Grace Ly~

772

171 Waterloo Ave
Downsview 55

Rm. 101
new arts Building

.2564 of Kmno4 N
.1019 of " "

5u Edgefield

P. Pendhaya

103
.098

P = 2(x+w)
$\frac{P}{2} - x = w$

P = 2(x+w)

Tables 2.
Friday the Dec 21
at 8.00 A.M.

Wed. Dec. 19th.
Philo 1. at 9 A.M.

49

McGraw-Hill Publications in the Zoological Sciences

E. J. BOELL, CONSULTING EDITOR

General Zoology

General Zoology

TRACY I. STORER

*Professor of Zoology and
Zoologist in the Agricultural Experiment Station
University of California at Davis*

SECOND EDITION

NEW YORK   TORONTO   LONDON

McGraw-Hill Book Company, Inc.

1951

GENERAL ZOOLOGY

THE MAPLE PRESS COMPANY, YORK, PA.

PREFACE

This text provides a general introduction to zoology, primarily for students in colleges and universities. Part I deals with the general principles of animal biology, and the subject matter is arranged to facilitate readings in connection with either lectures or laboratory and for reference use. In Part II each chapter describes the structure and physiology of common and representative types belonging to a major group of animals—from the one-celled protozoans to man. The accounts of natural history and reproduction show how structure and function serve in the life cycles of these and related animals. Some of the many interrelations between animals and their environments are discussed and there is frequent mention of the importance to mankind of various animals, both useful and harmful. The broader relations of animals are dealt with further in the general chapters on ecology, distribution, and evolution.

The synopses of classification, while intended mainly for reference, serve to show the extent and diversity of the animals comprising each of the larger groups, together with something of their mode of occurrence and their relations to other animals and mankind. Each synopsis extends down to orders, and in some the principal families are included. External or easily recognized characters are used where possible to facilitate identification of specimens. Common or notable representatives are mentioned by scientific and common names, using North American examples when available. Since the living animals are but the current members of a continuous procession of animal forms that have occupied the earth down through time, the geological ranges of groups and various fossil representatives (marked †) are mentioned.

Technical words in the text are distinguished by different type faces, as follows: anatomical and other terms, *humerus, monohybrid;* scientific names of genera or species, *Rana pipiens*, *Mus;* names of families and higher systematic groups, CULICIDAE, PROTOZOA, etc. Throughout the summaries of classification the pattern is: Phylum **ARTHROPODA;** Class *INSECTA;* Order **Diptera,** Family TABANIDAE.

Preparation of a second edition has afforded opportunity for various changes and additions. Advantage has been taken of many constructive criticisms received from teachers, students, and other users of the first edition. Each of these comments has been carefully considered and all those consistent with the general plan of the book and the space available have been included.

Significant developments in zoology during recent years have been followed and are incorporated where possible without undue expansion of the text. A later classification of the nematodes has been substituted and the Phylum Aschelminthes is recognized to include several miscellaneous groups of animals. A few other groups have been raised to the rank of phyla in keeping with recent trends in classification. Additions have been made on such subjects as vitamins, hormones, genetics of human blood groups, the Rh factor, symbiosis, populations, human evolution, and the relations of genetics to natural selection. Recent books and monographs have been added to the lists of references and the glossary has been slightly expanded, with new definitions for some terms.

Most of the illustrations are original. Anatomical figures, wherever possible, were made from special dissections and those of bilateral animals are shown from the left side to facilitate comparisons. In series showing embryological or larval development the individual figures are brought into comparable positions so that changes during growth or metamorphosis can be traced or compared directly with drawings of the adult animals. For the second edition a considerable number of illustrations have been replaced by better figures, others have been altered, and some new ones added for groups or structural features not previously illustrated. These later figures were drawn by Mrs. Emily Patterson Thompson, who, for the first edition, provided most of the figures of invertebrates, some of vertebrates, and many in the general chapters. Others of the latter two groups were done by Norman C. Bilderback and W. Schwarz and a few by Mrs. Marion P. Rosenberg. Photographs have been furnished by J. R. Slevin, the San Diego Zoological Society, the National Zoological Park, and others. These, together with illustrations supplied through the courtesy of various publishers, are credited as to source in the legends.

The following persons provided critical comments and suggestions for the first edition: L. H. Hyman (Chaps. 12–22, 24); J. T. Allen (Glossary); G. H. Ball (Chaps. 12, 21); S. C. Bishop (Chap. 29); R. M. Eakin (Chap. 5); W. K. Fisher (Chap. 19); P. W. Gregory (Chaps. 5, 6); Harold Kirby (Chap. 12); C. D. Leake (Chap. 10); G. S. Myers (Chap. 28); M. A. Stewart and G. M. Spurlock (Chaps. 16, 17); R. L. Usinger (Chaps. 7, 8, 9, 23, 24); Alexander Wetmore (Chap. 31, part). General aid was given by R. L. Usinger, G. M. Spurlock, J. T. Emlen, Jr., and L. E. Rosenberg. A host of correspondents, in the United States and abroad, have been generous with suggestions since the book first appeared in January, 1943. For the second edition there has been important help from A. W. Bell, B. G. Chitwood, C. L. Hubbs, T. H. Jukes, G. S. Myers, and K. P. Schmidt. To all these persons, including many unnamed, the author is grateful for their willing and useful cooperation.

TRACY I. STORER

DAVIS, CALIF.
March, 1951

CONTENTS

PART I
General Animal Biology

FIG. 1-1. The Animal Kingdom. A "genealogical tree" to indicate the probable relationships and relative position of the major groups (named in boldface type). All groups above a given characteristic (named in italics) possess that character. Figures not to same scale.

2

CHAPTER 1

INTRODUCTION

A tremendous variety of animals now inhabits the earth, and many other kinds have lived and died out through past geological time. These animals differ from one another in size, structure, manner of life, and other features. Mankind has acquired a vast amount of detailed knowledge about animals—enough to fill a large library—but there is still much more to be learned, even about the most familiar kinds. The average person has more or less **common knowledge** about animals, that birds are covered with feathers and lay eggs, that dogs are covered with hair and give birth to living young, and many similar facts. He is usually acquainted with common birds, fishes, and insects and a few others but knows little or nothing about the many additional forms of animal life. Besides such common knowledge there are many items of **natural history** known to certain people, such as the songs, habits, manner of nesting, and other details about birds or other conspicuous animals. The **science of zoology** (Greek *zoön*, animal + *logos*, discourse) includes all these matters and all other knowledge about animals, both popular and technical. Zoology deals with the structure and bodily functions of animals, their habits, where and how they live, their relations to one another and to their environments, their classification, and many other features.

1-1. Science (Latin *scientia*, knowledge) may be defined as any body of exact knowledge or as tested and verified human experience. A **scientist** is one who endeavors to observe and record, as accurately as possible, the things or processes relating to any particular subject. Absolute honesty is the basis of all scientific work. The raw materials of science are **facts,** the real state of things as contrasted with belief. The simpler facts are determined by close and careful observation, by use of the senses of sight, hearing, and touch. Scientific instruments enable this to be done more accurately and permit the observations of one person to be compared with those of another. In many fields of science the extent and accuracy of knowledge are dependent upon the instruments that are available and their precision. Thus the smallest animals and the finer structure in larger animals were unknown before the invention of the microscope, knowledge has grown with improvements in this and other instruments, and some paths of inquiry are blocked today because of certain limitations in the best of instruments.

3

The records of science are accumulated facts, or **data.** These may be **qualitative** data about different kinds of things and phenomena or **quantitative** data such as dimensions or weights that can be expressed in numerical terms. If a particular group of data suggests some general principle or some relation of cause and effect, the scientist formulates a temporary working explanation, or **hypothesis.** Then, if the subject matter permits, he plans and conducts **experiments** to test his hypothesis. Should the experiments disprove the hypothesis, the latter is discarded. If, however, they indicate its correctness, he formulates a more definite **theory** to explain the observed facts. Finally, when conditions permit actual proof of the cause-and-effect relation, this can be stated as a **scientific law** or **principle.** The latter, however, is never beyond criticism. If additional facts do not agree, the principle must be discarded or restated.

1-2. Zoology. All the facts, conclusions, theories, and laws that relate to animal life constitute the science of zoology. Together with **botany,** or the science of plants, it forms **biology** (Gr. **bios,** life), the science of living things, or organisms. Biology, in turn, is one of the **natural sciences** that consider the phenomena of nature. Other natural sciences are geology, which deals with the structure of the earth; mineralogy, which deals with the compounds in the earth's crust; physiography, which deals with the external form of the earth; and meteorology, which deals with the conditions of the atmosphere. The natural sciences may be contrasted with the **exact sciences**—physics, which deals with the properties of matter, and chemistry, which deals with its constitution.

Long in the past, one man might know and teach all science or all natural science, but scientific knowledge has become so vast and detailed that the sciences are now divided into many fields, and a scientific worker can master but one or a few of them. Some of the principal subdivisions of zoology together with the chapters in which they are discussed are:

ANATOMY (Gr. *ana,* up + *temno,* cut), structure as revealed by dissection.
MORPHOLOGY (Gr. *morphe,* form), structure as a whole.   (Chaps. 2, 4, 12 to 33)
HISTOLOGY (Gr. *histos,* tissue), microstructure of tissues.   (Chap. 3)
CYTOLOGY (Gr. *kytos,* hollow), structures and functions within cells.   (Chap. 3)
PHYSIOLOGY (Gr. *physis,* nature), living processes or functions within animals.
                                                    (Chaps. 2, 4 to 6, 12 to 33)
NUTRITION (L. *nutrio,* feed), use and conversion of food substances.   (Chap. 4)
EMBRYOLOGY (Gr. *en,* in + *bryo,* swell), growth and development of the new individual
    within the egg.   (Chap. 5)
GENETICS (Gr. *genesis,* origin), heredity and variation.   (Chaps. 6, 9)
PATHOLOGY (Gr. *pathos,* suffering), nature, symptoms, and cause of disease.
PARASITOLOGY (Gr. *para,* besides + *sitos,* food), study of animals that live and subsist
    on or in other animals.   (Chaps. 7, 12 to 24)
NATURAL HISTORY, life and behavior of animals in their natural surroundings.
                                                    (Chaps. 2, 12 to 33)

Ecology (Gr. *oikos*, house), relations of animals to their environments.

(Chaps. **2, 7,** 12 to 33)

Zoogeography (Gr. *zoön*, animal + geography), distribution of animals in space.

(Chap. 8)

Paleontology (Gr. *palaios*, ancient + *ont*, being), fossil animals and their distribution in time. (Chaps. 8, 9, 12 to 33)

Evolution (L. *e*, out + *volvo*, roll), origin and differentiation of animal life. (Chap. 9)

Taxonomy (Gr. *taxis*, arrangement + *nomos*, law), classification of animals and principles thereof. (Chaps. 11, 12 to 33)

Psychology (Gr. *psyche*, mind), the animal mind.

Sociology (L. *socius*, companion), societies of animals and man. (Chaps. 7, 23, 33)

Zoology is also divided for the study of animal groups that are of especial interest or importance into such fields as

Protozoology, study of the one-celled animals, or Protozoa.

Entomology, study of insects; further subdivided into insect morphology, insect taxonomy, economic entomology, etc.

Ornithology, study of birds.

Mammalogy, study of mammals.

Medical zoology, study of animals that affect the health of man.

1-3. Living vs. nonliving matter. Most living organisms, whether animals or plants, can usually be distinguished from nonliving or inor-

Fig. 1-2. The largest animals as compared with man. About $\frac{1}{250}$ natural size. (*Adapted from C. R. Knight.*)

ganic materials, but this is not easy with some of the lower forms of life. The dormant seeds of plants and the "resting stages" or eggs of some animals may appear inert, but when placed under appropriate conditions each will reveal its living nature. Perhaps the lowest forms of living substance are the viruses (see Chap. 9).

The main differences between living and nonliving things are as follows:

Form and size. Each kind of living organism is usually of definite form and of a characteristic size (Figs. 1-2, 1-3), within certain limits; most of them are also arranged as definite individuals. A whale, a flea, or any common plant is recognized by such features. Nonliving materials vary widely in such respects, as from a sand grain to a mountain or a drop of water to an ocean.

CHEMICAL COMPOSITION. Living organisms are composed chiefly of carbon, hydrogen, oxygen, and nitrogen in various but definite proportions, together with small amounts of calcium, phosphorus, sodium, potassium, iron, copper, sulphur, chlorine, etc. These materials are organized into complex organic molecules, often of great molecular weight, and collectively form the living substance or **protoplasm** (Chap. 3). The same and other chemical elements occur as compounds in non-living minerals, etc., but the molecular weights are small (below 2,000).

ORGANIZATION. The parts of each living organism are composed of microscopic cells, and these are assembled into interrelated systems for

FIG. 1-3. Some of the smallest animals and some animal cells, all included within the outline of a *Paramecium*. Magnified to 500 times natural size.

performing the life processes. Any structural organization in rocks or minerals depends upon the constituent materials or manner of formation, as with crystals.

METABOLISM. Various vital processes, collectively known as **metabolism,** are constantly in progress within living organisms, including the intake and use of food, respiration, secretion, excretion, and others. Nonliving things are relatively stable.

IRRITABILITY. The protoplasm and living organisms react to changes in the environment. These changes act as **stimuli** that produce changes in, or **responses** by, the organism. Stimuli may be external, such as heat, light, moisture, pressure, or contact, or else internal. The degree of response is often disproportionate to that of the stimulus, and the organism is often not permanently altered by the stimulus. If inanimate materials react, there is a definite quantitative relation between the intensity of the environmental change and the reaction produced, as in the expansion of metal with heat; such materials may undergo permanent change in form, as with the melting of ice to water or the chemical weathering of rocks.

REPRODUCTION. Each kind of living organism has the ability to duplicate itself in kind—pine seeds produce pine trees and not oaks, and chicken eggs yield little chicks and not ducklings or puppies. Organisms reproduce by using materials within their bodies, produced by metabolism; the manner of reproduction is varied (Chaps. 5, 12 to 33). Nonliving things cannot reproduce.

GROWTH AND LIFE CYCLE. Living organisms grow by development of new parts between or within older ones (intussusception) and may replace parts during life. Each individual has a definite life cycle of birth, growth, maturity, life span, and death. If nonliving things increase, they do so by external addition (accretion), as with crystals, and there is no orderly cycle of change.

1-4. Animals vs. plants. Most living organisms can be quickly referred to either the ANIMAL KINGDOM or the PLANT KINGDOM, but some defy such ready segregation. Most animals can move about or move parts of the body, but so can a few plants. Some animals become fixed early in life, such as the sponges, sea anemones, oysters, and barnacles; other fixed forms (hydroids, bryozoans) are of plantlike form. The green flagellates that contain chlorophyll and move about are considered plants by botanists and animals by zoologists. The microscopic wavy-outlined spirochaetes, many of which are disease producers, seem to be on the borderline between bacteria (plants) and PROTOZOA (animals).

The principal differences between animals and plants include:

FORM AND STRUCTURE. In animals the body form is rather invariable, the organs are mostly internal, the constituent cells are within delicate membranes, and the tissues are bathed in a solution of sodium chloride (NaCl). Growth is usually differential, producing changes in proportions of body parts with age. In plants the body form is often variable, organs are often added externally, the cells are usually within thick rigid walls of cellulose, and sodium chloride is toxic to most plants. Growth in plants is usually terminal, at the ends of organs, and often continues throughout life.

METABOLISM. Animals require complex synthesized organic materials as food, which can be obtained only by eating plants or other animals (heterotrophic nutrition). These are broken down (digested) and rearranged chemically within the body. Oxygen is needed for respiration. The end products of metabolism are chiefly carbon dioxide, water, and simple organic materials such as urea, $(NH_2)_2CO$. Most plants utilize carbon dioxide from the air together with water and inorganic chemical substances derived in solution from the soil (autotrophic nutrition). By photosynthesis—the action of sunlight on the green pigment, chlorophyll—

these simple materials are formed into various organic compounds, and oxygen is released as a by-product (Fig. 7-1).

IRRITABILITY. Most animals have a nervous system, and they respond quickly to stimuli. Plants have no such system, and their responses to stimuli are slower.

1-5. Numbers and kinds of animals. More than 900,000 *species* of living animals are known (Fig. 1-5). Some of these are represented by enormous numbers of individuals, but others are extremely scarce. For convenience in study and to indicate relationships between the different kinds, the animal kingdom is divided into various groups, large and small. The principal large divisions, or *phyla* (singular *phylum*) are listed here, with a few characteristics for each. Representatives of these are shown in Figs. 1-1 and 1-4. Chapter 11 contains a classification of the animal kingdom, and the phyla are discussed in detail in Chaps. 12 to 32.

Phylum **PROTOZOA.** UNICELLULAR ANIMALS. Mostly one-celled and of microscopic size; in fresh or salt waters or as parasites of other animals.   (Chap. 12)

Phylum **PORIFERA.** SPONGES. Shape various, body surface with many pores through which water passes; usually with a "skeleton" of lime, silica, or organic material; all aquatic, mostly in salt waters.   (Chap. 13)

Phylum **COELENTERATA.** HYDROIDS, JELLYFISHES, SEA ANEMONES, AND CORALS. Body saclike with central digestive cavity; aquatic, mostly in salt waters.   (Chap. 14)

Phylum **PLATYHELMINTHES.** FLATWORMS, FLUKES, AND TAPEWORMS. Soft, flat, thin, not segmented. Flukes and tapeworms are parasites of other animals.   (Chap. 16)

Phylum **ASCHELMINTHES,** Class *NEMATODA.* ROUNDWORMS. Body slender, often tapered toward ends, not segmented; digestive tract extends through body. In salt or fresh waters or soil, or parasitic in animals or plants.   (Chap. 17)

Phylum **ECHINODERMATA.** STARFISHES, BRITTLE STARS, SEA URCHINS, SEA LILIES, AND SEA CUCUMBERS. Body usually with 5-part symmetry, and a limy skeleton. All in salt waters.   (Chap. 19)

Phylum **MOLLUSCA.** CHITONS, CLAMS, SNAILS, SQUIDS, ETC. Body soft, usually enclosed by a limy shell and with a fleshy "foot" for locomotion. In salt or fresh waters and on land.   (Chap. 20)

Phylum **ANNELIDA.** SANDWORMS, EARTHWORMS, AND LEECHES. Body long, slender, usually conspicuously divided into segments. In salt or fresh waters or in soil.   (Chap. 21)

Phylum **ARTHROPODA.** CRUSTACEANS, INSECTS, SPIDERS, CENTIPEDES, MILLIPEDES, ETC. Body segmented, with jointed legs; entirely enclosed in an organic covering "skeleton" (of chitin); in all sorts of environments.   (Chaps. 22 to 24)

Phylum **CHORDATA.** THE "VERTEBRATES" (fishes; frogs and salamanders; turtles, lizards, and snakes; birds; mammals) AND SOME LOWER FORMS. The vertebrates have a jointed spinal column; the body typically comprises a head, trunk, and tail, usually with two pairs of fins or limbs; in all kinds of environments.   (Chaps. 25 to 33)

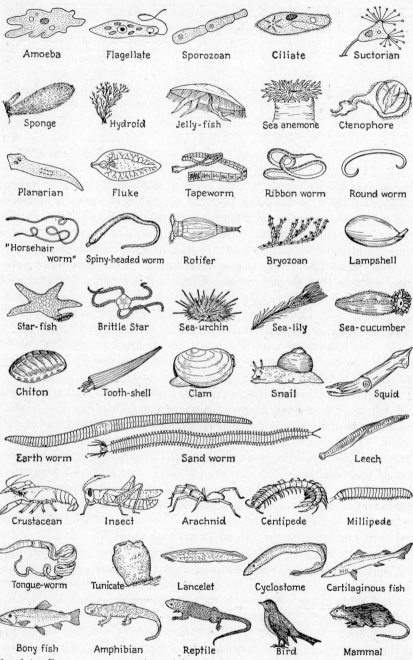

FIG. 1-4. Common representatives of the principal groups (phyla and classes) of animals.

FIG. 1-5. Approximate numbers of species in major divisions of the Animal Kingdom.

1-6. The environments of life. We do not know whether life occurs elsewhere in the universe. On the earth it exists under certain physical conditions; these include the presence of (1) those chemical elements that go to make up the protoplasm of living organisms (Chap. 3); (2) energy from the sun as solar radiation for plants to synthesize organic compounds usable as animal food; (3) an atmosphere containing oxygen; (4) water; and (5) certain temperature limits. Exceptions occur with some animals that do not require direct sunlight and a few that gain their oxygen indirectly. Life usually occurs within temperature limits of about 3° and 45°C. Many animals can exist only within a much narrower range, and a few survive higher or lower temperatures.

Through millions of years the earth's crust has been pushed up and folded by volcanic or other forces and has been worn down by weathering and erosion. These opposing agencies have produced the surface relief of mountains, valleys, plains, continents, islands, ocean basins, rivers, and lakes. These seem large to human eyes, but from the highest mountain to the greatest ocean deep is but 0.3 per cent of the earth's radius. The soil, rocks, and other land features vary in texture and other characteristics depending upon the minerals from which they have been formed and their geological history. Water covers about 72 per cent of the earth's surface. The fresh waters of lakes and streams contain sparse amounts of dissolved chemicals. Other inland brackish or alkaline waters have a larger mineral content. The salt waters of the oceans and their connecting bays and inlets average about 3.5 per cent in dissolved minerals, sodium chloride (NaCl) being the major component.

The daily rotation of the earth on its own axis results in the alternations of day and night, and the longer movement on its elliptical and inclined orbit around the sun is responsible for the seasons. Because of these two types of movement, the solar radiation received from the sun at any place varies in amount. This in turn brings about local differences in the temperature of the earth and its waters and atmosphere, in the distribution of water as rain, snow, ice, or water vapor, and in local movements of the atmosphere as winds. Collectively these differences form what we call climate; the several parts of the earth's surface are subjected to various kinds of climate, hot or cold, wet or dry, windy or still.

The end result of the differences in topography, water relations, and climate is to produce a wide variety of physical environments over the earth; these are the *habitats* or places where plants and animals grow and live (Fig. 1-6).

1-7. Distribution. Animals inhabit practically all parts of the earth from great depths in the sea to the highest mountains and from the poles

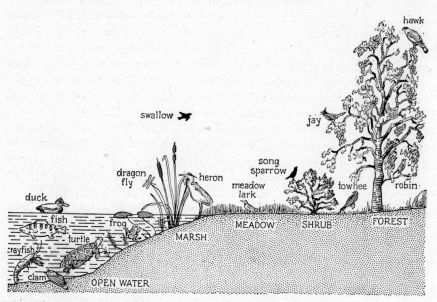

Fig. 1-6. Some common animals in their natural habitats. Each species lives in a particular kind of environment.

to the equator. Each species of animal has a definite *range* or area of distribution, determined by its needs as to food, shelter, and reproduction. Various kinds of animals live in all sorts of waters, fresh or foul, alkaline or salt. Others are found in land environments from the hottest and driest desert wastes to the most humid of tropical forests and in all sorts of plant growths.

The majority of animals are *free-living,* able to move about independently, but some water dwellers are fixed in place, or *sessile.* Still others are *parasites* that live on or within other animals at the expense of the latter (Chaps. 7, 8).

1-8. Interrelations. No animal lives entirely to itself. Each is affected in varying degree by the features of its physical environment and by the other animals and plants that constitute its biological environment. The distribution of many land animals is determined by the kinds of plants or plant growths upon which they rely for food or shelter. Most animals are affected by enemies, diseases, and competitors. The total of all these interactions comprises the "web of life" or the "balance of nature," a dynamic complex of forces, physical and biological, that affects every living organism, including man.

1-9. Relations of animals to man. Animals bear many relations to human affairs, some being very useful and others harmful (see Chaps. 12 to 33 for details). The domestic mammals and birds, together with fishes, are the principal sources of human protein food and of various oils and fats. Oysters, crabs, lobsters, shrimps, and other aquatic animals also are eaten. The wool of sheep and the pelts of various fur-bearing mammals provide clothing, and bird feathers are used in pillows and quilts. The hides of animals provide leather and glue, the hair is made into felt, and the glands and other internal organs yield many medicinal preparations. Honey, beeswax, tortoise shell, and natural sponges are other useful animal products. The livestock and meatpacking industries, the commercial fisheries, the fur trade, and beekeeping provide profitable employment for thousands of persons.

Premedical and other students learn elementary anatomy by use of lower animals. Research on frogs, rats, rabbits, and dogs has provided much of our understanding of physiological processes in mankind. These and other "laboratory animals" are used in studies of nutrition, in work with vitamins and hormones, and in testing the action of drugs, all of which find application in human medicine.

Man finds great recreational and aesthetic interest in watching wild animals in their natural surroundings and in the healthful outdoor pursuit of those species classed as fish and game.

Among the harmful animals the larger predatory animals are no longer dangerous to man in civilized countries, but they kill domestic livestock and useful wild animals. The insects and rodents that feed upon crop plants, grasses, herbs, or trees take a toll from farmers that amounts to many millions of dollars annually and necessitates large expenditures for control. Other insects and the "house" rats and mice damage stored foods and other property. Some insects, spiders, scorpions, and snakes are dangerously poisonous. The many kinds of parasites—protozoans, worms, insects, and ticks—bring illness and death to man, his domestic livestock, and useful wild species. The parasites of malaria and yellow fever carried by mosquitoes, the bacteria of plague transmitted by fleas, the typhus spread by lice, and other diseases carried by animals have exercised a dominant role in the history of mankind down through the ages.

References

The vast literature of zoology includes thousands of separate books and many periodicals, both technical and popular. The items listed here and in other chapters are a few selected works in which the student will find elementary and advanced materials dealing with various aspects of zoology. There are many elementary text-books of zoology and animal biology that deal with parts or all of the animal kingdom and with various general biological phenomena and principles.

The following works include systematic accounts of the animal kingdom:

HARMER, S. F., and A. E. SHIPLEY (editors). 1895–1909. The Cambridge natural history. London, Macmillan & Co., Ltd. 10 vols. PROTOZOA to MAMMALIA.

LANKESTER, E. R. (editor). 1900–1909. A treatise on zoology. London, A. & C. Black, Ltd. 8 vols. Incomplete; omits annelids, insects, land vertebrates, etc.

PARKER, T. J., and W. A. HASWELL. 1897. A text-book of zoology. London, Macmillan & Co., Ltd. 1940–1941. 6th ed. Revised by Otto Lowenstein and C. Forster-Cooper. 2 vols., lv + 1,528 pp., 1,173 figs. PROTOZOA to MAMMALIA.

SEDGWICK, A. 1898–1900. A student's text-book of zoology. London, Swan Sonnenschein & Co. 3 vols., 2,565 pp., illus. PROTOZOA to MAMMALIA.

The principal comprehensive works in foreign languages are:

BRONN, H. G., and OTHERS. 1859– . Klassen und Ordnungen der Thier-Reichs. Leipzig. "6 vols." (actually about 50, still incomplete).

CLAUS, C., KARL GROBBEN, und ALFRED KUHN. 1932. Lehrbuch der Zoologie. 10th ed. Berlin, Julius Springer. xi + 1,123 pp., 1,164 figs.

DELAGE, M. Y., et E. HÉROUARD. 1896–1902. Traité de zoologie concrète. Paris. 5 vols. Incomplete; chiefly lower invertebrates.

GRASSÉ, PIERRE P. (editor). 1948– . Traité de zoologie, anatomie, systématique, biologie. Paris, Masson et Cie. 17 vols. planned, 4 issued to date.

KÜKENTHAL, W., und T. KRUMBACH (editors). 1925– . Handbuch der Zoologie eine Naturgeschichte der Stämme des Tierreichs. Berlin, Walter de Gruyter & Co. "7 vols." (actually 14 or more, still incomplete).

PERRIER, J. O. E., et R. PERRIER. 1893–1928. Traité de zoologie. Paris, Masson et Cie. 10 vols., 3,610 pp., 2,352 figs.

The following deal with invertebrates:

BORRADAILE, L. A., and F. A. POTTS. 1936. The Invertebrata. 2d ed. New York, The Macmillan Co. xv + 725 pp., 483 figs. Modern, technical. PROTOZOA to TUNICATA.

BROWN, F. A., JR. 1950. Selected invertebrate types. New York, John Wiley & Sons, Inc. xx + 597 pp., 235 figs. PROTOZOA to TUNICATA.

BUCHSBAUM, R. 1948. Animals without backbones, an introduction to the invertebrates. 2d ed. Chicago, University of Chicago Press. xiii + 405 pp., 456 photographs, 312 drawings. Elementary.

BULLOUGH, W. S. 1950. Practical invertebrate anatomy. London, Macmillan & Co., Ltd. xi + 463 pp., 168 figs. PROTOZOA to CEPHALOCHORDATA.

CARTER, G. S. 1940. A general zoology of the invertebrates. New York, The Macmillan Co. xxviii + 509 pp., 172 figs. General problems, physiology, ecology.

CROWDER, W. 1931. Between the tides. New York, Dodd, Mead & Co., Inc. 461 pp., 36 pls., 451 figs. Seashore animals of the Atlantic coast.

GALTSOFF, P. S., F. E. LUTZ, P. S. WELCH, J. G. NEEDHAM, and OTHERS. 1937. Culture methods for invertebrate animals. Ithaca, N.Y., Comstock Publishing Co., Inc. xxxii + 590 pp., 82 figs.

HYMAN, L. H. 1940. The invertebrates: Protozoa through Ctenophora. xii + 720 pp., 221 figs. 1951. Platyhelminthes and Rhynchocoela. Vol. 2, vii + 550 pp., 208 figs.; Acanthocephala, Aschelminthes, and Entoprocta. Vol. 3, vii + 600+ pp., 223 figs. New York, McGraw-Hill Book Co., Inc. Modern general, other volumes planned.

JOHNSON, M. E., and H. J. SNOOK. 1927. Seashore animals of the Pacific coast. New York, The Macmillan Co. xiv + 659 pp., 11 pls., 700 figs.

MACGINITIE, G. E., and NETTIE MACGINITIE. 1949. Natural history of marine animals. New York, McGraw-Hill Book Co., Inc. xii + 473 pp., 282 figs.

PRATT, H. S., and OTHERS. 1935. A manual of the common invertebrate animals exclusive of insects. 2d ed. Philadelphia, The Blakiston Co. xviii + 854 pp., 974 figs. Chiefly for North America; keys for identification.

RICKETTS, E. F., and J. CALVIN. 1948. Between Pacific tides. 2d ed. Stanford University, Calif., Stanford University Press. xxvii + 365 pp., 46 pls., 129 figs. Marine invertebrates, arranged by habitats.

WARD, H. B., G. C. WHIPPLE, and OTHERS. 1918. Fresh-water biology. New York, John Wiley & Sons, Inc. ix + 1,111 pp., 1,547 figs. Chiefly invertebrates; keys for identification.

Comprehensive books on animal physiology include:

PROSSER, C. L. (editor). 1950. Comparative animal physiology. Philadelphia, W. B. Saunders Co. ix + 888 pp., 312 figs. Deals with PROTOZOA to MAMMALIA, but subject matter arranged by physiological processes.

ROGERS, C. G. 1938. Textbook of comparative physiology. 2d ed. New York, McGraw-Hill Book Co., Inc. xviii + 715 pp., 158 figs. Many data, especially on invertebrates.

SCHEER, B. T. 1948. Comparative physiology. New York, John Wiley & Sons, Inc. x + 563 pp., 72 figs. By groups, from PROTOZOA to VERTEBRATES.

CHAPTER 2

THE FROG AS A REPRESENTATIVE ANIMAL

The body of any animal exhibits a definite form, or *morphology*, and is composed of various structural parts, both gross and microscopic. By use of these features it carries on the activities necessary for life, the *physiological processes* within its body and the *external relations* with its environment. The frog is especially suitable for an introductory study because of its size and availability and because it shows many resemblances in form and function to the higher vertebrates and man (Chaps. 4, 30 to 33). It is large enough so that the details of its structure can be determined easily by dissection, its physiology is well known and readily demonstrated, and

Fig. 2-1. The leopard or grass frog (*Rana pipiens*) and the bullfrog (*R. catesbeiana*), both about half natural size.

its life habits, or *natural history,* are simple and easily observed. The following account will apply to any common species such as the leopard frog, *Rana pipiens*, or the bullfrog, *R. catesbeiana*[1] (Fig. 2-1).

2-1. General habits and external relations. Frogs live in water and in moist places on land; hence they are said to be amphibious (Gr. *amphi,* both + *bios*, life). Each species lives in a particular kind of surroundings, or *habitat,* such as marshes, pools, or streams (Chap. 29). On land a frog *rests* with its short angular forelegs upright and the long hind legs folded or flexed beside the body. When disturbed it jumps, or *leaps,* by suddenly extending the hind legs and feet. In the water it *swims* by alternately flexing and extending the hind legs, when the broad webs

[1] These and other North American frogs are described in the classification of Chap. 29.

between the toes push against the water and carry the animal forward. It may *float* with all legs extended and only the eyes and nostrils above water; from this position it can turn and *dive* to the bottom by swimming.

In its external relations the frog does those things which enable it to survive as an individual and to continue as a species. It must find *food* of the proper kind and amount. This consists exclusively of living moving animals, chiefly insects and worms, which are caught by a quick flip of the sticky mucus-coated tongue and swallowed entire. Motionless animals or objects are ignored, and undesirable food is rejected. The

Fig. 2-2.   The separate organ systems of a frog (compare Fig. 2-4).

frog seeks *shelter* in the water to escape enemies, to avoid unfavorable very hot or very cold weather, to moisten its skin, and to absorb water. In winter it avoids being frozen by burrowing into the bottom mud of a pond for a "winter sleep," or hibernation. Frogs seek shallow quiet water as a *breeding place* where their jelly-coated eggs are laid and fertilized. The eggs develop into embryos that hatch out as tadpoles or larvae. These feed and grow in the water and later transform into young frogs (Fig. 2-20). Various *enemies* capture and eat frogs, thus reducing their numbers. Snakes, turtles, herons, raccoons, and man are the chief enemies. From them the frogs endeavor to escape by leaping away, diving into water, and hiding in the bottom debris. Certain internal parasites and some *diseases* tend also to reduce the frog population. The *competitors* of frogs include other frogs and various animals living in the same habitat that seek insects and similar food.

2-2. Organ systems and physiological processes.   The body of a frog (like that of most animals) consists of several *organ systems,* each specialized by structure and function to perform some essential physiological process such as digestion, circulation, etc.   These systems are integrated to work harmoniously with each other.   Each system is composed of several *organs,* which individually perform some part of the general function; in the digestive system, the mouth is for food taking, the stomach for storage and digestion, and so on.   An organ, in turn, is formed of several layers or parts known as *tissues;* and each tissue is composed of many microscopic *cells,* usually of like kind.   The wall of the stomach contains four principal tissue layers, including digestive and gland cells, muscle cells, connective tissues, and others.   The many substances comprising the cells are known collectively as *protoplasm* (Chap. 3).   The frog's body is made up of the following organ systems (Fig. 2-2) which are described in detail later:

1. Integument, or skin.
2. Skeletal system.
3. Muscular system.
4. Digestive system.
5. Circulatory system.
6. Respiratory system.
7. Excretory system.
8. Nervous system and sense organs.
9. Glands of internal secretion.
10. Reproductive system.

2-3. External features.   The frog's body comprises a *head* and *trunk* that are broadly joined and two pairs of *legs,* or *limbs;* there is no neck region or tail.   The entire animal is covered by soft smooth moist *skin,* of distinctive color and pattern on each species.   Some frogs have a thickened dorsolateral fold along the back from behind each eye, and some have rounded warts on the legs or elsewhere.   The head (Fig. 2-3) bears a wide transverse *mouth* for taking food, two small *nostrils* (external nares) near the tip of the snout that serve in respiration, two large spherical *eyes* (organs of sight), and behind each eye a flat *eardrum* or *tympanic membrane* that receives sound waves.   Each eye has a fleshy opaque *upper eyelid* and a lesser *lower lid.*   Beneath these is a transparent third eyelid, or *nictitating membrane,* that can move upward over the eyeball to keep it moist in the air and as a protection when under water.   At the hind end of the body is the *vent,* or *anus,* a small opening through which are discharged undigested food wastes, the urine or liquid excretory wastes from the kidneys, and the sex cells (eggs or sperm) from the reproductive organs.

The short "arm," or *front leg,* comprises an upper arm, forearm, wrist, and hand; the latter has a small palm with tubercles beneath, four fingers (digits), and a vestigial "thumb."   The inner digit is thickened on males, especially in the breeding season.   Each of the long powerful **hind legs** consists of a thigh, shank or lower leg, ankle (tarsal region), and the long foot with a narrow sole (metatarsus) and five slender toes connected by broad thin webs.

The frog is **bilaterally symmetrical,** with equivalent right and left sides.   Structures on or toward the central longitudinal axis are termed **medial,** and those toward the sides are said to be **lateral.**   The regions of the body are the **anterior end,** which moves forward; the opposite or **posterior end;** the back or **dorsal surface,** which is habitually uppermost; and the lower or **ventral surface** (see Fig. 11-2).   The latter comprises the broad **chin** and **throat** beneath the head; the chest, thorax, or **pectoral region** adjacent to the forelegs; the belly, or **abdomen,** behind; and the **pelvic region** between the hind legs.

maxillary teeth

internal nares

vomerine teeth

tongue

opening of Eustachian tube

opening to vocal sac

external nares

upper eyelid

entrance to esophagus

glottis

FIG. 2-3.   Head and mouth of a male bullfrog.

2-4. Mouth cavity.   Within the **upper** and **lower jaws** is the broad **mouth** or **buccal cavity.**   This narrows behind as the **pharynx,** which connects to the gullet, or esophagus.   The **tongue** is flat and fleshy, attached anteriorly to the mouth floor but notched and free behind.   Taste buds occur in small papillae on its upper surface.   The mucus-coated posterior end of the tongue can be flipped forward through the opened mouth to capture food.   Swallowing is accomplished by raising the mouth floor, in which a flat **hyoid cartilage** is embedded, and is aided by depressing the eyeballs.   The upper jaw is margined by fine conical **maxillary teeth,** and on the roof of the mouth are two patches of **vomerine teeth.**   These all attach to the bone surfaces and are replaced if lost.   They serve to hold food but not for chewing.   Near the vomerine teeth are two openings, the **internal nares,** which connect with the external nares and through which air passes to and from the mouth cavity in respiration. The **glottis** is a median ventral slit in the pharynx, behind the tongue, that guards the entrance to the lungs.   It is opened for breathing but closes when food is being swallowed.   Behind each eyeball and near the

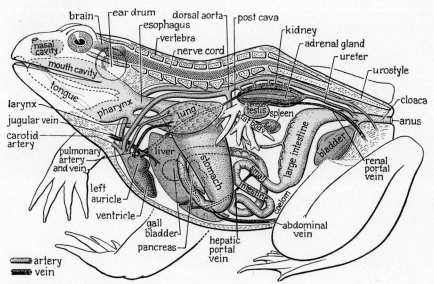

FIG. 2-4.   The frog.   Internal structure (compare Fig. 2-2).

corner of the mouth there opens a small **Eustachian tube;** this connects
to the middle ear chamber, beneath the eardrum, and allows the air
pressure to be equalized on the two surfaces of the eardrum.   Male
frogs of many species have near by an opening into a *vocal sac* in the
chin.   The two sacs can be inflated to amplify the croaking notes.

2-5. Internal structure.   If the skin and muscular body wall are cut
away on the ventral side, the *internal organs* or *viscera* will be found within the large *body cavity* or *coelom.*   A smooth transparent membrane,
the *peritoneum,* lines the cavity (parietal peritoneum) and covers the
organs (visceral peritoneum).   Most of the organs are suspended from
the middorsal region by double layers of peritoneum known as ***mesenteries*** through which blood vessels and nerves connect to the organs
(Figs. 2-4, 2-5).

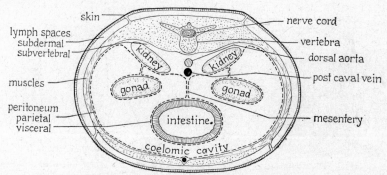

FIG. 2-5.   The frog.   Diagrammatic cross section of the body to show relations of the
peritoneum (broken lines) to internal organs.   The skin is multilayered (compare Fig. 2-6).

Far anterior in the coelom is (1) the reddish pear-shaped *heart* within
a tissue sac (pericardium) filled with watery lymph.   Besides the heart
are (2) the two thin-walled elastic *lungs,* and behind these is (3) the firm
brown *liver* of three rounded lobes with (4) the saclike greenish *gall
bladder* between the middle and right lobes.   Parts of the digestive tract
include (5) the short *esophagus* above the liver, (6) the long whitish
stomach along the left side, (7) the slender and coiled *small intestine,*
and (8) the bigger and dark *large intestine* or *rectum* that passes posteriorly.   Along the fore part of the small intestine is (9) a slender
irregular and whitish *pancreas.*   Behind the stomach lies (10) a rounded
reddish *spleen.*   At either side of the middorsal line, above the peritoneum, are (11) two dark elongate *kidneys.*   The *bladder* (12) is a thin-
walled sac midventrally at the posterior end of the coelom.   Between the
intestines and kidneys are (13) the *gonads* or *sex organs.*   A female has
two large *ovaries,* containing many small dark spherical eggs, and two
convoluted whitish *oviducts* extending along the dorsal wall of the
coelom.   In a male there are two small dark bean-shaped *testes.*   To

each sex organ is connected (14) a branched *fat body.* The rectum and the ducts from the kidneys and sex organs all enter (15) the *cloaca,* which opens at the anus.

2-6. Integument. The thin flexible *skin* covers the entire animal. It provides physical protection, excludes disease organisms, serves in respiration, and is the means of water absorption, as a frog does not drink. As in all land vertebrates, it comprises an outer stratified *epidermis* and a *dermis* (corium) beneath, both of several cell layers (Fig. 2-6). In the epidermis, the basal cells (stratum germinativum or Malpighian layer) produce successive layers of cells that move outward and flatten, the outermost becoming a thin cornified covering. Every month or so during the season when the frog is active, a new layer forms beneath

Fig. 2-6. The frog's skin. Enlarged stereogram showing the component cell layers, fibers, and other parts. The section is cut at 45 degrees to the main body axis as indicated in the small outline figure.

and the old covering is molted, or sloughed off; the latter splits down the back, is worked off in one piece by the "hands," and usually is swallowed. The dermis is mainly of connective tissue. Its outer spongy portion contains glands and pigment cells over a dark-staining layer of granules or fibers. The deeper part is a compact bed of crossed connective tissue fibers, each layer at about 45 degrees with the body axis, making the skin flexible either along or across the body. In and beneath the dermis are nerves and blood vessels, the latter of importance in cutaneous (skin) respiration. The skin of frogs and toads, unlike that of other vertebrates, is attached to the body only along certain lines (Fig. 2-5).

The glands produce useful fluids, or *secretions,* that pass out on the epidermis through fine ducts. The many small *mucous glands* secrete a colorless watery fluid that keeps the skin moist, glistening, and sticky. If a frog is roughly handled or chloroformed, the scarcer but larger *poison glands* pour out a thick whitish alkaloidal secretion with a burning taste

that protects the animal in some degree from enemies.   Each gland
has a spherical base of secreting cells that discharge into a central cavity,
whence the secretion can be forced out of the neck or gland duct by the
action of muscle fibers around its base.   The loose attachment of the
elastic skin and its mucus-covered surface often enable the frog to slip
from the grasp of enemies.

The skin is colored by scattered **pigment granules** in the epidermis and
pigment cells, or **chromatophores,** in the dermis—melanophores with
black or brown pigment, lipophores with red or yellow, and guanophores
that contain whitish crystals.   The skin of a tadpole may have over
300 chromatophores per square millimeter.   Frogs are usually **protectively colored** to resemble their surroundings, green on the dorsal and
lateral surfaces and pale to whitish beneath.   There is no green pigment;

A   B

FIG. 2-7.   Pigment cells (melanophores) of frog skin.   *A.* Expanded.   *B.* Contracted,
pigment being withdrawn into body of cell.   (*After Hewer.*)

the prevailing color results jointly from the pigments that absorb some
light rays and reflect others (chemical color) and interference phenomena
in the outer layers of the skin (physical color).   Dark spots are due to
groupings of melanophores and golden flecks to yellow lipophores.   On
most amphibians the patterns are stable, but the colors of some undergo
marked changes (Fig. 29-3).   Darkening results when the pigment
granules in the chromatophores are scattered, and paling occurs when they
are concentrated; changes in color result from both external conditions
and internal states.   Low temperature produces darkening; under higher
temperatures, drying, or increased light, the color pales.   Some of these
changes are induced through the eyes, as experimentally blinded frogs do
not change.   Pigment control is due in part to a hormone (intermedin)
of the pituitary gland, in part to a hormone of the adrenal glands, and in
part to the nervous system.

2-7. Skeletal system.   The body framework is a jointed internal
skeleton that supports the soft parts, protects vital organs, and affords
attachments for muscles used in movement and locomotion.   In an early

frog larva it is entirely of soft gristle or **cartilage,** but many parts later become hard **bone** (Chap. 3).   Cartilage persists on the ends of limb bones to form smooth joint surfaces and in parts of the skull and limb girdles. The skull, vertebral column, and sternum comprise the **axial skeleton,**

Fig. 2-8.   Skull of the bullfrog in dorsal, lateral, and ventral views.   The lower jaw and hyoid cartilages are shown only in the lateral view; cartilage stippled; II, X, etc., exits for cranial nerves.

and the limbs and girdles form the **appendicular skeleton** (Figs. 2-8, 2-9, Table 4-1).

The broad flat skull comprises (1) a narrow brain case, or **cranium;** (2) the paired **sense capsules** of the nose and ear and large **orbits** for the eyes; and (3) the **jaws, hyoid,** and cartilages of the **larynx** (visceral skeleton). The cranium is roofed mainly by the frontoparietals, the nasals cover the nasal capsules, the prootics house the inner ears, and posteriorly each exoccipital bears a rounded *occipital condyle.* The two condyles fit depressions in the first vertebra and permit slight movement of the head on the spinal column. Between the condyles is the large opening, or *foramen magnum,* through which the brain and nerve cord connect. Over the roof of the mouth are two vomers that bear teeth, and the dagger-shaped parasphenoid. Each half of the upper jaw (maxillary arch) includes a premaxilla and maxilla with teeth and a quadratojugal, all fused to the cranium. The lower jaw (mandibular arch) on each side is a rodlike (Meckel's) cartilage, encased by the dentary and angulo-splenial bones; the latter bone articulates to the quadrate cartilage on the cranium.

Fig. 2-9. Skeleton of the frog.

The spinal or *vertebral column* supports the body, connects to the head and limbs, and protects the nerve cord. It consists of nine *vertebrae* and a long thin *urostyle.* In the frog it is short, of few segments, and scarcely flexible, being thus unlike the column in most vertebrates. Each vertebra is made up of a spool-like *centrum* surmounted by a *neural arch* to house the nerve cord. Above the arch is a low *neural spine,* at either side is a broad *transverse process,* and at either end is a pair of *articular processes* that fit to similar processes on adjacent vertebrae. A frog has no ribs.

The anterior or *pectoral girdle* is a ○-shaped framework around the thorax that shelters organs within and supports the fore limbs; it is attached to the vertebrae by muscles. Each half includes a broad cartilaginous *suprascapula* dorsally, a narrower *scapula* laterally, and the slender *clavicle* and wider *coracoid* ventrally. The latter join to the midventral breastbone, or *sternum,* which is largely cartilaginous and of several parts (epi-, omo-, meso-, and xiphi-sternum from before backward). Where the scapula and coracoid meet there is a shallow depression (glenoid fossa) in which the head of the humerus in the fore limb articulates.

The posterior or *pelvic girdle* is a stout rigid V-shaped frame that connects the hind limbs to the vertebral column and transmits the power in locomotion from the hind limbs to the body. It consists of three bones on each side, the long *ilium* anteriorly, the *ischium* posteriorly, and *pubis* ventrally. Where these join, there is a cuplike socket, or *acetabulum,* in which the head of the femur of the hind limb articulates. Each ilium has a long process, parallel to the urostyle, that attaches to a stout transverse process on the ninth (sacral) vertebra.

The two pairs of limbs differ in size but have similar component bones and parts as follows:

FORE LIMB   Humerus   Radius and Ulna (fused)   Carpals   Metacarpals   Phalanges
    (arm)   *(upper arm)*   *(forearm)*   *(wrist)*   *(palm of hand)*   *(fingers)*

HIND LIMB   Femur   Tibia and Fibula (fused)   Tarsals   Metatarsals   Phalanges
    (leg)   *(thigh)*   *(shank or lower leg)*   *(ankle)*   *(sole of foot)*   *(toes)*

The most complete skeletal protection is provided for the brain in the solid skull; the nerve cord is in a bony flexible conduit of neural arches with openings between adjacent vertebrae through which spinal nerves pass out; the vertebrae, pectoral girdle, and sternum encircle the thorax; the pelvic girdle shields the abdomen dorsally; and the limb skeletons afford only support.

The form of each bone is related to the function it serves and is built on good "engineering" principles in both gross and microscopic structure. Those subject to heavy stresses are reinforced within, and where stout muscles or tendons attach the exterior is roughened. *Fixed* bones of the brain case and pelvic girdle are immovably joined to each other, but most of the bones are *movable* with smooth *articular surfaces* at the joints where one bone moves on another. At the shoulder and hip there are *ball-and-socket joints* that permit rotation of the movable member (humerus, femur); *hinge joints* that allow movement in one plane occur at the elbow, knee, and elsewhere. Movable bones are attached to one another by *ligaments* formed of dense connective tissue, besides the muscles and tendons that operate them. The centrum of each vertebra and each long bone in a limb or foot comprises a larger central *diaphysis* and a smaller *epiphysis* at either end. The fixed bones are joined to each other and each epiphysis to its diaphysis by irregular and interlocking *sutures.* The latter remain cartilaginous throughout life in a frog; hence, its bones may continue to grow.   In birds and mammals, however, each suture becomes bony at a certain age, after which increase in size is impossible.

2-8. Muscular system.   The body of a frog or any other vertebrate contains three kinds of muscle fibers—smooth, cardiac, and striated— which differ in microscopic structure and physiology (Chap. 3).   The external muscular system (Figs. 2-10, 2-11) consists of *skeletal* or *voluntary muscles* that are attached to the bones; under willful control they produce movement and locomotion.   A skeletal muscle includes many

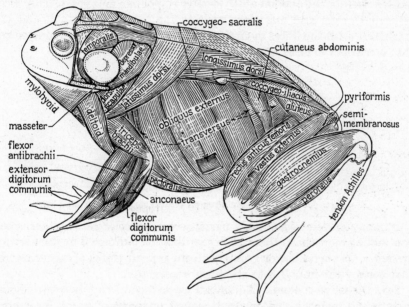

Fig. 2-10.   Muscles of the bullfrog.

parallel striated fibers, bound together by connective tissue.   Its opposite ends are fastened to separate bones or other parts by extensions of the connective tissue.   The more central or less movable end is called the *origin,* and that on the more distal or movable part is the *insertion.* Many muscles are tapered toward their ends, some connect broadly to the bones, and other have the connective tissue prolonged as a slender *tendon* that inserts at some distance from the muscle itself.   Tendons occur especially on the lower limb segments, feet and toes, where some pass under transverse (annular) ligaments that serve as pulleys.   The *action* of a muscle is to contract, or shorten in length, and thus the two structures to which it is attached are brought closer together.   Muscles are commonly arranged in opposed groups.   The following are the general types, as to mode of action, and an example of each:

Flexor, bends one part on another; *biceps,* flexes forearm toward upper arm.

Extensor, straightens or extends a part; *triceps,* extends forearm on upper arm.

Abductor, draws a part away from axis of body (or of a limb); *deltoid.*

Adductor, draws a part toward axis of body (or of a limb); *latissimus dorsi.*

Depressor, lowers a part; *depressor mandibulae,* moves lower jaw down to open
mouth.

Levator, elevates or raises a part; *masseter,* raises lower jaw to close mouth.

Rotator, rotates a part; *pyriformis.*

Voluntary muscles are of three general structural forms: (1) broad thin sheet muscles, such as the external oblique and transversus that form a flexible wall for the abdomen; (2) slender ribbonlike muscles, usually with restricted origin and insertion, such as the biceps or deltoid; and (3) sphincters with the fibers in circular arrangement, as in the sphincter ani that constricts to close the anus.

Fig. 2-11.   Muscles of the bullfrog on ventral surface of left hind leg.

In many movements of body parts, several muscles act together, some contracting more than others; such coordination is directed by the nervous system.   On each fiber or group of fibers are end plates of motor nerves that convey the impulses to stimulate contraction.

2-9. Digestive system.   An animal needs food to supply materials for growth and maintenance, for replacement or repair of parts, for energy to move, and for producing sex cells.   Plants synthesize the materials they need for life and growth from simple chemical substances in the soil and air.   Animals require complex organic substances as food and obtain these by eating plants or other animals.   Their food must be subjected to physical and chemical changes, or *digestion,* before it can be *absorbed* and used in the body.   The digestive system consists of the alimentary canal, or *digestive tract,* and the *digestive glands.*   The tract is essentially a tube that extends from the mouth to the anus, being of differing diameter and structure in its several parts.

The insects and other small animals taken as food into the frog's mouth are lubricated by the mucus secreted there (a frog lacks salivary glands) and pass through the *pharynx* to enter the *esophagus.*   This is a short tube lined by glands that secrete an alkaline digestive fluid and with muscular walls that move the food along.   Food passes at once to the

stomach, which is an organ for storage and digestion, larger at the anterior or cardiac end and tapering to the posterior or pyloric end. The thick stomach walls comprise four layers: (1) the **mucosa,** or inner lining, with many glands, both unicellular and multicellular (Chap. 3), some of the latter being tubular or branched and those of the cardiac end larger; (2) the **submucosa,** a network of connective tissue containing blood and lymph vessels and nerves; (3) the **muscularis** with both circular and longitudinal bundles of smooth muscle fibers; and (4) the **serosa,** or outer covering which is the peritoneum (Fig. 4-12).

Muscular contractions of the stomach wall serve to crush the food into smaller particles and to mix it with the secretions of the glands. These secretions contain **enzymes** or digestive ferments. An enzyme is a chemical substance, an organic catalyst, that speeds up certain chemical reactions and converts large amounts of material without being changed or used up itself in the process. Many kinds of enzymes perform essential vital processes in the bodies of animals. Each kind of digestive enzyme changes certain classes of chemical molecules of the food into simpler compounds (Chap. 4) that can be absorbed through the wall of the digestive tract and enter the blood. Food is not a part of the body until it is absorbed.

The digestive enzymes in the stomach and intestine of the frog include pepsin, trypsin, and erepsin, which act on proteins; lipase, which acts on fats; and amylopsin and maltase, which act on starches. Hydrochloric acid secreted in the stomach activates the digestive fluid secreted in the esophagus. The muscular movements that mix and gradually move food along the digestive tract are termed **peristalsis.** Some absorption may occur in the stomach, but most of the mixed and finely divided contents is passed through the **pyloric valve** (a sphincter muscle) at the posterior end and enters the **small intestine.** The intestinal wall is comprised of four tissue layers as is the stomach.

Two large **digestive glands,** the liver and pancreas, supply secretions to the small intestine besides those from glands in the intestinal wall. The **liver** is a large multilobed gland that secretes **bile.** This passes through bile capillaries and is stored in the **gall bladder,** whence it is poured through the **bile duct** to the small intestine when food enters the latter. The bile serves to emulsify fats. The **pancreas** is also a multicellular gland. It produces several digestive enzymes that pass into the **pancreatic duct,** which joins the common bile duct. The principal work of digestion and absorption takes place in the small intestine. Undigested residues are slowly moved by peristalsis into the **large intestine,** there are formed into feces, and finally are egested through the **cloaca** and **anus.** Absorbed materials pass by way of the blood and lymph to various parts of the body for immediate use in growth or activities or for storage.

Much reserve food is stored in the liver as glycogen ("animal starch"), a carbohydrate that can be converted into glucose for use in the body as needed. Fats may be stored in various parts of the body.

2-10. Circulatory system. The transporting of materials within the body is performed by the *circulatory system.* Its principal functions are to carry (1) oxygen and carbon dioxide between the respiratory organs and body tissues; (2) digested foods and water from the digestive tract to other organs; (3) stored foods from place to place as needed; (4) organic wastes and excess minerals in solution, together with water, to the excretory organs; and (5) hormones from the endocrine glands where they are produced to the places where they are used. Other functions are mentioned later. The circulatory system consists of the heart, the arteries,

erythrocyte   large monocyte   lymphocyte   thrombocyte

neutrophil   basophil   eosinophil

Fig. 2-12.   Blood cells of the frog.

capillaries, veins, and lymph vessels, and the fluid blood and lymph. The heart is a chambered muscular pump that forces the fluids to circulate constantly through the closed system of tubular elastic vessels.

The *blood* consists of a clear fluid *plasma* containing free cells, or *blood corpuscles* (Fig. 2-12). The plasma comprises water, distinctive blood proteins, and mineral salts, including about 0.65 per cent of sodium chloride; it is the medium that carries soluble materials. The *red blood cells* or *erythrocytes* are elliptical, flattened, and nucleated. They contain a yellow to red respiratory pigment, *hemoglobin,* that serves to carry oxygen to the tissues. Each cell measures about 0.014 by 0.023 mm. (14 by 23 micra), and they number 400,000 or more per cubic millimeter of blood. The *white blood cells,* or *leucocytes,* are colorless and nucleated; they number about 7,000 per cubic millimeter and are of several kinds (Chap. 4). Most of them can move independently (by amoeboid movement). Certain kinds (phagocytes) police the body against invading bacteria or other foreign organisms and remove dead or old tissue cells.

When a blood vessel is injured, the blood **coagulates,** or forms a clot, to stop up the wound and prevent loss of blood.   Certain small spindle cells, or **thrombocytes,** floating in the plasma provide the substance thrombin that acts upon the fibrinogen in the plasma to bring about clotting. Blood cells are formed chiefly in the **marrow** contained in cavities within the bones.   Some are formed in the **spleen,** which also disposes of old cells.

The **heart** comprises a connected series of chambers enclosed by muscular walls (Fig. 2-13).   It consists of (1) a conical thick-walled **ventricle** posteriorly; (2) the left and right **auricles** anteriorly, with thin muscular walls; (3) a thin triangular **sinus venosus** dorsally; and (4) a stout tubular

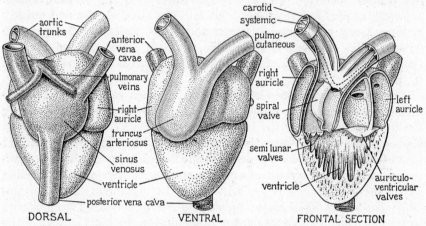

FIG. 2-13.   Heart of the bullfrog, enlarged.

truncus arteriosus that leads forward from the anterior base of the ventricle.   Between these chambers there are **valves** to prevent backward flow of blood.   The auricles are separated by an interauricular septum.   In the truncus is a thin, flat, and twisted spiral valve.   The heart is covered by a thin membrane, the **pericardium,** and is enclosed in a thin sac of the same material.

The **arteries** are blood vessels (Fig. 4-15) that carry blood away from the heart.   They are lined by a glassy-smooth endothelium and have stout walls containing smooth muscle cells and connective tissue fibers to maintain the **blood pressure** produced by contractions of the heart.   The arteries branch again and again into successively smaller vessels, with thinner walls, that extend to all parts of the body.   The finest arteries, or arterioles, connect to the microscopically fine **capillaries,** which have walls only of endothelium and are scattered densely among the tissue cells of the body.   Here food and oxygen are distributed by osmosis through the capillary walls, some plasma and lymph cells escape, and both carbon dioxide and other wastes are taken into the blood.   The capillaries join to form small *veins,* and these in turn combine into larger veins.   The veins carry blood toward or to the heart.   Their structure is essentially like that of the arteries, but the walls are thinner, with less muscle and connective tissue, since the blood pressure in veins is lower than in arteries.

The course of circulation (Fig. 4-16) is as follows: Blood accumulates in the sinus venosus, which contracts to force it into the right auricle. Blood from the lungs accumulates in the left auricle.   The two auricles then contract and force their contents into the ventricle.   Earlier it was thought that when the ventricle contracted the spiral valve deflected unoxygenated blood from the right side into the pulmocutaneous arch and oxygenated blood from the left side into the carotid and systemic arches. Injecting opaque but inert materials into the blood stream and quickly making X-ray photographs (Foxen and Wells) indicates that the two streams mix.   Cutaneous respiration, both in water and on land, is thought to compensate for failure of all unoxygenated blood to be pumped to the lungs.

The truncus divides into left and right branches, each of which is sub-divided into three major vessels or "arches," the *common carotid* serving the head, the *systemic* the body and viscera, and the *pulmocutaneous* the lungs and skin.   Where the carotid divides, there is a spongy carotid gland that equalizes blood pressure in the vessels beyond.   The two sys-temic arches pass dorsally around the esophagus and join as a median *dorsal aorta* extending posteriorly below the vertebrae.   Each pulmo-cutaneous artery divides into a *pulmonary artery* proceeding to capillaries in the lungs and a *cutaneous artery* branching on the inner surface of the skin.   In general, the arterial system has the pattern of a tree, with repeated branchings (Fig. 2-14).

The venous system is somewhat more complex.   Two *precaval veins* return blood to the sinus venosus from veins in the head, fore limbs, and skin.   A median *postcaval vein* collects from the kidneys, gonads, and dorsal musculature.   There are also three special venous paths.   (1) The paired *pulmonary veins* return blood that has been oxygenated in the lungs to the left auricle; all other veins deliver eventually to the sinus venosus and right auricle.   (2) The *hepatic portal system* gathers blood from the digestive tract (stomach and intestines) and carries it to the liver where the veins break up into capillaries through the liver and then the blood is assembled in hepatic veins that enter the post cava.   The hepatic portal circulation allows certain materials in blood from the digestive tract to be either stored or filtered out during passage through the liver.   In the frog the hepatic portal also receives an abdominal vein that collects from the hind limbs (femoral veins), bladder, and ventral body wall.   (3) The *renal portal system* gathers blood from the hind limbs (sciatic and femoral veins) and posterior body wall and divides into capillaries within the kidneys.   This blood is collected by the renal veins and returns to the heart in the postcaval vein.

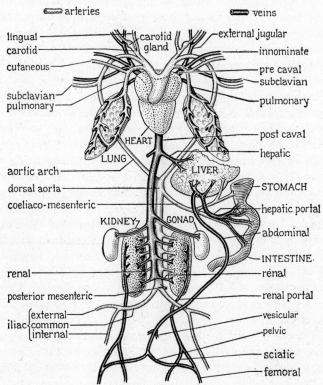

arteries   veins

lingual — carotid gland — external jugular
carotid — innominate
cutaneous — pre caval
— subclavian
subclavian — pulmonary
pulmonary —
HEART
LUNG — post caval
— hepatic
aortic arch — LIVER
dorsal aorta — STOMACH
coeliaco-mesenteric — hepatic portal
KIDNEY — GONAD — abdominal
— INTESTINE
renal — renal
posterior mesenteric — renal portal
iliac { external / common / internal } — vesicular
— pelvic
— sciatic
— femoral

FIG. 2-14.   Circulatory system of the bullfrog in ventral view showing the principal arteries and veins in relation to the internal organs.

aorta   arteries

LUNG   HEART — LIVER ← DIGESTIVE TRACT   blood BODY TISSUES capillaries

lymph capillaries

veins

lymph   vessels

FIG. 2-15.   Plan of the circulation in a frog or other vertebrate, with both blood vessels (solid lines) and lymph vessels (broken lines); arrows indicate the direction of flow.

The *lymphatic system* includes many delicate *lymph vessels* of varied diameter and shape that penetrate the organs and tissues but are difficult to see.   Frogs and toads, unlike other vertebrates, have also several large *lymph sacs* or spaces between the skin and body (Fig. 2-5).   Behind the shoulder girdle and beside the anus are two pairs of *lymph hearts* that pulsate frequently in a living frog.　Dorsal to the coelom and peritoneum there is a large **subvertebral lymph sac** about the kidneys.　The watery **lymph** in these structures contains leucocytes but lacks red cells and some proteins of blood plasma.　It filters out from blood capillaries into the tissues, enters the lymph vessels, and later returns to the veins.　Some small openings (stomata) in the peritoneum communicate with lymph vessels.

2-11. Respiratory system.　The energy for life and growth is derived by the oxidation, or "physiological burning," of absorbed food.　This is analogous to the burning of coal in the presence of oxygen to yield heat and carbon dioxide ($C + O_2 \rightarrow CO_2 + heat$).　**Respiration** is the process of supplying oxygen to the body; the removal of carbon dioxide that results from metabolism is really a matter of excretion but is commonly included as a part of respiration.　The oxygen-carbon dioxide exchange between the air or water and the blood is termed **external respiration,** and that between the blood and body cells is **internal respiration.**

The **respiratory organs** of a frog are the **lungs, skin,** and **lining of the mouth cavity.**　They all have moist surfaces (epithelium) close over blood vessels.　Oxygen from the air dissolves in the surface moisture and diffuses inward to the blood, whereas carbon dioxide passes in the opposite direction.　The **hemoglobin** in red blood cells combines with oxygen where plentiful and releases it as the blood passes through body tissues where oxygen is scarcer and needed.　The hemoglobin enables the blood to transport much more oxygen than if the latter were dissolved in the plasma.　Carbon dioxide, however, is carried mainly by the plasma.　The laws of simple diffusion of gases probably account for the exchanges in respiration as the concentration of oxygen in the air (about 20 per cent) is far greater than in blood and that in the blood is greater than in tissues; the reverse is true for carbon dioxide.

The frog's **lungs** (Fig. 2-16) are two thin elastic sacs with low internal folds that increase the inner surface to form many small chambers, or alveoli.　These are lined with capillaries of the pulmonary circulation.　Each lung connects by a short **bronchus** to the voice box or **larynx** behind the glottis.　The mechanics of breathing involve **inspiration,** or drawing in air, and **expiration,** or forcing it out, both performed with the mouth closed.　At inspiration (1) the glottis closes, the mouth floor is depressed, and air is drawn through the nares into the mouth cavity and pharynx; (2) the external nares close (by valves), and the mouth cavity is compressed to force the air through the opened glottis into the lungs.　At expiration the muscles of the body wall contract to force air in the lungs out the mouth cavity and nares.　Much of the frog's respiration, however, is performed by merely pumping air in and out of the mouth cavity, where the gaseous exchange occurs through the mucous membranes of its lining. The frog's skin contains large blood vessels that serve in respiration either in air or water and especially during hibernation. Oxygen dissolved in the water then passes through the moist skin to the blood, and carbon dioxide moves in the reverse direction. The frog tadpole has **gills** for respiration (Fig. 29-4). These are slender extensions of the epithelium of the pharynx containing many blood capillaries; their function is comparable with that of the skin or lung of a frog (Fig. 4-17).

The **larynx** is reinforced by cartilages and contains two elastic bands, the **vocal cords.** When air is forced vigorously from the lungs, the cords vibrate and produce croaking notes, the pitch of the sound being regulated by muscular tension on the cords.

Fig. 2-16.   Respiratory organs of the bullfrog in laterodorsal view.   *Left.*   Larynx opened with right vocal cord in place.

2-12. Excretory system.   The animal body is a delicately balanced system from which excess materials and the wastes, or end products, of metabolism must be removed. The process of removal is termed **excretion.**   Some wastes are disposed of by the skin and lungs, others are discharged from the liver in the bile, and some are excreted from the intestine with the feces. The principal **excretory organs** of the frog are the two elongate brown **kidneys** (Fig. 2-17). These lie dorsal to the coelom and peritoneum in the subvertebral lymph sac. The kidneys are selective filters that remove soluble organic wastes (especially urea), excess mineral salts, and water gathered from the body cells and fluids by the blood.

Each kidney is a compact mass of about 2,000 **renal corpuscles** (Malpighian bodies) bound together by connective tissue. A renal corpuscle comprises (1) a coiled knot, or **glomerulus,** of small arteries within (2) a double-walled cup, or **Bowman capsule,** that is connected to (3) a **uriniferous tubule** surrounded by capillaries (Fig. 4-20). The latter joins through collecting tubules to the **ureter** (Wolffian duct), a fine white tube that extends along the outer margin of the kidney to the dorsal wall of the cloaca.   Blood with both oxygen and wastes is brought to the kidneys in the renal arteries, which divide into arterioles in the glomeruli and continue as capillaries about the tubules; the renal portal veins also join these capillaries.   Blood reduced in wastes leaves the kidneys by the renal veins.   On the ventral surface of each kidney are many ciliated funnels, or **nephrostomes,** that may drain wastes from the coelom.   They connect to uriniferous tubules in frog larvae and later to the renal veins.

The liquid waste collected in the kidneys is known as **urine.**   It passes down the ureters to the cloaca and may be voided at once through the

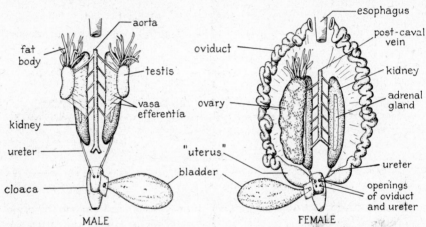

FIG. 2-17.   Excretory and reproductive organs (urogenital system) of the frog in ventral view.   Cloaca opened ventrally to show entrance of ducts (enlarged), and the bladder turned aside.   Aorta and arteries shown in male, and postcaval vein in female; left ovary omitted.

anus or may be stored temporarily in the thin-walled **bladder** that connects to the ventral side of the cloaca.   The daily output of urine in summer amounts to about one-third of the frog's weight.

2-13. Nervous system.   The complex physiological processes of the many organs within the body and the frog's relations with its external environment are controlled and coordinated by the **nervous system** (Fig. 2-18).   This is an intricate structure composed of nerve cells, or **neurons** (Chap. 3).   The system includes (1) the **central nervous system,** or brain and spinal cord and (2) the **peripheral nervous system** of the paired cranial and spinal nerves together with the sympathetic nervous system.

The **brain** is housed in the "brain box," or cranium.   In dorsal view it shows (1) two **olfactory lobes** with nerves to the nasal chambers; (2) two **cerebral hemispheres** closely joined to the preceding and also attached to (3) the median **diencephalon,** or 'tween-brain.   Behind this are two rounded **optic lobes,** supported on (4) the **midbrain** below, and followed by (5) a small transverse **cerebellum;** this is over (6) the open-topped **medulla oblongata,** which tapers to join the spinal cord.   The diencephalon has a dorsal **pineal body** or **epiphysis.**   Below the diencephalon is the **optic chiasma,** or crossing of the optic nerves, followed by the **infundibulum** as a bluntly triangular outgrowth, with the **hypophysis,** or **pituitary body,** at its posterior end.

The **cavities** within the brain are the first and second **ventricles** in the cerebral hemispheres; these connect to a third ventricle in the diencephalon.   From the latter a small aqueduct of Sylvius leads to the fourth ventricle located in the medulla.   The fourth ventricle is continuous with a minute central canal through the spinal cord.   Cerebrospinal fluid fills the ventricles and other cavities and surrounds the brain.   Metabolic exchanges for the brain are performed by arteries and veins over its sur-

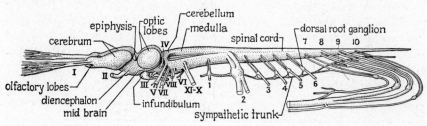

FIG. 2-18.   Nervous system of the bullfrog in laterodorsal view, with the nerves and sympathetic trunk of the left side.   I–X, cranial nerves; 1–10, spinal nerves (see Table 4-7).

face and by two dense networks of blood vessels, the **anterior choroid plexus** over a dorsal opening in the diencephalon and the **posterior choroid plexus** over the medulla.   The brain and spinal cord are surrounded by two membranes, a thicker **dura mater** adhering to the enclosing bones and a delicate **pia mater** close over the nervous tissue itself. Ten pairs of **cranial nerves** extend from various parts of the brain to sense organs, muscles, and other structures (Table 4-7).

The functions of the brain have been determined by studying the behavior of frogs after experimentally injuring or removing parts and by stimulation with electric currents.   The olfactory lobes serve the sense of smell.   The cerebral hemispheres are areas of memory, intelligence, and voluntary control in higher animals, but in the frog their function is less clear.   Removal impairs memory, the frog is lethargic, and its movements are more machine-like.   The diencephalon is related to vision and balance.   The optic lobes inhibit reflexes in the spinal cord, each controlling the opposite side of the body.   In higher vertebrates the cerebellum is a center of coordination; in the frog it controls equilibrium in part. The medulla directs most bodily activities.   If all the brain but the medulla is removed, the frog can leap, swim, capture and swallow food, recover normal position if inverted, and breathe normally. Death soon follows removal of the medulla.

The **spinal cord** extends backward from the medulla and within the neural arches of the vertebrae, to end as a slender filament in the urostyle. It has lengthwise dorsal and ventral *fissures* and contains a **central canal** already noted. The outer portion, or **white matter,** is chiefly of nerve fibers; and the inner part, or **gray matter,** consists largely of nerve cells. Ten pairs of **spinal nerves** emerge laterally from the cord, between the vertebrae, and can be seen as shiny white strands on the dorsal wall of the abdomen above the peritoneum. Each nerve has two roots. The **sensory** or **dorsal root** carries nerve impulses from parts of the body *into* the spinal cord, and on this root is a **ganglion** containing nerve cells. The **motor** or **ventral root** comprises fibers that transmit directive impulses *outward* from the cord to the tissues. The two roots of each join outside the cord as a nerve that extends to a definite part of the body or limbs. On either side, the large second or **brachial nerve** joins in a network, or **brachial plexus,** from which nerves run to the fore limb and shoulder region. The seventh to ninth form a **sciatic plexus** that distributes to the hind limb.

The **sympathetic nervous system** shows as two threadlike nerve strands above the dorsal wall of the coelom. Each has 10 ganglia and many fibers connecting to the brain, spinal cord, and viscera. The system directs many internal or "vegetative" functions that are not under conscious or voluntary regulation such as the rate of heartbeat, secretion of digestive juices, muscular movements in the stomach and intestine, and the muscular "tone" of blood vessels.

2-14. Sense organs. Changes in either the external or internal environment of an animal act as stimuli that affect **sensory structures,** or **receptors,** in its body. The receptors are connected to sensory nerves and give rise to nerve impulses, which are transmitted to the central nervous system. Each kind of stimulus affects a particular kind of receptor. We know accurately only the sensations of man; from these we interpret the sensory reactions of lower animals. In the frog, receptors for **touch,** or **tactile stimuli,** are present as microscopic structures under the epidermis. Others probably respond to irritating substances such as strong chemicals and possibly to heat. The tongue bears small papillae containing **taste buds** which evidently pass judgment on items taken into the mouth for food, since some are rejected. The sense of **smell** is ascribed to endings of the olfactory nerves in the nasal cavities.

The vertebrate **ear** serves the dual function of **hearing** and adjusting the **equilibrium** of the body. The latter sense resides in the semicircular canals and ampullae of the inner ear (Chap. 4). The frog has a **tympanic membrane** or **eardrum** exposed on either side of the head to receive sound waves from both air and water. Vibrations induced in an eardrum are transmitted across the space beneath (middle ear) by a rod (columella) connecting between the eardrum and inner ear. The latter lies within the prootic bone and contains a lymph-filled compartment with sensory endings of the eighth cranial or auditory nerve where sound impressions are registered. Frogs seem insensitive to most sounds but react to the croaking notes of males during the breeding season.

The *eye* is the most complex of vertebrate sense organs and responds to *light* or ether waves having certain frequencies of vibration. The frog's eyes are much like those of man (Fig. 4-34). The *eyeball* lies in the orbit, beneath the eyelids, and may be rotated by six muscles attached to its outer surface. Its structure is analogous to that of a camera, having a transparent biconvex lens that forms an image on the sensitive interior. The outer covering or *sclerotic coat,* of connective tissue, forms a supporting case, with the *cornea* as a transparent front. The next or *choroid coat* contains blood vessels and much black pigment to exclude all light save that entering the front. The innermost layer or *retina* contains the *rods* and *cones,* or receptors for vision, that connect to the second cranial or *optic nerve.* Inside the cornea, part of the choroid coat is specialized as the *iris,* a pigmented disc with a central opening, or *pupil,* through which light enters the spherical *lens* just behind. The pupil contracts or dilates to regulate the amount of light entering the eye. The frog's lens does not change in either shape or position, and its eye is like a "box camera" for forming images of objects beyond a certain minimum distance. The space before the lens contains a watery *aqueous humor* and that behind contains a jelly-like *vitreous humor,* both serving to maintain the form of the eyeball.

2-15. Endocrine glands. The frog, like other vertebrates, has several *endocrine* or *ductless glands.* These produce substances known as *hormones* or *internal secretions* since they are carried by the blood instead of being passed out through ducts. The hormones regulate various physiological processes (see general discussion in Chap. 4).

At the base of the brain is a minute *pituitary gland,* of three lobes. The *anterior lobe,* in larvae and young, secretes a *growth-stimulating hormone* that controls growth, especially of long bones, and also affects the thyroid. Removal of the gland in larvae delays their growth, and they do not metamorphose into frogs; replanting the gland restores these functions, and by feeding or injecting an extract of the gland larvae of greater than normal size result. In adult frogs the anterior lobe secretes a *gonad-stimulating hormone* responsible for release of ova or sperm from the reproductive organs. If two or more fresh anterior lobes are implanted on successive days in an adult but nonbreeding female, her eggs will soon mature and be laid. Similar implants into a male will hasten sexual maturity, the clasping reflex, and the discharge of spermatozoa. The *intermediate lobe* produces *intermedin,* which regulates the behavior of chromatophores in the skin. Its removal is followed by a marked bleaching due to concentration of the pigment; if then implanted, the pigment spreads and normal coloration results. The *posterior lobe* evidently regulates water intake by the skin; its removal seems to inhibit molt of the cornified epidermis and to cause deposition of pigment there.

The small *thyroid gland* behind the hyoid cartilage produces *thyroxin,* which regulates general metabolism. The gland enlarges and its secretion increases in larvae before they metamorphose into frogs. If it is removed, the larvae do not transform. If the gland or its extract is injected into young bullfrog larvae, which normally have a two-year larval life, their metamorphosis is hastened.

The *pancreas* secretes, besides digestive enzymes, the hormone known as *insulin,* which regulates sugar metabolism. This is produced by special cell groups, the *islets of Langerhans.* Its action is less conspicuous in the cold-blooded frog than in birds and mammals.

Along the ventral surface of each kidney is a slender *adrenal gland* that produces *epinephrin,* or *adrenalin.* This hormone causes increased blood pressure and also contracts the dark pigment in the skin.

2-16. Reproductive system. The organ systems discussed previously are all concerned with the life of the individual animal, whereas the *reproductive system* serves to maintain the species. It consists of the reproductive organs or *gonads,* which produce sex cells, and the *reproductive ducts* through which these cells leave the body (Fig. 2-17). Frogs are of two *sexes,* the *females* which lay eggs or *ova* (sing. *ovum),* and the *males* which produce sperm or *spermatozoa* to fertilize the eggs and cause them to develop into new individuals. Each individual frog is either female or male, the sexes being separate.

The female's two gonads, or *ovaries,* are attached dorsally in the coelom, near the kidneys, each supported by a mesentery (mesovarium). In early spring the ovaries of an adult female contain several thousand small black eggs that swell out the abdomen, but a summer specimen has only a small mass of grayish ovarian substance. Each ovary is a hollow sac of four to seven lobes with thin double walls, and every egg is enclosed in a delicate follicle formed of cells between the two layers. The ovary is supplied with arteries that bring materials for growth of the ova. Along either side of the middorsal line of the coelom is a whitish convoluted *oviduct;* its anterior end is an open ciliated funnel (ostium) and its posterior end joins dorsally to the cloaca.

When the eggs become mature, in the breeding season, each follicle ruptures (by action of a pituitary hormone), and the eggs escape into the coelom. There they are moved anteriorly by the action of cilia covering

the peritoneum and enter the oviduct funnels.   They are moved down
the ducts by cilia on lengthwise ridges lining the interior.   Between
these ridges are gland cells; these secrete albuminous material to form
the jelly coatings that swell out around the eggs after laying (Figs. 2-20,
29-6).   At 22 to 25°C. the eggs pass through the oviduct in about 4
hours, and they may be accumulated in the enlarged posterior portion
("uterus") before being laid by passing out of the cloaca.

The male has two small bean-shaped *testes* attached near the kidneys
by mesenteries (mesorchia).   Each testis is a mass of coiled *seminiferous
tubules* in which spermatozoa are produced.   The minute sperm, when
mature, enter several fine ducts, or *vasa efferentia,* that pass through the
mesorchium and connect to uriniferous tubules in the anterior part of
the kidney.   The sperm then pass down the tubules and ureter (which

FIG. 2-19.   The earliest illustration of frogs and tadpoles in their natural habitats.
(*From Rondelet, De piscibus marinis,* 1551.)

are joint urinogenital canals) and may be stored in the dilated posterior
end, or *seminal vesicle,* of the ureter.   At mating, the sperm are discharged through the cloaca to fertilize the eggs.   Mature and functional
sperm are present from September to March in *Rana pipiens.*

Anterior to the gonads in either sex are paired fingerlike growths, the
fat bodies.   These are largest just prior to hibernation and far reduced
after breeding.   They provide reserve nutriment, possibly of aid in formation of the sex cells, and for subsistence during hibernation.   They
are of special importance during the breeding season for the males, which
then take little or no food.   The fat bodies are used up in frogs kept for
some time at laboratory temperatures, and females then may also draw
on their yolk-laden eggs for sustenance.

In most species of frogs and toads there are differences between
mature females and males known as *secondary sexual characteristics.*
The males have heavier arm muscles, shorter but stouter inner fingers,
and roughened "nuptial pads" on their fingers.   Male toads and tree
toads have a median resonating pouch on the chin, and there are paired

pouches in some frogs.   The eardrum is larger in the male of the bull-frog and green frog, and there are differences in coloration between the sexes of some toads.   With birds and mammals such differences are due to endocrines produced in gonads, but this is not clearly so in all amphibians.   Implants of testes into female toads will produce thick nuptial pads on the inner fingers such as occur in males.   Conversely, removal of the testes in the European newt (a salamander) is followed by loss of the secondary sexual characteristics.

2-17. Natural history and life cycle.   The general habits of frogs were described earlier in this chapter.   Frogs require a damp environment so that the soft glandular skin will be kept moist.   Most species live in or near ponds or streams (Fig. 2-19), but a few, like the wood frog, inhabit the damp floor of forests.   In such environments they find food, shelter, and breeding places.   Frogs are "cold-blooded" or variable-temperatured (poikilothermous); their body temperature is dependent upon that of the environment so that their distribution and seasonal activities are controlled by climatic conditions.   A few live in cold regions, in high mountains or even within the Arctic Circle, but frogs are most abundant as to species and individuals in the moist regions of temperate or tropical lands.   They reproduce, feed, and grow during the warmer weather; where the winter is cold, that season is spent in hibernation.   In this inactive state, all metabolism in the body drops to a low level, and the heartbeat is very slow.

Each species of frog has a definite time of spring emergence, based upon temperature, and most species proceed at once to reproductive activities (Fig. 2-20).   The males gather in appropriate waters and begin croaking to attract the females.   The latter, when their eggs are "ripe," enter the water where each is clasped by a male.   He mounts her back and holds tightly with his forelegs around her thorax, with the roughened nuptial pads on his inner fingers pressed tightly against her breast.   As the female extrudes her eggs into shallow water, the male discharges milt, or seminal fluid containing spermatozoa, to fertilize them.   The jelly coats about the eggs swell in the water and adhere to plant stems or other objects, the eggs from each female forming a large tapioca-like mass.   Development begins at once, and each egg becomes an embryo, which after some days emerges from the jelly as a small "polliwog," tadpole, or larva.   It has an ovoid head-and-body, a slender compressed tail, and horny jaws used to scrape green algae from objects in the water for food.   The intestine is then long and spirally coiled in the abdomen. The larva has three pairs of external gills on the pharynx, and later these are replaced by three pairs of internal gills within the gill slits (Fig. 29-4). Later the hind legs appear, but the forelegs are hidden under a membrane (operculum) over the ventral surface of the body.   Finally, after some weeks or months, depending upon the species of frog and the prevailing temperature, the larva undergoes a gradual metamorphosis.   Its lungs have developed, and it seeks shallow water where it may gulp down air. The forelegs burst into evidence, and the part larva–part frog lives at the water's edge as its mouth widens, its gills and tail are resorbed, its

limbs appear

internal gills

metamorphosis

mouth parts

external gills

larvae hatch

1 year old

2 years old

3 years old

adults spawn in water

jelly swells

embryonic development

sperm   eggs

Fig. 2-20.   Life cycle of the frog.   (*After Rosel*, 1758.)   Magnified figures show newly hatched tadpoles clinging to vegetation by their adhesive "discs," and the face of an older larva with its dark horny jaws and minute "teeth."

intestine shortens, and other changes occur.   The tadpole thus changes into a frog which, after one or more years, becomes sexually mature and reproduces.

Each female lays several hundred or thousand eggs.   Some eggs fail to develop, and some are eaten by enemies.   Many larvae are devoured by fishes, snakes, turtles, water insects, and other animals, some larvae die because the water dries up before they transform, and young frogs fall victim to many enemies. Of the great numbers of eggs laid each season, only a few become adult frogs; but under normal conditions these are enough to maintain the frog as a species.

References

(See also Chap. 29)

Gaupp, E.   1896–1904.   A. Ecker und R. Wiedersheim's Anatomie des Frosches. 2d ed.   Brunswick, Germany, Friedrich Vieweg & Sohn.   3 vols., 1,774 pp., 500 figs.   A classic, with great detail.

Holmes, S. J.   1928.   The biology of the frog.   4th ed.   New York, The Macmillan Co.   ix + 396 pp., 112 figs.   Simple account of structure, physiology, and behavior.

Howes, G. B.   1902.   Atlas of practical elementary zootomy. . . . London, Macmillan & Co., Ltd.   Pls. I–VIII, the frog, gross and microscopic anatomy.

Marshall, A. M.   1928.   The frog, an introduction to anatomy, histology and embryology.   12th ed.   London, Macmillan & Co., Ltd.   xi + 182 pp., 40 figs.

CHAPTER 3

PROTOPLASM, CELLS, AND TISSUES

A. PROTOPLASM

The living substance in the cells of all plants and animals is called *protoplasm*. It is a complex mixture of various materials, including water, mineral salts, and many organic compounds. The latter are known in nature only as components or products of living organisms. In different species and in the parts and organs of any one animal the protoplasm differs in its chemical, physical, and biological properties. It has, however, certain common characteristics and so was called "the physical basis of life" by T. H. Huxley.

3-1. Chemical composition. Protoplasm contains about 20 of the 93 known chemical elements. The proportions of these and the specific compounds into which they are organized differ in various animals and in the different cells and tissues of any one animal. These elements are among the most common in the rocks, soils, and waters of the earth; they are present in foods taken by animals, in their useful products or secretions, and in the wastes of animal metabolism. An average percentage chemical composition of animal protoplasm (by weight and apart from intercellular substance) is as follows:

Oxygen (O)	76.0	Sulphur (S)	0.2	Magnesium (Mg)	0.02
Carbon (C)	10.5	Phosphorus (P)	0.3	Calcium (Ca)	0.02
Hydrogen (H)	10.0	Potassium (K)	0.3	Sodium (Na)	0.05
Nitrogen (N)	2.5	Iron (Fe)	0.01	Chlorine (Cl)	0.10

Traces of silicon (Si), copper (Cu), aluminum (Al), manganese (Mn), boron (B), cobalt (Co), iodine (I), fluorine (Fl), and bromine (Br) are also present in many animals. No single element is peculiar to living things, but carbon and nitrogen are more abundant in protoplasm than among inanimate materials.

The *inorganic constituents* are water (H_2O), some salts (NaCl, $CaCO_3$, etc.), and some gases, especially oxygen (O_2) and carbon dioxide (CO_2). *Water* makes up from 50 to 96 per cent, by weight, of protoplasm. It is more abundant in young cells or animals than in older ones and in the lower aquatic animals than in the higher terrestrial types. Water: (1) is the best solvent for inorganic substances and for many organic compounds; (2) favors the dissociation of electrolytes dissolved in it; (3) has high surface tension; (4) has great fluidity; and (5) has a large capacity to absorb heat. All the necessary processes of protoplasm are dependent upon these characteristics of water, and the life of organisms on this earth would be impossible without it. Watery body fluids (lymph and blood plasma), with both inorganic and organic content, surround cells in the animal body and transport materials within it. Terrestrial animals usually have a suitable body covering and other means to restrict undue loss of water.

The *inorganic salts* are chiefly those found in sea water, notably sodium chloride (NaCl), and are present in small concentrations; the ions of these are important in the composition of protoplasm, its chemical activities and electrical properties, and for growth, maintenance of health, and reproduction. The skeletons or shells of many animals are composed of inorganic salts [$CaCO_3$, $Ca_3(PO_4)_2$, etc.] secreted by specific cells or tissues.

Organic compounds are those of carbon and hydrogen in which some or all of the hydrogen may be replaced by other elements or chemical radicals. Organic compounds in animals usually contain oxygen, many also contain nitrogen, and some have other elements. Protoplasm consists principally of carbohydrates, lipids, and proteins.

Carbohydrates are compounds of carbon, hydrogen, and oxygen, generally with the latter two in a 2 to 1 ratio, as in water. The most common in animals are sugars and glycogen ("animal starch"). Carbohydrates taken into the body are usually transformed into glucose ($C_6H_{12}O_6$) while being absorbed. This substance is ready soluble, is easily oxidized in the tissues, and is the most important source of energy for protoplasmic activities. Starches with the formula ($C_6H_{10}O_5$)$_x$ (x may be 200 to 300) are common as stored food substances in plants. Starches eaten by animals are broken down (hydrolyzed) into simple sugars by the digestive enzymes before being absorbed. The cellulose that forms the walls of plant cells has the same empirical formula as starch, but x is much larger and the molecule is of different structure; cellulose is relatively insoluble and can be digested by only a few animals. Glycogen ($C_6H_{10}O_5$)$_x$ (x being small) is stored in animal tissues, especially the liver and muscles. Lactose, or milk sugar ($C_{12}H_{22}O_{11}$), is present in the milk secreted by all mammals to nourish their young.

Lipids (fatty and related substances) contain carbon and hydrogen, with less oxygen than carbohydrates. They are all "greasy" and are soluble in organic liquids such as ether, chloroform, or benzene, but rarely in water. Some are fluid at ordinary temperatures, such as cod liver oil or whale oil; others are solid fats, such as butter, lard, and tallow; and a few are waxes such as that in the human ear or that produced by bees. The true fats, both liquid and solid, are combinations of glycerol (glycerin) and fatty acids, of which oleic acid ($C_{18}H_{34}O_2$) in butter is an example. Fats may be decomposed (saponified) by alkalies such as sodium or potassium hydroxide, yielding glycerol and soaps, which are soluble in water. The compound lipids may contain nitrogen, with or without phosphorus, in addition to carbon, hydrogen, and oxygen; lecithin, abundant in egg yolk, is an example. The sterols are complex waxlike lipids, with many carbon and hydrogen atoms and at least one OH radical. Cholesterol, vitamin *D*, some sex hormones, and certain cancer-producing substances belong in this group. The compound lipids and sterols are essential components of all protoplasm. Many fats are received in food of both plant and animal origin and are variously transformed either for immediate use or else for storage in the animal body. They are readily oxidized in protoplasm, yielding energy that is largely transformed into heat.

Proteins are the most abundant organic compounds in animal protoplasm. They contain carbon, hydrogen, oxygen, and nitrogen, usually with small amounts of sulphur, sometimes phosphorus, and occasionally iron, iodine, or other elements. Protein molecules are very complex, with molecular weights of 35,000 (gelatin) to 5,000,000 (hemocyanin) or more. They are composed of structural units known as amino acids, characterized by nitrogen in an amino radical (NH_2). More than 20 amino acids are known, and the many ways in which they can combine make possible an almost infinite variety of proteins or nitrogenous substances. "Simple" proteins consist entirely of amino acids; examples are the soluble proteins in blood serum, milk albumen, and egg white, and the very insoluble proteins known as keratins that form cuticle, hair, and nails. "Conjugated" proteins contain other radicals or organic compounds besides amino acids; examples are the hemoglobin in red blood cells, and the nucleoproteins of cell nuclei.

Protoplasm contains additional organic substances, some of unknown composition, that either direct the activities of individual cells and tissues or else control and coordinate the functions of the entire animal. These *regulatory substances,* the enzymes, hormones, vitamins, and respiratory pigments, are discussed further in Chap. 4.

3-2. Physical characteristics. Typically protoplasm is a translucent, grayish slimy substance, somewhat viscous, but capable of flowing. It usually consists of a matrix containing minute particles. Such a combination is termed a *colloid* (Gr. *kolla*, glue), which is a state rather than a kind of matter. The matrix is the *continuous* or *external phase,* and the inclusions constitute the *dispersed* or *internal phase.* Colloid particles measure 1/10,000 to 1/1,000,000 mm. in diameter; thus they are larger than most chemical molecules but cannot be seen with ordinary microscopes. Colloids do not diffuse through parchment or similar membranes and upon drying ordinarily yield formless masses, whereas crystalloids such as salts or sugars usually form true solutions that can diffuse through membranes and that upon drying yield crystals of definite structure. *Emulsions* with particles of larger than colloid size are exemplified by droplets of oil or fat in protoplasm and by the fat (cream) in milk. A colloid system may be either a somewhat rigid *gel* or a more liquid *sol,* and in living matter these states may interchange during metabolic processes.

Division of material into minute particles results in an enormous increase in its total surface. Thus, a solid cubic centimeter of any substance has a surface of 6 sq. cm. (about 1 square inch); but if dispersed in particles 1/100,000 mm. in diameter, the total surface is about 6,000 sq. m., or 1⅜ acres. As the life processes in protoplasm occur at surfaces between cells and particles, the enormous areas provided by colloid dispersion are highly important.

The physical structure of protoplasm has been variously interpreted to be (1) granular; (2) foamlike or alveolar; (3) an emulsion; or (4) fibrillar or reticular, of small fibers or threads. Actual differences in kind, difficulties in observing the fine details, and changes incidental to removing protoplasm from living organisms or the fixing of tissues for study are responsible for some differences in the interpretation of its structure.

3-3. Biological activities. Protoplasm and living organisms are characterized by activity and change. A human being develops as an embryo, is born, grows, lives actively, and dies. Within its protoplasm, as in all animals, many processes are going on constantly. In contrast to nonliving materials, protoplasm is characterized by (1) *metabolism,* the physical and chemical changes by which materials are transformed and used for growth, maintenance, and repair and to yield energy; (2) *irritability,* the response to stimuli from changes in its environment; and (3) *reproduction,* the ability of an organism or its parts to produce new individuals of its own kind. Constructive metabolism (anabolism) includes the synthesis of components from foods into compounds, often more complex, which are incorporated into the protoplasm, stored for later use, or formed into essential products such as secretions. By destructive metabolism (catabolism, dissimilation), various components are broken down (oxidized, etc.) to simpler compounds, providing energy for work or heat, with consequent yield of waste products. Both types are occurring simultaneously in living protoplasm, but anabolic processes, leading to growth, predominate during embryonic development and early life.

3-4. Enzymes. Many of the chemical processes within living protoplasm are extremely rapid; yet the same substances, when removed from the body, react slowly if at all. The difference is due to the presence in animal cells and tissues of organic catalysts, known as **enzymes,** responsible for specific types of reaction.   A catalyst is a substance that speeds a chemical reaction without affecting the end point, or being used up, or being combined in the end product.   Minute amounts of an enzyme will transform large amounts of the substance acted upon.   The enzymes are protein in nature.   Many kinds are known, and 20 to 30 have been crystallized but none synthesized.   Some writers believe there may be a thousand kinds in one animal cell.   Digestion, respiration, secretion, excretion, and other vital processes depend upon enzymes.   Each enzyme acts on a particular class of chemical substance (carbohydrate, fat, protein) and in a particular constructive or destructive type of reaction. Each does best at some optimum temperature and a certain acid or alkaline reaction (pH) of the surrounding fluid medium.   Most enzymes lose their catalytic power when heated to 40 to 50°C.   This may be one reason many animals die at such temperatures.   Many enzymes are formed in the cells where they are produced as inactive **zymogens;** only in the presence of another substance, an **activator,** does the enzyme become functional.   For example, the inactive trypsinogen, secreted in the pancreas, becomes the active protein-splitting enzyme, trypsin, after it has passed through the pancreatic duct into the cavity of the small intestine and been activated there by enterokinase secreted by cells in the intestinal wall.   Some vitamins (B_1, B_2) exert their action by combination with certain oxidizing enzymes.

3-5. Diffusion and osmosis. The living protoplasm in an animal requires a supply of materials for metabolism and must dispose of the wastes or end products.   This continuing traffic between exterior and interior, body fluids and cells, is of substances in solution.   Not all materials can pass these routes.

If a quantity of gas is enclosed in a container, it **diffuses** or becomes distributed equally throughout the container because of forces that repel each gas molecule from the others; the resulting **diffusion pressure** is proportional to the number of molecules present per unit volume of space. If two gases are present, each becomes diffused equally and the total pressure is the sum of the two partial pressures.   In like manner, a gas or a soluble solid diffuses in a liquid, and one liquid diffuses in another.   If crystals of either salt or sugar are dropped into water, they subsequently disappear by going into solution.   There is mutual and uniform diffusion of the molecules of water and of sugar or salt.

The physiological processes and exchanges of living cells depend in part on some physical properties of the enclosing membranes and contents. The cells and some of their components are enclosed by ultramicroscopic thin layers, of colloidal nature, known as **semipermeable membranes.** These contain submicroscopic pores through which certain kinds of molecules can pass but other larger molecules cannot.   Membranes regulate the movement and exchange of foods, respiratory gases, other essential materials, and wastes between the cells and fluids in animal bodies. Some pass larger molecules than others, and the rate of passage varies with the kind of membrane and kinds and amounts of material present on the two sides.   When unequal concentrations of dissolved substances occur on the opposite sides of such a membrane, the resulting differences in diffusion pressure will tend to force exchange of water and of the substances through the membrane until there is equilibrium between the two sides.   Such diffusion of water is termed *osmosis* (some authors also use this term for the diffusion of dissolved substances).   When two fluids contain equal concentrations of dissolved substances, they are said to be *isotonic*.   Solutions used to immerse living cells or tissues for study are made isotonic with the natural fluids that surrounded the cells or tissues in the body, as to the kinds and amounts of the principal salts (0.9 per cent NaCl for mammalian blood or tissues, etc.).

Experiments with artificial semipermeable membranes (of collodion or cellophane) serve to demonstrate these principles.   A container is divided into two parts by a membrane; one part (A) contains salt (NaCl; molecular weight, 58) dissolved in water and the other (B) only pure water. Some salt will diffuse through the membrane from A to B and some water from B to A until an equilibrium occurs with equal parts of salt and water in each.   If a solution of salt is placed in A and of cane sugar ($C_{12}H_{22}O_{11}$; molecular weight, 342) in B, the exchange will be slower but eventually will reach equilibrium with like amounts of salt and sugar in each.   When a solution of hemoglobin is placed in A and water in B, water will move from B to A by osmosis, but no diffusion of hemoglobin into B will occur because of its much greater molecular weight (63,000 to 68,000).

B. CELLS

3-6. History.   The finer structures of living organisms were unknown until after the invention of the compound microscope (about 1591).   In 1665 Robert Hooke reported that cork and other plant materials contained numerous small partitions separating cavities that he named *cells*. In 1824 Rene Dutrochet stated that " . . . plants are composed entirely of cells, and of organs that are obviously derived from cells . . . ," and that the same applied to animals.   In 1833 Robert Brown described the nucleus as a central feature in plant cells.   In 1838 M. J. Schleiden put forth the thesis that cells were the unit of structure in plants; and 1839 his coworker Theodor Schwann, having studied many animal tissues in detail, applied the thesis to animals.   This generalization is known as the *cell theory*.   Greater emphasis was given at first to the cell wall and less to the contents.   In 1840 Purkinje named the cell contents protoplasm.

Research during the past century has extended the theory and shown that the cell content is by far the important part and has recognized that intercellular material is produced by certain cells. According to the cell theory *all animals and plants are composed of cells and of cell products.* The cell is the fundamental unit, both structural and physiological, in all organisms, and there is a constant exchange of matter and energy within cells in the process of living. In multicellular animals the cells are integrated for proper functioning, whereas in unicellular animals the cell and organism are one. A multicellular animal generally starts life as a single cell that divides repeatedly to form its body.

3-7. The cell. A *cell* is a mass of protoplasm enclosed in a membrane and containing a nucleus; both nucleus and cytoplasm arise by division of the corresponding elements of a preexisting cell. As exceptions, the red blood cells of mammals lose the nucleus after growth, and cells of striated muscles and a few other kinds have more than one nucleus in each.

Since most animal cells are quite small, the unit chosen for their measurement is 1/1,000 of a millimeter, a *micron* (plural *micra*), designated by the Greek letter μ. Human red blood cells average 7.5 μ in diameter, and many other cells are from 10 to 50 μ, but some nerve cells in large animals are several feet in length. The largest cells are the yolks of bird and shark eggs; that of the chicken is about 30 mm. in diameter.

The typical animal cell (Fig. 3-1) is bounded by a delicate *cell membrane* within which is an invisible *plasma membrane* surrounding the *cytoplasm* (cytosome) that fills the interior of the cell and contains the *nucleus.* The cytoplasm is translucent and viscous. Near the nucleus is a globular *centrosome* (cell center) containing one or two dotlike *centrioles* (central bodies). The cytoplasm commonly contains various inclusions such as (1) *mitochondria* (chondriosomes), formed as minute granules or filaments; (2) *Golgi bodies,* small

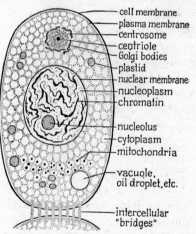

cell membrane
plasma membrane
centrosome
centriole
Golgi bodies
plastid
nuclear membrane
nucleoplasm
chromatin

nucleolus
cytoplasm
mitochondria

vacuole,
oil droplet, etc.

intercellular
"bridges"

Fig. 3-1. Diagram of an animal cell. Not all parts shown will be present or evident in any one cell, either living or fixed and stained.

networks or groups of granules believed to have a part in forming secretions; (3) *fat,* as droplets or as yolk in egg cells; (4) *vacuoles,* filled with either granular or fluid material; and (5) *secretion granules,* especially in gland cells, later to be transformed and pass out as secretions. These inclusions serve various special purposes in cell physiology, not all understood; some require special techniques to be seen.

The nucleus is commonly oval or spherical but in some kinds of cells is elongate or lobed; it may be centered in the cytoplasm or at one side or end. It is surrounded by a distinct **nuclear membrane** enclosing the nuclear sap (karyolymph). Most important within the nucleus is the **chromatin,** seemingly of isolated granules but actually parts of continuously spiraled filaments, the **chromonemata.** Chromatin is so named

Fig. 3-2. *A.* One pair of giant chromosomes from the salivary glands of a fruitfly (*Drosophila*); The dark crossbands may be the loci (location) of genes. *B.* Chromosomes of the gonads in *Drosophila* to the same scale, the arrow pointing to the chromosomes (IVth pair) shown in *A.* (*After Bridges, American Genetics Association, 1936.*)

Fig. 3-3. The 48 human chromosomes. *Left.* During mitosis in an embryonic mesenchyme cell; deeper lying chromosomes are stippled; the *Y* chromosome of the male is marked. ×1500. *Right.* Arranged in homologous pairs to show differences in size and shape. (*After Evans and Swezy, 1931.*)

because it stains intensely with basic dyes such as hematoxylin. Each nucleus usually contains a spherical **nucleoleus** (one or more). The nucleus controls much of cell metabolism; if removed the cell cannot perform anabolic activities and lives only a short time. An isolated nucleus cannot form cytoplasm.

The study of cell structure and activity is known as **cytology**. For most cytological study, cells or pieces of tissue are fixed (killed) in chemical reagents or by freezing, cut in thin sections (10 μ or less), mounted on microscope slides, and stained to differentiate the internal details. Care is necessary that these procedures do not alter the original details within the cells. Living cells may be treated with "vital dyes" that stain and render parts more visible without injury.   Apparatus for microdissection permits removal of cell parts or injection of reagents for special studies. Isolated cells and tissues may be kept alive to grow for days (or years) in nutrient solutions.   The phase microscope and the electron microscope are new research tools permitting study of the finer details of cell structure.

C. CELL DIVISION

Growth in organisms is chiefly by multiplication of cells.   In the unicellular PROTOZOA, the animals themselves are multiplied; in other animals the number of cells in the individual is increased.   Living cells, when not dividing, are termed metabolic cells, because metabolic processes are going on constantly within them.

FIG. 3-4.   Diagram of stages in mitosis, the division of one cell into two.

3-8. Mitosis.   Cells multiply chiefly by *mitosis,* a somewhat complex process that involves, importantly, an equal division of the nuclear chromatin as to kind and amount (Fig. 3-4).   Mitosis is active during embryonic development, in growth, in repair of injury, and in replacement of body covering at molting.   As seen in living cells it is a continuous dynamic process, but for study purposes is divided into several stages, as follows: (1) prophase, (2) metaphase, (3) anaphase, and (4) telophase. Cells not undergoing mitosis are said to be in the interphase.

PROPHASE.   The centrosome usually contains two centrioles (if but one this divides); the two move to opposite sides of the nucleus.   Around each centriole fine short radiating fibers appear in the cytoplasm to form an aster; and other longer *spindle fibers* extend between the separating centrioles.

Meanwhile the chromatin within the nucleus becomes evident as distinct chromosomes that shorten, thicken, and stain deeply.   Each chromosome is actually composed of two wavy parallel filaments, the *chromatids* (daughter chromosomes). In the cells of any one species the several chromosomes are of characteristic size and shape—long or short, thick or thin, and shaped like a rod, J, or V (Figs. 3-2, 3-3). Careful preparations show a constriction or dot (centromere) where the two arms of a chromosome join; this is the point of attachment by spindle fibers. At the end of the prophase the nuclear membrane and nucleolus disappear, the chromosomes become associated with the spindle fibers and move toward the equatorial plane of the cell.

The total number of chromosomes present at the end of the prophase is the *diploid number*.[1] This is constant and characteristic in any species of animal for all its cells except mature germ cells.

METAPHASE. The chromosomes lie radially in an equatorial plate across the cell midway between the two asters, each chromosome being connected to the spindle fibers. Other fibers extend continuously between the poles. The two halves of each chromosome become more evident.

ANAPHASE. The halved chromosomes move apart, those of each group toward its respective pole (centriole). In living cells there is an active pulling back and forth of the opposing sets as they separate. Each daughter chromosome consists of an equivalent half of the material formerly in one chromosome.

TELOPHASE. As the groups of daughter chromosomes end their polar movement they become less conspicuous, a nuclear membrane forms about each group, a nucleolus is produced in each, each centriole divides into two, and the spindle disappears. Finally the cytoplasm constricts in the former plane of the equatorial plate. When this has ended, mitosis is complete. The chromosomes in each daughter cell revert to the netlike pattern of the interstage or metabolic cell.

3-9. Significance of mitosis. The equal division of chromatin whereby each daughter cell receives half of that in each parent chromosome is of great significance from the standpoint of heredity (Chap. 6), since the genes or determiners of hereditary characters are believed to be carried by the chromosomes and to split with the latter. Such partitioning distributes identical lots of genes to all cells in the body.

---

[1] The diploid numbers for a few animals are as follows:

Amoeba, *Entamoeba histolytica*..	6	Fruitfly, *Drosophila melanogaster*.....	8
Radiolarian, *Aulacantha scoly-*		Dogfish, *Scyllium canicula*.........	24
mantha.....................	1,600+	Bullfrog, *Rana catesbeiana*..........	26
Hydra, *Hydra fusca*...........	12	Chicken, *Gallus domesticus*.........	18
Roundworm, *Ascaris megalo-*		Man, *Homo sapiens*...............	48
cephala (germ cells).........	4	Dog, *Canis familaris*..............	78
Earthworm, *Lumbricus terrestris*	32	Horse, *Equus caballus*.............	60
Crayfish, *Cambarus virilis*......	200		

3-10. Amitosis.   Direct nuclear division, or *amitosis,* has been reported in several types of cells and tissues; the nucleus simply constricts and separates into two portions without formation of spindles or chromosomes. This may occur without division of the cytoplasm, resulting in a syncytium, or multinucleate cell.   Many cases of cells undergoing amitotic division are considered to have been abnormal or pathological.

D. TISSUES

The parts of any multicellular animal consist of different kinds of cells. Those of similar structure and function are arranged in groups or layers known as *tissues;* hence multicellular animals (METAZOA) are "tissue animals."   *Histology,* or microscopic anatomy, is the study of the structure and arrangement of tissues in organs, in contrast to gross anatomy which deals with organs and organ systems by dissection.   In each tissue

FIG. 3-5.   Types of epithelial tissues.

the cells are essentially alike, being of characteristic size, form, and arrangement, and they are specialized or *differentiated,* both structurally and physiologically, to perform some particular function such as protection, digestion, or contraction, whence a *division of labor* results among different tissues.

The cells in a multicellular animal may be divided into (1) *somatic cells* or *body cells* (and their products), constituting the individual animal throughout its life; and (2) *germ cells* having to do only with reproduction and continuance of the species (Chap. 5).   There are four major groups of somatic tissues, as follows: (1) epithelial or covering; (2) connective or supporting, including vascular or circulatory; (3) muscular or contractile; and (4) nervous.

3-11. Epithelial tissues.   These cover the body, outside and inside, as in the skin and the lining of the digestive tract (Fig. 3-5).   The cells are compactly placed, with little intercellular material, and often supported beneath on a basement membrane.   Protoplasmic processes, or "bridges," are present between adjacent cells in the skin of vertebrates.   Structurally the cells in epithelial tissues may be (1) squamous, or flat; (2)

cuboidal; (3) columnar; (4) ciliated; or (5) flagellated. The tissue may be either (6) simple, with the cells in one layer; or (7) stratified, with multiple layers. Functionally an epithelial tissue may be (8) protective; (9) glandular, or secretory; or (10) sensory.

Simple squamous epithelium is of thin flat cells, like tiles in a floor; such cells form the peritoneum that lines the body cavity and the endothelium lining the inner surface of blood vessels in vertebrates. *Stratified squamous epithelium* forms the outer layers of the human skin and lines the mouth and nasal cavities. *Simple cuboidal epithelium,* with cubelike cells, is common in salivary glands and in kidney tubules. *Simple columnar epithelium* consists of cells taller than wide, with their long sides adjacent; this type lines the stomach and intestine of vertebrates.

FIG. 3-6. Action of an individual cilium: 1–6*a*, forward stroke, in direction of arrow, cilium rigid; 6*b*–12, recovery stroke, cilium bends from base to tip. (*After Gray*, 1928.)

A *ciliated cell* bears on its exposed surface numerous short hairlike protoplasmic processes known as *cilia* (Fig. 3-6). These beat in one direction, the adjacent cilia acting in unison, so that small particles or materials on the surface are moved along. *Cuboidal ciliated epithelium* lines the sperm ducts of earthworms and other animals, and *columnar ciliated epithelium* lines the earthworm's intestine and the air passages (trachea, etc.) of land vertebrates. The embryos and young larvae of many aquatic animals are covered with ciliated cells by which they are able to swim about. *Flagellated cells* each have a single slender whiplike cytoplasmic process or flagellum on the exposed surface; such cells line the inner digestive cavities of hydra and sponges.

Protective epithelium guards animals from external injury and from infection. It is of a single layer or simple on many invertebrates but stratified on land vertebrates. In the latter case, the basal layer of columnar cells (stratum germinativum) produces successive layers of cells by mitosis; these pass outward, flatten, and lose their soft protoplasmic texture to become cornified or "horny," as they reach the surface. The epithelium on the earthworm secretes a thin homogeneous *cuticle* over its entire exterior surface, and the exterior chitinous covering on arthropods is similarly produced.

Glandular epithelium is specialized for secreting products necessary for use by an animal. Individual gland cells of columnar type (goblet cells) that secrete mucus occur on the exterior of the earthworm and in the intestinal epithelium of vertebrates (Fig. 3-7). *Cuboidal glandular epithelium* forms the salivary and sebaceous glands of man and various mammals.

Sensory cells receive stimuli from without the body. For example, certain groups of cells in the general epithelium on the tongue in vertebrates become specialized as receptors for the sense of taste.

3-12. Connective and supportive tissues. These serve to bind the other tissues and organs together and to support the body. They are derived mainly from embryonic mesenchymal cells that have many delicate protoplasmic processes. Tissues of this group later become diverse in form and usually produce much intercellular substance, so that the cells themselves are less conspicuous. The supportive tissues may be classified as (1) vesicular; (2) gelatinous or mucous; (3) reticular; (4) fibrous; (5) adipose; (6) tendon; (7) cartilage; (8) bone; and (9) pigment (Fig. 3-8). Vascular tissues, blood, and lymph also are included in this group.

UNICELLULAR   SAC-LIKE   TUBULAR   COMPOUND ALVEOLAR
(earthworm)   (frog skin)   (human intestine)   (salivary gland)

FIG. 3-7.   Types of glandular tissues.

Vesicular connective tissue forms the notochord of chordates during early stages of development; it contains large polygonal cells filled with fluid, but little intercellular substance. In *gelatinous connective tissue* the cells have branching processes and the spaces between are filled with a jelly-like matrix, as in the umbilical cord of mammals. *Reticular tissue* is a network of cells with stiffened protoplasmic fibrils, the spaces between being filled with other types of cells; it makes the framework of blood-forming organs such as lymph glands, red bone marrow, and the spleen. *Fibrous connective tissue* consists of scattered cells, rounded or branched in form, with the intercellular spaces occupied by delicate fibers. The *white fibers* consist of numerous fine parallel fibrils, pale in color and often wavy in outline, forming bundles that are crossed or interlaced, but not branched; they occur commonly in tendons and around muscles and nerves. The *elastic fibers* are sharply defined and straight, bent, or branched; they bind the skin to the underlying muscles, attach many other tissues and organs to one another, and are present in walls of the larger blood vessels and elsewhere. Both kinds of fibers occur in the wall of the intestine and in the deeper part (dermis) of vertebrate skin. In *adipose* or *fat tissue* the cells are rounded or polygonal, with thin walls and the nucleus at one side; they contain droplets of fat, which may form larger globules.

Fat is usually dissolved out in prepared microscopic sections, leaving only a framework of cell outlines.

A *tendon* is a bundle of parallel white fibers surrounded by a sheath of the same material, with inward projections of the sheath that form septa, or partitions. *Cartilage,* or gristle, is a supportive tissue consisting of a firm yet elastic matrix (chondrin) secreted by small groups of rounded cartilage cells embedded within it. The exterior surface is covered by a thin membrane, the perichondrium. Three kinds of cartilage are distinguished. *Hyaline cartilage* is bluish white in color, translucent, and of homogeneous texture; it covers the joint surfaces and ends of the ribs and is present in the nose and in the rings of the

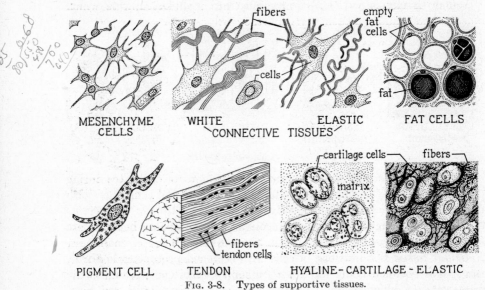

MESENCHYME CELLS   WHITE CONNECTIVE TISSUES   ELASTIC   FAT CELLS

PIGMENT CELL   TENDON   HYALINE - CARTILAGE - ELASTIC

Fig. 3-8.   Types of supportive tissues.

trachea. It is the skeletal cartilage in the embryos of all vertebrates and in the adults of sharks and rays. It may become impregnated with calcareous salts but as such does not become bone. *Elastic cartilage* contains some yellow fibers in the matrix; it is present in the external ears of mammals and in the Eustachian tubes. *Fibrocartilage* is the most resistant type, containing a preponderance of fibers, with fewer cells and less matrix. It occurs in the pads between the vertebrae of mammals, in the pubic symphysis, and about joints subject to severe strains.

True *bone* or *osseous tissue* occurs only in the skeletons of bony fishes and land vertebrates (Fig. 3-9); it differs in structure and composition from the calcareous skeletons of echinoderms, mollusks, and other invertebrates. Bone consists of a dense organic matrix (chiefly collagen) with deposits of mineral substance, largely tricalcium phosphate, Ca_3

$(PO_4)_2$, and calcium carbonate, $CaCO_3$; the mineral part averages about 65 per cent of the total weight.   Bone forms either as replacement for previously existing cartilage (cartilage bone) or follows embryonic mes- enchymal cells (membrane bone).   Both types are produced by **bone cells,** or **osteoblasts,** that secrete both the matrix and the hard material. The cells become separated and embedded but retain many minute protoplasmic connections with one another and with blood vessels. Bone is, therefore, a living tissue that may be resorbed in part or changed in composition.   During the life of an individual the proportion of mineral gradually increases and the organic material decreases, so that bones are resilient in early youth and brittle in old age.

A bone is closely surrounded by thin fibrous **periosteum,** to which muscles and tendons attach.   Within the periosteum are bone cells that

FIG. 3-9.   Structure of bone (enlarged and diagrammatic).   *A*. Portion of a long bone in longitudinal and cross section.   *B*. Three concentric lamellae around a Haversian canal, as seen in a thinly ground cross section.

function in growth and repair.   The mineral substance is usually depos- ited in thin layers, or **lamellae.**   Those beneath the periosteum (periosteal lamellae) are parallel to the surface.   Within this wall, especially in long bones, are many small tubular **concentric lamellae,** forming cylin- drical **Haversian systems.**   The wall of each system is of several such lamellae with a central cavity, or **Haversian canal.**   The systems are mainly longitudinal, but the canals cross-connect providing channels for blood vessels and nerves to pass from the periosteum to the interior **marrow cavity** of a bone.   Individual bone cells occupy small spaces, or **lacunae,** left between the lamellae as the mineral is deposited, and these are connected to one another by many minute radiating canals (canaliculi) occupied by the protoplasmic processes.   In flat (cancellous) bones as of the skull and in the ends of long bones, the interior lacks regular systems and is of more spongy texture.   Gross sections made by sawing such bones will show that the bone fibers are arranged, like beams in arches and trusses, to resist compression stresses from the exterior.   Sections made by grinding slices of bone until of microscopic thinness will show the lacunae and canaliculi, which then become filled with air and appear black by refraction. The central cavity in a long bone is filled with yellow marrow; the ends and the spaces in other bones contain red marrow, where blood cells are produced.

Pigment cells or *chromatophores,* derived from mesenchyme cells, provide the color of many animals (Figs. 2-7, 29-3).

3-13. Vascular or circulatory tissues. The blood and lymph that serve as means for transport and distribution of materials within the animal body consist of a fluid *plasma* containing free cells, or *corpuscles* (Fig. 3-10, Table 4-3). Colorless *white blood cells,* or *leucocytes,* are found in all animals with body fluids; they differ considerably in structure and function in different groups, but some of them always have the function of "policing" the body by engulfing bacteria and other foreign materials, when they are known as *phagocytes.* Some white blood cells have the power of independent movement and of changing shape, whence they

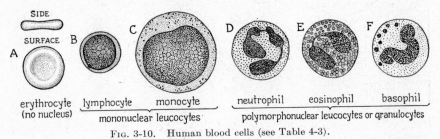

FIG. 3-10. Human blood cells (see Table 4-3).

are called *amoebocytes* (amoeba-like). The leucocytes of vertebrates can pass through the walls of blood vessels and invade other tissues of the body. The blood of vertebrates also contains *red blood cells,* or *erythrocytes,* colored red by the *hemoglobin* that serves for transport of oxygen. In mammals the red cells are nonnucleated, biconcave, and usually round, but in other vertebrates they are nucleated, biconvex, and oval. The fluid plasma transports most materials carried in the blood stream; it is colorless in vertebrates, but in some invertebrates is colored either blue or red by dissolved respiratory pigment (either hemocyanin or hemoglobin).

3-14. Muscular or contractile tissues. Movements in most animals are produced by long, slender muscle cells (Fig. 3-11) that contain minute fibers or *myofibrils.* When stimulated, they shorten in length or contract, thus drawing together the parts to which the muscles are attached.

In *striated muscle* the fibrils have alternate dark and light crossbands of different structure or density, producing a distinctly cross-banded or striated appearance; the dark bands shorten and broaden upon contraction. The cells are cylindrical, scarcely 50 μ in diameter; but some measure an inch or more in length. Each cell is surrounded by a delicate *sarcolemma* and contains several to many long nuclei. Groups of striated muscle cells in the vertebrates are bound together by connective tissue sheaths to form *muscles* of various shapes. These sheaths either attach to the periosteum on bones or gather to form tendons by which the muscles are attached to the skeleton. The simultaneous contraction of many fibers causes a muscle to shorten and bulge, as easily seen in the biceps of the upper arm. Since striated muscle in vertebrates is attached to the skeleton, it is called skeletal muscle and being under conscious control is also termed voluntary muscle.

Nonstriated or *smooth muscle* consists of delicate spindle-shaped cells, each with one central oval nucleus and homogeneous fibers; the cells are arranged in layers, or sheets, held by fibrous connective tissue. Such

A- Smooth or involuntary

B- Striated or skeletal

C- Cardiac or heart

Fig. 3-11.   Types of muscular cells and tissues.

muscle is found in the internal organs or viscera of the vertebrate body, as in the walls of the digestive tract, blood vessels, respiratory passages, and urinary and genital organs; hence it is also called visceral muscle; not being under control of the will, it is also termed involuntary muscle. The heart muscle of vertebrates is called *cardiac muscle;* it contains delicate cross striations, and the fibers are branched to form an interconnecting network. In some lower invertebrates the contractile and protoplasmic portions of a muscle cell are of distinct parts, as in nematodes.

Nonstriated muscle is usually capable of slow but protracted contraction; in mollusks, it forms the voluntary muscles of the body. Striated muscle can contract rapidly but intermittently and requires frequent rest periods; it occurs in the wing muscles of the swiftest flying insects and in the bodies and viscera of arthropods generally. Cardiac muscle is striated yet involuntary; throughout the life of an individual its only rest period is between successive contractions of the heart.

3-15. Nervous tissues. These are specialized for the reception, storage, transmission, and discharge of stimuli either from without or inside the body. The individual nerve cell, or **neuron,** usually has a large cell body, a conspicuous nucleus, and two or more protoplasmic processes (Fig. 3-12). The process that transmits stimuli toward the cell body is the **dendrite,** and that carrying impulses away from it is the **axone. Bipolar cells** have one dendrite and one axone; **multipolar cells** have a multiple dendrite and single axone. The dendrite is often short and commonly much branched (like a tree) near the cell body, whereas the axone may be short or long and is unbranched save for an occasional **collateral fiber.** A

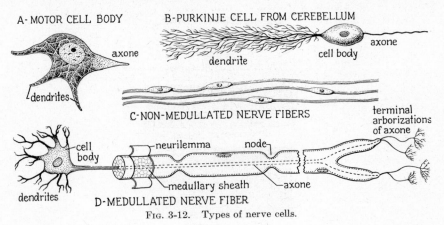

A- MOTOR CELL BODY   B- PURKINJE CELL FROM CEREBELLUM

axone

dendrite

cell body

axone

dendrites

C- NON-MEDULLATED NERVE FIBERS

terminal arborizations of axone

cell body

neurilemma

node

medullary sheath

axone

dendrites   D- MEDULLATED NERVE FIBER

Fig. 3-12.   Types of nerve cells.

group of nerve cell bodies, with their conspicuous nuclei, when outside the central nervous system, is termed a **ganglion** (pl. *ganglia*). A group of fibers or processes, bound together by connective tissue, is a **nerve.** The central nervous system of animals consists of an aggregation of nerve cells and fibers. Nerve fibers without any surrounding sheath are termed **nonmedullated** and are gray in appearance. A **medullated fiber** has the axone surrounded by a medullary (myelinated) sheath containing fatty material and appears white. A delicate membrane, or **neurilemma,** surrounds a nonmedullated fiber and likewise the outside of a medullated fiber. The medullated substance is constricted at intervals, forming the **nodes of Ranvier.**

Nonmedullated fibers are common among invertebrates and in vertebrates are found in the sympathetic system, in certain fiber tracts of the spinal cord (internally), and of the brain (externally). Medullated fibers in nerves and on the outside of the spinal cord give these parts a whitish appearance.

Interspersed among nerve cells and fibers throughout the central nervous system are the **neuroglia** (or glia) of several cell types that seem to serve as delicate packing to hold neurons apart.

References

DAHLGREN, ULRIC, and W. A. KEPNER. 1908. A text-book of the principles of animal histology. New York, The Macmillan Co. xiii + 515 pp., 470 figs.

DAWSON, HELEN. 1948. Lambert's histology. 2d ed. Philadelphia, The Blakiston Co. ix + 696 pp., 296 figs.

DE ROBERTIS, E. D. P., W. W. NOWINSKI, and F. A. SAEZ. 1948. General cytology. Translated by Warren Andrew. Philadelphia, W. B. Saunders Co. xi + 345 pp., 143 figs.

MAXIMOW, A. A., and W. BLOOM. 1948. A textbook of histology. 5th ed. Philadephia, W. B. Saunders Co. xi + 700 pp., 562 figs.

NONIDEZ, J. F., and W. F. WINDLE. 1949. Textbook of histology. New York, McGraw-Hill Book Co., Inc. xiii + 450 pp., 287 figs.

SEIFRIZ, WILLIAM. 1936. Protoplasm. New York, McGraw-Hill Book Co., Inc. x + 584 pp., 179 figs.

SHARP, L. W. 1934. Introduction to cytology. 3d ed. New York, McGraw-Hill Book Co., Inc. xiv + 567 pp., 230 figs.

WILSON, E. B. 1928. The cell in development and heredity. 3d ed. New York, The Macmillan Co. xxxvi + 1,232 pp., 529 figs.

CHAPTER 4

ORGANS AND ORGAN SYSTEMS

The relations between structure and function were described for the frog as a representative animal in Chap. 2, and the characteristics of protoplasm, cells, and tissues were given in Chap 3. The present chapter provides a comparative account of the organ systems in animals, contrasting those of invertebrates and vertebrates and describing briefly those of the human body. Matters pertaining to reproduction and development are considered in Chap. 5, and the structure and function of each phylum and class are described in detail in Chaps. 12 to 32. Names of animal groups used here are given in Chaps. 1 and 11 together with characteristics of each. The term vertebrate applies to all members of the Phylum CHORDATA (cyclostomes to mammals) having a segmented spinal column and many other common characteristics (Table 25-1) and the invertebrates comprise all other animals including the lower chordates.

FIG. 4-1. Diagram of the essential functions in an animal.

4-1. Body parts. In the one-celled "bodies" of PROTOZOA structural parts are known as *organelles*. The terms *organ* and *organ system* refer to structures formed of tissues in the multicellular animals, or METAZOA. Essential vital functions are usually performed by definite structural parts, as in the frog. Most of the higher invertebrates and all the vertebrates have systems for the various functions discussed here. The functions of some structures in lower animals are not clearly understood because their small size makes experimental determination difficult. In certain cases, functions are performed without structural differentiation as in the coelenterates that lack respiratory and excretory organs and the flatworms and roundworms that have no circulatory or respiratory organs.

An organ that continues in use maintains its efficiency, but if unused it tends to degenerate. Thus, muscles of the human body retain their normal "tone" if used, but if bandaged or rendered inactive by accident or disease they decrease in size and functional ability. In sedentary animals and many parasites various organs have disappeared. For example the tapeworm, which absorbs nutriment directly from its host, has no digestive tract; and insects such as fleas, lice, and others of parasitic or burrowing habits have no wings.

A. BODY COVERING

4-2. Invertebrates. The body in all animals has some covering to conserve the protoplasm within, to give physical protection, and to exclude disease organisms. Many protozoans (*e.g.*, *Amoeba*) are covered only by the delicate cell membrane, whereas others (*Paramecium*) have also a firm elastic pellicle. All multicellular animals are covered by a tissue, the *epidermis.* On many soft-bodied invertebrates of the water or moist environments on land, such as coelenterates, flatworms, and slugs, this is a single layer of cells. The epidermis on many worms secretes an external, noncellular *cuticle* as additional covering; this is delicate on earthworms but resistant on flukes, tapeworms, and roundworms. On some other animals the epidermis secretes a protective external skeleton or shell.

4-3. Vertebrates. The body covering is a *skin,* or *integument,* consisting of an outer *epidermis* over an underlying *dermis* that contains blood vessels, nerves, and pigment. On fishes the thin epidermis contains many glands that provide mucus to lubricate the exterior of the body. Sharks and rays have enamel-covered exposed scales, and most bony fishes are protected by dermal scales that sheathe the body. The land vertebrates (amphibians to mammals) have a *stratified epidermis* of several cell layers (Figs. 2-6, 4-2). The outermost layer becomes hardened, or *cornified,* as a more resistant covering and is continually renewed by growth of new layers from the base of the epidermis. Amphibian skin is glandular and moist, as in the frog. On reptiles, birds, and mammals the cornified part is dry and tougher, the better to resist wear in dry environments. It also limits the loss of moisture by evaporation and thus conserves body fluids. The skin of reptiles usually contains dermal *scales* that afford added physical protection, and on lizards and snakes the cornified exterior is molted at intervals. Birds are covered by *feathers;* these are dry, nonliving cornified products of the epidermis that insulate the body, provide streamlined exterior contours of bodily form, and make the broad surfaces of the wings and tail used for flight. The skin of mammals is covered by *hairs,* another type of cornified epidermal product, also serving for insulation. Both feathers and hair are replaced periodically by molt of the old and growth of new coverings.

Only the birds and mammals with their heat-conserving body coverings are "warm-blooded" (homoiothermous), with regulated body temperatures. All other animals are "cold-blooded" (poikilothermous); like the frog, their body temperatures are essentially at those of the environments in which they live. Seals, whales, and other aquatic mammals have deep layers of fat (blubber) under the skin that insulate their bodies from heat loss in the water. The human skin (Fig. 4-2) resembles that of other mammals but is scantily haired on most parts. Evaporation of the watery perspiration secreted by the **sweat glands** helps to cool and regulate the body temperature in hot environments.

Other cornified epidermal products include the horns of cattle and sheep (but not the calcareous antlers of deer), the claws, nails, hoofs,

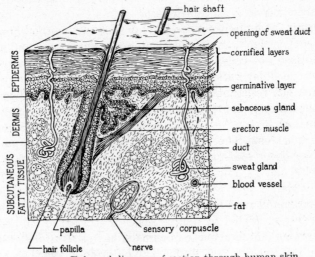

Fig. 4-2.   Enlarged diagram of section through human skin.

and horny pads on the feet of various land vertebrates, the beak and shank coverings on birds, and the outer scutes on turtle shells. Cornified materials are all highly insoluble proteins (keratins) that are quite resistant to wear and chemical disintegration. Some other keratins are the horny coverings on fish eggs and the horny skeletons of bath sponges and sea fans (coelenterates).

B. SKELETAL SYSTEMS

All animals in some phyla and some in most of the others have a firm framework, or **skeleton,** that gives physical support and protection for the body and often provides surfaces for the attachment of muscles. A skeleton is not absolutely essential, however, since many aquatic invertebrates and a few land forms have none. Parts of the skeleton in arthropods and vertebrates form jointed appendages that serve as levers in locomotion.   In such cases there is a close mutual relation of structure and function between the skeletal parts and muscles, whereby their interaction is more efficient.

The skeleton may be a shell or other *external* covering (exoskeleton), as on corals, mollusks, and arthropods, or *internal* (endoskeleton) as with vertebrates.   It is *rigid* on corals, many mollusks, and others, but variously *jointed* and movable in echinoderms, arthropods, and vertebrates.   Exoskeletons serving as defensive armor were present on fossil animals such as the trilobites, primitive fishlike ostracoderms, early amphibians (labyrinthodonts), and some ancient reptiles (dinosaurs); they occur also on living barnacles, some fishes, the turtles, and the armadillo.

An exoskeleton limits the ultimate size of an animal and may become so heavy that the organism must remain fixed.   This is because the internal muscles cannot be large and powerful enough to move the heavy framework.   The internal skeleton of a vertebrate involves far less limitation, and some vertebrates have attained to huge size; these include the brontosaurs and other fossil reptiles and the living elephants and rhinoceroses.   Certain sharks and whales, whose weight is partly supported by the water, are even larger (Fig. 1-2).

4-4. Invertebrate skeletons.   Some protozoans (Sarcodina, Mastigophora) secrete or otherwise form skeletons of calcareous, siliceous, or organic substances, often of intricate pattern.   Sponges secrete microscopic internal rods (spicules) or fibers of the same classes of materials. The skeletons of corals, brachiopods, echinoderms, and mollusks are mainly of lime ($CaCO_3$) and are retained throughout the life of the individual, growing at the margins and becoming thicker with age. All arthropods—crustaceans, insects, and others—are covered completely by jointed exoskeletons of organic materials containing *chitin* (p. 464).   This is flexible at the joints between segments of the body and appendages but more rigid elsewhere.   On crabs and related crustaceans the external covering is reinforced by internal deposits of limy salts that produce a hard "crust."   The appendages number one pair per body segment (somite) or fewer and are variously developed as sensory antennae, jaws or other mouth parts, and legs for walking or swimming. Since the skeletons of arthropods when once hardened cannot expand, these animals undergo complete molt of the old covering at intervals to permit of growth; the body parts enlarge immediately after a molt, before the new covering has hardened.   The exoskeletons of arthropods resist the loss of body fluids; and this, with other adaptations to life in air, enables the insects, spiders, and relatives to inhabit dry environments on land.   The secreted tubes in which some aquatic worms live, the cases built of bottom debris by some protozoans and certain insect larvae, and the empty snail shells used by hermit crabs all serve as protective exoskeletons.

4-5. Vertebrate skeletons.   The internal skeleton has a common basic pattern with the fundamental features seen in a frog.   From the cyclostomes to the mammals a progressive sequence may be traced, although there are many differences in the size and form of component parts and in the presence or absence of certain elements.   The essential features in a land vertebrate are given in Table 4-1.   The skeleton supports the body, provides for attachment of muscles, and houses the brain and nerve cord. In all but the cyclostomes it includes framework for the jaws and the paired fins or limbs.   The skeleton consists of *cartilage* in adult cyclostomes and sharks and in the embryos of all higher vertebrates, but in the adults of bony fishes to mammals it is largely of *bone* with cartilage over joint surfaces and in a few other places.   The skeletal parts increase gradually in size by growth at the ends or margins.   This continues throughout life in all except the birds and mammals, which reach a definite size and then cease to grow.

TABLE 4-1.   GENERAL DIVISION OF THE SKELETON IN A LAND VERTEBRATE

Axial skeleton (*median*)			Appendicular skeleton (*lateral, paired*)	
Skull	Vertebral column	Thoracic basket	Pectoral (*anterior*)	Pelvic (*posterior*)
Cranium (brain box)	Vertebrae	Ribs (paired; bony or cartilaginous)	Shoulder girdle	Hip girdle
Sense capsules (nose, eye, ear)	Cervical (*neck*)	Sternum	Scapula (*dorsal*)	Ilium
Visceral arches (jaws, hyoid, larynx)	Thoracic (*chest*)	(breastbone)	Clavicle (*anterior*)	Pubis
	Lumbar (*lower back*)		Coracoid (*posterior*)	Ischium
	Sacral (*hip*)			
	Caudal (*tail*)		Fore limb	Hind limb
			Humerus (*upper arm*)	Femur (*thigh*)
			Radius and ulna (*forearm*)	Tibia and fibula (*shank*)
			Carpals (*wrist*)	Tarsals (*ankle*)
			Metacarpals (*palm*)	Metatarsals (*sole*)
			Phalanges (*fingers*)	Phalanges (*toes*)

In all chordates the first skeletal element to appear is a slender unsegmented and gelatinous rod, the *notochord,* that extends along the body axis between the digestive system and the nerve cord.   It persists thus in amphioxus and cyclostomes but in fishes and higher types is later surrounded and supplanted by the backbone, or spinal column, of separate *vertebrae* (Fig. 4-3).   The spool-like *centrum* of each vertebra has a dorsal *neural arch* to enclose the nerve cord.   In the tails of fishes each vertebra has also a ventral *hemal arch* around the main artery and vein of the tail. In the body or trunk region this arch is spread open and forms riblike structures shielding the internal organs. In land vertebrates the centrum bears a pair of *transverse processes* as points of attachment for the true *ribs* of these animals (except frogs). At either end of the centrum are two *articular processes* by which one vertebra may turn slightly on those directly before and behind. The vertebral column of fishes comprises only *trunk* and *tail* regions, but in salamanders, reptiles, and mammals there are five regions: neck, or *cervical;* chest, or *thoracic,* with ribs; lower back, or *lumbar;* pelvic, or *sacral,* joining the hind-limb girdle; and tail, or *caudal.* The caudal vertebrae are reduced in man and birds. Long-bodied swimming vertebrates have the vertebrae numerous and much alike as seen in eels and similar fishes, in some salamanders (*Siren*), in some fossil reptiles, and in whales. The living snakes that literally swim on land have many vertebrae (Fig.

Fig. 4-3.   Vertebrae (antero-lateral views).   *A.* Tail region of bony fish.   *B.* Trunk region of bony fish.   *C.* Cervical vertebra (twelfth) of domestic turkey.   *D.* Relation of vertebrae, ribs, and sternum in a mammal.   *E.* Human lumbar vertebra.

30-8). The ribs of land vertebrates usually join ventrally to a breast-bone, or *sternum,* but this is lacking in snakes. The sternum of birds has a large keel for attachment of the stout flight muscles.

The vertebrate *skull* begins in the embryo as cartilage and consists of (1) the *cranium,* or brain box, which houses the brain; (2) three pairs of *sense capsules* for the organs of smell, sight, and hearing; and (3) the *visceral skeleton,* which is a series of paired arches providing the jaws, the support for the tongue (hyoid apparatus), and the supports for the gill region. It continues in this state in adults of sharks and rays, but in bony fishes and higher forms the cartilaginous cranium is replaced and added to by numerous bones; also the capsules and upper jaw become more completely joined to the cranium. In land vertebrates parts of the visceral arches are put to other uses (Fig. 9-7). Both the general form and detailed structure of the skull in adults of various vertebrates are diverse, and a comparative study from fishes to mammals shows many differences, including reduction in the number of bones; yet there is an underlying homology throughout the entire series.

Cyclostomes have no lateral appendages, but the sharks and bony fishes have two pairs, the *pectoral* and *pelvic fins,* with skeletal elements consisting of *fin rays.* Each pair is supported on a framework, or girdle (Chaps. 27, 28). Land vertebrates have two pairs of *limbs* in place of the fins, and these are supported by the *pectoral* and *pelvic girdles,* respectively, as in the frog. Each limb characteristically ends in five *toes,* or *digits.* The component bones of the girdles and limbs are homologous from amphibians to mammals, although variously modified in adaptation to special modes of life (Fig. 9-2). Loss of digits, fusion

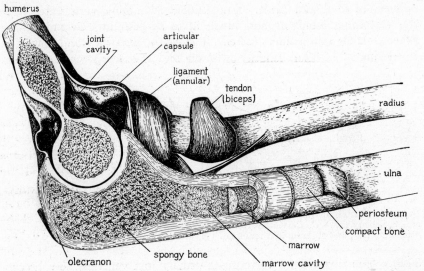

Fig. 4-4. Structure of a long bone and joint. The human elbow joint, in longitudinal section. The rounded trochlea of the humerus fits the semilunar notch of the olecranon to make a hinge joint, which is enclosed in the articular capsule. Ulna cut to show bone structure (diagrammatic).

of other bones, and reduction or complete loss of fins, limbs, and girdles have occurred in various vertebrates. Some salamanders have only four or three toes on each foot, and no living bird has more than three "fingers" or four toes. Reduction in number of toes occurs in many mammals, the horse being an extreme case, with only one functional toe on each foot (Fig. 9-13). The radius and ulna and the tibia and fibula are fused in many species that have slight rotational movement of the limbs. The limbs and digits are far reduced in some salamanders and lizards and are absent in a few lizards and all snakes. Whales and sirenians have no hind limbs, and among fishes the eels lack pelvic fins. Vestiges of the limbs or girdles in whales, boas, and other limbless vertebrates indicate that these have descended from ancestors with limbs.

C. MUSCULAR SYSTEMS

The ability to contract is a fundamental property of protoplasm, but in most animals the contractions that bring about changes in shape or form and locomotion are produced by special fibrils or muscular tissues. Most multicellular animals that are capable of locomotion have opposed sets of muscles to perform these movements.

4-6. Invertebrates. Simple protozoans such as *Amoeba* can contract or extend the one-celled body in any direction. Others of more specialized structure such as the stalked *Vorticella* have special contractile fibrils (myonemes). The body wall of coelenterates contains ⊥-shaped epitheliomuscular cells with contractile fibers in the basal part; these cells lie in opposed sets in the body wall (Fig. 14-3), whereby the body can be contracted in either length or diameter. Flatworms usually have muscle fibers in three planes—longitudinal, transverse, and dorsoventral (Fig. 16-4*B*); contraction of those in any one plane will force the soft but fluid-filled body to extend in the other planes, much as the human tongue can be moved. In roundworms the muscle cells somewhat resemble those of coelenterates, but all are aligned against the body wall and parallel to the main body axis (Fig. 17-2). The alternate contraction of fibers along opposite sides of the body enables the worm to bend and straighten, but it can neither twist freely nor extend the body in length. In an earthworm the body wall includes two layers of muscles, an outer circular and an inner longitudinal layer (Fig. 21-4). Contraction of the outer layer causes the fluid-filled body to elongate, and the longitudinal muscles produce shortening in length. The crustaceans, insects, and other arthropods are the only invertebrates that depart from the "layer" arrangement of muscles; they have many separate muscles, varied in size, arrangement, and attachments, that move the body segments and the parts of the jointed legs and other appendages. These muscles are attached to the internal surfaces of the exoskeleton and act over hinge joints between adjacent parts of it. A caterpillar may have nearly 2,000 separate muscles.

4-7. Vertebrates. The muscles of vertebrates attach to various parts of the skeleton. Those of the fishlike forms—cyclostomes to permanently-gilled amphibians—and of the limbless reptiles are predominantly segmental (Fig. 28-3). These muscles alternate with the vertebrae and provide the undulating movements by which the animals travel. In land vertebrates, from frogs to mammals, the nonsegmented muscles that move the limbs and head are larger and more important (Figs. 2-10, 32-3). In the higher forms some segmental muscles persist, however, between the vertebrae and the ribs and (rectus abdominis muscles) in the ventral body wall (Fig. 4-6). The contraction of muscles is controlled by end plates of motor nerve fibers that attach to the muscle fibers (Fig. 4-28).

In a living animal the contraction (shortening) of a muscle results from impulses passing from the central nervous system along a nerve. This may be demonstrated with a nerve-muscle preparation such as the sciatic nerve and gastrocnemius muscle dissected out together from a frog. One end of the muscle is attached immovably and the opposite end to a lever

FIG. 4-5.   The human skeleton.

that will magnify or record any change in length of the muscle. Impulses, in the form of brief electric shocks, are applied to the nerve. Beginning with one too weak to produce any result and gradually increasing the intensity a *threshold* of stimulation is reached at which slight contraction results. Further increase will produce a greater contraction, but soon a point is reached when still stronger impulses have no further effect. If all fibers but one in the nerve are cut and the remaining one, to a few muscle fibers, is stimulated at increasing intensities, nothing happens until the threshold is reached when the response is at once a

maximum. This is the ***all-or-none effect.*** The graded increase in an
entire nerve-muscle preparation results from different fibers having
slightly unlike thresholds. When the individual shocks are well spaced
in time, the muscle relaxes completely to its original length between them.
But if repeated at close intervals it does not; this state is called ***clonus.***
With still higher frequency of shock stimulus there is no relaxation but a

Fig. 4-6. The superficial muscles of the human body (pectoralis major and external
oblique removed on left side).

smoothly maintained contraction termed ***tetanus.*** Normal movements
in the entire animal and also the maintained tensions or ***tonus*** of the body
—as when a person remains seated or standing—all result from tetanic
contractions.

   In locomotion each pair of opposed muscles shows a rhythm of alternate activity. If more than one such pair is involved, their action
shows a regular sequence. The primitive pattern, as in an eel, snake,
or other slender animal, is a series of waves of contraction passing
alternately along either side of the body. The movement of limbs in

land forms is also alternate, in both vertebrates (Fig. 4-8) and insects. In lower vertebrates the stimulus for movement comes mainly from the environment and is controlled by nerve centers in the medulla oblongata but is modified by sensory stimuli from the eyes, nose, or other special receptors. Among invertebrates such as earthworms, crustaceans,

Fig. 4-7. *A.* Internal segmental muscles connected to hardened jointed and telescoping parts of the exoskeleton in an arthropod. *B.* Internal muscles in the leg of an insect. *C, D.* A few of the external muscles on the endoskeleton of the left hind leg in a frog, showing the opposed action of flexors and extensors; leg flexed in *C,* extended in *D.* (*Adapted partly from Guyer, Animal biology, Harper & Brothers.*)

and insects, destruction of the "brain" does not seriously disturb the normal pattern of locomotion which depends upon contact with the ground or other environmental material.

4-8. Cilia and flagella.   Certain movable processes on cells (see Chap. 3) serve in locomotion and for many vital processes in the bodies of ani-

Fig. 4-8.   Locomotion in the toad, a four-footed animal.   Beginning at the upper left, the 15 figures show the normal pattern of limb movement; 1 to 4, sequence of flexing the limbs. (*After J. Gray,* 1939.)

mals.   A *flagellum* is a beating whiplike process arising from a granule (blepharoplast) within a cell.   Flagella occur on some protozoans, on the collar cells of sponges, and on internal cells of hydra (Chaps. 12 to 14). When many short processes are present, they are termed *cilia.*   External cilia provide for the locomotion of ciliate protozoans, ctenophores, rotifers, some flatworms, and aquatic larvae of many invertebrates. Cilia occur on the tentacles of bryozoans, some marine worms, and certain coelenterates, on the exterior of starfishes, and on gills of bivalve mollusks. They line parts of the respiratory and genital tracts of vertebrates, the intestines of mollusks and earthworms, the feeding groove (endostyle) of lower chordates, and the excretory organs of many invertebrates. Some rates of beat, per second, for cilia are: *Vorticella,* 6 to 8; *Stentor,* up to 42; gills of a mussel, 10; flagella in a sponge, 20.

In multicellular animals **mucus** is often secreted by gland cells adjacent to those bearing cilia, and materials entrapped in the mucus are carried by the continual beating of many cilia in one direction (Fig. 3-6). Cilia and mucus carry food to the mouth on anemones, bivalves, and bryozoans, and foreign particles trapped by mucus in the respiratory passages of land vertebrates are carried outward by ciliary action. The cilia in egg and sperm ducts aid in carrying sex cells to the exterior.

D. DIGESTIVE SYSTEMS

The foods utilized by animals for life and growth are obtained by eating plants or other animals. Certain kinds of insects subsist upon the tissues or juices of a single species of plant or the blood of a particular species of animal, but other animals utilize several or many kinds of materials. The cattle, deer, rodents, and insects that eat leaves and stems of plants are said to be **herbivorous;** the cats, sharks, flesh flies, and many marine animals whose food is entirely or largely other animals are termed **carnivorous;** and those such as man, bears, rats, and others that utilize a variety of both plant and animal sources are called mixed feeders, or **omnivorous.** The digestive system in various animals differs in general form, structural details, and physiological processes according to the nature of the food, the manner of life, and other factors.

4-9. Invertebrates. Many protozoans have no permanent structures for taking or digesting food. An amoeba pushes out lobes of protoplasm (pseudopodia) at any part of its one-celled body to surround an item of food; the latter is taken into a fluid-filled **food vacuole** within the cytoplasm for digestion (Fig. 12-4). In *Paramecium* and other ciliate protozoans a permanent external **oral groove** lined by beating cilia carries food particles to a definite "cell mouth" where they pass into food vacuoles and are digested (Fig. 12-21). The microscopic food of sponges is captured by and digested in flagellated **collar cells** that line certain interior canals of the animal; digestion is thus intracellular, as in protozoans. Coelenterates have a definite **mouth** connected to a saclike digestive or **gastrovascular cavity** (enteron) within the body that is lined by a tissue layer of special digestive cells (Fig. 14-3). The flatworms have a mouth and a branched **digestive tract** extending to all parts of the body (Fig. 16-2).   In both the latter groups the tract is *incomplete* in that foods enter and undigested residues pass out the same opening, the mouth.   In the coelenterates and flatworms, food that has entered the digestive tract is acted upon by enzymes secreted from gland cells in the interior lining.   This is intercellular digestion, in a digestive cavity, such as occurs in all higher animals; some partly digested food, however, is taken into cells lining the cavity for intracellular digestion.

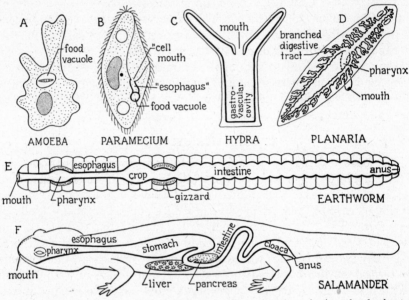

FIG. 4-9.   Types of digestive systems in animals; diagrammatic.   *A.* Amoeba, food enters any part of cell.   *B.* Paramecium, with definite "cell mouth."   *C.* Hydra, a mouth and digestive sac.   *D.* Planaria, mouth and branched digestive tract, but no anus.   *E.* Earthworm, tubular digestive tract, complete with terminal mouth and anus.   *F.* Vertebrate, complete and partly coiled tract with anus at base of tail.

In most other invertebrates the digestive tract is essentially a tube, short or long, straight or coiled, and is termed *complete* because food enters the mouth and passes through various organs for storage, digestion, or absorption and any residues pass out the *anus,* or *anal opening,* at the opposite end of the system.   The differentiated parts are unlike in animals belonging to different groups (Chaps. 17 to 24), but the names applied to them give some indication of the function of each part.   An earthworm, for example, has a *mouth* with fleshy lips to grasp food, a muscular *pharynx* that sucks in the food and lubricates it by mucous secretions, a slender *esophagus* to carry food on to the dilated *crop* for storage, a muscular-walled *gizzard* where food is ground against particles of sand, and a long *intestine* with pouchlike lateral extensions providing a large surface for absorption of digested portions.   Undigested residues pass out the **anus** at the posterior end of the body. Jaws with teeth occur in the mouths of some other annelid worms, in squids and octopuses, and in many arthropods. The mouth in all mollusks except the bivalves has a radula (Fig. 20-4) bearing many fine horny teeth that serve to rasp off particles of food. The mouth parts of insects may be adapted either for chewing or sucking (Chap. 23, Table 23-1).

4-10. Vertebrates.[1] The digestive system of almost every vertebrate resembles that of a frog in having the following essential parts: (1) The **mouth** and **mouth cavity,** commonly with teeth to grasp, tear, or chew food, and a **tongue** that may help in capturing or manipulating food; in most land vertebrates the cavity contains **salivary glands** to lubricate the food. (2) The **pharynx,** which contains gill slits in fishes and aquatic amphibians but has no digestive function. (3) The **esophagus,** which is

Fig. 4-10. Diagram of structure and activities in the digestive tract of a vertebrate.

an elastic tube carrying food past the region of the heart and lungs. (4) The **stomach,** which is an enlarged sac or pouch where food is stored and digestion begins. (5) The **small intestine,** which is a slender elongate tube, usually coiled, that is the principal region for digestion and absorption of food. (6) The **large intestine,** or **colon,** where absorption is completed and undigested residues are formed into masses, or feces, for expulsion through (7) the terminal **cloaca,** which ends with (8) the **anus,** at the end of the trunk. The cloaca is also an exit for excretory wastes and sex cells in sharks, amphibians, reptiles, and birds, but these pass out of separate orifices in most mammals. Two large digestive glands, the **liver** and **pancreas,** joined by ducts to the small intestine, are present in all vertebrates and are of the general form and structure seen in the frog; no pancreas occurs in cyclostomes. Typically all vertebrates have teeth except the living birds, although a few representatives in other classes are toothless. The teeth in some fishes and reptiles and in most mammals are differentiated into specialized types for piercing, shearing, crushing, or grinding, according to food habits (Chap. 32).

4-11. Food and digestion. The plant and animal foods taken by animals consist of protoplasm (Chap. 3) which is made up of proteins, carbo-

---

[1] For a comparison of the digestive and other organ systems in the various classes of vertebrates see the figures on "general structure" in Chaps. 26 to 28, 2, and 30 to 32.

hydrates, and fats, together with vitamins, minerals, and water. The water and inorganic salts can be absorbed from the digestive tract without change, but the protoplasmic materials must be altered before they can be utilized. The digestive system is a "laboratory" where these changes occur.

The processes of digestion, absorption, and utilization of food may, by analogy, be likened to a miscellany of large and small buildings (food),

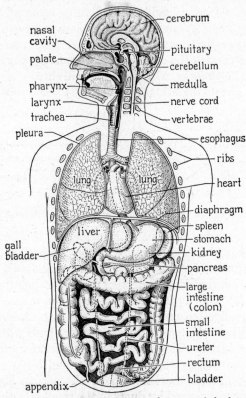

Fig. 4-11. The digestive system and other internal organs of the human body. Greater omentum removed; reproductive organs omitted (see Figs. 33-3, 33-4).

which are taken apart, the wooden portions into boards, the plumbing into pipes and fittings, and so on (digestion). Each must be of such size as to pass through a series of holes in a great wall (absorption). On the other side the various parts may be stored or recombined into new structures of different kinds from the original ones, and some are burned to supply energy (utilization).

Some foods are subjected only to chemical alteration, as with the microscopic organisms taken as food by protozoans and other small animals, the fluids of plants sucked up by bees and aphids, the blood pumped in by parasitic worms, leeches, or insects, and the larger prey taken by coelenterates and starfishes. Many other animals use food that must be reduced physically before chemical digestion can proceed effectively. This is accomplished by teeth in the mouth or elsewhere (pharynx of some fishes, stomach of crayfishes) and by grinding in the gizzard of earthworms and birds. Flesh eaters such as the sharks, large fishes, snakes, hawks, owls, cats, and others bolt down their food entire or in large pieces, and its physical reduction is accomplished by muscular action in the stomach. Other fishes and the herbivorous mammals that subsist upon plant materials chew their food thoroughly before it is swallowed. Insects and many land vertebrates have salivary glands that provide secretions to moisten the food while it is being chewed and swallowed.

4-12. Enzymes. The chemical aspects of digestion involve the reduction of complex organic substances in the food into simpler molecules that can be passed through cells of the digestive epithelium to enter the fluids and cells of the body. Proteins are reduced to amino acids, fats to fatty acids and glycerol, and carbohydrates to simple sugars (monosaccharides) such as glucose. These changes are performed by the digestive ferments, or enzymes (Chap. 3). Many enzymes bring about *hydrolysis:* by action of the enzyme a molecule of water is added to the molecule acted upon, and the combined molecule then separates into two of like or unlike size. One or both cleavage products may again be hydrolyzed; with proteins this is repeated until they are divided into the constituent amino acids, and with carbohydrates until the end products are simple sugars. Many reactions catalyzed by enzymes are reversible; under one set of surrounding conditions a substance will be split into two products, whereas under other conditions these two will be synthesized into the original substance.

4-13. Digestive enzymes. In general, digestive enzymes can act only upon dead protoplasm and are unable to penetrate living cells. They are produced by all animals from protozoans to mammals, but the same number or kinds of enzymes are not present in all animals. The food in a vacuole within a protozoan can be seen to change gradually in form and size as it is acted upon by enzymes. The reaction of the vacuole changes from acid to alkaline during the process as can be shown by indicator dyes. The cytoplasm therefore has the ability to secrete enzymes and also substances to change the reaction of fluid in the vacuole. In the lower invertebrates, enzymes are secreted by cells in various or all parts of the digestive tract but in higher animals only by glands or cells in certain parts. In the vertebrates, some are produced in the salivary glands or the esophagus and others regularly in the stomach, small intestine, and pancreas. The account that follows pertains especially to human digestion.

The *saliva,* secreted by three pairs of *salivary glands,* contains *ptyalin,* an enzyme that acts in the normal alkaline medium of the mouth to reduce starches to the double sugar, maltose. Its action is more rapid on cooked starch but ceases when the food is acidified in the stomach. Gastric glands in the wall of the stomach secrete a fluid *gastric juice* that becomes mixed with the food by peristaltic contractions of the stomach wall. The secretions include *mucin,* which lubricates the food mass, *hydrochloric acid* (to about 0.2 per cent), which acidifies the stomach contents, and enzymes. Of these, *pepsin* splits proteins partly, to proteoses and peptones, and *rennin* causes the casein in milk to coagulate, or form a curd. (Rennin extracted from stomachs of calves is used to form the "curd" in cheese making.) There is possibly a third enzyme, *gastric lipase,* acting on emulsified fats. An estimated 1,500 cc. of salivary secretion and 2,000 to 3,000 cc. of gastric juice is secreted daily in an average person. Food in the stomach is gradually reduced to a soupy mass and then passes through the pyloric valve to enter the small intestine.

In the much-folded mucosa lining the small intestine there are tubular glands (Fig. 4-12) that secrete an alkaline *intestinal juice* (succus entericus) containing enzymes. *Erebsin* continues the gastric digestion of proteins, splitting the proteoses and peptones into amino acids. The carbohydrate-splitting enzymes are *maltase,* which converts maltose into glucose; *sucrase,* which changes sucrose (cane sugar) to glucose and fructose; and *lactase,* which divides lactose (milk sugar) into glucose and galactose. When the stomach contents enter the intestine, the acid (HCl) stimulates cells of the intestinal mucosa to release *secretin.* This is a hormone (p. 115) which passes in the blood stream to the pancreas and initiates the discharge of *pancreatic juice* into the intestine. The pancreatic juice contains *trypsin* (activated from trypsinogen), which splits intact or partly divided proteins into amino acids; *lipase,* which converts fats to fatty acids and glycerol; and *amylopsin,* which reduces entire or partly digested starches to sugars. The liver secretes *bile* (not an enzyme), which contains some wastes and also bile salts; the latter aid digestion by physically dividing fats into small droplets (emulsification).

4-14. Absorption. The intestinal contents are continually subjected to slow *peristaltic contractions* of the muscular wall. This serves to divide and redivide the contents, to mix it thoroughly with the secretions, to bring new portions against the mucosa, and to move the contents slowly along. The small intestine is the principal area for absorption. Its inner surface bears thousands of minute projections, or *villi,* each containing blood capillaries and also a central *lacteal vessel* connected to the lymphatic system.

The end products of protein and carbohydrate digestion (amino acids, simple sugars) pass through cells of the intestinal mucosa and into blood capillaries connecting to the hepatic portal vein, whence they are carried to the liver.   The protein materials serve first to repair or replace living protoplasm of the body.   The constituent amino acids are recombined

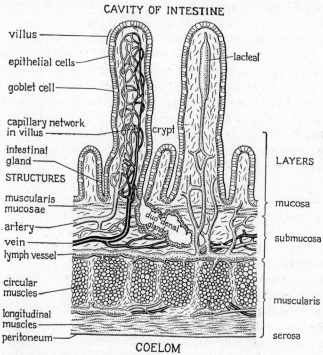

CAVITY OF INTESTINE

villus

epithelial cells

goblet cell

lacteal

capillary network in villus

crypt

intestinal gland

STRUCTURES

muscularis mucosae

duodenal gland

artery

vein

lymph vessel

circular muscles

longitudinal muscles

peritoneum

COELOM

LAYERS

mucosa

submucosa

muscularis

serosa

Fig. 4-12. Diagrammatic longitudinal section through the wall of the small intestine (duodenum); villus at left shown only with blood vessels, that at right only with a lacteal, but both occur in all villi.

(evidently under enzyme action) to form the various types of protoplasm characteristic of different tissues.   Any intake of protein beyond these requirements is believed to be promptly relieved of its nitrogen (deaminated) in the liver by the formation of urea, which passes to the kidneys for excretion.   The nitrogen-free residue from such protein can be used by the body as are carbohydrates.

In the liver the sugars are converted into glycogen (animal starch) and either stored or reconverted into glucose and released into the blood stream to maintain a rather constant glucose level (about 0.1 per cent) in the latter.   Muscle glycogen, derived from blood glucose, is oxydized to yield energy for muscular work and heat production.

Fats are digested into neutral soaps and glycerol, which are taken up separately by the intestinal mucosa; they enter the lacteal (lymph) vessels connected to the thoracic duct which joins the left jugular vein and thereby enter the blood stream. Later these components are resynthesized under the action of lipase into fats characteristic of the animal's own body. Fats can also be synthesized within the body from carbohydrates when the latter are received in excess of energy needs. Fats of any kind not utilized at once for energy are stored in fat cells (Fig. 3-8) in muscles, beneath the skin, or elsewhere in the body.

4-15. Utilization. Carbohydrates and fats serve as "fuel" for the metabolic processes in cells of the body and are "burned" by physiological oxidation to produce the energy necessary for vital activities, including muscular work and heat. The relative values, per gram, of the three classes of foodstuffs are as follows: protein, 5,000 calories; fat, 9,000 calories; carbohydrate, 4,000 calories. The end products of fat and carbohydrate metabolism are carbon dioxide and water; protein metabolism yields also various nitrogenous wastes.

4-16. Other digestive processes. At the junction of the small and large intestine in man there is a short pouch, or *caecum,* ending in a slender *vermiform appendix.* These serve no useful purpose in human digestion; the appendix may become infected and require surgical removal. In rodents, horses, and some other herbivorous mammals the caecum is a large thin-walled sac in which food is subjected to bacterial digestion, including the reduction of some cellulose; the useful end products are absorbed into the blood circulation. Some absorption may occur in the large intestine, but this region serves mainly to extract excess fluid from the undigested food residues before the latter are formed into feces and discharged through the anus.

In many birds the lower end of the esophagus is dilated into a *crop* for temporary storage for food. Most species also have the stomach divided into a slender soft glandular *proventriculus* and a thick-walled muscular *gizzard* lined by cornified tissue where food is ground up by grit swallowed for the purpose (Fig. 31-8). In cattle, deer, and other cud-chewing mammals or ruminants, the stomach has four compartments, the first three of which are specializations of the esophagus and have rough cornified linings (Fig. 32-14).

4-17. Water, minerals, and vitamins. Besides the organic food materials already discussed, animals require other substances to maintain normal health. *Water* is needed by all. Aquatic species obtain it with their food or by absorption, as in the frog. Insects living in wood or dry cereals obtain some water from their seemingly dry food and conserve the "metabolic water" from the oxidation of foodstuffs in their bodies. Many desert reptiles and mammals have no access to water and do not drink if it is offered.   Most birds and mammals drink water to supplement that taken with food so as to maintain adequate amounts in their bodies.   They are subject to greater losses of water because of their higher body temperatures and more rapid respiration.

Certain **mineral substances** are normal constituents of protoplasm (Chap. 3), and the small amounts lost in excretions are usually replaced with incoming food.   In some localities and in certain foods there are deficiencies in these minerals that result in abnormalities of animal metabolism.   A shortage of phosphorus affects adversely both appetite and the formation of bone.   Deficiency in the amounts of "trace elements" may be serious, as with a shortage of copper, which leads to anemia.   General metabolism, rate of growth, and reproduction are variously affected by mineral deficiencies.   By use of the cyclotron it is now possible to make common mineral substances radioactive.   When one of these is fed in the diet, its course, eventual location, and excretion can be traced by the emanations it gives off.

The **vitamins** (Table 4-2) are organic substances that regulate various vital processes in the bodies of higher (and probably lower) animals. Minute amounts of them are essential for normal health, growth, and reproduction.   Each vitamin evidently regulates one or more particular functions and must be present in the food in a certain minimal amount; this varies with different vitamins and different animals.   A lesser amount or complete absence leads to a "deficiency disease."   A well-balanced diet usually provides a sufficiency of all vitamins, but fads in eating and the restricted diets of some races of people lead to deficiency diseases.   Scurvy (vitamin C deficiency) was prevalent on long sea voyages of past centuries; the British sea captains who later carried limes for food to prevent scurvy were known as "lime juicers."   Beriberi (B_1 deficiency) is a prevalent disease among oriental peoples who live largely on polished rice, and pellagra occurs among southerners living on diets largely of corn.   Other vitamins of the B complex remain to be isolated.

E. CIRCULATORY SYSTEMS

The life processes of an animal require that food and oxygen be available continually for metabolism in its protoplasm and that wastes be removed promptly.   In protozoans these interchanges are effected by streaming movements of the cytoplasm; and in such simple multicellular animals as sponges, flatworms, and others, by diffusion between epidermal cells and the near-by body parts.   In more complex animals with organs and tissues well removed from the exterior or gut there is a **circulatory system** for internal transport.   Its essential parts are (1) the **blood,** consisting of fluid plasma and free cells or blood corpuscles; (2) the

TABLE 4-2. THE VITAMINS AND THEIR CHARACTERISTICS

Name, formula, and principal effect	Important sources	Physiological functions	Result of deficiency or absence (in man, except as noted)
A($C_{20}H_{30}O$) antixerophthalmic (fat soluble)	*Plant form* (carotene, $C_{40}H_{56}$) in green leaves, carrots, etc.; is changed in liver to *animal form* ($C_{20}H_{30}O$) present in fish-liver oil (shark); both forms in egg yolk and milk	Maintains integrity of epithelial tissues, especially mucous membranes. Needed to regenerate visual purple in retina of eye	Xerophthalmia (dry cornea, no tear secretion), phrynoderma (toad skin). Night blindness. "Nutritional roup" in birds
B *"complex"* (water soluble) Thiamine (B_1) ($C_{12}H_{17}ON_4S$) antineuritic	Yeast, germ of cereals especially wheat, peanuts, other leguminous seeds, egg yolk, liver, and lean pork	Needed for carbohydrate metabolism. Thiamine pyrophosphate is "co-carboxylase" which catalyzes metabolism of pyruvic acid to acetaldehyde and CO_2 (Stimulates root growth in plants)	Beriberi (on diet high in polished rice). Loss of appetite, with loss of "tone" and reduced motility in digestive tract. Cessation of growth. Polyneuritis in birds
Riboflavin ($C_{17}H_{20}O_6N_4$)	Green leaves, milk, eggs, liver, yeast	Essential for growth; forms active group of several enzymes concerned with intermediate metabolism of food	Cheilosis (inflammation and cracking at corners of mouth). "Yellow liver" of dogs. "Curled-toe" paralysis of chicks
Nicotinic acid or niacin ($C_6H_5NO_2$) antipellagric	Green leaves, wheat germ, egg yolk, meat, liver, yeast	Forms active group of di- and tri-phosphopyridine nucleotides essential to cellular function	Pellagra in man and monkeys. Swine pellagra in pigs. Blacktongue in dogs. Perosis in birds
Folic acid ($C_{19}H_{19}O_6N_7$)	Green leaves, liver, soybeans, yeast, egg yolk	Essential for growth and formation of blood cells; concerned with synthesis of certain components of desoxyribonucleic acid	Anemia (hyperchromicmacrocytic) and sprue in man. Nutritional cytopenia in monkeys. Slow growth and anemia in chicks and rats
Pyridoxine (B_6) ($C_8H_{12}O_3N$)	Yeast, cereal grains, milk, liver	Present in tissues as pyridoxal phosphate which serves in transamination and decarboxylation of amino acids	Anemia in dogs and pigs. Dermatitis in rats. Paralysis (and death) in pigs, rats, and chicks

Vitamin	Sources	Function	Deficiency
Pantothenic acid $(C_9H_{17}O_5N)$	Yeast, cane molasses, peanuts, egg yolks, milk, liver	Forms "coenzyme A" which catalyzes addition of acetyl group to choline and other substances	Dermatitis in chicks and rats; Graying of fur in black rats; "Goose stepping" and nerve degeneration in pigs
Biotin $(C_{10}H_{16}O_3N_2S)$	Yeast, cereal grains, cane molasses, egg yolk, vegetables, fresh fruits	Essential for growth; Functions in CO_2 fixation and oleic acid synthesis in bacteria	Dermatitis with thickening of skin in rats and chicks; Perosis in birds
B_{12} $(C_{61-64}H_{86-92}N_{14}O_{13-}PCo)$	Liver, fish, meat, milk, egg yolk, fermentations of *Streptomyces*	Catalyzes formation of purine and pyrimidine desoxyribosides; concerned in transmethylation	Pernicious anemia, caused by change in gastric secretion so that B_{12} is not absorbed from digestive tract; Slow growth and paralysis in young pigs; Slow growth in chicks
C or ascorbic acid $(C_6H_8O_6)$	Citrus fruits, tomatoes; animals (except primates and guinea pigs) produce vitamin C	Maintains integrity of capillary walls; involved in formation of "intercellular cement"	Scurvy (bleeding in mucous membranes, under skin, and into joints) in man and guinea pig
D $(C_{28}H_{44}O)$ antirachitic (fat soluble)	Fish-liver oils, especially tuna, less in cod; exposure of skin to ultraviolet radiation	Regulates metabolism of calcium and phosphorus; needed for normal growth and mineralization of bones	Rickets in young (bones soft, yielding, often deformed); Osteomalacia (soft bones), especially in women of Orient
E or Tocopherol $(C_{29}H_{50}O_2)$ antisterility (fat soluble)	Green leaves; wheat-germ oil and other vegetable fats	Essential to rapid cell proliferation and differentiation in vertebrates	Sterility in male fowls and rats; degeneration of testis with failure of spermatogenesis; Death of embryos; "Suckling paralysis" and muscular dystrophy in young animals
K $(C_{31}H_{46}O_2)$ antihemorrhagic (fat soluble)	Green leaves, also in certain bacteria as those of "intestinal flora."	Essential to production of prothrombin in liver, necessary for blood clotting	Blood fails to clot

heart, with muscular walls that contract periodically to pump the blood through the body; and (3) a system of tubular **blood vessels** through which the fluid is moved. The system is **closed** in vertebrates and annelids where the vessels convey blood from the heart in various circuits among the tissues and back to the heart. Mollusks and arthropods have **open** or lacunar systems, blood being pumped from the heart through blood vessels to various organs but returning partly or entirely through body spaces to the heart.

4-18. Invertebrates. The plasma is colorless in some invertebrates and in others is colored by dissolved **respiratory pigments** that carry oxygen (see respiratory organs, p. 95). The red plasma in earthworms and some insect larvae (*Chironomus*) contains hemoglobin, and in the "blue" blood of many mollusks and crustaceans this is replaced by hemocyanin. Invertebrate blood usually contains amoeboid corpuscles, or "white blood cells," of various form and function in different groups.

The heart of invertebrates is always dorsal to the digestive tract. In mollusks it is short, lies within a thin pericardial sac, and consists of one or two thin-walled **auricles** that receive blood from the body and deliver to a single muscular-walled **ventricle.** The latter contracts to force the blood through the vessels, or **arteries,** that distribute to various organs (Fig. 20-9).

In insects and many other arthropods the heart is a slender tube with segmentally placed lateral openings, or **ostia,** that receive blood from the body spaces, or **hemocoel,** and pump it through a median aorta to organs and tissues (Fig. 23-5). The earthworm has several lengthwise vessels through the body, with paired transverse connecting vessels in most body segments. The circulation is produced by contractions of the mid-dorsal vessel and by five pairs of lateral hearts in anterior body segments (Fig. 21-3, Table 21-1).

4-19. Vertebrate blood.[1] In all vertebrates the **blood** comprises (1) a nearly colorless plasma; (2) white blood cells or corpuscles (leucocytes), of several kinds; (3) red cells (erythrocytes) colored by their content of hemoglobin, which serves to transport oxygen; and (4) smaller cells (thrombocytes), or platelets. The **plasma** carries dissolved foods, wastes, some gases, and internal secretions. Human plasma consists of about 92

---

[1] The various functions of the circulatory system and the general structure of the blood, heart, and vessels of vertebrates are much as described for the frog (Chap. 2, Figs. 2-12 to 15). Human blood cells are shown in Fig. 3-10, and their characteristics are given in Table 4-3; the structure and action of the human heart are illustrated in Fig. 4-14, and the principal vessels of the human circulatory system in Fig. 4-13; the microanatomy of arteries, capillaries, and veins is indicated in Fig. 4-15; progressive differences in the heart and aortic arches of vertebrates are illustrated in Fig. 9-4; the general plan of vertebrate circulation is diagrammed in Fig. 2-15, and differences among fishes, amphibians, and birds and mammals are shown in Fig. 4-16.

per cent of water, proteins, and other organic compounds and about 0.9 per cent of inorganic salts, chiefly sodium chloride; in health, these vary but slightly in amount.   Physiological salt solution containing the same kinds and amounts of these salts can be used to dilute blood without injuring the corpuscles and to examine fresh tissues.   An average person (155 pounds) contains about 6,300 cc. of blood, equally plasma and cells (Table 4-3).

FIG. 4-13.   Principal blood vessels of the human circulatory system as related to internal organs; small intestine, bladder, and reproductive organs omitted.

4-20. Erythrocytes.   The *red cells* are nucleated and oval in all vertebrates but mammals where they are nonnucleated, biconcave, and circular (oval in camels).   Mammalian red cells are nucleated, however, during their development.   The red cells total about 30 trillion in a human being; each may live 100 to 120 days and make 50,000 or more circuits in the blood stream.   Red cells are more numerous in infants and in persons living at high altitudes; their numbers are altered in some diseases, being reduced in anemia.   Red cells are produced chiefly in red bone marrow, and an excess supply is often stored in the spleen. Old cells are destroyed chiefly in the spleen, whence much of the hemoglobin passes to the liver, its pigment being excreted in the bile and its iron content being largely returned to the marrow.

TABLE 4-3. AVERAGE CHARACTERISTICS OF HUMAN BLOOD CELLS

Kinds of cells and average number per cubic millimeter of blood	Structure; color with Wright's blood stain; diameter (μ = 0.001 mm.)	Source	Function
Erythrocytes (red blood cells): 5,000,000 (in males) 4,500,000 (in females)	Nonnucleated, circular, biconcave; orange-buff; 7.5 to 7.7 μ (8.6 μ in fresh blood)	Endothelium of capillaries in bone marrow	Transport oxygen; remain in blood vessels
Leucocytes (white blood cells): 8,000 to 10,000 1. Granulocytes,	Colorless in life Nucleus of lobes joined by thread, stains dark lilac; cytoplasm granular, pale blue; 10 to 12 μ	Reticuloendothelial cells outside capillaries of bone marrow	Amoeboid; can leave blood vessels and enter tissues; defend against infection
a. Neutrophil, 65 to 75%	Granules stain weakly		
b. Eosinophil, 2 to 5%	Granules eosin (red)		
c. Basophil, 0.5%	Granules deep blue		
2. Lymphocyte, 20 to 25%	Nucleus single, large, round, deep blue; scant cytoplasm, clear blue; 6 to 10 μ	Lymphoid tissue, spleen, and lymph glands	Nonmotile; related to immunity
3. Monocyte, 2 to 6%	Nucleus single, large, round, deep blue; much cytoplasm, muddy blue; 12 to 15 μ	Spleen and bone marrow	Very motile; phagocytic
Platelets: 200,000 to 400,000	Small, refractile, no nucleus; dark blue to lilac; 2 to 4 μ	Cytoplasmic fragments of megakaryocytes in bone marrow	Provide substance needed in clotting

4-21. Leucocytes. The several kinds of *white cells* have their principal activities in the tissues, and those seen in the blood stream are but a part of the "passing parade" on their way from their origins in the marrow, spleen, or lymphoid structures to the tissues or to their death. The lymphocytes, with a single rounded nucleus, are commonest in lymph vessels and in the lymph nodes along those vessels; the granulocytes with lobed nuclei are both in the blood stream and around tissues. Most white cells of both types can perform amoeboid movements and can crawl out between the endothelial cells lining capillaries into spaces between tissue cells. There many of them can act as *phagocytes* (Gr. *phagos*, eat) and protect the body by consuming bacteria that invade wounds. In an acute infection such as appendicitis or pneumonia the neutrophils and small lymphocytes increase markedly, the total leucocyte count rising to 20,000 or 30,000 per cubic millimeter, to battle the

infection.   The whitish pus of an infected area consists of dead leucocytes, tissue cells, and blood serum.

4-22. Clotting.   When a blood vessel is cut, the issuing blood is soon
stopped by a protective *clot.*   The injured tissues and disintegrating
blood platelets release *thromboplastin* which, in combination with *calcium
ions* always present in the plasma, act upon *prothrombin,* also in the
blood, to produce *thrombin.*   The latter converts a soluble blood protein,
fibrinogen, into *fibrin* which becomes a mass of fine fibers entangling
corpuscles to form the clot.   The fluid residue is the *blood serum.*   A
further substance, *heparin,* prevents the formation of thrombin in blood
flowing normally within blood vessels.   Decrease in the number of
platelets lengthens the clotting time.   Blood withdrawn for transfusion
or for laboratory use is kept from clotting by addition of sodium citrate.
In certain male persons known as "bleeders" clotting is long delayed or
fails; a slight cut or tooth extraction may result in death by loss of blood
(hemorrhage).   This condition is caused by a sex-linked hereditary
disease (hemophilia) transmitted by females; of the latter, only those
rare individuals homozygous for the defect suffer from this disease.

4-23. Antibodies.   When a "foreign protein" (*i.e.,* not naturally in the
body) is injected into the blood of an animal, a specific protective substance, or *antibody,* usually is formed.   Thus if a small (sublethal) dose
of rattlesnake venom is injected into a pigeon, the bird's plasma, after
several days, will contain antibodies capable of neutralizing a much
larger dose of venom.   The venom has served as an *antigen* stimulating some tissues to produce an antibody which is carried mainly in the
blood plasma.   Bacteria and other organisms may serve as antigens.
Recovery from any germ-caused disease results from the production of
antibodies, which often confer a degree of *immunity,* transient or permanent, to further attack by the organism in question.   Human beings and
domestic animals are now rendered immune to certain diseases by injecting the dead organisms (vaccine) of a particular disease or the immune
serum (antitoxin) from a horse or other animal that has previously been
immunized.

4-24. Human blood groups.   If red blood cells from one person are
mixed with blood plasma of another individual, the cells remain separate
in some cases and become clumped, or agglutinated, in others.   This
is a matter of great practical importance when blood from a healthy
donor is sought for transfusion into the veins of a sick or wounded
person to aid the latter; should clumping occur, the patient may die instead of being helped.   The blood of donor and patient must be "compatible."   Extensive tests show that two types of *antigens* (agglutinogens) called A and B occur in the red cells of different persons, and the
plasma contains two kinds of *antibodies* (agglutinins) known as a and b.

There are four **blood groups** among human beings: Group **O**, antibodies *a* and *b* but no antigens; Group **A**, antibody *b* and antigen *A*; Group **B**, antibody *a* and antigen *B*; and Group **AB**, antigens *A* and *B* but no antibodies. The results of mixing cells of any one group with plasma of another are summarized in Table 4-4.   Blood-group characteristics are inherited and remain constant throughout life.   Blood of any anthropoid ape is like one or another human group; monkeys and lower mammals also have blood groups but not identical with those of man.

TABLE 4-4.   RESULTS OF MIXING CELLS AND SERUM OF HUMAN BLOOD GROUPS
   −, *compatible; no agglutination*   +, *not compatible; agglutinates*

				Blood Group			
				O	A	B	AB
				Antigen in red cells			
				None	*A*	*B*	*A,B*
Blood Group	O	Antibodies in serum	*a,b*	−	+	+	+
	A		*b*	−	−	+	+
	B		*a*	−	+	−	+
	AB		None	−	−	−	−

Sterile dried plasma, without corpuscles, now serves extensively for blood transfusion.   It keeps indefinitely under varied climatic conditions, needs only to be mixed with sterile water before injection, and involves no problem of agglutination.

Human red cells have an additional pair of antigens, *M* and *N*, but the plasma lacks corresponding agglutinins; these antigens are of no concern in blood transfusion but of interest in human genetics.

4-25. The Rh factor.   About 85 per cent of white persons have another antigen in their red blood cells and their blood known as Rh+; those lacking this substance are termed Rh−, and the difference is one of heredity of the individual.   If Rh+ blood is repeatedly transfused into an Rh− individual, the antigen stimulates production of an anti-Rh agglutinin.   This is called iso-immunization since both the antigen (Rh) and antibody (anti-Rh) are in the same species.

An Rh− individual receiving blood from Rh+ donors shows no reaction at first but later becomes iso-immunized; if then transfused with Rh+ blood there is a severe or fatal reaction.   The anti-Rh agglutinins cause hemolysis of the Rh+ transfused blood.

An Rh− mother bearing an Rh+ foetus (that received the Rh+

factor from the father) may become immunized by Rh+ foetal erythrocytes entering the maternal circulation. Then in second or later pregnancies the maternal anti-Rh agglutinins cross the placenta, enter the foetal circulation, and hemolyze the foetal red cells, commonly with fatal results. This disease (erythroblastosis) in the foetus or newborn results in loss of about 1 pregnancy in 50 among the white population of the United States. Once so immunized such a mother, with a homozygous father (Chap. 5), is unlikely to bear a living child.

4-26. Lymph. This consists of blood plasma less some plasma proteins; it contains white cells, especially lymphocytes, but no red cells. Lymph diffuses through the walls of capillaries, circulates about the tissues, and enters the system of lymph capillaries, which join in larger lymph vessels that eventually empty into certain large veins. Scattered along the system are many *lymph nodes.* Besides producing lymphocytes, the nodes defend the body from infection by intercepting disease organisms. Throat infections, for example, may be accompanied by swelling of lymph nodes in the neck.

4-27. Heart. The entire circulatory system in any vertebrate comprises the heart; the blood system of arteries, arterioles, capillaries,

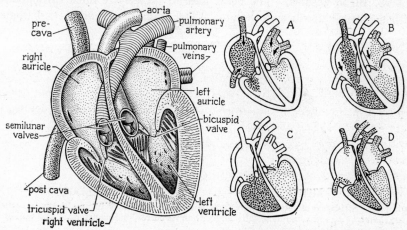

FIG. 4-14. The mammalian heart (frontal section, ventral view) and (*A–D*) its mode of action. Arrows indicate paths of blood flow. Heavy stipple, unoxygenated blood; light stipple, oxygenated blood. *A.* Auricles filling from veins. *B.* Blood entering relaxed ventricles. *C.* Auricles contracting, ventricles filling. *D.* Ventricles contracting, blood forced into aorta and pulmonary arteries. (*Modified from Best and Taylor, The human body and its functions, Henry Holt & Co.*)

and veins; and the lymphatic system. The heart comprises a series of chambers with slight or heavy muscular walls that receive blood from the veins and pump it through the arteries (Figs. 4-14, 9-4). In the two-chambered heart of fishes (1 auricle, 1 ventricle) all blood passing through the heart is unoxygenated; amphibians and most reptiles have two auricles that receive blood from the body and lungs, respectively, and a single ventricle; in birds and mammals the four-chambered heart (2 auricles, 2 ventricles) is really a dual structure, the right side pumping only from the body to the lungs, and the left side from the lungs to the body (Fig. 4-16).

Action of the heart is under involuntary nervous control; the auricle(s) fill and contract, followed almost at once by the ventricle(s). The short intervals while the chambers are filling provide the only rest for the heart muscle throughout life. The human heart in a quiet normal adult contracts, or "beats," about 72 times per minute; the rate is increased by exercise, emotional excitement, and some diseases. In some small birds and mammals the heart beats 200 to 400 times per minute. Blood moves from the heart in a series of spurts, which in an exposed artery as on the wrist or temple may be felt as the "pulse," greatest as the heart is contracted (systole) and least when filling (diastole). The pressure declines at progressive distances from the heart because of frictional losses especially in the arterioles; and the returning flow in the veins is practically smooth.

4-28. Blood vessels. The heart and all vessels are lined throughout with a glassy-smooth endothelium. The walls of the aorta and larger

Fig. 4-15. Structure of blood vessels (not to scale). An artery has a thicker muscular layer than a vein, and a vein is usually larger than its corresponding artery. The wall of a capillary consists only of endothelium.

arteries contain heavy layers of elastic and muscle fibers (Fig. 4-15), but the small arterioles are covered by smooth muscle fibers only. The capillary walls, where all exchanges of nutrients, gases, and wastes occur between the blood stream and tissues, consist only of endothelium. Frog muscle shows about 400 capillaries per square millimeter in cross section, and 1 cc. of blood in passing has contact with about 2,700 sq. mm. of capillary surface. In a dog the comparable figures (by Krogh) are 2,600 capillaries and 5,600 sq. mm. Veins are thin walled, with connective

FISH

AMPHIBIAN

BIRD OR
MAMMAL

FIG. 4-16. Paths of blood circulation in vertebrates. Fish, one auricle and one ventricle (Figs. 27-4, 28-3). Amphibian, two auricles and one ventricle (Fig. 2-13). Bird or mammal, two auricles and two separate ventricles (Figs. 31-7, 32-4). Arrows indicate paths of blood flow. Blue, unoxygenated blood; red, oxygenated blood. (Compare Fig. 9-4.)

tissue fibers but few muscles; unlike the arteries they collapse when empty. The walls of all blood vessels are elastic, and vasomotor nerve fibers control the muscle fibers, causing arterioles to dilate or contract so as to alter the amount of blood passing to any region. The blood in man controls the body temperature by regulating the loss of heat. Excess heat acts through a nerve center in the medulla to permit dilation of superficial blood vessels in the skin where heat may be lost; chilling results in contraction of such vessels. In a resting dog the rate of blood flow per second is 300 to 500 mm. in large arteries and 0.5 mm. in capillaries.

4-29. Aortic arches (Fig. 9-4). Six pairs of aortic arches appear in the embryos of all vertebrates, proceeding from a ventral aorta at the anterior end of the heart and passing between the gill slits that develop in the sides of the pharynx. The first and second pairs soon disappear. In adult fishes, arches 3 to 6 lead to the gills where respiratory exchanges occur and then join above to form the dorsal aorta; similarly, arches 4 to 6 supply the gills in permanently gilled salamanders. In land vertebrates, arch 3 forms the common carotid on each side, arch 5 disappears, and arch 6 becomes the pulmonary arteries to the lungs. In frogs, toads, and reptiles the two parts of arch 4 become the systemic arches to the dorsal aorta; in birds only the right half persists, and in mammals only the left half, the opposite in each forming a subclavian artery.

F. RESPIRATORY SYSTEMS

All animals need oxygen for the metabolism in their cells and must dispose of the resulting carbon dioxide. The exchange of these gases is termed *respiration.* Some animals can exist for months on fats or other foods stored in their bodies, many can live a shorter time without water, but few survive for long without oxygen, since none is stored in the body. Most animals obtain the oxygen from their environments. The air contains 21 per cent of oxygen (210 cc. per liter), but water contains only 0.7 per cent or less (7 cc. per liter); the oxygen in the water molecule (H_2O) is not available for respiration. The environments of some intestinal parasites and of some muck-inhabiting leeches, worms, and arthropods lack free oxygen; these *anaerobic* animals obtain oxygen by metabolism of foods (glycogen; fats?) in their bodies.

Ordinary respiration in different animals is performed by various *respiratory organs* or *systems,* such as the body covering, gills, lungs, or tracheae. These structures are unlike in appearance but fundamentally the same in function (Fig. 4-17); each comprises a moist permeable membrane through which molecules of oxygen and carbon dioxide diffuse readily. In accordance with the laws of gases each gas acts independently of others. When a difference in diffusion pressure (Chap. 3) exists on the two sides of a membrane, more molecules pass toward the region of lesser pressure than in the opposite direction. The partial pressure of oxygen in the air or water is greater than within an animal body, where it is constantly being used up, so that oxygen tends to enter any suitable membrane surface. The partial pressure of carbon dioxide is greater within the animal, so that it tends to pass outward. These exchanges occur simultaneously. Simple diffusion suffices for the respiration of small animals with permeable body coverings, but large species and those with dry or nonpermeable exteriors need special means to aid the gaseous exchange. *External respiration* is the exchange between the environment and the respiratory organs; *internal respiration,* or the exchange between the body fluids and tissue cells, is a part of general metabolism. The means whereby oxygen is utilized in cellular respiration to oxidize foodstuffs is obscure. It takes place at a relatively low temperature in an animal body, but the reaction does not occur readily with foodstuffs exposed to air in a laboratory. Certain enzymes and vitamins are probably involved in the process.

4-30. Aquatic respiration. In a protozoan, gaseous exchanges take place through the cell membrane to and from the surrounding water. In

Fig. 4-17. Diagrams showing the equivalent nature of the various respiratory mechanisms in different animals.

sponges, coelenterates, and other lower invertebrates the gases diffuse through the epithelial cells and thence to those deeper in the body. Starfishes have small fluid-filled gills, or *papulae,* projecting from the coelom into the sea water (Fig. 19-4), and sea cucumbers have an internal much-branched *respiratory tree,* joined to the cloaca, that fills with and empties of water for respiration (Fig. 19-13). *Gills* occur in many mollusks and crustaceans, some annelid worms, all fishlike vertebrates, and some amphibians. A gill consists of many fine filaments covered by a delicate epidermal membrane and containing blood channels. The O_2–CO_2 exchange occurs between the surrounding water and blood within. The gill filaments of salamander larvae (Fig. 29-4) and of some marine worms merely lie exposed to water currents. Tube-dwelling annelids (Fig. 21-13*A*), aquatic crustaceans such as the crayfish (Fig. 22-5), and many mollusks have special means to force water over their gills. In the lower vertebrates the gills are in chambers at the side of the pharynx, and water is taken into the mouth (or nostrils in amphibians) and forced over the filaments (Fig. 28-5, 28-6). The small amount of oxygen present in water limits the density of aquatic populations, especially in some inland waters.

4-31. Aerial respiration. Terrestrial flatworms have a moist epidermis through which respiratory diffusion occurs, and in earthworms the exchange takes place through the moist cuticle and epidermis to blood vessels in the body wall (Fig. 21-5). Land snails have an air cavity, or *lung,* lined with blood vessels, where air passes to and fro in respiration (Fig. 20-4). All such animals either live in moist places or are active only when the air is damp. Land animals that breathe dry air have a body covering that is impermeable to gases, and their respiratory organs are within the body where they can be kept moist. The bodies of insects and related arthropods have a series of openings, or *spiracles,* through which air is pumped to and from an internal branched system of air ducts, or *tracheae,* by movements of the abdomen (Figs. 23-2, 23-6). These ducts extend to all interior organs and end in microscopic fluid-filled *tracheoles* where oxygen and carbon dioxide diffuse to and from the adjacent tissue cells.

All "land vertebrates," including also the aquatic reptiles, birds and mammals, have *lungs* essentially like those of a frog. The *glottis* is an opening in the floor of the pharynx and is supported by a cartilaginous framework, or *larynx.* The latter connects to a flexible tube, or *trachea,* which extends into the thorax and forks into two *bronchi,* one to each lung. The trachea and bronchi are reinforced against collapse by rings of cartilage. The lungs contain many interior partitions in reptiles and are elaborately divided spongy structures in birds and mammals, affording large respiratory surfaces. The bronchioles end in microscopic compartments, or *alveoli,* surrounded by many blood capillaries (Fig. 4-18), where the respiratory exchanges occur. Bird lungs are dense, and air is forced through the bronchioles to and from a series of thin-walled *air sacs* (Fig. 31-9); these occupy spaces between internal organs and around or within some bones. The air sacs serve mainly to dissipate excess body heat and are not essential for respiration. The larynx in mammals contains two muscular *vocal cords* over which air is forced to produce sounds.   The songs and calls of birds are produced by vocal cords in a **syrinx** located at the lower end of the trachea.

The high rate of metabolism in birds and mammals requires a rapid respiratory exchange, and smaller animals have a higher rate than larger ones.   Bird lungs are joined to the ribs and vertebrae by connective tissue and are alternately dilated and compressed by slight movements of the bony thorax (Chap. 31).   In mammals, including man (Figs. 4-11, 32-4), a dome-shaped muscular partition, the **diaphragm,** separates the thorax containing the heart and lungs from the abdominal cavity.   The thoracic cavity is an airtight chamber, and the ordinary

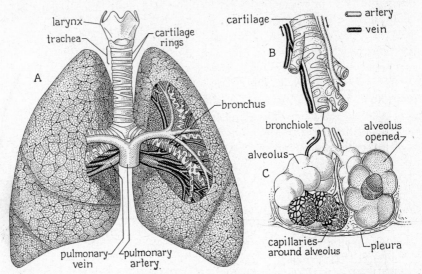

FIG. 4-18.   The human respiratory system.   *A.* Larynx, trachea, and lungs in ventral view; left lung opened.   *B.* Portion of a bronchiole, with cartilages; small blood vessels adjacent.   *C.* Alveoli and capillaries (diagrammatic).

atmospheric pressure of air in the alveoli keeps the elastic lungs expanded against the inner wall of the cavity.   At *inspiration* the ribs are raised and muscles in the diaphragm contract to flatten the latter; the thoracic space is thus enlarged, and pressure about the lungs is lessened; air then passes down the trachea and into the lungs.   *Expiration* results from lessening the volume of the thorax by relaxing the muscles that control the ribs and diaphragm.   The total oxygen capacity of the human blood averages about 1,200 cc., and 100 to 350 cc. of oxygen pass into the tissues at each circuit.   In an hour the body at rest uses about 15 liters (4 gallons) of oxygen, and in strenuous exercise up to 280 liters (75 gallons). The rate of breathing is controlled mainly by a respiratory center in the medulla of the brain, and this in turn is stimulated by a certain excess of carbon dioxide in the blood.   The respiratory rate increases during vigorous exercise because of the greater production of carbon dioxide in muscular metabolism. One may "hold his breath" for a limited time but eventually cannot withstand the demand for oxygenation of the blood. The respiratory rate is also subject to nervous control of other sorts, as seen in emotional states of anger or excitement. Death results from a lack of oxygen.

4-32. Respiratory pigments. Oxygen absorption is enormously increased by the presence of *hemoglobin* in the plasma of some invertebrates and in the red cells of vertebrates. This is a protein containing iron that combines loosely with oxygen to form oxyhemoglobin of bright red color in the respiratory organs and releases the gas for diffusion into the tissues. The blood loses about two-fifths of its oxygen in a second or two while passing through the capillaries. Carbon dioxide returns mainly in the plasma as bicarbonate, although a small amount combines with the hemoglobin. The respiratory pigment in blood of squids and octopuses is *hemocyanin* (with copper instead of iron); the latter is also in some other mollusks and some crustaceans.

G. EXCRETORY SYSTEMS

Excretion is usually defined as the process of ridding the body of wastes resulting from metabolism. The protoplasm and fluids of an animal, be it protozoan or human, comprise a delicately balanced physico-chemical system, and it is the function of excretion to maintain this constant internal environment. Excess water, salts, or organic materials, including metabolic wastes, are excreted, whereas substances essential for normal functions are conserved. As the excreted materials are usually in solution, excretion is essentially a process of selective filtering.

4-33. Invertebrates. Protozoans generally excrete wastes through the cell membrane and into the surrounding water. *Amoeba, Paramecium,* and various other protozoans have one or more *conrtactile vacuoles* that accumulate excess fluids from within the cell body and periodically discharge to the exterior (Figs. 12-2, 12-21). In sponges and coelenterates, excretions diffuse to the epidermal cells and into the water. Other invertebrates have *excretory organs* to withdraw wastes from the tissues and body fluids. Flatworms and ribbon worms contain many *flame cells* (protonephridia) scattered among the body cells from which wastes are drawn to pass out in a branched system of excretory ducts (Fig. 16-3). In the earthworm, each compartment of the segmented body cavity contains a pair of fine tubular *nephridia* (metanephridia). The inner end of each nephridium is a ciliated funnel, or *nephrostome,* draining wastes from the coelom, and about the tubule are blood vessels whence 'waste is also drawn; the tubule ends externally as a minute ventral *nephridiopore* (Fig. 21-7A). Mollusks and some other invertebrates have one or two pairs of nephridia-like organs that drain from the body or blood (Fig. 20-9).   Insects and other land arthropods possess a series of delicate *Malpighian tubules,* closed at their inner ends, that collect waste from the body fluid.   These attach to the junction of the mid- and hind-gut, and the excretions pass out with the feces (Fig. 23-5).

4-34. Vertebrates.   The principal excretory organs in every verte- brate are two *kidneys,* as in the frog.   They are short and posteriorly located in all except the fishes where they extend along most of the body cavity.   The kidneys of lower vertebrates (cyclostomes to amphibians) and the embryonic kidneys of the higher groups develop segmentally, a pair per body somite; some tubules have nephrostomes opening to the coelom, thus somewhat resembling the nephridia of earthworms (Fig. 4- 19, Table 4-5).   The adult kidneys of reptiles, birds, and mammals are nonsegmental and drain wastes only from the blood.   From each kidney, of whatever type, a common *excretory duct,* or *ureter,* carries the waste posteriorly.   In amphibians, reptiles, and birds the two ureters discharge into the cloaca, to which a *urinary bladder* connects in amphibians and some reptiles.   The waste, or *urine,* is always fluid except in reptiles and birds where the semisolid excretions are voided as whitish material with the feces.   In most mammals the ureters connect directly to the bladder, whence a single duct, or *urethra,* discharges to the exterior; in males the urethra passes through the penis.   The interrelated excretory and reproductive systems of vertebrates are commonly termed the *urogenital system.*

TABLE 4-5.   TYPES OF KIDNEYS IN THE VERTEBRATES

	Pronephros, or head kidney	Mesonephros, or mid-kidney	Metanephros, or hind kidney
Embryonic history and adult structure	First to appear in embryo; develops segmentally, far forward in body cavity; each unit with a nephrostome opening from the coelom; no glomeruli	Develops segmentally in middle part of body cavity; some nephrostomes open to coelom, but excretion chiefly by glomeruli	Last to develop; not segmental; posterior in body cavity; no nephrostomes; many glomeruli; all excretion from blood stream
Fishes and amphibians	*Functions in larva;* disappears in adult	*Becomes functional kidney of adult*	(Not developed)
Reptiles, birds, and mammals	Appears transiently in embryo and soon disappears	Appears after pronephros; *functions during embryonic life,* disappearing before hatching or birth; duct persists as vas deferens in male	Last to appear; becomes *functional kidney throughout life*

Each human kidney (Fig. 4-20) consists of an inner medulla and outer cortex, the latter containing about a million excretory units, or **nephrons.** A nephron is made up of (1) a **Malpighian** or **renal corpuscle** composed

FIG. 4-19. The urogenital systems of vertebrates; only one side or half of each is shown. *Top.* Diagram of the relations of units of the excretory system to the circulatory system and coelom.   For the male mammal the primitive (embryonic) positions of the testis and vas deferens are indicated by broken lines.

of a globular double-walled **Bowman capsule** around a knot of arterioles, or **glomerulus;** and (2) a **tubule,** both convoluted and straight, surrounded by blood capillaries.   The corpuscle is about 0.2 mm. in diameter, and the tubule is 0.015 to 0.025 mm. in diameter by 50 to 60 mm. long.   All tubules discharge into a central cavity, or **pelvis,** of the kidney that connects to the ureter.

4-35. Kidney function. Wastes from the body are brought in the blood stream by the renal arteries to the arterioles.   According to the modern theory of kidney function (by Cushny), protein-free fluid passes

FIG. 4-20. The human excretory system. *A.* Entire system, ventral view. *B.* One kidney in median section.   *C.* Relations of glomeruli, tubules, and blood vessels.   *D.* One renal corpuscle and adjacent tubule (shown also in cross section); solid arrows, blood path; broken arrows, excretory path; *C* and *D* diagrammatic and much enlarged.

from the arterioles in the glomerulus through the capsule and into the tubule; then certain materials are returned by selective resorption from the tubules to the surrounding capillaries and rejoin the blood stream to leave in the renal veins.

TABLE 4-6. CONCENTRATING ACTION OF THE HUMAN KIDNEY

	Water	Sodium (Na)	Chloride (Cl)	Potassium (K)	Phosphate (PO₄)	Sulphate (SO₄)	Uric acid	Urea
Blood plasma, %.....	92	0.30	0.37	0.02	0.009	0.002	0.004	0.03
Urine, %...........	95	0.35	0.60	0.15	0.150	0.180	0.050	2.00
Concentration by the kidney............	..	1x	2x	7x	16x	90x	12x	60x

The fluid urine comprises water, various salts, urea, and other organic wastes. Urea and sulphates are greatly concentrated in the urine (Table 4-6), whereas useful constituents such as glucose are conserved in the body. The excretion or retention of water depends upon the state of hydration of the body as a whole; an excess is quickly excreted, but less with a deficient intake. An excess of sodium chloride in the diet is soon excreted; but if the intake is scant or if much is being lost in perspiration, the kidney conserves the remainder and little enters the urine. The kidney deals selectively with a great variety of materials, useful or otherwise. The glomeruli are believed to excrete everything but proteins of high molecular weight (hemoglobin, molecular weight 68,000, being on the border line), so that disposal or retention depends upon activity of the tubules. Normal kidney function is essential to health, and any irregularity or disease in the kidney is serious. Certain salts, especially oxylates, may crystallize to form kidney stones in the pelvis of the kidney and sometimes require removal by surgery.

In a frog kidney, delicate experiments (by Richards) showed each glomerulus passes 1 to 4 cu. mm. of fluid per hour (2,000 glomeruli, a total of 4 to 16 cc.); this is ten to twenty times the output of urine, indicating much resorption by the tubules. In man the daily output of urine averages 1,500 cc., or 1 cc. per minute. An estimated 120 cc. of fluid per minute passes into the glomeruli, so that about 170 liters (45 gallons) of blood is filtered daily.

4-36. Other excretory organs. Air expired from the lungs contains water vapor, carbon dioxide, and small amounts of excretory wastes. The sweat glands of the skin give off water, salts, and some organic wastes (contributing to the "body odor"). The liver forms urea, which is excreted by the kidneys. It also produces the pigment bilirubin derived from the hemoglobin with the death of red cells; this colors the bile and is passed into the intestine to be eliminated in the feces. Certain drugs and metallic poisons are also disposed of by the liver.

H. NERVOUS SYSTEMS

All living protoplasm is excitable or irritable (Chap. 1). Because of this, every organism is sensitive to changes or stimuli from both its external and its internal environments; to these it responds or reacts in various ways. Every type of organic response, from the simplest action of an amoeba to the most complex bodily function or mental process in man, results from this fundamental characteristic of excitability. To perceive stimuli, to transmit these to various body parts, and to effect responses, most animals have a *nervous system.* This system (together with endocrine glands in some) serves also to coordinate and integrate the functions of cells, tissues, and organ systems so that they act harmoniously as a unit.

A *stimulus* is any physical or chemical change capable of exciting an organism or its parts. Common external stimuli derive from temperature, moisture, light, gravity, contact, pressure, oxygen supply, salt concentrations, and odors (chemical emanations). Internal stimuli result from the quantity of food, water, oxygen, or wastes in the body and from fatigue, pain, disease, or other conditions.

Some stimuli act directly upon cells or tissues and elicit a direct response (*e.g.*, sunburn), but most animals have various kinds of specialized *receptors* (sense organs) to receive stimuli. A receptor is a cell or organ having an especial sensitivity (lowered threshold) to some particular kind or kinds of stimulus, as the eye to light and the ear to sound. *Exteroceptors* receive stimuli from the external environment, and *interoceptors* from within the body, as with hunger or thirst.

Receptors induce the transmission of nerve impulses through the nervous system, which in turn excites terminal structures, or *effectors,* to bring about responses. Some stimuli are gradual and elicit slow response, as the chilling that precedes a sneeze; others are abrupt and produce a quick response, as the jab of a pin. Beyond a certain minimum there may be no quantitative relation between the intensity of a stimulus and the kind or magnitude of the response that it produces; this depends upon the kinds of cells or organs excited and their physiological condition. Upon being excited, muscles contract to produce movements, and gland cells pour forth the secretions previously synthesized within them.

Nervous systems are composed of nerve cells, or *neurons,* with cell processes known as *dendrites* and *axones.* The neurons are of varied form (Fig. 3-12) in the systems of different animals and in the several parts of any one nervous system. According to the "neuron theory" each neuron is a distinct anatomical unit, having no protoplasmic continuity with other neurons, and is also physiologically distinct. Injury to the nucleus or cell body destroys a neuron but does not affect adjacent neurons. The neuron is the functional unit of the nervous system, which consists solely of neurons in orderly arrangement, they alone performing the nervous functions. Between any two neurons related in function there is a delicate contact, or *synapse;* this is a "physiological valve" that passes nerve impulses in only one direction, from the axone of one neuron to the dendrite of the other.

The *nerve impulse* that passes along a nerve fiber is possibly a chemical change. It requires the presence of oxygen and produces a minute but measurable amount of carbon dioxide and a rise in temperature; an electrical change occurs, but this is far slower than the speed of electricity. A nerve impulse travels 6 to 12 m. per second in a lobster,

28 to 30 m. per second in a frog, and up to 120 m. per second in some mammalian fibers. Transmission is slower in nonmedullated fibers than in those with a medullary sheath. There is a short delay in passage at each synapse. An impulse, upon reaching the finely branched ends of an axone, causes the latter to produce a chemical **neurohumor** which sets up an impulse in the next neuron. Acetylcholine is produced in most synapses including those at effectors on skeletal muscle. In at least some sympathetic synapses the neurohumor is sympathin, an adrenalin-like substance.

Sensory or **afferent neurons** are those which conduct impulses from receptors to or toward the central nervous system; and **motor** or **efferent neurons** conduct from the central nervous system to various effectors. Still other **adjustor neurons** (internuncial or associative) in the brain and nerve cord join variously between sensory and motor neurons. A **nerve** consists of one to many **nerve fibers** (axones or dendrites) bound together by connective tissue; some nerves contain only sensory fibers, others only motor fibers, and many are mixed nerves including both types. A **ganglion** is a unit containing the cell bodies of few or many neurons, and certain ganglia in the brain are known as **centers.** In all but the lowest animals the nervous system may be termed a receptor-adjustor-effector system or a sensory-neuro-muscular mechanism.

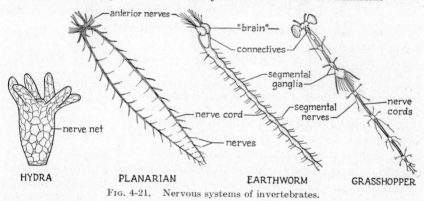

FIG. 4-21.   Nervous systems of invertebrates.

4-37. Invertebrates (Fig. 4-21).   Most protozoans show no structures for coordination, but many ciliates such as *Paramecium* have a definite system of fibrils or a **neuromotor apparatus** (Figs. 12-22, 12-29); this evidently receives stimuli, conducts impulses, and coordinates movements of the cell body. In sponges the cells about the openings (oscula) in the body wall will contract slowly if touched, and these reactions may be communicated slowly to near-by cells, but there are no definite nerve cells or structures. In hydra (Fig. 14-5) and other coelenterates there is a diffuse **nerve net** around the body in or under the epithelium, but no central ganglion. The net is composed of nerve cells (protoneurons), but these are unlike typical neurons in being joined to one another by protoplasmic processes. They connect both to receptors (modified epithelial cells) in the epidermis and to the bases of epitheliomuscular cells that contract slowly to alter the body shape. Nerve nets occur in some other animals and even on the blood vessels of vertebrates.

In bilaterally symmetrical animals the nervous system is linear, usually comprising one or more pairs of **ganglia** or a **brain** in the anterior end connecting to one or more **nerve cords** extending posteriorly through the body. The nerve cords of invertebrates are all ventral and solid, and nerves pass from the ganglia and cords to various organs. Flatworms

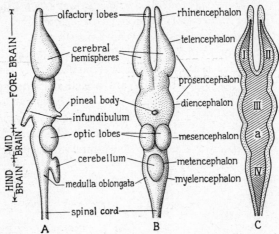

FIG. 4-22. General pattern of the vertebrate brain; diagrammatic. *A.* Left side. *B.* Dorsal surface. *C.* Frontal section with ventricles numbered (I–VI); (*a*) aqueduct.

(Fig. 16-2) have two anterior ganglia, with nerves to the head region, and two separated nerve cords which are joined by cross connectives. In mollusks, annelids, and arthropods the paired anterior ganglia (supraesophageal, subesophageal) lie above and below the esophagus and are joined by connectives. The more specialized mollusks lack ventral nerve cords but have large ganglia joined by connectives in the head, foot, and viscera (Fig. 20-9*A*). In annelid worms and the more primitive arthropods, including some insects and their larvae, the two ventral nerve cords have a pair of ganglia and a pair or more of nerves in each body segment (Fig. 21-6). In the higher crustaceans, insects, and arachnoids the ventral ganglia are concentrated anteriorly (Fig. 24-3). The starfishes and other echinoderms have a radially arranged nervous system in keeping with their symmetry (Chap. 19).

4-38. Vertebrates. The nervous system in all vertebrates has a comparable embryonic origin (Chap. 5) and is always single, hollow, and

dorsal to the digestive tract.   In basic pattern it is like that of the frog
(Fig. 2-18) and consists of (1) the **central nervous system** comprising an
enlarged anterior **brain** (Figs. 4-22, 4-23) connected to a spinal or **nerve
cord** and (2) the **peripheral nervous system** of 10 or 12 pairs of **cranial
nerves** from the brain (Table 4-7), a pair of **spinal nerves** from the cord
for each primitive body segment, and
the **autonomic** (or sympathetic) **nervous
system** (Fig. 4-25).   The description of
the frog's nervous system will suffice
for almost any vertebrate save for proportional differences in the brain, the
length of the spinal cord, and the
number of cranial and spinal nerves.

4-39. Brain.   In the adult shark
(Fig. 27-6) and frog the parts of the
brain are in linear arrangement.   In
the higher vertebrates this primitive
brain stem becomes folded or flexed,
and the **cerebrum** and the **cerebellum**
become progressively enlarged (Fig.
4-23) until in mammals and especially
in man (Fig. 4-27) the cerebrum over-
lies all other parts.   Furthermore, the
outermost gray matter, or **cortex,** of
the cerebrum is thickened and also
increased in area, so that it becomes
folded or convoluted.   In man it contains several billion neurons and their
synapses.   The cortex is the seat of all
conscious sensations and actions, memory, the will, and intelligence; its increase in bulk among the higher vertebrates is in keeping with their greater
mental abilities.   The cerebellum is
concerned with muscular coordinations
and shows especial development in
fishes and birds whose movements are

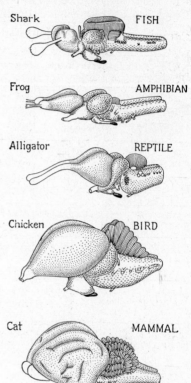

FIG. 4-23.   The brains of representative vertebrates, showing progressive
increase, especially in the cerebral
hemispheres and cerebellum.   *Olfactory
lobes,* clear; *cerebrum,* lightly stippled;
optic tracts and lobes, coarsely stippled;
base of midbrain, wavy lines; *cerebellum,*
vertical lines; *medulla oblongata,* horizontal dashes; *pituitary body,* black.
Stubs of cranial nerves are outlined.

quick and well balanced.   The connections and functions of the cranial
nerves are given in Table 4-7.

4-40. Spinal cord and nerves.   The outer or **white matter** of the spinal
cord consists of bundles of medullated fibers connecting between various
parts of the brain and the nuclei of spinal nerves and adjustor neurons.
The inner **gray matter** contains adjustor neurons and the nuclei of motor

TABLE 4-7. THE PAIRED CRANIAL NERVES OF VERTEBRATES

Number and name of nerve	Origin (in brain)	Distribution (external connections)	Function (chiefly as in man)
I Olfactory	Olfactory lobe (or bulb)	Olfactory epithelium in nasal cavity	*Sensory:* smell
II Optic	Optic lobe on midbrain	Retina of eye	*Sensory:* sight
III Oculomotor	Floor of midbrain	Eye: 4 muscles of eyeball; iris, lens, upper lid	*Motor:* movements of eyeball, iris, lens, and eyelid
IV Trochlear	Floor of midbrain (emerges dorsally)	Eye: superior oblique muscle of eyeball	*Motor:* rotation of eyeball
V Trigeminal	Side of medulla	Top and sides of head, face, jaws, and teeth	*Sensory:* feeling on forehead, scalp, upper eyelid, side of nose, in teeth *Motor:* movement of tongue and of muscles used in chewing
VI Abducens	Side of medulla	Eye: external rectus muscle of eyeball	*Motor:* rotation of eyeball
VII Facial	Side and floor of medulla	Tongue (anterior $\frac{2}{3}$), muscles of face, of mastication, and of neck	*Sensory:* taste *Motor:* facial expression, chewing, movement of neck
VIII Auditory (acoustic)	Side of medulla	Inner ear: (1) organ of Corti in cochlea (2) semicircular canals	*Sensory:* (1) hearing (2) equilibrium
IX Glossopharyngeal	Side of medulla	Tongue (posterior $\frac{1}{3}$); mucous membrane and muscles of pharynx	*Sensory:* taste and touch *Motor:* movements in pharynx
X Vagus (pneumogastric)	Side and floor of medulla	Pharynx, vocal cords, lungs, heart, esophagus, stomach, and intestine	*Sensory:* vocal cords, lungs *Motor:* pharynx, vocal cords, lungs, esophagus, stomach, heart; inhibits heartbeat
XI* Spinal accessory	Floor of medulla	Muscles of palate, larynx, vocal cords, and neck	*Motor:* muscles of pharynx, larynx, and neck
XII* Hypoglossal	Floor of medulla	Muscles of tongue (and neck)	*Motor:* movements of tongue

* Nos. XI, XII are lacking in amphibians, fishes, and cyclostomes.

neurons; nuclei of sensory neurons are in the **dorsal root ganglia** of spinal nerves. If the dorsal root of a spinal nerve is cut, any sensory impulses from the entering fibers fail to reach the cord and brain. Destruction of the ventral root blocks all motor control by fibers in that nerve. The ventral roots are variously injured or destroyed in infantile paralysis, leading to impairment of muscular function.

Fig. 4-24. The human spinal cord, spinal nerves, and sympathetic nervous system and their relation to the vertebrae and the membranes (meninges) about the cord.

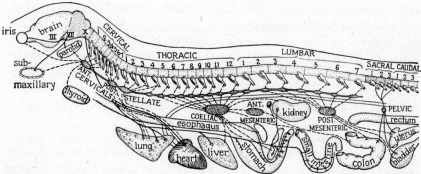

Fig. 4-25. The automatic nervous system of a mammal and its connections with the central nervous system and the internal organs; diagrammatic. Sympathetic trunk and main ganglia (coeliac, etc.), heavy stipple; sympathetic nerves, broken lines; parasympathetic nerves, solid lines; cranial nerves, III, VII, X; spinal nerves numbered for each region of spinal cord.

4-41. Autonomic nervous system. The somatic nerves (cranial, spinal) connect mainly to skeletal muscle and direct the adjustment of an animal to its surroundings. By contrast, the **autonomic nervous system,** of ganglia and fibers connecting to all smooth muscles, glands, and the viscera, deals with the internal environment of the body. It controls routine (vegetative) functions such as rate of metabolism, action and tone of internal muscles, and maintaining constancy (homeostasis) in components of the blood, body fluids, and tissues. In birds and mammals, it closely regulates the body temperature by increasing metabolism and ruffling out the feathers or fur in cold weather or by promoting loss of heat in a warm environment.

The thoracolumbar portion, or **sympathetic system,** includes two lengthwise chains of connected ganglia beside the trunk vertebrae and aorta. Efferent fibers from the spinal cord pass in spinal nerves to enter the sympathetic ganglia as preganglionic fibers. Upon leaving, as postganglionic fibers, those of each group unite as a **plexus,** then distribute to various organs, as with the nerves from the coeliac plexus to the stomach, liver, etc. Afferent sympathetic fibers pass directly from organs to the dorsal roots of spinal nerves and into the spinal cord. Still other fibers connect to the erector muscles of the hairs and to sweat glands and small blood vessels. The craniosacral portion, or **parasympathetic system,** includes fibers in certain cranial nerves, to the iris of the eye (III), the glands and mucous membranes of the mouth (V, VII), and the heart, lungs, stomach, and upper small intestine (X or vagus); and other fibers from sacral nerves connect to organs in the lower abdomen.

Some organs are innervated by both systems, and the two are somewhat antagonistic. The parasympathetic promotes secretion of saliva and digestive juices, increases motility in the intestines, constricts the bronchi, and slows the heartbeat. Besides its routine control, the sympathetic also mobilizes bodily resources for an emergency—fright, flight, or fight, and injury. It increases the rate of heartbeat, dilates the bronchi, slows gastrointestinal action, and stimulates the adrenal gland to increase the secretion of epinephrin. The latter constricts blood vessels of the skin and viscera, dilates those of the heart and skeletal muscle, releases glucose from the liver for muscle metabolism, and accelerates the clotting time of the blood.

4-42. Stimulus and response. Certain responses in animals can be classified readily, but many cannot, because they differ from one another in degree and not in kind. In lower animals a larger percentage are invariable, whereas in higher forms the variable responses predominate. The amoeba exhibits many fixed responses, yet it can learn in a simple way. Man's behavior is highly variable, but he has many invariable and involuntary responses.

The essentially invariable type of response by which an animal orients itself toward or away from a given stimulus is termed a **taxis.** (The term tropism now is reserved for the turning movements of plants.) A fish that heads into a current so that the two sides of its body are stimulated equally by the passing water exhibits **positive rheotaxis** (Gr. *rheos*, current), and an insect that climbs directly upward in opposition to gravity is said to show **negative geotaxis** (Gr. *geos,* earth). The moth that flies directly to a light is **photo-positive** or shows positive phototaxis (Gr. *photos,* light), whereas a cockroach that scuttles for cover when spotted by a light at night is **photo-negative** (negative phototaxis). These several types of response are considered to depend upon reflexes.

The simplest invariable coordinated response involving a nervous system is a **reflex act** and occurs in animals with nerve cords and nerves, such as annelid worms, arthropods, and vertebrates. If when the human leg is bent and suspended freely, the knee tendon is tapped, the leg jerks forward. This knee-jerk reflex is an automatic, unlearned, and involuntary response to the stimulus. The **reflex arc** (Fig. 4-26*A*) (1) involves

FIG. 4-26. Simplified stereogram of the vertebrate spinal cord and nerves to show relations of neurons involve in reflex arcs. Afferent neurons, solid; efferent neurons, outlined; association neurons, broken lines; receptors, as in skin; effectors, as on muscles. Arrows show paths of nerve impulses. Each nerve contains many fibers. *A.* Simple reflex arc. *B.* Reflex arc with one adjustor neuron. *C.* Reflex arc with cross connections. *D.* Reflex arc with cross connections and also others to and from the brain.

a receptor excited by the stimulus and (2) induces a nerve impulse in the dendrite of a sensory neuron, which passes through the nerve cell body (in the dorsal root ganglion) and along the sensory axone into the gray matter of the spinal cord. There the impulse (3) crosses a synapse, or center of correlation, to (4) a second conductor, the motor (efferent) neuron, and continues out its axone in the ventral root to (5) the end organ in contact with an effector; if the latter is a muscle, it is excited to contract. Other simple reflexes are the winking of the eyelids when an object is thrust before the eyes and the sudden secretion of tears by the tear glands when a bit of dust lodges on the cornea. A reflex may or may not evoke a conscious sensation. Few if any reflexes in vertebrates are really simple. The majority are **compound reflexes** wherein an impulse entering on one sensory neuron influences several motor neurons through intermediate or **adjustor neurons** (Fig. 4-26*B, C*); or impulses from several sensory neurons are compounded to act on one motor neuron.

Allied reflexes are combined to produce a harmonious effect, such as the muscular movements in a person when walking or in an earthworm or caterpillar when crawling. These actions may be modified or inhibited through *association neurons* extending to other portions of the nerve cord and to the brain (Fig. 4-26*D*). *Chain reflexes* act in sequence, the response of one becoming the stimulus for the next. A frog responds to a near-by moving insect by opening its mouth and flipping its tongue forward and back; the arrival of captured prey in the mouth acts on receptors there to bring about closing of the mouth and start swallowing reflexes in the pharynx and esophagus. By training, a reflex may be conditioned to follow upon some environmental stimulus other than the original one that evoked it. In a dog the sight of food induces reflexly a flow of saliva, whereas the ringing of a bell does not. The Russian physiologist Pavlov rang a bell whenever food was offered to a dog. After some repetitions the mere sound of the bell, without food, induced salivary secretion in the animal. This Pavlov termed a *conditioned reflex*. Many human acts become conditioned reflexes, often of complex character. Repeated performance of a particular act or procedure becomes a *habit* by some more or less enduring change in the mode of response to a stimulus. Many of the routine activities of human beings are thus reduced to habits so that they are induced by particular stimuli without the intervention of conscious control.

An *instinct* is a complex and invariable form of behavior. Most instincts serve to maintain the individual or the species. In many kinds of animals the choice and means of using food are instinctive acts throughout life, whereas instincts pertaining to reproduction are manifested only when the individuals become sexually mature. In animals that live more than one year the reproductive instincts are active only during the breeding season. The migrations of birds and fishes and the manner of making nests and caring for young among insects and vertebrates are governed entirely or largely by instinct. The mud dauber wasp exemplifies a complex cycle of instincts. Each female makes a tube of mud; then just before it is sealed, she captures and paralyzes spiders with her sting, lays an egg on each, and seals them in the tube. The wasp larvae hatch and feed on the living prey, and when mature the young wasps cut their way out. The parent female never sees her offspring, but her instinctive behavior and later that of the young serve to maintain the species. In social insects such as the honeybee (Chap. 23) each caste has separate instincts that function together for the well-being of the colony.

Beyond hereditary taxes, reflexes, and instincts are the higher aspects of nervous function by which these innate *patterns of behavior* become modified in adaptation to special needs. These grade upward to the display of *intelligence* among the higher vertebrates and man, in

which the brain contains a greater number and more intricate arrangement of conduction paths and larger numbers of association neurons in
the cerebral cortex. All the neurons ever to be present develop early
in the life of an individual, but new synapses presumably are established
throughout life according to the kinds and intensity of stimuli received.
There is a functional localization for certain kinds of sensory and motor
phenomena in the cortex; these have been ascertained (Fig. 4-27*D*)

FIG. 4-27. The human brain. *A.* Left side. *B.* Ventral surface; I–XII, cranial nerves.
C. Median section; III, IV, ventricles. *D.* Left side, showing localization of certain functions
on the surface of the cerebral cortex.

partly by experiment and partly by study of the effects of brain injuries.
A discussion of the nature of consciousness, memory, and the will is
beyond the scope of this text.

I. SENSE ORGANS

Receptors that yield conscious sensations are called **sense organs.**
The functions of these are well known only in man; we cannot always
determine their functions clearly in animals. The human "special
senses" are as follows: **touch,** including contact, pressure, heat, and
cold; **taste,** for certain substances in solution; **smell,** for volatile chemicals

and gases in the air; *hearing,* for vibrations in air, water, or solids; and *sight,* for light waves. Compared with man, the dog has a more delicate sense of smell, the cat hears sounds of higher pitch, the eagle has keener sight, and the honeybee sees farther into the violet but less of the red. Sensory structures are located so as to meet the environment, being around the body in sessile animals and more numerous anteriorly in bilaterally symmetrical species.

4-43. Touch. Tactile receptors are common on the tentacles of coelenterates and annelid worms and on the antennae of arthropods; the latter commonly have tactile hairs on the body (Fig. 23-4*D*). On vertebrates, tactile receptors occur over most of the exterior surface. Some are *free nerve endings,* and others are special *corpuscles* that contain the

Fig. 4-28. Receptors and effectors, the end organs related to sensory and motor nerves. *A.* Free sensory nerve endings in cornea of eye. *B.* Meissner corpuscle (sensory) under human epidermis. *C.* Nerve endings on gland cell in pancreas. *D.* Motor fibers on muscle fibers in frog. *E.* Motor end plates on muscle fibers in rabbit. (*Adapted from Cajal, Histology, The Williams & Wilkins Co.*)

sensory nerve terminations (Fig. 4-28). On man these are most sensitive and closely spaced on the face and palmar surfaces of the fingers. At the finger tip a pressure of only 3 grams per square millimeter is detected and two points 2.3 mm. apart will receive separate sensations, whereas on the back of the body the minima are 48 grams and 67 mm.

4-44. Taste and smell. A common *chemical sense* to irritating chemicals is present in the human mouth and nasal cavities and over all the body in amphibians, fishes, and other aquatic animals. *Taste,* or gustation, is the perception of dissolved materials by *taste buds.* These are groups of narrow receptors with fine tips in a small external pore (Fig. 4-29). They are usually in or about the mouth but occur over the body in catfishes and carp and on the fins of some other fishes. Human taste buds distinguish sweets, salts, acids, and bitter (alkaloidal) substances, and differ in sensitivity as to the concentrations of various materials that can be detected: cane sugar, 1 part in 200; table salt, 1 in 400; hydrochloric acid, 1 in 15,000; and strychnine 1 in 2,500,000. The olfactory organs of fishes and other aquatic animals respond like taste buds to substances dissolved in the water.

Besides their ordinary service, the taste buds may help in maintaining the constancy of the body's internal environment. Rats suffering from

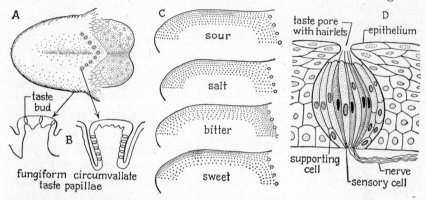

FIG. 4-29. The mechanism of taste in man. *A.* Dorsal surface of tongue. *B.* Two types of taste papillae in section and enlarged. *C.* Relative sensitivity on the tongue for the four tastes. *D.* Section of a taste bud; enlarged and diagrammatic. (*Partly after Parker, Smell, taste and allied senses in the vertebrates, J. B. Lippincott Co.*)

experimental dietary or endocrine deficiencies, when offered a choice of foods or solutions, chose those containing the needed substances.

Smell, or olfaction—"taste at a distance"—depends in man on slender neurons with directly exposed tips that lie in mucous membrane high in the nasal cavity (Fig. 4-30). Eddy currents of air carry volatile sub-

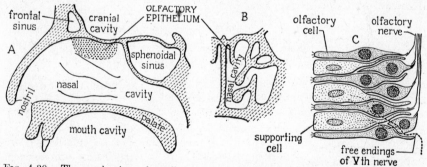

FIG. 4-30. The mechanism of smell (olfaction) in man; diagrammatic. *A.* Section of the head showing olfactory epithelium on lateral wall of right nasal cavity. *B.* Transverse section of nasal cavity. *C.* Enlarged microscopic section of the olfactory epithelium. (*Adapted from Parker, Smell, taste and allied senses in the vertebrates, J. B. Lippincott Co.*)

stances directly to these cell endings, which have much greater sensitivity than taste buds. Man can detect oil of peppermint at 0.024 mg. per liter of air and artificial musk at 0.0004 mg. per liter. Much of our "taste" for food depends upon smell, as shown by the fact that when a cold congests the nasal membranes all food tastes much alike. The sense of smell is vastly more delicate among wild mammals and insects and serves these animals variously in finding food and mates and sometimes in avoiding enemies. In some moths the odor of a female may attract a male for a mile or more.

4-45. Hearing and equilibration. A *statocyst* (Fig. 4-31) is a small organ of equilibration in which a particle rests among hairlike projections on sensory cells. A change in position of the animal brings the particle, or *statolith,* against one or another of the receptors, which transmits an impulse indicating the body position in respect to gravity. In mollusks the statolith is a small limy concretion, whereas in the crayfish (Chap. 22) a particle of sand serves this purpose.

Fig. 4-31. Statocyst of a mollusk (enlarged section).

The inner ear of vertebrates contains three semicircular canals, each in a separate plane and with a swelling, or *ampulla,* containing a statocyst-like organ of equilibrium. The organ of *hearing* in mammals (Fig. 4-32) has an external sound-collecting appendage, or *pinna,* around a tubular *external auditory canal.* At the end of the canal, sound waves act to set the eardrum, or *tympanic membrane,* into vibration. These movements pass through three *auditory ossicles* (malleus, incus, stapes)

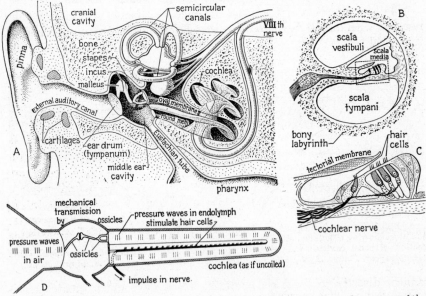

Fig. 4-32. The mechanism of hearing and equilibrium in man. *A.* General structure of the ear. *B.* Cross section of one part of cochlea (area of Fig. *C* in dotted lines). *C.* Enlarged section through spiral organ of Corti with sensory hair cells. *D.* Diagram of sound transmission from the air to an impulse in the auditory nerve.

and produce vibrations in the fluid filling the spiral *cochlea* of the inner ear. In the latter are many *hair cells,* each evidently the receptor for a particular frequency, that induce stimuli in the auditory nerve. In lower land vertebrates there is no pinna, the cochlea is represented by a small outgrowth (lagena), and one bone (columella) replaces the three ossicles. The human ear responds to sound frequencies of about 30 to 10,000, or higher, per second. Sound receptors among invertebrates occur only in certain insects (Fig. 23-15).

4-46. Light and sight. Photoreceptors sensitive to light are present in earthworms (Fig. 21-2), and there are "eye spots" on various coelenterates and mollusks. From such simple structures various types of eyes have been developed (Fig. 4-33). Among arthropods there are both simple and compound eyes (Fig. 22-8; Chaps. 22, 23). The cephalopod

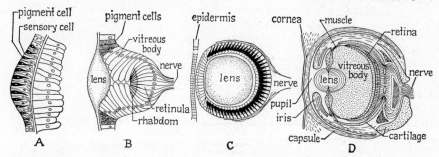

FIG. 4-33. Eyes of some invertebrates, seen in median section. *A.* Medusa (coelenterate). *B.* Beetle larva (insect). *C.* Snail (mollusk). *D.* Cuttlefish (mollusk). (*Altered from Claus, Grobben, and Kuhn.*)

mollusks have eyes much like those of vertebrates, but they are derived differently.

The *eye* in all vertebrates (Fig. 4-34) is much as described for the frog. It is of the "camera" type with a lens which focuses images of external objects on the receptors in the *retina,* as on a photographic film. The receptors consist of *rods* (about 115 million in a human eye), which form colorless sensations in dim light, and the *cones* (6.5 million), which are active in bright light and are sensitive to both white and colored light.

After exposure to bright light, some time is needed for dark adaptation (vision in very dim light). The rods contain a protein pigment, visual purple or rhodopsin, that is bleached by light and must be present for vision in the dark. Rhodopsin is related to carotene compounds, and vitamin A is considered a stage in its regeneration; severe vitamin A deficiency interferes with dark adaptation.

The human eye is sensitive to a visible spectrum from violet to red (397 to 723 mμ, and most acute at 510 mμ = yellow); it cannot perceive vibrations of other wavelengths. Focusing in mammals is accomplished by change in curvature of the lens through action of the ciliary muscle, whereas in birds the lens moves to and fro as in a camera. The size of the opening or pupil in the iris diaphragm, which admits light to the interior, is changed reflexly according to the intensity of the light. Many mammals, some birds, and a few other vertebrates have **binocular vision** in that both eyes can focus on an object in part of the visual field. Such vision facilitates detecting movement in the line of sight and enables man and some animals to judge distances accurately.

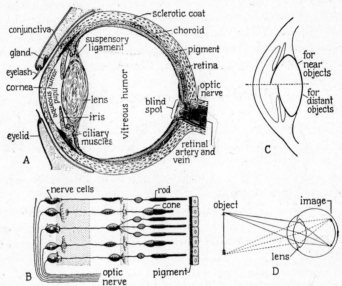

Fig. 4-34.   The mechanism of sight in man.   *A.* Median vertical section of the eye.   *B.* Enlarged diagram of the structure of the retina.   *C.* Changes in shape of the lens (accommodation) to focus on near and distant objects.   *D.* Manner in which lens serves to form an image on the retina.   (*A, modified from Dakin, Elements of general zoology, Oxford University Press.*)

J. ENDOCRINE GLANDS

Most multicellular glands in animals discharge their secretions through ducts and are called glands of external secretion (exocrine); such are the salivary glands and liver that have ducts to the digestive tract and the mammary and sweat glands with ducts opening on the body surface. Vertebrates contain other glands, without ducts, the secretions of which are carried by the blood stream to various parts of the body. These are the **glands of internal secretion, ductless glands,** or *endocrine glands;* their products are called **internal secretions, hormones,** or *endocrines.* Minute amounts of these substances exercise a profound regulatory control over many bodily functions, stimulating or inhibiting the development, growth, and activities of various tissues and influencing the behavior of the individual.   Most or all endocrine activities are inter-related in various degrees.

The endocrine glands include the pituitary, thyroid, parathyroids, islets of Langerhans, adrenals, gonads, parts of the gastric and intestinal mucosa, and, in some mammals, the placenta (Fig. 4-35).   The pineal and thymus were earlier thought to produce internal secretions, but this view is not supported by clear-cut evidence.   The location, structure, and functions of the endocrine glands are enough alike throughout the vertebrates as to suggest a homologous series, differing as to details. Glands of internal secretion are present in some invertebrates (Chaps. 22, 23), but information about them is limited.   Knowledge of vertebrate endocrines has advanced enormously through experimental research since about 1920.   The functions are studied by (1) removing the glands from either young or adult animals; (2) implanting them into subjects of various ages; (3) feeding the gland substance or an extract of it; (4) injecting the extract into the body; and (5) observing individuals with diseased glands.   The science of endocrinology has important appli-cations in human medicine and some bearing on the production of domesticated animals. ،

The structure and function of the endocrines will be described with particular reference to man.

4-47. Thyroid.   This gland, of two lobes joined by an isthmus, lies on either side of the trachea below the larynx.   It consists of many spherical closed sacs or follicles of microscopic size that are lined with cuboidal cells and surrounded by blood vessels and nerves.   The follicles are filled with a colloid material containing the active principle *thyroxin* ($C_{15}H_{11}O_4NI_4$; about 65 per cent of iodine by weight) which regulates the general meta-bolism of the body, its growth, and sexual development.   If the thyroid is removed in a young animal, skeletal growth is arrested and sexual maturity fails; if removed from tadpoles, they do not transform into frogs. Normal development is restored, however, if thyroid is implanted or fed or an extract of it is injected.   Overgrowth or overfunction (hyperthyroid-ism) in man speeds up bodily activities (basal metabolism) and in-creases heat production and heartbeat.   Such conditions are usually relieved by surgical removal of part of the gland, which reduces the amount of thyroxin in the body.   Extreme cases of hyperthyroidism often exhibit nervous excitability and *exophthalmic goiter* or protrusion of the eyeballs.   The latter may follow partial removal of the thyroid (to relieve hyperthyroidism).   One causative factor is oversecretion of thyrotropic hormone by the pituitary which in turn stimulates formation of excess fluid behind the eyeballs.

A deficiency of iodine in the soil and water occurs in glaciated regions and others far from the sea (which contains much iodine), as in the Great

Lakes region, the Alps, The Himalayas, and elsewhere. A chronic enlargement of the thyroid, known as *goiter,* often occurs to compensate for the deficiency. If the deficiency is severe, *cretinism* results among children. Cretins are dwarfed in size, with thick puffy skin and coarse facial features, the basal metabolism is decreased, and the sexual organs do not develop; mental growth is seriously retarded, many are imbeciles

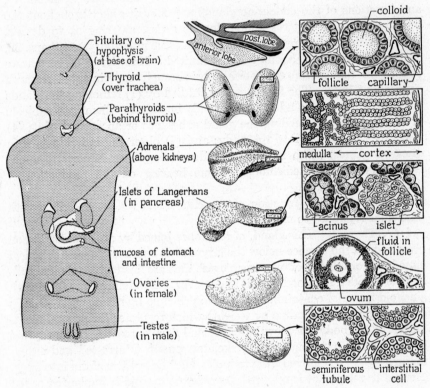

Fig. 4-35.   The endocrine glands of mankind.

or idiots, and deaf-mutes are common. Comparable deficiency in adults causes *myxedema,* characterized by thick puffy skin, scant dry hair, lowered metabolism, disturbance of sexual function, and mental lethargy. Treatment with thyroid extract, if commenced early, stimulates young cretins to normal development and commonly restores myxedematous adults. In regions of iodine deficiency the addition of iodine to the diet, as iodized salt, prevents the occurrence of such defects.

4-48. Parathyroids.   Behind or partly embedded in the thyroid are two pairs of small oval *parathyroids.* Their secretion regulates the concentration of calcium in the blood plasma and affects the calcium metabolism in the body. Removal of the glands is followed by muscular twitchings and spasmodic contractions of increasing violence, leading to severe convulsions (*parathyroid tetany*) and death. Injection of parathyroid extract stops these effects. Overproduction of parathyroid secretion raises the level of calcium in the blood, and calcium may be withdrawn from the bones.

4-49. Gastric and intestinal mucosa. There is evidence of several hormones produced in cells lining the stomach and small intestine that control secretion of digestive enzymes. *Secretin* from the intestinal wall stimulates secretion of the pancreatic juice, and *gastrin* from the mucosa of the stomach serves similarly for gastric juice.

4-50. Islets of Langerhans. Within the substance of the pancreas, in addition to the glandular tissue that provides digestive enzymes passing through the pancreatic duct to the intestine, there are numerous groups of cells, of different form and staining reaction, not connected to the duct. These *islets of Langerhans* produce the endocrine *insulin* which regulates the metabolism of carbohydrates, including sugars, and fats. Disease in the islets or removal of the pancreas is followed by an increase of sugar in the blood and urine, a condition known as *diabetes.* This formerly was fatal in children and young adults and a considerable cause of death in older people, but its effects can now largely be prevented by daily injections of insulin. The latter is extracted from the pancreases of cattle and sheep obtained in slaughterhouses.

4-51. Adrenals (suprarenals). These two glands lie adjacent to the anterior ends of the kidneys in man and mammals. Each consists of an outer cortex and inner medulla, of different microscopic structure. In frogs the adrenal lies along the ventral surface of the kidney, and in sharks the cortex and medulla are separate structures.

The medulla produces *epinephrin* (adrenalin), which, when injected into an animal, causes contraction of smooth muscle fibers in some arterioles, chiefly in the abdomen and skin, with consequent rise in the blood pressure, while arterioles in skeletal muscle are relaxed. The heart is stimulated. It relaxes smooth muscle on the bronchioles of the lung (and hence relieves attacks of asthma) and retards muscular movements in the intestine; it also hastens the transformation of glycogen into glucose. One or two parts per billion of epinephrin are normal in the blood stream of man; but under emotional stress, such as fear or anger, additional amounts are suddenly secreted, and blood is shifted from the viscera to the muscles and the brain, so that the individual is ready for "fight or flight." This hormone is also produced in many invertebrates. Clearcut evidence shows that two substances are produced by the medulla (epinephrin and nor-epinephrin) that differ only qualitatively in biological effect.

The adrenal cortex produces several endocrine substances. Chemically these are steroids, some of the more important being ***desoxycorticosterone, corticosterone,*** and ***cortisone.*** The last of these is beneficial in treating some types of arthritis. Complete removal of both adrenals is followed by death in 10 to 15 days. Earlier symptoms are loss of appetite, vomiting, weakness and prostration, reduction in bodily temperature and metabolism, and loss of water and sodium chloride from the blood. Destruction of the adrenal cortex (Addison's disease) in man results in bronzing of the skin, gradual decline, and finally death.

4-52. Pituitary. At the base of the brain is the **pituitary gland,** or hypophysis, formed during embryonic development of (1) an anterior lobe from a pouch (Rathke's pocket) on the roof of the mouth and (2) a posterior lobe from the infundibulum of the brain. In an adult human being it consists of four parts, as follows: anterior, intermedia, posterior (nervosa), and tuberalis. Extracts of the ***posterior lobe*** affect smooth muscle, cause a rise in arterial blood pressure resulting from contraction of all blood vessels (thus being unlike adrenalin), and also contract smooth muscle in the intestine, gall bladder, ureters, urinary bladder, and uterus. These effects may be due to either one or two hormones. ***Pituitrin*** is a commercial extract that produces all these effects. In cold-blooded vertebrates ***intermedin*** from the ***intermediate lobe*** causes extension of the melanophores, or pigment cells.

The ***anterior lobe*** of the pituitary produces several hormones, the number varying in the judgment of different investigators. The principal activities of these hormones are as follows:

1. Growth stimulating. Excessive secretion or overgrowth of the gland causes *gigantism*. If this occurs during early youth, it results in elongation of the long bones; human giants 8 to 9 feet tall are produced by extreme overfunction. An excess later in life causes *acromegaly* in which the forehead, nose, and lower jaw becomes massive and the facial skin is thick and coarse. Deficiency of this hormone results in *dwarfing*, the individual retaining the proportions of a child.

2. Gonadotropic. In female mammals this hormone (1 or more) causes normal growth of the Graafian follicle in the ovary. Injection of it into immature females causes precocious sexual maturity within a few days; overdoses in rats cause a doubling or trebling of the number of eggs (up to 33) released from the ovaries at one time. In male mammals it stimulates growth of both the seminiferous tubules and interstitial tissue. Implantation of pituitary gland into amphibians results in rapid maturing and laying of eggs within a few days. Removal of the pituitary is followed by atrophy of the gonads and the accessory sex organs.

3. Lactogenic. Stimulates milk secretion in the mammary glands of mammals and secretion of "crop milk" in pigeons; it is present in birds when they are "broody."

4. Adrenotropic. Stimulates growth and secretory activity of the adrenal glands.

5. Thyreotropic. Stimulates the growth and secretory activity of the thyroid gland.

6. Diabetogenic. Raises the sugar content of the blood (thus being antagonistic to insulin).

4-53. Gonads, or sex glands. The testes of the male and ovaries of the female are the *gonads,* or *primary sex organs.* The sperm ducts, associated glands, and the penis of the male and the oviducts, uterus, and vagina of the female are the *accessory sex organs;* these are related in various ways to reproduction (Chap. 5). External differences between the sexes, or *secondary sexual characteristics,* appear in many animals upon attaining sexual maturity. The gonads, besides producing eggs and sperm, respectively, secrete hormones that affect the accessory organs and sexual characteristics. Other endocrine glands, especially the pituitary and thyroid, also influence the sexual structures and functions.

The thick neck, deeper voice, and belligerent manner of bulls, the antlers of male deer, and the larger comb, wattles, and spurs and crowing habits of roosters are some familiar secondary sexual characteristics. Castration or removal of the gonads, before sexual maturity, produces striking changes in the form and temperament of these animals. The steer (castrated bull) has a smaller neck and more cowlike voice and is docile, the castrated deer grows no antlers, and the capon (castrated rooster) has smaller comb and spurs and does not crow. In all such castrates the secondary characters are lacking, the accessory sex organs are reduced, sexual behavior is slight or absent, and the individuals tend to accumulate fat.

The endocrine of the testis that is responsible for these changes is known as *testosterone* ($C_{19}H_{30}O_2$) and is thought to be produced by the Leydig or *interstitial cells,* which occur between the seminiferous tubules of the testis. If this hormone is injected into a castrated individual, the accessory sex organs enlarge, the secondary sexual characters develop, and the behavior becomes that of a normal (uncastrated) animal.

The follicles of the ovary produce a female sex hormone, *estradiol* (and closely related estrogenic hormones), responsible for the phenomenon of estrus, or "heat," in female mammals. Removal of the ovaries from immature females prevents them from becoming sexually mature, their accessory sex organs remain infantile, and the sex instincts are not shown. Injection of estradiol into castrated females corrects these effects. If it is injected into normal (uncastrated) but immature females, they are quickly brought to sexual maturity, the accessory organs develop, but their ovaries remain infantile.

The accessory reproductive organs of females, especially after estrus, are under control of another ovarian hormone known as *progesterone* (progestin); this is produced by the corpus luteum that forms in a Graafian follicle of the ovary after discharge of the ovum. Progesterone, in conjunction with estradiol, prepares the uterus for receiving a fertilized ovum. Both these hormones, either directly or indirectly, are also concerned in preparing the mammary glands for their subsequent function, bringing about enlargement of the glands; later the lactogenic hormone of the pituitary causes milk secretion. A third ovarian hormone, *relaxin,* serves to relax ligaments of the pelvic girdle and thus facilitate birth.

References

BAITSELL, G. A. 1950. Human biology. 2d ed. New York, McGraw-Hill Book Co., Inc. xvii + 730 pp., 361 figs.

CARLSON, A. J., and VICTOR JOHNSON. 1948. The machinery of the [human] body. 3d ed. Chicago, University of Chicago Press. xix + 660 pp., 220 figs.

FULTON, J. F. 1943. Physiology of the nervous system. 2d ed. New York, Oxford University Press. x + 614 pp., 112 figs.

HANSTRÖM, BERTIL. 1939. Hormones in invertebrates. Oxford, Clarendon Press. xi + 198 pp., 13 pls., 21 figs.

MARSLAND, DOUGLAS. 1945. Principles of modern biology. New York, Henry Holt & Co., Inc. ix + 774 pp., 350 figs.

MITCHELL, P. H. 1948. Textbook of general physiology. 4th ed. New York, McGraw-Hill Book Co., Inc. xviii + 927 pp., 200 figs.

PROSSER, C. L. 1950. Comparative animal physiology. Philadelphia, W. B. Saunders Co. ix + 888 pp., 312 figs.

ROGERS, C. G. 1938. Textbook of comparative physiology. 2d ed. New York, McGraw-Hill Book Co., Inc. xviii + 715 pp., 158 figs.

TURNER, C. D. 1948. General endocrinology. Philadelphia, W. B. Saunders Co. xii + 604 pp., 164 figs.

CHAPTER 5

REPRODUCTION AND DEVELOPMENT

Reproduction, the ability to produce new living individuals, is a basic characteristic of all plants and animals. Aristotle and other early biologists understood correctly how the higher animals reproduce, but for centuries people believed that many forms of life arose from non-living materials by *spontaneous generation.* Worms and tadpoles were thought to generate from mud and flies from the carcasses of dead animals. These erroneous ideas were gradually abandoned after critical experiments by Francesco Redi (Italian, 1626?–1697) who showed that maggots and flies are produced from meat only if living flies have laid eggs on such material. An increasing knowledge of the eggs and larvae in the life histories of lower animals helped also to dispel the earlier beliefs. Until about a century ago it was thought that bacteria and other micro-organisms could develop spontaneously in nutrient solutions. Finally, in 1861, Louis Pasteur (French, 1822–1895) proved that when such cultures were heated enough to kill the organisms and properly stoppered to prevent reinvasion by germs or their spores from the air they would remain without life. The principle of *sterilization* that he demonstrated is the basis for destroying microorganisms by heat or chemicals. It is used in present-day surgery and medicine, in preserving food by canning, in the keeping of *pasteur*-ized milk, in safeguarding public water supplies, and in other aspects of modern life.

All reliable evidence indicates that new life comes only from pre-existing life (*omne vivum ex vivo*); this is the process of *reproduction* (biogenesis).

A. REPRODUCTION

5-1. Asexual reproduction. Reproduction that involves only one "parent" and no special reproductive structures is termed *asexual reproduction.* It occurs in many plants and in protozoans, coelenterates, bryozoans, and tunicates (Fig. 5-1) but is unknown in mollusks, arthropods, vertebrates, and other groups. Protozoans multiply by *binary fission* in which an individual divides into two halves, usually equal, after which each grows to the original form. The nucleus divides, and then the cytoplasm is constricted in two. Fission is transverse in some (*Paramecium*) and longitudinal in others (*Euglena*). A type of multiple fission, or *sporulation,* occurs in the sporozoans (*Plasmodium*, etc.), where the nucleus divides repeatedly and then the cytoplasm fragments so that a part of it surrounds each of the many daughter nuclei (Chap.12). **Budding** is a type of reproduction in which a new individual arises as an outgrowth, or **bud,** on an older animal, later to assume the form and size of the latter. It may either remain attached or become separate. In sponges, coelenterates, bryozoans, and tunicates, budding results in

FIG. 5-1.   Types of asexual reproduction.   *A*. Binary fission in *Paramecium*.   *B*. Budding in *Hydra*.   *C*. Fragmentation in a flatworm, *Microstomum;* numbers indicate the sequence of fission planes that will divide the animal into sixteen parts.   (*After von Graf*.)

colonies of many individuals.   Fresh-water sponges also produce internal buds, or **gemmules,** each (Fig. 13-7) of several cells within a dense covering.   These escape, and later each gemmule gives rise to a new individual.   Bryozoans produce internal buds known as **statoblasts** which likewise develop into new animals.

In some flatworms (TURBELLARIA) and ribbon worms (NEMERTINEA)

an individual may **fragment** itself into two or more parts, each capable of growing to be a complete animal. Some sea anemones reproduce from fragments at the base of the stalk.

5-2. Regeneration. The capacity to **regenerate** parts lost by injury or otherwise is allied to growth after fragmentation. Young animals and species low in the evolutionary scale usually have greater regenerative powers than older or higher animals. A cutting of willow or geranium placed in moist soil will

FIG. 5-2.   Regeneration in a flatworm, *Euplanaria*. Portions cut from an entire worm (indicated by dotted lines) gradually regenerate (dark stipple) to form entire small worms. (*After Stempell*.)

grow into a complete plant, and pieces of some hydroid coelenterates (*Tubularia*) if set into sand under sea water will form complete animals. If a flatworm (*Euplanaria*) is cut into pieces, each will usually regenerate to form a complete but smaller individual (Fig. 5-2). Starfishes and other echinoderms regenerate lost arms or other parts. Appendages of crabs and other crustaceans and the tails of some salamanders and lizards may be cast off under stress, a process termed **auto-**

tomy (Gr. *auto*, self + *toma*, to cut). Then the animal regenerates the lost part. Regeneration may involve either a local part or a complete reorganization of tissues to produce organs and other structures anew.

Regeneration (and embryonic differentiation) have been explained by the axial-gradient theory of Boveri, Child, and others. This involves different rates of metabolic activity in the parts of an animal, highest commonly at the anterior end and lowest posteriorly. A short anterior fragment of a planarian would have a high metabolic rate and may produce a second head, whereas a short piece removed toward the posterior end leaves the main axial gradient undisturbed and a tail end will regenerate. Complete reversal of polarity may occur if a fragment of *Tubularia* is "planted" upside down, when the former basal end will produce a mouth and tentacles.

5-3. Sexual reproduction. All kinds of animals and most plants increase by **sexual reproduction** in which new individuals develop from sex cells produced by the parents. Typically two sex cells of different kind (male and female) join to produce a new individual. Among protozoans there are reproductive processes resembling the sexual phenomena of higher animals (Chap. 12). In the **conjugation** of ciliates (*Paramecium*, etc.) two individuals of apparently like kind fuse together, exchange micronuclear materials, and then separate to continue binary fission. Among the sporozoans (*Plasmodium*, etc.) two kinds of individuals, macrogametes and microgametes, are produced at certain stages. These fuse permanently in pairs to continue the life cycle. In the colonial flagellate *Volvox*, the same or different colonies produce two kinds of free individuals that combine in pairs, one of each, and give rise to new colonies.

In multicellular animals, sex is the total of all structural and functional characteristics that distinguish **male** ($\male$) and **female** ($\female$) animals. Both produce free **sex cells,** or **germ cells.** Those of males are minute and known as sperm, or **spermatozoa** (Gr. *sperma*, seed + *zoon*, animal); the female releases somewhat larger **eggs,** or **ova** (sing. *ovum*). Besides the necessary differences in reproductive organs, individuals of the two sexes may differ in external or internal form, in physiology, in behavior, and among the higher animals, even in psychological characteristics.

The germ cells are produced in organs known as **gonads,** the sperm being formed in **testes** (sing. *testis*), or spermaries, and the ova in **ovaries.** These are the **primary sex organs,** and the only sex structures present in coelenterates. Most animals have ducts lined with glands and other parts associated with the gonads to form a **reproductive system** that aids in the reproductive process (Fig. 5-3). Any or all of these parts are single, paired, or multiple in different animals (Chaps. 14 to 32).

If both male and female systems are in one individual, as in flatworms,

earthworms, and others, the animal is said to be **monoecious** (Gr. *monos,*
one + *oecium,* house). In nematodes, arthropods, various other invertebrates, and practically all vertebrates each individual is either male or
female; the sexes are **separate,** and such animals are **dioecious** (Gr. *di,*

FIG. 5-3. Reproductive systems. *Left.* Earthworm (monoecious), both systems in one
individual. *Right.* Cat (dioecious), male and female systems in separate individuals.

two + *oecium*). The term **hermaphrodite** is applied to monoecious
species and also to occasional abnormal individuals of dioecious species
that contain both male and female systems. A condition known as
protandry occurs in some oysters and the hag fishes (cyclostomes) where
the same gonad produces sperm and eggs alternately.

5-4. Reproductive systems. Although there is great variety in the
structural details of the reproductive systems of different animals, there is

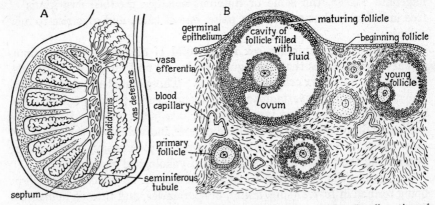

FIG. 5-4. The gonads of mammals. *Left.* Section of a testis. *Right.* Small section of
an ovary, much enlarged, with several Graafian follicles.

a basic similarity in their pattern, even between those of the two sexes
(Table 5-1). In the **male reproductive system** the spermatozoa are
produced in a series of compartments, or tubules, of the **testis** (Fig. 5-4).
Thence they travel through small ducts, or **vasa efferentia,** to a larger

duct, or **vas deferens.**   The lower end of the latter often is enlarged as a **seminal vesicle.**   The vas deferens either leads directly to the exterior of the body or through a copulatory organ, or **penis,** in those species which mate, or copulate, for transfer of sperm directly from the male to the female.   **Accessory glands** that provide secretions to activate the sperm or for other purposes are sometimes present along the sperm duct.   In mammals these are the prostate and bulbourethral glands.

The **female reproductive system** produces the ova as individual cells in the **ovary.**   In some animals each ovum during its growth is surrounded by "nurse" or follicle cells, as in the frog.   Each ovum in a mammal develops within a special **Graafian follicle** that enlarges as the egg matures and finally ruptures to release it (Fig. 5-4*B*).   The fluid of these follicles contains hormones important in reproduction (Chap. 4). The ovaries of mammals and some other animals are solid, those in a frog are saclike, and those of insects comprise several tubular ovarioles.   The ovum usually acquires its yolk while still in the ovary.   Mature eggs are released from the ovary and pass down the conducting tube, or **oviduct,** being moved by the action of muscles in its walls or by cilia lining its interior.   **Glands** in the wall of the oviduct may surround the egg with

TABLE 5-1.   THE ESSENTIAL FEATURES OF REPRODUCTIVE SYSTEMS

Sex	Gonads (*produce sex cells*)	Sex ducts	Accessory glands	Storage (*of sperm*)	Terminal organs (*extrusion or transfer*)
Male (♂)	testis (*spermatozoa*)	vasa efferentia, vas deferens	sperm activating	seminal vesicle	penis
Female (♀)	ovary (*ova*)	oviduct (+uterus)	albumen, yolk, shell	seminal receptacle	vagina (+ovipositor)

various materials such as the albumen (egg white) and shell in reptiles, birds, and other animals.   The lower end of the duct may be enlarged as a temporary storage reservoir for eggs before they pass out of the body. This part of the duct is expanded as the **uterus** in the mammals and other animals that retain their eggs for development inside the body.   In species that copulate, the terminal part of the female tract is specialized as the **vagina** to receive the male's penis; some have also a **seminal receptacle** for storage of the sperm received.

5-5. Origin of sex cells.   There is great interest in the ultimate origin of the sex cells because they give rise to new individuals and serve to transmit hereditary characteristics between successive generations.   The doctrine of germinal continuity of August Weismann (German, 1834–

1914) held that the sex cells, or *germ plasm,* comprised a substance apart from external influences and from the body, or *somatoplasm.* For each new generation the parent germ plasm produces both the body (soma) and the germ plasm of new individuals. The continuity of germ plasm is clear in some invertebrates (*Ascaris, Sagitta, Miastor*) where one cell in the early cleavage of the egg can be traced as the ultimate origin of the future sex cells. In birds, mammals, and others, however, no such early recognition of future germinal material is possible. Indeed, all the early ova in young mammals degenerate, and others form later from germinal epithelium (modified peritoneum) over the ovaries. The subject is less important now because we recognize a direct continuity in the chromosomes whereby each cell of the new animal contains the hereditary mechanism established in the egg (zygote) as it starts to develop.

In some animals the gonads appear during embryonic development but do not enlarge until the individuals approach sexual maturity. In others they form at the latter stage. Early germ cells in the gonads multiply by mitosis like somatic cells (epithelium, muscle, etc.); every chromosome divides longitudinally into strictly equivalent halves so that each daughter cell receives an identical set of chromosomes. The nucleus in each contains a dual set of chromosomes, the diploid number, $2n$ (except in some "haploid" bees, etc.). In every pair, one chromosome was derived from the male parent and the other from the female parent of the individual in question. The two members of each pair are termed *homologous chromosomes.* At the approach of sexual maturity the germ cells multiply rapidly; they are then known as *spermatogonia* in the male and as *oögonia* in the female. Before being able to participate in reproduction, however, their physical and physiological characteristics must change.

5-6. Maturation and meiosis. The process by which spermatogonia become spermatozoa and oögonia become ova is known as *gametogenesis* or *maturation,* and the resulting matured cells are called *gametes* (Figs. 5-5, 5-8). The accompanying nuclear changes are termed "reduction of the chromosomes" or *meiosis.* The gametes of the male and female differ in form, size, and physiology, but the meiotic changes in their nuclei are comparable.

Meiosis consists of two nuclear divisions that follow one another without an interval, known as the *first and second meiotic (maturation) divisions.* These differ from mitosis in two important features: (1) The final number of chromosomes in a gamete is only half (or the haploid number, n) of that present in a spermatogonium or oögonium (or somatic cell), and the set of chromosomes in a matured gamete includes but one member from each homologous pair that was present in the unmatured cells. (2) There is a random assortment in this reduction so that each gamete receives either *one or the other* member of each pair.   Hence, when two gametes of opposite sex later join in fertilization, the chromosome number in the new individual will be that of the species.   The manner of division and segregation of the chromosomes during maturation, together with the random meeting of eggs and sperm in fertilization, afford a logical basis for many of the observed phenomena of inheritance on the premise that the chromosomes are the bearers of the determiners, or genes, for hereditary characters.   The random sorting provides for variation in the characters that will appear in different individuals of the new generation (Chap. 6).

5-7. Spermatogenesis. As a male matures sexually, the spermatogonia in the testis multiply by mitosis until a great many are present. After the last mitosis, maturation begins. Each spermatogonium grows in size, and then is termed a *primary spermatocyte.* During the prophase of the *first meiotic division,* the diploid number of chromosomes ($2n$) appears in the nucleus, each chromosome being a single strand of particles (chromomeres). The 2 chromosomes of each homologous pair come to lie more or less parallel to one another, a phenomenon called *synapsis* (conjugation). Soon each chromosome divides longitudinally into 2 chromatids, but the latter do not immediately separate.   Every bundle then includes 4 components (chromatids) and is termed collectively a *tetrad.*   There is no further splitting of chromosomes during maturation.

In each primary spermatocyte the chromosomes shorten and thicken; a spindle forms with the tetrads arranged at random on the equatorial plate.   At the metaphase the paternal and maternal pairs of chromatids separate slightly; at the anaphase one pair goes to one pole of the spindle and the other pair to the opposite.   From different tetrads the manner of segregation is by chance—free assortment; some maternal and some paternal pairs of chromosomes go to one pole and those of opposite origin to the other pole.   Each of the resulting 2 cells (with n chromosomes or $2n$ chromatids) is called a *secondary spermatocyte.*[1]

---

[1] Further details are as follows.   At the beginning of meiosis the chromosomes first appear as long filaments with the chromomeres spaced out on the chromonemata, like beads on a rosary (leptotene stage).   The homologous chromosomes then pair, side by side, eventually joining along their entire length (zygotene-synapsis).   The pairs then shorten and thicken (pachytene), and during this stage each individual chromosome splits longitudinally (or reproduces) to yield 2 daughter chromatids (the tetrad, latterly called bivalent).   At this time transverse breaks may occur whereby parts of the pair of daughter chromatids of one chromosome may be exchanged for equivalent parts of the 2 chromatids of the other homologous chromosome (this is crossing over; see Chap. 6, Fig. 6-9; the points of crossing over are termed chiasmata).   Then the homologous chromosomes (each of 2 chromatids) begin to separate (diplotene stage) and there is further contraction in length (diakinesis).   Finally they become arranged in an equatorial plate, the two members of each homologous pair having their centromeres toward opposite poles of the cell.

Fig. 5-5.   Maturation of germ cells and fertilization; diagrammatic.   The maturation process is similar in the two sexes as to nuclear divisions and chromosomes, but differs as to the cytoplasm.   The species is assumed to have 6 chromosomes (diploid number); chromosomes derived from the previous generation are shown as white (maternal) and stippled (paternal) respectively.

Shortly a spindle forms in each secondary spermatocyte, and the chromosomes take an equatorial position.   The **second meiotic division** then occurs; the two chromatids of each pair separate from each other as distinct chromosomes and go to opposite poles of the cell: the resulting 2 cells are called **spermatids.**   A primary spermatocyte thus yields

4 spermatids, each containing *n* chromosomes, the haploid number. From each pair of homologous chromosomes in a primary spermatocyte, any one spermatid contains one representative, either paternal or maternal.

Following the second division, each spermatid undergoes a *metamorphosis.* Much of the cytoplasm is cast out, the nucleus compacts to a small (densely staining) head, behind this is a mid-piece containing one or two centrioles, and the posterior end of the cell becomes a slender cytoplasmic tail. This is the mature male gamete, or *spermatozoan.*

FIG. 5-6.   Maturation of the ovum, sperm entrance, and fertilization in the roundworm, *Ascaris megalocephala.*

Both maturation and metamorphosis are usually completed before the sperm is released from the testis.

5-8. Oögenesis.   The gonads of females produce fewer sex cells than do those of males. In the ovary the oögonia become *primary oöcytes,* often enlarging with the addition of yolk. Synapsis, tetrad formation, and chromosome reduction occur as in the male. The division spindle forms near the cell margin. At the first meiotic division practically all the cytoplasm remains with one nucleus to form the *secondary oöcyte;* the other nucleus passes out on the surface of the cell as a microscopic *first polar body.* Likewise, in the second meiotic division, the cytoplasm with one nucleus forms the *oötid,* and the other nucleus is passed out as the *second polar body.* The chromosome content of an oötid results from chance assortment as with a spermatid. With slight change in nuclear position the oötid becomes a female gamete, or *ovum.*

Thus each oögonium yields but one ovum; yet the nuclear divisions that produce the ovum and polar bodies are equivalent to those by which four spermatozoa are derived.   The animal egg acquires most of its physical features before maturation.   In different species, meiosis either occurs in the ovary, or after the egg is set free, or requires that a sperm must penetrate the egg cytoplasm before it will be completed.

FIG. 5-7.   Protective coverings of some animal eggs.

5-9. Gametes.   The gametes of various animals differ in form and size, and those of the two sexes in any one species are quite unlike (Fig. 5-8). The ovum (any covering or shell being disregarded) is spherical or oval and nonmotile and may contain yolk (deuteroplasm) to nourish the newly developing individual.   The largest ova are those of some huge sharks, these being the largest animal cells known.   The hen's ovum ("yolk") is about 30 mm. in diameter, many amphibian eggs are about 2 mm.,

FIG. 5-8.   The gametes of several animals.   Ova; natural size, diameters in millimeters. Spermatozoa, greatly enlarged, but not to same scale.   (*Mostly after Retzius.*)

those of mammals are about 0.05 to 0.25 mm. (human ovum about 0.15 mm.), and some invertebrate eggs are even smaller.   Spermatozoa are small and motile, able to swim in fluid.   While usually threadlike, some are amoeboid, and others of peculiar shapes.   Their size is usually microscopic.   Those of amphioxus are 16 to 20 μ long, and those of man 52 to 62 μ; among the largest are those of a toad (*Discoglossus*) which measure 2,000 μ (2 mm.).   The sperm cell is usually but a minute fraction of the egg in volume; with human gametes the ratio is about 1 to 195,000.   Enough human ova to provide the present world population of two billion people could be put in a top hat and the sperm to fertilize them in a thimble!

5-10. Fertilization.   The union of a mature spermatozoan and an ovum is known as *fertilization,* and the resulting cell is a *zygote.*   Two haploid nuclei (n) fuse (Fig. 5-6) as a zygote having the diploid number ($2n$) of the species.   Fertilization involves the physical entry of the sperm and also physiological processes in both egg and sperm, as follows: (1) A sperm cannot effect the fertilization of an unmatured egg.   (2) Fertilization is an irreversible process.   (3) Fertilization is usually species-specific as only in exceptional cases will "foreign" sperm fertilize an egg.   Fertilization stimulates the egg to active cleavage and development and also provides for combining of hereditary characteristics from both male and female parents.   In different species, sperm penetrate the egg at various stages during maturation (from oögonium to oötid), but fusion of the egg and sperm nuclei occurs only after maturation in the egg is completed.   Experimental evidence suggests that the outer (cortical) portion of the egg secretes a substance, *fertilizin,* to which the sperms react in effecting fertilization.   On some eggs a *fertilization membrane* forms after entrance of one sperm and excludes others; the egg cytoplasm then separates slightly from its cell membrane.   Additional sperms may enter (polyspermy) eggs with much yolk, but only one fuses with the egg nucleus.

A few monoecious or hermaphroditic animals may be self-fertilizing; but *cross-fertilization,* the combining of gametes from two different individuals, is the general rule.   A monoecious animal commonly produces its eggs and sperm at different times, but if formed simultaneously they are usually self-sterile.

Fertilization is accomplished by various physical means.   In *external fertilization* (1) the eggs and sperm are shed freely into open water (many invertebrates, some marine fishes); (2) the male and female are close together, as over a nest, when eggs and sperm are extruded (lampreys, trout); or (3) there is simultaneous extrusion of eggs and sperm by clasped pairs (frogs and toads).   In *internal fertilization* (4) the male places sperm packets (spermatophores) on the bottom that are taken into the seminal receptacle of the female (aquatic salamanders); or (5) by definite copulation sperm are transferred by the male into the female's vagina, later to fertilize eggs in her reproductive tract (nematodes, some mollusks, earthworms, arthropods, some fishes, all reptiles, birds, and mammals).   Many water dwellers practice internal fertilization, and it is necessary for all terrestrial species as sperm can travel only in a fluid medium.   In vertebrates having internal fertilization, the sperm travel up the oviduct and usually fertilize eggs soon after they enter.

5-11. Artificial insemination. In some mammals normal copulation may be replaced by artificial insemination, whereby seminal fluid is removed from a male and placed in the vagina of a female to initiate pregnancy. This now is a common practice for some kinds of domestic animals; the desirable characteristics of a high-quality stallion or bull may be transmitted to hundreds of offspring rather than to relatively few as by ordinary mating. Furthermore, semen properly prepared may be shipped long distances for such use. About 2,500,000 dairy cows are now inseminated annually in the United States. Under medical supervision, artificial insemination is used among human beings in special cases as where a husband is sterile or where some physiological abnormality in husband or wife prevents normal conception.

5-12. Cryptorchidism. In males of most terrestrial mammals, upon reaching sexual maturity, the testes descend from the abdominal cavity into the scrotum, either permanently or during the mating season. Failure to descend, a condition termed cryptorchidism, renders a testis sterile. If both testes remain abdominal, no viable sperm are produced because of the higher temperature within the abdomen as compared with the scrotum. Descent is considered to be conditioned by a pituitary hormone.

5-13. Special types of sexual reproduction. Development of an egg without the entrance of a sperm is known as *parthenogenesis* (Gr. *parthenos*, virgin + *genesis*, origin). It occurs naturally and regularly in rotifers, plant lice and thrips, many ants, bees and wasps, some crustaceans, and certain other invertebrates. Indeed males are unknown in some thrips and rotifers. Aphids have successive generations of parthenogenetic females during the spring and summer, but later both sexes are produced by parthenogenesis. These then mate in ordinary sexual reproduction, and the females lay fertilized eggs from which females hatch the next spring to continue parthenogenesis (Fig. 23-32). The queen honeybee produces fertilized eggs (with sperm from her seminal receptacle) that develop into females, either workers or queens; but she also lays unfertilized eggs that yield males or drones (Chap. 23). These and the parthenogenetic males of other bees are haploid in chromosome number. Their spermatogenesis is of a peculiar type, omitting a reduction division.

The larvae of the gall fly, *Miastor*, produce eggs that develop parthenogenetically to yield other larvae. In the liver flukes (TREMATODA) one larval stage, the sporocyst, produces unfertilized eggs that give rise to another known as the redia (Chap. 16). These instances of parthenogenesis among larvae are termed *paedogenesis*. The larvae of the tiger salamander and some others (Family AMBYSTOMIDAE) under certain conditions will become sexually mature, mate, and produce fertile eggs; this phenomenon is called *neoteny.*

Mature eggs of certain species that normally are fertilized may, by certain types of stimulation, be induced to develop by *artificial parthenogenesis.* This was first clearly demonstrated by Jacques Loeb in 1900. Many experiments have been conducted by various investigators using eggs of sea urchins and other marine invertebrates. The stimuli employed included shaking, heat, dilute organic acids, and hypertonic solutions (water with greater than normal concentrations of salts). By pricking thousands of frog eggs with needles, Loeb induced development in many eggs, obtained over 200 tadpoles, and reared nearly a hundred frogs through or beyond metamorphosis. Both sexes were obtained. Other experimenters have produced lesser numbers of frogs by this method. The frogs are diploid as to chromosome number and not haploid, as might be expected. At least one "fatherless" rabbit has resulted from the artificial stimulation of an egg that was later implanted in the uterus of a female. Although the means for inducing artificial parthenogenesis seem diverse, all the successful methods evidently achieve the same result as that produced by spermatozoa—activation of the egg.

5-14. Polyembryony is the production of two or more individuals from one egg by separation of the cells in early stages of cleavage. This occurs in cases of identical twins in man, also in some armadillos (4 young per egg), in bryozoans, and in some parasitic HYMENOPTERA. In the last-named group some eggs produce single embryos whereas others yield 8 to 20 young (*Platygaster*) or about 1,000 (*Litomastix*).

5-15. Reproduction in general. Most species have definite *reproductive seasons.* In temperate and cold regions these are usually in spring or summer when food is abundant and other conditions for survival of the offspring are favorable. Many invertebrates do not reproduce until the environmental temperature reaches a certain minimum. Other species are influenced by the kind of food available. With some birds and mammals the increasing length of daylight has been shown to act on the gonads through the pituitary gland to induce breeding.

Most animals are *oviparous,* the females release or lay eggs from which the young later hatch out. Many aquatic invertebrates, most insects, and all birds are of this sort. Other animals give birth to living young. Some of them are *ovoviviparous;* producing eggs with much yolk that develop within the oviducts ("uterus") of the female. Certain insects, sharks and lizards, and the garter snakes and rattlesnakes are examples. The mammals and occasional other animals are *viviparous,* producing small eggs that are retained and nourished in the female's uterus.

The **number of eggs** produced by each female of a species is inversely proportional to the average chance for survival of any one offspring to complete maturity. The number is largest where the hazards are greatest. Some parasites produce millions of eggs, the codfish lays up to 6,000,000, a brook trout up to 5,600, a quail averages 14, a robin 3 to 5, a deer or sheep 2 or 1, and the horse only 1. Some species produce repeated layings of eggs or broods of young. The **rate of development** until hatching is rather constant in birds and mammals, but with other animals it varies according to the environmental temperature or other conditions. The approximate time required is characteristic for each species, ranging from a few hours or days for some invertebrates to many months for the largest mammals.

Animals often have special **breeding habits** that make for greater success in reproduction. These include the courting performances of many vertebrates that ensure successful matings, the use of nests to provide protection for eggs, and the parental care given to eggs and young. The eggs are carried on the body or in brood pouches by the females of some crustaceans, insects, and spiders and by either the male or female among certain fishes and amphibians. Birds sit on and incubate their eggs, and thus heat from the parent's body causes the eggs to develop at a uniform rate. In mammals the development of the young within the mother's uterus achieves a similar result. Young of some spiders, wasps, and bees are provided with food in the nest, the termites and social bees feed and tend the young in their colonial nests, the nestlings of birds are fed with food gathered by the parents, and young mammals are nourished by milk secreted from the mammary glands of their mothers.

5-16. Sex ratio. The numerical relations between the sexes in a species is the **sex ratio.** The primary ratio is that in embryos when sex is first evident, the secondary when the young are born or hatched, and the tertiary thereafter. Differences between the ratios within a species reflect unlike mortality in the two sexes. In mankind the primary ratio is high, but males experience greater mortality both prenatal and postnatal. The ratio is important in livestock production, and there would be decided practical benefit if sex could be controlled to produce more females—but this has not been possible.

The sex ratio is usually stated as numbers of males per 100 females. Some well-known secondary ratios are: mankind, 103 to 107; horse, 98.3; cattle, 107.3; sheep, 97.7; pig, 111.8; dog, 118.5; rabbit, 104.6; house mouse, 100 to 118; chicken, 93.4 to 94.7; pigeon, 115.

The ratio varies with race or breed, season, and other factors not all understood. Theoretically there should be equal numbers of male- and female-producing gametes; either there is a differential in gamete production or in mortality among early embryos.

B. DEVELOPMENT

5-17. Development. The starting point for the production of a new individual by sexual reproduction is the activated egg, or zygote. Repeated mitotic divisions result in many cells that differentiate to form the tissues and organs of the developing individual, or **embryo.** This is the process of embryogeny (Gr. *embryo* + *genesis,* generation), and the science that deals with the subject is **embryology.** The following account outlines early development of the frog (Fig. 5-10) and mentions some features of that in birds and mammals.

5-18. Cleavage. Soon after an egg is fertilized, the single-celled zygote becomes two cells (by mitosis), the two divide into four, and so on. This process of **cleavage** partitions the egg substance into an increasing number of smaller cells, or **blastomeres,** each with an equal number of chromosomes.

5-19. Blastula. As cleavage continues, the cells become arranged in the form of a hollow ball, or **blastula,** within which a segmentation cavity, or **blastocoel,** appears. Two major regions may then be distinguished, an upper **animal hemisphere** or pole of small dark cells that contain little yolk and an opposite **vegetal hemisphere** below of larger pale-colored cells rich in yolk granules. Between them is a **marginal zone** of medium-sized cells.

5-20. Gastrula. Cleavage is followed by a somewhat complex process of **gastrulation.** Cells of the vegetal and marginal regions gradually move inward and are overgrown by those of the animal hemisphere. A double-walled cup results, as might be produced by pushing in one side of a hollow rubber ball. This is termed a **gastrula.** The blastocoel is gradually obliterated, and the cavity resulting from gastrulation is the primitive gut, or **archenteron.** The external opening of the archenteron is called the **blastopore.**

Gastrulation involves three related activities: (1) the yolk-laden endoderm cells of the vegetal pole push or cup inward (invagination); (2) the germ ring, and especially the dorsal lip of the blastopore, is inturned (involution); and (3) the ectoderm grows downward eventually to cover the cells of the vegetal pole (epiboly, or overgrowth).

When complete the gastrula consists of (1) an outer cell layer of **ectoderm,** from cells of the animal hemisphere; (2) an inner layer, of **endoderm,** from cells of the vegetal pole; and between these (3) a third layer, of **mesoderm,** derived from the marginal zone. These are the **germ layers** from which various tissues and organs will form. The ectoderm will produce the external covering of the body, the nervous system, and the sense organs; the endoderm provides the lining of the digestive tract, its glands, and associated structures; and the mesoderm

FIG. 5-9. Sample stages of cleavage and gastrulation in eggs of chordates. *A*. Amphioxus, cleavage holoblastic, little yolk; egg diameter 0.1 mm. (*After Hatschek.*) *B*. Frog, modified holoblastic cleavage, much yolk; diameter 2 mm. (*Various sources.*) *C*. Bird, meroblastic discoidal cleavage in small blastodisc on large yolk mass; diameter 30 mm. (*After Blount; and Patten, Embryology of the chick, The Blakiston Co.*) *D*. Mammal, cleavage holoblastic, practically no yolk; an outer and inner cell mass formed in blastula (6); gastrula formed by migration of endoderm cells from inner cell mass (7); egg surrounded during early cleavage by zona pellucida (from Graafian follicle of ovary) which later disappears. (*After Gregory; and Patten, Embryology of the pig, The Blakiston Co.*)

gives rise to the supportive tissues, muscles, lining of the body cavity, and other parts (Table 5-2).

5-21. Body symmetry and axes.[1]   An *egg axis* may be visualized through the animal and vegetal poles.   A *gray crescent* forms on a meridian 180 degrees from the point of sperm entrance, usually being bisected

Fig. 5-10.   Early embryology of the frog.   Long arrow indicates egg axis.   *A.* Sperm at surface of egg.   *B.* Entrance path of sperm (in plane of paper) bisects gray crescent and determines plane of first cleavage.   *C.* Late blastula.   *D.* Blastopore formed, gastrulation begins.   *E.* Processes in gastrulation.   *F, G.* Gastrulation continues, rotation of egg on axis, anteroposterior and dorsoventral relations established.   *H, I.* Gastrula completed.   *J.* Beginning of organ systems.   *D–H.* Longi-sections; *I, J.* Cross sections.   (Compare Figs. 5-9B, 5-11, 2-20.)   (*A–G*, redrawn by permission from W. C. Curtis and M. C. Guthrie, *Textbook of general zoology*, John Wiley & Sons, Inc.; *H–J*, redrawn from H. Spemann, *Embryonic development and induction*, Yale University Press.)

by the first cleavage plane.   The latter usually proves to be the future median plane of the embryo; hence the path of sperm entrance establishes bilateral symmetry (right and left sides).   The dorsal lip of the blastopore, where endoderm and marginal zone meet, shifts upward from the

---

[1] The movement and fate of local portions of the egg may be determined by spotting the surface with vital dyes that stain but do not injure the protoplasm and then tracing the subsequent location of these color spots.

lower surface as gastrulation proceeds; when all the endoderm is inside, the original egg axis has rotated about 90 degrees.   The former lower end of the axis is then at the completed blastopore, marking the posterior end of the future animal, so that the longitudinal body axis is indicated. The plate of mesoderm cells inturned at the upper lip of the blastopore indicates the dorsal region; and shortly after gastrulation the paired neural folds on the surface, forward from the blastopore, provide an external indication of the dorsal surface.

5-22. The embryo. After gastrulation the *differentiation* of the embryo begins.   From the three germ layers there are outpocketings, inpocketings, thickenings, divisions, and other changes that lead to establishment of the organs and organ systems (Fig. 5-11).

The nervous system starts dorsally as a pair of **neural folds.**   The ectoderm between these sinks down, and the folds come together to

Fig. 5-11.   Stereogram of early frog embryo cut away to show beginnings of organ systems.

form a **neural tube,** which is larger at the anterior end to become the **brain.**   On either side, in the angle between the neural tube and ectoderm, a thin line of cells forms as the **neural crests;** these will produce the dorsal or sensory roots of the spinal nerves that grow into the cord. Motor roots later grow out ventrally from the cord.   The early brain is of three primary vesicles, the *fore-, mid-,* and **hindbrain.**   The forebrain produces the cerebral hemispheres and diencephalon, and from the hindbrain the cerebellum and medulla oblongata are derived.   A rounded **optic vesicle** grows laterally on either side of the forebrain; as each meets the ectoderm on the side of the head region, the latter is stimulated to form a thickened **lens vesicle** that subsequently produces the lens of the eye.   Meanwhile, the outer surface of each optic vesicle becomes concave by invagination and forms the **retina.**

The endoderm of the primitive archenteron cavity elongates forward from the blastopore to become the lining of the **digestive tract.** Anteriorly, at the future pharynx, three outpocketings of the tract on either side meet three corresponding inpocketings from the side of the neck; these break through to form the **gill slits.**   A single ventral outpocket, behind the pharynx, forms the **liver bud,** later to yield the liver and bile duct. The blastopore closes, and for a time the digestive tract is sealed at both ends. A later inpocketing of ectoderm (stomodeum) forms ventrally on the head region and a similar one (proctodeum) at the posterior end. In later embryonic life these break through to join the endoderm of the digestive tract, the stomodeum becoming the mouth cavity and the proctodeum becoming the cloaca, both lined by ectoderm. During larval life a ventral outpocket of the pharynx grows posteriorly, with two lobes, and gives rise to the **larynx, trachea,** and **lungs.**

As gastrulation is ending, the plate of mesoderm cells from the dorsal lip of the blastopore grows forward between the ectoderm and endoderm.

Table 5-2. General Outline of Embryonic Differentiation in a Vertebrate

Its middorsal portion folds off as a solid rod of cells, the **notochord,** between the developing nerve cord and primitive gut, to serve as a supporting body axis.   Later in larval life, groups of mesenchyme cells gather about it to form the **vertebrae.**   The latter are first of cartilage and become bony in the young frog.

The lateral mesoderm at either side of the notochord early grows down as a curved plate between the ectoderm and the endoderm, and the two meet ventrally beneath the primitive gut.   Each plate gradually splits into two layers, and the space produced between them is the body cavity, or **coelom.**   The outer layer is applied to the ectoderm as the **parietal peritoneum,** and the inner layer surrounds the gut (and other organs later) to make the **visceral peritoneum** and other structures. Mesoderm on either side of the notochord and nerve cord forms a lengthwise series of segmental pouches or **somites.**   The upper part (epimere) of each somite has a thick inner layer (myotome) that later produces the **voluntary muscles** while the thin outer layer becomes the **dermis** of the skin.   The midportion of the somite gives rise to the pronephros and later the mesonephros of the excretory system.

The further details of embryonic development are too numerous to be followed here.   After some days (depending on the species of frog and the water temperature) the embryo escapes from its gelatinous covering to hatch as a tadpole, or **larva.**   Shortly it begins to feed and grow.   Development continues for some months, and then a **metamorphosis** occurs by which the larva transforms into a frog (Fig. 2-20).

5-23. Development of the chick.   Eggs of birds, reptiles, and many fishes contain so much yolk that cleavage of the entire mass is impossible. The process begins in a small area of protoplasm, or **blastodisc,** at the animal pole.   By this meroblastic cleavage a plate of cells is formed that corresponds to the spherical blastula of a frog (Fig. 5-9*C*).   At gastrulation, one edge (the future posterior end) turns under, resulting in two layers of cells, the ectoderm and endoderm.   The site of the inturning (invagination) is called the blastopore lip.   A median **primitive streak** then develops anteriorly from the blastopore, on the ectoderm, and from its anterior portion parallel edges turn up to form **neural folds.**   The **notochord** appears between the neural tube and endoderm, as in the frog. The endoderm spreads in a flat sheet over the surface of the yolk mass. Mesoderm forms between the ectoderm and endoderm at either side of the notochord, then splits into two sheets with the future coelomic cavity between; somites develop in the mesoderm at either side of the notochord. Meanwhile, a **head fold** appears at the anterior end of the primitive streak; this contains the first evidence of the future brain and of the foregut.   The subsequent development of the chick embryo has much in common with that of the frog, as to the way in which organs become established (Fig. 5-12).   Gill pouches and *gill slits* appear in the first few days but soon close.   The endoderm and mesoderm on all sides spread around the yolk to form a *yolk sac* (Fig. 5-14) finally enclosed by the ventral body wall just before hatching.   A calcareous *egg tooth* then

FIG. 5-12.   The chick embryo during the first 72 hours of development ($\times 6\frac{1}{2}$).   Gastrulation (Fig. 5-9C) probably occurs before the egg is laid.   At 21 hours of incubation the first somite appears; after 26 hours the heart begins beating and food material is brought by vitelline veins from the yolk surface (not shown).   During the second day the anterior end turns so that the left side of the embryo lies toward the yolk; this turning is completed on the fourth day.   At 48 hours the amnion covers the anterior two-thirds of the embryo.   (*After Patten, Early embryology of the chick, The Blakiston Co.*)

forms on the tip of the beak, by which the embryonic bird cracks the shell and hatches out as a chick.

5-24. Development of the mammal.   The eggs of the lowest living mammals (MONOTREMATA) resemble those of birds in being of some size,

FIG. 5-13.   The rat embryo from the tenth to twentieth day of gestation, natural size; 10- and 12-day stages also enlarged three times.   Early development is slow; third day: 8-cell stage, in oviduct; fourth to seventh days: blastula, in uterus; eighth day: primitive streak; tenth day: somites 1 to 6 (comparable with 25-hour chick).   After the embryonic membranes and placenta are formed growth is rapid and birth occurs $21\frac{1}{2}$ to 22 days after fertilization.

with much yolk, and are laid externally.   Eggs of all the higher or placental, mammals are minute, practically yolkless, and retained within the female's body for development.   The entire egg divides (Fig. 5-9D), and a yolk sac is formed.   This has been taken to mean that the mammals are derived from a stock (the reptiles) with large-yolked eggs, but in acquiring other means for developing and nourishing the embryo they have not lost all features of their former mode of development. After the gastrula stage, the development of a mammalian embryo resembles that of the bird during its earlier stages (Fig. 5-13). Gill pouches and slits appear but soon close.

5-25. Embryonic membranes. The embryos of reptiles, birds, and mammals are provided with a series of **embryonic membranes** that protect against desiccation and shock and serve in respiration, excretion, and other necessary functions during embryonic life. These are the **amnion, chorion, yolk sac,** and **allantois** (Fig. 5-14); each is composed of two layers of embryonic tissue. The amnion forms a closed sac about the embryo and is filled with a watery **amniotic fluid** that keeps the embryo moist and protects it against shock or adhesions. The chorion surrounds the amnion. The yolk sac in reptiles and birds gradually incorporates the egg yolk into the digestive tract for nourishing the embryo. The allantois pushes out from the hind-gut to lie against the chorion and shell membranes. Blood vessels then grow out on its surface to serve as an

Fig. 5-14. Three stages in development of the embryonic membranes of the chick; diagrammatic longitudinal sections; shell, shell membranes, and albumen omitted; compare Figs. 5-7, 5-12, 5-15*B.*

embryonic respiratory and excretory organ. These membranes are ruptured and discarded when the young hatch.

5-26. Placenta and umbilical cord. The minute mammalian egg passes down the oviduct to lie on the inner surface of the maternal uterus. An amnion soon forms and fills with fluid. The chorion and allantois grow out and soon make contact with the surface of the uterus, whereby embryonic blood vessels on the allantois are brought close to maternal blood vessels in the uterine wall. Processes, or **villi,** of the chorion become embedded in depressions of the uterine surface, and the joint embryonic-maternal structure so formed is called the **placenta** (Fig. 5-15). Nutrients and oxygen then pass from the maternal blood vessels through the several intervening cell layers to the blood of the embryo, and carbon dioxide and excretory wastes move in the opposite direction, but no direct connection exists between the maternal and embryonic circulations. The degree of intimacy between the maternal and embryonic structures varies with different mammals, as does the form of the placenta. The latter may be *diffuse,* with scattered villi (pig and cow); *discoidal,* or disclike (bats, rodents, and mankind); or *zonary,* a cylindrical band (cats and other carnivores). The human placenta is complex, as some lining tissues of the uterus disappear and embryonic blood vessels on the chorionic villi are bathed in maternal blood (Fig. 33-5). When the developing embryo has acquired its characteristic mammalian form, it is called a *foetus.* From the ventral surface of its abdomen a soft flexible **umbilical cord** extends, conveying the two arteries and a vein that connect to embryonic

FIG. 5-15. *A.* Entire reproductive tract of female cat, with uterus cut open to show the position of one embryo. *B.* Cat embryo with zonary placenta cut and part of embryonic membranes removed to show relation of umbilical cord, blood vessels, and membranes.

capillaries in the placenta. When the foetus has completed its growth within the uterus, *birth,* or *parturition,* occurs. The maternal vagina dilates, and slow rhythmic contractions of the uterus gradually force the foetus through the vagina to the exterior. The amnion is either ruptured in this process or else is quickly torn by the mother, so that the newborn young may breathe air, and shortly the umbilical cord is severed. The embryonic part of the placenta either passes out with the foetus or descends later, as the "afterbirth," and is usually eaten by the parent mammal.

5-27. Processes in development. Aristotle and the Romans recognized that mating of a male and female was necessary for the production of offspring in mankind, the domestic animals, and some animals in nature, but the causal relation of copulation to birth of young is still unknown to some primitive peoples. Spermatozoa were discovered by Hamm and Van Leeuwenhoek in 1677 and soon were thought to have a bearing on development. In 1824 Prevost and Dumas showed that if seminal fluid of frogs was filtered to remove the sperm before being poured

over unfertilized eggs, the latter failed to develop.   Penetration of the
egg by sperm and union of the sperm and egg nuclei in fertilization were
first observed by Fol and Oskar Hertwig, independently, with the sea
urchin in 1875.   Meanwhile, embryologists were evolving two contrasted
theories to explain development.   The *preformation theory,* supported by
Harvey and Malpighi, was well established by 1720 and was later elaborated by Bonnet (1720–1793), Von Haller (1708–1777), and others.   It
assumed that either the egg or the sperm contained a "germ" completely
preformed but minute and invisible, which expanded or enlarged to visible
size and form during development.   Some artists even figured the
"homunculus" (little man) presumed to occur in the head of a human
sperm.   Bonnet's theory of "encasement" assumed that, if the "germ"
contained a complete individual, then each germ in turn must contain
those for succeeding generations in smaller scale, like a series of boxes one
within another; all germs were assumed to have been created in the
beginning.   On this fantastic premise someone calculated that Eve, the
mythical mother of the human race, must have contained over 200 million
homunculi!   The opposing *theory of epigenesis* by Wolff (1759) and
others assumed that the egg lacked internal organization and some outside
force (vis essentialis) was responsible for its development.   Modern
descriptive and experimental embryology has shown that the cytoplasm
of eggs has some preformed elements and that both external and internal
factors operate in development.

   5-28. Organization.   The eggs of various species differ as to their
degree of organization before and after fertilization.   With those of some
jellyfishes the individual blastomeres may be separated, up to the 16-cell
stage, and each will produce a complete but proportionately smaller
embryo; that of *Amphioxus* will do likewise up to the 4- or 8-cell stage;
and if the blastomeres of the 2-cell stage in a salamander are carefully
separated, two complete embryos may result.   In such cases of "indeterminate cleavage" the blastomeres if undisturbed will combine to form a
single embryo, but if parted each can produce a separate and complete
individual.   By contrast, the separation of blastomeres or cell groups
during cleavage in eggs of some mollusks (*Dentalium*) and tunicates
(*Styela*) will result in each producing only that part of the embryo which
it would form in an undisturbed egg.   Such "determinate cleavage"
indicates an organization of material in the egg prior to cleavage.   One
part may influence another as is shown in eggs of *Amphioxus* or of
amphibians that are only partially separated in the 2-cell stage and yield
➤-shaped embryos with two anterior ends.   If dorsoventral separation
is attempted in the early gastrula of a salamander, the upper part may
produce a well-formed embryo and the lower only a mass of cells.
   Evidence of subsequent organization in the egg substances and of the

time or stage in which it occurs has been derived for amphibians by vital staining and also by transplanting small areas of formative tissue. By numerous studies of the first type an elaborate "presumptive organization" has been demonstrated in the late blastula and early gastrula, and the existence of the several processes in gastrulation has been confirmed. Between the 2-cell stage (when each blastomere may produce a separate embryo) and the beginning of gastrulation, materials for each of the principal regions of the early embryo become differentiated (Fig. 5-16).

The dorsal lip of the blastopore proves to be a region of strong influence in determining subsequent embryonic growth. If at the beginning of gastrulation a piece of presumptive epidermis is planted in the dorsal lip, it will be carried in and contribute to the production of muscle segments, gut wall, or other organs depending upon where it arrives; in any

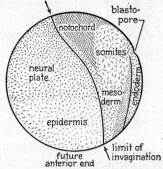

FIG. 5-16.   Localization of formative areas on the egg of a salamander, *Triton*, at the start of gastrulation.   (*After Vogt.*)

case, it contributes to either mesoderm or endoderm derivatives and not to ectoderm. Pieces of presumptive mesoderm transplanted into the ectoderm of a gastrula will become epidermis (ectoderm). If, however, somewhat later a portion of the dorsal lip is transplanted to the ectoderm, it will induce the formation there of a secondary embryo on the host embryo. The notochord and other dorsal-lip derivatives come from the transplant, but the nervous tissue arises from the local host ectoderm that otherwise would have become epidermis (Fig. 5-17).

Further evidence of time sequence in organization has been obtained by exchanging transplants of presumptive epidermis and neural plate (both ectodermal) between embryos of two salamanders that have eggs of different color. Dark presumptive epidermis from *Triton taeniatus* transplanted to the neural-plate region of the light-colored *T. cristatus* became neural plate if moved during the early gastrula stage but continued as dark epidermis, even in the brain, if transplanted in the late gastrula. The reverse transplant produced comparable results. In the early transplant the region determined the nature of the subsequent growth, whereas in the later one the material that was transplanted was already "determined" as to the kind of tissue it was to produce. Such determination of the fate of tissues in embryonic development is ascribed to "organizers" by Hans Spemann. An example of the presence of organizers in later stages is to be seen in the development of the lens for an eye only in the presence of an optic vesicle. If the vesicle is removed, no

Fig. 5-17. Effect of an organizer. *A.* Neural fold stage of a newt (*Triton taeniatus*) with secondary neural plate—the white stripe—induced by transplanted organizer from another species (*T. cristatus.*) *B.* Side view of early embryo (*T. taeniatus*) with secondary neural tube and somites. (*After Spemann.*)

lens develops; and if the vesicle is transplanted from the head to elsewhere in the body, a lens develops wherever ectoderm touches an optic vesicle.

References

ALLEN, EDGAR (editor). 1939. Sex and internal secretions. Baltimore, Williams & Wilkins Co. xxxvi + 1,346 pp., illus. Modern technical accounts.

BARTH, L. G. 1949. Embryology. New York, The Dryden Press. xii + 330 pp., 194 figs. Emphasis on processes and controlling influences, many diagrams.

BRAMBELL, F. W. R. 1930. The development of sex in vertebrates. New York, The Macmillan Co. xvi + 261 pp. 24 pls., 25 figs.

DAWYDOFF, C. 1928. Traité d'embryologie comparée des invertébrés. Paris, Masson et Cie. xiv + 930 pp., 509 figs.

DE BEER, G. R. 1934. An introduction to experimental embryology. Oxford, Clarendon Press. xii + 148 pp. Excellent concise summary.

HAMILTON, W. J., J. D. BOYD, and H. W. MOSSMAN. 1945. Human embryology (prenatal development of form and function). Cambridge, England, W. Heffer & Sons, Ltd. viii + 366 pp., 364 figs.

HUETTNER, A. F. 1948. Fundamentals of comparative embryology of the vertebrates. New York, The Macmillan Co. xiv + 416 pp., 168 figs. Amphioxus, frog, chick, and mammal.

HUXLEY, J. S., and G. R. DE BEER. 1934. The elements of experimental embryology. London, Cambridge University Press. xiii + 514 pp., 212 figs.

KERR, J. G. 1919. Text-book of embryology. Vol. 2, Vertebrata, except Mammalia. London, Macmillan & Co., Ltd. xii + 591 pp. 254 figs.

KORSCHELDT, E., und K. Heider. 1936. Vergleichende Entwicklungsgeschichte der Tiere. New ed. 2 vols. Jena, Gustav Fischer. xx + 1,314 pp., 1,312 figs. General embryology.

LILLIE, F. R. 1919. The development of the chick. 2d ed. New York, Henry Holt & Co., Inc. xi + 472 pp., illus. The American classic.

MACBRIDE, E. W. 1914. Text-book of embryology. Vol. I. Invertebrata. London, Macmillan & Co., Ltd. xxxii + 692 pp., 468 figs. Sponges to tunicates.

MORGAN, T. H. 1927. Experimental embryology. New York, Columbia University Press. xi + 766 pp., 263 figs.

———. 1934. Embryology and genetics. New York, Columbia University Press vii + 258 pp., 129 figs.

NEEDHAM, JOSEPH. 1934. A history of embryology. London, Cambridge University Press. xviii + 274 pp., illus. Scholarly review of ideas regarding development up to 1814.

PATTEN, B. M. 1929. The early embryology of the chick. 3d ed. Philadelphia, The Blakiston Co. xiii + 228 pp., frontispiece + 87 figs. Modern account for the first four days.

———. 1931. The embryology of the pig. 2d ed. Philadelphia, The Blakiston Co. ix + 327 pp., frontispiece + 168 figs. Only complete account of development of a mammal.

———. 1947. Human embryology. Philadelphia, The Blakiston Co. xv + 776 pp., 446 figs.

RUGH, ROBERTS. 1948. Experimental embryology a manual of techniques and procedures. 2d ed. Minneapolis, Burgess Publishing Co. vii + 480 pp., illus.

SPEMANN, HANS. 1938. Embryonic development and induction. New Haven, Yale University Press. xii + 401 pp., 192 figs. Experimental studies with amphibian embryos.

CHAPTER 6

HEREDITY AND GENETICS

It is a common observation that "like tends to beget like," in human beings, animals, and plants.   The young of dogs are always puppies and those of cats always kittens, never puppies.   Yet offspring usually differ among themselves and from their parents in varying degree.   Two pure-bred collies will produce pups that grow to resemble their parents closely, whereas the chance mating of two mongrel dogs often yields a litter of diverse sorts.   The Greeks observed that blue-eyed parents had blue-eyed children, that baldness and squint eyes followed in successive generations, and that certain eye defects ran in particular families.   This passage of characters from one generation to another is called inheritance or heredity.

Heredity is resemblance based upon descent, or the occurrence in living organisms of qualities, either expressed or latent, that are derived from their ancestors.   It involves both physical and physiological charac-teristics, instincts, and even psychological features in higher animals and man.   Differences among individuals of a species are called *variations,* and these may be divided into *random* or *fluctuating variations* due to food, temperature, or other environmental factors, and hereditary or *germinal variations* that appear in certain offspring without reference to the environment.   The science of *genetics* seeks to account for resem-blances and differences due to heredity, their source, and their behavior during development.

Genetics is already of great economic value to agriculture in improving the form, yield, resistance to disease, and other features of domesticated animals and cultivated plants.   Some knowledge of human heredity has been obtained and already has some practical applications.   Genetics has aided the study of evolution, of embryology, and of other sciences.   It has a cultural value in dispelling many of the erroneous beliefs regarding inheritance and the role of external influences in the development of human beings.

From the time of the Greeks, little of importance relating to heredity was discovered until about the eighteenth century, when knowledge of sexuality in plants and of plant hybridization increased considerably. Kölreuter (1733–1806) and others then produced various fertile hybrids, by artificial pollination, and described the characters of both parent and hybrid plants but obtained no satisfactory explanation of the hereditary process.

148

6-1. Mendel. The first person to conduct decisive experiments in heredity and to formulate the basic laws of genetics was Gregor Johann Mendel (1822–1884), a monk and later abbot of the Augustinian monastery at Brünn, Austria (Fig. 10-7). He recognized heredity as of major importance for understanding organic evolution. He saw clearly that all earlier experimenters with hybrids had failed to discover any general laws of inheritance because they had neither traced individual characters through successive generations nor kept complete numerical records of their results. To overcome these difficulties, Mendel planned careful experiments in the garden of the monastery. He chose the garden pea, *Pisum,* for study and spent 2 years in selecting races with distinctive and contrasted characters and in making certain that each of his original stocks was pure. During the next 6 years he made many crosses by

x ♂ y   ♂ male   female ♀   x ♀ x

FIG. 6-1. The fruitfly, *Drosophila melanogaster,* used for studies in genetics. Much enlarged. Diploid sets of chromosomes shown, with sex chromosomes marked (*XY, XX*). Male fly smaller with abdomen marked by three black bands, the last extending beneath the rounded posterior end. Female larger, abdomen swollen but pointed, with five black bands not joined ventrally.

artificial pollination, each of which was carried through three or more generations. Mendel kept an accurate statistical record of all plants and seeds of each kind that was produced, analyzed these results, and from them deduced the two most important fundamental laws of heredity. His report (44 pages) was published in 1866 in an obscure periodical but came to worldwide attention only in 1900 when three other investigators independently had then reached similar conclusions.

The discovery of Mendel's findings gave great impetus to the study of heredity, and an enormous amount of careful work has since been done by many geneticists working with various plants and animals. Of especial value has been the use of the fruitfly, or pomace fly, *Drosophila melanogaster,* by W. E. Castle, T. H. Morgan, and many others. This small insect (Fig. 6-1) is reared easily in bottles provided with a culture medium as food for the larvae; a pair will produce 200 or more offspring and successive generations are obtained every 10 to 14 days. With such abundant material it has been possible to investigate problems requiring many individuals and generations and to apply statistical (mathematical) analysis to the results.

6-2. Monohybrid cross. This is a cross in which the parents differ in one pair of alternative characters. When a true-breeding black or pigmented guinea pig and a white individual are mated (Fig. 6-2), all the (hybrid) individuals of the next (F_1)[1] generation are black, no matter which parent is black and which is white.   These black hybrids, when crossed among themselves, yield in the following (F_2) generation a population in which, *on the average*, three-fourths are black, like the black grandparent, and one-fourth are white, like the white grandparent.   The character of white coat disappears in the F_1 and reappears unchanged in the F_2.   If the F_2 white animals are then crossed among themselves, only white individuals result (F_3), whereas among the black F_2 animals some

TABLE 6-1. SOME MENDELIAN CHARACTERS IN DOMESTICATED ANIMALS

	Dominant	Recessive		Dominant	Recessive
Cattle	Black (Angus)	Red	Horses	Bay	Black or chestnut
	Polled (no horns)	Horned		Black	Chestnut
	White face (Hereford)	Colored face (in other breeds)		Gray	Any other color
	Black-and-white (Holstein)	Red-and-white		Trotting	Pacing
Sheep	White fleece	Black fleece	Dogs	Gray Intense color Stumpy tail	Black Dilute color Normal tail
Swine	Wild color (slaty, grizzled)	Black or red	Cats	Tabby Black Short hair	Black or blue Blue Long hair (Angora)
	Black	Red			
	Self-white	Colored			
	Uncleft hoof ("mule foot")	Normal hoof			
	Belted	Solid color	Mice	Gray	White

($\frac{1}{3}$) produce only blacks and the others ($\frac{2}{3}$) produce both blacks and whites, as in the F_2 generation.   Thus, as Mendel said, when two contrasting characters are brought together in a cross, one is **dominant** (expressed or evident) in the next (F_1) generation, and the other is **recessive** (latent, or recedes from view).   In the following (F_2) generation these two characters are **segregated**, in an average 3 to 1 ratio.   We may, therefore, state in modern terms, **Mendel's First Law:** *The factors for a pair of characters are segregated.*   The factors responsible for a pair of

[1] The parental generation of a cross is designated as P, the first generation of offspring following as the F_1 (first filial), the second as the F_2, and so on.

alternative or contrasted characters, such as Mendel studied, are now termed *alleles* (allelomorphs).

6-3. Mechanism of heredity. Mendel was the first to differentiate between the actual visible character and that "something" which caused its production.   Obviously the character as such cannot be present in the germ cells that join in fertilization to produce a new individual, but something representing it and responsible for its production must be there. This is now called the *gene* or *factor* for the character.   A gene is the unit of inheritance that is transmitted in a gamete and controls the development of a character, by interaction with the other genes, the cytoplasm, and the environment.

Since the gametes are the only materials that pass onward from parents to form new individuals of the next generation, the mechanism of heredity must be sought in them.   It will be recalled (Chap. 5) that (1) in meiosis each cell destined to become a gamete receives, by random sorting, either one or the other member of each pair of homologous chromosomes; (2) at fertilization there is a random meeting of an egg and a sperm; (3) the chromosomes of the egg nucleus and sperm nucleus join to form a zygote; and (4) during embryonic growth and later, each cell in the new individual receives by mitosis an equal and like number of chromosomes derived from the zygote.   As inheritance in sexual reproduction involves the transmission of characteristics from both parents, the chromosomes are considered to be the means by which this occurs.   In certain experiments it has been shown that (1) an egg deprived of its nucleus and then "fertilized" by a sperm produces an individual with only paternal characteristics; (2) mature eggs caused to develop by artificial parthenogenesis result in animals with only maternal characteristics; and (3) some of the cytoplasm may be removed from certain eggs and yet if the egg nucleus is fertilized by a sperm the resulting individual contains characteristics of both parents.   Thus hereditary transmission of characterisics is dependent upon the nucleus rather than the cytoplasm.

The modern **chromosome theory of heredity** assumes that genes are ultramicroscopic particles contained in the chromosomes.   Their physical and chemical nature is still unknown.   The giant salivary gland chromosomes of *Drosophila* (Fig. 3-2), contain many crossbands which possibly are the location (loci) of the genes.   Some indirect evidence on the presence and arrangement of genes in chromosomes is discussed later in this chapter under linkage, etc. (pp. 164-166).

6-4. Explanation of the Mendelian ratio. Since hybrid individuals result from combining two gametes from opposite sexes, a process of segregation must take place in the germ cells of such hybrids to account for the sorting out of genes to produce characters in the F_2 generation. Mendel realized this but knew nothing of the actual mechanism.   The reduction divisions during meiosis, discovered since his time, and the random union of egg and sperm provide a satisfactory explanation of this segregation.

If we represent the dominant gene for black (or pigmented) coat in guinea pigs by P and the recessive gene for white by p, then the genetic formulas for the parents (which contain the diploid number of chromosomes) are PP and pp and for their respective gametes are P and p. When the gametes of the parents join in fertilization, all the resulting offspring of the F_1 generation will be Pp and black. When the F_1 forms gametes, each sex will produce both P and p gametes. The possible combinations for the F_2 will be PP (black), Pp and pP (black), and pp (white), giving an average ratio of 3 blacks to 1 white individual. The events in this cross may be outlined as follows:

P_1		F_1		F_2
The animals	Their gametes	The animals	Their gametes	The animals
Black (PP)	P		male ($\male$) P and p	1 Black (PP)
		Black Pp		2 Black (Pp)
white (pp)	p		female ($\female$) P and p	1 white (pp)

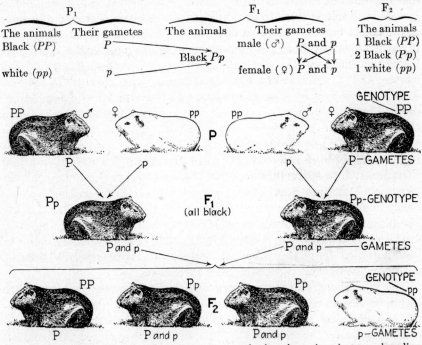

Fig. 6-2.   Monohybrid cross.   Inheritance of coat color in guinea pigs when pure-breeding black and white parents are mated.

Such individuals as the parents that are "pure," containing like genes for any one character (PP or pp), are termed **homozygous**.   The F_1 hybrid, which appears black and yet contains a gene for white (Pp), is said to be *heterozygous;* it contains two kinds of genes of an allelomorphic pair. The entire genetic constitution of an individual, both expressed and latent, makes up its **genotype;** and its appearance, or the assemblage of characters that are expressed or evident, constitutes its **phenotype.**   Both the parents and two of the F_2 (*PP* and *pp*) are homozygous, but the F_1 hybrid and two of the F_2 (*Pp*) are heterozygous; the F_1 hybrid is a black phenotype, and its genotype is *Pp*.   In the F_2, the whites are homozygous recessives; of the blacks, $\frac{1}{3}$ are homozygous dominants yielding only blacks, and $\frac{2}{3}$ are heterozygous.   The analysis may be restated thus:

	P			F_1			F_2	
phenotypes	genotypes	gametes	phenotype	genotype	gametes	phenotypes	genotypes
Black	PP	P	Black	Pp	♂ P and p	3 Black	1 PP
							2 Pp
white	pp	p			♀ P and p	1 white	1 pp

Many other characters have been found to follow Mendel's first law, and some examples are given in Table 6-1.

6-5. Incomplete dominance.   With some characters the F_1 hybrid is intermediate between the parents.   Such a case of incomplete dominance occurs in the Andalusian fowl, where the mating of a black and a splashed-white produces blue offspring in the F_1, and the F_2 results are 1 black,

FIG. 6-3.   Incomplete dominance of a Mendelian character in the Andalusian fowl.   The "blue" fowls are lightly stippled.   (*Modified from Hesse-Doflein.*)

2 blue, 1 splashed white (Fig. 6-3).   Here the homozygous dominant is black, the heterozygous individuals are blue, and the homozygous recessive is splashed white.

P			F_1			F_2	
phenotypes	genotypes	gametes	phenotype	genotype	gametes	phenotypes	genotypes
Black	BB	B			♂ B and b	1 Black	BB
			Blue	Bb		2 Blue	Bb
splashed					♀ B and b	1 splashed	
white	bb	b				white	bb

Mendel's first law obviously applies here as well as in cases of complete dominance, although the heterozygous individuals, being blue, can easily be recognized.

6-6. Backcross.   Offspring that show the dominant character in a cross are alike phenotypically but may be either heterozygous or homozygous for that character.   To determine their genotype the *test cross or backcross* is used by mating the dominant hybrid with a pure recessive individual.   If, with guinea pigs, the black individual under test is homozygous (PP), all the offspring from a backcross with the recessive (pp) will be black (Pp); if, however, it is heterozygous (Pp), the offspring will be about equally black (Pp) and white (pp).   Thus:

Backcross			Offspring	
phenotypes	genotypes	gametes	phenotypes	genotypes
Black	Pp	P and p	2 Black	Pp
white	pp	p and p	2 white	pp

In practical genetics the backcross is used as a rapid means for "purifying" (rendering homozygous) desirable stocks.

6-7. Dihybrid cross.   When parents differ in two pairs of characters, the F_1 offspring are termed *dihybrids;* in such crosses Mendel found that each pair of characters is inherited independently of the other.   This may be illustrated (Fig. 6-4) in the case of the guinea pig where black or pigmented coat (P) is dominant to white (p) and rough or rosetted coat (R) is dominant to smooth (r).   The mating of a black rough animal to a smooth white one may thus be outlined:

P				F_1		
phenotypes	genotypes	gametes	phenotype	genotype	gametes	
Black, Rough	$PPRR$	PR			PR	Pr
			Black, Rough	$PpRr$		
white, smooth	$pprr$	pr			pR	pr

Four kinds of gametes are formed by each sex and the Punnett checkerboard will show the 16 matings possible to produce the F_2 generation.

Possible matings for the F_2 generation					Analysis of the F_2 generation			
	Male gametes				Phenotypes			
	PR	*Pr*	*pR*	*pr*	9 Black Rough	3 Black smooth	3 white Rough	1 white smooth
PR	*PPRR* Black Rough	*PPRr* Black Rough	*PpRR* Black Rough	*PpRr* Black Rough	Genotypes			
Pr	*PPRr* Black Rough	*PPrr* Black smooth	*PpRr* Black Rough	*Pprr* Black smooth	1-*PPRR* 2 *PPRr* 2 *PpRR* 4 *PpRr*	1-*PPrr* 2-*Pprr*	1-*ppRR* 2-*ppRr*	1-*pprr*
pR	*PpRR* Black Rough	*PpRr* Black Rough	*ppRR* white Rough	*ppRr* white Rough				
pr	*PpRr* Black Rough	*Pprr* Black smooth	*ppRr* white Rough	*pprr* white smooth				

(Female gametes — left column label)

The F_2 phenotypes include 9 black rough (any with *PR* genes) like the dominant parent and 1 white smooth (*pr*) like the recessive parent. Two new combinations have appeared, of which there are 3 black smooth (*Pr*)

FIG. 6-4.   Dihybrid cross, with guinea pigs differing in two independent pairs of Mendelian characters of the hair—color and arrangement.

and 3 white rough (*pR*).   The 9:3:3:1 ratio is characteristic of a dihybrid cross.   There are $9 + 3 = 12$ black to $3 + 1 = 4$ white offspring and $9 + 3 = 12$ rough to $3 + 1 = 4$ smooth individuals.   The ratio of 3 dominant to 1 recessive in each case follows Mendel's First Law, as in a monohybrid cross.   This shows the independence of each pair of characters, which is **Mendel's Second Law:** *When races differ from each other in two (or more) pairs of factors, the inheritance of one pair of factors is independent of that of the other(s).*

The four phenotypes involve nine different genotypes as shown in the analysis of the F_2 population; *PPRR*, *PPrr*, *ppRR*, and *pprr* are homozygous, and the other five are heterozygous. The appearance of new phenotypes and genotypes in dihybrid (and multihybrid) crosses is a practical means of obtaining strains of animals or plants with combinations of characters different from those of the parents. In this cross, there are two new types of homozygous individuals, one black smooth (*PPrr*) and one pure white rough (*ppRR*).

6-8. Multihybrids. In a **trihybrid cross** each gamete carries 3 genes; 8 kinds of F_1 gametes are possible in each sex, giving 64 combinations for the F_2, with 8 phenotypes and 27 genotypes. By crossing a short, black, smooth-haired guinea pig with a long white rough-coat animal (Fig. 6-5) the results are as follows:

	P			F_1		
phenotypes	genotypes	gametes	phenotype	genotype	gametes	
Short					*SPR*	*SPr*
Black	*SSPPrr*	*SPr*				
smooth					*SpR*	*Spr*
			Short			
			Black	*SsPpRr*		
			Rough			
long					*sPR*	*sPr*
white	*ssppRR*	*spR*				
Rough					*spR*	*spr*

ANALYSIS OF THE F_2 GENERATION OF A TRIHYBRID CROSS

Phenotypes							
27 Short Black Rough	9 Short Black smooth	9 Short white Rough	9 long Black Rough	3 Short white smooth	3 long Black smooth	3 long white Rough	1 long white smooth

Genotypes							
1-*SSPPRR* 2-*SSPPRr* 2-*SSPpRR* 2-*SsPPRR* 4-*SSPpRr* 4-*SsPPRr* 4-*SsPpRR* 8-*SsPpRr*	1-*SSPPrr* 2-*SSPprr* 2-*SsPPrr* 4-*SsPprr*	1-*SSppRR* 2-*SSppRr* 2-*SsppRR* 4-*SsppRr*	1-*ssPPRR* 2-*ssPPRr* 2-*ssPpRR* 4-*ssPpRr*	1-*SSpprr* 2-*Sspprr*	1-*ssPPrr* 2-*ssPprr*	1-*ssppRR* 2-*ssppRr*	1-*sspprr*

Increasing the numbers of independent factor pairs greatly enlarges the chance for new combinations, thus:

Pairs of factors, n; kinds of F_1 gametes by each sex, 2^n; possible combinations for F_2 zygotes, 4^n; kinds of phenotypes in F_2, 2^n; different genotypes in F_2, 3^n.

FIG. 6-5. Trihybrid cross, with guinea pigs differing in three pairs of Mendelian characters of the hair—length, color, and arrangement.

The great variability in human beings may be due to the large number of chromosomes (24 pairs) and genes involved, together with inter-mingling of races through time. Since each gamete carries structurally different chromosomes, each probably with one to many genes, the possible F_2 combinations number millions or more.

6-9. Special types of inheritance. Besides the simple types of Mendelian inheritance already described, many others of more complex nature have been discovered that involve the interaction of two or more factors. A few examples of these will now be considered.

6-10. Supplementary factors. The form of comb differs on several breeds of domestic fowls, but each remains quite true within its breed (Fig. 6-6).   The Wyandotte has a low regular *rose* comb with papillae, the Brahma a narrow, higher three-ridged *pea* comb, and the Leghorn and others an upright blade, or *single* comb. When fowls with rose (or pea) and single comb are crossed, the former is dominant, and the F_2 averages 3 rose (or pea) to 1 single.   When rose is crossed with pea, how-ever, the F_1 hybrid bears a walnut comb (resembling half a walnut meat) and the F_2 gives 9 walnut, 3 rose, 3 pea, and 1 single. The results differ from ordinary dihybrids because the F_1 resembles neither parent, and two new types appear in the F_2. This is a case of *interaction of supplementary factors* in a cross of parents differing in two pairs of factors that affect

Fig. 6-6. Comb characters of male fowls. (*Adapted from Punnett, Mendelism, The Macmillan Co.*)

one structure, the comb. If the dominant gene for rose is represented by R and its allele by r and that for pea by P and p, respectively, the results may be explained thus:

P		F_1		F_2			
genotypes and phenotypes	gametes	genotype and phenotype	gametes → RP	Rp	rP	rp	
			↓				
			RP	$RRPP$ walnut	$RRPp$ walnut	$RrPP$ walnut	$RrPp$ walnut
$RRpp$ rose	Rp		Rp	$RRPp$ walnut	$RRpp$ rose	$RrPp$ walnut	$Rrpp$ rose
		$RrPp$ Walnut	rP	$RrPP$ walnut	$RrPp$ walnut	$rrPP$ pea	$rrPp$ pea
$rrPP$ pea	rP		rp	$RrPp$ walnut	$Rrpp$ rose	$rrPp$ pea	$rrpp$ single

9:3

Single comb is thus a double recessive ($rrpp$), rose comb contains either one or two R genes but only recessive p genes, pea comb has either one or two P genes but only recessive r genes, and walnut appears whenever at least one each of R and P are present.

Another modified two-factor ratio occurs in the color of Duroc-Jersey swine, where two factors are necessary for full color (red), either one alone yields partial color (sandy), and the absence of both yields colorless (white) animals. If the dominant factors are represented by R and S and the recessive by r and s, the relations of these *mutually supplementary factors* are as follows:

	P		F$_1$		F$_2$			
genotypes and phenotypes	gametes	genotype and phenotype	gametes →	RS	Rs	rS	rs	
			RS	$RRSS$ red	$RRSs$ red	$RrSS$ red	$RrSs$ red	
$RRSS$ red	RS		Rs	$RRSs$ red	$RRss$ sandy	$RrSs$ red	$Rrss$ sandy	
		$RrSs$ red	rS	$RrSS$ red	$RrSs$ red	$rrSS$ sandy	$rrSs$ sandy	
$rrss$ white	rs		rs	$RrSs$ red	$Rrss$ sandy	$rrSs$ sandy	$rrss$ white	

9:6:1:

White is thus a double recessive ($rrss$), sandy results when only one kind of dominant gene (either R or S) is present, and red is produced when both (R and S) are present.   The ratio of 9:6:1 is thus a modified 9:3:3:1 ratio.

6-11. Cumulative factors. In some cases either of two independent genes may alone produce a character but, when acting together, cause it to be accentuated; such **cumulative genes** are quantitative in expression. According to Davenport, the pigmentation of Negro skin is due to such genes.   He suggests that a pure-blooded Negro has two pairs of genes for black (melanin) pigmentation, BB and $B'B'$, whereas a pure-blooded white carries the paired bb and $b'b'$ for nonblack.   Mating of such individuals results in mulatto offspring (F$_1$) with skin of intermediate color; two of the latter in turn will have children of different skin colors. Thus:

	P		F$_1$		F$_2$		
genotypes and phenotypes	gametes	genotype and phenotype	gametes →	BB'	Bb'	bB'	bb'
$bbb'b'$ white	bb'		BB'	4	3	3	2
		$BbB'b'$ Mulatto	Bb'	3	2	2	1
			bB'	3	2	2	1
$BBB'B'$ Negro	BB'		bb'	2	1	1	0

The figures in the checkerboard indicate the number of genes for black color in each individual; the offspring average, as to skin color, one full-colored Negro (4 B or B' genes), four dark mulattoes (3), six half-color mulattoes (2), four pale mulattoes (1), and one white-skinned (no dominant genes).   The last might have other Negro characteristics, however, since other racial characteristics assort independently.   Marriages between pure-blooded whites and mulattoes yield white and mulatto offspring in various proportions, depending on the genotype of the mulatto parent.

6-12. Lethal factors. In various species of plants and animals *lethal factors* have been found which, in the homozygous condition, stop development at some stage and the individual dies. Their presence is usually detected by an abnormal ratio in the offspring. A conspicuous case is that of the yellow race of the house mouse, *Mus musculus*, which never breeds true. If a yellow mouse is mated to some nonyellow, half the young are yellow and half are nonyellow, a ratio to be expected from mating a heterozygous animal (yellow) with a homozygous recessive (any nonyellow such as agouti). If two yellows are mated together, the young average 2 yellow to 1 nonyellow, whereas the expected ratio among the young would be 1 pure yellow to 2 heterozygous yellow to 1 nonyellow. Autopsy shows that the homozygous yellow dies as an embryo; only young of the other two groups are born. The "creeper fowl" with short, crooked legs behaves genetically like the yellow mouse. Various lethals are known in *Drosophila*, 12 or more occur in cattle, others in sheep, hogs, and horses, and some human defects are thought to be due to such factors.

6-13. Multiple alleles. All the examples discussed heretofore have involved pairs of alternative factors. Many other cases are now known of more than two alternative factors that affect the same character; these are called *multiple alleles*. Thus, in the domestic rabbit, among various color forms, there are the normal "wild" type, the complete albino with solidly white coat and pink eyes, and the "Himalayan" albino with pink eyes and a white coat except for black or dark brown on the ears, nose, and feet. The albino is a simple recessive to the wild type, and the Himalayan albino is likewise recessive to the wild type. When Himalayan and pure albino are crossed, however, all the F_1 offspring are Himalayan, and the F_2 yields 3 Himalayan to 1 pure albino; there is no reversion to the wild type. Obviously, Himalayan and albino are alleles of one another, and both are alleles of the wild color. Other instances of multiple alleles are known for coat color in mice, guinea pigs, and rats. In *Drosophila* at least 14 alleles for eye color have been found, from white and ivory through buff and apricot to the wild-type red. Several series are known in plants, especially snapdragons and maize. No more than two alleles of a series can occur in any particular individual.

Still more complex types of inheritance include modifying factors, multiple effects of a single gene, and those in which either the external environment or conditions within the animal change the manner in which a gene regulates the development of a character. An instance of the last kind occurs with dwarfism in the house mouse, where a recessive gene halts growth at about two weeks of age and the animals are all sterile; the anterior lobe of the pituitary gland and the cortex of the adrenal are deficient.   Continued implantation of anterior pituitary in such young causes resumption of growth, the animals may reach normal size, and males may become fertile.   Thus hormones may exercise an influence on the manner in which genes are expressed in the formation of characters.

6-14. Sex and heredity.   No factor mentioned previously has any relation to sex; with all of them either the male or the female may carry one factor and the other parent its alternative.   The situation is different for some other characters, including that of sex itself.   Somatic and early germ cells in male animals contain a pair of homologous chromosomes in which one member is smaller than the other, and sometimes of different shape.   These are the ***sex chromosomes,*** the larger being the ***X chromosome*** and the other the ***Y chromosome;*** in some species the latter is lacking.   A pair of X chromosomes is present in females.   Thus a male may be designated as XY (or XO) and a female as XX.   All other pairs of strictly homologous chromosomes are termed ***autosomes.***

Human cells, except gametes, contain 48 chromosomes—the 2 sex chromosomes, and 23 pairs of homologous autosomes (Fig. 3-3).   During maturation the sex chromosomes segregate freely, like other chromosomes, so that an ovum contains 23 autosomes and an X chromosome, and a sperm has 23 autosomes and either an X or a Y chromosome.

If A is used to represent one haploid set of autosomes (23 in mankind), then the genetics of sex in human beings can be diagrammed as follows:

Any Parent Generation			Offspring	
sex	genotypes	gametes	genotypes	sex
male	$2A + XY$	$A + X$	$2A + XX$	female
		$A + Y$		
female	$2A + XX$	$A + X$	$2A + XY$	male

Thus sex is evidently determined by the kind of sperm that fertilizes an egg.   As approximately equal numbers of the two sexes appear in the offspring of most animals, it is reasonable to assume that X sperm and Y sperm are formed in equal numbers and that either kind has an equal chance of fertilizing an egg.   The results are the same in species (many insects) that lack the Y chromosome, save that the female has an even number of chromosomes and the male one less.   Among birds and moths the situation is reversed from that in other animals, there being two kinds of eggs and one of sperm; males are therefore XX (sometimes designated as ZZ), and females are XY (or ZW).

6-15. Sex determination.   Since other inherited characters result from genes, the question arises as to whether sex is dependent upon one or more genes or upon the entire X (or Z) chromosome. Some studies with *Drosophila*, involving peculiar individuals known as "intersexes" and "supersexes," provide information on this matter and suggest that autosomes are also involved in sex expression (Fig. 6-7). Such individuals result from abnormal meiosis (nondisjunction, etc.). The **intersexes** show a mixture of male and female features in the gonads, external genitalia, and secondary sexual characters. Their cells contain 3 *sets* of autosomes (chromosomes II, III, IV) but only 2 X chromosomes $(3A + 2X)$. The **super female** has modified female characters and abnormal ovaries; her cells contain 2 *sets* of autosomes and 3 X chromosomes $(2A + 3X)$. The **super male** has exaggerated male characters, and its cells have 3 *sets* of autosomes but only 1 X chromosome $(3A + X)$. From these findings C. B. Bridges proposed a theory of genic balance, which states that sex determination in *Drosophila* results from the inter-

Super female	Triploid female	Normal diploid female	Intersex	Normal diploid male	Super-male
3/2	3/3	2/2	2/3	1/2	1/3

Fig. 6-7. Sex determination in *Drosophila*, according to the theory of genic balance; effect of ratio between X chromosomes (black) and autosomes (outlined). (*Rearranged from Sinnott and Dunn, Principles of genetics.*)

action of numerous genes, located on all the chromosomes, some being female determiners and others male determiners; the X chromosome is thought to contain more female than male determiners. The ratio of autosomes to X chromosomes is believed to regulate the various types of sex expression, although the explanation of sex determination given earlier (*XX* female, *XY* or *XO* male) holds so long as the cells contain *two sets* of autosomes. The Y chromosome evidently carries no genes for sex or other characters; yet, in species where it normally occurs, males without a Y chromosome are sterile.

Prior to the discovery of sex chromosomes, many ingenious theories had been proposed to explain sex. Various schemes have been tried to control the sex of offspring, especially in domesticated animals and mankind, but none has been effective. Among some of the lower animals, alteration of environmental conditions affects the **sex ratio** (Chap. 5), which is the proportion of males to females among offspring; this has been accomplished with frogs and some invertebrates.

Some abnormalities of sex, other than intersexes, have been observed. Occasional fruitflies, bees, and other insects are **gynandromorphs,** with one part of the body showing male and the other female characteristics. Intersexes have been seen in gypsy moths reared experimentally and occur also among pigs. In rare cases **sex reversal** has been seen among vertebrates, especially poultry, when an individual originally female has become a male.

6-16. Sex-linked inheritance. The X (or Z) chromosome has been found to carry genes for **sex-linked** characters, the inheritance of which is therefore related to sex determination. This may be seen clearly in the fruitfly, *Drosophila*, where eye color is sex-linked (Fig. 6-8). The normal

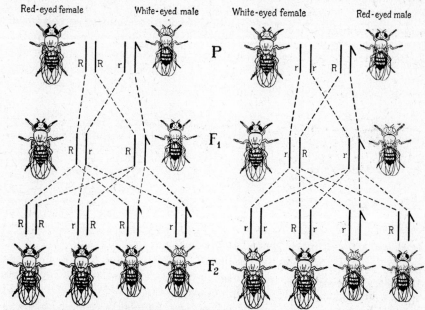

FIG. 6-8. Sex determination and sex-linked inheritance of eye color in *Drosophila*. The sex chromosomes are represented by vertical bars with symbols (R, r) for genes of eye color.

red eye color is dominant to the white eye color. If a homozygous red-eyed female and a white-eyed male are mated, all the F_1 flies are red-eyed; when the latter are intercrossed, the F_2 yields an average of 2 red-eyed females to 1 red-eyed male to 1 white-eyed male. If X_R represents the gene for red eye and X_r that for white eye, the results of this cross may be diagrammed thus:

	P				F_1			F_2	
genotypes	phenotypes	gametes		genotypes	phenotypes	gametes		genotypes	phenotypes
$X_R X_R$	red-eyed ♀	X_R		$X_R X_r$	red-eyed ♀	X_R		$X_R X_R$	red-eyed ♀
		X_R				X_r		$X_R X_r$	red-eyed ♀
$X_r Y$	white-eyed ♂	X_r		$X_R Y$	red-eyed ♂	X_R		$X_R Y$	red-eyed ♂
		Y				Y		$X_r Y$	white-eyed ♂

In the P generation each matured ovum carries an X chromosome with the gene for red eye, half the sperm carry an X chromosome with a gene for white eye, and the other sperm contain a Y chromosome with no gene for eye color. In the F_1 generation two kinds of eggs are produced, with the gene for either red eye or white eye, and of the sperm half have a gene (on the X chromosome) for red eye and half have no gene for eye color (Y chromosome). Four kinds of zygotes are thus possible. In the F_2, half the females are homozygous for red eye and half are heterozygous, and the males are equally red- and white-eyed.

A somewhat different result is obtained in the opposite or **reciprocal cross** with a homozygous white-eyed female and a red-eyed male. In the F_1 the males are white-eyed, and the females red-eyed. In the F_2 there result approximately equal numbers of red-eyed females, white-eyed females, red-eyed males, and white-eyed males. Thus:

P			F_1			F_2	
genotypes	phenotypes	gametes	genotypes	phenotypes	gametes	genotypes	phenotypes
X_rX_r	white-eyed ♀	X_r / X_r	X_RX_r	red-eyed ♀	X_R / X_r	X_RX_r	red-eyed ♀
X_RY	red-eyed ♂	X_R / Y	X_rY	white-eyed ♂	X_r / Y	X_rX_r	white-eyed ♀
						X_RY	red-eyed ♂
						X_rY	white-eyed ♂

About 150 sex-linked genes have been found in *Drosophila* (Fig. 6-10, chromosome I), and many sex-linked characters are known in other animals and in man; barred plumage in poultry and red-green color blindness in mankind (p. 171) are common examples.

6-17. Linkage. Independent assortment (Mendel's second law) was evident in the examples discussed earlier in this chapter, and in the preceding paragraphs instances of sex-linked inheritance were described. It has long been known that many other characters of animals tend to be inherited together. The number of pairs of Mendelian factors present in any animal far exceeds the number of chromosome pairs, and so each chromosome must carry several or many genes. Characters that tend to be inherited together are said to be **linked**. Extensive studies of the linkage relations in various animals and plants have shown that the genes occur in **linkage groups;** members within each group are linked to one another in varying degree, while a pair in one linkage group assorts or combines independently with pairs in other linkage groups. When the linkage relations of many genes in a species are known, it is found that there are as many groups of linked genes as chromosome pairs. About 500 linked genes are known in *Drosophila melanogaster;* there are 4 linkage groups (3 large, 1 small), and there are 4 pairs of chromosomes (3 long,

1 short).　*D. willistoni* has 3 linkage groups and 3 chromosome pairs, and *D. virilis* has 6 of each.　Among plants, maize has 10 of each, and the garden pea has 7 of each.　This evidence is highly important in showing that the genes are contained in the chromosomes.

6-18. Crossing over.　If the genes for two characters are in one chromosome and the latter remains intact through inheritance, the linkage will be complete, the two characters always occurring together; but such is not always the case (Fig. 6-9).　Linkage is usually only partial, and characters separate in a certain number of cases, the percentage of separations varying between different characters, although it is usually constant as between any two.　Thus albinism and yellow coat color in

synapsis　　segregation　　　　synapsis　　segregation　　　　synapsis　　segregation

NO CROSSOVER　　　　　SINGLE CROSSOVER　　　　　DOUBLE CROSSOVER

Fig. 6-9.　Diagrams of crossing over, the exchange of genes between homologous chromosomes.　*A, a*; *B, b*; *C, c*, represents pairs of allelomorphic genes in homologous chromosomes that pair during synapsis.

rats are linked in over 99 per cent of individuals, but other linked characters may separate in nearly 50 per cent of the cases.　Instances where characters (genes) originally together become separated are known as *crossovers*.　It will be recalled that during maturation the two chromosomes of a homologous pair are closely associated or intertwined at synapsis; ordinarily they separate as they come together, but at times they exchange homologous parts with one another, and this is the physical basis of crossing over.

If it is assumed that the genes on a chromosome are arranged in a linear manner, then two that are far apart will have their linkage transposed by an exchange at any point between them, whereas if they are close together the chance of crossing over is much less (Fig. 6-9).　On the assumption that the frequency of crossing over indicates the relative distance between genes on a chromosome, T. H. Morgan and his associates constructed "chromosome maps" for known genes in each linkage group with *Drosophila*.　In a mating involving any two linked characters 1 per cent of crossover is taken to represent 1 unit of distance between their respective genes.

This may be illustrated by the three characters of yellow body, white eye, and ruby eye, all sex-linked and therefore pertaining to chromosome I (X). In matings between yellow body and white eye, crossover occurs in 1.5 per cent of individuals, between white eye and ruby eye in 6.0 per cent, and between yellow body and ruby eye in 7.5 per cent; hence, the sequence is yellow-white-ruby, with 1.5 units of space between the genes for yellow and white and 6.0 units between white and ruby (1.5 + 6.0 = 7.5). Many crosses, between various linked characters, have provided data for constructing chromosome maps (Fig. 6-10).

Fig. 6-10. Chromosome maps for *Drosophila.* One chromosome of each pair is diagrammed with the relative positions for some of the many genes "mapped" by linkage studies; other genes are indicated by unlabeled bars. Numbers indicate relative distance of each from "left" end of chromosome. Inset shows chromosomes of gonads.

6-19. Giant chromosomes. For years the genetic evidence from *Drosophila* lacked support from cytological study of the chromosomes, since the latter, as seen in gonads, are minute. Recently, attention has been given to the large chromosomes in the salivary glands of this and other flies. These chromosomes occur in permanent homologous pairs and when stained show a varied series of dark-colored transverse bands, some wide and others narrow (Fig. 3-2). The bands give some clue to the location of genes, because in cases of **deletion,** where a certain character has disappeared from a laboratory stock of *Drosophila,* a portion of one chromosome is missing at the position indicated for the gene of that character in the chromosome map. This provides one further and important bit of evidence associating the genes with the chromosomes.

6-20. Theory of the gene. The evidence on characters, genes, chromosomes, and linkage as just outlined is summarized by T. H. Morgan in his *Theory of the Gene* (Yale Univ. Press) thus: (1) the characters of an individual are referable to paired genes in the germinal material, held together in a definite number of linkage groups; (2) at maturation each pair of genes separates (Mendel's first law), so that each gamete contains only one set; (3) the genes in different linkage groups assort independently (Mendel's second law); (4) orderly interchange or crossing over occurs at times between genes in corresponding (homologous) linkage groups; and (5) the frequency of crossing over furnishes evidence of the linear arrangement of genes in each linkage group and their relative position to one another.

6-21. Mutations.   At times, new characters appear in the offspring of animals and plants that upon test prove to be heritable; these are germinal variations, or *mutations,* and are caused by some change in the gene for the character concerned.   A historic case was the sudden appearance in a true-breeding stock of red-eyed *Drosophila* of one white-eyed individual; when the latter was bred, this character proved to be heritable and as it continued in succeeding generations the change was permanent.   Over a thousand mutations have been observed in *Drosophila* (Fig. 6-11) and

FIG. 6-11.   Some mutations of wings and eyes in *Drosophila* used in study of crossing over and linkage; compare Fig. 6-1.   (*After Morgan and others.*)

many in other animals and in plants.   Most of the mutations in *Drosophila* are abnormalities, recessive defects, or lethals such as would not survive in nature, but there have been distinctive and useful mutations among domestic animals and plants that have been preserved by selective breeding.   Examples are the polled (hornless) Hereford cattle, the short-legged (Ancon) sheep, and the short-legged dachshund and the long-legged greyhound among dogs.   The rate of mutation varies widely in different animals and for different genes, some being exceedingly stable whereas others change rather frequently.   Thus, 14 or more mutations of one gene for eye color in *Drosophila* have been noted.   Most mutant genes are recessive, but some dominants have appeared.

Prior to 1927 only spontaneous mutations, occurring naturally, were observed.   Since then the application of X rays (or radium) to animals or plants, especially *Drosophila*, maize, and barley, has been found to induce mutations in the offspring at greatly increased rates.   The frequency of mutation is increased two hundred fold in some cases and is in proportion to the dosage of X rays.   These mutations prove heritable, like natural mutations, but a majority of them are lethal.   Mustard gas and ultraviolet light also serve to induce mutations.

6-22. Inbreeding and outbreeding.   The mating of closely related individuals is called *inbreeding;* this may involve brother-sister matings or lesser degree of relationship.   Many races of domesticated animals and plants have been derived or improved by inbreeding, but there is a feeling among practical breeders that continued inbreeding leads to decline of vigor and the appearance of defects in offspring.   Close marriages in human society, as between cousins, are usually banned for fear that defective children may result.   Inbreeding tends to produce homozygous stocks, and since most genes for defects are recessive, it provides more opportunity for defective characters to appear.   The results will depend on the genetic constitution of the stocks that are inbred.   Guinea pigs carried through 23 generations of brother-sister matings by Sewall Wright and others ended with a stock reduced in size, fertility, and resistance to tuberculosis.   Helen D. King, however, carried similar matings in white rats through 25 generations, using only the most vigorous individuals in each, and at the end the inbred animals compared favorably with crossbred controls.   Similar experiments through more generations with *Drosophila* have ended with normal stocks.   Inbreeding with selection can produce satisfactory or improved stocks, combining desirable dominant characteristics in the homozygous condition.

Outcrossing, which is the mating of individuals not closely related, usually results in *hybrid vigor,* the offspring exceeding their parents in vigor and size.   The mule is a classical case, being larger and having more stamina than either of its parents, the mare and ass.   Outcrossing tends to produce heterozygous individuals in which any defective features are masked by dominant normal characters.   The great majority of human marriages may be classed as outcrosses; thus the human population is heterozygous, and defects are relatively rare.   People in an isolated community are more likely to be inbred and hence show a larger percentage of defects than in the general population.

6-23. Artificial selection.   By selective breeding and the perpetuation of mutations, mankind has produced many breeds of domesticated animals that differ markedly in physical, physiological, and psychological characteristics from the wild ancestors.   Choice among the resulting offspring and discarding those with unwanted features have yielded many useful forms.

The wild jungle fowl of India (*Gallus bankiva*) is small and slender, with variegated coloration, and the hens lay only 12 to 24 eggs per year. Continued selection has produced from it many domestic breeds of poultry that differ in size, coloration, and egg production.   The bantams are only about 10 inches high and weigh about 1½ pounds, whereas "meat fowls" such as the Cochins, Plymouth Rocks, and Rhode Island Reds are up to 16 inches tall and 6 to 8 pounds in weight. The White Leghorn hen now averages 120 eggs per year, and in some highly selected flocks each produces 200 or more eggs annually.

Beef cattle, such as the Hereford, Shorthorn and Aberdeen Angus breeds, are selected for shape (conformation) that yields desirable cuts of meat, and dairy breeds such as the Holstein-Friesian and Jersey have been developed for high milk production and high butterfat, respectively.

The greatest variety of characters perpetuated under domestication is among dogs (derived from wolves of Eurasia), over 100 breeds being recognized. These range from tiny Pekingese to great wolfhounds and from short-legged dachshunds and bulldogs to long-legged greyhounds. The coat color varies from white through shades of yellow, brown, and blue to black, and the character of the coat from nearly hairless in the Chihuahua to the dense sleek coat of the collie and curly hair of the Irish water spaniel (Table 32-1).

Artificial selection has perpetuated peculiar mutations that would not survive long in nature, such as the pouters and fantails among pigeons or the bulldogs and Pekingese dogs. Indeed, few domesticated animals survive as such in the wild; if they persist at all, they generally revert to resemble the ancestral species. When domestic rabbits are released on islands the offspring soon are like the European gray rabbit whence they were derived. Specialized breeds of swine, such as the Poland China, similarly come to resemble the European wild boar from which they arose.

A reversal of artificial selection was tried by Lutz Heck of Berlin to reestablish the ancestral aurochs or ur (*Bos primigenius*) from which modern breeds of cattle were derived. By crossing several of the most primitive existing breeds of the Mediterranean region he obtained animals that resemble old paintings of the aurochs, which has been extinct as a species for several centuries.

6-24. Twins. Since the sum total of characteristics in any one individual results from the action and interaction of many genes, it is obvious that the various offspring from one pair of parents will differ from each other. When a female produces more than one young at a birth, each usually develops from a separate egg, and so the young are genetically different. If, however, the early blastomeres of one egg separate and each gives rise to an individual, all the latter will have the same genetic make-up. The first condition produces *fraternal twins* (triplets, etc.) which may be of the same or of different sex; among human beings they are no more alike than the other children of any one family. The second condition produces *identical twins,* always of the same sex, with like physical features, agreeing in physiological characteristics such as susceptibility to disease and length of life, and showing practically the same mental traits and abilities. The five famous Dionne children are considered to be identical quintuplets. In the armadillo four young of identical kind result from partitioning a single egg. In various species a partial separation during cleavage or early embryonic development results in "double monsters," such as two-headed snakes or six-legged calves, and Siamese twins in which two bodies are joined in varying degree.

6-25. Erroneous ideas about heredity. Formerly it was thought that *acquired characteristics,* which are those resulting from environmental influences during the lifetime of individuals, were heritable. No reliable evidence in support of the idea has ever been presented, and biologists now agree that such characters are not inherited. Environment ("nurture"), however, may play an important role as to the degree in which hereditary characters ("nature") develop in an individual.

Modification of the embryo by *maternal impressions,* or experiences of the mother during pregnancy, is another erroneous idea about heredity. The embryo is, of course, influenced by the health or nutrition of the mother, but that is quite another thing.

It was once thought that when a female animal was bred to a male the latter might influence the progeny from subsequent mating with other males; this notion of *telegony* was long held by animal breeders but is now largely discarded.

Breeders of domesticated animals sometimes refer to the *prepotency* of one parent, implying that it has ability to transmit characteristics more fully or to the exclusion of the other parent. Since the chromosome and genetic contribution of the two sexes is equivalent, this idea possibly arose from the greater attention given to one sex, usually the male, in efforts at improvement of a breed of animals. Any actual difference results from dominance or heterozygosity in the animals mated.

FIG. 6-12. Examples of two hereditary abnormalities known in man. *A.* Syndactyly (fused fingers). *B.* Polydactyly (extra digit).

HUMAN INHERITANCE

The genetic characteristics of human beings are passed from generation to generation in the same way as those of animals and plants. The details are difficult to work out for mankind because of the long intervals between generations and the scarcity of records that specify the characteristics of numerous individuals. By tracing backward through family histories in which the peculiarities of many members have been listed, it has been possible to determine the manner of inheritance for some physical features, physiological characteristics, and mental traits (Figs. 6-12 to 6-14).

6-26. Eye color. The iris of the human eye is brown or blue or, rarely, pink. Pigment on the back of the iris causes blue eyes of various shades; if there is also pigment on the front of the iris, the color is hazel to dark brown. In rare instances pigment is lacking on both surfaces and the eyes appear pink (albino) because of the blood vessels in the iris. When both parents are blue-eyed, all their children have blue eyes; when one parent is heterozygous brown-eyed and one blue-eyed the children are partly brown-eyed, partly blue-eyed. Marriage of two brown-eyed persons usually results only in brown-eyed children; yet blue-eyed ones may appear. These facts indicate that eye color is a simple Mendelian character; brown is dominant to blue, and blue-eyed individuals are homozygous recessives for eye color.

6-27. Color blindness. The inability to distinguish red from green, is a sex-linked recessive character in mankind. Normal men neither have nor transmit the defect; "carrier" females enjoy normal vision but, being heterozygous for the character, may have color-blind children; color-blind males and females both transmit the defect. The inheritance of this character is diagrammed in Table 6-2.

TABLE 6-2. INHERITANCE OF COLOR VISION (RED-GREEN DISCRIMINATION) IN MANKIND

The gene for this factor, being sex-linked, is carried on the X chromosome. Color blindness (**X**) is recessive to normal vision (X). The heterozygous "carrier" female has normal vision.

Parents → ↓	gametes ↓ →	Normal ♂ XY		Color-blind ♂ **XY**	
		X	Y	**X**	Y
		Children			
Normal ♀ XX	X	XX ♀ normal	XY ♂ normal	XX ♀ *carrier*	XY ♂ normal
Carrier ♀ **X**X	X	XX ♀ normal	XY ♂ normal	XX ♀ *carrier*	XY ♂ normal
	X	XX ♀ *carrier*	XY ♂ color-blind	**XX** ♀ color-blind	XY ♂ color-blind
Color-blind ♀ **XX**	**X**	XX ♀ *carrier*	XY ♂ color-blind	**XX** ♀ color-blind	XY ♂ color-blind

6-28. Blood groups. The importance of blood groups in transfusion was described in Chap. 4. The heredity of these groups is based on three genes for antigen production: antigen A, gene A; antigen B, gene A^B; no antigen, gene a. Neither A nor A^B is dominant to the other, but both are dominant to a. The genotypes and blood groups of individuals are as follows:

Genotype............	aa	AA or Aa	A^BA^B or A^Ba	AA^B
Blood group..........	O	A	B	AB

The relations possible between parents and offspring are shown in Table 6-3. The blood group to which an individual belongs is useful in some but not all medicolegal cases involving parentage, as when two babies are accidentally interchanged in a hospital or when a woman claims a certain man as the father of a child. For example, if two parents, both of group O are given a baby of group A there obviously has been a mistake; likewise a couple of O × AB could not be parent to a group O baby. An A × B couple, however, could not make a valid claim for any particular baby.

TABLE 6-3. HEREDITY OF HUMAN BLOOD GROUPS

Parents	Children Possible	Children Not possible	Child	One parent known to be	Other parent May be	Other parent Cannot be
O × O	O	A, B, AB	O	O A B	A, B O, B O, A	AB
O × A A × A	O, A	B, AB				
O × B B × B	O, B	A, AB	A	O B	A, AB	O, B
A × B	O, A B, AB	—	B	O A	B, AB	O, A
O × AB	A, B	O, AB	AB	A B AB	B, AB A, AB A, B, AB	O, A O, B O
A × AB B × AB AB × AB	A, B, AB	O				

6-29. Mental characteristics. Some traits, both good and bad, are inherited like other characteristics, although evidence about them may be difficult to interpret. Certain families have shown outstanding ability and leadership through successive generations, with many individuals distinguished in scholarship, the professions, the fine arts, business, statesmanship, and other fields of human endeavor. Conversely, other family lines include many degenerate individuals. The "Jukes" family, studied by Dugdale and Estabrook, is one of bad pedigree that was traced through several generations. From the marriage of a shiftless

FIG. 6-13. Inheritance of musical ability. (*After Hurst*, 1908.)

farmer's son and a prostitute a total of 2,094 descendants were identified; these included 299 paupers, 118 criminals, 378 prostitutes, and 86 brothel keepers. There was a general record of intemperance and illegitimate births, and half the total were feeble-minded. The "Kallikak" family, analyzed by Goddard, presented an even more interesting situation. Martin Kallikak had a son by a feeble-minded girl, then married into a

TABLE 6-4. SOME MENDELIAN HEREDITARY CHARACTERISTICS OF MANKIND

	Character	Dominant	Recessive
NORMAL	Hair form	Curly	Straight
	Hair color	Dark	Light
	Skin color	Dark	Light
	Skin pigmentation	Normal	Albinism (no pigment)
	Eye (iris) color	Brown	Blue
ABNORMAL	Fingers and toes	Short (brachydactyly)	Normal length
		"Webbed" (syndactyly)	Normal, not fused
		Extra digits (polydactyly)	Normal, 5 on each member
	Epidermis of skin	Thickened (keratosis)	Normal
	Hair and teeth	Absent (hypotrichosis)	Present
	Nervous function	Normal	Hereditary epilepsy
		Normal	Feeble-minded
		Normal	Insanity (also caused by organic disturbance, not genetic)
	Eye	Opaque lens (hereditary cataract)	Normal
		Internal swelling and pressure (glaucoma)	Normal
	Ear	Normal hearing	Deaf-mutism
SEX-LINKED	Color vision	Normal	Color-blind (cannot distinguish red and green)
	Clotting of blood	Normal	Hemophilia (clots slowly if at all)

respectable family, and produced several children whose descendants became worthy members of society. The illegitimate feeble-minded son, however, sired a degenerate line comparable with that of the "Jukes" family.

Practically every organ in the human body may be subject to hereditary defects in structure or function (Table 6-3), but mental defects, such as feeble-mindedness and insanity, are much more important. Furthermore it seems that such defects are increasing in frequency. Several million persons in the United States have an intelligence quotient of 70 or lower, from high-grade morons to imbeciles and idiots. More than 300,000 cases are of hereditary origin, but only about 11 per cent of them are thought to be the progeny of feeble-minded parents (Fig. 6-14). The

Fig. 6-14. Inheritance of feeble-mindedness. *Black*, feeble-minded; *white*, normal; □, males; ○, females; *A*, alcoholic; *i*, died in infancy. In the two cases where both parents were feeble-minded note that all children were also feeble-minded. (*From Holmes, Human genetics and its social import.*)

remainder derive from normal persons who are heterozygous for this character. The feeble-minded become juvenile delinquents, problem children, and cases for public charity and relief. They breed early and often and so tend to increase their kind. Only a small percentage are cared for in institutions, public or private. The end result is a rapidly mounting bill for their care and for dealing with the crimes that they commit. At least 29 states have laws that permit insane and feeble-minded persons to be sterilized, but only about 35,000 had been so dealt with up to 1941. This reduces the cost and difficulty of dealing with such defectives in institutions but does not affect the remainder.

The human race has evolved through a long series of progressive changes to its present state (Chaps. 9, 33) and would seem capable of further modification for better or worse. When man lived a primitive life, many defective characters were probably weeded out by rigorous selective action of the environment. "Civilization" is mainly a control of man's environment, and it has increasingly tended to suspend such selection. Human races have crossed and recrossed so that mankind has become the most variable of all animals. In this process the human species has accumulated a long series of hereditary defects. The frequent outcrossing in human populations and the common bans on marriage between persons closely related have tended to make the human germ plasm heterozygous and thus mask any defects that are recessive genetically. Since there is little selective mating to rid the human population of such defects, they continue unabated. Although modern medicine helps the individual to survive, it may actually be harming the race. In earlier centuries many defective persons died before they became old enough to reproduce, whereas today such persons are repaired by medicine or surgery and survive to produce progeny that carry on their hereditary defects.

6-30. Eugenics. Many organizations and persons are now interested in *eugenics* (Gr. *eugenes*, well-born), a field of endeavor which seeks to better the human race by applying the principles of genetics. If it were possible to control the matings between human beings, the race could be improved by eliminating certain serious defects and in many other ways, but this is not practical. Eugenists seek to determine the facts of human heredity, to educate the general public on the effects of good and bad matings, and to encourage legislation that will prevent matings between obviously defective persons. The further field of *euthenics* tries to improve the environmental conditions under which human beings develop and live so as to give the best possible expressions to the genetic constitution that each one has. Such aid, while temporary, is of great value. No measurable aid in human genetics will be possible until much fuller records on human inheritance are available and until means are learned to recognize heterozygous individuals who carry genes of serious defects and to limit the mating of such persons.

References

BATESON, W. 1913. Mendel's principles of heredity. 3d imp. London, Cambridge University Press. xiv + 413 pp., illus.

CASTLE, W. E. 1940. Mammalian genetics. Cambridge, Mass., Harvard University Press. ix + 169 pp., 131 figs.

DEMEREC, M. (editor). 1950. Biology of Drosophila. New York, John Wiley & Sons, Inc. 572 pp., illus.

DOBZHANSKY, T. 1941. Genetics and the origin of species. 2d ed. New York, Columbia University Press. xviii + 446 pp., 24 figs.

DUNN, L. C., and T. DOBZHANSKY. 1946. Heredity, race and society. New York, Penguin Books, Inc. 115 pp.

GATES, R. R. 1946. Human genetics. New York, The Macmillan Co. 2 vols., xvi + 1,518 pp., 326 figs.

GOLDSCHMIDT, RICHARD. 1938. Physiological genetics. New York, McGraw-Hill Book Co., Inc. ix + 375 pp., 53 figs.

LUSH, J. L. 1945. Animal breeding plans. Ames, Iowa State College Press. viii + 443 pp., 50 figs.

MENDEL, G. 1866. Versuche an Pflanzen-Hybriden. *Verhandlungen der Naturf. Verein, Brünn*, vol. 4, pp. 3–47. Translated in Bateson (see above), pp. 335–379; also reprinted by Harvard University Press.

MULLER, H. J., C. C. LITTLE, and L. H. SNYDER. 1947. Genetics, medicine, and
man.   Ithaca, N.Y., Cornell University Press.   ix + 158 pp., 29 figs.

SINNOTT, E. W., L. C. DUNN, and TH. DOBZHANSKY. 1950. Principles of genetics.
4th ed.   New York, McGraw-Hill Book Co., Inc.   xiv + 505 pp., 202 figs.

STERN, CURT. 1949. Principles of human genetics.   San Francisco, W. H. Free-
man & Co.   xi + 617 pp., 198 figs.

STURTEVANT, A. H., and G. W. BEADLE. 1939. An introduction to genetics.   Philadelphia, W. B. Saunders Co.   11–391 pp., 1 pl., 126 figs.

CHAPTER 7

ANIMAL ECOLOGY

Every living organism, from the simplest bacterium to the ponderous elephant, has a distinctive manner of life that depends upon its structure and physiology and also upon physical, climatic, and biological factors of the environment in which it lives. All the plants and animals at any place comprise an integrated community which for convenience is often divided into the *plant community* and the *animal community*. The interrelations between organisms and their environments form the subject matter of *ecology* (Gr. *oikos*, house).

All energy used by organisms for growth, metabolism, and activities is derived from the sun. Plants absorb the radiant energy in sunlight and by the photosynthetic action of chlorophyll in their cells produce carbohydrates from carbon dioxide and water. They also synthesize proteins and fats. The energy stored in these compounds is the ultimate source of that used by all animals since none of the latter (except a few protozoans) can synthesize food.

The numbers and kinds of plants present at any place depend on (1) the physical and chemical characteristics of the soil; (2) the moisture cycle as to total amount and seasonal occurrence in the soil and air; (3) the temperature cycle as to daily and seasonal extremes and averages, and length of the growing season between killing frosts; (4) the duration and intensity of sunlight; and (5) other factors. The numbers and kinds of animals in a community are regulated directly by various environmental factors and indirectly by factors that affect the plants upon which many animals depend for food, shelter, and breeding places.

7-1. Chemical cycles in nature. The elements that go to form the bodies of plants and animals are all derived from the environment, and there is a constant interchange of these incident to the life and death of organisms (Fig. 7-1).

Carbon (C) is a constituent of all organic compounds in protoplasm (Chap. 3). From the carbon dioxide (CO_2) in air or water it is synthesized into the molecules of carbohydrates, and these, together with proteins and fats, make up the tissues of plants. The plants are eaten by certain animals, and after digestion and absorption (Chap. 4) the compounds of carbon become reorganized as animal protoplasm. In turn, this passes through other animals. Destructive metabolism in animals

177

yields carbon dioxide as a respiratory waste that returns to the air or water.

Oxygen (O_2) is taken up directly from the air or water (Fig. 4-17) to serve in oxidative processes in animal bodies and returns thereafter to the environment either combined with carbon (C) as carbon dioxide or with hydrogen as water. From the carbon dioxide used by plants the oxygen is returned to the environment, but plants also use some oxygen in respiration. A "balanced aquarium" contains animals and plants in

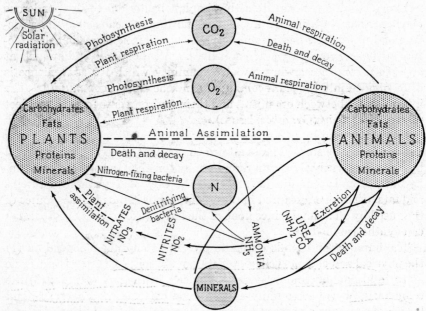

FIG. 7-1. The chemical cycles of carbon dioxide, oxygen, nitrogen, and minerals in nature. Arrows indicate the paths of movement of materials from the air (CO_2, O_2, N) and soil (minerals) to and from plants and animals.

such numbers that their mutual needs and output of oxygen and carbon dioxide are balanced.

Atmospheric *nitrogen* (N) can be used directly only by nitrogen-fixing bacteria in soil or in root nodules of some legumes, which combine it into nitrates (NO_3). Plants use nitrates to form vegetable proteins. These either return by decay to the soil or are eaten by animals and converted into animal proteins. In animal metabolism the latter are eventually broken into nitrogenous wastes, mostly urea, (NH_2)$_2$CO, and excreted. By action of other bacteria in soil or water such wastes are converted to ammonia and to nitrites; by further bacterial action either the nitrogen is returned to the air, or the nitrites are converted into nitrates.

Certain *minerals,* or inorganic chemical substances, are essential for both plants and animals (Chap. 3) in small but definite amounts that

differ in various species.   Plants obtain mineral constituents from the soil
solution about their roots, and these return to the soil only by decay or
burning of the plants.   The supply for animals is taken partly from their
food and partly from water, and in some cases directly from the soil.
Minerals from animals return to the soil or water in excretions and feces
and upon decay of their bodies (Fig. 7-2).

FIG. 7-2.   The mineral cycle.   Materials uplifted into mountains become disintegrated
into soil minerals.   By erosion and water or wind transport these move gradually toward
the lowlands and the sea; meanwhile, some pass once or many times through plants and
animals.

Water (H_2O) is essential in protoplasm and in all metabolic processes
of organisms, being the vehicle in which all materials are carried for
absorption and secretion by the cells.   In animal digestion, water is
utilized chemically in hydrolysis of starches to sugars, and metabolic
water is produced by oxidative processes in the tissues.

7-2. Climatic factors.   The environment is almost constant in some
tropical lands and seas, but over much of the earth the temperature,
moisture relations, and sunlight change with the seasons.   Such changes
variously affect different animals, some more than others.   The life
cycle of each species is closely adjusted to the climatic conditions in its
environment.

7-3. Temperature.   The birds and mammals, with insulated bodies
and regulated temperatures, are seldom affected directly by change of
environmental temperature, but the cold of winter or excessive heat of
summer may alter their food supplies.   Many birds that summer in
Arctic and temperate regions travel, or *migrate,* to warmer regions for
the winter to obtain appropriate food.   Birds, elk, and deer that summer
in high mountains, as in western North America, migrate to lower levels
for the same reason.

Ground squirrels, bears, and some insectivorous bats enter a winter
rest, or *hibernation,* when their food of the warmer seasons becomes
unavailable.   In hibernation the body temperature drops to about that
of the animal's shelter, the heartbeat and respiration become very slow,

and the reduced metabolism is supplied mostly by fat stored in the body before entering hibernation.

The cold-blooded animals—reptiles, amphibians, fishes, insects, and all other invertebrates—have no internal regulation of body temperature, the latter being always practically at that of the environment in which they live. The rate of chemical processes in their metabolism, and consequently their growth and activities, are directly influenced by environmental temperatures, being speeded up by warmth and delayed by cold. Each species has certain limits in these respects. Any and all are killed by prolonged freezing or by excessive heat. If freezing weather occurs after their eggs or larvae have begun to develop, many are killed and their populations are reduced.

Reptiles and amphibians feed and grow in warm weather but must hibernate in the ground or water to escape being frozen in regions that experience low winter temperatures. Some snakes of the arid West that are abroad by day in the spring become nocturnal in summer to avoid death by overheating. Most fresh-water fishes become rather inactive in cold weather, and each species has an upper limit of heat tolerance. Since temperature changes are slower and less extreme in the ocean, marine organisms are less abruptly affected by seasonal changes of climate, yet many kinds of salt-water fishes migrate north and south seasonally. Some adult insects can survive freezing temperatures, but most species have eggs, larvae, or pupae that overwinter as resting stages with lowered metabolism, either beneath the ground surface, within plants, or in the bottoms of ponds and streams, to escape being frozen. Some fresh-water crustaceans and many rotifers produce resistant eggs that survive freezing in water or on land.

Temperature changes also influence the growth, fruiting, and survival of the plants upon which various animals depend for food. A prolonged cold spring delays the development of grasses and leaves upon which many insects, rodents, and grazing animals forage and may determine the degree of survival of the latter. Unseasonable weather at blossoming time may reduce the subsequent crops of berries upon which robins, bluebirds, and other species levy for food, forcing the birds to wander elsewhere for food or starve; the same results with failure of seed crops utilized by sparrows and chipmunks.

7-4. Water relations. Many aquatic environments in eastern North America are relatively stable because water is retained by freezing in winter and that lost by evaporation in summer is replaced by frequent rains. In the western states, however, lakes fluctuate widely with changes in rainfall or snowfall. Many small ones and some of the larger dry out completely at times, killing all fishes and other strictly aquatic species. The margining marshes that shelter frogs, turtles, ducks, muskrats, and others also are destroyed. Abrupt changes in the flow of streams alter the conditions for their inhabitants. Severe floods modify the character of the bottom, covering gravel beds with silt, and the rushing waters may actually destroy many animals. The reduction of a creek to scant flow or scattered pools exposes the aquatic animals to attack by predators of the land and also permits the waters to become overheated. Certain toads, tree toads, insects, and other invertebrates breed in transient rain pools; and if the rains are scant or unseasonal, these animals may lack for spawning places or the pools may dry out and kill the young stages before their growth is completed.

Another important water relation affecting the occurrence and activities of land animals is the moisture content of the air, or relative humidity

FIG. 7-3. The water cycle. Constant interchange of water between the air, land, and sea produces various daily and seasonal alterations in the environments of plants and animals.

(percentage of water vapor in relation to saturation at any given temperature). Some animals are suited to arid deserts of low humidity, some exist only where the atmosphere is saturated, and others live variously at intermediate humidities. For small animals the **microclimate** of the little places where they feed or find shelter is all important, usually having a lower temperature and higher humidity than the general climate of the region in which they occur. In arid places many small animals remain in seclusion by day; else they would soon die of desiccation. They venture out at night when temperatures are lower and the humidity greater, especially close to the ground. In regions having frequent summer rains, or where fields and gardens are irrigated, the humidity near the ground is such that small invertebrates are active during the daytime.

All animals that inhabit soil are affected by change in its moisture content. Earthworms live close to the surface in moist soil during warm weather but go deeper as the surface layer dries, and the same occurs with some insect larvae. In turn, the moles that feed on such animals work in shallow or deeper layers as necessary.

7-5. Food. Members of a plant community all compete for the same things—sunlight, soil minerals, and water—but animals are diverse in their food habits. Each species has particular requirements, and every individual needs a certain amount of food of the right kind. Human beings, rats, houseflies, and others of generalized food habits can subsist on a variety of foods and change from one to another as necessity dictates. Many species, however, are narrowly specialized and can exist only where and when their particular foods are available. Thus the beaver eats only the inner bark of willows and poplars; the larvae of the cabbage butterfly require leaves of cruciferous plants; some leaf hoppers subsist only on the juices of certain plants; and horseflies require mammalian blood. Some food supplies are seasonal; and the species depending upon them must, at other times of the year, shift to other foods, become dormant, migrate elsewhere, or perish. Failure of a food supply by freezing or drought will result in starvation of animals restricted solely to it.

The ocean, unlike the land, has few conspicuous plants and therefore few strictly herbivorous animals. The sea hare (*Tethys*), a mollusk, eats seaweed as a rabbit does lettuce, and some snails and limpets browse by rasping off the dense short algae covering shore rocks. The foundation of ocean pasturage, however, is the *plankton,* composed mainly of microscopic plants (diatoms, algae) and protozoans (dinoflagellates) that float freely in the water. Plankton, which varies in amount and species composition through the season (like the wildflowers in a field), is the food of innumerable minute crustaceans, chaetognaths, and other animals and of the larvae of mollusks, annelids, echinoderms, and the like. Seaweeds are commonest in bays, estuaries, and shore waters, many of them being annuals. When they die and sink, they are reduced by a rich flora of bottom-dwelling bacteria. The resulting microscopic *detritus* (plant material plus bacteria) forms a bottom scum. This is the food of various worms and other invertebrates that secrete mucus nets or have special means to select fine particles from the water or mud. Sea cucumbers and some sea urchins ingest bottom mud in quantity to extract detritus for food. There is also a supply of larger organic particles or *debris* derived mainly from animals that sink after death (from rough weather, killing by predators, etc.). Debris is the food of scavengers— certain shrimps, crabs, sea urchins, and others. In the ocean, however, animals are the principal food supply. Minute creatures that feed on plankton are eaten by other swimming invertebrates; these in turn are the food of larger crustaceans and small fishes which then are captured by larger fishes; and so on.

Plant-eating animals thus are the basis of any animal community. They in turn serve as food for other animals, which in turn are eaten by still others. The energy originally derived from the sun by plants thus passes in material form through a *food chain;* all food chains in a community constitute a *food cycle* or *food web.* These relations are very complex (Figs. 7-4, 7-5) even in a small community but may be illustrated by two simplified examples. In a pond the bacteria and diatoms synthesize materials, and then in sequence small organisms are eaten by larger

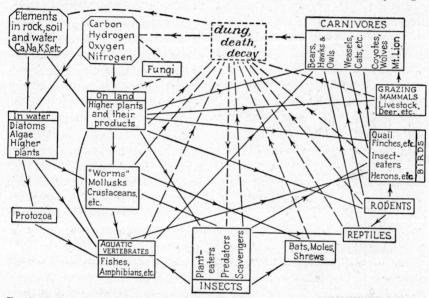

Fig. 7-4. Some interrelations among inorganic substances, plants, and animals in nature. Arrows indicate the path of materials from the primary (inorganic) sources through various organisms (solid lines) and back to the soil, water, or air (broken lines). Any one circuit constitutes a food chain. No parasites are included.

ones, thus: bacteria and diatoms → small protozoans → larger protozoans → rotifers, small crustaceans → aquatic insects → fishes. The large fishes, or any intermediate organisms, by death and decay become food for bacteria, thus completing the circuit. Or the fishes may be taken by herons, minks, or men and end up elsewhere. On land a food chain may include the following: soil minerals, carbon dioxide, and water → plants → plant-eating insects, rodents, or grazing mammals → predaceous insects or small carnivores → larger carnivores; this ends with death and decay as in the water. In any chain the successive members are larger in size but fewer in total numbers. Chains are not strictly linear but have many branches and alternative links so that the results of a change in numbers of any one member are difficult to predict. Any animal, above the smallest, takes food (prey) in relation to its size, neither so small that it cannot profitably gather enough nor too large for it to overcome successfully. The huge whalebone whale that sieves enormous quantities of minute crustaceans from the sea thus has a short food chain.

The food web of any community has been characterized by Elton as a *pyramid of numbers.* Animals at the base are small and abundant whereas those at the apex are few but large, and there is progressive increase in size of individuals but decrease in numbers of those between. In a deciduous woods, for example, aphids and other minute herbivorous insects may be enormously abundant, spiders and carnivorous beetles are fairly common, insectivorous birds are fewer, and the hawks and weasels preying on the birds are sparse numerically. The smallest kinds, because of their size, can reproduce rapidly, whereas larger members of the chain multiply more slowly. The largest predators at the apex are relatively so scarce that in turn they cannot serve profitably as prey for another species.

FIG. 7-5. The "boll weevil complex" as an example of the varied interrelations in nature. Besides the cotton plant and the boll weevil that feeds directly upon it, there are involved other plants and plant-feeding insects, predators, parasites, and hyperparasites. (*After U.S. Bureau of Entomology Bull.* 100.)

7-6. Cover, shelter, and breeding places (Fig. 8-5). Animals that live in large bodies of open water can avoid enemies only by superior ability in locomotion, but many species of smaller waters and of the land live in various types of *cover* and resort to retreats, or *shelters,* to avoid enemies or unfavorable environmental conditions. Small mammals, birds, lizards, and insects live in cover such as grassland, shrubbery, or trees; various marine fishes and invertebrates live amid seaweeds, rocks, or coral in shore waters, and some fresh-water fishes inhabit growths of aquatic plants; moles, pocket gophers, some snakes, various insects, earthworms, and other invertebrates live more or less continually within the soil. In all these cases the animals find their appropriate types of food in such surroundings and are able to escape enemies and avoid extremes of weather or other adverse influences. Most species also have special requirements for *breeding places* where the eggs or young are produced.   For some the shelter serves, but others build special **nests** for this purpose as is done by many birds, some fishes, and various insects. Small animals breed wherever conditions are suitable, but in many kinds of birds and some mammals each pair establishes a **territory** to supply the food requirements of the parents and offspring for the breeding season; the territory is defended against invasion by other individuals of the same species.

7-7. Competition.   The members of a species have the same requirements as to food and therefore compete with one another; representatives of different species that subsist on the same types of food are also in competition.   Thus grasslands may be the common forage area of grasshoppers and other plant-eating insects, rodents, rabbits, deer, and domestic livestock.   In times of food shortage, survival becomes a critical matter, determined by the quantities taken by each species according to its population and the amount eaten by individuals.   Species that have some latitude in choice of food may utilize other sources, whereas those restricted to but one type may be far reduced.   In times of "crop failure," of either plant or animal materials, death by starvation is the lot of many animals; and if an animal species has built up to excessively large numbers, it may come to the same end.

7-8. Enemies.   Every animal that consumes another animal is called an **enemy,** or **predator,** and the animal eaten is its **prey.**   An animal that consumes members of its own species is termed **cannibalistic,** and one that eats dead animals is a **scavenger.**   Any food chain, after the first plant-eating animal, is a succession of predations.   Predation differs from parasitism in that a predator destroys its prey outright, but a parasite usually continues to feed on its living host.   As Elton says, predators live on capital and parasites on income.   In a food chain each predator is usually larger than its prey, whereas the parasite is always much smaller than its host.

The predator is commonly believed to "control" the numbers of its prey, and in a sense it does so, but the relation is somewhat balanced. If a prey population increases, it will support more predators; if the latter then also increase, a heavier toll will be exacted of the prey, whereupon the latter will be reduced.   In either type of change the numbers of the predator tend to lag behind those of the prey because the predator being larger has usually a slower rate of increase, although it lives longer.   The amount of cover available in relation to the prey population also is a factor; more of the prey will escape the predators if there is much cover. Beyond a certain point of decrease in the population of prey it becomes unprofitable for the predator to pursue that particular kind of prey; it must then shift to using some other source or else suffer decline.   The red fox, for example, preys variously on woodchucks, cottontail rabbits, squirrels, mice, birds, and insects and also eats fruits and berries; its "diet" changes with season and place according to the things most readily available. Such a predator is less likely to vary so greatly in numbers than is the arctic fox, which lives mainly on lemmings or rabbits in the far North where the populations of both those rodents fluctuate widely.

7-9. Disease. Practically every animal species is subject to diseases produced by various types of organisms—viruses, rickettsias, bacteria, protozoans, parasitic worms, and arthropods. The disease organisms themselves must be considered as populations that in turn are affected by various factors in their respective environments, and they influence the numbers and well-being of the animals on which they live. Disease is probably one of the greatest agencies in regulation of other species. Attention here will be confined to parasites.

A *parasite* is an organism that lives on or in another species, the *host,* obtaining food and shelter at the latter's expense. The host can live without the parasite, but the latter cannot exist without its host. The parasitic animals include many PROTOZOA such as those causing malaria, amoebic dysentery, and other diseases; flukes, tapeworms, and other PLATYHELMINTHES; hookworms, root nematodes, and many other NEMATODA; all hairworms (NEMATOMORPHA) and spiny-headed worms (ACANTHOCEPHALA); various leeches (ANNELIDA); and many ARTHROPODA including fish lice, some barnacles and other CRUSTACEA, the mosquitoes, flies, fleas, and various other INSECTA, and the ticks and many mites (ARACHNOIDEA). No vertebrates are real parasites.

A species of parasite either inhabits one host species, or a group of similar hosts, or alternates between two or more host species; each kind of parasite is usually restricted to a certain site in its host. *Ectoparasites* such as leeches and lice live on the skin, and *endoparasites* dwell within the body, in the gut cavity (many worms) or other organs, in muscles (trichina) or other tissues, in the blood (some worms and protozoans), or even in blood cells (malarial parasite). Some parasitic insects and ticks in turn are *intermediate hosts* for parasitic protozoans or other organisms that they transmit to other or *definitive hosts.* (Chaps. 12, 16, 17, 18, 22, 23, 24.)

Different parasites evidently arose separately in various phyla from free-living ancestors, possibly starting as commensals, and have become variously specialized or degenerate for the parasitic mode of existence. Many have hooks or suckers for holding to their hosts; the gut is simplified (absent in tapeworms) because their fluid food is obtained directly by pumping or absorption from the host; and the reproductive organs are usually elaborated to produce enormous numbers of eggs or larvae so as successfully to overcome the hazards of reaching new hosts.

Some parasites have little or no effect on their hosts, others injure the latter temporarily or permanently by the destruction of tissues or production of toxic secretions, and some parasites kill their hosts. Harmful parasites are termed **pathogenic.** A host that recovers from the initial attack or damage often becomes a **carrier,** retaining some of the parasites, which continue to pass out eggs or larvae for infecting other hosts. Parasitism is the mode of life for many species; for survival as a species the parasite should not unduly injure its host. Parasitism, along with some diseases, is one factor in the regulation of populations of host animals. Some of the most notable instances of such control occur among insects where the matter is further complicated by secondary parasites, or **hyperparasites,** that parasitize the primary parasites (Chap. 23).

7-10. Symbiosis.[1] Parasitism and some other special types of interrelations between organisms of different species are termed **symbiosis.** Instances where an animal of one species gains benefit by living on or in another species, without harm or benefit to the latter, are known as **commensalism.** The commensal "lives aboard his neighbor's vessel but does not eat his provisions." Examples are the remora (Fig. 28-30) that attaches by its dorsal sucker to some other kind of fish for transport; the crabs that live regularly in the tubes of some echiurid and annelid worms (Fig. 21-13A) and other crabs in the mantle cavities of sea mussels; the special types of barnacles that attach only to whales or sea turtles; and the hydroids that gain support and a wider forage range by fastening to shells of certain crabs. Some commensals do get scraps from the host's "table."

A more intimate relation is that of **mutualism** (formerly termed symbiosis) in which two species have acquired such close interdependence that life apart is impossible. A striking example is that of certain termites and flagellate protozoans. The termites eat wood but cannot digest cellulose; however, the flagellates in the termite gut can do so and thus food is available for both. Termites experimentally rid of the flagellates soon die of starvation, and the protozoans cannot live a free existence. The green hydra (*Chlorohydra*) contains green algae (zoochlorellae), the one giving off carbon dioxide and the other oxygen as a by-product; sealed in a tube of water both live for some time by mutual aid. Similarly yellow or brown algae (zooxanthellae) are present in various protozoans, sponges, coelenterates (corals, sea anemones), and flatworms, where a similar O_2-CO_2 exchange occurs. Some species of beetles, ants, and termites grow and tend "gardens" of peculiar types of

---

[1] Originally symbiosis was used broadly as a term for all types of close plant-animal and animal-animal relationships; then it was narrowed to describe instances of close mutual advantage; recently biologists have reversed their usage to make symbiosis again the more general term.

fungi—that grow only under such care—and the fungi serve those insects as their sole food. Even man has a mutualistic relation with his crops of wheat and maize which grow only with his aid. Something approaching mutualism, but often termed *slavery,* is the practice of ants that gather and tend aphids. The ants provide shelter and protect the aphids, and the latter produce secretions used as food by the ants. Both ants and aphids, however, can also live independently.

7-11. Colonies and societies. All vertebrates, most arthropods, and many other invertebrates are *free-living* in that each individual gets about by its own efforts. By contrast, sponges, many hydroids, corals, bryozoans, tunicates, and others are *sessile,* in being fixed to some substratum of rocks, plants, or the shells of other animals. Among both categories, many species are *solitary* in that each individual is more or less independent, whereas others live in groups, or *colonies.* The many "individuals" of a colony among sponges, bryozoans, and tunicates are bound together structurally. In other aggregations such as colonies of insects, schools of fishes, flocks of birds, and herds of hoofed mammals the individuals are structurally separate but integrated by behavior into various types of *social organization.*

Persistently solitary animals such as carnivores (mountain lions, minks, etc.), hawks, flycatchers, snakes, and predaceous insects forage best independently and pair up only for reproduction. Members of species that are *gregariously asexual* assemble without reference to age or sex. In the winter flocks of robins, ducks, or starlings, many eyes and ears are of greater service when foraging or sleeping; groups of bats, rattlesnakes, or ladybird beetles gather for hibernation with some advantage. Among active groups of mammals or birds there is often a "leader," and a graduation in dominance among individuals, as seen in the "pecking order" among fowls of one sex in a flock. *Gregariously sexual* assemblages bring males and females together for mating, as with frogs, toads, gulls, and fur seals. *Societal organization* occurs where many individuals of a species live together in an integrated manner so that each contributes in some specialized way to the welfare of all. The social habit has arisen independently in several orders of insects and is highly developed among the termites, and in many bees, wasps, and ants. These have distinct castes, unlike in structure, physiology, and habits, none of which can live independently. Success with them is measured in terms of the colony, and not of the individual, which is unimportant. Human society comprises integrated groups of like individuals that specialize in different trades or professions to the benefit of both the individual and the group.

7-12. Populations. Few people realize the numbers of animals and plants that exist. Diatoms and protozoans may exceed 1,000,000 per liter of sea water. Censuses of the upper half inch of soil near Washington, D.C., revealed small organisms at the rate of 1,200,000 animals and 2,100,000 seeds or fruits per acre of forest soil; meadow soil contained 13,600,000 animal items and 33,800,000 of plant materials. On croplands, grasshoppers sometimes number 20,000 to 200,000 per acre, and in heavy infestations of the alfalfa weevil the eggs and larvae occur at 8,000,000 to 22,000,000 per acre. The numbers of larger organisms are naturally much smaller—birds at 2 per acre over the United States, deer at 1 to 25 or 40 acres, and black bears at 1 per several square miles.

Some recent winter flocks of ducks included over 200,000 birds; the bison on the Great Plains originally numbered several millions, as about 3,000,000 were killed in 1872–1874 alone; in eastern North America,

FIG. 7-6.　Age composition and changes in numbers of a valley quail population at Davis, Calif., through several years, as determined from banded birds. Despite the large production of young in 1936 the total population decreased in that and following years. (*After Emlen, Journal of Wildlife Management*, 1940.)

flocks of the now extinct passenger pigeon once darkened the skies for days during migration, and nearly 12,000,000 were killed and sold in one Michigan town in 40 days.

The potential rate of increase for all animals is very great, although slower in the larger forms. Any species would soon overrun the earth if it went unchecked, but none has ever done so, although some spread with considerable rapidity. For example, from about 80 pairs of the European starling released in New York, N.Y., in 1890–1891 the species has multiplied and spread to Canada, Arizona, and California.

Because of the many factors that affect animal populations it is not surprising to learn that all are subject to fluctuation (Fig. 7-6). The numbers change from month to month, season to season, and year to year. Yellow jackets, certain caterpillars, and various other insects may be excessively numerous one year and scarce in another. In any one locality the population of meadow mice or of other small rodents will rise and fall in a rather regular manner about every 4 years. Snowshoe rabbits, foxes, and other fur bearers of northern North America fluctuate in numbers, as shown by fur returns of the Hudson's Bay Company and by more recent censuses. Thus the "balance of nature" is a dynamic one, ever changing with the successes and failures of the many species of plants and animals that comprise any community and with the many other environmental factors that also are subject to cyclical or other types of changes.

7-13. Ecology and conservation. Any change in the physical or biological character of an environment obviously will affect different species of animals in varying degree. To the natural forces that thus act upon the animal populations, the influences of man have been added in many places and with increasing vigor during recent centuries and years. Civilization is essentially an attempt by man to control the environment for his own advantage, usually immediate; civilization is applied ecology or ecological manipulation. Mankind has cut forests, drained swamps, irrigated arid lands, planted huge acreages of crops, and tried to kill off a wide variety of competitors and enemies from wolves and bison down to small insects and the many native or introduced plants classed as weeds. Agriculture, forestry, reclamation and irrigation, public health activities, and aid to game or fur species are all direct or indirect ecological manipulations. Invention and perfection of heavy power-driven bulldozers, gang plows, and power saws, and of chemical poisons that can be distributed in quantity by airplane or from the ground to control insects or weeds have greatly multiplied man's ability to alter his surroundings. All of this, however, is not constructive; accelerated erosion by wind and water after plowing up grass sod, stripping forests faster than they will regenerate, and various other effects are evident in many places. The disappearance of former populous civilizations that once flourished in the Near East and the decline in human "carrying capacity" of many other areas demonstrate that much of this manipulation has been too hasty and ill-advised. Some current efforts at conservation of renewable (biological) natural resources are tending to correct the evils of former environmental manipulations which were largely exploitation with little regard for the future. A human civilization, like any plant or animal community, cannot long continue if its environment becomes damaged beyond recovery.

7-14. Adaptations. Many animals are specialized, or **adapted,** by structure, physiology, and habits, for particular modes of life in their respective environments. Some examples are mentioned earlier in this chapter and others in Chaps. 12 to 32. The honeybee (Chap. 23, Figs. 23-12 to 14) shows many adaptations such as sucking mouth parts for obtaining nectar, the ability to subsist on sugars, the hairs and brushes used to gather pollen, the production and molding of wax into shelters for food and young, and the intricate pattern of habits of three castes in a social colony.   Man is a generalized species, able to do many things in various ways and to live in diverse environments.   The brown rat (Fig. 32-1), although specialized in being a rodent, is generalized enough to live successfully in a wide variety of conditions as to climate, shelter, and food. The mole (Fig. 32-21), by contrast, is narrowly adapted for life in the ground, with slender teeth to grasp worms, eyes covered and ears reduced, short fore limbs with huge palms bearing heavy claws to dig and "swim" through soil, and short reversible fur, which is not disarranged by moving forward or backward.   Different mammals show adaptive modifications of teeth for various kinds of food (Fig. 32-11), and the bills of birds are adapted in relation to their food habits (Fig. 31-11).   Other conspicuous examples are seen in the many parasites that can live in only a single host

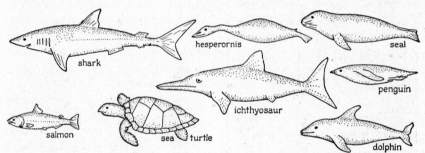

FIG. 7-7.   Oceanic vertebrates—sharks to mammals—showing adaptive convergence for swimming, with streamlined bodies and paddle-like fins or limbs.

species, and others like the malarial parasite and liver fluke that must alternate between two particular hosts to complete their life cycles (Chaps. 12, 16, 17, 22 to 24).   *Adaptive radiation* is seen in the one order of marsupial mammals in Australia that has "radiated" into diverse forms that run, jump, climb, burrow, or glide (Chap. 32).   *Adaptive convergence* often occurs when animals of different groups come to live in a common habitat.   Large vertebrates of the ocean, from sharks to mammals (Fig. 7-7), all have streamlined bodies and paddle-like fins or limbs, which enable them to swim more effectively.   Such adaptive characters are superimposed on the fundamental ones that make the shark a cartilaginous fish and the whale a mammal.

Many adaptive features are *protective* in various ways.   Some *structural adaptations* that afford protection from enemies are the shells of armadillos, turtles, and various mollusks, the quills of porcupines, the stings of bees and wasps, and the venom of poisonous snakes.   Still other adaptive characters tend to render many animals less easily detected by their enemies.   In this category, *animal coloration* has excited much discussion among biologists.   Some believe that it is highly adaptive in many species and serves them importantly in evading enemies, whereas other biologists discount its purposiveness and hold that animals are taken as prey in proportion to their respective numbers. Arguments on these two viewpoints are presented in the works of Cott and McAtee (see References).

The coloration of black crows and white herons obviously bears no particular relation to their respective environments, but by **protective coloration** many species harmonize more or less with their surroundings. The hares, weasels, and ptarmigan of the far North molt into white coats when snow covers their surroundings. The ruffed grouse (Fig. 31-25)

A   B   C

FIG. 7-8. Mimicry and protective resemblance. *A.* Viceroy butterfly, *Basilarchia archippus*, above, which mimics the monarch butterfly, *Danaus plexippus*, below. *B.* Moth larva in resting attitude resembling a twig. *C.* South American leaf insect, *Phyllium* (Order ORTHOPTERA). All ×⅔. (*B and C after Wolcott, Animal biology.*)

has a variegated pattern that blends with the leafy backgrounds of its woods habitat, and many oceanic invertebrates and fish larvae are transparent. Bark-inhabiting insects are commonly flecked with the colors of the backgrounds on which they usually occur. Many of these are cited as instances of camouflage, or **obliterative coloration,** whereby the outlines of the animal are obscured, save when it moves. **Warning coloration** is ascribed to some butterflies and other insects, considered to be distasteful to their enemies—they "advertise" their unpalatability. Bees and wasps with stout stings are often marked conspicuously with black and yellow.

There are many instances in which harmless or palatable species "copy," or **mimic,** other stinging or unpalatable species. The viceroy butterfly thus mimics the presumably unpalatable monarch butterfly (Fig. 7-8); certain moths, beetles, and flies mimic different species of wasps. Some long-horned beetles (CERAMBYCIDAE), for example, mimic wasps in form and color and also hover about flowers in wasp fashion. One African butterfly (*Papilio dardanus*) mimics in turn the color and form of three other distasteful species of butterflies with which it occurs, each in a separate geographic area.

Some insects show *protective resemblance* to objects in their surroundings by both form and color. A certain geometrid caterpillar rests in a position that resembles a twig of the tree on which it lives; a butterfly (*Kallima*) of India when resting with folded wings resembles a dead leaf; and some walkingsticks (ORTHOPTERA) are like dead or green twigs and others like green leaves.

Finally, some species of animals are considered to bear *recognition marks,* or *signals,* useful for identification by others of their species and to warn the latter of danger. The white outer tail feathers of juncos, meadow larks, and other birds, the white rump patch on the American antelope, and the cottony-white tail of cottontail rabbits are all flashed into view when these animals are frightened.

References

ALLEE, W. C., A. E. EMERSON, ORLANDO PARK, THOMAS PARK, and K. P. SCHMIDT. 1949. Principles of animal ecology. Philadelphia, W. B. Saunders Co. xii + 837 pp., 263 figs.

CHAPMAN, R. N. 1931. Animal ecology—with especial reference to insects. New York, McGraw-Hill Book Co., Inc. x + 464 pp., 153 figs.

COTT, H. B. 1941. Adaptive coloration in animals. New York, Oxford University Press. xxxii + 508 pp., 48 pls., 84 figs.

ELTON, C. 1935. Animal ecology. Revised. London, Sidgwick & Jackson, Ltd. xx + 207 pp., 8 pls., 13 figs.

HESSE, R., W. C. ALLEE, and K. P. SCHMIDT. 1937. Ecological animal geography. New York, John Wiley & Sons, Inc. xiv + 597 pp., 135 figs.

MCATEE, W. L. 1932. Effectiveness in nature of the so-called protective adaptations. . . . *Smithsonian Miscellaneous Collections*, vol. 85, pp. 1–201.

PEARSE, A. S. 1939. Animal ecology. 2d ed. New York, McGraw-Hill Book Co., Inc. xii + 642 pp., 133 figs.

RUSSELL, E. S., and C. M. YONGE. 1936. The seas: Our knowledge of life in the seas and how it is gained. Rev. ed. London, Ferderick Warne & Co., Ltd. xiii + 379 pp., 127 pls. (some colored).

SVERDRUP, H. U., M. W. JOHNSON, and R. H. FLEMING. 1942. The oceans: their physics, chemistry and general biology. New York, Prentice-Hall. x + 1,087 pp., illus.

CHAPTER 8

DISTRIBUTION OF ANIMALS

No animal species occurs uniformly over the whole world, but each is restricted to a definite *range*, or area of *distribution*. The entire extent of land or water over which a species may occur is termed its *geographical range*, and the kind of environment in which it lives is its *ecological range*. The immediate local situation that provides the essentials for existence is called its *ecologic niche*. The *geological range* of a species is its occurrence in the past (Figs. 8-1, 8-8). The term *habitat* is loosely used to indicate the place inhabited by a species. The study of animal distribution and of the factors controlling it is known as *zoogeography*.

Fig. 8-1. Relations among the three types of animal distribution: geographical, ecological, and geological.

All the animals living in a particular area, large or small, are collectively termed the *fauna*.

The beaver, for example, has a geographical range that embraces much of North America and Europe; its ecological range comprises fresh-water lakes and streams; its ecologic niche is provided by quiet waters bordered by aspens, poplars, or willows that may be cut to serve for food and for building dams; and its geological range includes, besides the present or Recent geologic time, also the Pleistocene and Pliocene epochs when it had a wider geographical range. Some animals are of widespread or *cosmopolitan* distribution, such as the harbor seal, which lives along most seacoasts of the world, and the sperm whale, which occurred in most oceans between 56°N. and 50°S. before it was reduced by man. Other species are *local* in occurrence like the recently extinct heath hen, latterly found only on an island of a few square miles (Martha's Vineyard off Massachusetts); some insects are known only from patches of plants covering but a few acres. Other animals have geographical and ecological ranges of various sizes and kinds. The mallard duck inhabits fresh-water marshes through much of the Northern Hemisphere, the polar bear is restricted to Arctic shores and ice, and living elephants dwell in the forests of Africa, India, and near-by regions.

194

8-1. Factors regulating distribution.   Since every species produces off-spring in excess of the numbers that can survive within its normal range, there is a "population pressure" by which individuals tend to expand the boundaries of the range.   Other factors such as competition, enemies, disease, shortage of food, adverse seasonal weather, and decrease in available shelter act to reduce the population.   The distribution of all animals, from protozoans to mankind, is consequently dynamic rather than static and always subject to change.

The external factors that limit distribution are termed **barriers.** These include (1) **physical barriers** such as land for aquatic species and water for most terrestrial forms; (2) **climatic barriers** such as temperature (average, seasonal, or extreme), moisture (as rain, snow, air humidity, or soil moisture), amount of sunlight, and others; and (3) **biological barriers** such as absence of appropriate food or presence of effective competitors, enemies, or diseases.   Many kinds of insects are limited to particular species of plants for their food, shelter, or breeding places, so that their distribution is controlled by factors that regulate these plants.   In the last analysis, the range and population of an animal rest upon the "law of the minimum," being controlled by the essential factor present in least amount or by some critical stage or condition for which the species has a narrow range of adaptability.   Oysters, for example, can live in various waters but breed only if the temperature exceeds a certain minimum; the species survives only where the minimum is passed.

8-2. Methods of distribution.   Free-living animals of some size become distributed by their own efforts.   Birds, fishes, and others that migrate are quick to settle in any suitable new situation.   Small aquatic animals and larvae and occasional large forms are carried about passively by water currents.   Many small insects are wafted about in the air, mostly within a few hundred feet of the earth but some at higher levels, and thus may be deposited in new places.   Rafts of trees, soil, and debris bearing animals may pass along large rivers and occasionally are seen far at sea; oceanic islands may have been populated by such means.   Violent hurricanes sometimes transport small living animals; some showers of organic matter in the United States have included earthworms deposited on a man's hat and on a buggy and many small fishes found after a heavy local rain in a previously dry cornfield in South Carolina.   Parasites and commensal animals are transported by their hosts into new localities.

A species does not necessarily occur in all places suitable for it, but only in those to which it has access, and this depends on its own past history or that of its ancestors.   Animal distribution of today is the joint result of existing barriers and of environmental conditions in the past. The continents have existed for long periods but have undergone many local alterations by elevation and erosion of mountain ranges, changes in the existence of lakes and streams, and the draining or flooding of low-lands.   Some continents have been connected at times by "land bridges" and separated by seas at other periods in earth history.   Warm climates extended to the polar regions in some periods, whereas glaciers blanketed much of the Northern Hemisphere in the Pleistocene epoch preceding the present.   All such changes have altered the distribution of plants and animals.   Older areas of land or water have been reduced or eliminated, and new ones have become available.   Living organisms have been

Fig. 8-2.   Geographical distribution of the muskrat, *Ondatra zibethica* (Fig. 32-27), a species divided into geographical races or subspecies (*O. z. zibethica, O. z. alba*, etc.) that differ from one another in average characters of size, coloration, skull features, etc.   Each subspecies occupies a distinct range (outlined by broken lines); in the east and north adjacent sub-species intergrade along their boundaries.   (*From data supplied by the U.S. Fish and Wild-life Service.*)

forced to move about, many species have been exterminated, and new species or groups have evolved to take advantage of new areas or environments.

Many North American animals are more closely related to species of eastern Asia than to those in South America.   From this we infer that the shallow Bering Sea now between Alaska and Siberia was a land bridge for terrestrial organisms in the late geological past (there are fossil remains of redwoods on the Aleutian Islands); the Isthmus of Panama is a replacement for the sea that earlier separated the Americas.   Terrestrial species need also appropriate "ecologic bridges" of suitable environment through which to migrate.   Forest monkeys of Panama cannot pass northward into tropical North America because there are not suitable forests to the north; likewise, the bison could not pass from North to South America because no open grasslands exist in the areas between.

GEOGRAPHICAL DISTRIBUTION

8-3. Major faunas. The *zoogeographic realms* (Fig. 8-3) are the largest units in distribution and are defined by the land animals native to each. The limits of each realm and its fauna reflect the past history of animal groups and also of changes in the earth's surface that either permitted or prevented animal migrations. The Australian Realm has

FIG. 8-3. The zoogeographic realms (separated by broken lines).

1. Australian. Australia, Tasmania, New Guinea, New Zealand, and oceanic islands of the Pacific. All monotremes, most marsupials (no placental mammals but bats and rodents), emu, cassowaries, brush turkeys, lyre birds, birds of paradise, most cockatoos, Australian lungfish. New Zealand has sphenodon and kiwi.

2. Oriental. Asia south of The Himalayas: India, Ceylon, Malay Peninsula, Sumatra, Borneo, Java, Celebes, and the Philippines. Tarsiers, macaques, gibbons, orang-utan, Indian elephant and rhinoceros, jungle fowl, peacock.

3. Ethiopian. Africa including the Sahara Desert, Madagascar, and adjacent islands. Gorilla, chimpanzee, African elephant, rhinoceros and lion, hippopotamus, zebra, giraffe, many horned antelopes, ostrich, guinea fowl, secretary bird. Many lemurs in Madagascar.

4. Neotropical. South and Central America, Mexican lowlands, and West Indies. Llama, alpaca, peccaries, arboreal sloths, armadillos, anteater, guinea pig, the., vampire bats, rheas, toucans, curassows and guans, most hummingbirds.

5. Nearctic. North America from the Mexican highlands to the Arctic islands and Greenland. Mountain goat, prong-horned antelope, caribou, muskrat.

6. Palearctic. Eurasia south to The Himalayas, Afghanistan, Persia, and Africa north of the Sahara. Hedgehog, wild boar, fallow and roe deer.

evidently been isolated longest and is the most distinct. Its mammals include the egg-laying monotremes and many marsupials, the latter having "radiated" into a great variety of forms from huge jumping kangaroos to small burrowing marsupial moles (Chap. 32). There is much evidence to indicate that the great Asiatic land mass was for long a center whence various animal stocks originated and migrated to other regions. Thus the great flightless birds are now in southern realms, the emu and cassowaries in the Australian, the ostrich in the Ethiopian, and the rheas in the Neotropical. Such *discontinuous distribution* occurs also with the tapirs in Malaysia and Central America, the limb-less amphibians (caecilians) in the tropics of the New and Old Worlds, and others. The Palearctic and Nearctic realms are least separated, and their faunas have much in common so that they are often combined as the *Holarctic Realm.* This is characterized by the elk (red deer), moose, bison, beaver, marmots, most bears and sheep, mallard duck, golden eagle, trouts, and salmons. Few or no species or groups occur throughout any single realm, and some range in parts of two. The tiger occurs from India to northern China, the opossums from South America into the United States, and the mountain lion and rattlesnakes through both the Americas. Various subdivisions of each realm can be dis-tinguished, each with a more or less distinct fauna.

8-4. Insular faunas. *Continental islands* stand in shallow waters close to the continents from which they were probably separated in the recent geologic past. The fauna of each resembles that of the near-by mainland, having identical species or closely related subspecies. It often includes various small mammals, reptiles, and amphibians probably resident on the area at the time of its separation from the continent, since they cannot travel through salt water. *Oceanic islands* arise by volcanic ac-tivity from great depths in the sea. The fauna lacks amphibians and small mammals save for bats and occasional rodents, the latter possibly transported in native boats. Wide-ranging fishes, sea birds, and marine mammals visit their shores. The land birds and insects are peculiar and often include wingless forms, which are less likely to be swept away by storms. The Galápagos Islands under the equator off Ecuador have bats and some land birds related to mainland species. The principal land birds (Family Geospizidae) comprise about 40 local forms, mostly finchlike but with some resembling warblers and woodpeckers. One of these is unique among all animals in employing a stick as a "tool" to probe for insects! The separate islands have various species of giant land tortoises, relatives of which occur only on certain islands in the Indian Ocean. The Hawaiian Islands, also oceanic, have one bat and one rat. The bird family Drepanidae has "radiated" into various forms resembling finches, warblers, creepers, and other ecologic types. New Zealand is a continent with the characters of an oceanic island. It lacked native mammals but had flightless birds, the now extinct moas and the living kiwi. Its one reptile (*Sphenodon*) is the sole liv ng species of an otherwise extinct order, and its one "frog" likewise belongs to an ancient group.

ECOLOGICAL DISTRIBUTION

The most obvious major divisions of environments used by animals are the *salt waters, fresh waters,* and *land,* but even these grade into each other (Fig. 8-4).   Water contains 7 cc. or less of oxygen per liter, its temperature changes slowly, it has less plant food than the land, and for animals the hazard of drying occurs only in temporary waters.   The displacement support of water permits some active marine animals to be of huge size.   On land, oxygen abounds (210 cc. per liter of air), temperatures may vary widely and change abruptly, and plant food often is abundant.   There is often a dearth of moisture so that land animals must

FIG. 8-4.   An ideal section at the margin of a continent to indicate some common ecologic environments available to animals; the region marked with an asterisk * is enlarged in Fig. 8-5.

adjust their habits to avoid desiccation or must have a drought-resistant epidermis.

8-5. Salt waters.   Oceans, seas, and bays cover about 71 per cent of the earth, providing habitats that are extensive and stable.   Their physical features include

(1) Temperatures from 32°C. (89°F.) in the tropics to −2.2°C. (28°F.) in some polar regions, but rarely with an annual variation more than 5°C. (9°F.) at any one place; (2) dissolved gases varying with temperature and depth; (3) salt content averaging 3.5 per cent (NaCl, 2.35; $MgCl_2$, 0.5; Na_2SO_4, 0.4; $CaCl_2$, 0.11; KCl, 0.07; $NaHCO_3$, 0.02; and others); (4) average depth of oceans about 12,500 feet, but 35,400 feet (6.7 miles) in the greatest "deep"; (5) pressure increasing about one atmosphere for each 33 feet of depth so that animals of deep waters live under enormous pressures but these are equalized throughout their bodies; and (6) light penetrating decreasingly down to 600 feet, a trace to 3,000 feet, with complete permanent darkness below.

Marine animals include representatives of all phyla and of all classes except the centipedes, millipedes, ONYCHOPHORA, and amphibians.   The ctenophores, brachiopods, chaetognaths, echinoderms, and lower chordates are exclusively marine.   Species and individuals are most abundant near the surface and decrease with depth, but some occur down to 18,000 feet.   Dredgings by the English "Challenger" expedition gave the following results:

Depth, feet	0–200	200–1,000	1,000–2,000	2,000–3,000	3,000–4,000	4,000–5,000	Below 5,000
Numbers of species	4,400	2,050	710	600	500	340	235

Marine animals are segregated ecologically as follows:

1. **Plankton.**   Organisms that float and are moved passively by winds, waves, or currents; mostly of minute or microscopic size with surface large in relation to bulk, often with elongate body parts or ciliated; includes many protozoans and crustaceans, some mollusks, a few worms, and a host of larvae (sponges to tunicates) and microplants (diatoms, algae).

2. **Nekton.**   Animals that swim freely by their own efforts; includes squids, fishes, sea snakes and turtles, sea birds, seals, whales, etc.   Plankton and nekton animals of the open sea are termed *pelagic.*

3. **Benthos.**   Strict bottom dwellers, segregated by depth and nature of the bottom.

a. LITTORAL or SHORE.   Between the tide lines, alternately exposed to air and covered by water twice daily; strong wave action brings much food and oxygen; segregated according to nature of bottom (mud, sand, or rock) and zoned according to length of exposure between tides; population dense, protozoans to tunicates.

b. NERITIC.   Below low tide line to depths of about 600 feet (100 fathoms) on the "continental shelf"; water well oxygenated, some wave action; many animals, protozoans to fishes.

c. BATHYAL.   At depths of 600 to 6,000 feet; water quiet, progressively colder, little to no light, fewer animals.

d. ABYSSAL.   Below 6,000 feet; permanently cold quiet water, complete darkness, oxygen scant; animals scarce, usually small and dark-colored, eyes large or none, often with light-producing organs.

In the benthos, some worms, echinoderms, mollusks, and crustaceans *crawl* over the surface; many worms and some bivalve mollusks are *embedded* or *burrow;* and many sponges, hydroids, anemones, corals, bryozoans, mollusks, barnacles, and tunicates are *sessile,* or *attached* to various objects.   The littoral and neritic vary in width according to the slope of the coast; the width of the littoral also varies with the height of the tides—12 inches at Galveston, Tex., and 18½ feet at Eastport, Me.

8-6. Fresh waters.   These differ from the sea in being scattered, of lesser volume and depth, and more variable as to temperature, content of gases and salts, light penetration, turbidity, movement, and plant growth.   "Pure" waters contain mere traces of salts, but some saline and alkaline waters have large amounts.   Carbonates (especially $CaCO_3$) are usually commoner than other salts.   Some fresh waters are constant in volume, but those of arid regions often fluctuate from flood stages to small volume or dry up completely during a single season.

Fresh-water animals include many protozoans, a few sponges, coelenterates and bryozoans, many worms, rotifers and snails, various bivalve mollusks, crustaceans, larval and adult insects, and vertebrates from fishes to mammals. Many of the invertebrates produce eggs or other "resting" stages resistant to drying or freezing that may be blown about by winds or carried accidentally on the feet of waterfowl. They rarely have floating larvae, since these might be carried by streams to the sea and lost. In any one place the species present usually change markedly through the year.

1. **Running waters.** The cold mountain streams, spring-fed brooks, slower brooks and creeks, and rivers of various sizes contain mobile animals that are segregated according to the rate of water movement, temperature, oxygen content, and character of the bottom. Thus trout live only in cool well-oxygenated waters whereas carp thrive in warm and even foul waters. Inhabitants of rapid waters often are flattened or have means for holding to the bottom.

2. **Standing waters.** These comprise lakes, swamps, and marshes (Fig. 8-5), either permanent or temporary, and occur in all regions from polar and alpine areas

Fig. 8-5. Ecological distribution of some common animals of fresh water and land. In general, each keeps to a particular plant association or other subdivision of the environment.

to the tropics. Lakes in cold climates may be frozen for a long time in winter and those of temperate regions for shorter periods, but lakes of hot regions are always open. Large lakes afford more stable environments than flowing waters; they have littoral, benthic, and pelagic divisions and a plankton fauna. Water in large temperate lakes undergoes circulation because of temperature differences and wind action. In winter this involves all depths; but in summer only the surface portion circulates, over a definite plane, or thermocline, separating it from the cold, poorly oxygenated, and stagnant water below, where there are but few animals.

8-7. Land.   The interaction of many physical, climatic, and biological factors produces a wide variety of ecologic conditions on the continents and islands.

Lands differ in (1) the chemical nature and physical texture of the soil, sand, and rocks exposed on the surface; (2) the topography, which includes plains, rolling lands, hills, valleys, and mountains; and (3) the altitude which varies from basins below sea level (Death Valley) to peaks exceeding 28,000 feet (Mount Everest).   Some of the climatic variants are as follows: (1) Air temperatures vary at different places from far below freezing (where soil also freezes) to 60°C. (140°F.) on some deserts; in many localities the temperature fluctuates widely, by day or through a season, but there is only slight change in many tropical areas.   (2) Moisture as rainfall amounts to 500 inches annually in a few tropical places but only mere traces on some deserts; the moisture content of air and soil vary from complete saturation to slight amounts according to place and time of year.   (3) Winds and sunlight affect both the temperature and the moisture content of the air and ground.   The physical and climatic conditions influence the plant cover that may grow on any land area, and the plants in turn affect the animal population, particularly where the latter depend directly upon plants for food and cover.

Forests, brushlands, grasslands, deserts, and other environmental complexes are variously repeated in different zoogeographic realms, and in parts of realms, with different species of native plants and animals in

Fig. 8-6.   Comparison of the latitudinal and altitudinal zones or associations of plants that provide the appropriate environments for various animals.

each.   Thus, rain forests of Africa and of Central America may be quite unlike as to constituent species, and the same is true as between deserts in Australia and in the southwestern United States.   Similarly, an ecologic niche such as that of insects living beneath bark on trees is repeated in many regions with different species of insects and various kinds of trees.   The principal terrestrial animals are mammals, birds, reptiles, and insects, with lesser numbers of amphibians, crustaceans, mollusks, worms, and protozoans.   They are all mobile save for some parasites, and live on the land surface, on plants, or at shallow depths in the ground. The subterranean habitat affords more uniform conditions than the surface.   All animals that fly or "live" in the air return to the ground or to trees or rocks.

Ecologic classifications of land habitats are based either upon climate (temperature, rainfall, relative humidity, etc.) or upon the various associations or communities (biomes) of terrestrial plants and animals that live in more or less interdependent relations.

8-8. Plant-animal associations.   There have been many attempts to define the distribution of plants and animals according to ecological factors—without entire success.   One system of *life zones,* based mainly on temperature, recognizes a series of latitudinal zones from the tropics

FIG. 8-7.   Ecologic segregation during the nesting season of seven species of birds, all members of one family (COMPSOTHLYPIDAE, wood warblers).   Habitats named below (fern glade, etc.) and the birds above (Tolmie, etc.)   Each has a separate forage niche and does not compete with the others.   (*After Grinnell and Storer,* 1924.)

to the polar regions and an equivalent sequence of altitudinal zones from the bases to the tops of mountains (Fig. 8-6).   Such zones, whatever their exact causes, are conspicuous on mountain ranges in western North America.   Another classification, of *plant-animal associations,* considers both temperature and moisture cycles, being defined in terms of the predominant type of plant cover (which affords food and shelter for animals).   The latter associations in North and Central America are as follows.

1. **Tundra.**   Treeless Arctic region; only the surface soil thaws out in the short summer; drainage poor, many ponds, marshes, and bogs; principal plants are bog (peat) mosses, lichens, sedges, grasses, and low herbs; mammals include musk ox, Barren Ground caribou, wolf, arctic fox, weasels, lemmings, arctic hare; conspicuous resident birds are snowy owl and ptarmigan (snow grouse); many migratory waterfowl and shore birds nest here in summer but go south to winter; no reptiles.

2. **Coniferous forest** (evergreen).   South of tundra to northern United States, with extensions southward along mountain systems (Sierra-Cascade, Rocky, and Appalachian) to central Mexico; winters bleak, summers cool, precipitation moderate; spruces, firs, pines, cedars; often includes shrubs and patches of grassland; mammals include moose and woodland caribou in the north and deer and elk toward the south, also the fur bearers—red fox, Canada lynx, pine marten, fisher, wolverine—with black bear and mountain lion, snowshoe rabbit, and some small rodents; birds are various grouse, warblers, chickadees, jays, etc.; few reptiles and amphibians; trout, grayling, etc., in waters.

3. **Broad-leaved deciduous forest** (summer-green). Especially from Mississippi Valley eastward; winters cold in the north, summers warm, with rain, and humid; oaks, maples, beeches, elms, walnuts, many shrubs and herbs; white-tailed deer, gray fox, wildcat, raccoon, fox, and flying squirrels; many warblers, vireos, and other small songbirds; many snakes and amphibians.

4. **Grassland** (prairies and Great Plains). Mississippi Valley westerly, Texas to Canada; winters of severe continental cold, summers hot, thundershowers. Great areas of hardy grasses (buffalo, bluestem, grama), trees locally along streams; bison, prong-horned antelope, wolf, coyote, badger, skunk, jack rabbit (= prairie hare), cottontails in thickets, ground squirrels; prairie chicken, burrowing owl, soaring hawks, meadowlarks.

5. **Sagebrush.** Great Basin plateau between Rocky Mountains and Sierra-Cascade system. Dry, winters cold with limited rain or snow, summers hot. Sagebrush (*Artemesia tridentata*) and other bitter-flavored shrubs, bunch grasses. Pronghorned antelope, jack rabbit, ground squirrels, other burrowing rodents, coyote, badger, sage hen (largest American grouse), water birds in local ponds and marshes, many reptiles.

6. **Deserts.** Southeastern California to western Texas and southward. Soil rocky or sandy. High summer temperatures, scant water at any time. Vegetation scattered, many herbs grow and flower soon after the occasional rains; cacti, yuccas. Smaller carnivorous mammals, many rodents active by night, few birds, many lizards, some snakes, few amphibians.

7. **Tropical rain forest.** Panama and parts of Central America. Sustained moderate temperatures, abundant rainfall. Forest of evergreen broad-leaved trees, many vines, orchids, etc. Marmosas, opossums, sloths, anteaters, bats, monkeys, great variety of birds and reptiles.

8-9. Distributional changes due to mankind. Human activities have altered the geographic and ecologic distribution of many animals in various ways. The bison, mountain lion, and wolf have been killed out in most of their original ranges. Trapping has reduced beavers and other valuable fur bearers. Excessive hunting has had a like effect on ducks, shore birds, wild turkeys, and other edible game birds. Clearing land of forest to plant crops and build cities has destroyed the food and shelter of tree-using species, but the planting of trees and shrubs in parks and gardens has provided habitats for various animals that previously could not live on those sites. Draining swamps and lakes has destroyed the essential environment for muskrats, beavers, ducks, some fishes, and other species, whereas the irrigation of once dry open areas has enabled some aquatic and marsh-dwelling species to replace the rodents, reptiles, and other original denizens of those arid localities. The planting of agricultural crops over wide areas has afforded enhanced food supplies for various birds, rodents, and insects.

Man has *introduced* many animals into regions where they were not native. Some introductions were deliberate and others accidental. Many such aliens soon disappear and some remain scarce, but others have become widespread and abundant. In each case the result depends on the suitability of the new environment, the availability of an unoccupied niche, the degree of competition with native species, and the extent to which the alien is affected by predators and diseases in its new home. Fleas, lice, tapeworms, and other parasites of man and domestic animals have been accidentally spread with their hosts to new lands; some have then shifted to native hosts, as the sheep tapeworm into American deer. The European corn borer, Japanese beetle, cotton boll weevil, codling moth, Argentine ant, and garden nematode are conspicuous alien pests now on important crops in the United States. The house mouse, Norway, black, and roof rats, housefly, and bedbug are aliens that are common domestic nuisances in most civilized regions.

Some deliberate but harmful introductions include the European gray rabbit in Australia and New Zealand where it competes for sheep pasturage, the Indian mongoose taken to Jamaica and Hawaii to control rats but which destroyed native birds instead, and the "English sparrow" brought into the United States in hope of controlling the introduced gypsy and brown-tail moths but which merely has become a nuisance.

Some deliberate introductions have been useful, such as the ladybird beetles imported to control various scale insects harmful to fruit trees, the ring-necked pheasant established in many states as an additional game bird for hunting, the trout transplanted into various waters, and the striped bass, shad, and other fishes placed in lowland waters of the Pacific coast to supplement the few native food and game fishes originally there. In general, the practice of transplanting alien animals has produced more harm than benefit.

GEOLOGICAL DISTRIBUTION

8-10. Fossils. The animals living today are only part of a vast and continuing population that has inhabited the earth through millions of years (Fig. 8-8, Table 8-1). Evidence of former animals and plants is provided by *fossils*. A fossil (literally something dug up) is an organic relic preserved by natural means in rocks or softer sediments that affords information as to the character of the original organism.

Dead animals are usually soon destroyed by scavenger organisms or by decay; but if soon covered by silt beneath water, by wind-blown soil, or by volcanic dust, decomposition will be slow and the hard parts may persist. If the surrounding material later becomes rock and is neither crushed nor heated, the remains will survive for long periods. A fossil may be (1) an *unaltered hard part* such as a skeleton, a tooth, or a shell; (2) a *mold,* where hard parts once present are dissolved away by percolating waters to leave a cavity showing the original form; (3) a *petrifaction* in which the original has been replaced particle by particle with other mineral substance to preserve all fine detail; or (4) a *cast* of mineral which fills a mold to show only exterior features. Even soft parts may leave impressions in fine sediments. Some fossil records of animal activities survive as tracks, burrows, tubes, and droppings. Fossil plants are common as impressions, or casts. Special types of fossils are the carcasses (with flesh, hair, etc.) of mammoths and woolly rhinoceros frozen in tundra soils of Siberia and Alaska; skin, hair, and dung of ground sloths in Nevada caves; skeletons of giant elk and other animals in peat bogs of Ireland and elsewhere; entire remains of insects and other small

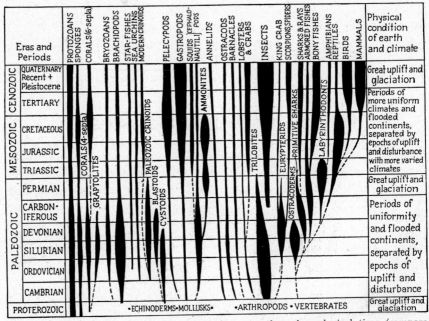

FIG. 8-8. Distribution of the major animal groups through geological time (compare Fig. 8-9 and Table 8-1). Changes in width of the black areas suggest relative numbers of species in each group during different eras and periods; broken lines suggest possible sources and time of origin for certain groups. (*After a chart by W. D. Matthew, University of California Museum of Paleontology.*)

animals embedded in amber ("fossil resin") as along the Baltic Sea; and skeletons of many species trapped in asphalt pits ("tar pools") of southern California.

Besides providing evidence of past life, fossils are used for identifying rock strata and for indicating a chronological or time sequence of such strata. They afford some information as to ancient environments and climates and as to the interrelations of bygone animals; and they furnish important data on the organic evolution of animals and plants down through time (Chap. 9). Many present-day species of animals occur also as fossils, showing that they lived in earlier geologic epochs. Fossils

Table 8-1. The Geological Column and Time Chart of Animal Life
(Compare Fig. 8-8)

Era (per cent)	Period and epoch, estimated years since each began	Principal animal life and changes	The environment
CENOZOIC (4%) — Age of Man	Quaternary Recent 20,000 Pleistocene 1,000,000	Rise of modern man; modern animals Primitive man; great mammals extinct at end	Postglacial; warm Alternate glacial cold and interglacial warm
CENOZOIC (4%) — Age of Mammals	Tertiary Pliocene Miocene Oligocene Eocene Paleocene 70,000,000	Some mammals decline Mammals at maximum; modern carnivores Rise of higher mammals Archaic mammals disappear; modern orders present Rise of archaic placental mammals and of later birds	Continents mainly above seas; Alps, Himalayas, other mountains rising; warm, gradually cooling; modern plants
MESOZOIC (9%) — Age of Reptiles	Cretaceous ("Chalk") 120,000,000	Small marsupial mammals and insectivores; toothed birds; great reptiles specialized, then disappear; first snakes; modern fishes and invertebrates; end of ammonites	Rocky Mountains and Andes forming; great swamps; cooling climates; rise of flowering plants
MESOZOIC (9%) — Age of Reptiles	Jurassic 155,000,000	First toothed birds; many giant reptiles; first lizards and crocodiles; modern sharks and bony fishes; many bivalves and ammonites	Continents near sea level; deserts widespread; many cycads
MESOZOIC (9%) — Age of Reptiles	Triassic 190,000,000	First mammals; rise of reptiles (ichthyosaurs, plesiosaurs, phytosaurs, pterodactyls, dinosaurs); end of armored amphibians; bony fishes in seas	Large rivers and flood plains locally; climate temperate to subtropical, some aridity; conifers and cycads
PALEOZOIC (24%) — Age of Amphibians	Permian 215,000,000	Primitive reptiles; decline of early amphibians; modern insects; last placoderms, trilobites, eurypterids, and other ancient marine life	Continued mountain building; widespread glaciation in Southern Hemisphere; climate various
PALEOZOIC (24%) — Age of Amphibians	Carboniferous (Pennsylvanian and Mississippian) 250,000,000	Amphibians dominant; first reptiles; insects suddenly common; brachiopods decline	Land low, sea over much of continents; mountain building at end; warm; seed ferns, lycopods
PALEOZOIC (24%) — Fishes	Devonian 350,000,000	First amphibians; many sharks and bony fishes; end of ostracoderms; tribolites decline; many mollusks; ammonites begin; first crabs and land snails	Much land submerged; some aridity on land
PALEOZOIC (24%) — Age of Invertebrates	Silurian 390,000,000	Many ostracoderms; placoderms appear; scorpions and spiders, the first air breathers on land	Much land submerged; mountain building later; first land plants
PALEOZOIC (24%) — Age of Invertebrates	Ordovician 480,000,000	Ostracoderms, the first vertebrates; corals and reefs; worms, bryozoans, some uni- and bivalve mollusks, many nautilids, echinoderms, and eurypterids	Great land submergence
PALEOZOIC (24%) — Age of Invertebrates	Cambrian 550,000,000	First marine fossils, most invertebrate phyla present; trilobites dominant; many brachiopods; probably no land life	Many lowlands; mild climates
PROTEROZOIC (25%) 925,000,000		Probably soft-bodied invertebrates, but fossils scarce; sponge spicules, worm casts	Great sediments, then much volcanic activity, and long period of erosion
ARCHEOZOIC (38%) 1,500,000,000		Possibly unicellular plants and animals; no fossils	Much igneous activity, some sediments, later much erosion

show that in the past various groups came to great prominence and later perished completely, others have a few living survivors, and some animals now numerous arose from small beginnings.   The fossil record is fragmentary at best.   Remains are more complete and numerous in rocks of later geologic periods, whereas in the older formations they are scarcer and less perfect because the rocks have been disturbed and crushed by earth movements or changed by heat.

8-11. Geological time.   Estimates of the age of fossils are derived mainly from study of radio-active minerals in fossil-bearing rocks.[1] The oldest recognizable rocks (Archeozoic) are considered to be about 1,500,000,000 years old, and the oldest rocks (Cambrian) with numerous

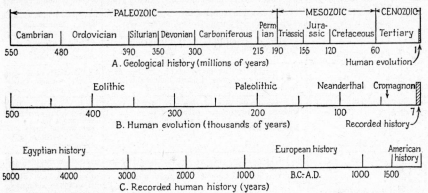

Fig. 8-9.   Time scales of the paleontologist *A*, archeologist *B*, and historian *C*; scales *A* and *B* are estimated.

fossils 550,000,000 years old.   The time since the Archeozoic may be visualized by comparing it to the distance from New York to San Francisco (about 3,300 miles).   One year is represented by 0.133 inch (3.4 mm.), a human lifetime by 9.3 inches, the Christian era by 21.5 feet, and the time since early Pleistocene when man appeared by about 2.1 miles— but a short distance down the road of time (Fig. 8-9).

[1] Uranium upon disintegration yields lead of atomic weight 206 (ordinary lead, atomic weight 207).   Precise study shows that 1 per cent of uranium thus disintegrates in 66,000,000 years.   Careful chemical analyses of the ratio of uranium to lead–206 in undisturbed rocks have provided an approximate time scale for the various strata of rocks containing fossils in the "geological column" and hence an estimate of the time when the animals there represented were living (Table 8-1).

References

Clements, F. E., and V. E. Shelford. 1939. Bio-ecology. New York, John Wiley & Sons, Inc. vii + 425 pp., 85 figs.

Elton, C. 1935. Animal ecology. Revised. London, Sidgwick & Jackson, Ltd. xx + 207 pp., 8 pls., 13 figs.

Flattely, F. W., and J. A. Walton. 1922. The biology of the seashore. London, Sidgwick & Jackson, Ltd. xvi + 336 pp., illus.

Hesse, R., W. C. Allee, and K. P. Schmidt. 1937. Ecological animal geography. New York, John Wiley & Sons, Inc. xiv + 597 pp., 135 figs.

Moore, Raymond C. 1933. Historical geology. New York, McGraw-Hill Book Co., Inc. xiii + 673 pp., 413 figs.

Pearse, A. S. 1939. Animal ecology. 2d ed. New York, McGraw-Hill Book Co., Inc. xii + 642 pp., 133 figs.

Romer, A. S. 1945. Vertebrate palaeontology. 2d ed. Chicago, University of Chicago Press. ix + 687 pp., 377 figs.

Wallace, A. R. 1876. The geographical distribution of animals. New York, Harper & Brothers. 2 vols., 1,108 pp., illus., and maps.

Welch, Paul S. 1935. Limnology. New York, McGraw-Hill Book Co., Inc. xvi + 471 pp., illus.

CHAPTER 9

ORGANIC EVOLUTION

For centuries, mankind has sought to learn how, where, and when life originated and the means whereby the many kinds of existing animals and plants have come into being. This chapter deals with some scientific theories on these matters and the evidence on which they are based.

We have no knowledge of life except on the earth. Of the billion or more "heavenly bodies" in the universe, all but a few are gaseous stars at temperatures of 2000°C. or over, or accumulations of interstellar dust not conceivably habitable, or nebulae of star aggregates at such vast distances that little can be learned of them. The remainder are mostly planets (asteroids) too small to retain an atmosphere. Of the seven major planets besides the earth in the solar system, Neptune, Uranus, Saturn, and Jupiter have cloudlike surfaces and low temperatures (−100°C.?); Mercury lacks water and atmosphere and undergoes wide temperature fluctuations; and Venus lacks water and oxygen but has moderate temperatures (+60 to −20°C.?). Only Mars, 35,000,000 miles from the earth, possibly could support life as we know it, having oxygen, water, and temperatures from 10 or 15°C. to freezing. White caps (snow?) form at the poles in the Martian winter, and some surface areas change seasonally from green or blue-gray to yellow or brown; also lines (canals?) in geometric pattern on light-colored areas have been reported. To some observers the color changes imply the presence of plant life on Mars, and the "canals" are evidence of intelligent beings on the planet. Difficulties in observation leave the subject of life on Mars one for debate.

9-1. Environments for life. The earth may have originated from the condensation of a mass of extremely hot gaseous material (nebular hypothesis) or as a molten mass (planetesimal hypothesis), in either case having been cast off from some other heavenly body. It cooled slowly, decreasing in volume, and because of its mass acquired in the course of time a gaseous atmosphere with sufficient pressure to retain water on the surface. The water filled depressions on the surface to form the oceans, which originally may have been very hot. The oldest exposed rocks indicate great volcanic activity on the then exposed lands. Life as we know it could not have existed until the waters and lands had cooled.

9-2. How life originated. The principal theories on the origin of life are as follows:

1. SPONTANEOUS GENERATION. Some or all life was earlier believed to originate from nonliving materials by spontaneous generation; this idea was discredited by experiments in the seventeenth and nineteenth centuries (Chap. 5).

2. SPECIAL CREATION. Life is presumed to have been created by some supernatural power either once, or at successive intervals, or each species is presumed to have been created separately.

3. COSMOZOIC THEORY. Protoplasm or simple living forms might have reached the earth accidentally from some other source in the universe. Life as we know it could not survive the extreme cold and dryness of interstellar space, and this theory permits no explanation as to the origin of life.

4. NATURALISTIC THEORY. When some environment on earth became suitable for life, possibly under conditions not since duplicated, some chemical mixture or compound was formed that may have had simpler living properties than any organism now existing. (In a sense, this is a special case of spontaneous generation!) Such material or protoplasm later became formed into units or cells containing differentiated parts—the earliest plants or animals. Once this stage was reached, aggregations to form multicellular groups, first of like units and later differentiated to form tissues with division of labor, become more readily understandable.

In the opinion of some biologists the characteristics of the viruses are suggestive as to the possible origin of living organisms.

9-3. Viruses. Low in the scale of living things are the forms known as viruses that occur and multiply only within cells of animals or plants and are the causative agents of various diseases. They can be cultured only in living tissues. Because of their small size (about 10 to 300 millimicrons) most viruses are invisible in ordinary microscopes, but images of them can be projected on the electron microscope. Some are larger than known bacteria and others smaller than certain protein molecules. Chemically some (influenza virus) are predominantly of nucleoprotein, whereas others (vaccinia virus) are almost as complex as a typical bacterium, containing nucleoprotein, carbohydrates, and lipoid, together with enzyme systems. Their chemical architecture is more complex than that of many proteins, yet several viruses have been reduced to crystalline form, and some may be stored for long periods at subfreezing temperatures which kill plants and animals. Viruses, however, behave as organisms. Recent researches indicate that they multiply only by genetic descent and none arises *de novo* from nonliving materials. The virus of mumps has remained true to type, as shown by clinical and epidemiological evidence, since the time of Hippocrates (460–377 B.C.), whereas the viruses producing smallpox, measles, and yellow fever give evidence of change (mutation) in virulence within the historic record. The characteristic of bacteria and viruses, the cell theory, and the atomic theory as to the constitution of matter thus come close together in considering these organisms, and the physical, chemical, and biological characteristics of "life" may depend upon structure.   Viruses, however, do not constitute the ultimate link between living and nonliving matter as was earlier thought.   They live only within the cells of plants or animals, obviously not a primitive environment.

9-4. Where life originated.   Since many simpler and lower animals are aquatic and marine and since the cells and body fluids of all animals contain salts (NaCl and others), it is inferred that life began in the oceans after the waters had cooled.   The earliest animal remains are all in rocks of marine origin.   Various marine organisms later invaded the fresh waters and land.   Some groups from the latter habitats have secondarily become marine such as the early sharks and bony fishes, the plesiosaurs and other ancient reptiles, and the whales, seals, and sirenians among living mammals.

9-5. When life originated.   An estimate by Aston places the beginning of the earth at 4,800,000,000 years ago.   The oldest recognizable surface rocks (Archeozoic) are estimated to be 1,500,000,000 years old, and the first (Cambrian) that contain numerous animal remains were probably formed 550,000,000 years ago (Chap. 8).   Since many groups of animals were then already differentiated, life may have begun fully 1,000,000,000 years ago.   Considering the entire earth, there is no conclusive evidence of any complete break in the record of life so that conditions suitable for its existence must have prevailed somewhere on the surface throughout an enormous period of time.

9-6. Evolution.   Data gathered by astronomers indicate that the stars and the solar and other systems of the universe have been undergoing gradual change, or *cosmic evolution,* through a vast length of time.   On the earth there is much evidence of gradual *geologic evolution* such as the elevation and later erosion of land masses, the transport of particles in water to form sediments, and the long-time changes in climates.

The animals now living and the many species of past times that are represented by fossils comprise a wide variety of forms progressively more complex, from the one-celled protozoans to the higher invertebrates and vertebrates.   Biologists interpret the history of animals (and plants) on the earth to have been a continuing process of *organic evolution* (L. *evolvo,* unroll), which has produced the existing species.   The doctrine of organic evolution states that existing organisms are the modified but lineal descendants of other species that lived in former geological times. This is "descent with modification," the process termed "the origin of species" by Charles Darwin.   The processes of evolution are considered to be still in operation and therefore capable of experimental study.

Existing knowledge as to the pattern of evolution is summarized in the natural classification (Fig. 1-1; Chap. 11), which is a "genealogical tree" of the Animal Kingdom. The similarities and differences between phyla and classes that provide data for classification are summarized after the lists of characteristics in Chaps. 12 to 32, and some are included in Tables 11-1 and 25-1.

Evidence for organic evolution is derived from comparative morphology, physiology, and embryology, from the study of fossils (paleontology), from animals and plants under domestication, from experimentation, and from other fields of biology. Scientists and many laymen now agree that there is abundant evidence for the *fact* that evolution has occurred, but there is difference of opinion as to the *processes,* or *methods,* by which evolution has taken place. The results of a process are naturally easier to determine than the process itself.

A. EVIDENCE OF EVOLUTION

9-7. Comparative morphology. All animals are alike in being composed of protoplasm, which is organized as cells (Chap. 3). If each species had been created separately, animals should be infinitely varied in structure, but they comprise an array of more or less distinct forms between which intermediates are lacking. Hence a system of classification is possible, in groups of smaller or larger size according to characteristics (Chap. 11). The larger groups of animals are variously unlike in appearance; but even such diverse forms as mollusks, insects, and birds agree in having organ systems for digestion, excretion, and other necessary functions. The members of any one such group show greater structural resemblance; all insects, for example, have one pair of antennae, six legs, and many other features in common. Finally, the members of a species comprise animals of like structure throughout.

In examining animals for structural evidences of evolution it is necessary to distinguish <u>characters that are of common origin (homology),</u> and hence indicative of common ancestry in descent, from purely adaptive <u>features that are of similar function (analogy) but of unlike origin.</u> Thus, the skeletal elements in the wings of bats, birds, and pterodactyls (extinct flying reptiles) are homologous in that all are modifications of the common pattern of fore limb in land vertebrates (Fig. 9-1). The wings of insects, however, are only analogous to those of vertebrates; although used for flight, they are derived as extensions of the body wall.

By studies in comparative morphology, embryology, and paleontology it is possible to trace the derivation of lateral appendages of vertebrates from lateral folds on the bodies of lower chordates (Figs. 25-11, 27-2) to the fins of sharks and bony fishes. The fins of some fossil fishes (Crossopterygii) furthermore contain skeletal elements that may be homologized with bones in the limbs of land vertebrates (Fig. 9-3). The limbs

of various species show a wide range in adaptive modifications for special
uses by changes in length or by fusion or reduction of parts (Fig. 9-2).
All, however, are homologous, being derived from the pentadactyl limb
(Gr. *penta*, five + *dactyl*, finger).

Among the vertebrates, from lowest to highest and including man,
homologies are present in practically every organ system. The comparative account of structural systems in Chap. 4 offers some of the most
striking evidence for evolution (compare also Chaps. 25 to 33). Thus,
in all vertebrates: (1) the nervous system includes an anterior brain with
comparable divisions, paired cranial nerves, a single dorsal nerve cord,

Fig. 9-1.   Analogy between wings of insects and vertebrates, of like function but different
origin.   Homology in the wing bones of vertebrates, all derived from the common pattern
of fore limb in land vertebrates, but variously modified.   Pterodactyl (extinct reptile) with
elongate 5th finger; bird with 1st and 5th lacking, 3d and 4th partly fused; bat with 2d to
5th fingers elongate.

and paired spinal nerves to each body somite; (2) the brain case is
followed by a jointed spinal column of separate vertebrae that support
the body and enclose the nerve cord; (3) the digestive tract is always
ventral to the vertebrae and always includes a liver and pancreas as the
major digestive glands; (4) the ventrally placed heart connects to a closed
system of vessels that contain blood with both white and red corpuscles;
and (5) the excretory and reproductive systems show many homologous
features. In all these organs there is agreement as to position in the body
and general form and even in the microscopic structure of the tissues in
each system. Because of this situation a frog, reptile, or mammal serves
equally well in obtaining a basic knowledge of vertebrate anatomy.

The organ systems, however, are not exactly alike but show progressive
changes from fishes to mammals. In the brain the trend (Fig. 4-23) is
toward enlargement of the cerebral hemispheres, which are centers of

higher mental activities, and also of the cerebellum, or center of coordination.   The heart is two-chambered in fishes, three-chambered in amphibians and most reptiles, and four-chambered in birds and mammals,

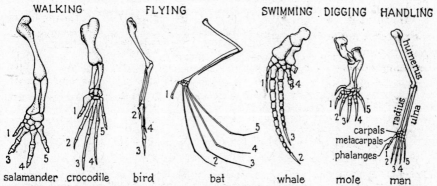

FIG. 9-2.   Homology and adaptation in bones of the left fore limb in land vertebrates. The limbs are *homologous* in being composed of comparable bones (humerus, carpals, etc.), which in each kind of animal are *adapted* for special uses by differences in the length, shape, and bulk of the various bones; 1–5, digits or "fingers."

eventually separating completely the venous and arterial blood (Figs. 4-16, 9-4).   In the excretory organs, drainage of wastes is first from the coelom and later only from the blood (Fig. 4-19).

FIG. 9-3.   Probable evolution of the fore limb.   *A*. Lobed fin of a Devonian crossopterygian fish.   *B*. Hypothetical intermediate.   *C*. Limb of an early amphibian. *H*, humerus; *R*, radius; *U*, ulna; *pr*, prepollex; 1–5, digits. (*After Gregory*, 1928.)

In like manner many homologies are found among invertebrates.   All the arthropods, for example, have segmented bodies with chitinous covering, a paired series of jointed appendages, a double ventral nerve cord, and many other features in common.   A double ventral nerve cord

FIG. 9-4.   Homology and embryonic sequence in the aortic arches and heart chambers of vertebrates.   *Above.*   Six pairs of arches develop in the embryos of all vertebrates, but parts indicated by dotted lines later disappear.   In land vertebrates the third pair always forms the carotid arteries; the fourth becomes the systemic arches to the dorsal aorta, but only the right persists in birds and the left in mammals; the sixth arch always forms the pulmonary arteries.   *Below.*   The embryonic heart always begins with one auricle (*A*) and one ventricle (*V*); it remains thus in fishes; the auricle becomes divided (*RA, LA*) in amphibians; the ventricle becomes partly divided in reptiles and completely so (*RV, LV*) in birds and mammals.   In embryos of higher forms the arches and chambers develop progressively through the succession of stages shown.   Arrows indicate paths of blood flow.   (Compare Fig. 4-16.)

is moreover present also in annelid worms, primitive mollusks, and some other invertebrates.

9-8. Comparative physiology.   The tissues and fluids of organisms show many basic similarities in physiological and chemical properties that parallel morphologic features.

1. From the hemoglobin in vertebrate blood, oxyhemoglobin crystals can be obtained; their crystalline structure, as shown by Reichert and Brown, parallels that of vertebrate classification based on body structure. Those of each species are distinct, but all from a genus have some common characteristic.   Furthermore, those of all birds have certain resemblances but differ from crystals obtained from blood of mammals or reptiles.

2. The precipitin tests are reactions of the blood serum.   In such tests human serum is least distinct from that of anthropoid apes (gorilla, chimpanzee, etc.), more so from other primates (monkeys), and still more distinct from that of other mammals.   Serums of mammals, in turn, are more sharply distinguished from those of other vertebrates.

3. Certain hormones derived from endocrine glands show like reactions when injected into widely different animals.   The thyroid gland in cattle controls their rate of metabolism.   Thyroid gland of cattle may be fed to human beings deficient in their own thyroid secretion to speed up their metabolism.   If beef or sheep thyroid is fed to frog tadpoles from

which the thyroid gland has been removed, the tadpoles will function normally and later metamorphose into frogs.

4. Many of the individual digestive enzymes present in different animals are essentially alike in their physiological action. The enzyme trypsin, which acts upon proteins, occurs in many animals from protozoans to man; and amylase, which acts on starches, is present from sponges to mammals.

9-9. Comparative embryology. Except for some specialized types of reproduction, every multicellular animal originates as a zygote, or fertilized egg (Chap. 5). The egg of each species of animal has the distinctive ability to produce an individual of that species, but there are many features of embryonic development common to any large group of animals. Fertilized eggs segment, pass through a blastula stage and a two-layered gastrula stage, and then become variously differentiated. In many kinds of invertebrates the egg yields a trochophore larva (Fig. 18-1). Eggs of vertebrates differ somewhat in mode of cleavage according to the amount of yolk present (Fig. 5-9), but the early embryos of all of them are much alike; later, those of each class become recognizable, and still later family and species characters become evident (Fig. 9-5). The beginning embryo in a hen's egg (Fig. 5-12) has at first the vertebrate characteristics of a notochord, dorsal nervous system, and somites; later, it acquires bird features such as a beak and wings; and, much later, there appear the features of a chick instead of a pigeon or duck.

A fish embryo develops paired gill slits, gills, aortic arches, and a two-chambered heart; these all persist in the adult to serve in aquatic respiration. Comparable structures appear in a frog embryo and are necessary during the fishlike life of the frog larva in water. When the larva transforms into an air-breathing frog, however, the gills and gill slits disappear, lungs become functional to serve for respiration in air, the aortic arches are altered to serve the adult structure, and the heart becomes three-chambered to effect circulation of the blood both to the body and to the lungs. The amphibian thus begins with certain fishlike features necessary to the aquatic larva, and later these are altered for terrestrial life. Astonishingly, the early embryos of reptiles, birds, and mammals also develop a fishlike pattern of gill slits, aortic arches, and two-chambered heart (Figs. 5-12, 9-6) although none of these vertebrates has an aquatic larva and all respire exclusively by lungs after birth. The embryonic gill slits soon close; the multiple aortic arches become the carotids and other arteries (Fig. 9-4); and the heart soon becomes three-chambered, later having four chambers in birds and mammals.

The presence of gill slits and multiple aortic arches in embryos of reptiles, birds, and mammals cannot be explained satisfactorily by a theory of special creation, but under a theory of evolution they are readily understandable as ancestral relics. The fossil record indicates that aquatic, gill-breathing vertebrates preceded the air-breathing land forms. In point of time the sequence of their appearance was fishes, amphibians, reptiles, birds, and mammals (Fig. 8-8). The amphibians represent a transitional phase, through which each frog still passes from aquatic respiration to air breathing (Fig. 2-20).

fish   salamander   turtle   chicken   pig   cow   rabbit   man

Fig. 9-5. Series of vertebrate embryos in three successive and comparable stages of development. *Top.* All are much alike in the earliest stage. *Middle.* Differentiation is evident but the four mammals (at right) are quite similar. *Bottom.* Later the distinctive characteristics of each become evident. (*After Haeckel, 1891.*)

Many other features in embryonic development and adult structure have a similar significance. In all land vertebrates the first embryonic gill pouch on each side is converted into a Eustachian tube connecting the pharynx and cavity of the middle ear. In a fish the gill region is supported by a series of visceral (branchial) arches (Chap. 28); and in higher vertebrates, including man, certain cartilages and bones of the jaws, middle ear, and larynx are derived from the embryonic "visceral arches" (Fig. 9-7).

The zoological position of some animals that are of degenerate form in the adult stages has been established only by study of their embryonic and larval stages. The larvae of barnacles (Fig. 22-14) show that these animals belong among the crustaceans, and the peculiar parasitic barnacle *Sacculina* (Fig. 22-16) can be recognized as a crustacean only during its larval existence.   Likewise, the tunicates (Fig. 25-7) were found to be chordates only by a study of their larval characteristics; the degenerate form of the adults gives no clue to their real position among animals.

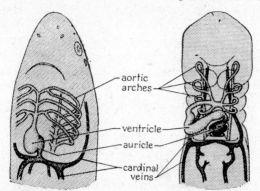

FIG. 9-6.   Embryological evidence of evolution.   *Left.*   Adult shark.   *Right.*   3 mm· human embryo.   With two-chambered heart, multiple aortic arches, and cardinal veins· (Compare Figs. 4-13, 4-15, 4-16, 9-4, 27-4.)

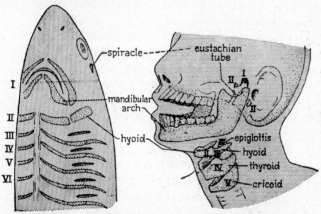

FIG. 9-7.   Derivatives of embryonic visceral arches in man compared with the branchial arches (I–VI) supporting the gills in an adult shark.   In man these become: I, lower jaw (only Meckel's cartilage) and malleus and incus of middle ear; II, styloid process of skull, stylo-hyoid ligament, lesser horn of hyoid, and stapes of middle ear; III, greater horn of hyoid; IV, thyroid cartilage of larynx and part of epiglottis; V, cricoid and arytenoid cartilages of larynx.   Auditory ossicles shown in heavy black.   The human maxilla (upper jaw) is a membrane bone of later origin.

These and many other facts illustrate the following "laws" of embryonic development formulated by Von Baer (German, 1792–1876): (1) General characters appear before special characters.   (2) From the more general the less general and finally the special characters develop. (3) An animal during development departs progressively from the form of other animals. (4) The young stages of an animal are like the young (or embryonic) states of other animals lower in the scale, but not like the adults of those animals. The oft-quoted "theory of recapitulation," or "biogenetic law," of Haeckel (German, 1834–1919) states that an individual organism in its development (ontogeny) tends to recapitulate the stages passed through by its ancestors (phylogeny). Haeckel's theory has been both stoutly defended and vigorously criticized by different biologists; Von Baer's "laws" provide a more accurate statement. Many factors complicate the picture of embryonic development in its bearing on evolution. To the ancient (palingenetic) characters of embryos have been added other modern (cenogenetic) characters. Some of the latter may appear early in the development of an individual, as is the case of the embryonic membranes of reptiles, birds, and mammals. These membranes are "new" features, not present in the lower vertebrates, but essential for protecting embryos of land vertebrates from their earliest stages, and they appear very early during development (Fig. 5-14). Another complication is the omission or "telescoping" of developmental features in relation to special environmental conditions, such as the absence of floating larvae in fresh-water crustaceans and the omission of larval stages of some tree-dwelling frogs (*Eleutherodactylus*) and some land salamanders (PLETHODONTIDAE).

9-10. Vestigial organs. Structures without use and of reduced size are present in many animals and are termed *vestigial organs.*

From the standpoint of special creation these are difficult to explain; from that of evolution they are obviously features in the process of disappearing from living organisms that were functional and necessary in their ancestors. Various species of cave-dwelling fishes, crayfishes, and insects have the eyes reduced or absent, whereas their respective relatives that live out in the open possess eyes. Traces of the pelvic girdle and hind limbs occur in boas (Fig. 30-9) and in whales. Whalebone whales lack teeth as adults, but tooth buds occur in their embryos. "Scarce as hens' teeth" does not apply to bird embryos, which have transient tooth buds; certain fossil birds (Fig. 31-17) had teeth as adults. The flightless kiwi (Fig. 31-19) of New Zealand has degenerate wings with only rudimentary bones, and the great moas of that land lacked wings completely. The living horses have splint bones, which are vestiges of toes present in ancestral horses (Fig. 9-13).

Fully 90 vestigial features are present in the human body according to Wiedersheim; conspicuous examples are shown in Fig. 9-8. The horse, rodents, and some other mammals have a large caecum or appendix as an accessory digestive chamber. In man the appendix is a slender vestige about $2\frac{1}{2}$ inches long that serves no useful function and often is a site of infection requiring surgical removal. The external ears of mammals are moved by special muscles; lacking need for such movement in man the muscles are usually reduced and nonfunctional.   In the inner angle of the human eye is a whitish membrane (plica semilunaris) representing the transparent nictitating membrane, or third eyelid, to be seen in the cat, bird, frog, and other land vertebrates.   The human "wisdom teeth," or posterior molars, are smaller and more variable than the other molars and irregular as to time or manner of eruption; this suggests that they are becoming useless and may eventually disappear.

9-11. Paleontology.   Important evidence of evolution comes from the study of *fossils.*   The nature of fossils, means for estimating their age, and their distribution in time are discussed in Chap. 8 (see Table 8-1; Figs. 8-8, 8-9).   Various fossils are discussed in Chaps. 12 to 32, and the fossil history of man is outlined in Chap. 33.

Fig. 9-8.   Some vestigial structures in the human body.   (*Partly after Kahn.*)

Leonardo da Vinci (Italian, 1452–1519) was the first to recognize that fossils were evidences of animal life in the past.   The first important studies of fossils were made by the French comparative anatomist, Georges Cuvier (1769–1832).   In 1800 he published an account of fossil elephants, relating them to living forms; later, in a classification of fishes, he employed both living and fossil species.   Cuvier, however, believed in special creation, and it was Darwin who first showed that fossils were evidence of the continuity and evolution of organisms. *Paleontology* (Gr. *palaios*, ancient), the study of fossils, is now an important science that links zoology and geology and provides many facts of evolution.

The geological record of past life is variously imperfect.   It is like the remnants of a book that lacks all the beginning chapters, contains only scattered pages or parts of pages in the central part, and retains an increasing number of intact pages or parts of chapters toward the end.   Any and all records of past life result from a succession of fortunate events, thus: (1) The remains of a dead animal escape destruction and (2) become buried in sediment or ash (3) that survives undue heating, crushing, or folding such as would destroy the fossil; (4) the sediment or rock becomes elevated as a part of the land and (5) escapes destructive erosion by water or wind; finally (6) the fossil becomes exposed or is dug out and comes to the attention of a paleontologist. Some fossil remains are complete, but many are fragmentary, and all the known fossils represent only a fraction of the many plant and animal species that have lived in the past. Some species or groups may never have become entombed as fossils because

Fig. 9-9. A sample of the geological column: Succession of strata in north wall of the Grand Canyon, Arizona (compare Table 8-1). Eras and periods are marked (names in parentheses are of local rock formations). One fault line is shown. Two unconformities (*Un*) mark long gaps in the record; below each the rocks were deformed, elevated, and finally far eroded before the layer next above was deposited. This site has no rocks of the Ordovician, Silurian, and Devonian periods or of the Mesozoic and Cenozoic eras. (*Photo by U.S. Geological Survey.*)

they were soft-bodied or because they lived where fossilization could not occur. Many fossils have been destroyed by alteration of the rocks or by erosion, and any fossils now in rocks deep in the earth or under the sea are inaccessible.

9-12. Invertebrates. Rocks formed prior to Cambrian time have since been much folded and distorted so that they reveal few organic relics. Yet animals must then have been in existence for a long time, because the

Cambrian rock strata, the oldest with many fossils, contain remains of a wide variety of well-differentiated invertebrates. These include protozoans, sponges, jellyfishes worms, brachiopods, echinoderms (sea cucumbers, crinoids), mollusks (gastropods, cephalopods), and arthropods (crustaceans, trilobites). The beginnings of most invertebrate phyla and of some classes cannot be traced, but the rise, continuance, and decline or extinction of others is well recorded. The trilobites (Fig. 22-17) were dominant when the record opens in the Cambrian; they increased in numbers and variety, then disappeared entirely in the Permian when there was continental elevation, greater aridity, and glaciation. The lamp shells (BRACHIOPODA, Fig. 18-13) were abundant throughout the

FIG. 9-10.　Representative fossils; covering matrix of rock removed. *Left*. Fossil bone bed from the Miocene of Nebraska containing remains of rhinoceroses and other mammals. *Right*.　Accumulation of Devonian trilobites.　(*From Moore, Historical geology.*)

Paleozoic era (456 genera) and less numerous in the Mesozoic (177 genera) but persist today with about 70 genera and 225 species. The living *Lingula* is much as it was in the Ordovician, 400,000,000 years ago, and is perhaps the oldest living genus of animals. The ammonites (Class CEPHALOPODA) began in the Devonian. Like the living pearly nautilus (Chap. 20) their shells comprise a succession of chambers, with the animal in the largest and terminal chamber. The gross form of the shell changed through time (Figs. 9-11, 9-12), and the sutures between successive chambers are simpler in the older stocks and more complex in those of later periods. The first chambers formed by some of the later ammonites were simple, like those of their ancestors. Then, surprisingly, some of the last of the ammonites had simpler sutures again and their shells were coiled in the young but straight in the adult parts. Finally the entire line of ammonites ended in the Cretaceous. The great Phylum ARTHROPODA was represented by the aquatic crustaceans, trilobites, and king crabs in

Bactrites   Anarcestes   Pronorites   Ceratites   Phylloceras   Ancyloceras

Fig. 9-11.   Trends in evolution of the fossil ammonites (Phylum Mollusca, Class Cephalopoda), showing the coiling and later uncoiling of the shell and the changes in form of
the sutures (shown by fine lines; black in *E*).   All reduced, but not to same scale.   (*From
University of California Museum of Paleontology.*)

Fig. 9-12.   An interpretation of evolution in the cephalopods.   Nautiloidea (solid lines),
Dibranchiata (broken lines), and †Ammonoidea (dots and dashes).   (Compare Figs. 9-11,
20-16).   (*After Raymond, Prehistoric life, reprinted by permission of the President and Fellows
of Harvard College.*)

the Cambrian period.   Scorpions, the first air-breathing and land animals,
appeared in the Silurian.   The insects appear suddenly in the Carboniferous, as several differentiated orders, and give no ready clue as to which
arthropod type they stem from.

9-13. Vertebrates.   The origins of the vertebrates are shrouded by
imperfections in the geological record.   Early stocks are thought to have
been in fresh waters, from which no fossil-bearing strata have survived.

The oldest vertebrate relics were evidently washed down to become embedded in marine deposits.

No vertebrate remains have been found in Cambrian rocks. Ordovician strata contain fragments possibly of ostracoderms, which were ancestral to cyclostomes, the lowest living vertebrates, without jaws or paired appendages. Silurian deposits have many ostracoderms and also spines and plates probably of placoderms, the earliest jawed vertebrates. By early Devonian time placoderms were abundant but ostracoderms less numerous. Further along in Devonian, however, both sharks (CHONDRICHTHYES) and bony fishes appeared and then became abundant. Amphibians, with paired limbs, also are in the record of late Devonian. The reptiles undoubtedly began during the Carboniferous because by the end of that period there were already several specialized types. Thenceforth, from the Permian to the Cretaceous, they were the dominant animals of land, sea, and fresh waters. Many became large in size, such as the brontosaurs, dinosaurs, and plesiosaurs. All the great reptiles disappeared at the end of the Cretaceous. Meanwhile, the first small reptile-like mammals began in the Triassic, and the first known birds appeared in the Jurassic. Early in the Tertiary (Paleocene) the mammals blossomed into a great variety, including some existing orders and others since vanished. The early forms were replaced by more modern types, and the mammals reached a peak of diversity in the Miocene. Since then they have declined, a considerable number having become extinct at the end of the Pleistocene, just preceding the present or Recent period in which we live.

Thus, despite the fragmentary nature of the early record, ascending the geological column the vertebrate types appear in an orderly time sequence that corresponds to the increasing structural complexity of groups living today.

9-14. Horses. The Family EQUIDAE provides about the most complete record of evolution in an animal series (Fig. 9-13), leading to the existing horses, asses, and zebras of the Old World. Much of their ancestral development occurred in North America, but horses died out there late in the Pleistocene (or early in Recent time), for reasons unknown. The wild horses of the western states in the last five centuries all derived from stocks that were brought in and escaped from early explorers and settlers.

The principal features of change in the horses through time include the following: (1) increase in size from that of a cat to some larger than existing horses; (2) enlargement and lengthening of the head anterior to the eyes; (3) increased length and mobility of the neck; (4) changes of the premolar and molar teeth from types suited for browsing, with roots, short crowns, and surface cusps, to those suited for grazing, with practically no roots, tall crowns, and many enamel ridges, accompanied by deepening of the lower jaw; (5) elongation of the limbs for speedy running, but with loss of rotational movement, and including fusion of bones in each foreleg to provide better hinge joints, together with support of the weight on the radius and tibia; and (6) reduction of the toes from five to one elongate toe (third) on each foot, which is covered by a hoof ("claw");

FIG. 9-13. Evolution of the horse. *Top row.* Progressive change in size and conformation from the little forest-dwelling *Eophippus* of the Eocene epoch to the large modern plains-inhabiting *Equus* (numbers are height at shoulder in inches). *Second row.* Bones of hind and fore feet showing reduction in lateral toes (solid black), from *Eohippus* with three hind and four front toes to *Equus* with only the third toe functional on each foot; the second and fourth represented by splints. *Third row.* Skulls showing changes in size and outline, and closing of postorbital process. *Bottom row.* Grinding surfaces of second upper molar showing increasing complexity of enamel pattern (black). (*Top row adapted from R. S. Lull, Fossils, courtesy of The University Society, New York; others from W. D. Matthew, 1913, and R. A. Stirton, 1940.*)

the lateral toes dwindle as "dew claws," and finally only small bones of the second and fourth toes persist as splints. By these changes the horse became a long-legged swift-running mammal suited to live and feed on open grasslands, with tall teeth having many enamel edges to grind harsh grassy vegetation through a relatively long life.

The real origin of horses is unknown. The record begins with †*Eohippus* in the lower Eocene of North America and Europe. It was a browsing forest dweller, about 11 inches high at the shoulder, with a short neck and head and a full set of 44 small short-crowned and rooted teeth that lacked cement. The front foot had four functional toes but the hind foot only three, the first and fifth toes being represented by tiny splints. †*Mesohippus* of the Oligocene was the size of a sheep, with taller but rooted molars and three functional toes on each foot; the lateral toes were smaller and only one splint (fifth) persisted on the forefoot. By Miocene time, several lines (†*Parahippus*, †*Merychippus*) had developed, including both browsing and grazing types. During Pliocene there were several distinct groups of horses (†*Pliohippus*, etc.) grazing on the plains of North America. Some spread to Eurasia, and †*Hippidium* to South America, the latter giving rise to some short-limbed genera that did not survive the Pleistocene. The lateral toes were reduced to dew claws that did not touch the ground. The cheek teeth were longer, with short roots, more folding of the enamel, and cement between the folds. Finally the earliest one-toed horses developed, during the Pliocene in North America, and later they spread to all the continents except Australia. In Pleistocene, there were ten or more species (*Equus*) of various sizes in North America, all of which disappeared in prehistoric time.

9-15. Elephants. The stout bones and teeth of elephants and their allies have left a well-documented record of evolution in the Order Proboscidea (Fig. 9-14). This begins in the late Eocene of northern Egypt with †*Moeritherium*, a creature about 2 feet high having a long narrow head that was elevated posteriorly and possibly a flexible snout since the nasal openings were behind the tip of the jaw. It had 36 teeth, the second incisors in each jaw were short tusks, and the molar teeth had crossrows of cusps. †*Palaeomastodon* of the Oligocene in Egypt was larger, with the skull and brain case more elevated and the nostrils farther back; there was probably a long snout or proboscis. The tusks were longer, other incisors and the canines had disappeared to leave 26 teeth, and all cheek teeth were functional at the same time. This and other forms (†*Phiomia*) spread to India and later to Eurasia. †*Trilophodon* of the Miocene reached North America. It had a long lower jaw, long upper tusks, and only two molars in each jaw, but these were bigger and had more transverse rows of cusps. Because of the length of its jaw, †*Trilophodon* may not have been a direct ancestor of later forms. Other collateral lines developed among the proboscidians but did not survive to later epochs. The long-faced †*Gomphotherium* of the Miocene and Pliocene was of wide occurrence and may have given rise to both elephants and mastodons.

No proboscidians are now native to the Americas, but four types inhabited North America during Pleistocene time, and mastodons lived in South America during the late Pliocene and Pleistocene. The mastodon (†*Mastodon americanus*) was about 9½ feet tall and had long coarse

hair.   It inhabited forests of Canada and the United States and probably
was hunted by the earliest Indians.   The mammoth (*Elephas* †*primigenius*) that ranged across the Northern Hemisphere was about 9 feet high
and covered with dense wool.   It was hunted by Paleolithic men in
Europe who pictured it in cave drawings; remains of mammoths have been
recovered in the frozen soil of Siberia and Alaska.   The Columbian elephant (*E.* †*columbi*) was 11 feet high and had incurved tusks; in early
Pleistocene it roamed the warmer parts of North America south to Florida
and the Mexican tablelands.   The huge imperial elephant (*E.* †*imperator*)
grew to 13½ feet high and was probably a plains dweller from Pliocene to

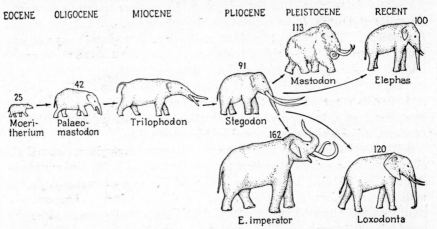

Fig. 9-14.   Phylogeny of the elephants, showing increase in size and in relative length
of tusks and proboscis since the Eocene epoch.   Additional lines of descent that later
became extinct are omitted.   Numbers indicate height at shoulder in inches.   (*Adapted
from Osborn, and from R. S. Lull, Fossils, The University Society, New York.*)

mid-Pleistocene.   The genus *Elephas* includes the living elephants of
India; both it and *Loxodonta* in Africa have two large tusks in the upper
jaw and but one molar functional in each jaw at a time.   The molars
have many transverse ridges of enamel, between which the softer dentine
and cement is worn down by the coarse foods.

   9-16. Human evolution.   Many kinds of evidence (Chap. 33) indicate
that man is a product of evolution.   In both gross and microscopic *structure* the human body resembles closely that of the anthropoid apes, is
much like that of other primates, and has much in common with mammals generally (compare Figs. 4-5, 4-11, 32-2 to 32-4).   Homologies with
other vertebrates are present in every organ system; some vestigial organs
of man have already been mentioned (Fig. 9-8).   Strictly human characteristics such as the upright posture, opposable thumbs, flattened vertical
face, scant body hair, and greatly increased brain are differences in degree
and not in kind from other mammals.   Many relationships in *function*

parallel those of structure; in both man and anthropoids there are comparable blood groups, human blood can be distinguished by immunological tests from all others except anthropoids, and some mouth protozoans are common to man and other primates. The earlier *embryonic development* of man is essentially as for other mammals (Fig. 9-5) and includes temporary gill slits and multiple aortic arches (Fig. 9-6). The *fossil record* of mankind includes a series of types (Fig. 33-8) that gradually approach the form of existing human races. Man's superior attainments over all other organisms are primarily matters of habits and behavior such as social organization, modification of the environment to his own advantage, development of tools and of language, and the ability to transmit learning by teaching.

Fig. 9-15. Evolution of molar teeth in elephants as to size and type of grinding surface, $\times \frac{1}{8}$. (*From Moore, Historical geology.*)

B. THEORIES OF EVOLUTION

Any attempt to account for existing organisms and fossils must explain their origins, their likenesses and differences, their adaptations to various environments, and their manner of occurrence on the earth. Theories of special creation assume organisms to have been produced by a supernatural agency that provided for all the above-mentioned features. Theories of organic evolution postulate that since life began on the earth it has been continuous and that later organisms have been derived from earlier forms by the inheritance of variations, either large or small, and induced either by the environment or by processes within the animals. Evolutionary processes are considered to be slow in action and therefore difficult to test experimentally.

Primitive human races have various myths to "explain" the origin of man and animals by the creative acts of supernatural powers. Until the last century most persons, including scientists such as Linnaeus, Cuvier, Agassiz, and Owen, believed that species had been created separately. Cuvier thought that the disappearance of fossil species had resulted from a series of catastrophes, the last being the Biblical flood, and that after each of these the earth had been repopulated by new special creations of higher types. The belief in catastrophes was dispelled by the Scottish geologist Charles Lyell (1797–1875) who showed in his *Principles of Geology* (1830–1833) that the geological processes of sedimentation, uplift, and erosion are essentially continuous.

Various early Greek philosophers had vague notions of an evolutionary process, but Aristotle (384–322 B.C.), the first notable zoologist, thought that organisms were molded by a "perfecting principle," and his ideas prevailed for centuries (Chap. 10). Buffon (French, 1707–1788) was the first modern biologist to discard the concept of special creation. He came to believe that animals were plastic, that small variations produced by the environment were accumulated to make larger differences, and that each animal in the ascending series of types was transformed from some simpler ancestor. Erasmus Darwin (English, 1731–1802), grandfather of Charles Darwin, added the further idea that functional responses to external stimuli were inherited.

9-17. Lamarck and the inheritance of acquired characteristics. The first general theory of evolution was proposed by Jean Baptiste de Lamarck (French, 1744–1829), a distinguished anatomist and student of classification. His theory was outlined in 1801 and set forth fully in his *Philosophie zoologique* (1809). Lamarck recognized a fundamental continuity underlying the diverse kinds of animals and believed that there had been a progressive development of forms. His theory, briefed from his own words, is as follows: The environment affects the shape and organization of animals; frequent continuous use develops and enlarges any organ, while by permanent disuse it weakens until it finally disappears; all acquisitions or losses wrought through influence of the environment and hence through use and disuse are preserved by reproduction.

Lamarck's theory may be illustrated by two of his examples. Birds, he assumed correctly, were originally terrestrial. A land bird going to seek food in water would spread its toes to strike the water in moving about. Thus the skin at the bases of the toes would be continually stretched, and muscular movements of the legs would promote an extra flow of blood to the feet. In consequence, the skin would become enlarged as webs between the toes, such as are to be seen in ducks, pelicans, and other water birds. Disuse he exemplified by the structure of a snake. In crawling through grass its body would be elongated repeatedly to pass through narrow spaces and the legs would not be used. Long legs would interfere with crawling, and four short legs would be incapable of moving the body. Legs are characteristic of reptiles, and yet the snakes lost theirs. The eyes became lateral or dorsal the better to see when on the ground, and the tongue developed as a protrusible sensory organ to serve in detecting objects in front of the snake.

There is little or no reliable evidence for Lamarck's theory of the "inheritance of acquired characteristics," and it has little support today. The muscles of an athlete increase in strength and bulk with extensive use but recede if exercise is discontinued; children never inherit such acquired characteristics of a father.   The docking of tails in horses, sheep, and bulldogs has been practiced through many generations, but none of these mutilations is ever inherited.   Pavlov trained mice to come for food at the sound of a bell and claimed that fewer and fewer trials were needed to teach mice of succeeding generations; and MacDougall has claimed similar results in the training of rats.   Neither of these experiments nor many others designed to test this theory have produced convincing results.   This conclusion is not surprising when it is recalled that a new organism develops from the germ cells of its parents, not from the somatic cells of the latter.   The germ cells are set aside early in the growth of an individual and are subjected to little or no effect from the body cells or environment (Chap. 5).   This was demonstrated by Castle and Phillips who replaced the ovaries of a white guinea pig with those from a black female.   The former was then bred twice to a black male.   All the six young produced were black and homozygous.

9-18. Darwin and the theory of natural selection.   Charles Darwin (1809–1882) was a methodical painstaking English naturalist with a broad vision.   As a young man he served (1831–1835) as naturalist on the "Beagle," a vessel that explored South America, the Galápagos Islands, and other regions.   From his detailed notes and studies he wrote excellent works on barnacles, mammalian fossils, geology, and coral reefs.   Many of the facts of animal distribution and of the relations between living and fossil animals learned in his travels led him to consider the origin of species.   He began taking notes on the subject in 1837 and the next year read Malthus's *Essay on Population*, wherein that author showed how populations increase in geometric ratio until checked by limiting factors.   Darwin then recognized the struggle for existence within all populations, and he concluded that in such a struggle favorable variations would be preserved and unfavorable ones eliminated.   In 1844 he wrote out a summary of his theory but continued to gather data from original researches and observations by himself and many other persons.   Meanwhile Alfred Russel Wallace (1823–1913), an English naturalist, while studying the rich fauna and flora of the Malay Archipelago, independently and rapidly arrived at similar conclusions.   In 1858 he sent an essay on the subject to his friend Darwin.   Through the interest of Charles Lyell and the botanist Joseph Hooker, Wallace's essay and a brief of Darwin's conclusions were published together in the same year.   In 1859 Darwin issued his theory in a book entitled *The Origin of Species by Natural Selection, or the Preservation of Favoured Races in the Struggle for Life.*

This was the most important book of the nineteenth century.   It contains (1) overwhelming evidence of the fact of evolution, and (2) arguments for natural selection as the process.   The doctrine of evolution was not original with Darwin, but his convincing presentation quickly won the support of scientists and of many laymen, which Lamarck had failed to do. Unscientific attacks on "Darwinism," as the theory was called, continued until after the author's death. In the meantime, there began a great scientific search for additional facts bearing on the theory, and there was much speculation on natural selection.

The essence of Darwin's theory is as follows:

1. *Variations* of all grades are present among individuals and species in nature.
2. By the *geometric ratio of increase* the numbers of every species tend to become enormously large; yet the population of each remains approximately constant because under various factors of climate, competition, etc., many individals are eliminated.
3. This involves a *struggle for existence;* individuals having variations unsuited to the particular conditions in nature are eliminated, whereas those whose variations are favorable will continue to exist and reproduce.
4. A *process of natural selection* therefore is operative, which results in:
5. The *survival of the fittest,* or "the preservation of favored races."

9-19. Variation. Among animals that reproduce sexually no two individuals (save identical twins) are exactly alike. The individuals of every species vary in size, proportions, coloration, external and internal structure, physiology, and habits. Darwin recognized the widespread occurrence of variations; his theory assumes but does not explain their origins. In his day the laws of inheritance (Chap. 6) were unknown, and often he could not distinguish the heritable variations, which alone are important in evolution, from nonheritable variations produced by differences in food, temperature, or other environmental factors. Darwin saw that domestic animals and plants are more variable in many ways than wild species. He knew that man has produced many domestic races by *artificial selection,* or breeding of individuals having heritable variations (characteristics) useful for human needs; also, that practical breeders have established and improved the many breeds of livestock and races of cultivated plants by gradually accumulating small but useful hereditary differences through many successive generations. He rightly believed that, in most cases, all the domestic breeds of a species had been derived from one wild ancestral species —all breeds of rabbits from the European gray rabbit, and all pouters, fantails, racers, tumblers, and other widely differing breeds of pigeons from the rock dove (Tables 31-1, 32-1). Many of these breeds now differ so greatly from one another that if they occurred in the wild any zoologist would classify them as distinct species and some as different genera! The domestic breeds of a species, however, all can mate with one another and produce fertile offspring. Having shown the wide diversity of domestic races produced from ancestral stocks by selection of small variations, Darwin assumed that small heritable variations in wild species were the materials of the evolutionary process in nature.

9-20. Geometric ratio of increase. All forms of life have the potentiality of rapid increase. The protozoan *Paramecium* (0.25 mm. long) can divide by fission about 600 times per year. If all survived and continued to divide their total bulk after some months would exceed that of the earth. The fruitfly, *Drosophila*, completes its life cycle from egg to egg in 10 to 14 days, and each female may lay 200 or more eggs. In 40 to 50 days, if all survived and bred, they would number 200,000,000; during one summer their numbers would become astronomical. Darwin assumed the elephant to breed at 30 years and live to 100 years, each female producing but 6 young; in 750 years about 19,000,000 would be alive.

The brown rat, English sparrow, and European corn borer in the United States and the European rabbit in Australia are examples of pests that have multiplied somewhat in keeping with their theoretical possibilities when introduced into new and favorable environments. Plagues of native insects and of meadow mice result at times when abundant food supplies are suddenly available and enable individuals to reproduce and mature rapidly.

9-21. Struggle for existence. Under ordinary conditions, however, animals never increase to such numbers as just indicated. The populations of most species tend to remain more or less stationary because of various checks. There are limitations in the food supply, shelter, and breeding places; individuals of a species compete with one another for these necessities and also with other species having similar requirements; an enlarged population of any species soon is levied upon by its predators and is a fertile field for parasites and diseases. The "struggle for existence" is not always a spectacular battle, as of a rabbit trying to escape from a fox, but is a continuing process in nature involving many factors, each of which eliminates some individuals. It acts at any stage in the life cycle of a species, from the egg, which may fail of fertilization, through embryonic development, larval stages, and adult life. Any individual animal is "successful" in the struggle for existence if it survives long enough to reproduce its kind.

9-22. Natural selection. Darwin assumed that in the struggle for existence individuals with slightly favorably variations enabling them to meet the conditions of life more successfully would survive in the struggle for existence and propagate their kind; this process Herbert Spencer termed "the survival of the fittest." Under this sort of **natural selection** those lacking such variations would perish or fail to breed so that the characters which they possessed would be eliminated from the population. In succeeding generations the process would continue and result in gradually adapting animals more successfully to their environments. With a change in environmental conditions there would be a change in the sort of characters surviving under natural selection. A species in a changing environment or one that had migrated to some new environment would be gradually altered to suit the new conditions. Animals failing to develop suitable new variations under any particular environmental conditions would soon be eliminated. In this manner, Darwin conceived the development of adaptations of whatever sort, the "origin of species" in changed or new environments, and also the disappearance of species in past geological time. Two portions of a species population having to meet slightly differing conditions would tend to diverge from one another and in time would be separated, first by small differences as varieties or subspecies, later as species that could not interbreed. A continuation of such divergence would lead to the production of still other species and in time to the divergence of larger groups. In this manner, he conceived the great number of species and larger categories of the animal kingdom to have been established through the long duration of geological time.

Most biologists accept Darwin's theory as the best general explanation of evolution. They differ mainly in their later and better understanding of some of the essential biological processes involved, which were unknown in his day, but which have been learned by later research.

9-23. Origin of heritable variations. Darwin realized clearly that heritable variations occur in both wild and domesticated animals, but he had no knowledge as to how they are produced or of the exact manner in which they are inherited. (Mendel's precise laws, although published in 1866, were not generally known until 1900.) Starting about 1875, however, biologists began to study the processes in germ cells and their relation to reproduction; a little later careful attention was given to experimental breeding. Soon there was a wealth of new knowledge that afforded a clear understanding of the manner of origin of heritable variations and of the ways they are passed from generation to generation. Outstanding contributors and their major discoveries are listed in Table 9-1. These researches showed that the details of chromosome behavior and of genetics are all-important for understanding certain evolutionary processes. In summary, the most important points are as follows:

1. Chromosomes in cell nuclei carry in linear arrangement the ultramicroscopic genes that are responsible for development of characteristics in an individual.
2. Meiosis segregates members of homologous chromosome pairs and halves the total number for each gamete (see Chap. 5).
3. Fertilization, the random union of 2 gametes of unlike sex, brings together assortments of chromosomes (and therefore of genes) from 2 parents, resulting in production of individuals with different gene combinations (see Chaps. 5, 6).
4. Mutations (changes) occur in genes, and chromosome rearrangements take place; both result in altering the assortment of genes (hence characteristics) passed on to succeeding generations (Chap. 6).

Table 9-1. Important Contributions to Cytology and Genetics

1866.   Mendel. Basic laws of genetics (Chap. 6).
1875.   Hertwig. Role of sperm nucleus in fertilization.
1880–1885.   Flemming; van Beneden. Chromosome constancy and longitudinal
             splitting.
1885.   Hertwig; Strasburger. Nucleus considered basis of heredity.
1885–1887.   Weismann. Germ plasm theory. Constancy in chromosome number,
             importance of fertilization; predicted meiotic reduction.
1885.   Boveri. Meiosis observed; realized somatic nuclei were diploid but
             gametes haploid.
1900.   De Vries; Correns; Tschermak. Independently discovered Mendel's
             1866 paper, recognized its importance, and confirmed his principles
             by their own experiments on plants.
1900.   De Vries. Mutation used as basis for a theory of evolution.
1901.   Castle. Reared *Drosophila* in laboratory.
1902.   Cuénot; Batson. Mendelian principles applied to animals.
1902.   McClung. X chromosome related to sex in male.
1903.   Sutton; Correns; Boveri. Noted close parallel between chromosome
             behavior and Mendelian segregation.
1905.   Stevens; Wilson. Two X chromosomes in female.
1906.   Bateson and Punnett. Linkage discovered (sweet pea).
1909.   Janssens. Cytological basis for crossing over.
1910.   Morgan. Mutants, including sex-linked white eye, in *Drosophila*.
1911.   Morgan. Genes sex-linked in female.
1912.   Morgan. Theory of linkage.
1913.   Sturtevant. Linear arrangement of genes; first chromosome map.
1916.   Bridges. Nondisjunction proved relations between genes and chromo-
             somes.
1917.   Emerson. Mutable gene in maize.
1927.   Muller; Stadler. Mutation rate greatly increased by radiation.
1932.   Darlington. Chromosome cytology clarified.
1933.   Heintz and Baur. Chromosomes seen in giant salivary nuclei.
1934.   Painter. Giant chromosomes in *Drosophila*.

9-24. Mutations and chromosome rearrangements.

The chromosomes in cell nuclei contain particles known as genes which are the basic elements in heredity, the separate units of the germ plasm. A gene starts and regulates a sequence of processes that leads to the appearance of a hereditary character. Earlier (Chap. 6) it was shown that hybridizing, under Mendelian inheritance, makes possible recombination of parental characters in subsequent generations. In addition, it is well known that "new" characters appear in offspring from time to time. These are termed *mutations*. A gene mutation is any change of a gene which results in a recognizable alteration of the original character. Upwards of 1,000 mutations, large and small, are recognized in *Drosophila* (Fig. 6-11) and lesser numbers in other animals and plants; the manner of inheritance for many is well known.

One source for heritable variations thus is by gene mutations; another is by *chromosome rearrangement* during meiosis. Cytological studies during maturation show that portions of chromosomes may come together (1) in different linear order (inversion); (2) with some part omitted (deletion); (3) with repeated parts in one chromosome (duplication); or (4) with part of one chromosome attached to another nonhomologous chromosome (translocation). Any such rearrangement leads to variation expressed as differing assemblages of characters in offspring. The ways in which genes give rise to characters in organisms are imperfectly known, as are the causes of gene mutations and of chromosome rearrangments. Both of the latter may be increased in frequency by X-ray treatment of animals or plants. In earlier years the evidence for genic change was obtained only from experimental breeding but more recently has been accompanied by study of the related changes in germ cells; the two fields thus combined are called *cytogenetics.*

Many mutations first detected in laboratory stocks of *Drosophila* now are known to occur in wild populations. Similarly, the "black" and "silver" mutations of the red fox, first known in nature, are now found in captive foxes on fur farms, where still other mutations have been discovered. From these and many other records it now seems likely that new mutations are constantly appearing in nature and that species populations are highly heterozygous. These conditions then provide a wide range of hereditary variations in wild species. Whether any particular variation will become a persistent characteristic in a species depends upon the size of the population, the degree of isolation or segregation of small groups of individuals, and other factors.

9-25. Kinds of mutations. Different mutations may be beneficial, neutral, or harmful. The huge mass of experimental data (importantly from *Drosophila* and some plants) indicate that most of those found are harmful or neutral. Mutations useful to man are well known among domestic animals and crop plants. In wild species mutations with superior adaptive value seem scarce but this is to be expected, since any that appear are probably soon incorporated in the gene complex of the species to its advantage. Many harmful genes are damaging, however, only when homozygous (as those of lethal characters); in the heterozygous condition, paired with their normal alleles, the majority have no unfavorable effect. A characteristic that is harmful by itself or under one set of environmental conditions may be beneficial in combination with others or under different conditions. Indeed, some experimental data show that two characters, each harmful when alone, prove beneficial when combined.

9-26. Adaptive characters. Many animals are highly specialized for existence in the environments they inhabit. The degree of adaptation differs in various species and higher groups, some being narrowly or closely adapted and others being quite generalized (pp. 190–193; 501–503). Adaptations commonly involve a combination of characteristics—structure, physiology, behavior, and mode of life. Many of these adaptive adjustments probably have evolved over long periods of time, but there are some instances during recent decades of rapid adjustments.

For many years hydrocyanic acid gas proved successful in the control of a red scale (Family COCCIDAE) on citrus trees in southern California; but by 1914 the standard fumigation dosage had become inadequate in one district, and later the same occurred in adjacent localities. Investigation by Quayle and others showed that there were two races of the insect, one cyanide-resistant and the other not. At a certain concentration of the gas 45 per cent of the former but only 4 per cent of the latter survived. Crossing the two races showed them to differ in one sex-linked gene of "HCN resistance." Resistant stocks have appeared similarly after years of spray control for other citrus pests and in the larvae of codling moth in apples. More recently among house fly populations sprayed with DDT, resistant stocks resulted after only about 3 years. Either of two assumptions is possible: the initial variability of these several insects included genes for both resistance and nonresistance, or mutations favoring resistance appeared.

Another instance of rather quick adjustment is that of "industrial melanism" among moths in factory districts of England, Germany, and other European countries. With the increased outpouring of coal smoke that blackened the local vegetation, melanic variants appeared and spread in several species of moths. Over several decades they became more frequent and finally replaced the original paler stocks. Breeding experiments showed the darker moths to differ in one or a few genes and to have greater vigor. Darkish mutants presumably did not survive in earlier times because they were not protectively colored on the vegetation then present.

9-27. Genic change and natural selection. Chromosome recombinations and mutations result in stocks of individuals having altered assemblages of old characters and some new characters, thus increasing the total variability in species. This wealth of potential variability, however, is unlike the relative constancy as to characters of most species in nature. It is the role of natural selection to work in the direction of narrowing species variability, more particularly to weed out characters that are nonadaptive or of no value for survival. The total effect that the physical and biological environment imposes on individuals is the "screen" of natural selection—it passes or permits those better suited to survive and eliminates all others. Sexual reproduction provides for abundant multiplication of individuals (geometric ratio of increase), and the cellular phenomena in gene mutations, chromosome rearrangements, and fertilization add to the supply of variability; then these abundant resources are screened by natural selection.

9-28. Population size and isolation. The total of individuals in many species is enormously large, numbering hundreds of thousands in common birds or mammals and millions or billions in some widespread insects. Such populations, however, are not distributed uniformly and broadly throughout the entire geographic range of the species. On the contrary, in the great majority, the total is subdivided into small areal groups or colonies that do not freely intermingle with other groups because of limited powers of locomotion or for other reasons. In consequence, matings actually occur only among the sexually mature individuals of small sectors of a species population.

It has been clearly shown, by methods that cannot be detailed here (but see Dobzhansky, 1941), that with random mating in a large and freely interbreeding population the variability will be relatively high and will remain rather constant, whereas in any of limited size the extent of variability is reduced rather rapidly and the genotype becomes more homozygous. Different small populations will, purely by chance, tend to differ from one another in slight ways and become distinct stocks or races (incipient species), each genetically rather uniform but not necessarily alike. Evidence from several fields of study—taxonomy, migration, homing behavior, cytology, serology—shows that many a "species" in the ordinary sense is actually composed of numerous biological strains, stocks, or races.

Isolation, the segregation of stocks into smaller units, may be brought about in several ways: (1) *geographical,* by physical separation in distance; (2) *ecological,* in different types of environments although in the same region; (3) *seasonal,* where two populations breed at different times of year; (4) *physiological,* where there is functional incompatibility in mating or in the production, fertilization, and survival of gametes; and (5) *behavioral,* where animals of two different groups will not mate for one reason or another.

Classical examples of the effects of isolation are afforded by land snails, which have but limited powers of locomotion. Studies of snails of the genus *Achatinella* by Gulick (1905) in the Hawaiian Islands and of *Partula* by Crampton (1916, 1932) on Tahiti and Moorea have revealed diverse local races of each, confined to small valleys or even a few acres. The characters of each race as to size, form, and coloration of the shell are not related to the immediate environment and are without adaptive significance. Populations of adjacent valleys may be more unlike than those more remote in distance. Similarly, the gall insects (CYNIPIDAE) of oaks, studied by Kinsey, are often alike over large areas in the eastern states where oak forests are practically continuous; but in the Southwest and

Mexico where oaks occur only on scattered "islands" in the higher mountains there are many "insular" species of gall wasps. All such examples may be explained by the chance survival of different mutations in different localities without implying any natural selection as to survival value.

9-29. Other factors in evolution. In a subject of such widespread and absorbing interest as evolution it is to be expected that some of the evidence will be interpreted in more than one way by various biologists. For example, Goldschmidt considers that there are two different genetic processes: (1) *microevolution,* based on accumulation of small genetic changes within a species, leads to production of subspecies differing in size, proportions, tone of color, etc., but not to the formation of other species; and (2) *macroevolution,* by a repatterning of the entire genetic system, produces sudden abrupt changes of form ("hopeful monsters") to yield new species or higher groups. Organisms derived by such changes would at once differ markedly from the stocks whence they arose; hence the search for "missing links" would be futile. Examples of such major changes among domestic animals are hairless breeds in dogs, the short- and bow-legged dachshund from some other breed of hound, the long-legged greyhound from a similar source, the short-legged Ancon sheep, and the tailless Manx cat. This explanation is, however, not accepted by many biologists.

The term *orthogenesis* (Gr. *orthos,* straight) has been used for some stocks of fossil and recent animals in which evolution seems to have proceeded along rather direct courses. Examples are the progressive reduction of digits and enlargement of teeth in horses; the increase in tusk size and reduction in number of molar teeth in elephants; the successive elaboration of horns from small "nubbins" to great unwieldly growths on titanotheres (fossil mammals); and the pattern sequences traceable from species to species among some living snakes, fishes, and insects. The term implies that evolution has been directed by some internal but unknown factor. No experimental evidence has supported this theory, which receives less attention now than formerly.

References

The following are a few selected items from the enormous literature on evolution.

CLODD, E. 1907. Pioneers of evolution. From Thales to Huxley. Rev. ed. London, Cassell & Co., Ltd. xi + 252 pp., illus.

DARWIN, CHARLES. 1859. On the origin of species by means of natural selection, or the preservation of favoured races in the struggle for life. 6th ed., 1875. New York, D. Appleton-Century Co., Inc. xxi + 458 pp.

DE VRIES, HUGO. 1909. The mutation theory experiments and observations on the origin of species in the vegetable kingdom. La Salle, Ill., The Open Court Publishing Co. 2 vols., xv + 582 pp., 119 figs; vii + 683 pp., 6 pls., 147 figs.

DOBZHANSKY, THEODORE. 1941. Genetics and the origin of species. 2d ed. New York, Columbia University Press. xvii + 446 pp., 24 figs.

GOLDSCHMIDT, RICHARD. 1940. The material basis of evolution. New Haven, Yale University Press. xi + 436 pp., 83 illus.

HUXLEY, JULIAN (editor). 1940. The new systematics. Oxford, Clarendon Press. viii + 583 pp., 55 figs.

————. 1942. Evolution the modern synthesis. New York, Harper Brothers. 645 pp.

LAMARCK, J. B. 1809. La philosophie zoologique. (Translated by Hugh Elliot, 1914, as Zoological philosophy.) London, Macmillan & Co., Ltd. xcii + 410 pp.

LULL, R. S. 1947. Organic evolution. 3d. ed. New York, The Macmillan Co. xix + 743 pp., illus.

MAYR, E. 1942. Systematics and the origin of species from the viewpoint of a zoologist. New York, Columbia University Press. xiv + 334 pp., 29 figs.

MOORE, R. C. 1933. Historical geology. New York, McGraw-Hill Book Co., Inc. xiii + 673 pp., 413 figs.

MORGAN, T. H. 1932. The scientific basis of evolution. 2d ed. New York, W. W. Norton & Co., Inc. xii + 14–306 pp., 45 figs.

ROMER, A. S. 1945. Vertebrate paleontology. 2d ed. Chicago, University of Chicago Press. ix + 687 pp., 377 figs.

SIMPSON, G. G. 1944. Tempo and mode in evolution. New York, Columbia University Press. xviii + 237 pp., 36 figs.

————. 1949. The meaning of evolution a study of the history of life and of its significance for man. New Haven, Yale University Press. xv + 364 pp., 38 figs.

WEISMANN, AUGUST. 1904. The evolution theory. London, Edward Arnold & Co. 2 vols., xvi + 827 pp., 3 pls., 131 figs.

CHAPTER 10

HISTORY OF ZOOLOGY

10-1. Early zoology. Prehistoric man had a practical interest in animals that provided food, clothing, and other essentials and in the wild beasts that menaced him. Later the animals began to play a part in his religion and medicine. In time, these and other factors led to the development of art. The Cro-Magnon peoples who lived in the caves of southwestern Europe have left many paintings of horses, deer, bear, and other animals and some animal statues (Fig. 10-1). These show a good

Fig. 10-1. Drawings of reindeer, elephants, horses, and chamois by prehistoric men in the cave of Les Combarèlles, France. (*From Rickard, Man and metals, after Breuil.*)

appreciation of life postures and considerable ability in drawing and painting with crude materials. Much later the early civilizations about the eastern Mediterranean produced pottery, sculpture, tapestries, and other decorative objects that show notable skill in portraying animals.

The language of all primitive races include many terms pertaining to animals; and as these differ from tribe to tribe, they indicate that knowledge of animals is as old as the languages themselves. Thus, American Indians had words to describe the species, sexes, and ages of animals native to their territories, including some that served in no practical ways. Besides providing many of the necessities of life, the animals were the bases of religious beliefs and ceremonials and as such are frequently mentioned in myths and legends. The raven, bear, seal, and eagle were figured on the symbolic totem poles of Indians along the North Pacific coast, and the wolf, coyote, bison, and rattlesnake were important to Plains Indians.

The earliest known civilization was in Babylon. The Babylonians made clay models of the organs in the human body, and their records show that they believed the heart to be the center of intelligence. The early Egyptians embalmed their dead but learned little of human anatomy. They acquired some knowledge of animals, and before 1500 B.C. they used the parts and excretions of animals for many medical treatments. The domestication of animals by early civilizations (Chap. 33) yielded practical information on breeding, growth, and nutrition.

The early eastern Greeks, however, made the first real contributions to biology. Among the Ionian tribes, which had no political or religious restrictions, were the first natural philosophers to speculate on the

centaur   mantichora   merman

unicorn   dragon   chimaera

FIG. 10-2. Some mythical animals. These creatures of the imagination are figured in some early books about animals, on sculpture and mosaics, and on vases and tapestries. A unicorn supports the arms of England, and the dragon of St. George is stamped on English coins. (*After Ashton, Curious creatures in zoology, Cassell and Co., Ltd., London.*)

origin of the universe and of the earth and its animal inhabitants. Anaximander (611–547 B.C.), a western Greek, believed that living things arose from a primordial mud, with a sequence from lower life up to man, who had arisen from a fish form. Xenophanes (sixth century B.C.) was the first to recognize fossils as animal remains and to infer that their presence up on mountains indicated the latter had once been beneath the sea. Empedocles (fifth century B.C.) is said to have rid a town of malaria by draining the near-by swamps. The earliest zoological document is a Greek medical work of the fifth century B.C., which contains a simple classification of edible animals, chiefly fishes.

Aristotle (384–322 B.C.) was the first zoologist of record and one of the greatest. He studied under Plato, taught Alexander the Great, lectured to pupils at the Lyceum in Athens, and wrote extensively on philosophy, politics, and other topics besides zoology. His *Historia animalium* of nine "books" (about 500 pages in a modern printed translation) includes a great miscellany on the structure and habits of many animals native to Greece, Macedonia, and Asia Minor. The portions based on his personal observations (and dissections?) are accurate, but some items from other sources are erroneous or fantastic. About 520 species belonging to Greece have been identified in his writings. He showed how animals could be grouped according to structure, habitat, and habits but offered no system of classification; others have done this from his writings (Chap. 11). Parts of other manuscripts by Aristotle, *On the Parts of Animals* and *On the Reproduction of Animals*, also survive. He had followed the day-by-day development of a chick embryo within the egg, knew that drone bees develop by parthenogenesis, and knew that the young of some sharks develop within the mother.

Aristotle insisted on the importance of observation, recognized the regularity and law inherent in biological phenomena, and used the inductive method of forming conclusions from observed facts. He used the human body as a reference in comparative discussions. On physiological processes, however, he was usually vague or in error, but this was natural since there was no science of chemistry. He conceived an evolutionary development from lower to higher forms, which he ascribed to a supreme "guiding intelligence."

In the Greek medical schools of Alexandria, Egypt, during the second and third centuries B.C., there was study of human anatomy and even some experimental physiology under Herophilus and Erasistratus.

The Romans were mostly practical administrators and soldiers, and they made few contributions to zoology. Pliny the Elder (A.D. 23–79) was a soldier and administrator who wrote much. In A.D. 77 he produced a *Natural History* of 37 books, which was a compiled encyclopedia covering all natural phenomena and their applications, wild and domestic animals, animal husbandry, medicine, and other topics. Although there was little new material and much of fancy and fable among the 20,000 items that he culled mainly from other writings or tales, the work served for over 1,500 years as a major source of natural history information. Other Roman writers dealing with biology were Lucretius (96–55 B.C.) who discussed the general phenomena of nature; M. T. Varro (116–27? B.C.) who wrote in *De re rustica* on agriculture and domestic and wild animals; Vergil (70–19 B.C.) whose *Georgics* (Book III) is a manual of agriculture; and Celsus whose *De medicina* (A.D. 30?) was one of the best ancient works on medicine.

Galen (A.D. 130–200?), a Greek physician who later lived in Rome, was the last great biologist of antiquity. He was especially influential in developing a coherent system of physiology. Since dissection of human bodies was impossible, he used other animals, especially the

Barbary ape on which his account of the human hand is obviously based. He described various internal organs and the blood vessels, showing that the arteries and left side of the heart contained blood and not air as believed by earlier writers; he also inferred that arteries and veins must be connected. He gave good accounts of the brain and nerves, and by experiment he had differentiated the sensory and motor nerves. Food he assumed was "transformed" in the stomach, passed to the liver, and there converted into blood. Galen localized various qualities of the soul in different organs and believed that all organs had been created in the most perfect form; hence, his long and detailed writings were acceptable in the ages of Christianity that followed. For a thousand years they were considered infallible and formed almost the only text on medical anatomy in western Europe.

FIG. 10-3. The mythical "barnacle tree." The common barnacle goose (*Branta bernicla*) of Europe is so named in reference to an old belief that "birdes" came forth from "shels" (goose barnacle, *Lepas anatifera*) which grew on timbers of wrecked ships on beaches of northern Scotland. (*From Riverside natural history, Houghton Mifflin Co.*)

A downward trend in scientific inquiry began before the end of Greek civilization. This continued throughout the existence of the Roman Empire and for the centuries when Europe was overrun by barbarians and divided into small states. After Galen a thousand years elapsed with no biologist who made critical observations. The church held the people to narrow and dogmatic beliefs and discouraged original inquiry. From before the time of Pliny the older writings were copied repeatedly with commentaries (and errors), but no copyist himself ever looked at the animals to verify or deny the writings that he copied. Pliny, Galen, and Aristotle were the chief sources of biological information. Aristotle's writings were acceptable to the church because he believed that the earth was the center of the universe and that a supreme intelligence directed all natural phenomena.

Meanwhile, in the Near East, men continued to read the old Greek writings. They did some original work in mathematics, astronomy, and chemistry but little in biology. Later, the biology of the Greeks was translated into Arabic and spread with Mohammedism, even to Spain. In Europe, universities were founded in the eleventh to thirteenth centuries, under control of the church, and the Arabic copies of Greek authors were then translated into Latin. The "scholastics" of these early schools were men interested in words and reason and not in things. A few able thinkers, however, sought the original Greek texts, and a few developed an interest in original observation.

The revival of learning, or Renaissance, was a slow process, contributed to by various factors. Two friars who taught at the University of Paris had important parts in this revival. Roger Bacon (English, 1214?–1294) had an especial interest in optics and in the philosophy of learning and of science. Albertus Magnus (Bavarian, 1206–1280) wrote a treatise *On Animals* that was a commentary on Aristotle but included some original observations. An interest in travel began to develop, first for commercial purposes and later for discovery, that brought to Europe knowledge of the animals in distant lands. Some early travelers were Marco Polo (1254–1323), Vasco da Gama (1469?–1524), Columbus (1446?–1506), and Magellan (1480?–1521); the last-named disproved the ancient notion of a flat world by circumnavigating the earth. Practical anatomy, with dissection, began again with Mondino (1270?–1326) at Bologna, Italy. Rediscovery of Greek and Roman statuary paved the way for revived interests in accurate portrayal of the human body and of animals and plants by the Italian Renaissance painters. Among the latter was Leonardo da Vinci (Italian, 1452–1519) who was an engineer and inventor, a painter ("Mona Lisa"), an anatomist of the human and of animal bodies, and a physiologist. He was a pioneer in many fields and far ahead of his age in his thinking and achievements, but his findings remained hidden in his notes and drawings only to be published many years later.

10-2. Manuscripts and printing. All early human records were manuscripts (L. *manus*, hand + *scribo*, write), on clay tablets and later on sheets of papyrus or parchment. The Greek library of the second century B.C. at Alexandria had over 700,000 scrolls, or "books," and both the Romans and Arabs later had similar but smaller libraries. Ancient documents survived by being copied repeatedly, but a vast number were lost. The oldest existing copies of Aristotle and Pliny date from about the ninth century A.D. Upon the invention of printing (about A.D. 1450) copies of the older works were multiplied in number and made available to many more persons. Printing was thus an important aid in the revival of learning.

10-3. Human anatomy. Andreas Vesalius (Belgian, 1514–1564) who studied at Paris and at Padua in Italy and later taught anatomy was a powerful factor in the return to original observation. Finding that Galen's writings were incomplete, contradictory, and erroneous, he made original dissections and published a large illustrated text *On the Structure of the Human Body* (1543). This book is notable for careful figures of the skeleton and muscles (Fig. 10-4) but contains some errors on function borrowed from Galen. His rejection of the ancient authority was distasteful to many conservative anatomists of his day, and he was forced out of teaching, never to return.

10-4. Natural history. The earlier general works on animals after the Renaissance and the invention of printing were patterned on Aristotle but gradually broke away from the ancient tradition and included increasing amounts of original observations. The first book on birds (1544) was that of William Turner (English, 1510?-1568); it dealt with the kinds noticed by Aristotle and Pliny but had some observations by Turner. Other notable early authors and their works were: Edward Wotton (English, 1492-1555), *De differentiis animalium* (1552); Konrad Gesner (Swiss, 1516-1565), *Historia animalium* (1551 and later), of four volumes and over 3,500 pages, with a fifth volume published by others (1621), the first illustrated work on zoology, with many good figures; Guillaume Rondelet (French, 1507-1566), *De piscibus marinis* (1554), including all sorts of marine animals from the Mediterranean and the first figure of a dissected

FIG. 10-4. The first accurate portrayal of the human body. Much reduced from a plate in *De fabrica corporis humani* by Andreas Vesalius, 1543.

FIG. 10-5. An excellent early zoological drawing, the snail (*Helix*). (*From Rondelet, De piscibus marinis*, 1551.)

invertebrate, the sea urchin (Figs. 2-19, 10-5, 19-9); Pierre Belon (French, 1517-1564), *Histoire naturelle des étranges poissons marins* (1551), dealing with sea anemones to whales and figuring the attachment of the embryo whale to the mother. Belon's was one of the earliest zoological books printed in a language other than Latin. Carlo Ruini (Italian) is remembered for his *Dell anatomia del cavallo* (1598), with beautiful figures on the anatomy of the horse.

From the sixteenth century to the present day there has been an unending series of natural-history works dealing variously with one species, a family or larger group, with certain or all animals of a region (faunal works), or the entire animal kingdom. A famous comprehensive work was the *Histoire naturelle* of Georges, Comte de Buffon (French,

1707–1788); the author was wealthy and influential, long director of the Jardin des Plantes in Paris, and a friend of Louis XV. The *Histoire* covered animals, plants, and minerals in 44 volumes (1749–1804) and was completed by assistants after the author died. It was often reprinted entirely or in part and was translated into English and German.

10-5. Blood circulation. As Vesalius had shifted from ancient authority to original observation in the study of anatomy, so William Harvey (English, 1578–1657) introduced the experimental method and quantitative deductions into physiology. Both had been students at Padua in Italy, where scientific study was on a high level. Harvey's researches,

Fig. 10-6. Development of the microscope. *A.* One of Leeuwenhoek's "microscopes," about 1673, a simple magnifier used in bright sunlight. *B.* Robert Hooke's microscope, 1665, with lamp and condenser to concentrate light on the object. *C.* A modern microscope.

after returning to England, dealt with the circulation of the blood. His book *De motu cordis* (1628) contained convincing proof that replaced the partial or erroneous ideas of all earlier times. He described the way in which the blood fills and then empties from the auricles and then the ventricles by the muscular contractions of these chambers (direct observations on lower animals); how blood spurts from a cut artery in keeping with the contractions of the heart; and how when a vein is clamped it empties on the side toward the heart but becomes engorged behind the clamp (experiment). Finally (by quantitative calculations), he showed that so much blood is pumped through the heart in an hour or day that it must be recirculated constantly. It could not, as earlier believed, all be generated in the liver from food as "natural spirits" for a single passage in the blood vessels. Harvey also studied embryology. In *De generatione animalium* (1651) he described the embryology of the chick and of lower forms and inferred that mammals are produced from eggs; lacking a powerful microscope he could not prove the latter or other important matters.

10-6. The microscope. Prior to the invention of the microscope (Gr. *mikros*, small + *skopos*, watcher), animals invisible to the unaided eye and the finer structures in larger animals were unknown. Hand lenses for magnification (and reading spectacles) were known in the thirteenth century or earlier. The first compound microscope with two separated lenses is ascribed to J. and Z. Janssen, spectaclemakers of Middleburg, the Netherlands, in 1590–1591, but Galileo is considered the effective inventor. Since the kinds of work possible with the microscope depend on its optical features (Fig. 10-6), the dates of a few significant improvements may be noted.

1610. First binocular (double compound).	1860. Water-immersion objective.
1635. Condenser added.	1873. Wide-angle condenser.
1660. Huygenian ocular designed.	1878. Oil-immersion objective.
1712. Mirror beneath stage.	1885. Compensating ocular.
1823. Achromatic (color corrected) doublet lenses.	1886. Apochromatic objective.
	1888. Achromatic condenser.
1851. Mono-objective with double oculars.	1897. Twin-objective binocular with erecting prisms.

The best compound microscopes now magnify about 2,000 times and resolve objects about 1.0 μ apart. The ultraviolet microscope (1903) magnifies up to 10,000 times and will resolve to about 0.1 μ. Since 1934 the electron microscope with magnifications to 30,000 times or more has been used with extremely thin preparations of many biological materials to learn the finer architecture of cell parts. The phase microscope, a recent development, differentiates many details of structure in living cells.

10-7. Early microscopists. Robert Hooke (English, 1635–1703) was the first to report the presence of cells in plant tissue; his *Micrographia* (1665), with 83 plates of figures, described a great variety of minute objects. The real founder of microanatomy for both plants and animals was Marcello Malpighi (Italian, 1628–1694). He investigated tissues and organs fresh, cooked, or injected. In various short papers he described the finer anatomy of the lungs, liver, and spleen and saw capillaries joining arteries and veins. He wrote a detailed account of the anatomy of the silkworm (1669), including the structure and respiratory function of the spiracles and tracheae. Another work described many small features in the development of the chick (1672). Antony van Leeuwenhoek (Dutch, 1632–1723) was a self-taught individual who ground his own lenses and made many simple microscopes, with magnifications up to 270 times. He examined many materials, and his discoveries included blood corpuscles, spermatozoa, striated muscles, protozoans, and rotifers. His results were reported in a long series of letters to the Royal Society of London. Another Hollander, Jan Swammerdam (1637–1680), was an intensive microscopist for a few years. His writings, published after his death in a *Biblia naturae* (1737–1738), included detailed studies on small invertebrates and insects, especially the anatomy of the honeybee. The student of elementary zoology retraces in some degree the work of these early microscopists and the host of others that have followed down to the present day.

10-8. Classification and nomenclature. For centuries, naturalists either listed their animals in no particular order or followed the system extracted from Aristotle. Plant classification began in the sixteenth century and was advanced by John Ray (English, 1627-1705). He was the first to narrow the concept of a species to organisms of like kind derived from similar parents, to recognize variation in species, and to establish larger groups based upon anatomical features. Besides a three-volume work on plants (1686–1704), he published small books on quadrupeds and serpents (1693) and on insects.

The first great systematist was Carolus Linnaeus (Swedish, 1707–1778). The growing knowledge of plants and animals in the eighteenth century was leading to confusion; descriptions were wordy, and species were designated by names that varied with locality and country. Linnaeus established a rigid system of classification and nomenclature with concise descriptions. Beginning in 1735 he published a *Systema naturae* that passed through 12 editions, the last in 1768. It was a methodical catalogue of plants, animals, and minerals, arranged in larger and subsidiary groups. He gradually evolved a binomial nomenclature by which each kind of organism is designated by a genus and a species name. This was first employed consistently for animals in his tenth edition (1758), which is the starting point for the binomial nomenclature used today. Linnaeus stimulated great interest in collecting and classifying, and he attracted many students to work under his guidance. He believed in the special creation and fixity of species but later recognized some variations. His plan for classifying and naming was of great help, but his insight into the fundamental aspects of animals was slight. Other contributors to classification are mentioned in Chap. 11.

10-9. Embryology. Aristotle had some knowledge about the development of certain animals, but not until the seventeenth century were detailed accounts of the embryology of the chick available, in publications by Fabricius (1621), Harvey (1651), and Malpighi (1672). Malpighi reported a small embryo in the unincubated egg (probably resulting from actual development in the hot Italian summer), and this observation was later elaborated into the theory of preformation by Charles Bonnet (Swiss, 1720–1793) and others (see Chap. 5). This was contested by Kaspar F. Wolff (German, 1738–1794) in his *Theoria generationis* (1759),

Aristotle
384–322 B.C.

Andreas Vesalius
1514–1564

William Harvey
1578–1657

Marcello Malpighi
1628–1694

Antony van Leeuwenhoek
1632–1723

Carolus Linnaeus
1707–1778

Georges Cuvier
1769–1832

Jean Baptiste Lamarck
1744–1829

Theodor Schwann
1810–1882

Karl Ernst von Baer
1792–1876

Charles Darwin
1809–1882

Gregor Johann Mendel
1822–1884

Louis Agassiz
1807–1873

Louis Pasteur
1822–1895

Thomas Henry Huxley
1825–1895

Fig. 10-7.   Some leaders in the development of zoology and related sciences.

who gave a poorer account than Malpighi but found no preformation of the embryo and ascribed development to an external force (epigenesis).   A useless controversy between these ideas was waged for half a century.   Karl Ernst von Baer (German, 1792–1876), the "father of modern embryology," set high standards in study, established the germ-layer theory, and introduced the comparative viewpoint in his *Development of Animals* (1828; 1837).   Francis Balfour (English, 1851–1882) summarized the great mass of detailed knowledge up to his day in a masterly *Comparative Embryology* (1880–1881).

10-10. Physiology.   The ancient and medieval writers speculated and made many erroneous inferences as to functions in animal bodies.   The experimental approach, which yields more accurate knowledge, was initiated by Harvey. René Descartes (French, 1596–1650) extended Harvey's method to include nervous phenomena and reflex actions. Albrecht von Haller (Swiss, 1708–1777) established physiology as a separate science not necessarily joined to medicine. His *Elements of Physiology* (1759–1766) was the first text. He was followed importantly by Charles Bell (Scottish, 1774–1842), Johannes Müller (German, 1801–1858), Dubois-Reymond (German, 1818–1896), and Claude Bernard (French, 1813–1878).

10-11. Comparative anatomy. Aristotle and Galen included a few notes that compared the structure of different animals, but until the eighteenth century practically all anatomical studies were treatises on separate animals. Baron Georges Cuvier (French, 1769–1832) established comparative anatomy as a new branch of biology. He made early independent studies at the seashore and in 1797 went to the Jardin des Plantes in Paris where he remained for a long period of intensive research. He became the leader in French science, a favorite of Napoleon, and director of higher education in France. His *Leçons sur l'anatomie comparée* (1801–1805) gathered the fruits of his earlier studies, and his work on the animal kingdom (*Règne animal*, 1816) included his theory of types. H. Milne-Edwards (French, 1800–1885) introduced the idea of division of physiological labor and wrote a treatise on comparative physiology and anatomy (1857–1881). Richard Owen (English, 1804–1892) carried on the influence of Cuvier in a more enlightened manner and developed the concepts of analogy and homology; his three-volume *Comparative Anatomy and Physiology of Vertebrates* (1866–1868) is still useful. Thomas H. Huxley (English, 1825–1895) brought rare ability in observation and judgment into this field and wrote on many topics. Johannes Müller (German, 1801–1858) was the greatest physiologist and comparative anatomist of his century. In America Edward D. Cope (1840–1897) contributed importantly to the comparative study of living and extinct vertebrates.

10-12. Paleontology. The nature of fossils as relics of animals that had lived in former times was noted by Xenophanes, by Leonardo da Vinci, and by Steno (1638–1686), but it was Cuvier who first gave attention to such materials and founded the science of paleontology. His *Ossemens fossiles* (1812–1813) was based on specimens from calcareous rocks where building stones were quarried near Paris. Cuvier believed in the fixity of species and that there had been a succession of catastrophes through time, each of which had killed off all life, after which new life had been created. The theory that fossils were remains of animals that had perished in the Biblical deluge was current before and after Cuvier's time, but the final recognition of their true nature was firmly established by the work of Charles Lyell (Scottish, 1797–1875) and his successors.

Lamarck (French, 1744–1829) did for invertebrate paleontology what Cuvier had accomplished for vertebrates.

10-13. Histology and the cell theory. In 1665 Hooke had figured the dead cells in cork and Van Leeuwenhoek later depicted the nuclei in blood corpuscles, but no early microscopist had any hint of cellular structure as a general phenomenon. François Bichat (French, 1771–1802) at the end of his short life issued a treatise on membranes, or "tissue"; he did no investigations with the microscope, but his work stimulated others to do so. By 1824 René Dutrochet (French, 1776–1847) announced that plants and animals were composed of cells. In 1823 Hunter had figures of blood cells with a "nucleus," and in 1833 Robert Brown (English, 1773–1858) described nuclei in plant cells. In 1838 M. J. Schleiden (German, 1804–1881) put forth the thesis that cells were the units of structure in plants, and in 1839 his coworker Theodor Schwann (German, 1810–1882), having studied many animal tissues in detail, applied the thesis to animals. This generalization, the cell theory, has been one of the most fruitful of all biological concepts, and today is at the basis of all understanding of the structure and functions within living organisms.

10-14. Evolution. Some history of evolutionary thought is given in Chap. 9. Up to the end of the eighteenth century there were only vague and crude speculations on the origin of organisms and their differentiation. With few exceptions there was general belief in special creation. Buffon discarded that viewpoint and speculated on the origins of organisms. Lamarck was the first to propose a general theory of evolution based upon influences of the environment, the effects of use and disuse of organs, and the inheritance of acquired characters. This was set forth in his *Philosophie zoologique* (1809). Cuvier strongly opposed Lamarck's theory in debates before the French Academy of Sciences in 1830 with Geoffroy Saint-Hilaire (French, 1772–1844). The convincing arguments of Charles Robert Darwin (English, 1809–1882) finally established the theory of evolution based on natural selection (1859) as a guiding principle for all subsequent biological work.

10-15. Heredity and genetics. The Greeks had recognized that some features were transmitted from generation to generation in man, but there was little further attention to this important subject for many centuries. Darwin endeavored to learn some facts of inheritance from practical breeders, but most biologists gave little attention to the matter. The pioneer work of Gregor Johann Mendel (Austrian, 1822–1884) was published in 1866 (see Chap. 6) but lay unnoticed until a revival in studies of inheritance around 1900. Since then the new science of genetics has made enormous strides, both practical and theoretical.

10-16. Biological education. Until less than a century ago there was only meager training in science, including biology, and that was mainly by lectures. Louis Agassiz (1807–1873) a Swiss zoologist and student of Cuvier, later professor at Harvard University, initiated the present practice of firsthand study and dissection of specimens by students. He also carried popular instruction to laymen by public lectures on zoology in many American cities. His dictum "Study nature not books" today is applied at all levels from nature study in the lower schools to the wide offerings of college and university instruction in the biological sciences.

10-17. Modern biology. The achievements and trends in modern biology cannot be stated or appraised briefly, since rapid progress over the great body of knowledge already available is being made by a vast number of investigators. The older fields of descriptive and comparative anatomy, embryology, taxonomy, and others continue to be developed but from enlightened viewpoints. Experimental zoology and genetics occupy major roles. Refinements in techniques and instruments make possible closer study of the structure and physiology of cells and tissues. Entirely new fields of inquiry have opened and expanded in the study of hormones, vitamins, and mineral metabolism. Chemical elements can now be made radioactive by use of the cyclotron, and such "tagged" materials may be fed and traced in their passage within the bodies of living organisms so that much new information is available as to the storage, utilization, and disposal of elements in food and metabolism. For animals living in nature the earlier descriptive natural history is being supplanted by quantitative ecologic measurements of populations and environmental factors, yielding a better understanding of interrelationships.

References

GARRISON, F. H. 1929. An introduction to the history of medicine. 4th ed. Philadelphia, W. B. Saunders Co. 996 pp., illus.

LOCY, W. A. 1915. Biology and its makers. 3d ed. New York, Henry Holt & Co., Inc. xxvi + 477 pp., 123 figs.

———. 1925. The growth of biology. New York, Henry Holt & Co., Inc. xiv + 481 pp., 140 figs.

NORDENSKIÖLD, E. 1924. The history of biology. New York, Alfred A. Knopf. x + 629 + xv pp., illus.

PEATTIE, D. C. 1936. Green laurels, the lives and achievements of the great naturalists. New York, Simon & Schuster. xxiii + 368 pp., illus.

SINGER, CHARLES. 1950. History of biology a general introduction to the story of living things. Rev. ed. New York, Henry Schuman, Inc. xxxv + 579 pp., illus.

CHAPTER 11

CLASSIFICATION AND NOMENCLATURE

11-1. Numbers of animals. Many kinds of animals now inhabit the earth, and many others have lived here during past geological time. The conspicuous kinds of land and sea are now well known as are many lesser sorts in the more civilized regions, but of those living elsewhere our knowledge is imperfect and only crude estimates of their numbers are possible.

The first enumeration of all known animals was made by Linnaeus in 1758 and included 4,236 kinds. In 1859 Agassiz and Bronn counted 129,370, and by 1911 Pratt estimated that 522,400 had been named. New forms are still being described, and the total is now well over 900,000 (Fig. 1-4). For certain groups in particular regions there are more precise figures. Thus, in North America there are over 2,500 mammals from Panama northward, and the fishes of fresh and salt waters total 4,137; north of Mexico the birds number 1,420, the reptiles 445, and the amphibians 167. California contains 460 kinds of mammals, 608 birds, 104 reptiles, and 41 amphibians. Even small areas may have many kinds; Lake Maxinkukee, Indiana, of 1,854 acres, has 64 fishes, 18 amphibians, and 130 mollusks. The numbers given for animal groups at the ends of chapters in Part II of this book are mostly estimates by specialists because there are few actual counts.

A. CLASSIFICATION

No one person can become familiar with more than a small proportion of the known animals. Since one objective in zoology is to obtain a perspective of the whole animal kingdom, some means of grouping animals for study is necessary. This is the function of the subscience of *classification, taxonomy,* or *systematic zoology.*

11-2. Methods of classification. Upon examining any mixed assemblage of animals, it is evident that various degrees of resemblance and difference exist between the several kinds. For example, among the domestic animals on a farm, the cow and sheep differ in size, color, and texture of the body covering, but they are alike in having horns and cloven hoofs. A horse differs in lacking horns and having solid hoofs, but it agrees with the cow and sheep in having long legs and teeth of the grinding type. A dog differs from all three in having nails and soft pads on its

255

toes instead of hoofs, and in having teeth of the stabbing and shearing types; it agrees in being covered with hair.   The cat resembles a dog more closely than it does any of the preceding three.   All these animals have hair and teeth, bear living young, and show other features in common. As a group they differ importantly from the chickens and ducks, which are covered with feathers, lack teeth, and lay eggs.   So it is that animals may be classified or divided into minor and major groups.

The classification of animals is based upon their **characters,** or inherent peculiarities.   These include structural features, external or internal, gross or microscopic, and those of size, proportions, and coloration. A character is more useful if it is constantly associated with others; thus every bird has, besides feathers, a beak, wings, clawed feet, a four-chambered heart, and warm blood.   Adaptive or superficial characters often serve to distinguish minor groups, and more fundamental or deep-seated features of structure separate the larger ones.

The first purpose of classification is that of convenience, but a more important one is to arrange animals in groups so as to show their presumed relationships.   They may be classified in many ways, as by grouping all with appendages, all the "wormlike" forms, or all with limy skeletons. Early zoologists actually used such features, but increasing knowledge has shown that such arrangements brought together animals that differ in more fundamental respects.   The modern or "natural system" of classification employs all available data as to structure, physiology, embryology, distribution, and other features; each group is distinguished by several to many characters.   The natural classification is based on the theory of evolution and is an effort to indicate "blood relationships" and the "genealogical tree" of the Animal Kingdom and its subdivisions (see Fig. 1-1).

In such a classification it is essential to distinguish characters that show **homology,** or similarity of origin (and hence relationship), from those that exhibit **analogy,** or similarity of function (but not necessarily of origin or relationship).   The arms of man, forelegs of mammals, wings of birds, and forelegs of frogs are essentially similar as to structure of the bones, muscles, blood vessels, and nerves, hence are homologous, although used for widely different purposes.   In contrast, the wings of birds and butterflies serve for flight but differ as to both embryonic development and adult structure and so are analogous (Fig. 9-1).

11-3. Species.   The basic group in biological classification is the **species** (not specie; the plural is also species).   There is no single means to determine the limits of a species, and no one definition serves in all cases.   Typically a species is a group of individuals (1) having many characters in common; (2) differing from and not intergrading with other groups; (3) usually having a geographic range separate from related groups; and, most importantly, (4) that is infertile with related groups. Members of a species are all derived from a common ancestry and can breed with one another to yield fertile offspring. Examples of common species are the house fly, yellow perch, bullfrog, and American robin. The individuals comprising a species often can be subdivided into smaller groups known as geographic races or **subspecies** that differ from one another by average rather than absolute characters. Each subspecies occupies a separate geographic range, and specimens from the boundaries of such ranges are usually intermediate in their characteristics (Fig. 8-2).

11-4. Higher groups. Two or more species having certain characters in common constitute a **genus** (pl. *genera*). In turn, genera with some common characters are grouped as a **family,** the families into **orders,** the orders into **classes,** and the classes into **phyla** (sing. *phylum*). All the phyla together comprise the **Animal Kingdom** (Fig. 1-1), which is comparable with the Plant Kingdom. The scheme of classification is like a tree having many leaves (species), with one to many on a fine stem (genus), several of these on a larger twig (family), several twigs on a little branch (order), a number of these on a larger branch (class), and the latter borne on the main framework (phyla), the whole forming a tree (kingdom). Intermediate groups such as subgenera, subfamilies, superfamilies, suborders, subphyla, etc., often are necessary to indicate the proper degrees of relationship.

The wide occurrence of some characters makes it possible to recognize groups larger than phyla (Fig. 1-1, Table 11-1, and Classification beyond). Members of the Subkingdom Protozoa consist of single cells or colonies of like cells in contrast to those of the Subkingdom Metazoa, which are many-celled (tissue animals). Within the Metazoa, the sponges (Porifera) comprise the Branch Parazoa with no digestive cavity in contrast to the Branch Enterozoa of all higher animals having such a cavity. The digestive tract is **incomplete,** having only a mouth in the Coelenterata, Ctenophora, and Platyhelminthes, but it is **complete** with both mouth and anus in all others. The Enterozoa are further divisible according to the number of germ layers laid down in the embryo; those with two layers (Porifera, Coelenterata) are termed **diploblastic,** and all the others which have three germ layers are **triploblastic.** The higher phyla (Bryozoa to Chordata) are termed the *Eucoelomata* because their body cavity is a **coelom** lined by peritoneum, from which excretory and reproductive ducts lead to the exterior. In Mollusca and Arthropoda the coelom is far reduced and the blood circulates in spaces between the internal organs which are known as a **hemocoel.** Body spaces in the Entoprocta and Aschelminthes are not lined and are called a **pseudocoel.** Still other lower phyla that lack body spaces are termed the *Acoelomata.* **Invertebrates** include all

animals without a backbone of vertebrae in contrast to the *Vertebrates*
(Phylum CHORDATA, cyclostomes to mammals) that have a segmented
vertebral column.

In addition to the preceding characteristics there are some other
general features of animals important in distinguishing the larger groups
(Figs. 11-1, 11-2).

1. SYMMETRY. Many PROTOZOA are *asymmetrical,* not being divisible into equivalent parts, but a few show *spherical symmetry.*
The COELENTERATA, CTENOPHORA, and ECHINODERMATA are *radially
symmetrical,* around a median axis through the mouth or oral region.

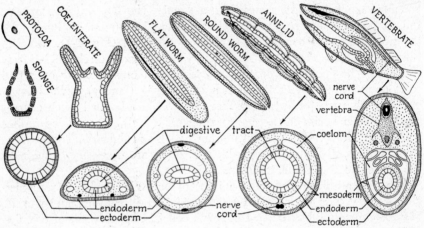

FIG. 11-1.   Diagrams of body structure in various types of animals.   *Above.*   In median
section.   *Below.*   In cross section, with indication of embryonic germ layers.

Planes through this axis will divide such an animal into radial sectors, or
antimeres.   The members of most phyla are *bilaterally symmetrical;*
a lengthwise vertical or sagittal plane will divide each individual into
equal and opposite right and left halves.   In such animals the part that
moves forward (and usually contains the mouth) is termed *anterior,* and
the opposite end is termed *posterior;* the back, or upper surface, is termed
dorsal, and the undersurface, usually toward the ground in locomotion,
is termed *ventral* (L. *venter*, belly).

2. SEGMENTATION.   In the ANNELIDA, ARTHROPODA, and CHORDATA
there is a linear repetition of body parts, known as *metamerism;* each
repeated unit is a *somite,* or *metamere.*   The segments may be essentially
alike (homonomous), as along the body of an earthworm, or unlike
(heteronomous), as in different body regions of a crayfish or insect.
Metamerism is conspicuous both externally and internally in most
annelids, is chiefly external with arthropods, and is largely internal with

the body muscles, vertebrae, nerves, and some blood vessels of man and other chordates.

3. APPENDAGES. Protruding structural parts that serve for loco-motion, feeding, or other purposes are termed *appendages;* examples are the tentacles of sea anemones, the minute setae of earthworms, the antennae and legs of arthropods, and the fins, legs, and wings of vertebrates.

4. SKELETON. Most land animals and many water dwellers have a *skeleton* for support or protection. It may be internal (endoskeleton), as in a frog or man, or external (exoskeleton), as with corals, crabs, or

Fig. 11-2.   Types of symmetry, and the axes, planes, and regions in animal bodies.

insects. The constituent materials may be calcareous or limy ($CaCO_3$), siliceous (SiO_2), or of organic material as in the chitin of arthropods.

5. SEX. An animal is termed *monoecious,* or *hermaphroditic,* if both male and female sex organs are contained in one individual. Mem-bers of most of the higher phyla are *dioecious,* with the sexes separate, each individual being either male or female.

11-5. History of classification. Aristotle (Greek, 384–322 B.C.), the "father of zoology," indicated how animals might be grouped according to their characteristics, and from his writings other persons outlined the fol-lowing classification that served for about 2,000 years:

I. Enaima (Vertebrates), with red blood.
   A. Viviparous.
     1. Man.
     2. Whales.
     3. Other mammals.
   B. Oviparous.
     1. Birds.
     2. Amphibians and most reptiles.
     3. Snakes.
     4. Fishes.

II. Anaima (Invertebrates), no red blood.
   A. Cephalopods.
   B. Crustaceans.
   C. Insects, spiders, etc.
   D. Other mollusks, echinoderms, etc.
   E. Sponges, coelenterates, etc.

John Ray (English, 1627–1705) was the first biologist to have a modern concept of species and to make some efforts to classify a few groups. It was Carolus Linnaeus (Swedish, 1707–1778) who laid the real basis for modern classification and nomenclature. He divided and subdivided the animal kingdom down to species on the basis of structural characters and gave each species a distinctive name. In his *Systema naturae* (tenth edition, 1758) he recognized six "classes," as follows: Mammalia, Aves (birds), Amphibia (reptiles and amphibians), Pisces (fishes), Insecta, and Vermes (all other invertebrates). Linnaeus thus did not divide the invertebrates with as much discrimination as Aristotle had done long before him. Because of the limited knowledge then available, a Linnaean "genus" might include animals now divided among several orders or families or placed in different phyla. The principle of his system is, however, the basis for our present method of classification.

In 1829, Cuvier (French, 1769–1832) divided animals into four branches: Vertebrata (mammals to fishes), Mollusca (mollusks and barnacles), Articulata (annelids, crustaceans, insects, spiders, etc.), and Radiata (echinoderms, nematodes, coelenterates, rotifers, etc.). Anatomy and classification were of great interest through the nineteenth century, and many systems were proposed, the important ones being by Lamarck (1801, 1812), DeBlainville (1822), Ehrenberg (1836), Von Siebold and Stannius (1845), Leuckart (1848), Owen (1855), Milne-Edwards (1855), and Agassiz (1859). Ernst Haeckel in 1864 and E. Ray Lankester in 1877 outlined the principal features of the zoological classification that is used today.

11-6. Difficulties in classification. All divisions in classification, from subspecies to phyla, are human concepts. Only individuals and populations of animals exist in nature. Whether a particular group shall be called a subspecies, species, genus, etc., is a matter of judgment based upon study of specimens. Biologists differ in appraising the relative importance of various characters and the amount of variation to be recognized in any group before subdividing it. Taxonomic "splitters" make many subdivisions, whereas conservative "lumpers" recognize fewer categories in the same material. Thus different recent authorities recognize 16 to 33 phyla, 20 to 40 orders of insects, and so on in other groups. As new facts are discovered, there is a tendency toward further subdivision. Zoologists are in fair agreement on much of animal classification, but no two may have exactly the same opinions on all details; as a result, no two books contain identical schemes of classification.

Because animal groups differ in their previous history, there is no uniformity in the content of groups above species. A certain genus may contain one or a few species, and another includes a hundred or more; different phyla have one to several classes. Attempts to indicate lines of descent by constructing "genealogical trees," especially in the higher units of classification (family, order, etc.), are difficult because intermediate forms that may once have existed have died out. Efforts at indicating probable origins and relationships are based on judgments that employ all available facts, but our knowledge is rarely adequate for final decisions.

In the above discussion and that on higher groups given earlier, animals are viewed **synthetically;** groups recognized as species are aggregated successively into genera, families, etc., up to the phyla and animal kingdom. The synopses of classification given in this book are **analytic,** subdividing the Animal Kingdom into phyla, classes, and orders; some important families are mentioned in a few chapters. Only a few common or representative genera and species are named. Limitations of space preclude further details.

B. NOMENCLATURE

11-7. Common or vernacular names. Each country has its own names for well-known animals. Thus a common sparrow of western Europe that is now established throughout the United States is known in different countries as follows:

United States: English sparrow.	Italy: Passera oltramontana.
England: House sparrow.	Germany: Haussperling.
France: Moineau domestique.	Holland: Musch.
Spain: Gorrion.	Denmark and Norway: Graaspurv.
Portugal: Pardal.	Sweden: Hussparf.

Within one country a species may have different local names; for example, in the United States, the mallard duck is also called wild duck, greenhead, gray duck, English duck, stock duck, and by some 30 other names. Still other names apply to the male (drake), female (duck, hen mallard), and young (ducklings). Confusion is thus likely between peoples of different nationalities or even within one country in naming a particular species.

11-8. Latin names. Until about the eighteenth century, manuscripts and most books were written or printed in Latin, the language of scholars. Few ordinary people then could read. When printed books began to appear in the languages of various countries, Latin was retained for the technical descriptions and names of animals, the names being long, descriptive "polynomials" that were useful but cumbersome. Thus in the first real natural history book in North America, Mark Catesby's *Natural History of Carolina, Florida* . . . (1731–1743), which had the text in parallel columns of English and French, the mockingbird was designated as

Turdus   minor   cinereo-albus   non   maculatus

meaning

Thrush   small   grayish-white   without   spots

11-9. Binomial nomenclature. When Linnaeus began his *Systema naturae*, which described and named all known animals (plants and minerals) with terse Latin descriptions of each, he started with Latin polynomials but later contracted these. In the tenth edition (1758) he consistently used but two names for each, a genus name and a species name. This *binomial nomenclature* soon became a universal means in all countries for naming animals and plants scientifically. Linnaeus designated the mockingbird of America as *Mimus polyglottos*, the English sparrow (to him, "hussparf") as *Passer domesticus*, and the mallard as *Anas platyrhynchos*. When a species is divided into subspecies, the latter are designated by *trinomials;* thus *Passer domesticus domesticus* is the subspecies of continental Europe, and *Passer domesticus niloticus* (*P. d. niloticus*) is the slightly differing form of the Nile Valley.

11-10. Rules of scientific nomenclature. With so many kinds of animals and numerous taxonomists at work in naming and describing them in different countries, some confusion in nomenclature has arisen. The same name has been given to different animals and different names to the same animal. Some rules of nomenclature were used by Linnaeus and others proposed later. The International Congress of Zoologists in 1898 created a permanent Commission on Nomenclature to prepare an International Code of Nomenclature and to render decisions on difficult cases. The code deals with names for families to subspecies and provides as follows:

(1) Zoological and botanical names are distinct (the same genus and species name may be used, but is not recommended, for both an animal and a plant); (2) no two genera in the Animal Kingdom may bear the same name, and the same applies to two species in a genus; (3) no names are recognized prior to those included by Linnaeus in the "Systema naturae," tenth edition, 1758; (4) scientific names must be either Latin or latinized and preferably are printed in italics; (5) the genus name should be a single word (nominative singular) and begin with a capital letter; (6) the species name should be a single or compound word beginning with a small letter (usually an adjective agreeing grammatically with the genus name); (7) the author of a scientific name is the person who first publishes it in a generally accessible book or periodical, with a recognizable description of the animal; (8) when a new genus is proposed, the type species should be indicated; (9) a family name is formed by adding -IDAE to the stem of the name of the type genus, and a subfamily name by -INAE.

In publishing the description of a new species it is now common practice to designate a particular or type specimen, to describe it, and to indicate the collection in which it is placed. Early authors often indicated no types and gave imperfect descriptions so that confusion has arisen as to which of their species are actually distinct and as to who were their authors. If a genus or species has been described more than once, the earliest name and author, according to the above rules, is recognized under the *law of priority* and duplicate names are termed *synonyms*.

TABLE 11-1   SOME CHARACTERISTICS OF THE PRINCIPAL GROUPS OF ANIMALS

Cells	Germ layers	Symmetry	Digestive tract	Excretory organs	Coelom	Circulatory system	Respiratory organs	Segmentation	PHYLUM (Class)	Distinctive features (exceptions omitted)
1	..	v	..	..	..	..	..	..	I PROTOZOA	Microscopic; one-celled or colonies of like cells
Cells many, arranged in layers or tissues (METAZOA)	2, diploblastic	Radial	Incomplete	0	0	0	0	0	III PORIFERA	Body perforated by pores and canals
				0	0	0	0	0	IV COELENTERATA	Nematocysts; digestive tract sac-like
				0	0	0	0	0	V CTENOPHORA	Comb plates for locomotion
	3, triploblastic	Bilateral	Complete (with anus)	+	0	0	0	0	VI PLATYHELMINTHES	Flat, soft; digestive tract branched or none
				+	0	+	0	0	VII NEMERTINEA	Slender, soft, ciliated; soft proboscis
				+	ps	0	0	0	IX Cl. ROTIFERA	Microscopic, cilia on oral disc
				+	ps	0	0	0	IX Cl. NEMATODA	Cylindrical, tough cuticle; no cilia
				+	+	0	0	0	XI BRYOZOA	Grow as mosslike or encrusting colonies
				+	+	+	0	0	XIII BRACHIOPODA	Dorsal and ventral limy shell; a fleshy stalk
		Radial		0	+h	+	+	0	XIV ECHINODERMATA	Symmetry 5-part radial; tube feet; spiny endoskeleton
				+	+	0	0	0	XV CHAETOGNATHA	Small; arrow-shaped, transparent; lateral fins
				+	+h	+	+	0	XVI MOLLUSCA	External limy shell of 1, 2, or 8 parts, or none; body soft
		Bilateral		+	+	+	+0	+	XVII ANNELIDA	Slender, of many like segments; fine setae as appendages
				+	+h	+	+	+	XXI ARTHROPODA	Segmented, with jointed appendages; exoskeleton of chitin
				+	+	+	+	+	XXII CHORDATA	Notochord, dorsal tubular nerve cord, gill slits; usually fins or limbs

+, present; 0, absent; *ps*, pseudocoel, not lined by peritoneum; *h*, coelom reduced, body spaces a hemocoel; *v*, symmetry various, or none.

In technical works the name of the author, sometimes abbreviated, is written after the genus or species—thus, *Passer domesticus* Linnaeus (or as Linn. or L.).

CLASSIFICATION OF THE ANIMAL KINGDOM

The following outline of the Animal Kingdom will serve for identification of most specimens to phylum and class. Other characters for these groups and for the orders are given in the more detailed classifications ending Chaps. 12 to 32. Some alternative names, used in other books, are included in parentheses. Groups marked † are extinct. Names of a few representative genera are given in italics, followed by common names when available.

Subkingdom A. *PROTOZOA.* Unicellular Animals.

Phylum I. **PROTOZOA.** Protozoans. Each individual one-celled or in colonies of similar cells; no tissues; size usually microscopic....................(Chap. 12)
Subphylum A. PLASMODROMA. Organelles for locomotion are flagella, pseudopodia, or none.

SARCODINA   MASTIGOPHORA   SPOROZOA   CILIATA   SUCTORIA
Fig. 11-3.   Phylum Protozoa.   Representatives of the five Classes.

Class 1. *MASTIGOPHORA.* Flagellates. One to many flagella for locomotion. *Ceratium; Euglena; Trypanosoma; Volvox.*
Class 2. *SARCODINA* (Rhizopoda). Pseudopodia for locomotion. *Amoeba; Actinophrys; Globigerina; Badhamia.*
Class 3. *SPOROZOA.* No locomotor organelles; all parasitic. *Monocystis, Eimeria, Plasmodium.*
Subphylum B. CILIOPHORA. Cilia at all or some stages in life history.
Class 1. *CILIATA* (Infusoria). Ciliates. Cilia or cirri always present. *Opalina; Paramecium; Oxytricha; Vorticella.*
Class 2. *SUCTORIA.* Suctorians. Cilia in young, adults with suckerlike tentacles. *Podophrya.*

Subkingdom B. *METAZOA.* Multicellular or Tissue Animals. Body of many cells, usually arranged in layers or tissues.
Branch 1. Mesozoa. Digestive cells few, external, ciliated.

Phylum II. **MESOZOA.** Symmetry radial; body slender, small; an external layer of ciliated digestive cells surrounding one or several reproductive cells; parasitic in cephalopods and other invertebrates. *Dicyema*....................(Chap. 18)

Branch 2. Parazoa. Digestive cells many, internal, flagellated; no digestive cavity.

Phylum III. **PORIFERA.** Sponges. Symmetry radial; body cylindrical, globose, branching, or irregular; skeleton internal, of minute spicules or of fibers (spongin); surface with many pores, connecting to canals and chambers lined by flagellated collar cells (choanocytes), and one or more large exits (oscula); aquatic, sessile.

(Chap. 13)

Class 1. *CALCAREA.* Calcareous Sponges. Spicules limy ($CaCO_3$), 1-, 3-, or 4-rayed; body surface bristly; marine, in shallow waters. *Leucosolenia, Scypha.*

Class 2. *HEXACTINELLIDA.* Glass Sponges. Spicules siliceous, 6-rayed, and in definite arrangement; marine, at 300 feet or deeper. *Hyalonema; Euplectella,* Venus's flower-basket.

Class 3. *DEMOSPONGIAE.* Skeleton siliceous, of spongin, of both, or none; canals complex; some large and brilliant; mostly marine. *Halisarca; Spongilla,* fresh-water sponge; *Spongia,* bath sponge.

Branch 3. Enterozoa. A digestive cavity or tract.

Division *A.* radiata. Symmetry radial.

Phylum IV. **COELENTERATA** (Cnidaria). Symmetry radial; the individual a sessile cylindrical polyp often in colonies, or a bell-like free-floating medusa with much gelatinous mesoglea; stinging capsules (nematocysts) present; digestive cavity saclike, sometimes branched; mouth surrounded by soft tentacles; no anus, head, or other organ systems; all aquatic, chiefly marine..............................(Chap. 14)

Porifera Hydrozoa Scyphozoa Anthozoa Ctenophora

Fig. 11-4. Phyla Porifera, Coelenterata (three Classes), and Ctenophora.

Class 1. *HYDROZOA.* Hydroids (and some medusae). Mouth opens directly into a digestive cavity that lacks partitions; hydroid stage usually in colonies; medusa with velum. *Hydra,* fresh-water polyp; *Obelia,* colonial hydroid, marine; *Millepora,* "stinging coral"; *Physalia,* Portuguese man-of-war.

Class 2. *SCYPHOZOA* (Scyphomedusae). Jellyfishes. Small to large medusae, chiefly of gelatinous mesoglea, and of bell or umbrella shape, margined with tentacles; digestive cavity with branched canals; polyp stage minute; all marine. *Aurelia,* common jellyfish.

Class 3. *ANTHOZOA* (Actinozoa). Sea Anemones, Corals, etc. All polyps (no medusae); a flat oral disc with tentacles; mouth connects to stomodeum (gullet); digestive cavity divided by radial partitions; corals with limy exoskeleton; all marine and attached, some gregarious. *Metridium,* sea anemone; *Gorgonia,* sea fan (horny); *Astrangia, Orbicella,* stony corals.

Phylum V. **CTENOPHORA.** Comb Jellies. Symmetry biradial; body subspherical with much mesoglea, or flat; 8 external rows of ciliated comb plates for locomotion; no nematocysts; digestive cavity with branched canals; no anus; marine; solitary. *Pleurobrachia; Cestum,* Venus's girdle; *Beroë*..................(Chap. 15)

Division *B.* bilateria. Symmetry bilateral (secondarily radial in Echinodermata); with organ systems and mostly with spaces between body wall and internal organs; digestive tract complete, with anus; mesoderm present.

Section a. acoelomata. No body cavity; space between body wall and internal organs filled with parenchyma.

Phylum VI. **PLATYHELMINTHES.** Flatworms. Body depressed, thin and soft, leaf- or ribbonlike, digestive tract branched and without anus, or absent; parenchyma fills spaces between organs; a pair of anterior ganglia or a nerve ring and 1 to 3 pairs of longitudinal nerve cords; usually hermaphroditic·..............(Chap. 16)

TURBELLARIA   TREMATODA   CESTOIDEA   NEMERTINEA   NEMATODA
Fig. 11-5. Phyla Platyhelminthes (three Classes), Nemertinea, and Nematoda.

Class 1. *TURBELLARIA.* Free-living Flatworms. Body ribbonlike to disclike, epidermis ciliated, no hooks or suckers; usually a digestive tract with ventral mouth; mostly free-living; marine, fresh-water, or terrestrial. *Euplanaria; Leptoplana.*

Class 2. *TREMATODA.* Flukes. Body often leaflike, with thick cuticle and no cilia; ventral suckers or hooks or both; mouth usually anterior, digestive tract 2-branched; all parasitic. *Fasciola,* liver fluke.

Class 3. *CESTOIDEA.* Tapeworms. Body narrow, flat, elongate, comprising a scolex, with suckers or hooks or both (for attachment), and a chain of few to many proglottids (pseudosegments), each with complete reproductive organs; cuticle thick, no cilia; no mouth or digestive tract; all parasitic. *Taenia; Dipylidium.*

Phylum VII. **NEMERTINEA** (Rhynchocoela). Ribbon Worms. Body slender, soft, very elastic, and covered with cilia; no segmentation; mouth anterior and with a long eversible proboscis; digestive tract complete, with anus; a blood vascular system; body spaces filled with parenchyma; no coelom; nervous system with anterior ganglia (brain) and 3 longitudinal nerve trunks; sexes separate; free-living, mostly marine, few fresh-water and terrestrial. *Cerebratulus; Stichostemma*......(Chap. 18)

Section b. pseudocoelomata. Spaces between body wall and internal organs not a coelom; anus present.

Phylum VIII. **ENTOPROCTA.** Individuals minute, solitary or colonial, each on a stalk, with calyx bearing single circle of many ciliated tentacles; digestive tract U-shaped, both mouth and anus within circle of tentacles; body spaces a pseudocoel filled with parenchyma; monoecious or dioecious; attached to objects or animals in salt or fresh waters. *Pedicellina, Urnatella*..........................(Chap. 18)

Phylum IX. **ASCHELMINTHES.** Size small or minute, body commonly slender; digestive tract complete, intestine usually straight, anus posterior; no anterior cilia (except rotifers).

Class 1. *ROTIFERA* (Rotatoria). Wheel Animalcules. Body of trunk and tapering "tail," the latter often jointed and with "feet" having adhesive glands for attachment; anterior end with trochal disc bearing cilia, used for locomotion and feeding, that move so as to produce a wheel-like appearance; males minute. *Hydatina* (Chap. 18)

Class 2. *GASTROTRICHA.* To 0.54 mm. long; slender, flexible; ventral surface flat, with 2 lengthwise rows of cilia for locomotion; mouth anterior, surrounded by bristles; aquatic. *Chaetonotus*......................................(Chap. 18)

Class 3. *KINORHYNCHA* (Echinodera). To 1 mm. long, cylindrical, head of 2 rings, encircled by spines; mouth with spiny retractile proboscis; body of 11 (or 12) rings covered by stout cuticle and bearing spines; sexes separate; marine. *Echinodera*..(Chap. 18)

Class 4. *NEMATODA* (Nemathelminthes). *ROUNDWORMS.* Body rounded, slender, often tapered at ends; covered with tough cuticle; longitudinal muscles only, producing flexing motions but no elongation or contraction; an anterior nerve ring and 6 lengthwise nerve cords; sexes separate; free-living in soil or water, or parasitic. *Ascaris*, roundworm; *Necator*, hookworm.............................(Chap. 17)

Class 5. *NEMATOMORPHA* (Gordiacea). "HAIR SNAKES," or "HORSEHAIR WORMS." Body threadlike, not tapered, anterior end blunt; cuticle rough, opaque; body spaces lined with cells; sexes separate; larvae parasitic in insects, adults free-living in water. *Gordius*...(Chap. 18)

NEMATOMORPHA ACANTHOCEPHALA   ROTIFERA   BRYOZOA   BRACHIOPODA
FIG. 11-6. Miscellaneous phyla.

Phylum X. **ACANTHOCEPHALA.** SPINY-HEADED WORMS. Body flat and rough in life, cylindrical and smooth when preserved; cuticle thin; anterior end with retractile proboscis bearing rows of recurved spines; no digestive tract; sexes separate; parasitic, larvae in arthropods, adults in vertebrates. *Echinorhynchus; Gigantorhynchus*...(Chap. 18)

Section c. EUCOELOMATA. With true coelom, usually lined with layer of cells.

Phylum XI. **BRYOZOA.** (Polyzoa). MOSS ANIMALS. Colonies branched and plantlike, or as low incrustations on rocks or shells, or as gelatinous masses; individuals many, minute, each in separate housing (zooecium); ciliated tentacles around mouth; digestive tract U-shaped, complete; coelom developed and lined; hermaphroditic; free-living in salt and fresh waters. *Bugula; Pectinatella*...............(Chap. 18)

Phylum XII. **PHORONIDEA.** Body wormlike, cylindrical, unsegmented, within a self-secreted membranous tube; anterior end bearing ciliated tentacles and a horseshoe-shaped lophophore; digestive tract complete, U-shaped, mouth and anus within lophophore; coelom of 6 compartments, with lining; blood vessels present. contractile; hermaphroditic; marine. *Phoronis*........................(Chap. 18)

Phylum XIII. **BRACHIOPODA.** LAMP SHELLS. External limy shell of dorsal and ventral valves, attached to rocks by a fleshy stalk; interior with 2 spiral arms (lophophores) bearing ciliated tentacles; digestive tract with or without anus; coelom well developed; heart small; sexes separate; marine. *Lingula; Terebratulina.*

(Chap. 18)

ASTEROIDEA   OPHIUROIDEA   ECHINOIDEA   CRINOIDEA   HOLOTHURIOIDEA
FIG. 11-7. Phylum ECHINODERMATA. The five living Classes.

Phylum XIV. **ECHINODERMATA.** ECHINODERMS. Symmetry radial, usually 5-parted, around an oral-aboral axis; no segmentation; body wall with calcareous plates, usually forming a rigid or flexible endoskeleton with external spines; digestive tract with (or without) anus; coelom includes water vascular system; with external tube feet for locomotion; sexes usually separate; all marine.............(Chap. 19)

Class 1. *CRINOIDEA.* Sea Lilies, Feather Stars. Body flowerlike, a box-like calyx of many plates bearing slender branched arms; some species on aboral stalk. *Anteodon.*

Class 2. *ASTEROIDEA.* Starfishes or Sea Stars. Body star-shaped or pentagonal with 5 to 50 arms (rays) not sharply distinct from central disc; skeleton flexible, usually with short spines and pedicellariae; ambulacral grooves with 2 or 4 rows of tube feet. *Asterias; Pisaster.*

Class 3. *OPHIUROIDEA.* Brittle Stars. Body with central disc and 5 distinct slender jointed arms (sometimes branched); tube feet in 2 rows; no anus. *Ophiura*, brittle star; *Gorgonocephalus*, "basket fish."

Class 4. *ECHINOIDEA.* Sea Urchins, Sand Dollars. Body hemispherical, disc- or egg-shaped, in shell (test) of fused plates that bear movable spines and pedicellariae; digestive tract elongate, coiled. *Arbacia, Strongylocentrotus*, sea urchins; *Dendraster*, sand dollar.

Class 5. *HOLOTHURIOIDEA.* Sea Cucumbers. Body elongate to wormlike, wall soft, fleshy; no arms, spines, or pedicellariae; mouth anterior, surrounded by retractile tentacles; digestive tract S-shaped, anus posterior. *Holothuria; Thyone.*

Phylum XV. **CHAETOGNATHA.** Arrow Worms. Small, slender, transparent; body of head, trunk, and tail; bristles or hooks about mouth; paired fins on trunk and a terminal tail fin for locomotion; digestive tract complete; coelom of 3 paired cavities; hermaphroditic; free-living, marine. *Sagitta* .... (Chap. 18)

Phylum XVI. **MOLLUSCA.** Mollusks. Symmetry bilateral (viscera and shell coiled in some); no segmentation; body soft, covered by a mantle that usually secretes a limy shell of 1, 2, or 8 parts; usually an anterior head and a ventral muscular foot for locomotion; digestive tract complete; a heart and blood vessels; respiration usually by gills; coelom reduced; nervous system of a few paired ganglia and connectives; sexes usually separate; in salt and fresh waters, some on land ...... (Chap. 20)

Class 1. *AMPHINEURA.* Chitons. Body elongate, often elliptical, shell of 8 dorsal plates (or none); head reduced; no tentacles; marine. *Chiton.*

Class 2. *SCAPHOPODA.* Tooth Shells. Shell and mantle tubular, slenderly tapered; foot conical; no gills. *Dentalium.*

Class 3. *GASTROPODA.* Univalve Mollusks. Viscera usually asymmetrical in spirally coiled shell (shell in some reduced or conical; in some, none); head distinct, with 1 or 2 pairs of tentacles; foot large, flat. *Helix*, snail; *Limax*, slug (shell internal), *Acmaea*, limpet (shell conical); *Haliotis*, abalone.

AMPHINEURA   SCAPHOPODA   PELECYPODA   GASTROPODA   CEPHALOPODA
Fig. 11-8.   Phylum Mollusca.   The five Classes.

Class 4. *PELECYPODA.* Bivalve Mollusks. Body enclosed in shell of 2 lateral valves (right and left), with dorsal hinge; no head or jaws; foot often hatchet-shaped, extends between valves when moving. *Ostrea*, oyster; *Mya*, clam; *Teredo*, "shipworm."

Class 5. *CEPHALOPODA.* Squids, Octopuses, etc. Shell internal or external, or none; head large, with conspicuous complex eyes; mouth with horny jaws and surrounded by 8, 10, or many arms or tentacles; marine. *Loligo*, squid; *Octopus*, devilfish or octopus; *Nautilus*, pearly nautilus.

Phylum XVII. **ANNELIDA.** Segmented Worms. Body elongated, usually of many like segments with fine bristle-like setae for locomotion; cuticle thin; digestive tract complete, tubular; coelom usually large; blood vascular system closed; nervous system of dorsal "brain" and a ventral nerve cord having ganglia and lateral nerves in each somite; mostly free-living............................(Chap. 21)

Class 1. *ARCHIANNELIDA.* Small; segmentation chiefly internal; no parapodia or setae; marine. *Polygordius.*

Class 2. *POLYCHAETA.* Sandworms, Tube Worms, etc. Segmentation conspicuous, with many somites having lateral projections (parapodia) that bear numerous setae; head region evident, with tentacles; sexes usually separate; chiefly marine. *Neanthes (Nereis),* clamworm, in sand; *Chaetopterus,* in tube.

Class 3. *OLIGOCHAETA.* Earthworms, etc. Segmentation conspicuous; no head or parapodia; setae usually few per somite; hermaphroditic; chiefly in fresh waters and moist soil. *Enchytraeus; Lumbricus,* common large earthworm.

Class 4. *HIRUDINEA.* Leeches. Body flattish; somites inconspicuous, each divided externally into several annuli; no setae or parapodia; a large posterior sucker, and often a smaller one at anterior end; coelom reduced; hermaphroditic; in salt and fresh waters or on land. *Hirudo, Macrobdella.*

OLIGOCHAETA   POLYCHAETA   HIRUDINEA

Fig. 11-9.   Phylum Annelida.   The three commoner Classes.

Phylum XVIII. **SIPUNCULOIDEA.** "Peanut Worms." Body slenderly gourd-shaped, highly contractile; slender anterior end (introvert) retractile, with short hollow tentacles around mouth; no segmentation or setae; digestive tract slender, spiraled, anus dorsal at base of introvert; coelom large, undivided, ciliated, containing blood with corpuscles; anterior dorsal nerve ganglion and ventral nerve cord; sexes separate; marine. *Sipunculus, Phascolosoma*................(Chap. 18)

Phylum XIX. **PRIAPULOIDEA.** Sausage-shaped; anterior end with swollen introvert bearing lengthwise rows of spines; body narrower, with transverse striations (not segmented); digestive tract straight, anus in posterior end surrounded by gill lobes; coelom large; adult lacks blood system, nephridia, and sense organs; sexes separates; marine. *Priapulus*.......................................(Chap. 18)

Phylum XX. **ECHIUROIDEA.** Body sausage-like; anterior end with trough-shaped elastic proboscis (nonretractile) leading to mouth; intestine spiraled, anus at posterior end, joined by 2 anal pouches; circulatory system of dorsal and ventral vessels; 1 to 3 pair of nephridia anteriorly; one pair of large ventral setae below mouth; adults unsegmented, larvae with 15 vestigial somites; monoecious; marine. *Echiurus, Urechis*...(Chap. 18)

Phylum XXI. **ARTHROPODA.** Joint-footed Animals. Body typically of head, thorax, and abdomen formed of segments and with body segments (somites) like or unlike, variously separate or fused; 4 or more pairs of jointed appendages; chitinous exoskeleton covering all parts, molted at intervals; digestive tract complete, straight; coelom reduced, body spaces a hemocoel; heart dorsal; respiration by gills, tracheae, or lung books; "brain" dorsal, nerve cord ventral and paired, with ganglia in each somite or concentrated anteriorly; sexes usually separate; terrestrial or aquatic, free-living, commensal, or parasitic....................................(Chap. 22)

Class 1. *CRUSTACEA*. LOBSTERS, CRABS, WATER FLEAS, BARNACLES, ETC. Two pairs of antennae, a pair of jaws, and 2 pairs of maxillae; body often with dorsal shield, or carapace, and tail ending in telson containing anus; some appendages biramous; respire usually by gills; mainly aquatic. *Daphnia*, water flea; *Balanus*, barnacle; *Astacus, Cambarus*, crayfishes..............................(Chap. 22)

Class 2. †*TRILOBITA*. †*Triarthrus*..............................(Chap. 22)

CRUSTACEA   INSECTA   ARACHNOIDEA   CHILOPODA   DIPLOPODA

FIG. 11-10.   Phylum ARTHROPODA.   Representatives of the five principal Classes.

Class 3. *INSECTA*. INSECTS. One pair of antennae; head, thorax, and abdomen distinct; thorax typically with 3 pairs of legs and 2 pairs of wings; mainly terrestrial. *Melanoplus*, grasshopper; *Musca*, fly; *Apis*, bee...............(Chap. 23)

Class 4. *ARACHNOIDEA*. SPIDERS, SCORPIONS, MITES, TICKS, ETC. No antennae; body of cephalothorax, with 6 pairs of appendages (chelicerae, pedipalpi, and 4 pairs of walking legs) and abdomen; chiefly terrestrial. *Epeira*, spider; *Sarcoptes*, itch mite; *Ornithodorus*, tick; *Limulus*, king crab..................(Chap. 24)

Class 5. *CHILOPODA*. CENTIPEDES. Form elongate, depressed; head with 1 pair of antennae; body of 15 to 173 somites, each with a pair of legs; terrestrial. *Lithobius; Scolopendra*...(Chap. 24)

Class 6. *DIPLOPODA*. MILLIPEDES. Body elongate, cylindrical; 1 pair of antennae; thorax of 4 somites, with a pair of legs on each; abdomen of 20 to more than 100 double somites, each with 2 pairs of legs; terrestrial. *Julus; Spirobolus*.
(Chap. 24)

Class 7. *ONYCHOPHORA*. Elongate; no head, but anterior end with paired short "antennae" and oral papillae; body somewhat cylindrical, unsegmented; 15 to 43 pairs of stumpy, unjointed legs; terrestrial. *Peripatus*................(Chap. 24)

The following groups of Arthropoda are of uncertain position.

PYCNOGONIDA (Pantopoda). SEA SPIDERS. Small to minute; body short, thin; 7 pairs of appendages including 4 pairs of long thin legs; marine. *Pycnogonum.*
(Chap. 24)

PENTASTOMIDA (Linguatulida). Wormlike, soft, unsegmented, but abdomen ringed; 2 pairs of ventral hooks beside mouth; parasitic in vertebrates. *Linguatula, Porocephalus*...(Chap. 24)

TARDIGRADA. BEAR ANIMALCULES. To 1 mm. long; cylindrical unsegmented body and 4 pairs of stumpy unjointed legs with claws; in moss or fresh waters. *Echiniscus*...(Chap. 24)

SYMPHYLA. GARDEN CENTIPEDE. Small, slender, white, 12 pairs of legs plus head appendages including antennae; in damp places. *Scutigerella*.......(Chap. 24)

PAUROPODA. Minute; cylindrical body of 10 to 12 somites, 9 pairs of legs, and 6 dorsal plates; in damp places. *Pauropus*......................(Chap. 24)

Phylum XXII. **CHORDATA**. CHORDATES. Having, at some stage or throughout life, the following: an axial rodlike notochord for support of the body, a single dorsal tubular nerve cord, and paired gill slits between the pharynx and exterior; segmentation usually evident; tail behind anus........................(Chap. 25)

Group α. **ACRANIA**. No cranium, jaws, vertebrae, or paired appendages.

Subphylum A. HEMICHORDATA (Enteropneusta, Adelochorda). TONGUE WORMS. Body wormlike, anterior end usually with fleshy proboscis and collar;

notochord short, anterior; nerve tissues both dorsal and ventral in epidermis; many permanent gill slits; marine. *Balanoglossus, Saccoglossus. Cephalodiscus*. . (Chap. 25)

Subphylum B. TUNICATA (Urochordata). Tunicates. Larvae minute and tadpole-like with gill slits, and with both notochord and nerve cord in tail; adults tubular, globose, or irregular in form, covered with tunic or test, often transparent; with many gill slits but notochord usually absent and nervous system reduced; marine. (Chap. 25)

Class 1. *LARVACEA* (Appendicularia). Individuals are minute persistent larvae, separate and free swimming, with notochord, "brain" and nerve cord, and 2 gill slits; test not permanent. *Appendicularia.*

Class 2. *ASCIDIACEA.* Ascidians. Size and form various; solitary, colonial, or compound; usually sessile after metamorphosis when tail, nerve cord, and notochord are lost and "brain" is reduced to a ganglion, but many gill slits persist; test well developed, permanent. *Cione, Molgula*, simple ascidians; *Botryllus*, compound ascidian.

Class 3. *THALIACEA.* Chain Tunicates. Size various; adults free-living, with no tail or notochord; test permanent, with circular muscle bands. *Salpa, Doliolum.*

Subphylum C. CEPHALOCHORDATA (Leptocardii). Lancelets. Body small, slender, elongate, "fishlike," distinctly segmented; notochord and nerve cord extending entire length of body, and many gill slits enclosed in an outer atrium, all permanent. *Branchiostoma*, amphioxus or lancelet . . . . (Chap. 25)

HEMICHORDATA   TUNICATA CEPHALOCHORDATA   CYCLOSTOMATA   CHONDRICHTHYES

OSTEICHTHYES   AMPHIBIA   REPTILIA   AVES   MAMMALIA

Fig. 11-11. Phylum Chordata. Representatives of the three lower Subphyla, and of the seven Classes of living vertebrates.

Group β. CRANIATA. Vertebrates. With cranium (skull), visceral arches, and "spinal column" of segmental vertebrae, all cartilaginous in lower forms but bony in higher ones; notochord extends from tail to base of cranium; anterior end of nerve cord with enlarged brain of specialized parts; head region with paired special sense organs (smell, sight, hearing); paired semicircular canals for equilibration; circulatory system closed, with heart of 2 to 4 chambers, and red blood cells.

Subphylum D. AGNATHA. Jawless Vertebrates. No true jaws or paired appendages.

Class 1. †*OSTRACODERMI.* Extinct Armored Fishes. Head and body armored with large scales, often fused into a cephalothoracic shield. †*Cephalaspis;* †*Pterolepis.*

Class 2. *CYCLOSTOMATA* (Marsipobranchii, Monorhina). Lampreys and Hagfishes. Body cylindrical, slender, with median fins only; skin smooth, no scales; heart 2-chambered; aquatic; mouth suctorial, with horny teeth; one nasal opening; 6 to 14 baglike pairs of gill pouches opening on side of body. *Petromyzon*, lamprey; *Myxine*, hagfish. . . . . (Chap. 26)

Subphylum E. GNATHOSTOMATA. Jawed Vertebrates. One pair of visceral arches modified as biting jaws; 2 nasal capsules or tubes; 3 pairs of semicircular canals; usually with paired appendages (fins or limbs); sexes separate.

Superclass a. pisces. Fishes. With median fins supported by fin rays; paired fins usually present; skin usually with scales containing limy material; nasal capsules not connected to mouth cavity; heart with one auricle; respiration by gills; aquatic.

Class 1. †PLACODERMI (Aphetohyoidea). Ancient Fishes. Jaws primitive; hyoid unspecialized, followed by a complete gill slit, no spiracle; paired fins variable; body covering of bony scales or plates; skeleton bony. †Climatius, acanthodian; †Dinichthys, arthrodire; †Pterichthyodes, antiarch......................(Chap. 27)

Class 2. CHONDRICHTHYES. Cartilaginous Fishes. Skeleton cartilaginous, notochord persistent; skin covered with placoid scales; chiefly marine. Squalus, shark; Raja, ray; Chimaera, chimaera.................................(Chap. 27)

Class 3. OSTEICHTHYES. Bony Fishes. Skeleton more or less bony; mouth usually terminal; gills covered by opercula; scales usually cycloid. Acipenser, sturgeon; Salmo, trout, salmon; Perca, perch; Neoceratodus, lungfish..........(Chap. 28)

Superclass b. tetrapoda. Four-legged "Land" Vertebrates. Typically with two pairs of 5-toed limbs, variously modified, reduced, or absent; skeleton of bone; nasal capsules connect to mouth cavity; some with external auditory canals; heart with 2 auricles and double circulation of blood.

Class 1. AMPHIBIA. Amphibians. Living forms covered by a soft, moist, glandular skin; heart 3-chambered; larvae typically aquatic, respiring by gills; adults commonly terrestrial, usually respiring by lungs. Ichthyophis, caecilian; Ambystoma, salamander; Bufo, toad; Rana, frog.................................(Chap. 29)

Class 2. REPTILIA. Reptiles. Body covered with dry cornified skin, usually with scales, or scutes; toes usually ending in claws; feet and limbs reduced or absent in some; respire by lungs; heart imperfectly 4-chambered; mostly terrestrial, some aquatic. Chrysemys, turtle; Sphenodon, tuatera; Sceloporus, lizard; Thamnophis, garter snake; Alligator, alligator...................................(Chap. 30)

Class 3. AVES. Birds. Body covered with feathers; fore limbs modified as wings for flight; respire by lungs; heart completely 4-chambered; "warm-blooded" (homoiothermous); terrestrial or aquatic. Struthio, ostrich, Larus, gull; Anas, duck; Corvus, crow; Passer, sparrow.......................................(Chap. 31)

Class 4. MAMMALIA. Mammals. Body usually covered with hair; respire by lungs; heart as in birds; "warm-blooded"; females with mammary glands providing milk for nourishment of young. Ornithorhynchus, duckbill; Macropus, kangaroo; Didelphis, opossum; Homo, man; Rattus, rat; Canis, dog, wolf; Equus, horse.

(Chaps. 32, 33)

PART II
The Animal Kingdom

CHAPTER 12

PHYLUM PROTOZOA. ONE-CELLED ANIMALS

The PROTOZOA (Gr. *protos*, first + *zoön*, animal) are mostly one-celled animals of microscopic size. In the Animal Kingdom they comprise the lowest of the great groups, or phyla, and stand in contrast to all the others, which are the multicellular tissue animals, or METAZOA (Gr. *meta*, after). As to structure, a protozoan is comparable with one cell of a metazoan, but functionally it is an entire organism, physiologically balanced, and performs all the essential life processes of an animal. Some protozoans are very simple in structure and others are complex, with "cell organs,"

Amoeba	Euglena	Gregarina	Paramecium	Podophrya
SARCODINA	MASTIGOPHORA	SPOROZOA	CILIATA	SUCTORIA

— Classes.

FIG. 12-1.   Common representatives of the Phylum PROTOZOA.

or *organelles,* that serve particular vital processes and that are functionally analogous to the organ systems of multicellular animals. Fully 30,000 kinds of PROTOZOA are known, and as individuals they far exceed all other animals in numbers. Each species lives in some particular moist habitat—in ocean waters or on the ocean bottom; in fresh, brackish, or foul waters inland; in soil or decaying organic matter. Many are free-living and free-swimming, whereas others are sessile, and some in both categories form colonies. Still others live on or in some species of plants and all sorts of animals from protozoans to man. In different cases the relationships vary from casual occurrence to strict parasitism. In turn, some kinds of bacteria live on or in certain protozoans as casuals, symbionts, or parasites. Many protozoans serve as food of other minute animals. Some are helpful in the purification of filter and sewage beds, but disease-producing species such as those causing amoebic dysentery, malaria, and African sleeping sickness are a scourge of mankind.

The PROTOZOA are divided, according to the structures they possess for locomotion (Fig. 12-1), into five Classes: (1) MASTIGOPHORA, or flagellates, with one or more whiplike flagella; (2) SARCODINA, or rhizopods, with pseudopodia; (3) SPOROZOA, with no locomotor organelles; (4) CILIATA, or ciliates, with cilia throughout life; and (5) SUCTORIA, with cilia in the young and tentacles in the adult stages. In the pages that follow, each class is discussed separately, and there is a classification of the phylum to orders at the end of the chapter.

12-1. Characteristics. 1. Small, usually one-celled, some in colonies of few to many similar individuals; symmetry none, bilateral, radial, or spherical.

2. Cell form usually constant, oval, elongate, spherical, or otherwise, varied in some species and changing with environment or age in many.

3. Nucleus distinct, single or multiple; other structural parts as organelles; no organs or tissues.

4. Locomotion by flagella, pseudopodia, cilia, or movements of the cell itself.

5. Some species with protective housings, or tests; many species produce resistant cysts or spores to survive unfavorable conditions and for dispersal.

6. Mode of life free-living, commensal, symbiotic, or parasitic.

7. Nutrition various: (a) *holozoic*, subsisting on other organisms (bacteria, yeasts, algae, other protozoans, etc.); (b) *saprophytic*, subsisting on dissolved substances in their surroundings; (c) *holophytic*, or autotrophic, by photosynthesis as in plants. Some combine two methods.

8. Asexual reproduction by binary fission, multiple fission, or budding; some with sexual reproduction by fusion of gametes or by conjugation (in CILIATA).

The PROTOZOA are descended from ancient unknown stocks of the earliest living organisms on the earth. The soft-bodied species have left no fossil record, but the extreme age of the phylum is proved by finding the hard remains of RADIOLARIA and FORAMINIFERA in Pre-Cambrian rocks. Most protozoans are one-celled and solitary, but some flagellates and ciliates grow as colonies. Many of the flagellate Subclass PHYTO-MASTIGINA have the cells embedded in a common gelatinous matrix and show physiological coordination between the individuals; some are connected to one another by protoplasmic threads. In some (*Volvox*) there is differentiation into vegetative and reproductive cells. These conditions parallel the formation of tissues and the segregation of somatic and germ cells in METAZOA. Certain PROTOZOA, ordinarily free-living, are occasionally found living within the bodies of other animals, thus affording a hint as to how strictly parasitic species may have been derived from free-living forms. Some chlorophyll-bearing flagellates resemble the green algae in structure and physiology and suggest common origin for plants and animals. The MASTIGOPHORA are probably the most primitive group, the CILIATA are the most specialized as to structure, and the SPOROZOA are probably simplified in structure as a result of their strictly parasitic manner of life. For convenience, the SARCODINA are discussed first.

12-2. Size. PROTOZOA are mostly so small that they are measured in microns (one micron, μ, = 1/1,000 mm., or 1/25,400 inch). Some are only 2 or 3 μ in length. A dozen *Babesia* (sporozoan) may inhabit one red blood cell or several hundred *Leishmania* (flagellate) a single tissue cell.

Most species are less than 250 μ long; but *Spirostomum* (ciliate) grows to 3 mm., and *Porospora gigantea* (sporozoan) to 16 mm.

CLASS *SARCODINA*. AMOEBAS, ETC.

This class includes both the "naked" amoebas and various shell-bearing types, the FORAMINIFERA, HELIOZOA, RADIOLARIA, and MYCETOZOA. The common amoeba, *Amoeba proteus,* of clean fresh waters that contain green vegetation, serves well as an introduction to the PROTOZOA and to the SARCODINA (Gr. *sarcodes*, fleshy).   The amoeba (Fig. 12-2) appears to be about the simplest possible living animal, an independent cell with nucleus and cytoplasm but no permanent organelles.   It has been studied intensively in the hope of discovering some of the fundamental features of life.   Despite its seeming simplicity it can move, capture, digest, and assimilate complex food, egest indigestible residues, respire, produce secretions and excretions, respond to changes (stimuli) of various kinds in both its internal and external environment, grow, and reproduce itself in kind.   It thus performs all essential animal activities and shows physiological specialization in various processes without having many structurally differentiated parts to perform these functions.

FIG. 12-2.   Structure of *Amoeba*.

12-3. Structure. The living amoeba is a minute mass of clear, colorless, and jelly-like protoplasm, up to 0.60 mm. long, that is flexible, of irregular shape, and undergoes frequent change of form.   It consists of (1) a very thin elastic external cell membrane, or *plasmalemma,* and beneath this (2) a narrow zone of clear nongranular *ectoplasm* surrounding (3) the main body mass of *granular endoplasm.* The latter consists of (*a*) an outer stiffer *plasmagel* and (*b*) an inner *plasmasol* in which streaming movements are visible.   Within the endoplasm are (4) a disclike *nucleus,* not easily seen in the living animal; (5) a spherical fluid-filled *contractile vacuole,* which at intervals moves to the surface, contracts, discharges its contents into the surrounding water, and then re-forms; (6) one or more *food vacuoles* of various sizes, containing bits of food under digestion; and (7) various other *vacuoles, crystals, oil globules,* and other *cell inclusions* ranging downward in size to or below the limit of microscopic visibility.

Briefly, the functions of these parts are as follows: (1) The cell membrane retains protoplasm within the cell, but permits the passage of water, oxygen, and carbon dioxide; (2) the ectoplasm lends form to the cell body; (3) the endoplasm contains the other structures and serves in locomotion;

(4) the nucleus controls vital processes of the organism; (5) the contractile vacuole regulates water content; (6) the food vacuoles contain food undergoing digestion; and (7) the other cell inclusions are reserve foods or other materials essential to metabolism.   If the amoeba is cut in two, the cell membrane soon surrounds each piece and prevents loss of the protoplasm; the part without a nucleus can still move and ingest food but is unable to digest or assimilate the food and soon dies, whereas that with the nucleus will continue to grow and reproduce.   An isolated nucleus, however, cannot survive.   Thus the nucleus and cytoplasm are interdependent.

12-4. Locomotion.   The amoeba moves by forming and extending temporary fingerlike extensions, or ***pseudopodia*** (Gr. *pseudos,* false +

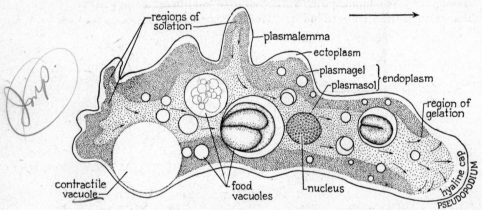

Fig. 12-3.   Locomotion in *Amoeba.*   The fluid inner plasmasol flows forward and is converted into plasmagel at the forward-moving pseudopod; the reverse process occurs in the opposite end and in pseudopodia that are being withdrawn.   Large arrow indicates direction of movement of entire animal; small arrows that of endoplasm.   (*After Mast*, 1926.)

podos, foot) at any place on its cell body (Fig. 12-3).   This sort of irregular flowing is termed ***amoeboid movement;*** it occurs in many Protozoa and also in the amoebocytes of sponges and the white blood cells of vertebrates.   Amoeboid movement is probably a basic characteristic of unspecialized protoplasm and like most fundamental processes is difficult to explain.   Various theories have been offered to account for it.   It can be imitated in part by some mixtures of nonliving materials, where differences in surface tension account for certain kinds of movement. S. O. Mast holds that movement in the amoeba is the result of changes within the colloidal protoplasm, from the fluid "sol" to the more solid "gel" condition, and vice versa.   Three outstanding features of locomotion are (1) attachment to the substratum, possibly by a secretion; (2) transformation of plasmagel to plasmasol at the hinder end and the opposite process at the forward end of the animal; and (3) an increase in the elastic strength of the plasmagel as it passes backward.   Attachment is best on rough surfaces but depends on the nature of the fluid about the animal and on the physiological condition of the amoeba.

12-5. Feeding.   The amoeba eats other protozoans, algae, rotifers, and dead protoplasm, preferring small live flagellates and ciliates.   It may eat several paramecia or several hundred small flagellates daily and exhibits choice in selecting food.   The amoeba is attracted by movements of the intended prey or by substances diffusing from it; unwanted or indigestible materials are usually avoided, as are organisms that show intense activity.   Food may be taken in at any part of the cell surface. The amoeba extends pseudopodia that encircle the food (Fig. 12-4), which, with some water, is taken into the endoplasm as a *food vacuole.* More water is included with an active item than with one that is quiet. The vacuoles are moved about by streaming movements in the endoplasm

Fig. 12-4.   *Amoeba.*   States in ingestion of food; total time 8 minutes.   Arrows indicate movement of protoplasm in pseudopodia.   (*After Schaeffer,* 1917.)

and thus come in contact with various parts of it.   A recently formed vacuole gives an acid reaction (to litmus or neutral red), probably because of a secretion that kills the prey quickly.   Later the reaction becomes alkaline, and the action of enzymes secreted by the endoplasm is evident. Food particles lose their sharp outlines, swell, become more transparent, and then lessen in amount as the products of digestion are absorbed by the surrounding protoplasm.   Evidence is clear as to the digestion of proteins, but less certain as to fats, starches, and sugars.   The absorbed materials serve for growth and reproduction as well as providing the energy for locomotion.   The vacuoles decrease in size as digestion proceeds, and any undigested residues are egested by being passed to the outside (Fig. 12-5) at any place on the cell surface.

If various materials are offered experimentally globulin, grain gluten, carmine, and tyrosin will be taken most readily; fibrin, egg or milk albumen, and keratin are less attractive.   Starch, silicic acid, salt, and iron are not taken.   Particles of glass and carbon or fragments of algae are ingested if moved by the investigator, but only the algae are retained.

The amoeba does not ingest sand grains, as often reported. Undesired items may be egested quickly and selectively (Fig. 12-4). The amoeba can live in highly purified water for about 13 days, and from 18 to 22 days if certain salts are added in the proper concentration, but it cannot long survive without proper food. It can digest various animal and vegetable oils if these are injected into the cell body with a micropipette.

12-6. Respiration and excretion. Stored food materials must be oxidized ("burned") to provide the energy for locomotion and other activities. Respiration is the process of obtaining oxygen for this purpose. The water in which the amoeba lives contains dissolved oxygen. This diffuses through the cell membrane, as in the internal respiration of cells in higher animals that derive their oxygen from the blood or other body fluids. Metabolism results in the production of waste products such as carbon dioxide and urea. For the well-being of the organism these must

Fig. 12-5. *Amoeba verrucosa.* Stages in egestion of a waste pellet; *xy*, ingrowth of new pellicle to prevent loss of endoplasm. (*After Howland, 1924.*)

be eliminated; their disposal, mainly by diffusion through the cell membrane, is the process of excretion.

The contractile vacuole probably serves in part for excretion, but its principal function is to regulate the water content of the cell body. Water enters in food vacuoles, is a by-product of oxidation, and also probably passes into the cell by osmosis, since the protoplasm contains a higher concentration of salts than the surrounding water. An amoeba placed in water with a higher salt content than usual forms a smaller vacuole that discharges less often than before; and some marine amoebas have no vacuole. The contractile vacuole forms gradually by fusion of smaller vacuoles that start from fine droplets. When filled, it is surrounded by a temporary "condensation membrane" that vanishes as the vacuole discharges through the cell membrane into the surrounding water. In some amoebas, however, the vacuole may be dissected out under water with the membrane intact.

12-7. Behavior. The responses of an amoeba to stimuli, or changes in its environment, either internal or external, constitute its *behavior* (Fig. 12-6). Hunger is an internal stimulus to which the amoeba responds by searching for food. Contact with a food item is an external stimulus to

which it responds by sending out pseudopodia to capture the food.   The
response to **touch** or **contact** is varied.   A floating amoeba, with spread
pseudopodia, responds positively to contact with a solid object by fastening to it, but a creeping amoeba, touched lightly with a needle, responds
negatively by drawing back and moving away.   Since the amoeba is
exposed to **light** of varying intensity in nature, it does not respond to a
gradual change in illumination.   But if a strong beam is suddenly flashed

FIG. 12-6.   *Amoeba.*   Reactions to stimuli.   Arrows indicate direction of movements.
E. Successive stages at about 30-second intervals in reaction to strong light focused continuously on a microscope slide.   (*After Jennings,* 1904; *E, after Mast,* 1910.)

on an individual in weak light, it responds negatively; the protoplasm
streams away from the stimulus, and pseudopodia soon form to aid the
withdrawal.   Furthermore, if an amoeba comes repeatedly into a field of
intense light (Fig. 12-6*E*), the number of attempts to continue in the
original direction decreases as the number of trials increases—a change in
behavior similar to the learning process of higher animals.   Response to
temperature is shown by changes in both locomotion and rate of feeding.
These both lessen as the water temperature approaches freezing.   Locomotion is speeded in higher temperatures but ceases above 30°C.   To
strong **chemicals,** the amoeba responds negatively (Fig. 12-6*D*), but to

substances diffusing from food it responds positively.   Thus the responses
by the amoeba to stimuli are such as to benefit the individual and the
species, by avoiding unfavorable conditions and seeking those useful to it.

12-8. Reproduction.   When the amoeba attains a certain size, reproduction by *binary fission* occurs (Fig. 12-7).   The cell body becomes spherical and covered by short pseudopodia, then elongates somewhat, and
finally constricts into two parts; meanwhile, the nucleus has divided by
mitosis.   Under ordinary laboratory conditions, the amoeba divides every
few days, and mitosis requires about 33 minutes at 24°C.   Other methods

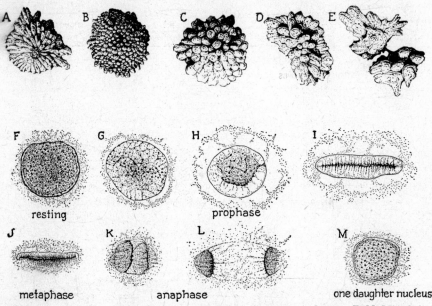

resting   prophase

metaphase   anaphase   one daughter nucleus

Fig. 12-7.   *Amoeba.*   Binary fission.   *A–E.* External appearance, ×10.   *F–M.* Mitosis in
the nucleus during fission, ×133.   (*After Chalkey and Daniel,* 1933.)

of reproduction have been reported but not confirmed; the same is true as
to the formation of resistant cysts to protect the animal from drought.

12-9. Other Sarcodina.   The Genus *Amoeba* includes many species
that differ from *A. proteus* in size, shape of pseudopodia, and other features.   These and members of other genera of amoeba-like protozoans
inhabit fresh, brackish, and salt waters.   Still others produce a shell, or
test, to enclose the cell body, examples being *Arcella,* which secretes a
thick test, and *Difflugia* (Fig. 12-8), which cements together a test of sand
grains or other foreign particles.   Besides these free-living forms the
Order AMOEBINA includes many commensal or parasitic amoebas.   Species of the Genus *Endamoeba* inhabit the gut in cockroaches and termites,
and those of the Genus *Entamoeba* live chiefly in the digestive tract of

land vertebrates.   Each is usually restricted to certain organs in a particular species of host animal.   These amoebas may form resistant cysts
by which they pass from an infected host to other individuals.

Six kinds of harmless amoebas may occur in man; of these, *Entamoeba
gingivalis* lives in the mouth, and *E. coli* in the intestine.   Another intestinal species, *E. histolytica*, however, is pathogenic and may produce the
disease known as "amoebic dysentery" (Fig. 12-9).   When food or water

| *Difflugia*
(×94)
AMOEBINA | *Rotalia*
(×22)
FORAMINIFERA | *Actinosphaerium*
(×22)
HELIOZOA | *Heliosphaera*
(×195)
RADIOLARIA |

FIG. 12-8.   Class SARCODINA.   Representatives of four Orders.   (*After Wolcott, Animal biology.*)

containing cysts of *E. histolytica* enters the digestive tract, the amoebas
are soon liberated and may invade glands of the intestinal wall to feed on
the blood and tissues and to multiply.   They cause the formation of
abscesses that rupture and discharge blood and mucus into the intestine,
when the feces become thin and a diarrhea results.   After such an acute
condition the patient may recover somewhat and become a carrier, with
less severe symptoms but continuing to discharge thousands of encysted

| TROPHOZOITE IN FECES | PRECYSTIC STAGE | MATURE CYST | EXCYSTING |

FIG. 12-9.   *Entamoeba histolytica*, the parasitic amoeba of man that causes amoebic
dysentery.   (*After Cleveland and Sanders, 1933.*)

amoebas and so able to spread the disease.   In some persons an intestinal
infection never produces any severe symptoms, but in others the amoebas
may invade the liver, spleen, or brain with fatal results.   Microscopic
examination of fecal smears for cysts of *E. histolytica* is the basis for
diagnosis, and medical treatment with drugs is necessary for a cure.
The intestinal abscesses may heal very slowly.   Fecal contamination of
drinking waters and raw vegetables or contamination of other foods by

infected and careless food handlers are the means of spread.   About 10 per cent of people in the United States are infected.

The Order FORAMINIFERA (Fig. 12-10) includes about 18,000 species, mostly marine, that have a covering test through which the long thread-like reticulate pseudopodia stream out and in.   Some fix to plants and hydroids or the sea bottom, others creep, and still others are pelagic, but all have some free-moving stage.   The tests of various species are 0.01 to 190 mm. in diameter and of spherical, tubular, spiral, or other shapes. They are composed of gelatinous, chitinous, or limy material or of selected

bits of sand, sponge spicules, or other debris.   FORMAMINIFERA have inhabited the oceans since Pre-Cambrian time, and their tests have accumulated as bottom deposits that became rock strata. About 48,000,000 square miles (35 per cent) of the present ocean bottom is covered with "ooze" formed of tests of certain pelagic forms, particularly *Globigerina*.   The great pyramids near Cairo, Egypt, were carved from limestone deposits made of tests of an Early Tertiary foraminiferan, †*Nummulites*.   The

FIG. 12-10.   Shells of FORAMINIFERA, ×5½. (*Specimens from G. Dallas Hanna.*)

petroleum industry of today studies the foraminiferans obtained in drilling test wells to identify oil-bearing strata.

Members of the Order HELIOZOA are spherical; the cell body may be naked, in a gelatinous matrix or in a lattice-like test.   The many fine radiating pseudopodia suggest the name "sun animalcules."   Most of the species live in fresh waters.   Protozoans of the Order RADIOLARIA somewhat resemble the HELIOZOA, but the cytoplasm is divided into outer and inner portions by a central capsule, and the skeleton is either of silica or of strontium sulphate.   They are all marine and pelagic, from the ocean surface to depths of 15,000 feet, and very abundant as to species and individuals.   About 2,000,000 square miles of ocean bottom, at depths of 12,000 to 24,000 feet, are covered with radiolarian ooze derived from empty skeletons of these animals.   Many rock formations contain fossil radiolarians.

The Order MYCETOZOA (MYXOMYCETES of botanists) includes the slime molds.   The species form masses of granular protoplasm (plasmodia), up to several inches in diameter, that contain thousands of nuclei and contractile vacuoles.   They live on wood or other decaying vegetation in damp places on land.

Reproduction among the Sarcodina is varied. Besides binary fission, the parasitic amoebas undergo multiple division of the nucleus while in the cysts. The Foraminifera multiply alternately by multiple fission and by "gametes," which are either flagellated or amoeboid. The Heliozoa multiply by fission, as do the Radiolaria, and some of the latter may have flagellated swarmers. The Mycetozoa produce multinucleate cysts to survive dry conditions.

Class *MASTIGOPHORA*. Flagellates

The presence of one or more long slender *flagella* (sing. *flagellum*) at some or all stages in the life cycle is characteristic of the Mastigophora (Gr. *mastix*, whip + *phoros*, bearing), The flagella serve for locomotion and food capture and may be sense receptors. The cell body is usually of definite form, oval, elongate, or spherical, covered by a film pellicle, and armored in certain groups of flagellates. Many species contain plastids with colored pigments; those with chlorophyll can synthesize food by the aid of sunlight and, as they seem akin to algae, are often classified as plants. Many flagellates are free-living and solitary, some are sessile, and some form colonies of a few to thousands of individuals. Various species abound in fresh and salt waters where they constitute, with diatoms, a major part of the food supply for minute aquatic animals. A number of species inhabit the soil. Many others are parasites of mankind and all kinds of animals, and some of them cause diseases of major importance. Reproduction usually is by longitudinal fission, but some undergo multiple fission, and there is sexual reproduction in one group. Free-living flagellates may encyst to avoid unfavorable conditions. Some Sarcodina possess flagella at times, and certain Mastigophora have amoeboid stages; so these two classes are rather closely related.

12-10. Structure. *Euglena viridis* and *E. gracilis* are common, solitary, and free-living flagellates that contain chlorophyll; they may be cultured

Fig. 12-11.   Structure of *Euglena viridis*, a free-living flagellate (Class Mastigophora).

and studied easily in the laboratory. The slender and elongate cell body is up to 0.1 mm. in length (Fig. 12-11). Euglena is of constant shape, with a blunt *anterior end* that habitually travels forward; the opposite or *posterior end* is pointed. The body shape is maintained by a thin flexible covering membrane, or *pellicle,* that is marked spirally by parallel striations or thickenings. Within this is a thin layer of clear *ectoplasm* around the main mass of granular nonflowing *endoplasm.* The anterior end contains a funnel-like *cytostome,* or cell mouth, that leads into a short tubular cell gullet, or *cytopharynx.* A long *flagellum* extends out through the cytostome; it consists of a contractile axial filament surrounded by a delicate sheath and arises from a granule, the *blepharoplast,* within the anterior cytoplasm. Behind the cytopharynx is a permanent spherical *reservoir,* and near by a vacuole into which several minute *contractile vacuoles* empty. Fluid collected from the cytoplasm by the vacuoles passes into the reservoir and out the cytopharynx. Near the reservoir is a red *stigma,* or "eyespot," that is sensitive to light. The round *nucleus* is located near the center of the cell. Euglena is of green color owing to the *chloroplasts* (chromatophores) containing chlorophyll that often crowd its cytoplasm. Other cell inclusions are the *paramylum bodies,* which consist of a carbohydrate allied to starch.

12-11. Movements. The flagellum beats back and forth to draw euglena through the water with a spiral rotation that enables the animal to follow a straight course (see *Paramecium,* p. 297). The animal may also crawl by spiral movements of the cell body. At times it performs wormlike "euglenoid movements" by local expansions and contractions that suggest the peristalsis in a vertebrate's intestine. Euglena reacts positively to light by swimming toward a source of favorable intensity, as a green plant turns to the light, but it performs an avoiding reaction to direct sunlight.

12-12. Nutrition. Some free-living flagellates capture small organisms, which are ingested through the cytopharynx and digested in food vacuoles in the cytoplasm, but such *holozoic nutrition* is rare or lacking in euglena. The latter utilizes *holophytic nutrition* whereby some food is synthesized within the body. This is done by photosynthesis, as in green plants, through the action of chlorophyll in the presence of light. Euglena commonly subsists by *saprophytic nutrition,* which is the absorption of nutrient materials dissolved in the water where it lives. In rich nutrient solutions, cultures of some euglenas will persist and multiply rapidly in weak light or darkness.

12-13. Reproduction. In active cultures, euglena reproduces frequently by longitudinal *binary fission* (Fig. 12-12). The nucleus divides in two by mitosis, then the anterior organelles—flagellum, blepharoplast, cytopharynx, reservoir, and stigma—are duplicated, and the organism splits in two lengthwise. Euglena also has inactive stages when it becomes nonmotile and secretes a surrounding cyst. In hot weather, *E. gracilis* may do this temporarily as a protective measure, without undergoing any change while encysted. Euglena may also lose the flagellum, encyst, and then divide by longitudinal fission. Further multiplication by longitudinal fission may also occur, resulting in cysts that contain 16 or 32 small daughter euglenas.   Encystment is stimulated by lack of food or by the presence of chlorophyll (as in strongly illuminated cultures).

12-14. Other Mastigophora.   Many members of the Subclass PHYTO-MASTIGINA, to which *Euglena* belongs, are free-living, colored by chroma-tophores, and holophytic in nutrition.   Species of the Order DINOFLAGEL-LATA are mostly marine, and they generally possess a cellulose-like armor

Fig. 12-12.   *Euglena viridis.*   Stages in longitudinal fission.   (*Modified from Tannreuther*, 1923.)

of two to many plates (Fig. 12-13).   *Ceratium* and *Peridinium*, along with diatoms, are important members of the microscopic plankton, or "ocean meadows," on which the minute larvae of crustaceans and other animals feed.   *Gonyaulax* when abundant (there may be up to 40,000,000 per cubic meter of water) causes "red water" in the sea by day and makes it luminescent at night.   *G. catenella* is an important food of sea mussels and clams.   It produces an alkaloid substance, harmless to the bivalves but which causes "mussel poisoning" in man if these mollusks are eaten in summer when subsisting largely on this protozoan.   About 350 cases of illness and 25 deaths occurred from this source on the Pacific coast in re-cent years and a few in Nova Scotia.

The Order PHYTOMONADINA in-cludes several green fresh-water flagel-lates (*Pandorina, Pleodorina, Volvox,* etc.) that form floating colonies (Fig.

Fig. 12-13.   Class MASTIGOPHORA. Two common marine flagellates.   *A. Peridinium,* ×120. *B. Noctiluca,* ×30.

12-14).   <u>*Volvox globator*</u> is a <u>hollow sphere</u> (0.5 mm. in diameter), filled with watery jelly.   Embedded in the gelatinous exterior wall are 8,000 to 17,000 minute (4 by 8 μ) individual cells, each with nucleus, contractile vacuole, red stigma, green chloroplast, and two flagella. Protoplasmic threads connect adjacent cells and provide physiological continuity between them.   The flagella beat collectively to roll the colony through the water.   Beginning in the spring, the first colonies develop from zygotes formed the previous season.   Several asexual generations follow. In each colony a few cells (gonidia) lose flagella, enlarge, and divide to form hollow masses of small cells within the parent colony; the latter disintegrates, and each "embryo" mass grows asexually into a new colony. Then a sexual generation ensues. From 20 to 30 non-flagellated cells within a colony enlarge, each to become a **macrogamete** ("female sex cell" or "ovum"); a larger number of others divide repeatedly to form flat packets of 128 or more slender **microgametes** ("male sex cells," or "sperm"). Both types of gametes are discharged into the fluid interior of the colony, each "ovum" is penetrated by a "sperm" and

Pandorina   Eudorina   Pleodorina

Platydorina   Volvox   Proterospongia

Fig. 12-14. Class Mastigophora. Colonial flagellates. (*After Hyman, The invertebrates.*)

the two fuse as a **zygote**. The latter secretes a cyst about itself and is released into the water when the parent colony disintegrates. It remains as a dormant stage until the following year, then escapes from the cyst to start a new colony by asexual fission.

The Volvox colony thus bears some resemblance to a multicellular animal. It is composed of cells of two kinds, unlike in structure and function. The **somatic cells** of the colony wall can synthesize food and cooperate in swimming but cannot reproduce and eventually die as does the body of a higher animal. The **germ cells** are unable to feed, are of two distinct kinds (sexes), and serve only to maintain the species by sexual reproduction.

The Subclass Zoomastigina comprises flagellates, lacking chloroplasts, that are simple to complex in structure. The free-living forms are holozoic in nutrition, and the many parasitic species are saprozoic. The

Order PROTOMONADINA includes both types. *Bodo* (Fig. 12-15) and *Oicomonas* are common small solitary types in fresh waters and soil. *Codosiga, Proterospongia,* and some other colonial aquatic forms have each flagellum surrounded by a collar, like the choanocytes of sponges.

All of the Family TRYPANOSOMIDAE are parasitic. *Phytomonas* lives in the latex cells of milkweeds and is carried from one plant to another by a bug (*Oncopeltus*). *Crithidia* and *Herpetomonas* are gut parasites of insects and spread by cysts. The Genus *Trypanosoma* comprises slender leaflike flagellates that inhabit the blood of vertebrates, form no cysts, and are carried from one host to another by bloodsucking

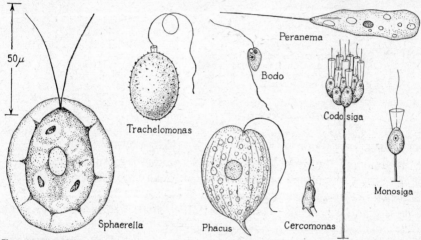

FIG. 12-15.   Class MASTIGOPHORA.   Representative free-living flagellates of fresh waters; all enlarged to about same scale.

invertebrates. Species in fishes, salamanders, frogs, and reptiles are transmitted by leeches. *T. lewisi* of the rat, spread by rat fleas (Fig. 12-16), usually does no harm to its host; but many other species are disease producers. *T. evansi* causes surra in domestic animals of the Orient and is carried by biting flies (*Tabanus*). *Trypanosoma brucei* occurs in antelope and other game mammals of Africa and is carried by native tsetse flies; in domestic livestock, it is the cause of nagana disease. *T. gambiense* and *T. rhodesiense* are the causative agents of two types of human sleeping sickness[1] in Africa, both carried by tsetse flies and both fatal unless treated in early stages. *T. cruzi* causes Chagas' disease in Central and South America, being transmitted by bugs (*Triatoma, Rhodnius*). The organism occurs in these insects and in wood rats (*Neotoma*) and other mammals in the southwestern United States, but evidence of human cases there is uncertain. Flagellates of the Genus *Leishmania* attack the endothelial cells in blood vessels of man. *L. dono-*

[1] Encephalitis, or "sleeping sickness," in the United States is caused by a virus.

vani causes kala azar and *L. tropica* the skin disease called Oriental sore; both occur in Asia, the Mediterranean region, and parts of South America. The related *L. brasiliensis* of Mexico, Central and South America also produces a skin disease. The spread of leishmanias is variously from rodents by blood-sucking flies (*Phlebotomus*), by direct contact between people, and by dogs.

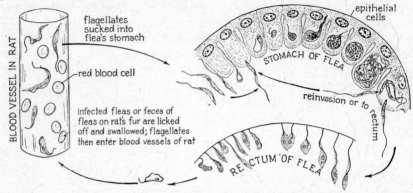

flagellates sucked into flea's stomach

red blood cell

BLOOD VESSEL IN RAT

infected fleas or feces of fleas on rat's fur are licked off and swallowed; flagellates then enter blood vessels of rat

epithelial cells

STOMACH OF FLEA

reinvasion or to rectum

RECTUM OF FLEA

Fig. 12-16. Class Mastigophora. Life cycle of the rat trypanosome, *Trypanosoma lewisi;* natural size, 25 μ long. (*Adapted from Minchin and Thompson, 1915.*)

Members of the Order Polymastigina have 3 or more flagella. *Tetramitus* and a few others are free-living, but many are intestinal parasites. *Hexamita* occurs in fishes and birds, *Eutrichomastix* in frogs, snakes, etc., *Devescovina, Oxymonas,* etc., in termites, and *Trichomonas* in both invertebrates and vertebrates.

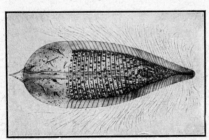

Fig. 12-17. Class Mastigophora. *Spirotrichonympha bispira,* a complex flagellate that lives only in the gut of termites. (*After Cleveland, 1928.*)

The Order Hypermastigina comprises species with many flagella and complex internal structure. They abound in the gut of a cockroach (*Cryptocercus*) and in about one-fourth of the species of termites, where (with polymastigotes) they constitute an outstanding example of mutualism (Fig. 12-17). Termites (p. 516) eat wood, but many of them are unable to digest the cellulose that it contains. The flagellates that receive "lodging and board" are able to digest this material for themselves and their hosts. Termites experimentally defaunated (by exposure to an oxygen atmosphere or kept at 36°C. for 24 hr. to kill the flagellates) will starve and die in 10 or more days, even when wood is eaten. If, however, they are reinfected with the flagellates, they can thenceforth utilize the wood and will survive. The flagellates form pseudopodia to ingest the wood fragments in the termite's gut, the cellulose is digested, and the soluble products become available for absorption by the termites.   Other nonsymbiotic protozoans occur in termites.

Class *SPOROZOA*. Gregarines, Coccidia, Haemosporidia, etc.

The Sporozoa (Gr. *spora*, seed + *zoön*, animal) are practically all parasites.   The simple cell body is rounded or elongate, with one nucleus and no locomotor organelles or contractile vacuole.   Some move by change in shape of the cell body.   Food is absorbed directly from the host (saprozoic nutrition), and respiration and excretion are by simple diffusion.   Most sporozoans increase rapidly by multiple asexual fission, or *schizogony;* the cell becomes multinucleate by repeated mitoses, and then

Fig. 12-18. *A*. Class Mastigophora.   Structure of *Trypanosoma*. *B*. Class Sporozoa.
A gregarine from the mealworm.   Both greatly enlarged.

the cytoplasm divides.   They also produce sexual *macro-* and *micro-gametes;* these join in pairs of opposite kind to form *zygotes.* The latter, in many species, form seedlike *oöcysts* by *sporogony,* and in this stage the organisms are spread from one host individual to another.   The typical coccidian life cycle is thus:

Sporozoa are possibly the most widely occurring of animal parasites. Distinct species occur in various animals from protozoans to mammals.   Some live within the host's cells and others in its body fluids or cavities.   They inhabit variously the digestive tract, muscles, blood, kidneys, or other organs.   Malaria in man, coccidiosis in fowls and rabbits, certain fevers in cattle, and the pebrine disease of silkworms are examples of serious diseases caused by sporozoans.

12-15. Order Gregarinida.   These are extra- or intra-cellular parasites of invertebrates (Fig. 12-18*B*).   A common example is *Monocystis*, which lives in the seminal vesicles of earthworms.   The minute *spore* is a spindle-shaped case containing 8 *sporozoites.* Upon escaping from the spore, each sporozoite enters a clump of immature sperm cells and transforms into a ***trophozoite*** that consumes the cells. The trophozoites then become grouped as pairs of ***gametocytes,*** each pair being surrounded by a ***cyst.*** Sporulation follows, each nucleus dividing many times with later partitioning of the cytoplasm so that many ***gametes*** of about equal size result. A pair of gametes, each from a different parent cell, then unite as a ***zygote,*** which secretes a thin hard spore case, or ***oöcyst,*** around itself while still within the cyst. The zygote nucleus inside divides successively into 2, 4, and 8 daughter nuclei, each of which combines with part of the cytoplasm to become a sporozoite. The manner by which spores are spread from one worm to another is unknown.

12-16. Order Coccidia. These parasites live in epithelial cells of many vertebrates, some myriapods, and a few other invertebrates. They occur

Fig. 12-19.   Class Sporozoa.   Life cycle of *Eimeria stiedae*, a coccidium from the liver of the rabbit.   (*Adapted from Wasielewski*, 1924.)

chiefly in the lining of the intestine, but also in the bile duct, kidneys, testes, blood vessels, and coelom. The life cycles involve alternate schizogony and sporogony, with change of host by some species. Coccidia produce the disease coccidiosis, which may be serious and even fatal. Species of economic importance occur in poultry, domestic mammals, and many kinds of wild animals. *Eimeria stiedae* (Fig. 12-19) is common in both domestic and wild rabbits. When food contaminated with oöcysts is swallowed, the host's digestive juices dissolve the cysts and release the sporozoites. These enter epithelial cells in the bile duct and enlarge as feeding trophozoites that undergo rapid schizogony to produce many merozoites. In turn, the merozoites invade other cells to repeat the cycle. A considerable destruction of epithelial tissue in the bile duct and liver may ensue, with consequent harm to the host. Later some merozoites develop into gametocytes, also within epithelial cells; some become enlarged macrogametes, and others divide to yield many microgametes.

Union of a macrogamete and a microgamete forms a zygote that secretes an elliptical covering oöcyst.   In this stage the coccidia pass out of the rabbit, in the feces.   Later the zygote within divides into 4 spores, each enclosing 2 sporozoites, and this is the infective stage for a new host.   Among domestic rabbits this parasite often causes severe epidemics with many deaths, particularly in young animals.   The common practices of rearing rabbits in separate hutches, of keeping their food off the floor, and of cleaning the hutches frequently are all essential to keep down losses from coccidiosis.

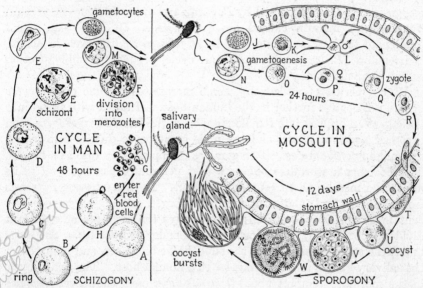

Fig. 12-20.   Class Sporozoa.   Order Haemosporidia.   Life cycle of *Plasmodium vivax*, the tertian malarial parasite of man and anopheline mosquitoes.   Sporozoites injected during the biting of the mosquito enter red blood cells and multiply asexually (schizogony); the resulting merozoites enter other cells to repeat the cycle.   Later gametocytes are formed; if drawn up by a biting mosquito they transform into gametes in the insect's stomach.   The zygotes encyst externally on the gut wall and form enlarged oöcysts.   By asexual multiplication (sporogony) many sporozoites are produced to invade the salivary glands.

12-17. Order Haemosporidia.   These Sporozoa are parasites of blood cells and tissues in birds and mammals; they form no resistant spores but are transferred by bloodsucking arthropods as intermediate hosts.   The most familiar example is *Plasmodium*, which causes malaria (Fig. 12-20). This disease, a scourge of man since ancient times, has caused an enormous amount of illness and innumerable deaths, especially in tropical and subtropical regions.   Possibly it is the most important of all diseases. The parasites are transmitted to man by females of certain species of mosquitoes of the Genus *Anopheles* (p. 528).   When the mosquito's mouth parts pierce the skin to obtain blood, the infective *sporozoites* pass from its salivary glands into the wound.   Each enters a red blood cell and becomes an amoeba-like *trophozoite.*   It grows to be a *schizont,* which by multiple fission (schizogony) divides into 6 to 36 daughter *merozoites* according to the species.   By rupture of the corpuscle these escape into the blood plasma, to invade other red cells and repeat the cycle.   After about 10 days the parasites are so numerous that the shock of their nearly simultaneous release produces a chill, followed by a violent fever in response to toxins from the liberated parasites.   The chill-and-fever cycle thenceforth depends upon the species of parasite: every 48 hours in benign tertian malaria caused by *P. vivax;* and every 72 hours in quartan (fourth day) malaria caused by *P. malariae.*   In aestivo-autumnal (malignant tertian) malaria caused by *P. falciparum,* the cycle is lacking or irregular.   *P. ovale,* with a 48-hour cycle, produces a mild infection ending in about 15 days.

After a period of schizogony, some merozoites become *gametocytes* but do not change further in the human host.   If taken with blood into the gut of an appropriate female *Anopheles,* the female gametocyte soon becomes a *macrogamete,* and the male gametocyte divides into 6 to 8 spermlike *microgametes.*   Two gametes of opposite sex fuse as a zygote. This becomes a wormlike *oökinete* that penetrates the gut wall to lie under the membrane surrounding the gut.   It then absorbs nutrients from the insect and enlarges as a rounded *oöcyst.*   A single mosquito may contain 50 to 500 oöcysts.   In 6 or 7 days the contents of each cyst divides (sporulation) into thousands of slender sporozoites.   The cysts burst, the sporozoites migrate through the body spaces, and many enter the salivary glands to await transfer to a human host.   The sexual cycle in the mosquito requires about 7 to 19 days until the insect becomes infective.

Acute symptoms of malaria in man usually continue for some days or weeks and then often subside as the body develops an *immunity* to the disease, but relapses may occur at irregular intervals.   In different persons the infection disappears in time, or lingers and causes damage to other organs, or may result in death.   Malaria patients are treated with quinine, atabrine, or plasmochin.   Healthy persons living in malarial regions often take small doses of quinine or atabrine daily as a prophylactic to kill any plasmodia received in mosquito bites.   General reduction or control of malaria in a region requires (1) treating the human victims, (2) effectively screening dwellings to exclude mosquitoes, and (3) draining off, oiling, or poisoning the water to reduce mosquitoes by killing the larvae.   DDT and other new insecticides are highly effective in killing adult mosquitoes and larvae, thereby reducing the malarial hazard.

Other species of *Plasmodium* occur in mammals, birds, and reptiles; several in primates closely resemble the species in man.

Babesia bigemina is a minute parasite of the red blood cells in cattle that causes red water, or Texas cattle fever.   The intermediate host is a tick, *Boöphilus annulatus* (Fig. 24-7A).   Following asexual stages in the blood of cattle, the merozoites are withdrawn when the tick feeds. The sexual stages occur in the blind gut of the tick, and the zygotes then penetrate to the ovary and eggs.   Later they multiply in the developing salivary glands of the embryo tick.   When the latter hatches and feeds on a bovine animal, the sporozoites are injected into the new host individual. Control of this disease, which once ravaged herds in many southern states, has been accomplished by dipping the cattle to remove ticks and rotation of their pasturing so that clean herds have no chance to acquire infected ticks.

CLASS *CILIATA*.   CILIATES, OR "INFUSORIA"

The CILIATA (L. *cilium*, eyelid) possess cilia throughout life, which serve for locomotion and food getting.   Each species is of constant and characteristic form, and most of them have one large macronucleus (or more) concerned with the routine or vegetative functions and one or more small micronuclei that are important in reproduction.   Ciliates are the most specialized of PROTOZOA in having various organelles to perform particular vital processes.   This results in a division of labor between parts of the organism, analogous to that between organ systems in a multicellular animal.   Ciliates abound in fresh and salt waters.   Many are free-living; some are commensal or parasitic in other animals; and a few grow in colonies.   They are much used in experimental studies because of their relatively large size and the ease with which they may be reared.

Paramecium (Fig. 12-21) is a ciliate common in fresh waters that contain some decaying vegetation.   It multiplies rapidly in the laboratory in an "infusion" made by boiling a little hay or some wheat grains in water.   The 8 or 9 species differ in size, shape, and structure.   *P. aurelia* is 0.12 to 0.25 mm. long and *P. caudatum* measures 0.15 to 0.3 mm. in length.   The following account deals mainly with *P. caudatum*.

12-18. Structure.   The elongate cell body is blunt at the forward-moving or ***anterior end,*** widest behind the middle, and tapered at the ***posterior end.***   Over the exterior surface is a distinct elastic membrane, the ***pellicle.*** This is covered by fine ***cilia*** that are arranged in lengthwise rows and are of uniform length save for a posterior ***caudal tuft*** of longer cilia.   Within the pellicle, the cell contents, as in *Amoeba*, consist of a thin clear external layer of dense ***ectoplasm,*** around the larger mass of more granular and fluid ***endoplasm.***   The ectoplasm contains many spindle-shaped ***tricho-***

cysts, alternating between the bases of the cilia, that may be discharged as long threads to serve perhaps in attachment or defense. From the anterior end a shallow furrow or *oral groove* extends diagonally back about halfway along the lower or *oral surface,* and has the cell mouth or *cytostome* at its posterior end. The cytostome opens into a short tubular gullet or *cytopharynx,* ending in the endoplasm. In the gullet cilia are fused to form two lengthwise dense bands (the penniculus). On one side, just behind the cytopharynx, is the "cell anus" or *cytopyge,* which can be seen only when particles are discharging through it. In the endoplasm are *food vacuoles* of various sizes that contain material under-

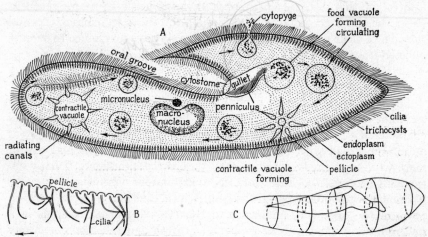

Fig. 12-21. Structure of *Paramecium caudatum,* a ciliate of fresh waters (Class Ciliata). *A.* The entire animal. Lines of dots indicate rows of cilia over the surface. Arrows show path of food vacuoles in endoplasm. *B.* Enlarged sketch of a few cilia showing how they beat in coordinated waves to drive the paramecium forward (to the left). *C.* Outline of body form (cross sections) at different positions along its length.

going digestion, and toward each end of the cell body is a large clear *contractile vacuole.* The small rounded *micronucleus* is partly surrounded by the larger *macronucleus.* *P. aurelia* has two micronuclei.

When specimens of *Paramecium* and similar ciliates are prepared by special methods (with nigrosin or silver salts) and studied under high magnification, the pellicle shows a hexagonal pattern of ridges, surrounding cuplike depressions with a cilium projecting from the center of each cup. Beneath the pellicle each cilium connects to a basal granule, and the granules are joined by longitudinal fibrils. Most ciliates have both transverse and longitudinal fibrils (Fig. 12-22), which in some are joined to a body (motorium) near the cytopharynx (Fig. 12-29). The granules and fibrils comprise a *fibrillar* or *neuromotor system,* probably sensory-motor in function, that coordinates the ciliary action. Experimental destruction of the motorium in some ciliates (*Euplotes patella*) is followed by loss of coordination in movements of the membranelles and cirri. Contractile fibrils (myonemes) occur in ciliates such as *Stentor* and *Vorticella*, but not in *Paramecium*.

12-19. Locomotion.   The cilia beat backward to carry the paramecium forward in the water, and as their stroke is oblique the animal rotates on its longitudinal axis.   The cilia in the oral groove beat more vigorously than the others, so that the anterior end swerves aborally.   The combined effect is to move the body forward in a spiral course, which is

FIG. 12-22.   *Paramecium multimicronucleata.   A.* Structure of the pellicle and associated organelles.   *B.* The neuromotor system in part of the cell body.   (*After Lund*, 1935.)

counterclockwise as viewed from behind (Fig. 12-23).   Thus the asymmetrical animal may travel in a direct path.   To swim backward the ciliary beat is reversed, as is the path of rotation.   If when swimming forward the paramecium meets some unfavorable chemical stimulus, it executes an *avoiding reaction* (Fig. 12-24)—the ciliary beat reverses, the animal moves backward a short distance, and then it rotates in a conical path by swerving the anterior end aborally while pivoting on the posterior tip.   While it is doing this, the cilia in the oral groove bring "samples"

FIG. 12-23.   *Paramecium.*   Locomotion.   The animal swims in a spiral manner so that the asymmetrical body progresses on a direct course.   (*Adapted from Jennings, Behavior of the lower organisms, Columbia University Press.*)

from the water immediately ahead; when these no longer contain the undesirable stimulus the animal moves forward again.   The reaction is similar upon encountering a solid object: it reverses, rotates, and goes forward, repeating the process if necessary until a clear path is found.

12-20. Feeding and digestion.   Paramecium feeds upon bacteria, small protozoans, algae, and yeasts.   The constant beating of cilia in the oral groove sweeps a current of water containing food toward the cytostome, and movements of the penniculus gather the food at the posterior end of the cytopharynx in a watery vacuole.   The vacuole becomes of a certain size, constricts off, and begins to circulate in the endoplasm as a *food vacuole;* another then begins to form in its place.   Streaming movements (cyclosis) in the endoplasm carry the vacuoles in a definite route, first posteriorly, then forward and aborally, again posteriorly to near the oral groove.   The contents of the vacuoles are acid at first and gradually become alkaline, as shown by use of congo red and other indicator dyes. As in *Amoeba*, the food is digested by the action of enzymes secreted by the endoplasm.   This process continues until the digested material is absorbed by the surrounding protoplasm and either stored or used for vital activity and growth.   The vacuoles gradually become smaller, and any indigestible residues are egested at the cell anus.

Paramecium caudatum will live and multiply in a bacteria-free suspension of liver extract, dead yeast, and kidney tissue to provide the necessary organic materials.   *P. aurelia* requires certain salts and bacteria. *P. bursaria*, which contains spherical green algae (zoochlorellae) in its endoplasm, will multiply in a solution of salts alone if kept in the light. This is a case of mutualism where the organisms are interdependent. The carbon dioxide produced by the protozoan in respiration serves the algae with their chlorophyll to synthesize organic materials and produce oxygen, both of which are necessary for the paramecium.

12-21. Respiration and excretion.   As with amoeba, respiration in paramecium corresponds to the internal respiration of cells in multicellular animals.   Oxygen dissolved in the surrounding water diffuses through the pellicle and then throughout the organism; carbon dioxide and organic wastes resulting from metabolism are probably excreted by diffusing outward in the reverse direction.

The contractile vacuoles regulate the water content of the body and may serve also in excretion of nitrogenous wastes such as urea and ammonia.   Liquid within the cytoplasm is gathered by a series of 6 to 11 *radiating canals* that converge toward and discharge into each vacuole. The canals are most conspicuous as a vacuole is forming.   When each vacuole has swelled to a certain size, it contracts and discharges to the exterior, probably through a pore.   The vacuoles contract alternately, at intervals of 10 to 20 seconds.   If the water containing a paramecium is densely filled with particles of carbon or carmine, the discharged contents from a vacuole will be evident momentarily as a clear spot in the surrounding clouded fluid before being dispersed by action of the cilia.

The rate of vacuole discharge varies with temperature, is higher in an inactive animal than in one that is swimming about, and is higher in water with a scant supply of dissolved salts than with stronger concentrations. Since the body of a paramecium contains dissolved substances, there is a tendency for water to pass through the pellicle, which functions as a dialyzing membrane.   Presumably it is the function of the contractile vacuoles to offset this tendency and maintain an optimum concentration of water in the body protoplasm by disposing of the excess.

FIG. 12-24.   Some reactions of *Paramecium*.

CONTACT.   Negative or avoiding reaction: *A.* Successive positions (1–6) in avoiding a solid object; rotation on the long axis not shown.   *B.* Weak reaction, anterior end swings in small circle.   *C.* Strong reaction, swings in large circle.   Positive reaction: *D.* At rest against a food mass; arrows indicate water currents produced by the cilia.   *E.* Resting on a cotton fiber; cilia in contact are motionless.

CHEMICALS.   Negative reaction: *F.* Drop of 0.5 per cent NaCl solution introduced into a paramecium culture under a coverslip.   *G.* Drop still empty 4 minutes later.   Positive reaction: *H.* Path of an individual within a drop of acid.   *I.* Individuals gather about a drop of 0.02 per cent acetic acid.   *J.* Culture 2 minutes after bubble of air and another of CO_2 are introduced; individuals gather densely about CO_2 (weak acid).   *K.* Twenty minutes later; the paramecia spread in a ring as the CO_2 diffuses outward.

TEMPERATURE: *L, M, N.* On slides at various temperatures the paramecia avoid extremes of cold and heat.   (*After Jennings, Behavior of the lower organisms, Columbia University Press.*)

12-22. Behavior.

The responses of paramecium to various kinds of stimuli are learned by study of its avoiding reaction and of the grouping or scattering of individuals in a culture.   The response is *positive* if the animal moves toward the stimulus and *negative* when it moves away. To an adverse stimulus the animal continues to give the avoiding reaction until it escapes.   All adjustments are made by *trial and error.*   The intensity of the reaction may differ according to the kind and intensity of the stimulus.   Experiments indicate that the anterior end of the animal is more sensitive than other parts.

To *contact,* the response is varied; if the anterior end is lightly touched with a fine point, a strong avoiding reaction occurs, as when a swimming paramecium collides with some object in the water, but if touched elsewhere there may be no response.   A slow-moving individual often responds positively to contact with an object by coming to rest upon it; since food organisms are common about masses of algae or plant stems, this response is advantageous, and individuals often concentrate about such materials.   Paramecium seeks an optimum as to *temperature,* between 24 and 28°C.; in a temperature gradient the animals congregate

in spots between these limits (Fig. 12-24). Greater heat stimulates rapid movement and avoiding reactions until the animals escape or are killed; in ice water, they also seek to escape but may be benumbed and sink.   To *gravity,* there is generally a negative response, as seen in a deep culture where many individuals gather close under the surface film with their anterior ends uppermost.   In a gentle *water current* the paramecia will mostly align with the flow, their anterior ends upstream.   Likewise, to a constant or direct *electric current,* the animals "head" toward the negative pole (cathode) from which electrons stream toward the positive pole (anode).   To most *chemicals,* the response is negative.   If a drop of weak salt solution (0.5 per cent) is introduced in a paramecium population on a microslide, the animals respond with the avoiding reaction and none enters the drop.   To acids, however, the response is positive even when the concentration is of sufficient strength to kill them.   This latter phenomenon probably is related to the fact that, although paramecium often lives in alkaline waters, the local concentrations produce sufficient carbon dioxide to render the immediate environment acid, and it is to this condition that they are most adapted.   The trichocysts of paramecium (Fig. 12-25) and certain other ciliates have been thought to be organelles of defense against enemies, but even when discharged they seldom save the animal from its predator.

FIG. 12-25.   *Paramecium* (below) discharging trichocysts upon attack by *Didinium,* another protozoan.   (*After Mast,* 1909.)

Although paramecium is of almost universal occurrence in fresh waters, its means of dispersal is unknown.   It has been reported to form cysts, but this observation lacks general confirmation.

12-23. Reproduction.   Paramecium reproduces by fission and also undergoes several types of nuclear reorganization known as "conjugation," "autogamy," and "endomixis." In *binary fission* (Fig. 5-1) the micronucleus divides by mitosis into two micronuclei that move toward opposite ends of the cell, and the macronucleus divides transversely by amitosis; a second gullet forms, two new contractile vacuoles appear, and then a transverse furrow divides the cytoplasm into two parts. The resulting two "daughter" paramecia are of equal size, each containing a set of cell organelles. They grow to full size before another division occurs. Fission requires about 2 hours to complete and may occur one to four times per day, yielding 2 to 16 individuals. A single paramecium thus gives rise to 2, 4, 8, 16 . . . 2^n individuals; all individuals produced by fission (uniparental reproduction) from a single individual are known collectively as a *clone*. Upward of 600 "generations" per year may be produced. The rate of multiplication depends upon external conditions of food, temperature, age of the culture, and population density and also on internal factors of heredity and physiology. If all descendants of one individual were to survive, they soon would equal the earth in volume. Stocks of *P. aurelia* have been maintained artificially for 25 years through 15,300 generations of fission without conjugation, by continually isolating daughter individuals in a fresh culture medium. In ordinary laboratory cultures with many individuals, the rate of fission gradually declines and some type of nuclear reorganization ensues.

12-24. Conjugation. In paramecium, other ciliates, and the SUCTORIA, there is, at intervals, a temporary union of individuals in pairs with mutual exchange of micronuclear materials that is known as *conjugation* (Fig. 12-26). The animals become "sticky," adhering to one another by their oral surfaces, and a protoplasmic bridge forms between them. The pairs continue to swim about during this process. A sequence of nuclear changes then occurs in each animal. The macronucleus begins to disintegrate and eventually disappears into the cytoplasm. The micronucleus enlarges, its chromatin forms long strands, a division spindle appears, and the micronucleus divides by mitosis; a second division of each follows at once, yielding four micronuclei. Three of the four micronuclei degenerate, and the remaining one divides again to yield two "pronuclei" in each animal. One from each then migrates through the protoplasmic bridge into the opposite individual, to unite there with the other pronucleus, which remains in place. Soon thereafter the two paramecia separate as exconjugants. In each the fused micronucleus or "zygote" divides successively into two, four, and eight micronuclei (the first two divisions are meiotic). Four of these then enlarge to become macronuclei, and three of the others degenerate. Then the micronuclei and animals divide twice, so that from each exconjugant there are four paramecia, each with one macronucleus and one micronucleus. Thenceforth, the organisms multiply by binary fission as already described.

Conjugation differs from the sexual union of gametes in other PROTO-ZOA and in METAZOA because progeny are not a direct product of the fusion; after conjugation each individual continues asexual fission. The

macronucleus — micronucleus

A
Two Paramecia fuse

B
each micronucleus divides, the macronucleus degenerates

C
the micronuclei divide again

D
3 of 4 nuclei in each disappear

E
each nucleus divides unequally

F
smaller pronuclei are exchanged

G
2 pronuclei in each unite as zygote nucleus

H
Paramecia separate (as exconjugants)

I

J

K
nuclei in each divide 3 times

L
4 become macronuclei, 3 disappear, I remains as micronucleus

M
micronuclei and Paramecia divide

N
a second division yields 4 Paramecia from each exconjugant

FIG. 12-26. *Paramecium caudatum.* Diagram of conjugation.

net result, however, is like the fusion of gametes (syngamy) in other animals. Conjugation is a process that provides for hereditary transfer, as the two exconjugants are genetically altered by their exchange of micronuclear materials (chromosomes). The nuclear changes bear comparison with those of meiosis and fertilization in METAZOA, with divisions (reduction) of the micronucleus, the joining (fertilization) of one micronucleus (egg pronucleus) by a migrant micronucleus (sperm pronucleus) to form a fusion micronucleus (zygote). The macronucleus which directs the vegetative processes in a paramecium has been compared to the body (soma) of the multicellular animal and its disintegration to the death of the body. The fusion micronucleus (zygote) then produces another macronucleus (soma) and continues as the reproductive component (germ plasm) of the exconjugant.

There have been many experimental attempts to learn the conditions that bring about conjugation. It was formerly believed that conjugation was essential to rejuvenate old stocks, which otherwise would die out; however, conjugation is not necessary under certain conditions, some stocks are more prone to conjugate than others, and conjugation is induced by various external and internal factors that are not clearly understood.

12-25. Mating types. For years no differences were detected between the two paramecia joining in conjugation. In 1937 Sonneborn reported stocks of *P. aurelia* containing two kinds ("sexes") of individuals; only members of opposite kinds would conjugate. These two categories were termed *mating types* I and II. By separating progeny of exconjugants that then multiply by binary fission, some clones produced only Type I, others only Type II, and still others both Types I and II. Later it was shown that the first two, so-called single-type clones, were not changed by endomixis, whereas the third or double-type clone after endomixis yielded all three sorts. By crossing and back-crossing (Chap. 6) the two types, Sonneborn further showed that mating types were determined by a single Mendelian factor. Single type clones were *AA* or *aa*, and double types *Aa*.

In *P. bursaria* Jennings determined three groups, each with several mating types (I—*A,B,C,D*; II—*E,F,G,H,J,K,L, M*; III—*N,O,P,Q*). Mating will occur between certain members of one group, but not between members of different groups. In Group I, an *A* individual will conjugate with one of the *B, C,* or *D* types but not with another *A* individual; one of *B* type will mate with any *A, C,* or *D* individual but not with another *B* animal, and so on. No individual of Group I will mate with any of Groups II or III, and none in II with a representative of III. These are not "sexes," but strains that will not inbreed and will not mate with individuals outside their groups. The mating response is quick and spectacular; for example, when numerous *A* and *B* individuals are placed together, they become "sticky" at once and aggregate in large clumps, from which conjugating pairs later separate out.

12-26. Autogamy. Nuclear reorganization resembling conjugation but occurring within one individual (hence one cell generation) is termed *autogamy* (Diller, 1936). In *Paramecium aurelia* (Fig. 12-27) which has 2 micronuclei, these divide twice (prezygotic) to yield 8. The macronucleus becomes skeinlike, and later breaks up. Two of the 8 micronuclei, as gamete nuclei, enter a protoplasmic cone bulging near the cell mouth (the other 6 micronuclei disintegrate). The two fuse as a synkaryon (zygote), which then divides twice (postzygotic). Of the 4 resulting nuclei, 2 continue as micronuclei and 2 become macronuclei. The cell and micronuclei then divide to yield two daughter paramecia each with a (new) macronucleus and 2 micronuclei. Thereafter binary fission resumes.

A — macronucleus / micronucleus

B — 2 micronuclei

1ST PREZYGOTIC DIVISION

C — 4 micronuclei

2D PREZYGOTIC DIVISION

D — 8 micronuclei

E — 2 gamete nuclei enter paraoral cone

and

F — fuse as synkaryon

ST POSTZYGOTIC DIVISION

G — 2 micronuclei

2D POSTZYGOTIC DIVISION

H — 4 micronuclei

I — 2 become macronuclei / 2 remain as micronuclei

CELL AND MICRONUCLEI DIVIDE

J — Two daughter micronuclei; old macronucleus disintegrates

FIG. 12-27. *Paramecium aurelia.* Diagram of autogamy. (*Adapted from Diller*, 1936.)

Autogamy is a rhythmic process and one in which hereditary changes occur; lines homozygous as to mating type can be produced. There is decreased survival only when, as the result of a cross, the animals receive lethal genes.

12-27. Endomixis. At intervals, binary fission is interrupted by replacement of the macronucleus and a nuclear reorganization known as *endomixis*. In *P. aurelia* (with 2 micronuclei) the old macronucleus disintegrates and each micronucleus divides twice, but 6 of the 8 resulting micronuclei disappear. The paramecium divides, each daughter receiving a micronucleus. The latter divide twice, and 2 of the 4 in each animal become macronuclei. Then each paramecium and its micronucleus divide again, to yield 4 normal individuals. Endomixis in *P. aurelia* commonly occurs every 25 to 30 days, following some decline in rate of fission, and about every 50 to 60 days in *P. caudatum*. Some clones of *P. aurelia* and other species continue fission for years without either endomixis or conjugation.

12-28. Variation and heredity. A wild stock of *Paramecium* in nature will contain individuals that differ as to total length and other features. Such variations are of three kinds, as follows: (1) age variation due to the age of the individual; (2) random variations due to the influence of factors in the environment; and (3) inherited variations due to genetic factors. From a wild stock, Jennings isolated eight "races," or biotypes, that differed in average size. Within each race the individual and random variations produced animals of various lengths, but the average of these was the same in successive generations by asexual fission because of their hereditary make-up.

DeGaris obtained conjugation between individuals of races that differed greatly in size, one (198 μ long) being twenty times the bulk of the other (73 μ long). After the exconjugants had separated, each produced a series of generations by fission. Those from the larger individual became successively smaller, and the opposite occurred with the smaller animal; after 24 days the offspring of both lines were alike. Before conjugation each race continued at its characteristic size; after conjugation the two individuals had like nulear content but differed as to cytoplasm. The subsequent divisions show that for a period of days the size of descendants was affected by *both cytoplasm and nucleus*, but finally only by nuclear constitution. In other crosses the final size from both conjugants was not strictly intermediate but might be more nearly like either one or the other. Thus in these PROTOZOA, as in METAZOA, recombining the chromosomal materials produces different combinations in different cases.

In summary, paramecium shows (1) structural specialization in organelles, (2) physiological division of labor between parts to perform special functions, (3) a stereotyped avoiding reaction, (4) reproduction by binary fission, (5) nuclear reorganization by endomixis, (6) conjugation as a mechanism providing for exchange of hereditary factors, (7) segregation into many mating types that are mutually exclusive in conjugation, (8) pure lines that are genetically distinct in a wild population, and (9) the relative influence of nuclear and cytoplasmic materials in inheritance.

12-29. Other Ciliata.   Examination of a drop of water from any quiet fresh-, brackish-, or salt-water source will usually reveal one or more species of ciliates and testify to the wide occurrence of these Protozoa (Fig. 12-28).   Free-swimming species are commonly ellipsoidal to spherical in shape, whereas creeping forms are often flattened.   Anterior-posterior and oral-aboral relations in structure and locomotion are usually evident.   The cilia on some types are reduced in numbers and grouped to form membranelles or cirri, by which their owners move about.   Some ciliates of both solitary (*Vorticella, Stentor*) and colonial habit (*Zootham-*

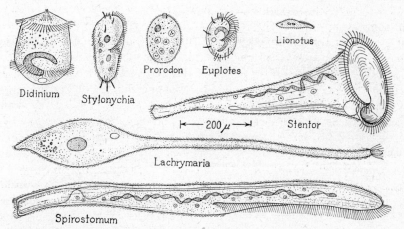

Fig. 12-28.   Class Ciliata.   Common fresh-water ciliates; all enlarged to about same scale. Macronucleus, heavy stipple; contractile vacuole, clear.

nium) are attached by stalks or other means.   The ciliates as a group exhibit tremendous variety in configuration, placement of cilia, form of the macronucleus, and other features.

The Subclass Protociliata comprises intestinal inhabitants (*Opalina*, etc.), mostly in frogs and toads, that have two to hundreds of nuclei all alike and no cytostome; permanent fusion of "gametes" occurs in their sexual reproduction.

Each individual in the Subclass Euciliata has a macronucleus (some have more than one) and one or more micronuclei.   Sexual reproduction (conjugation) involves only temporary union, as with *Paramecium*.   The orders of ciliates are distinguished primarily by the arrangement of the cilia around the cytostome.

Members of the Order Holotricha, like *Paramecium*, are uniformly ciliated and have no adoral membranelles.   They commonly encyst. The species are diverse in form and either live in various kinds of water or are parasitic; those of the Suborder THIGMOTRICHA occur chiefly in the mantle cavities of bivalve mollusks.

The order SPIROTRICHA contains, besides various free-living species, some of peculiar structure that inhabit parts of the digestive tract in herbivorous mammals, as in the caecum and colon of horses and the rumen and reticulum of sheep, cattle, deer, and other ruminants (Fig. 12-29). They may number up to 500,000 or 1,000,000 per cubic centimeter of gut contents so that a mature ox may contain 10,000,000,000 to 50,000,000,-000. These ciliates digest starches, fats, and proteins in the host's food. Various claims have been made as to their possible role, but they probably are only messmates (commensals) without either benefit or harm to their

FIG. 12-29. Class CILIATA. *Epidinium (Diplodinium) ecaudatum,* a complex ciliate from the rumen of cattle, as seen in median section. *(After Sharp, 1914.)*

hosts. *Balantidium coli* is a widely distributed and common ciliate parasite of the intestine in pigs that occurs rarely in man. Human infection probably is obtained by cysts carried into the mouth by the hands or with food. It sometimes invades the intestinal wall and produces ulcers.

The species of the Order PERITRICHA are distinguished by a disclike oral region that is conspicuously ciliated, with few or no cilia elsewhere, and the opposite end of the cell commonly bears some structure for temporary or permanent attachment to objects in the water. Some species are colonial, and some secrete a case or lorica, into which the organism may withdraw.

CLASS *SUCTORIA*

12-30. Adult SUCTORIA are sessile PROTOZOA that have delicate protoplasmic "tentacles" but neither cilia nor a cytostome (Fig. 12-1). Their young resemble the CILIATA in being ciliated and free-swimming. The cell body of suctorians is spherical, elongate, or branched in different species, usually attached by a stalk or disc to some object, and covered by a pellicle.   Some of the tentacles are tipped with rounded knobs that act as suckers to catch and hold the small ciliates that are used for food. Other tentacles are pointed and pierce the prey to take up its soft parts, which stream through these tentacles into the cell body.   Reproduction is by fission or budding; the young swim for a time and then settle to lose their cilia and transform into the adult stage.   Various species inhabit fresh, brackish, and salt waters and attach to inanimate objects, plants, and small aquatic animals; some are parasitic.   *Podophrya* is a common fresh-water representative; *Dendrosoma* is branched and up to 2.5 mm. tall; *Sphaerophrya stentoris* is parasitic in the ciliate *Stentor;* and *Allantosoma* attaches to ciliates in the colon of horses.

CLASSIFICATION

Phylum **PROTOZOA**. Protozoans. Single-celled or in colonies of like cells (no tissues); symmetry spherical, bilateral, or none; size usually microscopic; 30,000 species.   Pre-Cambrian to Recent.

Subphylum 1.   PLASMODROMA.   Locomotor organs are pseudopodia, flagella, or none; nuclei of one kind.

Class 1.   *MASTIGOPHORA* (Flagellata). Flagellates. With 1 to many flagella for locomotion in some or all stages of life cycle.

Subclass 1.   PHYTOMASTIGINA.   Usually with chromatophores; mostly free-living.

Order 1.   **Chrysomonadina.**   Small, solitary or colonial, often amoeboid; flagella 1 or 2; chromatophores yellow, brown, or none; no gullet; nutrition holophytic or holozoic; produce endogenous cysts of silica.   *Chromulina; Synura uvella* and *Uroglenopsis americana,* both colonial, in fresh waters, causing bad flavor in water supplies by aromatic oils released at death.

Order 2.   **Cryptomonadina.**   Small, oval, not amoeboid; flagella 2; chromatophores various or none; usually with gullet; mostly holophytic; some live as zooxanthellae in other Protozoa and in Metazoa.   *Chilomonas,* in foul waters, saprophytic.

Order 3.   **Phytomonadina** (Volvocales).   Small, solitary or in swimming colonies; some enclosed in cellulose membrane; flagella generally 2 or 4; no cytostome or gullet; chromatophores green or none; nutrition holophytic or saprophytic; mostly in fresh waters.   Solitary forms: *Chlamydomonas nivalis,* on snow; *Haematococcus pluvialis,* appears suddenly, causing "red rain" in pools.   Colonial forms (Volvocidae), in fresh waters: *Gonium,* as squares of 4 or 16 cells; *Pandorina,* globular, 16 cells; *Eudorina,* 32 cells near surface of gelatinous sphere; *Pleodorina,* 32, 64, or 128 cells in solid gelatinous ball; *Volvox,* to 15,000 cells on hollow gelatinous sphere, to 2 mm. in diameter (Fig. 12-14).

Order 4.   **Euglenoidina.**   Form elongate, usually definite; pellicle rigid or soft; flagella usually 1 to 3, in anterior cytopharynx, near contractile vacuole; chromatophores green or none; nutrition holophytic, holozoic, or saprophytic; mostly in fresh waters.   *Euglena,* some to 0.5 mm. long; *Astasia,* colorless; *Trachelomonas,* in shell; *Copromonas,* in feces of toads and frogs.

Order 5.   **Chloromonadina.**   Flagella 2; many chromatophores; reserve food as fat.   *Gonyostomum.*

Order 6.   **Dinoflagellata.**   Flagella usually 2, in grooves, one around body, one trailing; body often of fixed form, in cellulose-like armor of 2 to many plates; chromatophores many, brown, yellow, or green; many species important in marine plankton, some in fresh water, some parasitic. *Gymnodinium*, unarmored; *Peridinium* and *Ceratium*, both "armored," in salt or fresh waters; *Noctiluca*, spherical, to 2 mm. in diameter, marine, luminescent; *Gonyaulax*, in ocean, sometimes produces "red water," causes mussel poisoning on Pacific coast; *Blastodinium*, in intestine and eggs of copepods.

Subclass 2. ZOOMASTIGINA. No chromatophores; free-living or parasitic.

Order 1. **Protomonadina.** Flagella 1 or 2; body plastic or amoeboid; in fresh or foul waters, in feces, or parasitic. Free-living and holozoic: *Oicomonas, Monas, Bodo*, all solitary; *Codosiga*, on stalks, and *Proterospongia*, in gelatinous matrix, both colonial. Parasitic and saprozoic: *Herpetomonas*, in gut of flies; *Protermonas*, in gut of amphibians and reptiles; *Phytomonas*, in milky juices of milkweeds, euphorbias, etc., transmitted by plant-sucking bugs; *Trypanoplasma*, in blood of fishes, transmitted by leeches; *Trypanosoma*, narrowly leaflike, in blood of vertebrates, mostly transmitted by arthropods (by leeches to aquatic hosts).

Order 2. **Polymastigina.** Flagella 3 to 8 or more, one often trailing or bordering an undulating membrane; often with parabasal body and axostyle; holozoic or saprozoic; mostly commensal or parasitic, in gut and other organs of invertebrates and vertebrates. *Tetramitus*, in salt or fresh waters; *Chilomastix*, mainly in gut of vertebrates; *Devescovina*, in gut of termites; *Trichomonas*, in digestive and reproductive tracts of man and other animals; *T. foetus*, causes abortion in cows; *Hexamita, Giardia*, in intestines of vertebrates.

Order 3. **Hypermastigina.** Structure complex, many flagella and parabasal bodies; holozoic, mostly ingest wood; symbiotic in gut of termites and cockroaches and necessary for digestion of cellulose by these insects. *Trichonympha*, in termites and roaches; *Laphomonas*, in cockroaches; *Staurojoenina*, in termites.

Order 4. **Pantostomatida.** One flagellum; colorless; permanently amoeboid. *Mastigamoeba*, in fresh water and soil; *Mastigina hylae*, in intestine of frog tadpoles.

Class 2. *SARCODINA* (Rhizopoda). With pseudopodia for locomotion and food capture; mostly free-living.

Order 1. **Amoebina** (Lobosa). Pseudopodia short, lobose, changing; naked, in thin membrane, or in shell with 1 aperture; fresh and other waters or parasitic.

Naked forms: *Amoeba; Pelomyxa*, 2 to many nuclei, often many glycogen granules in body; *Hartmannella*, in foul waters, feeds on bacteria; *Entamoeba histolytica*, parasitic in intestine and tissues of man, causing amoebic dysentery; *E. gingivalis*, in human mouth, and *E. coli*, in intestine of man, apes, and monkeys, both harmless; others in frogs, cockroaches, etc. Shelled forms: *Arcella*, with secreted shell; *Difflugia*, shell of sand grains over organic base.

Order 2. **Foraminifera.** Body usually in shell (simple or chambered) of calcareous, chitinous, or foreign material, with one to many openings for branched or fused pseudopodia; shell 0.01 to 5 mm., some 150 mm. in diameter; reproduce asexually by multiple fission and sexually by flagellated or amoeboid phases; mostly marine and bottom dwellers, some pelagic; 18,000 species, living and fossil, Cambrian to Recent. *Allogromia*, no shell, in fresh water; *Nodosaria*, marine; *Globigerina*, pelagic (its empty shells in "globigerina ooze" cover about one-third of ocean floor at depths of 8,000 to 15,000 feet); †*Nummulites*, early Tertiary, shell to 190 mm. in diameter.

Order 3. **Heliozoa.** SUN ANIMALCULES. Spherical; pseudopodia radiating and stiffened by axial rods; chiefly in fresh water. *Actinophrys; Clathrulina*, in latticed sphere of tectin.

Order 4. **Radiolaria.** Often spherical; pseudopodia raylike; protoplasm separated into inner and outer parts by porous spherical capsule of chitin; usually with outer skeleton of silica or strontium sulphate, with radiating spines; diameter microscopic to several centimeters; marine, pelagic, ocean surface to depths of 15,000 feet; many species. Pre-Cambrian to Recent. *Acanthometron; Sphaerozoum; Collosphaera.*

Order 5. **Mycetozoa.** Adult phase as sheet of multinucleate cytoplasm up to several inches in breadth, with streaming movements; feed on decaying wood or leaves or live fungi; produce sporangia that release resistant spores. *Chondrioderma,* on beanstalks; *Badhamia,* on fungi.

Class 3. *SPOROZOA.* No locomotor organs or contractile vacuoles; reproduction by multiple asexual fission and sexual phases; all internal parasites, usually with intracellular stages.

Subclass 1. TELOSPORIDIA. Sporozoites elongate; no polar capsules in spores.

Order 1. **Gregarinida.** Trophozoite wormlike, 10 μ to 16 mm. long; zygote producing 1-walled spore containing 8 sporozoites; usually extracellular when mature; in digestive, coelomic, and other cavities of invertebrates. *Ophryocystis,* in Malpighian tubules of beetles; *Monocystis,* in sperm balls of earthworms; *Gregarina,* in grasshoppers, meal worms, etc.

Order 2. **Coccidia.** Zygote nonmotile; spores with one to many walls; with alternate asexual schizogony followed by sporogony; intracellular, chiefly in epithelial tissues of mollusks, annelids, arthropods, and vertebrates. *Hepatozoon,* in liver, marrow, etc., of mammals; *Haemogregarina,* in red blood cells of turtles, frogs, and fishes; *Eimeria (Coccidium),* chiefly in digestive epithelium of arthropods and vertebrates, especially domestic birds and mammals; *E. stiedae,* cause of coccidiosis in domestic rabbits.

Order 3. **Haemosporidia.** Zygote motile, producing naked sporozoites; reproduction alternately by schizogony, within red blood cells and blood system in vertebrates, and by sporogony in bloodsucking intermediate arthropod host. *Plasmodium,* in mosquitoes (*Anopheles, Culex*), cause of malaria in birds, mammals, and man; *Haemoproteus,* in bloodsucking flies (Hippoboscidae) and birds and reptiles; *Leucocytozoon,* in black flies (*Simulium*), causes disease in ducks; *Babesia bigemina,* carried by tick (*Boophilus annulatus*) causes Texas fever of cattle in United States; *Theileria parva,* causes East Coast fever of cattle in Africa.

Subclass 2. CNIDOSPORIDIA. Trophozoite amoeboid; spores with 1 to 4 polar capsules that discharge threads for attaching spore to host.

Order 1. **Myxosporidia.** Spores of 2 valves; polar capsules 2 (1 or 4); chiefly in cavities or tissues of fresh-water fishes, amphibians, and reptiles. *Myxobolus, Myxidium.*

Order 2. **Actinomyxidia.** Spores with 3 polar capsules, 3 valves, and 3 rays; in coelom or gut of annelids. *Triactinomyxon.*

Order 3. **Microsporidia.** Spores simple, polar capsule 1; intracellular in arthropods and fishes. *Nosema bombycis,* causes pebrine disease of silkworms; *N. apis,* causes nosema disease in honeybees.

Subclass 3. SARCOSPORIDIA. Spores naked, no polar capsules, many in large cyst to 50 mm. in diameter. *Sarcocystis,* in muscles or connective tissues of higher vertebrates, especially mammals.

Subclass 4. HAPLOSPORIDIA. Spores oval, no polar capsules; in aquatic invertebrates. *Haplosporidium,* chiefly in annelids.

Subphylum 2. CILIOPHORA. With cilia or cirri for locomotion in some or all stages of life cycle; nuclei of 2 kinds.

Class 1. *CILIATA.* Ciliates. Cilia usually present throughout life; no "tentacles."

Subclass 1. PROTOCILIATA. Opalinids. No cytostome; nuclei 2 to many; "gametes" fuse; parasitic. *Opalina, Cepedea,* in intestine of amphibians.

Subclass 2. EUCILIATA. Cytostome usually present; usually with macro- and micronuclei; with conjugation; mostly free-living, some commensal or parasitic.

Order 1. **Holotricha.** Cilia simple, over all or part of cell body; no adoral cilia. *Didinium*, *Paramecium*, free-living; *Anoplophrya*, parasitic in invertebrates; *Ichthyophthirius*, parasitic on skin of fishes; *Isotricha*, commensal in digestive tract of cattle.

Order 2. **Spirotricha.** With adoral row of membranelles, begining at right of peristome and passing around to left. *Stentor*, trumpet-shaped; *Spirostomum*, slender, to 3 mm. long; *Tintinnidium*, conical in a lorica; *Stylonychia*, *Euplotes*, *Oxytricha*, all with cirri on ventral surface; *Balantidium*, in intestines of various animals; *Diplodinium*, *Ophryoscolex*, of complex structure, commensal in digestive tract of ruminants.

Order 3. **Peritricha.** Adoral row of cilia beginning to left of peristome and passing around to right; few or no other cilia; body typically bell- or vaselike; mostly sessile, often colonial. *Vorticella*, solitary on stalk; *Epistylis*, *Zoothamnium*, *Opercularia*, in colonies; *Trichodina*, on aquatic animals.

Order 4. **Chonotricha.** Vaselike, cilia only on anterior funnel. *Spirochona*, on gills of amphipods.

Class 2. *SUCTORIA.* Cilia only in young stages; adults attached by stalk, with "tentacles" for feeding; no cytostome; mostly sessile; in salt or fresh waters. *Podophrya*, free-living; *Sphaerophrya*, spherical, parasitic in *Paramecium* and *Stentor*; *Trichophrya micropteri*, on gills of bass.

References

Borradaile, L. A., and F. A. Potts. 1932. The invertebrata. New York, The Macmillan Co. Protozoa, pp. 3–109, figs. 1–95.

Brumpt, E. 1936. Précis de parasitologie. 5th ed. Paris, Masson et Cie. Protozoa, pp. 181–545, figs. 69–270.

Calkins, G. N. 1933. The biology of the Protozoa. 2d ed. Philadelphia, Lea & Febiger. xi + 607 pp., 223 figs.

—— and F. M. Summers (editors). 1941. Protozoa in biological research. New York, Columbia University Press. xli + 1,148 pp., 4 pls., 226 figs. Modern summaries by leading American protozoologists.

Chandler, A. C. 1949. Introduction to parasitology. 8th ed. New York, John Wiley & Sons, Inc. Protozoa, pp. 31–235, figs. 1–56, especially human parasites.

Craig, C. F., and E. C. Faust. 1945. Clinical parasitology. 4th ed. Philadephia, Lea & Febiger. Protozoa, pp. 47–265, figs. 3–81.

Cushman, J. A. 1940. Foraminifera, their classification and economic use. Cambridge, Mass., Harvard University Press. viii + 535 pp., 79 pls.

Doflein, F., und E. Reichenow. 1927–1929. Lehrbuch der Protozoenkunde. 5th ed. Jena, Gustav Fischer. viii + 1,262 pp., 1,201 figs.

Hagelstein, Robert. 1944. The Mycetozoa of North America. Mineola, N.Y., published by the author. 5 + 306 pp., 16 pls.

Hartog, M. 1906. Protozoa. *In* Cambridge natural history. London, Macmillan & Co., Ltd. Vol. 1, pp. 1–162, figs. 1–62.

Hyman, Libbie H. 1940. The invertebrates: Protozoa through Ctenophora. New York, McGraw-Hill Book Co. Inc. Protozoa, pp. 44–232, figs. 6–67.

Jennings, H. S. 1906. Behavior of the lower organisms. New York, Columbia University Press. xiv + 366 pp., 144 figs.

Kudo, R. R. 1947. Protozoology. 3d ed. Springfield, Ill., Charles C. Thomas, Publisher. xiii + 778 pp., 336 figs. General account and classification.

Kükenthal, W., and others.   1925.   Handbuch der Zoologie.   Berlin, Walter de
    Gruyter & Co.   Protozoa, vol. 1, part 1, pp. 1–292, figs. 1–287.
Pratt, H. S.   1935.   A manual of the common invertebrate animals. . . . 2d ed.
    Philadelphia, The Blakiston Co.   Protozoa, pp. 11–74, figs. 1–126.
Ward, H. B., and G. C. Whipple.   1918.   Fresh-water biology.   New York, John
    Wiley & Sons, Inc.   Protozoa, pp. 210–300, figs. 274–559.
Wenyon, C. M.   1926.   Protozoology, a manual for medical men, veterinarians and
    zoologists.   New York, Wm. Wood & Co.   2 vols., xvi + ix + 1,563 pp., 20 pls.,
    565 figs.   Emphasizes parasitic and disease-producing species.

CHAPTER 13

PHYLUM PORIFERA. SPONGES

The sponges are lowly multicellular animals, incapable of movement, that variously resemble plants in appearance (Fig. 13-1). Different species are thin flat crusts, vaselike, branched, globular, or varied in form, and from a millimeter to over 6 feet in diameter. Many are gray or drab-colored, and others are brilliantly red, orange, yellow, blue, violet, or black. Most sponges are marine, living from the low tide line to depths of

Regadrella   Euspongia   Haliclona

Poterion

Sycon

Microciona

Fig. 13-1. Phylum Porifera. Class Calcarea: *Scypha* (formerly called *Sycon*). Class Hexactinellida: *Regadrella*, glass sponge. Class Demospongiae: *Poterion*, Neptune's goblet; *Euspongia*, bath sponge; *Microciona; Haliclona*, encrusting sponge. (*Regadrella and Scypha after Lankester, Treatise on zoology, A. & C. Black, Ltd.*)

$3\frac{1}{2}$ miles; one family is widespread in fresh waters. All are attached to rocks, shells, and other solid objects in the water. The name Porifera (L. *porus*, pore + *ferre*, to bear) refers to the porous structure of the body, with many surface openings. The commercial "sponge," used in the bathroom or on an automobile, is the flexible skeleton of a marine sponge with all the once living protoplasm removed.

13-1. Characteristics. 1. Symmetry radial or none; multicellular; 2 germ layers, cells imperfectly arranged as tissues and mesenchyme between.

2. Body with many pores, canals, or chambers through which water flows.

3. Some or all interior surfaces lined with choanocytes (flagellated collar cells).

4. No organs, movable parts, or appendages; digestion intracellular.

312

5. Usually with an internal skeleton of separate crystalline spicules, or of irregular organic fibers, or both.

6. Reproduction asexual by buds or gemmules; also sexual by eggs and sperm; larva ciliated, free-swimming.

Sponges were once thought to be plants, and their proper place in the animal kingdom was not settled until about 1857. They resemble some colonial flagellate protozoans (*Proterospongia*) in having groups of flagellated collar cells and intracellular digestion but differ in having some cells arranged as tissues and a body with many pores.

The sponges may have been derived from choanoflagellate Protozoa. Sponges are multicellular, with some evidence of tissue formation, thus comparing in a degree with the Metazoa, but differ in having intracellular digestion and in certain peculiarities of embryonic development. They are considered to be an aberrant stock, not on the direct line of evolution and hence often called the Parazoa (Gr. *para*, beside).

13-2. Structure of a simple sponge. The simplest of sponges is represented by *Leucosolenia* (Fig. 13-2), which attaches to the seashore rocks

Fig. 13-2. Structure of simple sponges. *A. Leucosolenia*, a small colony. *B. Leucosolenia*, enlarged section at top of body. *C. Scypha*, entire individual with part of body wall cut away (compare Fig. 13-3). *D–H*. Cells of sponges. (*Adapted from Hyman.*)

just below the low tide line. It consists of a small group of vaselike slender upright tubes united at their bases by irregular horizontal tubes. Each upright portion consists of a thin-walled sac, enclosing a central cavity, or ***spongocoel*** ("cloaca"), with one large opening, or ***osculum,*** at the summit. The wall is made up of (1) an outer ***epidermis,*** or dermal epithelium, of thin, flat cells and (2) a continuous inner lining of flagellated collar cells or ***choanocytes,*** in loose contact with one another; and between these two layers is (3) a gelatinous ***mesenchyme,*** which contains (4) free cells, or ***amoebocytes,*** of several kinds and (5) many minute crystal-like ***spicules*** of calcium carbonate supporting the soft wall. Some spicules are slender rods (monaxon), and others are three- or four-rayed (tri- or tetraxon). The wall is pierced by many minute incurrent openings, or *ostia,* that extend from the external surface to the central cavity, each pore being a canal through a tubular cell, or *porocyte,* of the epidermis.

The sponge cannot move and contraction is slight at best, but the porocytes can open or close. In life the amoebocytes move freely within the mesenchyme, which is soft, colloidal, or even watery in consistency. Each choanocyte is a rounded or oval cell, resting against the mesenchyme, its free end with a transparent contractile collar encircling the base of a single whiplike flagellum. The flagella whip back and forth, producing a continual flow of water into the many ostia, through the

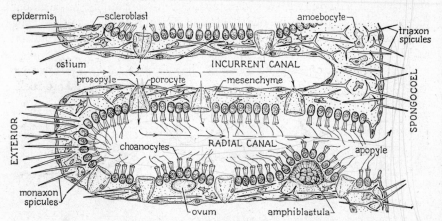

Fig. 13-3. Structure of the body wall of a *Scypha* sponge; diagrammatic section. Arrows indicate paths of water movements.

central cavity, and out the single osculum. The water brings oxygen and food and removes wastes. A sponge only 4 inches tall is estimated to pass 25 gallons of water daily through its body. The food is of plankton—microscopic animals and plants—and bits of organic matter, captured and digested in food vacuoles of the choanoytes or passed to the amoebocytes. There are no special sensory or nerve cells, and stimuli are conducted slowly from one part to another, presumably from cell to cell.

13-3. Other sponges. A somewhat more complex type is represented by *Scypha* (formerly called *Sycon* or *Grantia*), a slender form rarely over an inch tall, with one tubular central cavity and a single osculum (Figs. 13-2, 13-3). The body wall is thick and folded to form many short horizontal canals. The *incurrent canals* open from the exterior through small pores, or *ostia,* but end blindly toward the inner surface, whereas the *radial canals* begin blindly near the outer surface and open by minute *apopyles* into the spongocoel. Other smaller canals, or *prosopyles,* connect the incurrent and radial canals. The exterior surface is covered by thin *dermal epithelium,* the spongocoel is lined with a thin *gastral epithelium,* and the radial canals are lined with *choanocytes.* The canal systems greatly increase the surface exposed to the water. The body substance between these layers and outside the canals is of gelatinous *mesenchyme* containing amoeboid cells as in *Leucosolenia.* The spicules supporting the body are chiefly of four kinds, as follows: long straight (monaxon) about the osculum, short straight (monaxon) surrounding the ostia, T-shaped (triradiate) lining the spongocoel, and three-branched (triradiate) embedded in the body wall. Those about the osculum and incurrent pores protrude beyond the body surface, producing a bristly appearance.

13-4. Canal systems. In the great majority of sponges the structure becomes further complicated by branched canal systems of various kinds

FIG. 13-4. Canal systems of sponges; diagrammatic sections; epithelium, light lines; mesenchyme, stippled; areas with collar cells, heavy black; arrows indicate water currents. *D*, portion of an encrusting sponge; *E*, fresh-water sponge.

(Fig. 13-4). (1) The simplest or *ascon* type (*Leucosolenia*) has a thin body wall perforated by short straight ostia leading directly to the spongocoel, which is lined with choanocytes. (2) The *sycon* type (*Scypha*) contains two types of canals, but only the radial canals are lined with choanocytes. (3) The *leucon* type has a body of thick dense mesenchyme penetrated by complexly branched canal systems, and the choanocytes are restricted to small spherical chambers.

13-5. Skeleton. The soft bodies of sponges are supported by numerous minute crystalline spicules or by organic fibers, forming a "skeleton" (Fig. 13-5). In calcareous sponges such as *Leucosolenia* and *Scypha* the spicules are of calcium carbonate ($CaCO_3$), and those of "glass" sponges are of siliceous material (chiefly $H_2Si_3O_7$). Spicules are of many different kinds, sizes, and shapes; some of the simpler forms have already been mentioned, but there are others of even more complex form (polyaxon). In some glass sponges that live deep in the sea the spicules become fused together in a veritable framework. The bath sponges and others contain fine interjoined and irregular fibers of spongin. This material, like hair, nails, feathers, etc., is a sulphur-containing protein (scleroprotein) that is insoluble, inert chemically, and resistant to protein-digesting enzymes. Spicules are secreted by special cells in the mesenchyme known as scleroblasts, and spongin by others called spongioblasts. A monaxon spicule begins within a scleroblast as an organic axial thread around which calcium carbonate is deposited, the one cell dividing into two as the process continues, and both wander off when the spicule is complete. Each complex spicule is formed by the cooperation of several cells. The classification of sponges is based importantly on the kinds and arrangement of these skeletal materials.

Calcareous spicules   Siliceous spicules   Spongin network
                                                             of bath sponge

Fig. 13-5.   Spicules and fibers of sponges.   (*After Hyman, The invertebrates.*)

13-6. Histology. The outer or dermal epithelium and the lining of the central cavity in complex sponges are both of thin flat cells. The choanocytes form a loose layer of cells wherever they occur. These are the organized cell layers of sponges. The amoeboid cells in the mesenchyme include (1) *scleroblasts;* (2) *spongioblasts;* (3) *collenocytes,* or connective tissue cells, of stellate form with threadlike processes, or pseudopodia; (4) *myocytes* or elongate contractile cells, forming sphincters around pores and the osculum; and (5) *archeocytes* of amoeboid character and various functions; these last receive, digest, and circulate food and also form the reproductive elements (ova, sperm, gemmules).

13-7. Individuality in sponges. Though some of the cells in sponges are arranged in layers ("tissues"), much of the vital activity is by separate cells. Food is engulfed in vacuoles by the choanocytes after the manner of protozoans, and such material may be passed to the amoebocytes before being completely digested. Respiration and excretion are presumably performed by each cell independently. Sponges are thus cell aggregates without organs, and it is difficult or impossible to decide what is an "individual." Examples of *Leucosolenia* or *Scypha* each with a single osculum may be so designated, but in complex sponges with multiple canal systems and many oscula it is impossible to define the limits of an "individual."

13-8. Reproduction. Sponges multiply both asexually and sexually. Parts of a sponge lost by injury will be replaced by *regeneration,* an

$$3Pb + 2H_2SO_4 \rightarrow H_2O + 3Pb(HSO_4)_2 + SO_2$$

ability that is of value in the growing of bath sponges. Even greater ability to regenerate is shown if a sponge is squeezed through fine meshed silk so that the cells are separated. Such cells and cell clumps will come together by amoeboid movements, unite, and regenerate into a sponge like the original.   Many kinds of sponges increase commonly by **budding,** the buds either separating from the original sponge as growth proceeds or else remaining attached and thus increasing the number of parts, or the bulk, of the mass.

All fresh-water sponges (and some others) form internal buds, or **gemmules,** to carry the species through unfavorable conditions such as cold or drought (Fig. 13-7).   Groups of archeocytes (statocytes) enriched with food materials gather together in the mesenchyme and are sur-

FIG. 13-6.   Development of a calcareous sponge, *Sycandra*. (*After F. E. Schulze, 1875, 1878.*)

rounded by a resistant covering, sometimes containing spicules. As the sponge dies and disintegrates, the minute gemmules drop out and survive. When conditions again become suitable, as in spring, the cell mass escapes from within the covering and starts growth as a new sponge.

In **sexual reproduction** some sponges are dioecious and others, such as *Scypha*, are monoecious.   Ova and sperm develop from archeocytes, there being no special sex organs.   The ovum remains in the mesenchyme of the parent and is fertilized there by a sperm from another sponge.   The first three cleavages are vertical and produce a disc of eight pyramidal cells (Fig. 13-6).   A horizontal cleavage then yields eight large cells (future epidermis) and eight small (future choanocytes) arranged as a blastula.   The latter increase rapidly and elongate, and each acquires a flagellum on its inner end facing the blastocoel.   The few large cells become rounded and granular, and in their middle an opening forms that functions as a mouth to ingest adjacent maternal cells.   The embryo then turns inside out (like a stage in the protozoan *Volvox*) through its mouth, bringing the flagellated cells outside.   In this **amphiblastula** stage the oval larva escapes through the osculum of the parent to swim for some hours with the flagellated cells foremost. The flagellated half then invaginates into, or is overgrown by, the larger nonflagellated cells (= "gastrulation"). Soon the larva attaches to a solid object by the blastoporal end and begins growth as a young sponge (olynthus stage). Mesenchyme cells arise from both layers. Since the invaginated half seems to represent the animal hemisphere of the egg, the germ layers of a sponge are not considered comparable with those of metazoan embryos.

13-9. Fresh-water sponges. The Family SPONGILLIDAE includes about 15 genera and 150 species, of world-wide occurrence but restricted to fresh-water streams or ponds and lakes. They grow as tufts or irregular masses up to the size of a person's fist on sticks, stones, or plants (Fig.

entire "colonies"

Gemmule

exterior   in section

FIG. 13-7. Fresh-water sponge (Family SPONGILLIDAE). Gemmules about 1 mm. in diameter. (*After Jammes; Wolcott; and Hyman.*)

(13-7). Some are yellow or brown; others are green when exposed to sunlight because of zoochlorellae (fresh-water algae) in the mesenchyme. *Spongilla lacustris* is common in sunlit running waters, whereas *S. fragilis* avoids the light.

13-10. Relations with other animals. Sponges are seldom attacked or eaten by other animals, probably because of their skeletons and the unpleasant secretions and odors that they produce. The interior cavities of many sponges are often inhabited by crustaceans, worms, mollusks, and other animals. In a sponge the size of a washtub, A. S. Pearse counted 17,128 animals, mostly one kind of shrimp, but with a considerable variety of others including some slender fishes up to 5 inches long. Certain kinds of crabs tear off bits of living sponges, which are held against the shell until they attach; continued growth provides the crab with a protective covering of sponge having a disagreeable odor and containing spiny spicules. The sponge *Suberites* commonly grows on snail shells inhabited by some hermit crabs, soon absorbing the shell so that the crab actually inhabits a cavity in the sponge.   Another sponge, *Cliona*, grows on mollusk shells, boring into and eventually destroying the animal and its shell.   Some sponges that grow on bivalve mollusks, including oysters, become competitors of the latter since both sponge and mollusk feed on plankton; these sponges may become a nuisance on oyster beds.

13-11. The sponge industry. Since the days of ancient Greece, mankind has used the fibrous skeletons of the bath sponge (*Spongia*) for washing and mopping (Fig. 13-1).   The skeleton owes its water-holding capacity to capillary forces in the fine spaces of the irregular spongin network (Fig. 13-5).   The best and principal supplies of these sponges occur on rocky bottoms in warm shallow waters of the Mediterranean Sea and the Gulf of Mexico, about Florida and the West Indies, where over 2,000,000 pounds are taken annually.   The living sponges are brought up by divers either naked or in suits, by dredging or trawling, or by use of long-handled hooks.   They are killed by treading to loosen the living protoplasm, which is allowed to decay, then washed and beaten to remove all but the flexible skeleton.   The cleaned sponges are cut or trimmed, sometimes bleached, sorted, and marketed.   Decline in the natural supply has encouraged sponges culture in Florida and Italy.   Pieces of about 8 cubic inches are cut from desirable species and fastened to slabs of concrete or other supports on a shallow clean bottom where water currents provide abundant oxygen and food.   Several years are required to reach market size.   The largest living bath sponges may be 50 years old.

CLASSIFICATION

Phylum **PORIFERA.** Sponges. Form flat, vaselike, rounded, or branched; symmetry radial or none; color various; no organs; "body" perforated with many pores and chambers; some or all inner cavities lined with choanocytes; an internal supporting skeleton of crystalline spicules, irregular spongin fibers, or both, rarely none; sessile and marine, one family in fresh water; about 5,000 species.   Pre-Cambrian to Recent.

Class 1. *CALCAREA* (Calcispongiae). Calcareous Sponges. Spicules calcareous, monaxon or 3- or 4-branched; surface of body bristly, osculum often fringed with spicules; dull-colored; mostly under 6 inches long.

Order 1. **Homocoela.** Body wall thin, interior not folded, lined continuously with choanocytes (asconoid).   *Leucosolenia.*

Order 2. **Heterocoela.** Body wall thickened, folded internally; lining of choanocytes in radial canals not continuous (syconoid, leuconoid).   *Scypha; Grantia.*

Class 2. *HEXACTINELLIDA* (Hyalospongiae). Glass Sponges. Spicules siliceous and 6-rayed (hexactine), in definite arrangement, either separate or united in networks, some skeletons resembling spun glass; no surface epithelium; choanocytes only in finger-shaped chambers; body mass commonly cylindrical to funnel-shaped, some curved or flat or with basal stalk; length to 3 feet; exclusively marine, at depths of 300 feet to over 3 miles.   *Hyalonema; Euplectella aspergillum,* Venus's flower-basket.

Class 3. *DEMOSPONGIAE.* Skeleton of siliceous spicules, of spongin, of both, or none.

Order 1.   **Tetractinellida.**   Spicules tetraxon or none, no spongin; body mostly rounded or flattened, no branches or projections; in shallow waters. *Halisarca*, no skeleton; *Thenea; Geodea.*

Order 2.   **Monaxonida.**   Spicules monaxon; spongin in some; body form various; mostly in shore waters to 150 feet, but some to depths of 3½ miles; abundant; most common of all sponges. *Suberites; Cliona*, boring sponge; *Spongilla*, fresh-water sponges; *Haliclona.*

Order 3.   **Keratosa.**   Horny Sponges.   Skeleton a network of spongin fibers, no spicules; form usually rounded, often of considerable size; surface leathery, coloration dark, chiefly black. *Phyllospongia*, leaflike; *Spongia (Euspongia)*, bath sponge; *Hippospongia*, "horse" sponge.

References

Hyman, Libbie H.   1940.   The invertebrates: Protozoa through Ctenophora.   New York, McGraw-Hill Book Co., Inc.   Sponges, pp. 284–364.

Moore, H. F.   1923.   *In* D. K. Tressler, Marine products of commerce.   New York, Chemical Catalog Co., Inc.   Sponges, pp. 668–691, 11 figs.

CHAPTER 14

PHYLUM COELENTERATA. COELENTERATES

The COELENTERATA (Gr. *koilos*, hollow + *enteron*, intestine) or CNIDARIA are the lowest animals with definite tissues. The individuals are either separate or in colonies, and of two types: (1) the *polyp* with a tubular body having one end closed and attached and the other with a central mouth usually surrounded by soft tentacles; and (2) the free-swimming *medusa,* with a gelatinous body of umbrella shape, margined

Fig. 14-1. Phylum COELENTERATA. Some marine representatives in characteristic habitats, all reduced but not to same scale. Class HYDROZOA, Order HYDROIDA: *Tubularia, Plumularia;* Order TRACHYLINA: *Gonionemus;* Order SIPHONOPHORA: *Physalia,* Portuguese man-of-war. Class SCYPHOZOA, Order STAUROMEDUSAE: *Haliclystus;* Order CORONATAE: *Periphylla;* Order DISCOMEDUSAE: *Aurelia,* common jellyfish. Class ANTHOZOA, Order GORGONACEA: *Gorgonia,* sea fan; Order PENNATULACEA: *Pennatula,* sea pen; Order ACTINARIA: *Edwardsia, Epiactis,* sea anemones; Order MADREPORARIA: *Astrangia,* stony coral; Order CERIANTHARIA: *Cerianthus.*

with tentacles, and having the mouth on a central projection of the concave surface. Both are variously modified, and both appear in the life cycle of many species (Fig. 14-1). Each individual has a digestive cavity, some muscle fibers, and many minute stinging capsules (nematocysts). All are aquatic, and practically all are marine. The phylum includes the hydroids and hydromedusae, etc. (Class HYDROZOA), the jellyfishes (Class SCYPHOZOA), and the sea anemones and corals (Class ANTHOZOA). Many hydroids grow as small dense plantlike colonies, the jellyfishes and some hydroid medusae swim feebly, the flowerlike anemones abound on rocky ocean coasts, and the corals with their limy

321

skeletons form reefs on tropical shores.   Many anemones and corals are
brightly colored, some medusae are beautifully tinted, and many species
of coelenterates are luminescent.   Coelenterates are of slight economic
importance; some coral is used for jewelry and decorative art, and the
stings of certain jellyfishes and siphonophores occasionally injure bathers.

14-1. Characteristics.   1. Symmetry radial about an oral-aboral axis (biradial in
some ANTHOZOA); no head or segmentation.

2. Body of 2 layers of cells, an external epidermis (ectoderm), and an inner gastrodermis (endoderm), with little or much mesoglea between; nematocysts in either or
both layers.

3. Skeleton limy, horny, or none; muscle fibers in epithelia.

4. Mouth surrounded by soft tentacles and connecting to a saclike digestive cavity,
or enteron, that may be branched or divided by septa; no anus.

5. No blood, respiratory, or excretory organs.

6. A diffuse network of unpolarized nerve cells in body wall, but no central nervous
system; some with eyespots or statocysts.

7. Reproduction commonly by alternation of generations (metagenesis), with
asexual budding in the attached (polyp) stage and with sexual reproduction by
gametes in the free (medusa) stage; monoecious or dioecious; some with simple gonads,
but no sex ducts; cleavage holoblastic; a ciliated planula larva; mouth forms from
blastopore.

The stinging qualities of coelenterates were known to Aristotle, who
considered these organisms as intermediate between plants and animals.
They were long included in the Zoophyta (Gr., animal-plants) together
with various forms from sponges to ascidians.   When their animal nature
was established in the eighteenth century, Linnaeus and others classed
them with the echinoderms as Radiata because of their symmetry.
Leuckart in 1847 grouped the sponges, coelenterates, and ctenophores as
the COELENTERATA, and only in 1888 did Hatschek separate these as
distinct phyla, the PORIFERA, CNIDARIA, and CTENOPHORA.   The
coelenterates, or CNIDARIA, are distinguished from sponges in being
"tissue animals" (METAZOA) that have a distinct digestive cavity.
The coelenterates differ from ctenophores in being primarily radial
in symmetry, in possessing nematocysts, in having a polyp stage, and
in reproducing both asexually and sexually.   The polyp has been
considered an "arrested larva" and the medusa stage as the fullest
expression of the phylum.

14-2. Size.   Individual hydroid polyps are usually microscopic, but
colonies of various species are a few millimeters to 2 m. in length.   The
jellyfishes are from 12 mm. to over 2 m. in diameter, the largest (*Cyanea
arctica*) having tentacles up to 10 m. long.   Anemones range from a few
millimeters to a meter in diameter.   The individual polyps on corals are
minute, but their skeletons form massive growths in warm seas.

CLASS *HYDROZOA*.   HYDROIDS

14-3. Hydra.   The small solitary polyp known as hydra is one of the simplest of multicellular animals and serves well as an introduction to both the METAZOA and the COELENTERATA.   It is slender and flexible, 10 to 30 mm. long, with several delicate tentacles at one end (Fig. 14-2). It lives in the cool, clean, and usually permanent fresh waters of lakes, ponds, and streams, attaching to stones, sticks, or aquatic vegetation. Of the eight species in the United States, the "white" hydra, *Hydra americana*, is gray or tan with short tentacles and no stalk; the brown hydra, *Pelmatohydra oligactis* (formerly *H. fusca*), has a slender base or stalk to the body and tentacles three or four times as long as the latter; and the green hydra, *Chlorohydra viridissima* (formerly *H. viridis*),

FIG. 14-2.   Phylum COELENTERATA.   Hydra, the fresh-water polyp; natural size to 30 mm. long.   (*"Walking" after Wagner, 1905.*)

has symbiotic algae (zoochlorellae) in its inner cells, that make the body grass green.   The following account will apply to any common species.

14-4. General features.   The body (Fig. 14-3) is a cylindrical tube with the lower end closed to form a *basal disc,* or "foot," used for attaching to objects and for locomotion.   The opposite and free oral end contains the *mouth* as a small opening on a conical *hypostome,* encircled by 6 to 10 slender hollow *tentacles.*   The mouth leads into the digestive cavity, or *enteron,* which occupies the interior of the body and connects to the slender cavities in the tentacles.   The number of tentacles differs between species and increases with the age and size of an individual.   The entire animal is very flexible   The body may extend as a slender tube, may bend in any direction, or may contract to a short spherical form. The tentacles move independently or together and may extend as long delicate threads or contract down to slight knobs.   The side of the body may bear lateral *buds* that give rise to new individuals by asexual reproduction; at times, it bears other rounded projections, the *ovaries* or *testes,* concerned with sexual reproduction.

14-5. Cellular structure and function.   The wall of the body and tentacles consists of but two cell layers (Fig. 14-3), a thin external *epidermis,* of cuboidal cells, chiefly protective and sensory in function, and inside a thicker *gastrodermis,* of tall cells, serving mainly the digestive process.

Between the two is a thin noncellular *mesoglea,* or supporting lamella, secreted by and attached to both layers, that provides an elastic framework for both the body and the tentacles.

Both layers are composed of several cell types: (1) epitheliomuscular; (2) glandular; (3) interstitial; and (4) sensory. A network of nerve cells lies in or against the mesoglea. The cells of each type are specialized

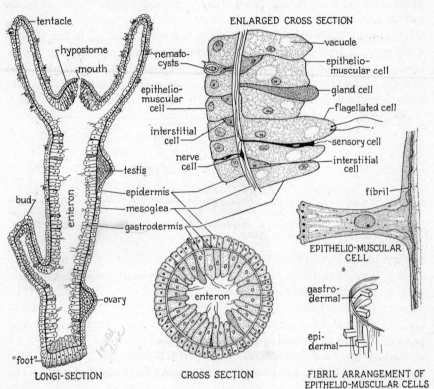

Fig. 14-3. Hydra. Structure as seen in microscopic sections. (*Epitheliomuscular cell after Hyman, The invertebrates.*)

in both structure and function to perform particular life processes; collectively, they are responsible for all the activities of the living hydra, as in all multicellular animals. Many of the cells in the gastrodermis bear one or two whiplike flagella, each arising from a blepharoplast within the cell.

EPITHELIOMUSCULAR CELLS. These cells are ⊥-shaped, having a bulbous outer portion and an elongate base containing a contractile fibril placed against the mesoglea. In the epidermis these cells are closely placed, collectively to form the exterior surface of the body; their fibrils attach lengthwise to the mesoglea and act as longitudinal muscles that contract to shorten the body stalk and tentacles. The epitheliomuscular (epitheliodigestive) cells of the gastrodermis form the principal part of the lining of the enteron and function actively in the digestion of food. Their contractile fibrils attach transversely inside the mesoglea so that they act as circular muscles to reduce the diameter and extend the length of the body. Circular contractile fibrils around the mouth and the bases of the tentacles act as sphincters to close off these openings.

GLAND CELLS. The basal disc is covered exclusively by tall gland cells that secrete a sticky mucus by which the hydra attaches to objects in the water; these cells can also produce a gas bubble. Gland cells are uncommon elsewhere in the epidermis, but large ones occur about the

Hydra tentacle with nematocyst "batteries"

VOLVENT

GLUTINANTS

cnidoblast
cnidocil
thread tube
nucleus
before discharge   discharged

cap

PENETRANT

discharged nematocysts on bristle of a crustacean

FIG. 14-4. The nematocysts or stinging capsules of hydra. (*After Schulze.*)

mouth, and many others are scattered in the gastrodermis where they secrete the enzymes by which the food is digested.

INTERSTITIAL CELLS. These are small round undifferentiated cells, found between the bases of the epidermal cells, that give rise to nematocysts, buds, and sex cells; few occur in the gastrodermis.

NEMATOCYSTS. The *nematocyst* is a minute rounded capsule filled with fluid and containing a coiled *thread tube* that may be everted to aid in the capture of prey or in locomotion. Each nematocyst is included in an interstitial cell that has been modified as a *cnidoblast,* on the exterior of which is a triggerlike *cnidocil.* Some nematocysts occur singly, but often one large and several small ones are grouped in a single large epithelial cell to form a small surface tubercle, or "battery." Nematocysts are most abundant on the tentacles, but some occur throughout the epidermis, except on the basal disc.

Hydra (Fig. 14-4) has four kinds of nematocysts, as follows: (1) The large spherical *penetrant* (16 μ in diameter) has a long thread tube that is coiled transversely and bears at its base three long spines and three rows of small thorns; when discharged the thread tube shoots out to pierce the skin of small animals and "inject" a fluid (hypnotoxin) that paralyzes the prey.   (2) The pear-shaped *volvent* (9 μ long) contains a short thick thread in a single loop; upon discharge this coils tightly around bristles or hairs on the prey.   (3) The oval *streptoline glutinant* (9 μ) has a long thread, in three or four transverse coils, that bear minute thorns and may coil upon discharge.   (4) The small *stereoline glutinant* (7 μ) discharges a straight unarmed thread.   The first two types are of particular value in capturing prey; the others produce a sticky secretion possibly used in locomotion as well as food getting.

The cnidoblast is an independent effector in that discharge of the nematocyst is due not to a nerve impulse but to some stimulus affecting the cnidocil directly.   It was formerly thought to act like a trigger, but direct mechanical stimulus as by touching with a glass rod or by the protozoans that live and move about on the surface of hydra is not ordinarily effective.   Substances diffusing in the water from the small crustaceans, worms, and larvae on which the hydra feeds will usually provoke discharge, as will acetic acid added to the water.   Eversion of the thread evidently is caused by increased osmotic pressure within the capsule.

The cnidoblast containing a nematocyst develops in the body epidermis, whence it migrates into and through the fluid in the enteron and again passes through the body or tentacle wall to its final location in the epidermis; none originates in the tentacles.   The thread tube when discharged cannot be withdrawn, and the cnidoblast cannot form another nematocyst; such parts return to the enteron and are digested, to be replaced by new cells and capsules arriving in the manner just described.

Sensory and nerve cells.   These require special staining methods for their demonstration.   Scattered through the epidermis are many slender *sensory cells* of several kinds, with delicate tips.   They are most numerous on the tentacles, about the mouth, and around the basal disc; a small number occur in the gastrodermis.   The bases of the sensory cells connect to the *nerve cells* that form a network in the epidermis and adjacent to the mesoglea.   The nerve cells have slender processes of various kinds, but these are not differentiated into dendrites and axones as with higher animals.   These processes join directly to sensory cells, between one nerve cell and another, and to contractile fibers of epitheliomuscular cells.   The combination provides a *sensory-neuromotor mechanism;* the sensory cells *receive* stimuli, the nerve cells *conduct* impulses, and the contractile fibers *react* to the latter.   Excluding the neuromotor organelles of some protozoans, this is the first and simplest neural mechanism to be seen among animals.   It provides for coordination in movement of the body and tentacles.   There is no central ganglion or brain such as occurs in flatworms and higher metazoan animals.

14-6. Locomotion. Hydra lives attached by its basal disc to objects in the water but is able to twist about, to perform movements for the capture of prey, and to change its location. It can move in several ways. Commonly it bends over, attaches the tentacles to the substratum by use of the glutinant nematocysts, releases and moves the basal disc to a new site, disengages the tentacles, and again assumes an upright position (Fig. 14-2). This "walking" resembles the looping action of a leech or measuring worm. Sometimes it travels inverted, using the tentacles as legs. Again, it may glide along the substratum by pseudopodia-like action of cells on the basal disc. Occasionally it uses a gas bubble secreted in mucus by the disc, to rise in the water and float at the surface. *P. oligactis* can "climb" by attaching its long tentacles to some object, releasing the basal disc, and then contracting the tentacles. The white and brown hydras often remain fixed for considerable periods, whereas green hydras move about often, especially when seeking food.

14-7. Feeding and digestion. Hydra feeds mainly on minute crustaceans, insect larvae, and similar animals; at times, it may swallow prey larger than itself. A hungry individual usually remains attached by its base with the body extended and the tentacles stretched to wave about in search of prey. When a tentacle touches any small animal, nematocysts are discharged into it at once. The penetrants puncture the victim and give off the paralyzing hypnotoxin, the volvents wrap about appendages or other parts, and the glutinants may fasten to its surface. Other tentacles may perform coordinated movements and discharge nematocysts to aid the capture. The tentacles bend inward and carry the food toward the mouth. The latter opens and moves around the food, which is swallowed and passed into the upper part of the enteron by contractions of the hypostome and body wall.

Gland cells in the gastrodermis then become active and discharge secretions containing enzymes that act upon the food. Expansion and contraction of the body wall and whipping movements of flagella on the digestive cells bring these secretions against all parts of the food. Soft parts of the latter soon become separated and liquefied, whereas harder portions (such as chitin) are unaffected. Some digestion is completed in the enteron, and the fully digested materials are absorbed by cells of the gastrodermis; this is *extracellular digestion* such as occurs in most multicellular animals. In addition, the free ends of epithelio-muscular cells in the gastrodermis send out pseudopodia that draw food particles into vacuoles within the cells, where *intracellular digestion* takes place as in protozoans and sponges. Hydra thus combines the digestive procedures of forms both lower and higher than itself. Indigestible residues are egested through the mouth, which thus functions also as an anus.   Absorbed food (especially glycogen) is stored locally in cells of the gastrodermis, whence the needs of the epidermis are probably supplied by diffusion.   There seems to be no general circulation of food in the gastrodermis or enteron.   Stored materials tend to be concentrated where metabolism is active and where buds or gonads are forming.

14-8. Respiration and excretion.   The oxygen necessary for respiration diffuses from the surrounding water directly into the cells of the hydra, and metabolic wastes such as carbon dioxide and nitrogenous compounds are lost by diffusion, mainly from the epidermis.

14-9. Behavior.   All movements result from action of the opposed sets of contractile fibers in the body wall and tentacles and show an obvious

coordination between the different parts of the organism that results from transmission of impulses through the *nerve net* (Fig. 14-5). The response of any individual hydra to stimuli from its environment will be conditioned by its physiological state at the time. A hungry individual usually responds more actively than one that has recently fed, and there are also differences in response between the species of hydra.

FIG. 14-5. Nerve cells in a young hydra. (*After Hadzi,* 1909.)

A slight touch, as with a needle, will cause the hydra to turn away the part so stimulated, and a stronger stimulus such as jarring the dish containing the animal will usually result in sudden and complete contraction of both tentacles and body.   Besides thus responding to external stimuli the hydra reacts also to internal stimuli; an undisturbed specimen will, from time to time, suddenly contract and then expand slowly.   Such spontaneous movements probably are related to food getting, being more frequent with hungry individuals.   Each species responds to a particular optimum of light intensity, the green hydra seeking a stronger intensity than other species.   In the main, they avoid either very strong or very weak illumination and usually move about by trial and error until the most favorable condition is found.   This probably also is related to food getting, since most of hydra's prey seeks well-lighted areas.   Hydra prefers cool waters and in a temperature gradient will seek the colder portion.   It endeavors to avoid injurious chemical substances.   Under rich feeding, high temperature, foul water, and other unfavorable conditions, hydra undergoes a lowered metabolic state known as "depression."   There is a gradual shortening and loss of the tentacles and column, beginning at the distal end; this may proceed to disintegration or may be followed by recovery.

Hydra occurs in enormous numbers in some lakes, to depths of 180 feet, but commonly disappears from surface waters at 70°F. or higher. At times it infests fish nets in such numbers as to irritate the hands of fishermen and sometimes kills quantities of young fishes in hatcheries.

14-10. Budding. Hydra produces new individuals either by asexual budding or by sexual means involving eggs and sperm.   A *bud* forms as a projection about midway on the body wall; it contains epidermis, meso-glea, and gastrodermis with an outpocketing of the enteron (Fig. 14-3). This lengthens, acquires blunt tentacles and a mouth distally, and later is constricted and detached at the base, to become an independent hydra. Occasionally, several buds form on a single "parent," and these in turn may produce secondary buds, to form temporarily a group somewhat resembling a colonial hydroid.   Prior to bud formation the gastroderm cells at the site become well supplied with food for the initial development; later, the bud receives food through the connection of its enteron with that of the parent individual.   Budding may occur at almost any season.

14-11. Regeneration and grafting. The ability of certain animals to restore or *regenerate* lost parts was first reported in 1744 by Trembley, an English naturalist, from studies on hydra.   If a living specimen is cut across into two or more pieces, each will regenerate into a complete but smaller hydra.   The hypostome and tentacles alone will form a new individual, and a hydra split part way through the mouth will form a "two-headed" polyp, if the portions are held apart.   Even minute frag-ments will regenerate completely, and pieces too small to grow inde-pendently may fuse and regenerate; but the "germ layers" will not mix. Epidermis joins only with epidermis and gastrodermis with gastro-dermis, cells of the latter sending out protoplasmic processes that inter-weave with one another.

Parts of two hydras may be brought together and *grafted* in various arrangements.   The parts usually retain their original polarity, that originally toward the oral end producing tentacles and the opposite end a basal disc, but an oral region grafted to an aboral end may *induce* an oral growth with tentacles in the latter.

14-12. Sexual reproduction. Most species of hydra are dioecious, any one individual producing only male or female sex organs and cells; a few species, however, are monoecious.   The formation of gonads and sexual reproduction ordinarily occur in the autumn but may be induced at other seasons by reducing the water temperature.   The *gonads* are the only reproductive organs (Fig. 14-6); these are temporary structures on the sides of the body, the *ovaries* producing eggs and the *testes* or spermaries producing sperm.   Both the male and female gonads arise from interstitial cells in the epidermis.

Each of the several testes is a conical outgrowth containing a number of elongate cysts.   The interstitial cell (spermatogonium) at the base divides repeatedly to produce many spermatocytes (*C*). These migrate outward, and the cysts become rounded. As each cell goes through two maturation divisions (*D*), four nuclei are produced, but the cytoplasm does not separate until later. The spermatids (*E*) transform into sperm, which escape in numbers to the distal end of the cyst and emerge through a pore in the testis to swim in the water (*F*); there they may remain active for a day or more.

The future egg forms from an interstitial cell beneath the epidermis; it enlarges and is joined by other interstitial cells, which become the yolk. Two maturation divisions ensue, with production of two polar bodies and reduction of the egg chromosomes from 12 to 6. The mature ovum

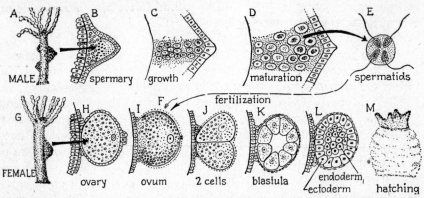

Fig. 14-6. Sexual reproduction of hydra. (*Adapted from Tannreuther*, 1908, 1909; *M*, *redrawn from W. C. Curtis and M. J. Guthrie, Textbook of general zoology, John Wiley & Sons, Inc.*)

(*H*) squeezes through a small opening in the epidermis to lie free on the surface of the latter (*I*). Fertilization then occurs with entrance of a sperm head, bringing 6 chromosomes.

The egg soon begins to divide (*J*), cleavage being total and equal. The blastula is a sphere formed of a single layer of cells, which enclose a small cavity. These cells shortly secrete a shell, or cyst, around the blastula (*K*). The outer ends of the blastula cells become the ectoderm, destined to form the epidermis, and their inner ends divide off to form the endoderm, which will produce the gastrodermis; the endoderm is solid (*L*) at first but later hollows out to make the enteron. Mesoglea is produced later between the two cells layers. The cyst containing the embryo soon hardens and drops into the water. After some time (10 to 70 days) the cyst softens and a young hydra with short tentacles hatches out. There is no larval stage.

14-13. Colonial hydroids. Unlike hydra, most other members of the Class HYDROZOA are marine and colonial. They include the hydroids, the stinging corals, some jellyfishes, and the free-floating siphonophores.

Obelia (Fig. 14-7) is a typical hydroid, of mosslike form, found on rocks or shells or piling in the shallow waters of seacoasts. .The small whitish **colony** is fastened by a rootlike base (hydrorhiza) bearing threadlike branched stems (hydrocauli) on which are hundreds of microscopic polyps of two kinds.   The feeding polyp, or **hydranth,** is hydralike, with 20 or more solid tentacles, and is set in a transparent vaselike **hydrotheca** that affords it protection.   These polyps capture minute animals by use of their nematocysts and tentacles.   The reproductive polyp, or **gonangium,**

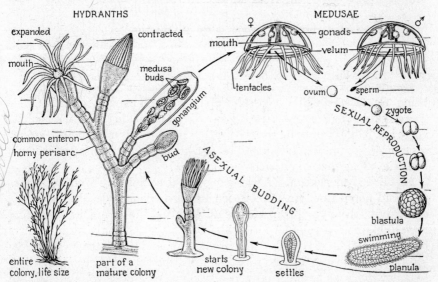

FIG. 14-7. Class HYDROZOA. Structure and life cycle of a colonial marine hydroid, *Obelia*. The colony comprises polyps of two types, the feeding hydranths and reproductive gonangia, both formed by asexual budding on branched stems attached to the substratum by a rootlike hydrorhiza. Free-swimming medusae of separate sexes bud off from the gonangia and later produce ova and sperm. The zygote develops into a ciliated swimming planula larva; this soon attaches and forms a new colony by budding. The three kinds of individuals illustrate polymorphism, and the alternation of asexual and sexual generations is termed "metagenesis." (*Modified from Wolcott, Animal biology.*)

is of cylindrical form, covered by a transparent gonotheca, and contains an axis or blastostyle on which lateral buds form that develop into medusae. The common stem supporting both kinds of polyps comprises an external transparent and noncellular **perisarc** that is continuous with the hydrotheca and gonotheca and an internal hollow **coenosarc** of cellular structure connecting the enterons of various polyps.   Digested food circulates through the coenosarc.   Both types of polyps are produced by buds on the stem.

The **medusa** is a minute jellyfish, shaped like an umbrella and rimmed with tentacles; on its concave side is a central projecting **manubrium.** This contains the mouth, which leads to an enteron in the middle of the bell, whence four *radial canals* extend to a *ring canal* in the bell margin. A gelatinous mesoglea fills the space between the epidermis over the bell, tentacles and manubrium, and the gastrodermis that lines the digestive tract and its branches.   Although the feeding polyps and the medusae differ markedly in appearance, their basic structure is essentially the same (Fig. 14-11).

The medusae escape from the gonangia to float and feed in the sea. They are of separate sexes, and their (epidermal?) gonads develop in the enteron, whence eggs and sperm are released into the water. There each zygote develops into a minute ciliated *planula* larva.   This soon settles and attaches with its blastopore uppermost, then grows to be a small polyp, which by asexual budding begins a new colony.   Such an alternation of sexual and asexual generations is termed *metagenesis*.

Hundreds of species of hydroids occur at various depths, a majority being found in shallow coastal waters.   In HYDROZOA of the Order TRACHYLINA the polyp generation is reduced or lacking, and the medusa stage is a jellyfish of some size with a thin narrow velum around the inner margin of the umbrella; *Gonionemus* is a common representative in some localities along the Atlantic coast (Fig. 14-1).

14-14. Polymorphism.   A wide range in the complexity of colony structure and polyp function is to be seen among various hydroids.   *Hydra* is an individual polyp that performs all essential life functions, including reproduction.   In colonial forms like *Obelia* the feeding hydranths perform all functions except that of reproduction, and the gonangia are solely reproductive in forming the medusae for dispersal.   *Hydractinia*, which lives on shells of hermit crabs, has feeding, reproductive, and fighting polyps, the last being of slender form, with no mouth, and bearing spherical growths on which are many nematocysts.   The greatest diversity is seen in members of the Order SIPHONOPHORA, which form floating or swimming colonies of specialized individuals.   Thus, in *Physalia pelagica*, the Portuguese man-of-war, and in *Velella*, *Porpita*, and others, each colony includes at least four types of polyps, as follows: (1) the pneumatophore, or float, into which gas is secreted to render the colony buoyant; (2) feeding polyps; (3) defensive or fighting polyps with nematocysts; and (4) reproductive polyps.   Some species also have sensitive or feeling polyps. In *Physalia* the float is used as a sail, attains to 8 or 10 inches in length, is crested, and may change in shape by contraction.   Such diversity in form and function of a basic type (the polyp) is known as *polymorphism*.

CLASS *SCYPHOZOA*.   JELLYFISHES

In the SCYPHOZOA (Gr. *skyphos*, cup + *zoon*, animal) the medusa stage is from an inch to 7 feet in diameter and consists largely of gelatinous

mesoglea, or "jelly," the polyp being minute or lacking. *Aurelia aurita*
is a common jellyfish of coastal waters, often seen singly or in companies.

14-15. Structure.   The body (Fig. 14-8) is shallowly convex above and
concave below and is fringed by a row of closely spaced delicate **marginal
tentacles.**   These are interrupted by eight equally spaced indentations,
each with a **sense organ** between two small **lappets.**   There is no velum.
Circular muscle fibers are numerous in the bell margin.   Central in the
concave oral surface is the **mouth,** on a short **manubrium,** between four
tapering **oral arms,** which are grooved and bear nematocysts along their
edges.   A short **gullet** through the manubrium connects to the **enteron,**
or digestive cavity.   Off the latter are four **gastric pouches** containing

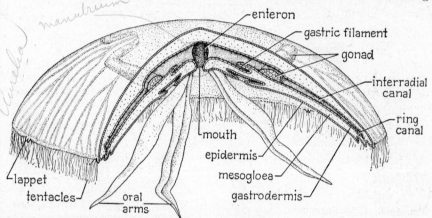

Fig. 14-8.   Class Scyphozoa.   Structure of a jellyfish, *Aurelia aurita;* one-quarter of the
body cut away to show internal structure.

slender tentacle-like **gastric filaments** with nematocysts.   Many **radial
canals** extend through the mesoglea from the pouches to a **ring canal**
in the bell margin.   There are four U-shaped **gonads,** one in the floor of
each gastric pouch.   The **nerve net** is best developed about the bell
margin.   Each sense organ comprises (1) a pigmented **eyespot** sensitive
to light; (2) a hollow **statocyst,** off the circular canal, that contains
minute calcareous granules and gives direction for swimming movements;
and (3) two **sense pits,** one lateral and one medial, probably chemoreceptors having to do with food recognition.   The exterior surface is covered
by epidermis; and the lining of the digestive system and canals from the
mouth inward, the gastric tentacles, and the gonads are of gastrodermis.

14-16. Natural history.   Jellyfishes may occur singly or in great
schools.   They float quietly and can swim feebly by rhythmic contractions of the bell but are largely at the mercy of currents and waves.
Great numbers are sometimes cast on shore during storms.   The food is
mainly of small invertebrates, seized and paralyzed by nematocysts on the

oral arms, then carried into the mouth; further quieting of the prey may be accomplished by nematocysts on the gastric tentacles. Some of the food digested in the enteron passes to the radial and circular canals for absorption, and undigested parts are cast out the mouth. Respiration and excretion are presumably performed by the whole body surface. The nerve net serves to coordinate the pumping contractions of the bell and action of the oral lobes.

The sexes are alike but separate (Fig. 14-9). Sperm from the gonads (testes) of a male pass out of its mouth and into the enteron of a female to fertilize the eggs produced in her gonads (ovaries). The zygotes emerge

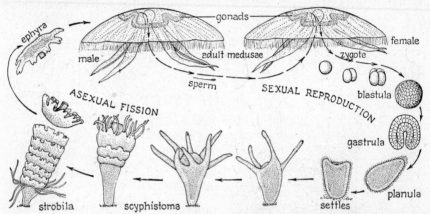

Fig. 14-9. Class Scyphozoa. Life cycle of the jellyfish, *Aurelia.* Adults of separate sexes produce eggs and sperm, and the zygotes develop on the oral arms of the female. The ciliated planula larva swims and later attaches to become a small scyphistoma; this by transverse fission (strobilation) yields several ephyrae which grow to be adult jellyfishes. Medusae reduced, other stages enlarged. (*After Agassiz; and Wolcott, Animal biology.*)

to lodge on her oral lobes, where each develops into a ciliated planula larva. This escapes to swim for a while, then settles and attaches to the sea bottom. Losing the cilia, it becomes a minute trumpet-shaped polyp (scyphistoma) with basal disc, mouth, and tentacles. It feeds and grows to about 12 mm. long and may produce lateral buds that become separate polyps, as with hydra. In autumn and winter a type of transverse fission (strobilation) ensues; horizontal constrictions form around the body and deepen so that the organism somewhat resembles a pile of minute saucers with fluted borders, the edge of each produced into eight double lobes. These flat eight-lobed ephyrae later separate, invert, and swim about, and each grows to be an adult jellyfish.

Class *ANTHOZOA.* Sea Anemones, Corals, etc.

The Anthozoa are marine polyps of flowerlike form (Gr. *anthos,* flower + *zoon,* animal), of small to large size and rather firm texture, with a tendency toward biradial symmetry in arrangement of the gullet and internal septa.   Besides the familiar sea anemones and stony corals, this class includes the soft, horny, and black corals, the colonial sea pens and sea pansies, and others, all of which lack a medusa stage.   They abound in warm shallow waters, but some inhabit polar seas, and various species occur from the tide lines to depths of 17,400 feet.

14-17. Structure.   A common sea anemone such as *Metridium* has a short cylindrical body (Fig. 14-10).   On the upper and flat **oral disc** are many short hollow **tentacles** around a slitlike **mouth;** the base, or **pedal**

Fig. 14-10.   Class Anthozoa.   Structure of a sea anemone, *Metridium*.   Part of the body has been cut away to show internal features.   Cross sections through and below the gullet show the arrangement of the septa.

disc, serves for attachment to solid objects in the sea.   The **gullet,** or stomodeum, is a flat tube connecting the mouth and internal cavity, or **enteron.**   Along one or both sides of the gullet is a smooth ciliated furrow, the **siphonoglyph,** in which water passes to the enteron.   Internally the body is divided into radial compartments by six pairs of complete **septa,** or mesenteries, that extend vertically from the body wall to the gullet; between these are other, incomplete septa (secondary, tertiary) attached to the body wall but not reaching the gullet.   In the septa, beneath the oral disc, are openings, or **ostia,** through which water can pass between the internal compartments.   The free inner margin of each septum is a thick convoluted **septal filament,** continued below as a threadlike **acontium;** both parts bear nematocysts and gland cells.   Other nematocysts occur on the tentacles.   The acontia can be protruded through pores in the body wall or through the mouth, to aid in subduing prey.   The *gonads* form along margins of the septa.

The exterior surface is covered completely by tough epidermis, with cilia on the oral disc, tentacles, and gullet, and the enteron is entirely lined by gastrodermis.   Both these cell layers contain strong muscle fibers, arranged as in hydra, and there are additional longitudinal fibers in the septa.   Between the epidermis and gastrodermis of the body wall and discs and within the septa there is mesoglea composed of cellular connective tissue.   The epidermis contains a nerve net and nerves occur in the septa, but no localized sense organs are present.

14-18. Natural history.   The sea anemone lives attached to some firm surface but can creep slowly on its pedal disc.   When undisturbed and

FIG. 14-11.   Phylum COELENTERATA.   Comparison of the hydroid polyp, the medusa (inverted), and the anthozoan polyp.

covered by water, the body and tentacles are widely extended.   If irritated or if exposed by a receding tide, the oral disc may be completely inturned and the body closely contracted.   Cilia on the tentacles and disc beat so as to keep these surfaces free of debris.   A constant current of water moves down the siphonoglyph to circulate in the enteron for respiratory purposes and to keep the body turgid, and an outward current passes up elsewhere in the gullet.

The food is of mollusks, crustaceans, other invertebrates, and fishes, paralyzed by nematocysts and carried by the tentacles to the mouth; some prey is gripped directly by the mouth and gullet, both of which can gape widely.   The food passes to the enteron, is digested by enzymes secreted from the filaments, and is absorbed by the gastrodermis.   Undigested wastes are cast out the mouth.

The sexes are separate.   Eggs and sperm leave the gonads through the mouth, and fertilization occurs in the water.   The zygote develops into an elongate ciliated gastrula; septa soon appear in the archenteron, the blastopore becomes a mouth, and long stiff cilia grow on the aboral end. This larva swims about, feeding on microorganisms, later creeps on the bottom, and then attaches by the aboral end.   With growth of the tentacles, septa, and mesoglea, it becomes a miniature anemone.

Most kinds of anemones are attached to rocks, shells, or other surfaces, but some can move readily, a few minute forms (*Boloceroides*) can swim by lashing their tentacles, and some slender types (*Edwardsia, Cerianthus*) burrow in the bottom leaving only the tentacles and oral disc exposed (Fig. 14-1).   Anemones are eaten by fishes, crabs, other crustaceans, starfishes, and nudibranch mollusks; cod, flounders, and other fishes use them in some quantity.   Some nudibranchs are immune to the toxins of anemones and even incorporate the undischarged nematocysts into their own bodies.   Certain kinds of anemones reproduce asexually by fission, either longitudinal (*Sagartia*) or transverse (*Gonactinia*), and others (*Epiactis*) fragment pieces off the base to form new individuals.   Some anemones regularly contain symbiotic algae (zooxanthellae) in the gastrodermis.   Several instances of longevity in captive anemones are recorded, one of *Cereus pedunculatus* to over 65 years.

14-19. Corals.   Members of the Order MADREPORARIA are the principal reef builders, growing as rigid masses able to resist the constant

Fungia (mushroom)   Acropora (elk-horn)   Oculina   Meandrina (brain)   (rose)   Tubipora (organ pipe)

FIG. 14-12.   Types of corals (Class ANTHOZOA).   *A.* Solitary and, *B–E,* parts of colonial stony corals (Order MADREPORARIA).   *F.* Horny coral (Order GORGONACEA).   (*After Wolcott, Animal biology.*)

pounding of waves.   Other coelenterates and invertebrates and marine algae also contribute to reef formation.   Many kinds of animals live among or in corals; some commensal crabs become imprisoned in galls on corals, and in the cells of some shallow water corals are brown algae (zooxanthellae).

The coral organism is a small anemone-like polyp, with short tentacles, scant musculature, and no pedal disc, that lives in a stony cup with radial ridges in the bottom.   Generations of such polyps in dense colonies produce the calcareous corals and coral reefs (Fig. 14-12).   They require waters at 20°C. or warmer and live from the surface to depths of about 120 feet between latitudes 28°N. and 28°S.   They abound about Florida and the West Indies, in the Caribbean Sea, and in the Coral Sea from Hawaii and the Philippines to Australia and East Africa.   A few stone corals (*Fungia*, etc.) are solitary, and some of these occur to depths of 25,000 feet.

Reef corals may form (1) a ***fringing reef*** extending out to a quarter mile from shore; (2) a ***barrier reef*** separated by a lagoon of some width and depth from a shore; and (3) an **atoll,** or circular reef, encircling a lagoon of water and not enclosing an island. Most famous is the Great Barrier Reef along northwest Australia, about 1,200 miles long and from a few to 90 miles off shore.

There are various theories as to the origin of coral reefs. Darwin inferred that growth began on a sloping shore and that as the shore sank this became a barrier reef and later an atoll when the land was completely submerged (Fig. 14-13). Daly's theory assumes that withdrawal of water to form the great icecaps of the last glacial period lowered the sea about 200 feet below its present level. Various terraces were then cut by wave action. Later, with rising temperatures, corals began growing and

FIG. 14-13.   Formation of a coral reef.   (*After Darwin.*)

built up with the gradual rise in sea level as the ice melted. Recent borings on Bikini showed sand containing Oligocene FORAMINIFERA at a depth of 2,500 feet. Previous theories of atoll formation are inadequate to explain this finding. Present-day reefs grow 5 to 200 mm. per year, and it is estimated that all existing reefs could have been developed in 10,000 to 30,000 years.

14-20. Fossil coelenterates. Relics of the HYDROZOA and ANTHOZOA occur from Cambrian time onward, and scant impressions of the SCYPHO-ZOA appear in Cambrian, Permian, and Jurassic rocks. Fossil reefs of stony corals occur in Iowa, Kansas, Kentucky, and Europe, and a great

TABLE 14-1.   TYPES OF REPRODUCTION IN THE COELENTERATES

Hydrozoa *Hydra*	small solitary polyp	→ bud → polyp → gametes → zygote → polyp
Obelia	polymorphic colony of minute polyps	→ bud → hydranth (feeding polyp) → bud → gonangium → bud → minute medusa → gametes → zygote → ciliated planula → polyp → buds → polyp colony
Scyphozoa *Aurelia*	large medusa	→ gametes → zygote → ciliated planula → minute polyp → bud → polyp → transverse fission → ephyra → medusa
Anthozoa *Metridium*	large solitary polyp	→ fission → polyp → fragmentation → polyp → gametes → zygote → ciliated larva → polyp

reef surrounds the "Michigan basin," from Wisconsin to Ohio. The †Tabulata of Silurian to Triassic times had colonies of many tubes with cross partitions, some pierced by pores; they are probably a subclass of Anthozoa. The †Stromatoporidea (†*Stromatopora*, etc.) of Ordovician to Devonian times left masses of wavy calcareous plates that formed reefs in ancient oceans; they have been variously classified, from algae to cephalopods! The †Graptozoa (†*Dictyonema*, etc.), of Upper Cambrian to Devonian, were colonial marine forms, either fixed or floating, with simple, branched, or bushlike stems of chitinous material that housed polyps in separate pits. The latter groups may both belong to the Hydroida.

CLASSIFICATION

Phylum **COELENTERATA** (Cnidaria). Coelenterates. Symmetry radial or biradial; the individual either a sessile cylindrical polyp, often in colonies, or a free-floating bell-like medusa with much mesoglea; with stinging nematocysts; digestive cavity (enteron) saclike, sometimes branched; soft tentacles about mouth; no anus, no head, no other organ systems; nervous system diffuse; some with eyespots, or statocysts; reproduction usually asexual in polyps and sexual in medusae; dioecious or monoecious; no sex ducts; all aquatic, chiefly marine, attached or floating; 10,000 species; Lower Cambrian to Recent.

Class 1. *HYDROZOA.* Hydroids (and some medusae). No stomodeum; enteron lacks partitions and nematocysts; mesoglea noncellular; medusa usually small and with velum (craspedote); chiefly in shallow salt waters; colonial or solitary; 3,700 species.

Order 1. **Hydroida.** Polyp generation well-developed, solitary or colonial, usually budding off small free medusae that bear ocelli and ectodermal statocysts. *Hydra, Pelmatohydra, Chlorohydra,* all in fresh water, solitary, no medusoid stage; *Cordylophora,* colonial, in rivers and brackish water; *Corymorpha,* solitary, marine; *Tubularia, Bougainvillia, Obelia, Eudendrium, Sertularia, Plumularia, Antennularia,* all sessile, colonial, and marine; *Polyorchis,* Pacific coast, no hydroid stage.

Order 2. **Hydrocorallina.** Polyps minute and dimorphic, protruding through pores in massive calcareous skeleton. Triassic to Recent. *Millepora,* stinging coral, with powerful nematocysts, on Florida coast and on tropical reefs down to 100 feet; *Stylantheca,* off California.

Order 3. **Trachylina.** Polyp generation reduced or none; medusa of some size, with velum beneath bell margin and tentacles attached above margin; with statocysts and endodermal tentaculocysts; sexes separate. *Liriope, Gonionemus, Aglantha,* all marine, warm seas, surface to depths of 10,000 feet; *Craspedacusta sowerbyi,* freshwater jellyfish, diameter to 20 mm., polyp stage 2 mm. tall, occasional in eastern North America.

Order 4. **Siphonophora.** Siphonophores. Swimming colonies comprising several kinds of polyps; no oral tentacles; upper end of colony usually a supporting float; nematocysts many, large, and powerful; medusae incomplete, attached to stem or disc, rarely free; marine, pelagic, especially in warm seas. *Physalia pelagica,* Portuguese man-of-war, Atlantic coast; *Velella; Porpita; Diphyes.*

Class 2. *SCYPHOZOA* (Scyphomedusae). Jellyfishes. Chiefly free-swimming medusae of bell or umbrella form, with strong 4-part radial symmetry and much gelatinous mesoglea; no true velum; no stomodeum; gastric tentacles about mouth; central gastrovascular "stomach" with pouches; notches in bell margin with sense organs (tentaculocysts) having endodermal statoliths; medusae sexual, dioecious, with gonads in gastral cavity; polyp generation none or reduced (scyphistoma), producing medusae directly or by transverse fission; all marine; 200 species.

Order 1. **Stauromedusae** (Lucernariida). Goblet-shaped; marginal sense organs none or as modified tentacles; sessile, attached by oral stalk to seaweeds; bays and coastal waters of colder regions. *Haliclystus; Lucernaria.*

Order 2. **Cubomedusae** (Carybdeida). Bell cubical; tentacles 4 or in 4 groups; bell margin bent inward; tropical and subtropical waters, shores, and open seas; feed mostly on fish. *Tamoya,* Atlantic coast.

Order 3. **Coronatae** (Peromedusae, part). Bell surrounded by circular furrow, above the scalloped margin; chiefly in deep waters. *Periphylla; Nausithoë; Linuche.*

Order 4. **Discomedusae.** Corners of mouth prolonged as 4 grooved oral arms; chiefly in coastal waters; includes most jellyfishes. *Aurelia,* common jellyfish; *Cyanea,* to 7 feet in diameter, from Arctic waters south along both coasts of North America; *Cassiopeia; Pelagia,* in open ocean, no fixed scyphistoma stage; *Rhizostoma, Stomatolophus,* no marginal tentacles, oral arms fused.

Class 3. *ANTHOZOA.* Corals, Sea Anemones, etc. All polyps, and attached (no medusae); oral disc flat, with hollow tentacles; mouth leading into stomodeum (pharynx), usually with siphonoglyph; enteron divided by vertical septa bearing nematocysts on inner margins; mesoglea a connective tissue; with or without skeleton; gonads (endodermal) in septa; all marine; solitary or colonial; 6,100 species.

Subclass 1. ALCYONARIA (Octocorallia). With 8 pinnately branched tentacles and 8 single complete septa; one ventral siphonoglyph; an endoskeleton; colonial.

Order 1. **Stolonifera.** Polyps arising separately from common stolon or mat; skeleton of separate spicules, sometimes fused as tubes. *Clavularia,* California coast; *Tubipora musica,* organ-pipe coral, in warm waters on coral reefs.

Order 2. **Telestacea.** Colonies of stems, each an axial polyp with lateral polyps, on a slender base. *Telesto.*

Order 3. **Alcyonacea.** Soft Corals. Polyps with lower parts fused in a fleshy mass and only oral ends protruding; skeleton of separate limy spicules, not axial; mostly in warm shore waters. *Xenia, Alcyonium; Anthomastus.*

Order 4. **Coenothecalia.** Skeleton massive, of crystalline calcareous fibers. *Heliopora,* blue coral of Indo-Pacific region.

Order 5. **Gorgonacea.** Horny Corals. Colony usually of plantlike form; axial skeleton of calcareous spicules, of hornlike gorgonin, or both; polyps short; 1,000 species. *Corallium,* red coral, used for jewelry; *Gorgonia,* sea fan.

Order 6. **Pennatulacea.** Colony fleshy, of one long axial polyp, with many dimorphic polyps along sides, above bare stalk; skeleton of limy spicules; 300 species. *Pennatula,* sea pen, featherlike; *Renilla,* sea pansy, disclike.

Subclass 2. ZOANTHARIA. Tentacles few to many (never 8), sometimes branched; siphonoglyphs 2, 1, or none; skeleton solid, if present.

Order 1. **Actiniaria.** Sea Anemones. No skeleton; polyp of some size, columnar, with muscular wall and usually a pedal disc; stomodeum usually with siphonoglyphs; septa paired, often in multiples of 6; on rocks, on sand, or on invertebrates; sessile, but not fixed; essentially solitary, some closely grouped; 1,000 species. *Gonactinia; Edwardsia,* in "burrows"; *Adamsia, Actinia,* habitually on shells of hermit crabs; *Sagartia; Metridium; Cribrina,* Pacific coast, to 30 cm. tall.

Order 2. **Madreporaria.** Stony Corals. Exoskeleton compact, calcareous; polyps small or minute, in cups on skeleton; tentacles in 6's usually; no siphonoglyph;

muscles feeble; mostly colonial in warm seas; Pre-Cambrian to Recent; 2,500 living, 5,000 extinct species. *Fungia*, solitary; *Balanophyllia*, California coast; *Astrangia danae*, Atlantic coast; *A. insignifica*, southern California. Reef-building corals: *Orbicella*, in Florida and West Indies; *Acropora, Montipora, Meandra, Isophyllia, Siderastrea*, in the Coral Sea (Hawaii to Australia and Africa).

Order 3. **Zoanthidea.** No skeleton or pedal disc; polyps usually united by basal stolons, some solitary with stalked base; many species on exterior of various invertebrates. *Epizoanthus*, on hermit crab.

Order 4. **Antipatharia.** BLACK CORALS. Skeleton plantlike, of stems (some branched) composed of horny material and bearing small polyps; tentacles 6; in deeper tropical waters. *Antipathes*, West Indies, etc.

Order 5. **Ceriantharia.** Slender, elongate, anemone-like; many tentacles in 2 circles; no pedal disc; one siphonoglyph; solitary. *Cerianthus*, inhabits slime-lined vertical tubes in sea bottom.

References

DARWIN, C.   1842.   The structure and distribution of coral reefs.   3d ed. 1896. New York, D. Appleton-Century Co., Inc.   xx + 344 pp., illus.

FOWLER, G. H., and G. C. BOURNE.   1900.   Coelentera.   *In* E. R. Lankester, Treatise on zoology.   London, A. & C. Black, Ltd.   Part 2, 165 pp., 107 figs.

FRASER, C. McL.   1937.   Hydroids of the Pacific Coast of Canada and the United States.   Toronto, University of Toronto Press.   207 pp., 44 pls.

———.   1944.   Hydroids of the Atlantic Coast of North America.   Toronto, University of Toronto Press.   451 pp., 94 pls.

GARDINER, J. S.   1931.   Coral reefs and atolls.   London, Macmillan & Co., Ltd. xiii + 181 pp., 15 pls., 33 figs.

HICKSON, S. J.   1906.   Coelenterata.   *In* Cambridge natural history.   London, Macmillan & Co., Ltd.   Vol. 1, pp. 243–411, figs. 124–179.

HYMAN, LIBBIE H.   1928.   Miscellaneous observations on *Hydra*, with special reference to reproduction.   *Biological Bulletin*, vol. 54, pp. 65–108, pls. 1–6.

———.   1940.   The invertebrates: Protozoa through Ctenophora.   New York, McGraw-Hill Book Co., Inc.   Coelenterates, pp. 365–661, figs. 106–208.

KÜKENTHAL, W., and OTHERS.   1924.   Handbuch der Zoologie.   Berlin, Walter de Gruyter & Co.   COELENTERATA (CNIDARIA), vol. 1, pp. 419–901, figs. 378–785.

MAYER, A. G.   1910.   Medusae of the world.   *Carnegie Institution of Washington, Pub.* No. 109, 3 vols., 735 pp., 76 pls.

SAVILLE-KENT, W.   1893.   The Great Barrier Reef of Australia. . . . London, W. H. Allen & Co.

STEPHENSON, T. A.   1928.   The British sea anemones.   London, Ray Society. 2 vols. I, xiv + 148 pp., 14 pls., 41 figs.

YONGE, C. M.   1930.   A year on the Great Barrier Reef.   New York, G. P. Putnam's Sons.   246 pp.

CHAPTER 15

PHYLUM CTENOPHORA. CTENOPHORES

The Phylum CTENOPHORA (Gr. *ktenos*, comb + *phoros*, bearing) comprises about 80 species of free-swimming marine animals with transparent gelatinous bodies. They are often called "comb jellies" because of the comblike plates on the body; some with lengthwise ridges are known as "sea walnuts." Ctenophores show some resemblance to jellyfishes and formerly were classified with the coelenterates but having distinctive

Mnemiopsis   Cestum   Beroë   Ctenoplana

FIG. 15-1. Phylum CTENOPHORA. Representative forms; not to scale. (*After Hyman, The invertebrates.*)

features of structure and biology are placed in a separate phylum (Fig. 15-1).

15-1. Characteristics. 1. Symmetry biradial (radial + bilateral), on an oral-aboral axis; 3 germ layers, with much mesoglea; no segmentation.

2. Body more or less spherical (flat in some); usually with 8 external rows of comb plates; no nematocysts.

3. Digestive system with mouth, "pharynx," stomach, and branched canals.

4. Nervous system diffuse, with an aboral sense organ (statocyst).

5. Sexes united; reproductive cells formed from endoderm in digestive canals beneath comb plates; development direct; no asexual development or alternation of generations.

The coelenterates and ctenophores are the only animals with a basic radial symmetry, as that of the echinoderms is a secondary feature of sessile life; both sea anemones and ctenophores show biradial symmetry. Ctenophores resemble coelenterates in having (1) radial symmetry; (2) parts arranged on an oral-aboral axis; (3) a gastrovascular cavity with branches; (4) gelatinous mesoglea; (5) no internal spaces except the digestive system; and (6) no other organ systems. The ctenophores differ in possessing (1) eight rows of comb plates; (2) mesenchymal or mesodermal muscles; (3) higher organization of the digestive system; (4) an aboral sensory region; and (5) no nematocysts. The eight-part system of comb plates (with evidence for eight-part distribution of nervous ele-

ments) is to some biologists a foreshadow of the eight nerve strands in
some flatworms, but to others this is not convincing evidence of evolutionary relationships.

15-2. Structure.   *Pleurobrachia* is a common ctenophore in the sea
along both coasts of North America (Fig. 15-2).   Its highly transparent
body is about ¾ inch in diameter and nearly spherical.   The **mouth** is at
the larger or oral end, and a **sense organ** at the opposite, or aboral end;
these establish the radial axis.   Eight equally spaced **comb plates,** or
paddle plates, extend as meridians from pole to pole.   Each plate is a
slight ridge, bearing a succession of small transverse paddles or combs,
formed of fused cilia.   In life, these combs beat with quick strokes toward

Fig. 15-2.   Structure of a ctenophore.   *A. Pleurobrachia*, entire specimen.   *B.* Sense
organ.   (*Both after Hyman, The invertebrates.*)   *C.* Reproductive cells in digestive canals
under comb plates.   (*From Bourne in Lankester, Treatise on zoology, A. & C. Black, Ltd.*)

the aboral end, and a wave of beats progresses along each row from aboral
to oral end.   This propels the ctenophore with the mouth end forward,
which is the opposite of progression in a coelenterate medusa.   Near the
aboral end, on opposite sides, are two blind sacs from each of which a long
flexible **tentacle** protrudes.   The tentacle is solid and contains muscle
fibers; it may be trailed out to about 6 inches in length or contracted but
does not assist in locomotion.   Its surface is covered with "lasso" or **glue
cells** (colloblasts) that secrete an adhesive material to entangle small
animals, which are then conveyed to the mouth.   The position of the
tentacles and some features of the digestive tract establish bilateral
symmetry.

The **mouth** leads into the **pharynx,** or stomodeum, where digestion
begins and is extracellular.   Beyond is the **stomach,** or infundibulum,
from which small **digestive canals** branch in definite pattern to beneath
the comb plates, tentacle sacs, and elsewhere.   The system is gastrovascular, serving for both the digestion and the distribution of food.
From the stomach a canal runs aborally and gives off four branches, two
of which open by "excretory pores" on opposite sides of the sense organ.
Undigested wastes pass out either the mouth or these pores.

The exterior surface, mouth, pharynx, and tentacles are covered with
thin ciliated **epidermis,** and the stomach and canals lined by ciliated

gastrodermis. Most of the body is of the gelatinous *mesoglea* that fills all spaces between structures and contains scattered muscle fibers, connective tissue cells, and amoebocytes of mesodermal origin. The animal is thus triploblastic.

The *sense organ* contains four elongated tufts of cilia that support a small rounded *statolith* of calcareous material, the whole in a covering like a bell jar. It is concerned in orientation with respect to gravity and in coordinating the beating of the comb plates. Beneath each comb plate is a nerve strand.

15-3. Natural history. Ctenophores abound in warm seas, and some occur in temperate regions. They are mostly in surface waters, but some live at various depths, even to 10,000 feet. They rest vertically in the water and can swim only feebly, so that currents or tides may concentrate them in large numbers. In the dark they emit a luminescence (light) from beneath the comb plates. Their food is of animals, including mollusk and crustacean larvae, fish eggs, and small fishes; digestion is rapid. Over oyster beds at spawning time they may consume numbers of oyster larvae. Ctenophores are eaten by some marine animals.

Ctenophores are monoecious, and both eggs and sperm are produced by the endodermal lining in digestive canals beneath the comb plates. Mature sex cells pass out the mouth, fertilization occurs in the water, and development is usually direct to the adult form. Cleavage is determinate, the fate of parts of the blastula being determined so early that experimentally separated blastomeres yield only fractional embryos.

CLASSIFICATION

Phylum **CTENOPHORA** (see Characteristics).

Class 1. *TENTACULA.* With tentacles.

Order 1. **Cydippida.** Body rounded; tentacles branched and retractile into sheaths. *Pleurobrachia; Hormiphora.*

Order 2. **Lobata.** Body laterally compressed; two large oral lobes; tentacles without sheaths. *Bolinopsis; Mnemiopsis leidyi,* Atlantic coast.

Order 3. **Cestida.** Body elongate, ribbonlike, compressed in plane of tentacles. *Cestum veneris,* Venus's girdle, to over 3 feet long and 2 inches wide, in tropical seas, travels by sinuous movements.

Order 4. **Platyctenea.** Body compressed on oral-aboral axis, to flattened creeping form, greatly modified. *Gastrodes,* early larva parasitic in tunicates (*Salpa*); *Coeloplana; Ctenoplana.*

Class 2. *NUDA.* No tentacles. Body thimble-shaped; mouth wide, pharynx very large. *Beroë,* to 8 inches tall, often pink-colored, in colder waters.

References

HYMAN, LIBBIE H. 1940. The invertebrates: Protozoa through Ctenophora. New York, McGraw-Hill Book Co., Inc. CTENOPHORA, pp. 662–696, figs. 209–221. Best recent account.

MAYER, A. G. 1912. Ctenophores of the Atlantic coast of North America. *Carnegie Institution of Washington, Pub.* No. 162, 58 pp., 17 pls., 12 figs.

CHAPTER 16

PHYLUM PLATYHELMINTHES. FLATWORMS

In classifications of animals made before the early nineteenth century, all creatures with elongate bodies but no conspicuous appendages were called "worms" (Gr. *helminthes;* L. *vermes*).   They differ from the radial sponges, coelenterates, and ctenophores in having an **anterior end** or head with sense organs that moves forward to "meet the environment" and a **posterior end** or tail behind; also, they travel or rest on a **ventral surface,** or undersurface, that remains downward against the ground or bottom, while the opposite **dorsal surface,** or back, is uppermost.   Furthermore, they are **bilaterally symmetrical,** their external features and many internal parts being arranged symmetrically on either side of a median or sagittal plane.   All these characteristics the worms share with most of the other higher animals.   Among themselves the various kinds of worms differ in many structural and biological features so that they must be separated into several phyla.

Lowest of the worms are the PLATYHELMINTHES (Gr. *platy*, flat), which have thin soft bodies.   This phylum includes three Classes, the TURBELLARIA, or free-living flatworms, most of which inhabit fresh or salt water or moist places on land; the TREMATODA, or flukes, which are either external or internal parasites; and the CESTOIDEA, or tapeworms, which are intestinal parasites of vertebrates.   Flukes and tapeworms are important parasites of mankind, livestock, and wild animals, some causing serious illness or death to these hosts.

16-1. Characteristics.   1. Symmetry bilateral; 3 germ layers; body usually flattened dorsoventrally; no true segmentation.

2. Epidermis soft and ciliated (TURBELLARIA) or covered by cuticle and with external suckers or hooks or both for attachment to host (TREMATODA, CESTOIDEA).

3. Digestive system incomplete, a mouth but no anus, and usually much branched; absent in CESTOIDEA.

4. Muscle layers well-developed; no body cavity; spaces between internal organs filled by loose parenchyma.

5. No skeletal, circulatory, or respiratory systems; excretory system with many flame cells connected to excretory ducts.

6. Nervous system a pair of anterior ganglia or a nerve ring connecting to 1 to 3 pairs of longitudinal nerve cords with transverse commissures.

7. Sexes usually united (monoecious); reproductive system of each sex with gonads, ducts, and accessory organs; fertilization internal; eggs microscopic, each enclosed with several yolk cells in a shell; development either direct (TURBELLARIA, monoge-

netic TREMATODA) or with one or more larval stages (digenetic TREMATODA, CESTOIDEA); asexual reproduction in some forms.

The PLATYHELMINTHES show many advances over the PORIFERA, COELENTERATA, and CTENOPHORA in having (1) bilateral symmetry, with anterior-posterior and dorso-ventral relations, (2) a nervous system of enlarged anterior ganglia and nerve cords extending along the body, (3) mesoderm as a third germ layer (in place of mesoglea) producing muscles and other organs between the ectoderm and endoderm, (4) layers and bundles of muscles making various movements possible, and (5) internal gonads with permanent reproductive ducts and copulatory organs. These features the PLATYHELMINTHES share with most of the higher groups of animals; they differ from many of the latter in having (1) no body cavity, (2) the gut branched to various parts of the body, (3) usually no anus, (4) the sexes united.

Most turbellarians are entirely free-living, a few dwell on the exterior of other animals, and a few are endoparasites. All flukes are either external or internal parasites, and all tapeworms are internal parasites. Structural and physiological specializations parallel this trend in habits. The turbellarians have a delicate ciliated epidermis, whereas both flukes and tapeworms are covered with cuticle resistant to digestion and have suckers and hooks for attaching to their hosts. Those which live internally lack sensory organs, and the tapeworms have no digestive tract. The species that are internal parasites produce enormous numbers of eggs, as is necessary for all organisms that have complex life histories.

16-2. Size. The turbellarians are mostly under 50 mm. long; but some ACOELA are microscopic, and a few land planarians become 300 mm. long. Various flukes are 0.5 mm. to 75 mm. in length, but most of them are small. Different species of tapeworms measure from 3 mm. to 12 m. (40 feet) in length.

CLASS TURBELLARIA. FREE-LIVING FLATWORMS

The common fresh-water planarians of North America, *Euplanaria maculata, E. agilis, E. dortocephala*, etc., are free-living animals. They inhabit cool, clear, and permanent waters, including streams, ponds, marshes, and springs, where they cling to the undersurfaces of submerged plants, rocks, and logs and avoid the light.

16-3. Structure. *Euplanaria* (*Dugesia*) is a thin slender and soft worm about 15 (5 to 25) mm. long, with a bluntly triangular anterior end, or "head," and tapered body patterned with dark pigment (Fig. 16-1). The head region bears two black **eyespots** middorsally. The **mouth** is on the ventral surface near the middle of the body. Through it a tubular **pharynx** or **proboscis,** with muscular walls, can be extended to capture food. Minute **excretory openings** are present laterally on the dorsal surface but are difficult to see.   Sexually mature worms have a small *genital pore* on the ventral surface behind the mouth.

The body (Fig. 16-4) is covered by *epidermis* of a single layer of cuboidal cells, resting on an elastic basement membrane.   The epidermis contains small bodies called *rhabdites* of uncertain purpose and many deep-lying *unicellular glands* that open on the surface.   The ventral epidermis is largely covered with *cilia* that serve for locomotion.   Beneath the basement membrane are layers of *muscle fibers,* circular, longitudinal,

FIG. 16-1.   Class TURBELLARIA.   Planaria.   External features.

and diagonal, also dorsoventral fibers.   Spaces between the muscles and internal organs are filled with *parenchyma,* a loose meshwork of cells lacking definite walls (syncytium); there is no body cavity.   In the parenchyma are scattered free *formative cells,* which by mitosis produce new parts in regeneration.

The digestive system (Fig. 16-2) consists of the *mouth,* the *pharynx,* and the *enteron,* or "intestine," of three main branches, one anterior and

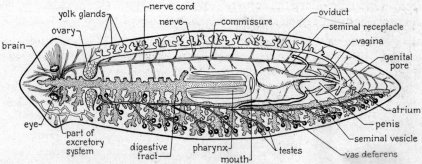

FIG. 16-2. Planaria. General structure (somewhat diagrammatic). On the right (upper) side the testes, vas deferens, and parts of the digestive tract are omitted; on the left (lower) side the nerve cord, yolk glands, and oviduct are omitted; only a bit of the excretory system is shown on the left anteriorly.

two posterior, with many smaller lateral subdivisions.   It is composed of columnar epithelium, derived from endoderm.

There is no skeleton other than the elastic basement membrane, and no respiratory system.   Oxygen-carbon dioxide exchange occurs through the epidermis and thence probably through the fluid about the parenchyma to other tissues.   The *excretory system* (Fig. 16-3) comprises two longitudinal ducts connecting to a network of tubules that branch throughout the body and end in many large *flame cells;* the latter are between various body cells, from which they collect excess water or fluid wastes. The central cavity within a flame cell contains a group of flickering cilia that drive the collected fluid into the tubules and to the canals that open on the body surface. Flame cells can be seen in unpigmented worms or in preparations made by crushing living worms between two glass slides.

PORTION OF EXCRETORY SYSTEM   A FLAME CELL

Fig. 16-3. Planaria. Part of the excretory system and one flame cell, both enlarged. (*Adapted from Lankester, Treatise on zoology, A. & C. Black, Ltd.*)

The **nervous system** of planarians is more highly organized than the diffuse nerve net of coelenterates. In the head region, beneath the eyes, are two **cerebral ganglia** joined to form a "brain," from which short nerves extend to the anterior end and the eyes and two **longitudinal nerve cords** pass back, one along either side, with many **transverse connectives** and **peripheral nerves.** The **eyespots** (Fig. 16-4) are sensitive to light from certain directions but form no image. Auricular sense organs on the sides of the head region may be chemoreceptors of "taste" or "smell."

SECTION OF EYE   CROSS SECTION OF BODY

Fig. 16-4. Planaria. *A.* Section through eye. *B.* Cross section of the body (excretory structures omitted)

A sexually mature worm has both male and female reproductive systems and hence is monoecious, or hermaphroditic. Both testes and ovaries develop from formative cells of the parenchyma. The *male reproductive system* includes (1) several hundred small spherical *testes* along both sides of the body, each connected by (2) a minute *vas efferens* to (3) a larger *vas deferens,* which extends along each side; the two ducts enter (4) a median *seminal vesicle* for sperm storage, which connects to

(5) the muscular *penis* opening into the (6) *genital atrium,* just within the genital pore. The *female reproductive system* consists of (1) two rounded *ovaries* near the anterior end of the body, connecting to (2) two *oviducts* paralleling the nerve cords, and along each duct are (3) many *yolk* or *vitelline glands,* which supply yolk cells when eggs are produced; the two oviducts join (4) the median *vagina* opening into (5) the *genital atrium;* to the vagina is connected (6) the rounded *seminal receptacle* ("uterus").

16-4. Natural history (Fig. 16-5).   Planarians avoid strong light and by day rest quietly on the undersurfaces of objects in water, often in groups of about 6 to 20.   After dark, they crawl actively in laboratory aquaria and presumably do so in nature.   They adhere to objects or surfaces by a sticky mucus secreted by the epidermal glands and do not swim independently in water.   Locomotion is usually by *gliding* with the anterior end forward and slightly raised.   This is accomplished by backward strokes of the cilia on the ventral surface, over a slime track produced by the glands. Less often a worm travels by *crawling.*   This results from muscular movements; contraction of the circular and dorsoventral muscles elongates the body, the anterior end is then affixed by mucus, and the posterior part drawn up by contraction of the longitudinal muscles.   Differential action of local muscle groups produces turning or twisting movements.   A moving worm tests its environment by turning the head portion from side to side.

On application of weak mechanical or chemical stimuli to the head region, either laterally or medially, the worm reacts positively by turning toward the stimulus, but strong stimuli result in a negative reaction.   The same is true in lesser degree upon stimulating the middle of the body; a strong stimulus at the posterior end causes the worm to move ahead. As compared with a coelenterate, the planarian thus shows a much higher degree of coordination in the action of its parts.   This results from the higher development of the nervous system, aided by sensory structures scattered in the epidermis, particularly those of the head region.   The more elaborate system of muscular fibers under direction of the nervous system makes a greater variety of movements possible.

Planarians are carnivorous and feed on other small animals, living or dead.   When hungry, they travel about actively, gathering quickly on any edible material.   They evidently feed on small crustaceans trapped in mucus that the worms secrete.   When one planarian begins feeding, others are soon attracted, either by substances diffusing from the food or by digestive juices from the worm.   A common method of collecting planarians is to place bits of meat in shallow water, when juices diffusing from the meat will soon attract them in numbers.   A small food item may first be "gripped" by the head region (Fig. 16-5).   Then the muscular pharynx is protruded on and into the food, bits of which are drawn into the mouth and enteron by suction of the pharynx. Digestion is reportedly both extra- and intra-cellular, fat being digested in the cavity of the enteron, but protein and carbohydrate within vacuoles of cells lining the enteron. Products of digestion gradually pass in solution to other body tissues; fluid in the parenchyma may assist in this distribution. The enteron is a gastrovascular cavity serving for circulation

Fig. 16-5. Some activities of planarians. (*Mostly after Pearl, 1903; eggs and hatching redrawn from W. C. Curtis and M. J. Guthrie, Textbook of zoology, John Wiley & Sons, Inc.*)

and digestion as in coelenterates. Any undigested material must be forcibly egested through the mouth, since there is no anus. A planarian that is starved for several weeks will exhaust its stored food; then certain organs degenerate and are utilized, and thus the worm gradually decreases in size.

16-5. Reproduction. Asexual multiplication occurs by **transverse fission;** a worm constricts in two, usually behind the pharynx, and the missing parts on each piece then grow and differentiate. Planarians possess great powers of regeneration; when injured either naturally or experimentally, any part of the body can be replaced and entire small worms will result from artificial cutting of a larger individual into pieces (Fig. 5-2)

In sexual reproduction two planarians bring their posterior ventral surfaces together, and copulation is mutual, the penis of each being inserted into the genital atrium of the other; sperm from the seminal vesicle in the male system of each passes to the female seminal receptacle of the other. Such exchange of sex products between separate individuals is called *cross-fertilization, and* the direct transfer of sperm from male to female organs is termed *internal fertilization.* The worms separate after mating, and sperm migrate up the oviducts to fertilize the eggs. Several zygotes and many yolk cells are later combined in a separate capsule, or egg shell; this is formed by the wall of the atrium and then passed outside. Development is direct, without a larval stage.

16-6. Other Turbellaria. The minute ACOELA are primitive marine forms with a mouth but no digestive cavity, food being digested in the solid mass of endoderm cells. They have no excretory organs, and the nervous system is diffuse. Many are free-living, and others live in the intestines of sea urchins and sea cucumbers. *Convoluta* is an acoel of seashore tide pools that is colorless when hatched but soon becomes green by acquiring small green algae in its tissues.

The RHABDOCOELA have a straight unbranched digestive cavity. Many of them are free-living, some are commensals on the exterior of marine animals, and a few are true endoparasites in other turbellarians, mollusks, echinoderms, and crustaceans. The free-living *Microstomum* feeds on hydra, the nematocysts of which pass from the worm's gut to become arranged in its own epidermis and serve there for defense against other animals. This worm reproduces asexually like a planarian, but the parts may remain attached to one another and form a chain of 8 or 16 individuals (Fig. 5-1*C*).

The Order TRICLADIDA, to which *Euplanaria* belongs, has other members in fresh waters and a few that are marine, and includes many land planarians in the humid tropics and subtropics. Some of the latter are large, and many are brilliantly colored. They travel in damp places on slime paths and can descend from leaves or branches by hanging on slime threads. *Bipalium kewense* is a common land planarian in greenhouses around the world, having been transported widely with potted plants. Three other alien species have become established locally in California. A few land planarians are native to the United States.

The POLYCLADIDA are exclusively marine, living among rocks, sessile animals, or plants of the seashore. Some dwell on the shells of echinoderms, mollusks, and crustaceans. They are leaflike, some quite broad.

some with numerous eyespots, some with tentacles; the gut is many-branched.   Some have a free-swimming larval stage.

Class *TREMATODA*.   Flukes

These flatworms are all parasitic, mostly in vertebrates.   The body of a fluke is usually covered with cuticle secreted by cells beneath and lacks cilia save in some larval stages.   There is usually a sucker about the mouth and one or several others on the ventral surface.   The mouth is anterior, and the digestive tract is usually somewhat λ-shaped with two main trunks having smaller branches.   The food consists of the tissues or body fluids of the host, which are sucked in by action of the muscular pharynx.   Complex muscle layers, excretory organs, and a nervous system are present as in the Turbellaria.   Sensory organs such as dorsal eyespots occur in some larvae and in some flukes that are ectoparasites. Two orders of flukes are commonly recognized, which differ in both structure and life history.

16-7. Order Monogenea.   Species of this group inhabit only one host. They are chiefly ectoparasites of fishes, amphibians, and reptiles, but some inhabit the mouth cavities or urinary bladders of such hosts.   A monogenetic trematode has at the posterior end a well-developed adhesive organ with one or more suckers, and often with chitinous hooks or anchors as well.   The reproductive organs resemble those of the Turbellaria.   Only one or a few eggs are produced at a time, either laid in water or attached to the host.   A ciliated larva hatches from the egg to swim about and find a host or die.   Development is direct to the adult form, so that each egg, if successful, yields one fluke.   A common example is the minute *Gyrodactylus*, which lives on the fins, skin, and gills of carp, trout, and other fresh-water fishes.   It produces living young and sometimes causes fatal epidemics among fish in hatcheries.

16-8. Order Digenea.   These flukes are all internal parasites.   Each species has a succession of stages that must live in certain organs of two or more host species in order to complete the life cycle, the larvae in a certain snail or other invertebrate and the adult in some vertebrate.   Various species of flukes are peculiar to parts of the digestive tract, lungs, urinary bladder, or blood vessels.   Some of them have about the most complex life cycles of any animals.

16-9. Sheep liver fluke.   Best known, perhaps, is the common liver fluke of sheep, *Fasciola hepatica*, adults of which inhabit the bile ducts and sometimes invade other organs.   They are commonest in sheep and cattle, are sometimes in other mammals, and occasional in man.   They produce the disease known as "liver rot."   Moderate infestations cause sheep to be unthrifty and subject to other diseases, and heavy infestations result in many deaths.   Fluke disease thrives only on ranges or pastures with marshy areas where the appropriate snails occur but is common in many parts of the United States, Europe, and other areas of the world.

The liver fluke has a leaf-shaped body up to 30 mm. long, rounded anteriorly and bluntly pointed behind (Fig. 16-6).   The *anterior sucker* is terminal, surrounding the mouth, and close behind is the *ventral sucker,* which serves for attachment in the host.   Between them is the *genital opening.*   The *digestive system* comprises the mouth, muscular pharynx, short esophagus, and two-branched enteron with many subdivisions throughout the body.   The *muscles* are complex as in planarians, and parenchyma occurs between the internal organs.   The *excretory system*

Fig. 16-6.   Class Trematoda.   Liver fluke of sheep, *Fasciola hepatica.*   *A*. Digestive system; *B*. Excretory system; both natural size.   *C*. Reproductive system in ventral view and enlarged; digestive system shown only at anterior end.   (*Modified from Sommer and Landois*, 1880.)

has many flame cells joined to one main canal opening in a single posterior pore.   The *nervous system* (visible when stained with methylene blue) includes a double ganglion near the esophagus, two lengthwise nerve cords, and various nerves.   Both sex systems are highly developed in a mature worm.   The *male reproductive system* has two much-branched testes along the middle of the body, each connected by a vas deferens to the single seminal vesicle, to which is also joined a prostate gland.   The vesicle connects to the penis just within the genital opening.   The *female reproductive system* comprises a branched ovary on the right side connected by an oviduct to the median oötype, which is surrounded by the Mehlis ("shell") glands.   Off the oviduct is a seminal receptacle.   Laurer's canal, of unknown function, extends dorsally from the receptacle.   Along each side of the body are many yolk glands, joined to two lengthwise yolk ducts with a common entry into the oötype.   From the latter an irregularly coiled uterus extends to the genital opening.

Each fertilized egg is combined with several yolk cells and surrounded by an egg shell in the oötype. Egg production is practically continuous; the uterus is crowded with eggs that segment en route to the outside. The eggs emerge from the genital pore, pass through the bile duct and intestine of the sheep, and are voided with its feces (Fig. 16-7). At temperatures below 50°F. they remain undeveloped but viable for several months; in warmer damp surroundings they develop in 9 days or more. From each egg there emerges a microscopic larva that is multicellular and ciliated, with a pointed anterior rostrum, two eyespots, a nerve ganglion, and two nephridia. If this *miracidium* (*A*) hatches in water, it swims

Fig. 16-7. Life history of the liver fluke of sheep, *Fasciola hepatica;* larval stages, about ×75. (*Details from Thomas,* 1883.)

about for not over 8 hours, to die unless it finds a certain kind of snail, *Lymnea* (*Galba*) *bulimoides*, or *L. columella* in the United States. In the latter event it burrows into the soft tissues and enters usually the pulmonary chamber or lymph vessels. Should many miracidia enter, the snail dies. The larva loses its outer cilia, enlarges, and becomes a saclike *sporocyst* (*B*). Within the sporocyst are germ cells, each of which can develop by parthenogenesis (without fertilization) into another larval stage termed the *redia* (*C*). Each sporocyst produces 3 to 8 elongate rediae, which are saclike, with a mouth and short gut. Within about 8 days they burst from the sporocyst and migrate to another organ, usually the liver. There the rediae may produce other rediae parthenogenetically for one or two generations. Finally, each original or daughter redia yields several larvae of another type, known as a *cercaria* (*D*). This has a slender tail and disc-shaped body, with both oral and ventral suckers and a forked gut. The cercaria burrows out of the snail to swim through the water by use of its tail.   After a few hours it settles on a grass blade or other vegetation near the water surface, loses the tail, and becomes a **metacercaria** (*E*); cells within the latter produce a tough enclosing cyst.   The encysted larvae remain viable for some weeks or months on grass or even on damp hay, if not subjected to high temperatures.   When infested vegetation bearing cercariae is eaten by a sheep or other suitable host, the cysts are digested off and the larvae burrow through the intestinal wall to the body cavity to reach the liver.   They burrow for several weeks and damage liver tissue before entering the bile duct to mature and live for several months.

Many chances of failure beset the path of a species that must complete such a life cycle.   These include the dropping of eggs in dry places, failure of miracidia to find quickly a snail of the right kind, death of infected snails, drying of ponds, or encystment on vegetation where sheep do not happen to graze.   As an offset of these hazards, each adult fluke may produce up to a half million eggs, and the parthenogenetic multiplication in the snail may yield up to 300 larvae from a single egg.

16-10. Other Trematoda.   About 3,000 species of digenetic flukes (Fig. 16-8) have been described from various hosts—fishes to mammals—

Fig. 16-8.   Class Trematoda.   Some representative flukes, variously enlarged.   *A. Prosthogonimus macrorchis.*   (*After Macy.*)   *B. Clonorchis sinensis.*   (*After H. B. Ward.*)   *C. Tristomum coccineum.*   (*After Lameere.*)   *D. Schistosoma haematobium.*   (*After H. B. Ward.*)

but the life histories of very few are known.   The principal parasitic flukes of mankind are as follows:

Intestinal Fluke, *Fasciolopsis buski.*   China, to India and adjacent islands. Larval stages in snails.   Cercariae encyst on water plants (water nuts, caltrop), used as raw vegetables in the Orient.   In parts of China, over half the human population is infected.   Also in pigs and dogs.

Liver Fluke, *Clonorchis sinensis.*   Japan, China and adjacent islands, to French Indo-China.   Also in dogs and cats.   Earlier larval stages in fresh-water snails and later ones (metacercariae) in muscles of many fresh-water minnows and carp. Human infections result from eating raw fish.   Adult flukes inhabit bile ducts, and infections may last from 5 to 20 years.   (Fig. 16-8*B*).

LUNG FLUKE, *Paragonimus westermani.* In Japan, China, the Philippine Islands, New Guinea, India, Africa, Yucatán, and Peru; occasional in oriental immigrants in the United States. Also in cats, dogs, pigs, goats, rats, and various wild mammals of regions where human infections are present, the flukes showing little host specificity. Eggs discharged in host's sputum, larvae occur in snails, and cercariae encyst in fresh-water crabs and crayfish. By eating these crustaceans uncooked the final hosts become infected; the young flukes occur in various organs, and the mature flukes encyst near the surface of the lungs.

BLOOD FLUKES: *Schistosoma haematobium* about the Mediterranean, in Africa, Madagascar, and southwestern Asia; *S. mansoni* in Egypt, South Africa, South America, and the West Indies; and *S. japonicum* from Japan to the Philippines and Celebes, Rhodesia and the Belgian Congo; the last also parasitizes cats, dogs, rodents, pigs, and cattle. Adult flukes inhabit veins of abdomen. Sexes separate and unlike (Fig. 16-8D), male (9 to 22 mm. long) with widened and infolded body permanently enclosing the slender female (14 to 26 mm.). Eggs deposited in veins, migrate to bladder or rectum, and leave in urine or feces. Larvae in various snails, and cercariae with forked tails burrow through human skin or are taken in drinking water.

Cercariae of some nonhuman schistosome flukes burrow into the skin and produce a "swimmer's itch" on persons frequenting fresh-water lakes in the north-central states, Canada, and Europe.

CLASS *CESTOIDEA.* TAPEWORMS

The cestodes (Gr. *cestus*, girdle + *oid*, like) are mostly slender and elongate, with a flat body usually formed of many short sections; hence the name "tapeworm." They are unlike other PLATYHELMINTHES in

| Fasciola hepatica | Diphyllo-bothrium | Taenia | Dipylidium |

FIG. 16-9. Eggs of the liver fluke and three species of tapeworms, ×250. (*After H. B. Ward.*)

external appearance; but their internal anatomy, particularly the reproductive system, indicates close relationship to the TURBELLARIA and TREMATODA. The cestodes lack cilia, are covered with cuticle, and have complex muscle layers, parenchyma, paired excretory ducts with flame cells, and a nerve ring with three pairs of nerve cords. They have no mouth, digestive tract, or endoderm, food being absorbed through the body wall. All are endoparasites, the adult worms in the intestines of vertebrates and the larvae (one exception) in tissues of some alternate host.

16-11. Subclass Cestodaria. This consists of a few species of small worms, each with a sucker for attachment, the body undivided, and a

single set of reproductive organs. *Gyrocotyle,* found in the ancient
chimaeroid fishes, is an example.   The group may be either primitive and
trematode-like, or a degenerate stock derived from other tapeworms.

16-12. Subclass Cestoda.   All other tapeworms belong to this group.
A common example is *Taenia solium,* the pork tapeworm of man, known
since ancient times, and from 6 to 25 feet long when mature (Fig. 16-10).
It has a minute knoblike "head," or *scolex,* with four muscular **suckers** on
the sides and a circle of **hooks** on the elevated tip, or *rostellum.*   A short
"neck," or budding zone, joins the scolex to the body, or *strobila,* which
consists of a series of up to 1,000 sections, or *proglottids.*   The suckers and
hooks serve to fasten the scolex to the intestinal wall of the host, and the
chain of proglottids lies free in the intestinal cavity.   New proglottids are

FIG. 16-10.   Class CESTOIDEA.   Scolex and one proglottid of the pork tapeworm, *Taenia solium.*

constantly forming by transverse budding in the neck and remain connected to be forced backward by growth of still others.   As they move
backward, the proglottids increase in size, mature, and finally become
detached.

The scolex contains a nerve ring, with nerves to the suckers and
rostellum and joined to three pairs of longitudinal nerves extending backward in the proglottids.   In it also is an excretory structure connecting to
a pair of excretory canals through the proglottids.   Each proglottid
contains muscles, parenchyma, sections of the excretory canals connected
by a cross canal, numerous flame cells, and the nerves.   A complete set of
both male and female sex organs develops in every proglottid when some
distance beyond the scolex.   Those in any proglottid are comparable
with the entire reproductive system in a turbellarian or trematode.   The
male system matures first.   Self-fertilization between the systems in one
proglottid, or in separate proglottids, or cross-fertilization between parts

in two worms in one host are all possible.   Eggs then develop in numbers, each including a fertilized ovum and several yolk cells enclosed in a resistant shell formed in the oötype.   These pass into the uterus, which gradually becomes a branched sac crowded with thousands of eggs; other organs degenerate.   Development of the eggs begins at once and continues as ripe proglottids are cast loose, pass out in the host's feces, and disintegrate (Fig. 16-11).   In eggs thus scattered on the ground, development continues to the formation of a six-hooked embryo (oncosphere) in each and then stops.

If such eggs are eaten by a pig, the shells are digested off in the pig's intestine and the six-hooked larvae burrow into blood or lymph vessels to be carried finally to the voluntary muscles where they encyst.   The cyst

Fig. 16-11.   Life cycle of the pork tapeworm, *Taenia solium*.   (*Adapted from Buchsbaum, Animals without backbones, University of Chicago Press.*)

enlarges, becomes filled with fluid, and is then called a "bladder worm" or **cysticercus.**   One side of the inner wall thickens and forms a hollow papilla projecting into the sac.   In the cavity of the papilla a scolex develops, with suckers and hooks, but there is no further growth.   When raw or imperfectly cooked pork containing such a cyst is eaten by man, the outer cyst wall is digested off, the papilla everts to form a scolex and "neck," and the bladder disappears.   The scolex attaches to the host's intestine, and a new tapeworm begins to form.   Larvae of this tapeworm may also occur in monkeys, dogs, cats, and sheep.   In man larval infections may involve the central nervous system, with severe results.

The budding, gradual maturing, and freeing of proglottids by a tapeworm resembles somewhat the production of ephyrae by the strobila of a scyphozoan coelenterate (p. 334).   The proglottids, however, degenerate to free the eggs, whereas each ephyra becomes a complete, free-living, and mature jellyfish that later reproduces sexually.

16-13. Other cestodes.   More than 1,500 species of tapeworms live in various vertebrates from fishes to mammals.   The adult stage of each is usually in a final host that preys upon the intermediate host, consuming the flesh of the latter which contains the infective stages.   Some tapeworms are harmless; others may produce severe symptoms but are rarely fatal.   Human infections are decreasing in civilized countries because of a wider knowledge as to how infections may be avoided, because of the detection and treatment of persons harboring tapeworms, and because of

Taenia   Taenia   Diphyllobothrium
saginata   solium   latum

FIG. 16-12.   Scolices and mature ("ripe") proglottids of three human tapeworms (beef, pork, and fish).

the inspection and refrigeration of meat to eliminate any containing cysticerci.   The following are a few of the common tapeworms:

Beef Tapeworm, *Taenia saginata.*   Larvae in flesh of cattle, adult worm in man; 4 to 12 m. (even 25 m.) long, proglottids up to 2,000 (Fig. 16-12).   About 1 per cent of cattle in the United States are infected; preference for rare beef may cause an increase in human infections.

Dog and Cat Tapeworm, *Taenia pisiformis.*   Larvae in liver and mesenteries of rabbits, adults in dogs and cats.

Dog Tapeworm, *Dipylidium caninum.*   Larvae in biting dog louse and fleas of dogs, cats, and man; adults in dogs and cats, occasional in man; 15 to 40 cm. long, not over 200 proglottids, each with 2 sets of genital organs.

Rat Tapeworm, *Hymenolepis diminuta.*   Larvae in earwigs, flour beetles, fleas, other insects, and myriapods; adults common in rats and mice, occasional in man; 20 to 60 cm. long, 800 to 1,000 proglottids.

Dwarf Tapeworm, *Hymenolepis nana.*   No intermediate host; larvae live in intestinal villi, and adults in intestines of man; 10 to 45 mm. long, to 200 proglottids; *H. fraterna*, in rats and mice.

Sheep Tapeworm, *Moniezia expansa.*   Larva in free-living mite (*Galumna*); adult in sheep, goats, etc.; up to 6 m. long.

Hydatid Worm, *Echinococcus granulosus* (Fig. 16-13).   Adult in intestine of dog, wolf, and jackal, only 3 to 6 mm. long, of 3 (or 4) proglottids; larva in man, monkeys, cattle, sheep, pig, dog, cat, and other domestic and wild animals; larval cysts up to

50 mm. in diameter in pig, sometimes larger in man, and in various organs; delicate inner lining of cyst forms brood capsules each with 5 to 20 scolices; daughter or "exogenous" cysts also form and may scatter to secondary centers in body; dangerous and sometimes fatal to man; almost cosmopolitan; upward of 500 human cases reported in United States.

Fig. 16-13.   Life cycle of the hydatid worm, *Echinococcus granulosus*.   The adult worm, 3 to 6 mm. long, of 3 (or 4) proglottids, lives in carnivorous mammals; the larval stage is in various domestic and wild herbivorous mammals and man, forming multiple cysts.

Fig. 16-14.   Life cycle of the broad tapeworm of fish, *Diphyllobothrium latum*.   Adult worm and fish host much reduced, larval stages variously enlarged.   (*Adapted partly from Kükenthal.*)

Fish Tapeworm, *Diphyllobothrium latum* (Fig. 16-14).   First larval stage (0.5 mm. long) in copepod crustaceans (*Diaptomus, Cyclops*), second (1 to 20 mm.) in perch, burbot, trout, and other fresh-water fishes; adult worms in man, pig, cat, dog, fox, or other fish-eating mammals; up to 10 m. long, with 3,000 to 4,000 proglottids; human infections from eating fish raw or insufficiently cooked; common in Europe and Japan, increasing in northern United States.

CLASSIFICATION

Phylum **PLATYHELMINTHES.**   Flatworms.   Body soft, usually depressed, often elongate, no true segmentation; covered by ciliated epidermis or by cuticle; some with external suckers or hooks or both; digestive tract incomplete, or none (Cestoidea); with flame cells and excretory canals; nervous system with anterior ganglia or nerve ring and 1 to 3 pairs of longitudinal nerve cords; sexes usually united; fertilization internal; eggs microscopic, with shell, and containing yolk cells; development direct (TURBELLARIA) or with larval stages; free-living, commensal, or parasitic; more than 7,000 species.

Class 1. *TURBELLARIA.* FREE-LIVING FLATWORMS. Epidermis ciliated, with many mucous glands and rodlike rhabdites; usually pigmented, some species brilliantly marked; usually with ventral mouth and no suckers; development usually direct; asexual reproduction in some.

Order 1. **Acoela.** Length 1 to 4 mm.; mouth anterior; no digestive cavity or excretory organs; marine. *Anaperus, Aphanostoma, Polychoerus.*

Order 2. **Rhabdocoelida.** Small; digestive cavity unbranched; mouth usually anterior; in salt, brackish, or fresh water, few commensal or parasitic. *Microstomum; Mesostoma,* viviparous; *Plagiostomum.*

Order 3. **Tricladida.** Size usually small, a few 150 mm. or longer; mouth midventral, with proboscis; digestive cavity 3-branched. *Euplanaria (Dugesia),* pigmented, and *Procotyla* and *Dendrocoelum,* milky white, all in fresh waters; *Bdelloura,* marine; *Bipalium (Placocephalus)* and *Geoplana,* terrestrial.

Order 4. **Polycladida.** Small to 150 mm. long; digestive cavity with many irregular branches; muscles complex; marine, few pelagic. *Planocera, Leptoplana, Eurylepta.*

Class 2. *TREMATODA.* FLUKES. Body covered with thick cuticle; mostly unpigmented; mouth usually anterior, digestive tract with 2 main branches; suckers on ventral surface and about mouth; monoecious (few dioecious); all parasitic.

Order 1. **Monogenea.** A large posterior ventral adhesive organ of 1 or several suckers, usually with chitinous hooks; mouth anterior, subterminal, with 2 ventral suckers near by; excretory pores 2, anterior; uterus with 1 or few eggs at a time; development with ciliated larva or direct; no intermediate host; chiefly ectoparasites on cold-blooded vertebrates, few in crustaceans, cephalopods, and mammals. *Gyrodactylus; Sphyranura osleri,* on gills of *Necturus; Tristoma coccineum,* 15 by 16 mm., on gills of swordfish; *Polystoma,* 2.5 to 6 mm., on gills of tadpoles, in bladder of amphibians and turtles and mouth or nose of latter; *Aspidogaster,* in renal and pericardial cavities of mollusks (UNIONIDAE); *Microcotyle,* 7 to 12 mm., on gills of marine fishes.

Order 2. **Digenea.** Suckers 2 or 1, one about mouth, the second ventral if present; no hooks; excretory pore 1, posterior; uterus long, many eggs; 1 or more larval stages reproducing in intermediate host(s) before metamorphosis to adult form; chiefly endoparasites, larvae in mollusks (also crustaceans, fishes), adults in vertebrates. *Bucephalus,* larvae in gonads or other parts of oysters, adults in marine fishes; *Fasciola, Fasciolopsis, Clonorchis, Schistosoma.*

Class 3. *CESTOIDEA.* TAPEWORMS. Body covered with thick cuticle; unpigmented; no digestive tract or sense organs in adult; a scolex with suckers and often also hooks for attachment; body usually of few or many proglottids, each sexually complete; all endoparasitic, usually with alternate hosts, adult worms in intestines of vertebrates.

Subclass 1. CESTODARIA (Monozoa). One small sucker, no proglottids, one set of sex organs; embryo with 10 hooklets. *Gyrocotyle,* intestine of *Chimaera.*

Subclass 2. CESTODA (Merozoa). Usually with scolex for attachment and 4 to many proglottids; embryo typically with 6 hooks.

Order 1. **Pseudophyllidea.** Scolex with 2 sucking organs, but no hooks; eggs operculate; 2 or 3 larval stages in crustaceans and fishes. *Diphyllobothrium latum,* fish tapeworm of man; *Ligula,* larva in perch and other fresh-water fishes, adult in gulls and other fish-eating birds.

Order 2. **Tetrarhynchidea** (Trypanorhyncha). Scolex long, with 2 or 4 sucking grooves, and 4 protrusible "proboscids" bearing many spines. *Tetrarhynchus*, larvae in marine invertebrates or fishes, adults in sharks and rays.

Order 3. **Tetraphyllidea.** Scolex with 4 flexible lappet-like suckers. *Phyllobothrium*, adults mostly in sharks and rays, also fresh-water fishes, amphibians, and reptiles.

Order 4. **Diphyllidea** (Heterophyllidea). Scolex $\frac{1}{4}$ to $\frac{1}{5}$ of total length, with long "shaft" bearing hooks; proglottids 4 to 20, may separate before maturity and live in intestine. *Echinobothrium*, in spiral valve of ray.

Order 5. **Cyclophyllidea.** Scolex with 4 cup-shaped suckers and usually a central rostellum often with hooks; sex openings lateral; proglottids either free or joined when mature; includes most tapeworms of man and higher animals. *Hymenolepis; Dipylidium; Taenia; Moniezia; Echinococcus.*

References

BAYLIS, H. A.   1929.   A manual of helminthology, medical and veterinary.   London, Ballière, Tindall & Cox.   xi + 303 pp., 200 figs.

BENHAM, W. B.   1901.   The Platyhelmia.   *In* E. R. Lankester, Treatise on zoology. London, A. & C. Black, Ltd.   Part 4, pp. 1–147, figs. 1–33.

BRUMPT, E.   1936.   Précis de parasitologie.   5th ed.   Paris, Masson et Cie.   xii + 2,139 pp., 4 pls., 1,085 figs.

CHANDLER, A. C.   1949.   Introduction to parasitology.   8th ed.   New York, John Wiley & Sons, Inc.   xii + 756 pp., 273 figs.

CRAIG, C. F. and E. C. FAUST.   1945.   Clinical parasitology.   4th ed.   Philadelphia, Lea & Febiger.   871 pp., 4 pls., 305 figs.

DAWES, BEN.   1946.   The Trematoda with special reference to British and other European forms.   Cambridge, England, Cambridge University Press.   xvi + 644 pp., 81 figs.

FAUST, E. C.   1949.   Human helminthology.   3d ed.   Philadelphia, Lea & Febiger. 744 pp., 313 figs.

GAMBLE, F. W.   1896.   Platyhelminthes.   *In* Cambridge natural history.   London, Macmillan & Co., Ltd.   Vol. 2, pp. 1–91, figs. 1–14.

HEGNER, R. W., F. M. ROOT, D. M. AUGUSTINE, and C. G. HUFF.   1938.   Parasitology with special reference to man and domesticated animals.   New York, D. Appleton-Century Co., Inc.   xxi + 812 pp., 308 figs.

HYMAN, L. H.   1951.   The invertebrates.   New York, McGraw-Hill Book Co., Inc. Platyhelminthes, vol. 2, pp. 52–458, figs. 13–173.

KÜKENTHAL, W., and OTHERS.   1928–1933.   Handbuch der Zoologie.   Berlin, Walter de Gruyter & Co.   Platyhelminthes, vol. 2, part 1, sections 1 and 2, xiii + 736 pp., 743 figs.

MONNIG, H. O.   1938.   Veterinary helminthology and entomology.   2d ed.   Baltimore, William Wood & Co.   xviii + 409 pp., 264 figs.

MORGAN, B. P., and P. A. HAWKINS.   1949.   Veterinary helminthology.   Minneapolis, Burgess Publishing Co.   ix + 400 pp., 58 pls.

NEVEU-LAMAIRE, M.   1936.   Traité d'helminthologie médicale et vétérinaire.   Paris, Vigot Frères.   xxiii + 1,514 pp., 787 figs.

SPREHN, C. E. W.   1932.   Lehrbuch der Helminthologie.   Berlin, Verlagsbuchhandlung Gebrüder Borntraeger.   xvi + 998 pp., 374 figs.

THOMAS, A. P.   1883.   The life history of the liver-fluke (*Fasciola hepatica*).   Quarterly Journal of Microscopical Science, ser. 2, vol. 23, pp. 99–133, pls. 2, 3.

CHAPTER 17

CLASS NEMATODA. ROUNDWORMS

The Class NEMATODA (Gr. *nematos*, thread) comprises the unsegmented roundworms with slender cylindrical bodies, resistant cuticle, and a complete and permanent digestive tract. Nematodes are much alike as to general appearance and morphology, but the species differ variously in structural details and natural history. Among multicellular animals they are probably second only to insects in numbers. Many are free-living in soil and water, and many others are parasites in the tissues or fluids of animals and plants. Different species are restricted to various peculiar habitats such as the roots of plants, seeds of wheat, gum of tree wounds, and the intestines, blood, and other organs in animal bodies. They are mostly small or minute, but a few grow to a meter in length. Their eggs are microscopic and resistant to adverse environmental conditions.

17-1. Characteristics. 1. Symmetry bilateral; 3 germ layers; no true segmentation, appendages, or proboscis.

2. Body slenderly cylindrical, covered with tough resistant cuticle somatic cells few, of fixed number.

3. Digestive tract complete and permanent; a straight tube with mouth and anus at opposite ends of body.

4. Body wall with longitudinal muscle fibers only; space within body an unlined pseudocoel.

5. No circulatory or respiratory organs; excretory organs simple, 2, 1, or none.

6. Nerve ring around esophagus connects to 6 anterior nerves and to 6 (or more) posterior nerves or cords.

7. Sexes usually separate, male smaller than female; gonads continuous with reproductive ducts, single (or double) in male, paired (or single) in female; fertilization internal; eggs microscopic, each covered by a chitinous shell; development direct, "larva" with several molts; no asexual reproduction.

The nematodes differ from flatworms in shape, in the absence of cilia and suckers, in the presence of a complete digestive tract and a body cavity, and in having the sexes separate. Nematode muscles are all aligned with the body axis and permit only dorsoventral bending and hence are less complex than those in flatworms, nemerteans, and annelids. The nematode body cavity compares with that of rotifers, gastrotrichs, and acanthocephalans in lacking a mesodermal lining and hence is unlike the true coelom of annelids and vertebrates or the parenchyma-filled body of flatworms and nemerteans. The nematodes, rotifers, and gastrotrichs

363

have a triradiate structure in the fore part of the gut, and the epidermis, which secretes the cuticle, is usually without cell boundaries. The complete digestive tract in nematodes allows food to move along without mixing successive meals, and undigested residues pass out the anus. Digested food diffuses through the gut and is distributed to other tissues by fluid in the pseudocoel; hence, a much-branched tract as in flatworms is unnecessary.

Zoological opinion has varied as to the proper place of the nematodes in classification. They have often been designated as a separate phylum (NEMATHELMINTHES, either with or without the acanthocephs and nematomorphs), but recently they have been placed as a class in the Phylum ASCHELMINTHES, along with the rotifers, gastrotrichs, etc.

17-2. Structure of Ascaris. The common intestinal roundworm of man and the pig (*Ascaris lumbricoides*) is a suitable species to show the

FIG. 17-1. Class NEMATODA. External features of the intestinal roundworm of the pig, *Ascaris lumbricoides*.

general features of a nematode (Fig. 17-1). The female is 8 to 16 inches long and about $\frac{1}{4}$ inch in greatest diameter; the male is of lesser size and only 6 to 10 inches long. Fresh specimens are yellow to pink in color. The *body* is slender and round, tapering toward either end. It is covered with smooth, tough, and elastic *cuticle,* bearing minute striations. Four whitish *longitudinal lines* extend along the body, one dorsal, one ventral, and two lateral. The *mouth* opens at the anterior end, between three rounded *lips;* the dorsal lip bears two double papillae, and each ventro-lateral lip has one double and two single papillae. The *anus* is a transverse slit close to the posterior end of the ventral surface. The *male* worm has a sharply curved posterior end, and two penial spicules project from the male genital pore just within the anus. The *female* worm is straighter, and the genital pore, or vulva, is midventral on the body at about one-third the distance from the anterior end.

The *body wall* (Fig. 17-2) is thin, consisting of (1) the *cuticle,* which is noncellular and secreted by the epidermis; (2) the *epidermis,* a thin protoplasmic layer that contains nuclei but no cell walls and hence is a syncytium; and (3) the *muscle layer,* of longitudinal fibers. Each muscle cell consists of a spindle-shaped fiber extending lengthwise beneath the epidermis and a club-shaped process that contains the nucleus and extends medially.   The muscle layer is divided into four lengthwise parts by the riblike inner projections of the four lateral lines.   These lines and the muscle cells are the irregular outer boundary of the body space, or *pseudocoel,* in which the other internal organs lie free.

The *digestive tract* (Fig. 17-3) is straight, extending the length of the body, and consists of (1) the *mouth;* (2) a small *buccal cavity;* (3) a muscular sucking *pharynx,* or esophagus, about ½ inch long, that acts to draw in food; (4) a long narrow *intestine,* which is nonmuscular, composed

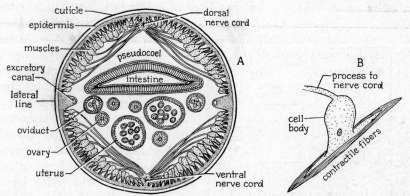

FIG. 17-2.   *Ascaris.*   *A.* Cross section of a female.   *B.* One muscle cell.   Both enlarged.

of a single layer of tall endoderm cells that absorb the digested food, and covered externally by cuticle; and (5) a short *rectum* discharging through (6) the *anus.*   No circulatory or respiratory organs are present.   The inner part of each lateral line contains an *excretory canal,* both emptying through a minute midventral pore just behind the mouth.   A *nerve ring* surrounds the esophagus; it connects to six short anterior nerves and to six posterior *nerve cords,* a larger dorsal and ventral cord each in the

FIG. 17-3.   *Ascaris.*   Internal structure of a female.

corresponding longitudinal line and others in the body wall, with various lateral branches and cross connectives.   Various papillae, probably sensory in function, occur on the body surface.

Each reproductive organ is a slender tube, closed at its inner end, of gradually increasing diameter, coiled back and forth in the body space, and unattached save where connected to the genital pore.   The gonad and reproductive duct are continuous.   The *male reproductive system* is single; its parts are (1) the *testis* for sperm production; (2) the *vas deferens* for conduction; (3) the *seminal vesicle* for storing mature sperm; (4) the *ejaculatory duct* for ejecting sperm; and (5) a sac containing two *penial spicules,* which are inserted in the female's vulva for attachment of the male and female during copulation.   The *female reproductive system* is ≺-shaped, each branch being up to 125 cm. long, and consisting of (1) an *ovary,* (2) an *oviduct,* and (3) a *uterus.*   The two uteri are joined in (4) a single short *vagina* opening at (5) the *vulva.*

17-3. Natural history.   The adult ascaris lives as a parasite within the intestine of its host and has problems of existence somewhat different

Ingestion of embryonated eggs

Adult worms found in the intestines

Eggs passed in feces

Eggs contaminate food

Migration in body
Eggs hatch in intestines, and larvae burrow into the wall. Then they penetrate capillaries, and pass to lungs via blood. Soon they enter the alveoli, grow and molt and migrate up the trachea to pharynx. Then they are swallowed.

Embryonated egg

Fig. 17-4.   *Ascaris.*   Life cycle in the pig. *(From Rebrassier, Ohio State University Press, 1938.)*

from those of a free-living animal. For obvious reasons, it is difficult to determine the physiological processes of an internal parasite while in its normal habitat, but the following inferences are probably correct: (1) Locomotion and maintenance of position are accomplished chiefly by dorsoventral bendings of the body; (2) the cuticle protects the living worm against the digestive juices of its host (antienzymes also may be a factor); (3) food is obtained from the semifluid materials in the host's intestine, being pumped in by the worm's muscular esophagus, and after digestion passes through its intestinal wall to be distributed by fluid in the body space to other tissues; (4) respiration is dependent upon the breakdown of glycogen within the worm's body, since the intestinal contents of its host contain little free oxygen; and (5) the sensory papillae probably are receptors for chemical and tactile stimuli.

17-4. Reproduction.   Male and female worms copulate within the host's intestine.   The eggs are fertilized in the oviducts of the female, and each (Fig. 17-6) becomes covered by a tough shell (measuring 45 to 75 by 35 to 50 μ).   A large female may contain 27,000,000 eggs at one time and lay 200,000 or more per day.   The eggs pass out of the female, into the host's intestine, and leave with the feces.   A period of development is necessary before they become infective for another host.   Under conditions of drought or cold they may lie dormant for many months.   In a warm, moist, but shady site development requires 2 or 3 weeks.   If such "embryonated" eggs (containing embryo worms) are swallowed by the proper host with food or water, they pass to the intestine.   There the larvae (0.2 to 0.3 mm. long) hatch, burrow into veins or lymph vessels in the intestinal wall, and travel through the heart and to pulmonary capillaries in the lungs, meanwhile growing in size.   In a few days they break into the air passages and move via the trachea, esophagus, and stomach to the intestine again, where they grow to maturity.

No intermediate host is necessary to complete the life cycle (Fig. 17-4). Young pigs usually acquire larvae from infected soil in pigyards or in dirt on the sow's udder when nursing.   Adult pigs are rather immune to infection; therefore any worms they contain were probably acquired when young.   Human infection with ascaris is not uncommon, and a majority of persons in some rural localities are infected.   Worms found in man and pigs are identical structurally, but differ physiologically in that infective eggs of the human ascaris do not ordinarily produce mature worms in pigs, and vice versa.   Passage of many larvae through the lungs may cause local inflammation and even a pneumonia.   Adult ascarids in the intestine may produce secretions toxic to the host, and the worms when numerous may obstruct the intestine.   Worms sometimes migrate up to the mouth or nose, or may even penetrate the intestinal wall to invade other organs, causing serious illness or death of the host.   Some animals and people become sensitized or allergic to the secretions of ascarids.

17-5. Other nematodes.   Many species, both parasitic and free-living, resemble *Ascaris* in general structure but differ as to various details.

| Xiphinema | Bunonema | Desmoscolex | Predaceous nematode |

FIG. 17-5.   Some free-living nematodes; all much enlarged.   (*After Cobb*, 1915.)

Some parasitic forms have teeth, hooks, or cutting plates in the mouth for attachment and feeding; and others that live on plant roots have a sharp hollow "spear" to puncture the cells and a muscular esophagus to withdraw the cell sap.   The cuticle on many free-living species bears minute bristles, spines, or even transverse rows of scales that aid them in crawling through soil.   Some predatory nematodes have enlarged mouths margined with teeth or other projections that make them appear like "micro-

scopic dragons" (Fig. 17-5). In different species and groups the mouth
and esophagus show much variety with lesser differences in muscles,
excretory organs, and reproductive structures. Males may have two,
one, or no penial spicules, and some have the posterior end with an
expanded caudal bursa serving to hold the female while mating. The
vulva is variously located, and the females of some species have a single
ovary, oviduct, and uterus.

There is a great host of free-living nematodes, the life histories of
which are practically unknown. They occur in moist soil and in some
deserts, in the sand of ocean beaches, in fresh, stagnant, and salt waters,
on the shores and bottoms of lakes and rivers, on the filter beds of water-
works, on mountain tops, in hot springs, and in the polar seas and ice.
The upper foot of an acre of alluvial soil may contain 3,000,000,000

FIG. 17-6.   Eggs of nematodes and an acanthocephalan (*Macracanthorhynchus*); all much
enlarged.   (*After H. B. Ward,* 1907.)

nematodes, and the top 3 inches of beach sand a third as many. Some
soil-inhabiting nematodes do severe damage to crop plants, others may be
of neutral status, and those that prey on other nematodes probably are
beneficial. Still other species live in various parts of plants, including the
roots, seeds, fruits, gums, leaf axils, bark crevices, and galls; the eggs or
larvae of some are transported by insects.

17-6. Relations to man. The many species of nematodes that are
parasitic in man, his domestic animals, and his cultivated plants are of
great practical importance and have been studied intensively. Some of
them do little or no damage, but others cause impaired efficiency, unthriftiness, illness, or death of the host. The effects depend upon the species of
worm, the numbers present, and other factors. More than 50 species are
parasites of mankind. Many others parasitize farm livestock and poultry,
all kinds of wild vertebrates, and various invertebrates. Almost any
organ of a vertebrate may be invaded by some kind of nematode. Each
species is usually confined to one or a few related hosts, occasionally
invades others, and usually occupies a particular organ. Most parasitic
nematodes have a free-living egg or larval stage in soil or water, but the
filarial worms require an intermediate host. Occasionally a host contains
enormous numbers, as a pint of stomach worms in man, or 40,000 in a
50-pound mammal. Infections with intestinal worms can be diagnosed
by searching for the microscopic eggs in the feces, those of most species

being of characteristic size, shape, and structure (Fig. 17-6). Treatment to eliminate them requires use of a drug, without too toxic an effect on the host, that will cause the worms to sicken and be carried out in the feces.

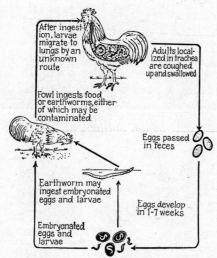

FIG. 17-7. Life cycle of the gapeworm, *Syngamus trachea.* (*From Rebrassier, Ohio State University Press,* 1938.)

The hosts and organs parasitized by some important nematodes are as follows:

MAN. Small intestine: *Ancylostoma duodenale* and *Necator americanus*, the hookworms; *Ascaris lumbricoides.* Caecum and appendix: *Trichuris trichiura*, whipworm, Large intestine: *Enterobius vermicularis*, pinworm, especially in children.

HORSE. Stomach: *Habronema megastoma*. Small intestine: *Parascaris equorum* (= *Ascaris megalocephala*). Large intestine: *Oxyuris equi*. Caecum and large intestine: *Strongylus vulgaris*.

SHEEP. Air passages: *Dictyocaulus filaria*, lung threadworm. Stomach: *Haemonchus contortus; Trichostrongylus axei.* Small intestine: *Bunostomum trigonocephalum*. Large intestine: *Oesophagostomum columbianum*, nodular worm.

PIG. Air passages: *Metastrongylus apri*, and others. Stomach: *Hyostrongylus rubidus.* Small intestine: *Ascaris lumbricoides.* Large intestine: *Oesophagostomum dentatum.*

DOG. Small intestine: *Ancylostoma caninum*, hookworm; *Toxocara canis*. Caecum: *Trichuris vulpis*, whipworm.

CHICKEN. Air passages: *Syngamus trachea*, gapeworm (Fig. 17-7). Gizzard: *Cheilospiura (Acuaria) hamulosa.* Small intestine: *Ascaridea galli; Capillaria columbae.* Caecum: *Heterakis gallinae*, caecum worm (also in turkey, where it carries the protozoan, *Histomonas meleagridis*, which causes the disease known as "blackhead").

17-7. Root nematodes. Many species of minute to microscopic nematodes live in or about the roots of plants. Some, such as the sugar beet nematode, *Heterodera schachtii*, are restricted to one or a few kinds of plants, but others are less specialized. The common garden nematode, *H. radicicola* or *marioni*, has been reported in over 1,000 varieties of plants and commonly infests over 75 garden and field crops, fruit and shade trees, shrubs and weeds (Fig. 17-8). Its eggs are deposited in roots or soil, and the young upon hatching penetrate rootlets to feed on the tissues within. The roots react by forming small galls of scar tissue—the "root knots"—about the worms. The adult male nematode is slender (1.2 to 1.5 mm. long), and the female becomes a whitish teardrop-like object (0.8 by 0.5 mm.) with a swollen body producing 500 to 1,000 eggs. Fertilization may occur but is unnecessary. The eggs are laid in a yellow gelatinous secretion. The life cycle requires nearly 3 months at 58°F. but

egg   larva   growing female   mature female   mature male   on tobacco   ROOT GALLS   on potato

FIG. 17-8. The root knot nematode, *Heterodera marioni*. Eggs, larvae, and adults, all greatly enlarged. Root galls produced by the worms, about natural size. (*After Tyler*, 1933.)

less than a month in soil at 81°F. Several generations per year are thus possible in the warm southern and western states. The larvae within galls can withstand some drying, and survive at 32°F. but die at lower temperatures. Root knot causes weakening or death of the plant, and soil infested with these worms often fails to yield profitable crops. The nematodes are carried into clean soils with plants, soil, manure, farm implements, or even irrigation water from infested lands. Once established, they are difficult to eradicate. Plant breeders have developed selected strains of some economic plants that are resistant to root nematodes. Certain chemicals (D-D, methyl bromide, etc.) are used to reduce the worms in infested soils.

17-8. Hookworm. This is one of the scourges of mankind in all moist tropical and subtropical regions. In populations of low economic level that go barefooted and use no sanitary toilets, from 50 to 95 per cent may be infected. Many of the "poor whites" in the southeastern states suffer from hookworm disease, and workmen in mines, tunnels, and brickyards often harbor hookworms. *Ancylostoma duodenale* and *Necator americanus* are both common in man, the latter especially in the United States.

The adult worm is 8 to 13 mm. long and has cutting plates or teeth in its mouth (Fig. 17-9). It attaches to the inner wall of the small intestine, where blood, lymph, and bits of mucous membrane are drawn into the worm's gut by action of the pumping pharynx. Feeding is aided by production of a secretion that prevents coagulation of the host's blood. The worm may pump more blood than it digests, and the wound it

Fig. 17-9.   Hookworms.   *A.* Mouth of *Ancylostoma duodenale* in anterior view, showing the teeth.   *B. Ancylostoma caninum* attached to intestinal wall in dog.   Both enlarged.   (*After Stiles; and Loess.*)

makes may bleed after the worm has moved elsewhere; the host, in consequence, loses blood into the intestine.

Hookworms mate while in the host's intestine. Each female produces several thousand fertile eggs daily, which pass out with the feces. In moist warm shady places these hatch in 24 to 48 hours (Fig. 17-10), and the larvae feed on excrement or other organic debris in the soil, later to

SEGMENTATION

EMBRYOS   HATCHING

Fig. 17-10.   Development of the hookworm, *Ancylostoma duodenale.*   (*After Stiles,* 1902.)

undergo two molts. When about 0.5 mm. long they become infective for man. Entry is usually by burrowing through the softer parts of the skin, as on the sides of the foot, and causes "ground itch." The larvae travel in blood and lymph vessels, passing through the heart and to the lungs, from capillaries to air cavities, and thence up the trachea into the esophagus and to the intestine. With two further molts they soon mature and may live some months or even several years.   Continued reinvasion of the host maintains the infection.

Children harboring a hundred or more hookworms are retarded in physical and mental growth, and persons of all ages with many worms become anemic from loss of blood, their energy is lessened, and their susceptibility to other diseases is increased.   Treatment under medical supervision with oil of chenopodium, carbon tetrachloride, tetrachlorethylene, or hexylresorcinol will rid a person of these parasites.   The wearing of shoes and the sanitary disposal of human feces will prevent infection.   Other species of hookworms occur in dogs, foxes, cats, cattle, sheep, and pigs.

17-9. Trichina worm.   *Trichinella spiralis* occurs as a minute living larva encysted in the striated muscles (Fig. 17-11) of pigs, house rats, and man, also in cats, dogs, and black bears.   If an individual of any of these

Fig. 17-11.   The trichina worm, *Trichinella spiralis;* enlarged.   Adults at left.

eats the flesh of another containing such larvae, the cysts are dissolved by the digestive juices and the larvae are liberated in the intestine of the new host.   In about 2 days they become sexually mature and mate; male worms are then about 1.5 mm. long and females 3 to 4 mm.   The females burrow into the intestinal wall to live for some time, and each produces up to 1,500 living larvae about 0.1 mm. long.   These enter lymph spaces, are carried in the blood stream, and burrow into skeletal muscles.   They grow to about 1.0 mm. then coil up and become enclosed in cysts, which later may be calcified.   Such larvae cannot mature unless the flesh containing them is eaten by another susceptible mammal, but may live for months or years in man.

Mild infections cause no particular symptoms, and some encysted trichinae occur in about 16 per cent of people in the United States. Heavy infections cause the disease *trichinosis,* which may be severe and can end in death.   Intestinal disturbances and abdominal pain occur first; with spread of the larvae there is fever, the muscles become swollen, hard, and painful, and there may be difficulty in swallowing and breathing.   There is no specific treatment, and recovery is slow.   Hogs, rats, and the other mammals become infected by eating slaughterhouse scraps, garbage, or animal carcasses that contain encysted larvae.   Man receives infection by eating pork (occasionally bear meat) containing the micro-

scopic cysts.   Examination of pork in slaughterhouses for trichinae is
economically impractical, and some infections may be missed.   The only
protection is to *cook pork thoroughly,* by heating all parts to at least
137°F.   Pink color in freshly roasted pork is evidence of inadequate
cooking.   Salami, headcheese, and other pork products may be dangerous
unless thoroughly cooked.   Refrigeration at −10°F. for 3 days will
usually kill all larvae, but cooking is safer.

17-10. Filarial worms.   The filariae of man and various vertebrates are
nematodes that require an intermediate arthropod host to complete the
life cycle.   One of these is *Wuchereria bancrofti* (Fig. 17-12), a human
parasite in all warm regions of the world, formerly present about Charles-

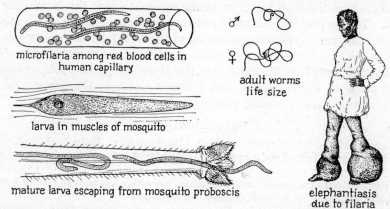

microfilaria among red blood cells in
human capillary

adult worms
life size

larva in muscles of mosquito

mature larva escaping from mosquito proboscis

elephantiasis
due to filaria

FIG. 17-12.   Stages in the life cycle of the filaria worm, *Wuchereria bancrofti.*   (*After
Francis; Fulleborn; and Sambon.*)

ton, S.C., where probably introduced with Negro slaves.   The minute
larvae, or microfilariae, are about 0.2 mm. long.   They live by day chiefly
in large blood vessels, passing at night to small vessels in the skin, but
cause no trouble even if numerous.   If taken up by certain kinds of
mosquitoes, the larvae pass to the insect's stomach, then to the thoracic
muscles, undergo metamorphosis, and when about 1.4 mm. long move into
the proboscis.   At the mosquito's next meal, the larvae crawl onto and
presumably puncture the human skin, pass into lymph vessels, coil up in
lymph glands, and later mature.   The adult female is about 80 mm. long,
the male 40 mm., but neither is over 0.3 mm. in diameter.   If both sexes
are present, they mate and each female produces perhaps 1,000 microfilariae.   The adults obstruct the lymph circulation and if present in
numbers may, after some years, cause the disease *elephantiasis,* in which
the limbs or other parts grow to enormous size.   An amazing biological
adjustment occurs in some localities where the microfilariae inhabit the
deeper circulation by night and superficial vessels by day and are transferred by diurnal mosquitoes.

17-11. Guinea worm. *Dracunculus medinensis,* possibly the Biblical "fiery serpent" (Num. 21:6), is a human parasite in India, Arabia, Africa, South America, and the West Indies. It occurs in several Old World mammals and has been found in dogs, foxes, raccoons, and mink in the United States but not in man. The larvae occur in water fleas (*Cyclops*) which may be swallowed by the final host in drinking water. Upon reaching the host's stomach the larvae escape and burrow to subcutaneous tissues, occasionally to the heart or meninges. There a year or less of growth yields a female up to 1,200 mm. long by 1 or 2 mm. in diameter (males are practically unknown). The mature gravid female migrates, usually to the host's lower leg or ankle where an ulcer forms. Upon immersion of the limb in water larvae escape to seek the intermediate host. Native peoples commonly remove a worm by winding it on a stick, a few turns per day; severe poisoning of the host follows if the worm is broken and its body contents enter the tissues. Another species (*D. ophidensis*) found in Michigan has the larval stage in *Cyclops viridis,* may occur in frog tadpoles, and becomes adult in the garter snake, *Thammophis sirtalis,* females growing to 250 mm. long.

CLASSIFICATION

Class NEMATODA (Nemathelminthes). ROUNDWORMS. Body slender, cylindrical, often tapered toward ends; covered with cuticle; no segmentation or cilia; digestive tract complete, straight; no proboscis; no circular muscles; body space (pseudocoel) usually not lined; sexes usually separate; male with cloaca, and usually 1 or 2 copulatory spicules; no cloaca in female; 12,000 species.

Subclass 1. APHASMIDEA. No phasmids (caudal sensory organs); amphids (anterior sensory organs) various, rarely porelike; excretory system often reduced or none; coelomocytes and mesenterial tissue well developed; females usually lack caudal alae.

Order 1. **Chromadorida.** Esophagus of 3 regions and not elongate; esophageal glands never duplicate, multinucleate, or opening anteriorly in esophagus.

Suborder 1. MONHYSTERINA. Esophago-intestinal valve not triradiate or vertically flattened; teeth none, 1 or 3 small, or 6 outward-acting; fresh or salt waters. *Monhystera, Plectus, Cylindrolaimus.*

Suborder 2. CHROMADORINA. Esophago-intestinal valve triradiate or vertically flattened; teeth 1 large, or 6 inward-acting, or 3 jaws; amphids spiral, circular, etc.; in salt and fresh waters. *Chromadora, Cyatholaimus, Desmoscolex.*

Order 2. **Enoplida.** Esophagus of 2 parts (anterior muscular, posterior glandular), often long, cylindrical or conoidal; amphids pocket-like, elongate, or porelike.

Suborder 1. ENOPLINA. Intestine lacks muscles; no caudal sucker or stylet; male with 2 spicules; free-living in salt, brackish, or fresh waters or in soil. *Enoplus, Trilobus.*

Suborder 2. DORYLAIMINA. (Trichurata). Intestine lacks muscles; no caudal sucker or glands; male with 2, 1, or no spicules. *Dorylaimus,* in soil and fresh or brackish water; *Trichinella spiralis; Trichuris trichocephala,* whipworm; *Capillaria,* hairlike in liver, gut, and elsewhere in vertebrates; *Mermis,* larvae in insects, adults free-living but do not feed.

Suborder 3. DIOCTOPHYMATINA. Intestine with 4 rows of muscles; male with caudal sucker and 1 spicule. *Dioctophyma renale,* giant nematode, male to 450 mm.

long, female to 900 by 15 mm., in body cavity of mammals; *Hystrichis*, in intestine of birds.

Subclass 2.   PHASMIDEA.   With phasmids; amphids porelike; excretory system with paired lateral canals; coelomocytes 4 to 6, mesenterial tissue scant; no caudal or lateral hypodermal glands.

Order 1.   **Rhabditida.**   Esophagus of 3 regions, especially in larvae.

Suborder 1.   RHABDITINA.   Lips 6, 3, 2, or 0; vagina short, transverse; caudal alae, if present, with papillae; no stylet; free-living and saprophagous in soil, or parasitic in plants or animals.   *Rhabditis*, some free-living in soil, others parasitic; *Strongyloides, Rhabdias*, alternate generations of parasitic females and of free-living males and females.

Suborder 2.   TYLENCHINA.   Lips 8, 6, or 0; stylet present; lateral excretory canals only on 1 side; vagina short, usually transverse; feed on fluids of living cells or in body spaces of insects.   *Tylenchus*, meadow nematode; *Heterodera*, root nematode (Fig. 17-8), in roots; *Anguina*, wheat eelworm; *Chondronema*, in insects.

Suborder 3.   STRONGYLINA.   Lips 6, 3, or 0, small; uterus heavily muscular, with ovejector; bursa with rays; parasitic in land vertebrates.   *Oesophagostomum; Syngamus trachea*, gapeworms; *Ancylostoma, Necator*, hookworms; *Trichostrongylus*, hairworms; *Haemonchus*, stomachworm; *Metastrongylus*, lungworm.

Suborder 4.   ASCARIDINA.   Lips usually 3 large, or 6 small, or none; some with 2 lateral jaws; vagina and posterior uterus muscular; caudal alae with papillae (no muscles or rays); parasitic in land snails, insects, and vertebrates.   *Ascaris; Enterobius*, pinworm; *Toxocara, Heterakis, Thelastoma*.

Order 2.   **Spirurida.**   Esophagus of 2 regions, anterior muscular and posterior glandular; adults in gut or tissues of vertebrates.

Suborder 1.   SPIRURINA.   Esophageal glands multinucleate; larval phasmids porelike; intermediate stages usually in insects.   *Gongylonema, Thelazia, Wuchereria; Onchocerca; Loa*, "eyeworm"; *Tetrameres*.

Suborder 2.   CAMALLANINA.   Esophageal glands uninucleate; phasmids in larvae large, pocket-like; copepods are intermediate host.   *Dracunculus medinensis*, Guinea worm; *Camallanus*, in turtles and fish.

References

See works by Baylis; Brumpt; Chandler; Craig and Faust; Faust; Hegner, Root, Augustine, and Huff; Monnig; Morgan and Hawkins; Neveu-Lemaire; and Sprehn cited in References to Chap. 16.

BAYLIS, H. A., and R. DAUBNEY.   1926.   A synopsis of the families and genera of Nematoda.   London, British Museum.   xxxvi + 277 pp.

CHITWOOD, B. G., and OTHERS.   1937– .   An introduction to nematology.   Baltimore, Monumental Publishing Co.   240 pp., 164 figs.   Technical; incomplete.

COBB, N. A.   1918.   Free-living nematodes.   *In* Ward and Whipple, Fresh-water biology.   New York, John Wiley & Sons, Inc.   Pp. 459–505, figs, 766–810.

GOODEY, T.   1933.   Plant parasitic nematodes.   New York, E. P. Dutton & Co.   xx + 306 pp., illus.

HYMAN, L. H.   1951.   The invertebrates.   New York, McGraw-Hill Book Co., Inc.   NEMATODA, vol. 3.

KÜKENTHAL, W., and OTHERS.   1928–34.   Handbuch der Zoologie.   Berlin, Walter de Gruyter & Co.   NEMATODA, vol. 2, part 1, section 4, pp. 249–402, figs. 267–426.

SHIPLEY, A. E.   1896.   Nemathelminthes.   *In* Cambridge natural history.   London, Macmillan & Co., Ltd.   Vol. 2, pp. 121–185, figs. 62–100.

YORKE, W., and P. A. MAPLESTONE.   1926.   The nematode parasites of vertebrates.   Philadelphia, The Blakiston Co.   xi + 536 pp., 307 figs.

CHAPTER 18

MISCELLANEOUS PHYLA AND GROUPS

Mesozoa	Kinorhyncha	Phoronida
Nemertinea	Nematomorpha	Chaetognatha
Entoprocta	Acanthocephala	Sipunculoidea
Rotifera	Bryozoa	Priapuloidea
Gastrotricha	Brachiopoda	Echiuroidea

Besides the major phyla described in other chapters, there are several additional groups of multicellular animals. While not often studied by beginners in zoology, they are described here to complete the account of the animal kingdom. All these animals are aquatic, in salt or fresh waters, some being abundant and of wide occurrence and others uncommon.

18-1. Difficulties in classification. Zoologists are not agreed as to the places these groups should occupy in classification; some obviously are low and others higher in the systematic scale, but they cannot be aligned definitely with the larger phyla. Some have long been recognized as separate phyla, and others have been attached as special Classes in certain of the well-established phyla. Several authorities now recognize a Phylum Aschelminthes to include as Classes the Rotifera, Gastrotricha, Kinorhyncha, Nematoda (Chap. 17), Nematomorpha, and Acanthocephala. Three other groups, the Sipunculoidea, Priapuloidea, and Echiuroidea, often have been brought together as a Class Gephyrea in the Phylum Annelida; but their peculiarities warrant each being placed in a separate phylum.

The sequence in which some phyla and lesser subdivisions should be listed is controversial. Obviously no linear or two-dimensional pattern is adequate to illustrate the differing degrees of relationship that result from the long and diverse history of sectors of the animal kingdom down through time. Some zoologists consider that the Echinodermata and Chaetognatha should be close to the Chordata, and some separate the Hemichordata from the latter for closer placement with the echinoderms; other authorities place the echinoderms lower in the system of classification.

18-2. The trochophore larva. In many aquatic invertebrates the early larva is a minute, transparent, and free-swimming organism called a *trochophore* or trochosphere. It is somewhat pear-shaped, with the large end uppermost, and encircled by two lines of cilia that beat so as to suggest a rotating wheel—hence the name "trochophore" (Gr. *trochos*, wheel +

376

phorus, to bear).   The upper end bears an apical plate with a tuft of cilia and a sense organ (eyespot).   The digestive tract is complete and ciliated internally, its position determining the median plane of bilateral symmetry.   The mouth opens between the ciliated bands, followed by a slender esophagus, expanded stomach, and straight intestine, with the anus in the smaller (ab-apical) end.   The body may contain a pair of nephridia for excretion, muscle and nerve fibers, and a band of mesoderm.

With various modifications this is the early larva of many marine flatworms, nemerteans, brachiopods, bryozoans, mollusks, and some

NEMERTEAN   BRYOZOAN   MOLLUSK   ANNELID
A   B   C   D

FIG. 18-1.   Early larvae of some invertebrates.   *A.* Nemertean pilidium.   *B.* Bryozoan trochophore.   *C.* Molluscan trochophore (*Patella*).   *D.* Annelid trochophore (*Polygordius*).   M, mouth; St., stomach; I, intestine; A, anus; N, nephridium.   (*After various authors.*)

annelids (Fig. 18-1).   Such a common larval pattern is suggestive of relationship between these groups in the distant past, for which no fossil record has survived.   In these various phyla adults are derived from the larval stages by modifications that often involve a major change of form, or metamorphosis.

PHYLUM MESOZOA

18-3. The MESOZOA are minute wormlike solid organisms with the simplest structure of any multicellular animals.   *Dicyema* (Fig. 18-2), a common parasite in the nephridia of octopuses and squids, is up to 8 mm. long, composed of an outer layer of about 25 (16 to 42) ciliated somatic cells surrounding one or more long axial reproductive cells.   The anterior 8 or 9 cells form a polar cap.   Repeated fission of the axial cell yields cells (agametes, with no observed maturation) that develop asexually into new individuals and then escape from the parent.   There is also a type of sexual reproduction.   *Rhopalura* is a rare parasite in tissues and cavities of flatworms, nemerteans, brittle stars, annelids, and a clam.   The MESOZOA resemble some colonial protozoans in having external cilia throughout much of the life cycle, in having intracellular digestion by the external cells, and in having special internal reproductive cells (as in *Volvox*). Their two cell layers, however, are not comparable with the ectoderm and endoderm of METAZOA, and they have no internal digestive cavity. Either they are intermediate between unicellular and multicellular animals or else degenerate forms, possibly related to the PLATYHELMINTHES.

FIG. 18-2. Phylum MESOZOA. *Dicyema.* *A.* Outline of full-grown individual, 3 mm. long; *B.* young nematogen stage, 0.4 mm. (*Adapted from McConnaughey,* 1949.)

References. HYMAN, L. H. 1940. The invertebrates. New York, McGraw-Hill Book Co., Inc. Pp. 233–247, figs. 68–71. McCONNAUGHEY, B. H. 1949. Mesozoa of the Family Dicyemidae from California. *University of California Publications in Zoology,* vol. 55, pp. 1–34, 7 pls.

PHYLUM NEMERTINEA. RIBBON WORMS

18-4. These slender worms have soft, flat, and unsegmented bodies, capable of great elongation and contraction. Some are only 5 mm. long, many are a few inches in length, and one species may stretch to 80 feet. The 500 species are variously red, brown, yellow, green, or white, some solidly colored and others striped or cross-banded. Most nemerteans are marine, living closely coiled beneath stones, among algae, or in burrows between the tides, but some inhabit deep water. The genus *Prostoma* lives in fresh waters, the tropical *Geonemertes* in moist earth, *Malacobdella* in the mantle cavities of bivalve mollusks, and *Carcinonemertes* among the gills or egg masses of certain crabs.

18-5. Characteristics. (1) Symmetry bilateral, 3 germ layers; (2) body slender, soft, highly contractile, and unsegmented; (3) an eversible proboscis; (4) digestive tract straight and complete; (5) no coelom or respiratory organs; body spaces filled with parenchyma; (6) 3 longitudinal blood vessels, 2 lateral excretory canals, branched, with flame cells; (7) nervous system with paired anterior ganglia and a pair of lateral longitudinal nerves, some species also with middorsal and midventral nerve trunks; (8) sexes separate, with multiple pairs of gonads, and development direct or through a pilidium larva; asexual reproduction by fragmentation.

The NEMERTINEA are commonly placed near or with the PLATYHELMINTHES because of the character of the integument and nervous system, the presence of flame cells, and the lack of external segmentation or a coelom; they differ from the flatworms in having a complete digestive tract, a simplified reproductive system, and in usually being dioecious. They show some features paralleling those of hemichordates and chordates, the nemertean dorsal nerve resembling the vertebrate spinal cord, the lateral nerves placed as the lateral line nerves of fishes, the cephalic ganglia like the brain of vertebrates, the transverse nerves comparing with spinal nerves, and the proboscis sheath suggesting the notochord.

18-6. Structure and natural history (Fig. 18-3).   The soft **integument** is of columnar cells, ciliated, mucous, sensory, and others; beneath this are both circular and longitudinal muscles.   Locomotion is by action of the external cilia and the muscles.   At the anterior end, above the mouth,

Fig. 18-3. Phylum NEMERTINEA. *A.* External form with proboscis extended. *B.* Internal structure, diagrammatic.   Left side removed except for part at middle of body and proboscis retracted into sheath.

is a pore through which the soft *proboscis* may be extended far out or completely withdrawn, like inverting the finger of a glove; the proboscis is contained in a *sheath* inside the body.   It is thought to serve or offense and defense, being armed with stylets or spines in some species. The *digestive tract* is a ciliated tube, extending the entire length of the body, having both a mouth and an anus, and sometimes also paired lateral caeca; the food is of other animals, both living and dead.   The *circulatory system* includes a pair of lengthwise lateral vessels and usually a middorsal vessel, with cross connections at the head and about the digestive tract.   The blood is either red or colorless and circulates back and forth as a result of movements of the body.   Respiration occurs by exchange of gases through the body wall.   The *excretory system* comprises a pair of lateral canals with numerous branches, some with flame cells that lie close to blood vessels.   There is no true body cavity, spaces between the body wall and internal organs being filled with gelatinous parenchyma.   The *nervous system* includes two large cerebral ganglia in the head region, with cross connectives and with anterior nerves especially to the proboscis.   A large lateral nerve extends along each side of the body, with ganglion cells and cross connectives; some species have also a middorsal and a midventral nerve trunk.   The *sense organs* include few to

many ocelli and receptors in the integument of the head and along the
sides of the body.

The sexes are usually separate (a few species are monoecious, some
protandric). The *reproductive system* consists of pairs of simple sacs
or multiple pairs of gonads between the intestinal pouches, developed
within the parenchyma and opening directly on the body surface when the
eggs or sperm are mature. Certain nemerteans (LINEIDAE) have a free-
swimming (pilidium) larval stage; development in others is direct, being
viviparous in some. The adults have great powers of regeneration, and
some reproduce regularly· during warm weather by fragmentation of
the body, each piece then growing into a complete worm.

Classification. Phylum **NEMERTINEA** (see Characteristics). Order 1. **Palae-
nemertea.** No stylets or intestinal caeca; usually no eyes. *Tubulanus.* Order 2.
Heteronemertea. No stylets or caeca; with "eyes." *Lineus; Cerebratulus.* Order 3.
Hoplonemertea. Usually with stylets and intestinal caeca. *Paranemertes, Geo-
nemertes, Amphiporus, Prostoma* (= *Stichostemma*), *Tetrastemma, Carcinonemertes.*
Order 4. **Bdellonemertea.** Body short, thick, with posterior sucker; no caeca.
Malacobdella.

References. COE, W. R. 1935. Nemertea. *In* H. S. Pratt. Manual of the
common invertebrate animals. Philadelphia, The Blakiston Co. Pp. 230–241,
figs. 325–335. BÖHMIG, L. 1929. Nemertini. *In* W. Kükenthal and others.
Handbuch der Zoologie. Vol. 2, part 1, section 3, pp. 1–110, figs. 1–75. HYMAN,
L. H. 1951. Rhynchoela. *In* The invertebrates. New York, McGraw-Hill Book
Co., Inc. Vol. 2, pp. 459–531, figs. 174–208.

PHYLUM ENTOPROCTA

18-7. The ENTOPROCTA (Kamptozoa) are small mossy organisms,
colonial or solitary, found attached to seaweeds or other submerged
objects in shallow waters. Formerly they were included among the
BRYOZOA, which they resemble superficially, but their fundamental
structure is quite different.

18-8. Characteristics. (1) Symmetry bilateral, no segmentation, 3 germ layers;
(2) individual zooids minute, each with calyx, stalk, and enlarged base; (3) edge of
retractile circular calyx surrounded by one row of many slender, active, ciliated
tentacles; (4) both mouth and anus open within circle of tentacles; (5) digestive tract
U-shaped, complete, ciliated, with esophagus, stomach, and rectum; (6) space within
body a pseudocoel filled with gelatinous parenchyma; (7) retractor muscles present;
(8) no circulatory or respiratory organs; (9) one pair of protonephridia for excretion;
(10) nerve ganglia present; (11) monoecious or sexes separate, 2 gonads, with ducts;
(12) eggs and larvae develop in ovary, then larvae swim freely in water before attaching to grow; (13) calyx often lost and regenerated from stalk.

Of the 40 or more known species, *Urnatella gracilis,* usually found in
pairs, is the only fresh-water form, living on the underside of stones in
running waters of the eastern and central states and in Lake Erie.
Loxosomella and *Loxosoma* grow from buds that separate so each indi-

vidual is distinct; large numbers live as commensals on marine annelid worms and less often on sponges or ascidians. Common colonial types are *Pedicellina* and *Barentsia*, that grow on shells or algae in shallow sea water.

References. CORI, C. J. 1930. Kamptozoa (Bryozoa entoprocta). *In* W. Kükenthal and others, Handbuch der Zoologie. Vol. 2, part 1, section 5, pp. 1–64, figs. 1–76. HYMAN, L. H. 1951. Entoprocta. *In* The invertebrates. New York McGraw-Hill Book Co., Inc. Vol. 3, pp. 521–554, figs. 209–223.

PHYLUM ASCHELMINTHES

This phylum includes several groups of animals that are mostly of small to microscopic size and slender in form. The digestive tract is complete and usually straight, the anus posterior, and the space inside the body is a pseudocoel. Except for the rotifers, none has anterior cilia.

CLASS ROTIFERA. ROTIFERS, OR "WHEEL ANIMALCULES"

18-9. The rotifers are minute to microscopic (under 1 mm. long), attractive in form and color, active in movements, and favorites of amateur microscopists. They abound in fresh-water lakes, ponds, and quiet streams, in muddy wayside ditches and eaves troughs, in street gutters and barnyard puddles, and occur even in the leaf axils of mosses. Most of the 1,300 species are free-living, but some are fixed in protective tubes, a few are external or internal parasites, and a few inhabit salt water. The class and common names refer to the beating cilia on the anterior end of the body, which suggest the rotation of microscopic wheels. This ciliated area, the absence of external cilia elsewhere, and movements of the chewing pharynx in life distinguish rotifers from all other minute aquatic animals.

18-10. Characteristics. (1) Symmetry bilateral, no true segmentation, 3 germ layers; (2) body somewhat cylindrical, with ciliated disc anteriorly and forked "foot" posteriorly; (3) body wall a syncytium covered with hardened cuticle (lorica); body cavity without special lining; (4) digestive tract complete or incomplete; (5) 2 nephridia, coiled and branched, with flame cells; (6) a dorsal nerve ganglion and various nerves (no cord), sense organs tuftlike or as eyespots; (7) sexes separate; males usually minute and degenerate or none; female with ovary, yolk gland, and oviduct; reproduction both parthenogenetic and sexual; usually oviparous; no larva.

The ROTIFERA resemble the PLATYHELMINTHES in having excretory organs with flame cells (protonephridia) and the NEMATODA in being composed of relatively few cells and having a body cavity without special lining. Some adult rotifers resemble a trochophore larva and may be somewhat like the ancestors of certain other invertebrates. As a group, the rotifers display an amazing variety in structure, suggesting that they have had a long geologic history. Unfortunately, they are unknown as fossils, probably because of their minute size.

18-11. Structure and function. The typical rotifer (Fig. 18-4) is elongate, with an anterior *head* region, an expanded *trunk,* and a narrow tail-like posterior *foot,* usually movable and often ending in two slender *toes.* Each toe contains a *cement gland* providing a sticky secretion by which the animal may attach temporarily to some object. The *body wall* is a thin syncytium with nuclei, covered by a thin glassy chitin-like cuticle (lorica). On the anterior end is a retractile disc, or *corona* (often double), rimmed with cilia. These cilia beat with a whirling motion that draws water containing oxygen and food toward the head end, carries off wastes, and serves for locomotion. The digestive tract

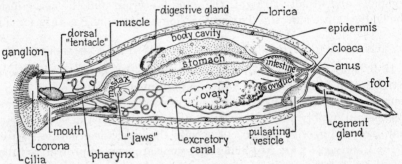

Fig. 18-4. Phylum Aschelminthes, Class Rotifera. General structure of a female rotifer, in section from the left side; much enlarged. (*After Delage and Herouard.*)

is lined by cilia, save in the pharynx, and includes (1) the *mouth* below the corona; (2) a rounded muscular pharynx, or *mastax,* that has a "dental mill" of chitin-like *jaws* with *teeth* used to grasp, cut, and grind the food; (3) a short *esophagus;* (4) a sizable *stomach,* of large cells and with a pair of digestive glands; (5) a short *intestine;* (6) the oval *cloaca;* and (7) the *anus,* which is dorsal at the end of the trunk. Some species lack digestive organs beyond the stomach. Between the body wall and digestive tract is a fluid-filled *body cavity,* without special lining and hence not a true coelom. Isolated *muscles,* chiefly longitudinal, serve to withdraw the corona and to move or contract the foot. Excretion is accomplished by two slender (proto) *nephridia* connected to an enlarged *pulsating vesicle* that discharges relatively large amounts of water into the cloaca; each nephridium is irregularly coiled and has several lateral branches beginning in flame cells. A large *nerve ganglion* dorsal to the mouth gives off nerves to various organs. There is usually a pair of short sensory tufts ("lateral antennae") on the sides of the body posteriorly; some rotifers have also a tuft (or two) above the brain, as also one to three dorsal eyespots. Ectoderm provides the external covering, the nervous structures, and the lining of the ends of the digestive tract, the mid-gut is of endoderm, and the other structures grow from mesoderm.

The preceding account applies to a typical female, which has also a single *ovary* and *yolk gland* connected to an *oviduct* emptying into the cloaca. The male, in species where known, is much smaller than the female, and its body cavity contains one large *testis;* this opens by a duct, either in a *penis* that can be protruded dorsally, or in the foot.

In various rotifers (Fig. 18-5) the body is slender (*R. neptunius*), broad (*Polychaetus*), saclike (*Asplanchna*), flattened (*Ascomorpha*), or even spherical (*Trochosphaera*). The lorica may bear ridges, rings, or spines.

FIG. 18-5. Phylum ASCHELMINTHES, Class ROTIFERA. Various rotifers, all enlarged. (*After Jennings*, 1901.)

The foot may be long, short, or absent; it serves for attachment and as a rudder in swimming, also as an organ for leaping in some. The corona may have one or two concentric wreaths of cilia; the jaws and teeth are of varied form. Many of these differences are used in classification.

18-12. Natural history. Rotifers are cosmopolitan, and the same species may occur in America, Eurasia, and Australia, wherever conditions are appropriate. Two lakes of like physical and biological characteristics but hundreds of miles apart may contain similar assemblages of rotifers; conversely, two others unlike but close together can have quite different kinds. The rotifer fauna of any body of water undergoes some change as to the constituent species during any one summer season.

The great majority are free-living and solitary. They are commonest in quiet fresh waters with much aquatic vegetation. Some species swim in open water, but more live about or on fresh-water plants, where some creep over the vegetation.   Several species live attached, each in a self-constructed protective case either of its own secretions or of foreign particles; thus, *Collotheca* (*Floscularia*) inhabits a transparent tube, and *Floscularia* (*Melicerta*) constructs a tube of microscopic "spherical bricks."   Certain species are colonial, some free-swimming, and others fixed.   The Bdelloidea can creep like leeches but also can swim. *Seison nebaliae* lives as a commensal on a crustacean (*Nebalia*), *Pleurotrocha parasitica* is an external parasite and *Alberta naidus* an internal parasite of fresh-water annelids, *Hertwigia* lives within colonies of the protozoan *Volvox*, and *Proales wernecki* forms microscopic galls in *Vaucheria*, an alga.

Rotifers that feed on unicellular algae have short broad teeth; those subsisting on the juices of larger plants have pointed teeth to pierce the plant cells and a muscular pharynx that acts like a piston to suck out the juices; and those of predatory habit have slender jaws armed with teeth that can be projected through the mouth to grasp the protozoans, rotifers, and other animals used as food.   Rotifers aid in keeping the water clean by feeding on bits of organic debris as well as on other organisms.   In turn, various rotifers serve as food for small worms and crustaceans and are an important part of the "food chain" in the fresh waters.

18-13. Reproduction (Figs. 18-6, 18-7).   The females, at different seasons, usually produce two kinds of eggs, "summer" and "winter." The first are thin-shelled, develop at once by parthenogenesis, and yield only females; in favorable waters a series of such generations may occur.

ADULTS   EGGS

female   male   "female"   "male"   "winter"

Fig. 18-6.   Stages in the life cycle of a rotifer, *Hydatina senta;* all enlarged.   (*After Whitney,* 1916.)

|←——— Sexual phase ———→|←——————— Parthenogenetic phases ———————→|

rest period ——→FEMALES ——→eggs ——→FEMALES——→eggs——→FEMALES
                                    (many generations)

winter eggs   *change in*
(zygotes)   *conditions*

                        small
          sperm◄——MALES◄————— male-producing◄——FEMALES
fertilization   eggs

                        large
          eggs◄——FEMALES◄————— female-producing◄—— FEMALES
                        eggs

Fig. 18-7.   Diagram of the life cycle of a rotifer, *Hydatina senta.*

Then, with some change in environmental conditions not clearly understood, a generation is produced in which some females lay small eggs yielding only males and others lay larger eggs yielding only females, both by parthenogenesis. The males then produce sperm, fertilize the females internally, and the latter lay eggs. These "winter eggs" (zygotes) have thick and resistant shells, like protozoan cysts. They require a rest period and may remain dormant for long periods, can survive drought or freezing, and may be blown about by winds or be carried on the feet or feathers of birds. Later, in favorable waters, they develop into females that resume the "summer" phase. Such means for surviving adverse conditions and for dispersal explain the universal distribution of rotifers.

Classification. Class *ROTIFERA* (see Characteristics). Order 1. **Monogonata.** Two lateral antennae on body; toes 0 to 2; one ovary; males usually present, but degenerate; includes most species of rotifers. *Proales, Salpina, Hydatina.* Order 2. **Bdelloidea.** No lateral antennae; toes 0 to 4, foot glands numerous; 2 ovaries; males unknow ·. *Habotrocha, Philodina, Rotifer.* Order 3. **Seisonida.** No lateral antennae or toes; 2 ovaries; males fully developed; only 2 species. *Seison,* commensal on crustaceans.

References. Jennings, H. S. 1918. The wheel animalcules (Rotatoria). *In* H. B. Ward and G. C. Whipple. Fresh-water biology. New York, John Wiley & Sons, Inc. Pp. 553–620, figs. 856–962. Wesenberg-Lund, C. 1929. Rotatoria. *In* W. Kükenthal and others, Handbuch der Zoologie. Vol. 2, part 1, section 4, pp. 8–120, figs. 2–131.

Class *GASTROTRICHA*

18-14. This includes about 100 species of microscopic forms (0.01 to 0.54 mm. long) common among the algae and bottom debris of quiet fresh and salt waters. In size and habits they resemble some ciliate proto-

Chaetonotus   Echinoderes

Fig. 18-8.   Phylum Aschelminthes.   *Left.* Class Gastrotricha, *Chaetonotus. Right.* Class Kinorhyncha, *Echinoderes.* Both enlarged. (*After Jennings; and Wolff and Krause.*)

zoans. A typical gastrotrich (*Chaetonotus maximus*) is elongate and flexible, with the posterior end forked and containing a cement gland for temporary attachment (Fig. 18-8). The flat ventral surface has two lengthwise bands of cilia used for locomotion, and on the arched dorsal surface are many slender spines. The mouth is anterior, surrounded by bristles and fine sensory hairs, the pharynx is muscular, the intestine straight, and the anus posterior. Unicellular algae are the chief food.

The body cavity has no special lining.   Six pairs of delicate muscles are present, one pair extending lengthwise of the body.   The two nephridia are coiled but unbranched, beginning with flame cells and opening mid-ventrally on the body.   A saddle-shaped nerve ganglion anteriorly connects to two longitudinal ventral nerves and by fibers to the sensory hairs. In fresh-water species only females are known; the marine forms are her-maphroditic.   The simple ovary fills much of the body cavity; each of the proportionately large eggs is encased in a tough shell bearing hooks that fasten to materials in the water.   There is no larval stage.   The GASTROTRICHA (Gr. *gaster*, belly + *trichos*, hair) are occasionally grouped with the NEMATODA, from which they differ especially in possessing cilia.

Reference.   REMANE, ADOLPH.   1929.   Gastrotricha.   *In* W. Kükenthal and others.   Handbuch der Zoologie.   Vol. 2, part 1, section 4, pp. 121–186, figs. 132–210.

CLASS *KINORHYNCHA* (ECHINODERA)

18-15.   This group consists of about 30 species (Genus *Echinodera* and others) of marine worms up to 5 mm. long, found in the bottom mud and sand of shallow to deep seas.   The body is of 13 (or 14) rings; two of them form the head, which is encircled by spines and has a short retractile proboscis (Fig. 18-8).   The trunk is encased in 11 rings of chitinous cuticle bearing lateral spines.   The mouth is at the proboscis tip, the stomach is expanded, and the anus opens in the terminal, retractile ring.   There are two excretory tubes, each with a flame cell connected to a ciliated duct opening dorsally on ring 9.   The nervous system is in the epidermis, beneath the cuticle, with a dorsal ganglion, connectives around the pharynx, and a midventral cord having a ganglion in each segment.   The sexes are separate, each with a pair of tubular reproductive sacs opening ventrally beside the anus.   *Echinodera* resembles the NEMATODA but differs in having paired excretory organs, which are ciliated internally, and unfused sex organs.

Reference.   REMANE, ADOLPH.   1929.   Kinorhyncha.   *In* W. Kükenthal and others.   Handbuch der Zoologie.   Vol. 2, part 1, section 4, pp. 187–248, figs. 211–266.

CLASS *NEMATOMORPHA* (GORDIACEA).   "HORSEHAIR WORMS"

18-16.   These worms are extremely long and slender, with a uniformly cylindrical body, a bluntly rounded anterior end, and a swollen and coiled posterior end (Fig. 18-9).   Different species are from a few millimeters to over a yard in length.   The exterior surface is opaque and often colored. The body wall consists of (1) a thin cuticle bearing minute papillae; (2) the epidermis, which secretes the cuticle; (3) a single layer of longitudinal muscles, incomplete at the ends of the body; and (4) an epithelium lining the body cavity.   The latter is nearly filled with loose parenchyma.   The digestive tract is complete in young worms and ends posteriorly in a cloaca, but it becomes closed at both ends or degenerate in adults. No circulatory, respiratory, or excretory organs are present. A nerve ring surrounds the esophagus, connecting to a single midventral nerve cord. There are two minute eyes and many sensory bristles. The sexes are separate, each with two gonads in the body cavity. The reproductive ducts are paired, not connected to the gonads, and empty into the cloaca.

The adult worms are often seen wriggling in the water of ponds, quiet streams, rain puddles, or drinking troughs. Their presence in such places, sometimes in numbers, is responsible for an old belief that they are long horsehairs that have "come to life" in water. The females deposit

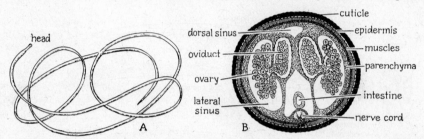

Fig. 18-9.   Phylum Aschelminthes, Class Nematomorpha. The "horsehair worm," *Gordius*. *A.* Entire specimen. *B.* Cross section of female, enlarged. (*After Kükenthal.*)

long strings (to 91 inches!) of minute eggs on aquatic vegetation. From these the small larvae emerge to swim about and bore into aquatic insects, often entering May-fly larvae. Later but while still immature they may enter the body cavity of beetles, crickets, or grasshoppers. After further growth in the second host they escape, probably by drowning of the insect, and soon become sexually mature.

These animals have often been included in the Phylum Nemathelminthes because of their body form, complete digestive tract, presence of a cuticle, simple musculature, and absence of segmentation. The lined body cavity filled with parenchyma, single nerve cord, separate gonads, and reproductive ducts are important differences from the Nematoda, and so they probably form a distinct group.

About 15 species occur in North America. *Paragordius varius* is common, growing to 300 mm.; *Gordius robustus* grows to 890 mm. by 0.5 to 1.0 mm. in diameter; *Nectonema agile* is marine, up to 200 mm. when adult, and its larva is parasitic in crustaceans (*Palemonetes*).

Reference. Rauther, Max. 1929. Nematomorpha. *In* W. Kükenthal and others. Handbuch der Zoologie. Vol. 2, part 1, section 4, pp. 403–448, figs. 427–480.

Phylum ACANTHOCEPHALA.   Spiny-headed Worms

18-17. These are parasites of peculiar structure and function that live as adults in the intestines of vertebrates and as larvae in arthropods.

The distinctive feature for which the group is named (Gr. *acanthos*, spine + *kephale*, head) is the anterior cylindrical **proboscis** that bears rows of recurved spines serving to attach a worm to the gut of its host (Fig. 18-10). The proboscis is contained in a sheath into which it may usually be completely retracted by muscles. The body of most species is elongate, flattened, and rough in life (but rounded and smoother in preserved specimens), and capable of extension and contraction. The body is covered by a thin cuticle secreted by the epidermis beneath, which is a syncytium with large nuclei and penetrated by minute fibers and canals. Beneath the epidermis is a layer of circular muscles, and within these a sheath of longitudinal muscles lining the fluid-filled body cavity. Nei-

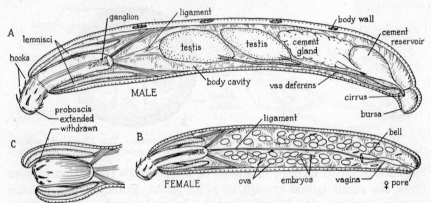

Fig. 18-10. Phylum Acanthocephala. Spiny-headed worm, enlarged and left side of body removed to show internal structure. *A*. Male. *B*. Female. *C*. Anterior end with proboscis withdrawn. (*Adapted from Lynch,* 1936.)

ther the larva nor the adult has a digestive tract, food being absorbed directly from the host's intestine. There are no circulatory or respiratory structures. Two branched nephridia with cilia are connected to a common posterior excretory duct. A nerve ganglion in the proboscis sheath sends nerves to the proboscis and posteriorly.

The sexes are separate. The male contains a pair of testes developed in a cordlike ligament extending from the proboscis sheath to the posterior end, and the sperm pass out a duct, through the posterior bell-like bursa containing the genital pore. The female has no persistent ovary. Ova develop on the ligament, are set free in the body cavity and fertilized there, then surrounded usually by three membranes. They are generally advanced in development before escaping into the host's intestine to pass out with the feces. When eggs are eaten by the intermediate host, the larvae develop in the latter. Completion of the life cycle requires that the larval host in turn be eaten by the host of the adult worm.

The 300 or more species of acanthocephs are 6 to 650 mm. in length and parasitize different vertebrates from fishes to mammals. Larvae of those in terrestrial hosts usually develop in insects, and those of aquatic vertebrates in crustaceans. *Macracanthorhynchus hirudinaceus* is common in pigs and occasional in man; the male worm is 50 to 100 by 3 to 5 mm. and the female 100 to 650 by 4 to 10 mm. Its intermediate host is the "white grub," or larva of the June beetle, which pigs often eat when in pastures.

The ACANTHOCEPHALA differ from NEMATODA in the presence of a proboscis, absence of a digestive tract, presence of circular muscles, presence of ciliated excretory organs, and peculiarities of the reproductive organs. Since they show no closer relationships to other animals, they are probably best considered as a separate phylum.

References. RAUTHER, MAX. 1929. Acanthocephala. *In* W. Kükenthal and others, Handbuch der Zoologie. Vol. 2, part 1, section 4, pp. 449–482, figs. 481–523. MEYER, A. 1933. Acanthocephala. *In* Bronn, Klassen und Ordnungen der Tierreichs. Vol. 4, part 2, book 2, section 2, pp. 333–582, illus.

PHYLUM **BRYOZOA.** MOSS ANIMALS

18-18. Many of the BRYOZOA (Gr. *bryon*, moss + *zoon*, animal) are tufted or branched colonies, a few millimeters high, and attached to

FIG. 18-11. Phylum BRYOZOA. Fresh-water bryozoans. *Plumatella*. *A*. Colony, natural size, on a twig. *B*. Part of colony much enlarged, showing both expanded and contracted individuals. *C*. Statoblast. *D Cristatella*, entire colony is free-moving. (*After Allman*, 1856.)

objects in shallow sea water. Some resemble colonial hydroids and corals in appearance, but their internal structure is much more advanced. Their form suggested the names "moss animals" or "zoophytes" (plant-like animals), and the numbers of microscopic individuals in a colony suggested the name POLYZOA (Gr. *poly*, many). They are often included among the "seaweeds" pressed and dried by amateurs at the seashore. Some bryozoans are matlike, and others form thin incrustations on rocks, shells, or kelp. All members of the phylum are aquatic, and most of them are marine, but one order is restricted to fresh waters (Fig. 18-11).

Bryozoans are known from Lower Ordovician time to the present; more than 2,000 species are Paleozoic, 1,500 are Mesozoic, and about 2,500 are living. Their exoskeletons have aided in forming lime-bearing rocks of many strata. Many of the species had a short geologic (time) range but wide geographic distribution; they are thus useful in correlating geologic strata. For this purpose they are of economic importance in studying the cores brought up in drilling test wells for petroleum.

18-19. Characteristics. (1) Symmetry bilateral, no segmentation, 3 germ layers; (2) colonial, individuals minute, each in separate housing (zooecium); (3) digestive tract complete, U-shaped; mouth surrounded by a retractile lophophore bearing tentacles; anus opens outside lophophore; (4) coelom well-developed, lined with peritoneum; no circulatory or respiratory organs; (5) no nephridia; (6) a nerve ganglion between mouth and anus; (7) usually monoecious with gonads developed from peritoneum; eggs fertilized in coelom and developed in a modified portion, or ooecium, serving as a brood pouch; larva a trochophore; colonies formed by asexual budding, also by statoblasts in fresh-water species.

The lophophore and tentacles of bryozoans suggest relationships with the brachiopods, as mentioned in discussion of that group. The trochophore larva suggests ancient origin from some "worm" stock. Four of the five bryozoan orders appear in Ordovician rocks and were probably evolving in Cambrian time but then had no calcified structures and consequently left no fossil record.

18-20. Structure and natural history. *Bugula* is a common bryozoan that grows as branched brown or purple tufts, 2 or 3 inches long, attached to objects in shallow sea water (Fig. 18-12). Each "stem" includes numerous individuals less than 1 mm. long, closely united in four longitudinal rows. An individual, or *zooid,* consists of a tubular chitinous housing, or *zooecium,* with the soft living parts, or *polypide,* inside. On the exterior of most zooids is an *avicularium* (modified zooid?) shaped like a bird's head, with jaws that open and snap shut to keep minute animals from settling on the surface. The anterior end, or *introvert,* of the living polypide is a rounded ridge, or *lophophore,* that bears a circle of slender, flexible, and ciliated *tentacles* around the mouth; it is attached to an opening in the zooecium by a flexible chitinous collar. The tentacles sweep microscopic food organisms toward the mouth and also aid in respiration. The introvert may be completely withdrawn, like the tip of a glove finger, by *retractor muscles.*

The *digestive tract* is complete, with a ciliated lining, and includes the *mouth* between the tentacles, a wide *pharynx,* a slender *esophagus,* an elongate *stomach* of U or V shape, and a slender *intestine* leading to the *anus,* which opens close outside the lophophore. The dorsal region is reduced so that the mouth and anus are close together.   A retractor muscle (*funiculus*) draws the stomach aborally.   There are no circulatory, respiratory, or excretory organs.   The body cavity is a true *coelom,* lined by thin peritoneum and filled with fluid containing corpuscles.   Some bryozoans have a *nerve ganglion* just below the lophophore, with fibers to the tentacles and elsewhere.   Ectoderm forms the epidermis of the body wall and secretes the zooecium, endoderm lines the digestive tract, and mesoderm provides the coelomic lining and muscles.

Bugula is monoecious; both ovaries and spermaries develop from the coelomic lining, the eggs in a portion of the coelom closed off as a brood

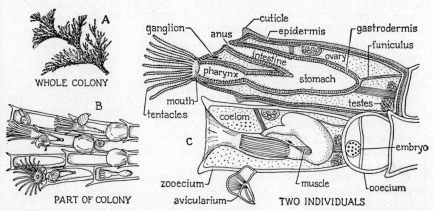

WHOLE COLONY

PART OF COLONY   avicularium   TWO INDIVIDUALS

Fig. 18-12.   Phylum Bryozoa.   Structure of *Bugula*.   *A*. Whole colony, natural size. *B*. Part of colony, enlarged.   *C*. Two individuals in longitudinal section, the upper expanded and the lower contracted.

pouch, or *ooecium.*   Each egg becomes a ciliated trochophore larva which is liberated in the sea, soon to settle, apical end downward, and found a new colony by asexual budding.

18-21. Other bryozoans.   The largest zooids are not over 3 mm. long by 1 mm. in diameter, and many are minute.   In different species the zooecium is tubular, conical, or urnlike and is usually calcareous or chitinous.   The fresh-water forms (Phylactolaemata) produce gelatinous housings bearing zooids on the surface, and they have a special mode of asexual reproduction to survive unfavorable conditions.   Internal buds called *statoblasts* form in the funiculus and are enclosed in a chitinous shell.   Upon the death and decay of the parent colony these are set free in the water either to float or to sink; they can survive freezing or drought and later produce new colonies.   Fresh-water bryozoans may grow in water pipes, occasionally in such quantity as to obstruct the flow.

Classification. Phylum **BRYOZOA** (Polyzoa or Ectoprocta). Mouth within and anus outside lophophore; coelom well-developed; lophophore retractile; no nephridia; colonies bushy, incrusting, or gelatinous. All aquatic, mostly marine, chiefly in shallow waters, but some down to 18,000 feet; others in fresh waters. Lower Ordovician to Recent.

Class 1. *PHYLACTOLAEMATA.* Lophophore horseshoe-shaped; a lip (epistome) overhanging mouth; overwintering egg a statoblast with chitinous shell; exclusively in fresh water. *Plumatella princeps,* zooecium calcareous, colony much branched, erect or creeping; *Pectinatella,* zooecia a gelatinous mass with zooids exposed on surface; *Cristatella mucedo,* forming an elongate creeping gelatinous mass to 10 inches long, in ponds.

Class 2. *GYMNOLAEMATA.* Lophophore circular; no epistome; predominantly marine; includes most fossil and living forms.

Order 1. **Ctenostomata.** Zooecium chitinous or gelatinous, with toothlike processes to close aperture; Ordovician to Recent. *Alcyonidium, Serialaria,* marine; *Paludicella,* fresh water. Order 2. **Cyclostoma.** Zooecium calcareous and tubular, no operculum; embryos in enlarged ovicells; Ordovician to Recent. *Crisia, Idmonea, Tubulipora.* Order 3. †**Treptostomata.** Zooecium calcareous, of 2 parts; some colonies to 2 feet in diameter; Ordovician to Permian. †*Amplexopora;* †*Hallopora.* Order 4. †**Cryptostomata.** Zooecium short, aperture hidden in a vestibule; Ordovician to Permian. †*Fenestella.* Order 5. **Cheilostomata.** Zooecium chitinous or calcareous, shape various; aperture usually anterior, with "lid" (operculum); ooecium present; Jurassic to Recent. *Bugula, Menipea,* colonies tufted; *Membranipora,* colonies incrusting on kelp.

References. BASSLER, R. S. 1922. The Bryozoa, or moss animals. *Smithsonian Institution Annual Report for* 1920, pp. 339–380, illus. TWENHOFEL, WILLIAM H., and ROBERT R. SHROCK. 1935. Invertebrate paleontology. New York, McGraw-Hill Book Co., Inc. Pp. 220–249, illus. HARMER, S. F. 1910. Polyzoa. *In* Cambridge natural history. London, Macmillan & Co., Ltd. Vol. 2, pp. 465–533, figs. 232–257.

PHYLUM BRACHIOPODA. LAMP SHELLS

18-22. The brachiopods bear a superficial resemblance to bivalve mollusks in having an external shell of two valves, but these are dorsal and ventral, rather than lateral as in the mollusks. Brachiopods have inhabited the sea bottom since animal life was first common in Cambrian time. Their shells are widespread and abundant fossils in rock strata of marine origin and are useful for correlating such deposits. Some 456 genera are known from Paleozoic rocks and 177 in the Mesozoic; the 70 genera and 225 living species are but a remnant of those now extinct. The living genus *Lingula* is much as it was in Ordovician time—over 400,000,000 years ago—possibly the oldest living genus of animals. All living brachiopods are marine, solitary, and usually attached to the bottom. Most of them are in shallow waters, but a few occur deeper, even down to 18,000 feet. The name of the phylum (L. *brachio,* arm + Gr. *pod,* foot) refers to the lophophore within the shell, and the term "lamp shell" applies to the resemblance of a valve of the concave shell to an old Roman oil lamp.

18-23. Characteristics. (1) Symmetry bilateral, no segmentation, 3 germ layers; (2) shell external, dorsal and ventral valves unlike, with a fleshy peduncle for attachment; (3) mouth preceded by tentacles on a fleshy lophophore; digestive tract with or without anus; (4) coelom well-developed; a small heart; (5) excretion by one or two pairs of nephridia, serving also as reproductive ducts; (6) a nerve ring about gullet; (7) sexes separate, each with paired gonads; eggs and sperm discharged into sea water; a free-swimming ciliated larva; no asexual reproduction.

The larvae of BRYOZOA and BRACHIOPODA may be considered as modified trochophores; the form of the lophophore and its dorsal lip in larval brachiopods resemble comparable structures in the phoronids and bryozoans. These groups are often assembled as classes of a Phylum MOLLUSCOIDEA, but they differ enough to be placed as distinct phyla.

18-24. Structure and natural history (*Magellania*). The soft parts are contained between two stout scoop-shaped calcareous shells, or **valves,**

FIG. 18-13.   Phylum BRACHIOPODA.   *A, B.* Typical positions of living lamp shells in life. *C. Magellania*, internal structure from left side; shells cut to midline, mantle and lophophore of left side removed.   (*A, B, after Twenhofel and Shrock, Invertebrate paleontology.*)

which are covered externally with organic periostracum (Fig. 18-13). The larger ventral valve has a posterior projecting **beak** perforated for passage of the fleshy stalk, or **peduncle,** by which the animal attaches permanently to the sea bottom. Within the dorsal valve is suspended a delicate calcareous **shelly loop** to support the lophophore. The actual **body** occupies only the posterior part of the space between the shells. The **body wall** consists of an external epidermis, stout connective tissue, and a ciliated coelomic lining. Two double folds of this wall extend anteriorly as the **dorsal** and **ventral mantle lobes,** which line the interior surface of the respective shells and have fine papillae penetrating the shell substance. A large W-shaped **lophophore** attaches to the anterior surface of the body and lies in the space between the mantle lobes; it is fringed with long ciliated **tentacles** that circulate water in the mantle cavity for respiration and whip small food organisms into a groove leading to the *mouth*. The latter opens from the base of the lophophore into a short *gullet,* followed by the larger *stomach* (with paired *digestive glands*) and a blind *intestine*. Three pairs of *muscles* serve to close and open the valves, and two other pairs attaching to the peduncle and shell permit the animal to turn about. The large fluid-filled *coelom* contains the internal organs, which are supported on mesenteries; branches of it extend into the mantle lobes and lophophore. A small contractile *"heart"* and blood vessels are present. At each side of the intestine is a large *nephridium* for excretion, with a fringed nephrostome opening from the coelom and a small exit into the mantle cavity. A *nerve ring* surrounds the gullet, with nerves to various organs, but special sense organs are absent. The sexes are separate; in each are two *gonads,* dorsal and ventral, respectively, and the nephridia serve as reproductive ducts, discharging eggs and sperm to the exterior. The fertilized egg grows into a free-swimming larva of somewhat peculiar character, which later attaches by a structure that becomes the peduncle.

Classification. Phylum **BRACHIOPODA** (see Characteristics).

Class 1. *INARTICULATA.* Two valves nearly alike, of chitinoid material containing calcareous spicules; no hinge, beak, or shelly loop; anus present. Order 1. †**Palaeotremata.** Lower Cambrian to Ordovician. Order 2. **Atremata.** Cambrian to Recent. *Lingula,* Pacific and Indian oceans, and *Glottidia,* both coasts of America, live between the tide lines and burrow in mud with long contractile peduncle. Order 3. **Neotremata.** Cambrian to Recent. *Crania,* ventral valve flat, fastened to rock, dorsal valve conical.

Class 2. *ARTICULATA.* Dorsal and ventral valves unlike, densely formed of oblique calcareous prisms; with hinge, and usually with beak for peduncle and shelly loop for lophophore; no anus. Order 1. **Prototremata.** Cambrian to Recent. *Rafinesquina.* Order 2. **Telotremata.** Ordovician to Recent; includes many fossil and most living forms. *Rhynchotremata, Terebratulina, Magellania.*

References. HELMCKE, J. G. 1939. Brachiopoda. *In.* W. Kükenthal and others, Handbuch der Zoologie. Vol. 3, part 2, section 5, pp. 139–158, figs. 152–271. TWENHOFEL, WILLIAM H., and ROBERT R. SHROCK. 1935. Invertebrate paleontology. New York, McGraw-Hill Book Co., Inc. Pp. 250–300, figs. 89–109.

Phylum **PHORONIDEA**

18-25. The phoronids are slender wormlike sedentary creatures of various sizes that inhabit the bottom under shallow seas. Some are scattered singly, and others are so densely placed as to fairly cover the sand for nearly an acre. Each is separately housed in a self-secreted tube of leathery, membraneous, or limy, texture from which its tentacles are extended to feed (Fig. 18-14). Some of the 15 or more species are less than 1 mm. long, but *Phoronopsis californica* grows to 12 or 15 inches, and its tube may be 18 inches long.

FIG. 18-14.   Phylum PHORONIDEA.   *Phoronis.   A.* Group of individuals as in life, in bottom sand or mud under shallow water, each in a self-excavated tube.   *B.* Internal structure, enlarged and partly diagrammatic; left side of lophophore and body wall removed; only part of left lateral mesentery shown.   (*After Benham,* 1889.)

18-26. Characteristics. (1) Symmetry bilateral, 3 germ layers, no segmentation; (2) body cylindrical, crowned by a double spiral of horseshoe shape (lophophore) bearing 60 to 300 hollow ciliated tentacles in 2 rows which are fused at their bases; (3) body wall of cuticle, epidermis, circular muscles (layer) and longitudinal muscles (bundles); (4) digestive tract U-shaped, mouth inside and anus outside lophophore, lining ciliated except in terminal part; (5) coelom throughout body and into tentacles, divided into compartments by transverse septum at base of lophophore and by 3 lengthwise mesenteries between body wall and gut; (6) circulatory system of 2 lengthwise trunks with lateral branches in body and vessels into bases of tentacles, blood with corpuscles containing hemoglobin; (7) no respiratory organs; (8) two ciliated nephridia opening near anus; (9) nervous tissue below epidermis, a ring surrounding mouth and fibers to parts of body; (10) monoecious, gonads (testis, ovary) develop beside blood vessels, gametes released through nephridia; (11) larva (actinotrocha) somewhat like a trochophore.

The systematic position of the phoronids has never been settled.   Once grouped with the GEPHYREA (sipunculids, etc.) they were later aligned with the bryozoans and brachiopods.   A resemblance also is indicated to *Cephalanthus* in the hemichordates, particularly because of the coelomic spaces.

18-27. Natural history. Phoronids feed by extending the mucus-coated tentacles to lay on the bottom and take minute organisms from the water or in the surface debris.   When uncovered by the receding tide or when disturbed, they withdraw to the shelter of their tubes.   The lophophore, if torn off, can be regenerated.   The bodies and tentacles of different species are red, orange, or green, and when numerous may give brilliant color to the sea floor.   At Naples colonies of *P. kowalevskii* form a network of their intertwined tubes 2 or 3 inches thick on submerged piling.

References. BENHAM, W. B.   1889.   The anatomy of *Phoronis australis.   Quarterly Journal of Microscopical Science,* n.s., vol. 30, pp. 125–158, pls. 10–13.   CORI, C. J.   1937.   Phoronidea.   *In* W. Kükenthal and others, Handbuch der Zoologie. Vol. 3, part 2, section 5, pp. 5–138, figs. 82–151.

PHYLUM CHAETOGNATHA. ARROW WORMS

18-28. These are little torpedo-shaped marine animals, from 20 to 70 mm. long, of which six genera and about 30 species are known. Some species are so abundant as to be important constituents of the ocean plankton. Many live at depths no greater than 100 feet and approach the surface at dusk and dawn when the light intensity is low. They feed actively on unicellular plants and animals, crustacean larvae, and other small marine life, darting about like arrows—hence the common name arrow worms and that of the principal genus, *Sagitta* (L., arrow); being transparent, they are also called glassworms. The phylum name refers to characteristic bristles about the mouth (Gr. *chaeton*, bristle + *gnathos*, jaw).

18-29. Characteristics. (1) Symmetry bilateral, 3 germ layers, no segmentation; (2) body elongate, with lateral fins; (3) digestive tract complete, anus ventral; (4) coelom well-developed as 3 pairs of cavities; (5) no circulatory, respiratory, or excretory organs; (6) nervous system with dorsal and ventral ganglia and sensory organs; (7) monoecious, development direct.

The chaetognaths show no obvious relation to other animals. They are not segmented, lack cilia on the epidermis and digestive tract, and the tail is post-anal as in no other phylum except the chordates. Their embryonic development has some resemblance to that of many annelids and some chordates.

18-30. Structure and natural history. The body is cylindrical, with *head, trunk,* and *tail* regions (Fig. 18-15). Two pairs of *lateral fins* are

FIG. 18-15. Phylum CHAETOGNATHA. Arrow worm, *Sagitta*, ventral view; natural size 20 to 70 mm.

located at the middle and end of the trunk, and a *caudal fin* across the tail. The *mouth* is a ventral slit on the broadened head, followed by the muscular *pharynx,* slender straight *intestine,* and *anus* at the end of the trunk. On either side of the mouth is a lobe bearing several sickle-shaped hooks, or *bristles,* of chitin; these are worked by muscles to serve as jaws in the capture of food, which is swallowed entire. The spacious *coelom* consists of three pairs of cavities separated by median *mesenteries* above and below the intestine and between the head, trunk, and tail. The *body wall* is made up of an *epidermis* with several layers of cells over a basement membrane, a thin layer of striated *muscles,* and the single-layered *coelomic lining.* Four lengthwise bands of muscles, two dorsolateral and two ventrolateral, provide for locomotion. The *intestinal wall* is of two cell layers, digestive epithelium internally and coelomic lining outside. The *nervous system* is of ectodermal origin and includes a pair of cerebral ganglia dorsal to the pharynx, a pair of connectives around the latter, and a ventral ganglion midway of the trunk, with nerves radiating to various parts. Dorsally on the head are two *eyes,* each with three lenses, and between the eyes a longitudinal *olfactory organ,* all with nerves to the cerebral ganglia. Small *tactile papillae* with stiff bristles occur over the body.

18-31. Reproduction. Chaetognaths are monoecious, and the sex cells are derived from the coelomic epithelium. In each trunk coelom is an elongate solid *ovary,* with a slender *oviduct* opening laterally at the end of the trunk. Each caudal coelom contains a narrow solid *testis* from which immature cells are released to mature as free sperm in the coelom, then collected by the ciliated funnel of a *sperm duct* opening laterally on the tail. Reproduction occurs through much or all of the year and fertilization is internal. A typical gastrula is formed, with the coelom produced as lateral outgrowths of the archenteron. The young at hatching resembles an adult.

Reference. MICHAEL, E. L. 1911. Classification and vertical distribution of the Chaetognatha of the San Diego region. . . . *University of California Publications in Zoology,* vol. 8, pp. 21–186, 8 pls.

PHYLUM SIPUNCULOIDEA

18-32. Searchers at the seashore commonly find small unsegmented worms, yellowish or grayish in color, living shallowly in the sand or mud or

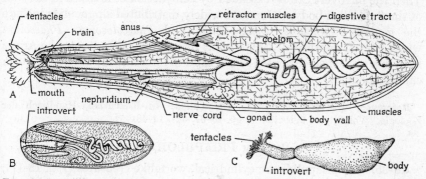

FIG. 18-16. Phylum SIPUNCULOIDEA. *Sipunculus.* *A.* Internal structure. *B.* Introvert retracted into body. *C.* External appearance, introvert and tentacles extended.

sheltering in empty shells about rocks. When disturbed the animals retract the anterior fringed end to assume the shape of a short club or even of a peanut kernel (Fig. 18-16). These are sipunculids, sometimes called peanut worms. About 250 species are known, a few being slender, even threadlike, but many are chunkier; the larger forms are 10 to 18 inches long.

18-33. Characteristics. (1) Symmetry bilateral, 3 germ layers, no somites; (2) body usually bluntly cylindrical posteriorly, with narrow anterior retractile portion (introvert) bearing fine chitinous papillae and ending in a circle of short, hollow fringelike ciliated tentacles; (3) body wall includes a slightly roughened cuticle, epidermis, dermis with glands and sense organs, and 3 layers of muscle: circular, oblique, and longitudinal (the layers of lattice-like pattern interiorly); (4) mouth centered in tentacles, digestive tract slender, extending to posterior end and spiraled back on itself, anus dorsal near base of introvert; (5) coelom large, undivided but traversed by many strands of connective tissue and muscle attaching to gut; peritoneum ciliated, coelomic fluid with several kinds of corpuscles; (6) circulatory system of dorsal and ventral vessels with ring sinus below tentacles; (7) nephridia (brown tubes) 2 or 1, opening near anus; (8) nervous system of dorsal bilobed ganglion near tentacles with connectives to single ventral unsegmented nerve cord through body, and many lateral nerves; (9) sexes separate but alike, no permanent gonads, sex cells develop in tissues on retractor muscles of introvert, and gametes escape through nephridia; (10) larva usually a trochophore (no trace of somites).

18-34. Natural history. Some sipunculids make burrows in mud or sand that are lined with mucus but not so distinct as the homes of other types of tube-dwelling worms.   When feeding the tentacles are extended on the sea bottom and the beating cilia entrap microorganisms in mucus which is swallowed along with much mud or sand.   Some sipunculids ingest sand as they burrow, then digest the adhering microorganisms. When a worm is disturbed, the introvert is drawn entirely into the anterior part of the body by retractor muscles but the tentacles are not inverted. Then the introvert can be extended by contraction of muscles in the wall of the fluid-filled body.   Common widely distributed sipunculids include the genera *Sipunculus*, *Dendrostoma*, and *Phascolosoma*. *Phascolion* which lives at depths to 1,000 fathoms from the West Indies to the Arctic lives in a snail shell cemented full of sand to form a tube, which the worm carries about.

Reference. BALTZER, F. 1931. Sipunculida. *In* Kükenthal, Handbuch der Zoologie.   Vol. 2, part 2, section 9, pp. 15–61, figs. 15–48.

PHYLUM **PRIAPULOIDEA**

18-35. The priapulids are cylindrical, wormlike creatures (Fig. 18-17), yellow or brown, and up to 80 mm. long, that inhabit mud or sand under shallow waters from Boston and the Belgian coast northward and from Patagonia south to Antarctica.   They live in crevices of rocks or between sessile animals or in empty mollusk shells but can burrow to leave piles of castings on the bottom.   Their food is of marine algae and bottom detritus.

18-36. Characteristics. (1) Symmetry bilateral, 3 germ layers, no segmentation; (2) body cylindrical and fleshy, comprising an anterior retractile proboscis with lengthwise rows of spines and papillae, a trunk with superficial rings and folds, and usually 1 or 2 posterior processes with soft hollow gill-like outgrowths; (3) body wall soft, of cuticle, epidermis, circular and longitudinal muscles; (4) digestive tract straight, with muscular pharynx, thin-walled intestine, and cylindrical rectum; (5) coelom throughout body, large and undivided, connecting to caudal outgrowths; (6) two excretory organs (protonephridia) connecting to sex ducts; (7) nervous system subepithelial, with ring around mouth (no dorsal ganglion) and ventral nerve cord lacking ganglia; (8) sexes separate, 1 pair of gonads; (9) a larval stage.

Priapulids (*Priapulus, Halicryptus*) formerly were grouped with sipunculids and echiurids in the *Phylum* ANNELIDA despite their lack of setae, segmentation, and ganglia in the nervous system; but their characteristics indicate no immediate relationships to any of the living phyla.

Fig. 18-17. Phylum PRIA-PULOIDEA. *Priapulus,* external form. × 1½. (*From Wolcott, Animal biology.*)

Reference. BALTZER, F. 1931. Priapulida. *In* Kükenthal, Handbuch der Zoologie. Vol. 2, part 2, section 9, pp. 1–14, 14 figs.

Phylum ECHIUROIDEA

18-37. The echiurids comprise about 60 species of peculiar worms, of gray, reddish, or yellowish color, that inhabit the mud or sand between rocks under shallow coastal waters of all warm and temperate seas (Fig.

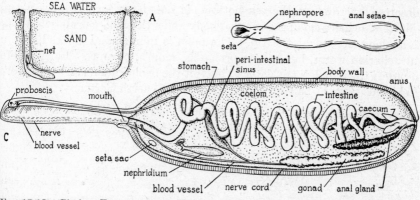

FIG. 18-18. Phylum ECHIUROIDEA. *Urechis caupo.* A. The echiurid worm in its burrow with mucous net spread for food capture. B. Ventral view, proboscis partly retracted. (*Both after Fisher and Macginitie, 1928.*) C. Internal structure with left side of proboscis and body wall removed.

18-18).   The commoner forms dig and live in widely U-shaped burrows in the bottom and have a narrow troughlike proboscis used in feeding.   A few species dwell in empty shells.   *Urechis caupo* of California grows to 450 mm. long, but others are smaller, down to 25 mm. or less.

18-38. Characteristics.   (1) Symmetry bilateral, 3 germ layers, no segmentation in adult (but 15 vestigial somites in larva); (2) body commonly sausage-shaped, soft, with anterior proboscis either spatulate or threadlike and long, that is flexible and contractile but cannot be withdrawn into body; (3) body wall thick, fleshy, epidermis with rings of fine papillae; (4) one pair of ventral anterior setae, some (*Echiurus*) also with 1 or 2 rings of setae around anus; (5) digestive tract complete, mouth at base of proboscis, pharynx muscular, intestine long and much coiled, rectum with 2 long vesicles, anus posterior and terminal; (6) circulatory system of dorsal and ventral vessels joined anteriorly, but no lateral vessels; (7) coelom large, undivided, crossed by many muscle strands supporting intestine; (8) nephridia 1 to 3 pairs anteriorly or 1 large, all serve as gonoducts; (9) a midventral nerve cord in body with paired lateral nerves and a nerve trunk around edge of proboscis but no anterior or body ganglia and no sense organs; (10) sexes separate, dimorphic in some, gonad single, median and posterior; (11) larva a trochophore.

18-39. Natural history.   The widely distributed *Echiurus* inhabits a burrow and feeds by extending the mucus-covered proboscis above the mud to trap plankton or debris.   If disturbed the proboscis is cast off and then regenerated.   *Urechis caupo* lives permanently in a tunnel dug by use of its setae and flushed with water expelled from the rectum.   To feed, a band of epidermal cells behind the setae secrete a mucous cylinder (with pores only 0.004 μ in size) attaching to the burrow walls and fore part of the body.   Then peristaltic contractions in the body wall draw water through the burrow.   Microorganisms are sieved by the mucous net which later is swallowed.   As commensals, a goby, a polychaete worm, and a small crab live also in the burrow.   *Bonellia*, which uses deserted burrows on the sea bottom, is noted for sexual dimorphism. The female has a small green ovoid body and a threadlike proboscis, up to 1 m. long, forked at the tip.   The male is minute and ciliated, like a turbellarian worm, but has no proboscis, mouth, or anus.   Early in life it enters the female's gut, later to inhabit the nephridium as a "parasite." Echiurids serve as bait for cod in Belgium and north Germany.

Reference.   BALTZER, F. 1931. Echiurida. *In* Kükenthal, Handbuch der Zoologie.   Vol. 2, part 2, section 9, pp. 63–168, figs. 49–132.

CHAPTER 19

PHYLUM ECHINODERMATA. ECHINODERMS

The ECHINODERMATA (Gr. *echinos*, hedgehog + *derma*, skin) include the starfishes, or sea stars (Class ASTEROIDEA), brittle stars (OPHIUROIDEA), sea urchins and sand dollars (ECHINOIDEA), sea lilies (CRINOIDEA), and sea cucumbers (HOLOTHURIOIDEA), besides several extinct classes (Fig. 19-1). All are radially symmetrical, and most of them have a limy endoskeleton with external spines. They live on the seashore

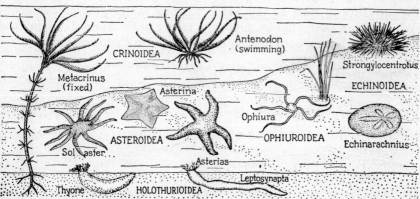

FIG. 19-1. Phylum ECHINODERMATA. Representative forms as they live in the sea; all reduced, but not to same scale. Class CRINOIDEA: crinoids (*Metacrinus*, attached; *Antedon*, free-swimming). Class ASTEROIDEA; common starfishes (*Asterias, Asterina*), sun star (*Solaster*). Class OPHIUROIDEA: brittle star (*Ophiura*). Class ECHINOIDEA: sea urchin (*Strongylocentrotus*), sand dollar (*Echinarachnius*). Class HOLOTHURIOIDEA: sea cucumbers (*Thyone, Leptosynapta*).

and sea bottom, from the tide lines down to over 12,000 feet, and are mostly free-living but slow-moving; a few are pelagic, but none is parasitic. Some are abundant, but none of them forms colonies; some sea lilies are permanently attached, and many others swim in open water. A few echinoderms are used as human food, and their eggs serve in many experimental researches. Starfishes may damage commercial beds of oysters or clams.

19-1. Characteristics. 1. Symmetry radial, usually 5-parted in adults, bilateral in larvae; 3 germ layers; most organs ciliated; no head or segmentation.

2. Body covered by delicate epidermis over a firm mesodermal endoskeleton of movable or fixed calcareous plates usually in definite pattern, and with spines (skin leathery and plates microscopic in HOLOTHURIOIDEA).

401

3. Digestive tract simple, usually complete (some lack an anus).

4. Circulatory system radiate, but reduced; coelom ciliated, usually large, its fluid containing free amoebocytes; part of larval coelom becomes a water vascular system usually with many tube feet serving for locomotion, food handling, or respiration.

5. Respiration by minute gills or papulae protruding from the coelom, by tube feet, and in Holothurioidea by cloacal respiratory trees.

6. Nervous system with circumoral ring and radial nerves.

7. Sexes separate (rare exceptions), alike externally; gonads large, with simple ducts; ova abundant, usually fertilized in the sea; larvae microscopic, ciliated, transparent, and usually free-swimming, with conspicuous metamorphosis. A few species are viviparous, a few reproduce also asexually by self-division, and many regenerate lost parts readily.

19-2. Relationships. Although the Echinodermata were once joined with the Coelenterata as the "Radiata," they belong well up among the invertebrates in a rather isolated position, being the only animals with complex organ systems that display conspicuous radial symmetry. Unique features such as the water vascular system, calcareous endoskeleton, and pedicellariae probably reflect their ancient origin, the echinoderms having been already differentiated in Cambrian time.

Fig. 19-2. Phylum Echinodermata. Diagrammatic sections showing for the 5 living classes the relations of the mouth (M), anus (A), tube feet (T), and spines (S). The digestive tract is outlined.

Some biologists believe that echinoderms have retrogressed from a type that once was more advanced and active, since the larvae are bilaterally symmetrical and free-living whereas the adults are radially symmetrical and of sedentary habit, with reduced blood and nervous systems and a saclike gut. Radial symmetry and the lack of a "head" are adjustments enabling a sedentary animal "to meet the environment on all sides."

The Echinodermata show some chordate-like features such as (1) a mesodermal endoskeleton (not external and from ectoderm as in other invertebrates); (2) the embryonic blastopore becoming the adult anus (not the mouth as in annelids and mollusks); (3) the mouth forming from an ectodermal inpocketing (stomodeum) that connects to the endodermal esophagus; and (4) the mesoderm forming as outpocketings of the primitive gut (not from special mesoblast cells as in annelids and mollusks). The larvae of some echinoderms resemble those of the HEMICHORDATA, which are variously included in or excluded from the Phylum CHORDATA.

19-3. External appearance (Fig. 19-1). Most starfishes have 5 tapering arms, some 6, and some up to 50; others are pentagonal without distinct arms. Their colors are variously yellow, red, brown, or purple. Brittle stars have a small rounded central disc with 5 slender, jointed, and flexible arms, sometimes marked with crossbands of color. The sea urchins are hemispherical with long movable spines, and sand dollars are disclike with short spines; many species are purple or blue. The crinoids are flowerlike with a cuplike disc bearing 5 branched arms and are of various colors. Sea cucumbers have soft sausage- or worm-shaped bodies covered by leathery skin, which may be white, red, brown, or black.

19-4. Size. No adult echinoderm is either very large or minute, the smallest being ½ inch in diameter. The largest starfish (*Pycnopodia helianthoides*) spreads to about 32 inches. The largest sea urchin (*Echinosoma hoplacantha*) has a shell about 12 inches in diameter, and the spines on some tropical urchins (*Diadema*) are up to 9 inches long. The biggest sea cucumber, *Synapta maculata*, becomes 6 feet long by less than 2 inches in diameter.

CLASS *ASTEROIDEA*. STARFISHES

Starfishes abound on most seacoasts, especially on rocky shores and about wharf piling. Various species live from the tide lines to considerable depths on sand and mud. Common North American species are *Asterias forbesi* from the Gulf of Mexico to Maine, *A. vulgaris* from Cape Hatteras to Labrador, and *Pisaster ochraceus* along the Pacific Coast.

19-5. Structure. The body (Figs. 19-3, 19-4) consists of a central *disc* and five tapering rays, or *arms.* The axes of the arms are termed "radii," and the spaces between them on the disc are "interradii." On the upper or *aboral surface* are many blunt calcareous *spines,* which are parts of the skeleton. Many small soft *dermal branchiae,* or papulae, project from the body cavity and between the spines to function as gills and for excretion. Around the spines and among the papulae are many minute pincerlike *pedicellariae.* Each pedicellaria has two jaws moved by muscles that open and snap shut when touched; they keep the body surface free of debris or small organisms and may help to capture food. The *anus* is a minute opening near the center of the aboral surface, and near by is the rounded *madreporite.* The *mouth* is in the middle of the lower or *oral surface,* surrounded by a soft peristomial membrane. A median *ambulacral groove,* bordered by large spines, extends along the

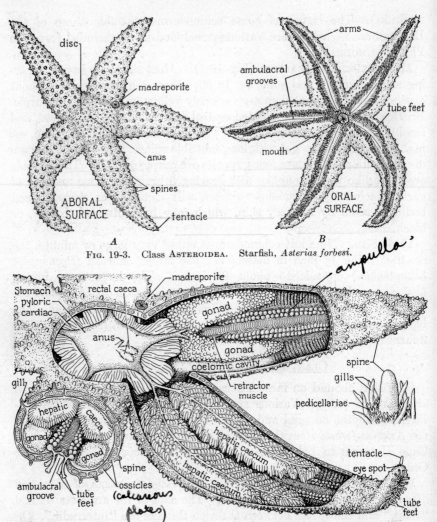

FIG. 19-3.   Class ASTEROIDEA.   Starfish, *Asterias forbesi*.

FIG. 19-4.   Starfish, general structure.   Three arms are cut off, one is seen in cross section at the left, the disc and aboral surface are removed on two arms, and the hepatic caeca removed in the upper of these.   Enlarged inset shows spine, gills, and pedicellariae.

oral surface of each arm, and from it many slender *tube feet* protrude in four (or two) rows.   On the tip of each arm is a small soft tactile *tentacle* and a light-sensitive *eyespot*.

The entire body is covered by ciliated *epidermis*.   Beneath is meso-derm that produces and contains the *endoskeleton,* a framework of many small calcareous *ossicles* of various but definite shapes and arranged in regular pattern (Fig. 19-5).   The ossicles are bound together by con-nective tissue and joined by muscle fibers.   Inside the skeleton is the large *coelom,* lined by ciliated epithelium, that contains the internal organs. It is filled with a lymph-like fluid containing free amoebocytes that participate in circulation, respiration, and excretion.   Extensions of the coelom into the dermal branchiae bring the fluid close to the surrounding sea water, separated only by the thin peritoneum and external epidermis,

FIG. 19-5.   Starfish, *Pisaster ochraceus.*   Part of skeleton showing the framework of ossicles.

where respiratory exchanges are easily made.   The amoebocytes gather wastes in the fluid and then escape from the branchiae to the exterior.

The water vascular system (Fig. 19-6) is a specialized part of the coelom.   Its parts are (1) the sievelike *madreporite* through which sea water may enter; (2) the *stone canal* connecting to (3) the *ring canal* around the mouth, whence (4) five *radial canals* extend, one in each arm above the ambulacral groove.   Each of the latter gives off many (5) *lateral canals,* one to each of (6) the *tube feet,* all with valves. The margin of the ring canal bears *Tiedemann bodies* that produce the free amoebocytes found in the fluid filling the system.   Each tube foot is a closed cylinder with muscular walls, having a sucker at the outer or free end, and a bulblike *ampulla* at its inner end within the body cavity. When an ampulla contracts, the fluid it contains is forced into the tube foot and extends the latter as a

FIG. 19-6.   Starfish.   Diagram of the water vascular system.   (*From Coe,* 1912.)

slender flexible process that can be twisted about by muscles in its walls. If the tip touches an object, the muscles may contract and return the fluid to the ampulla so that the foot shortens.   Withdrawal of fluid lessens the pressure within the tip and causes it to adhere to the object because of the greater pressure of the sea water or atmosphere outside; the foot thus acts as a suction cup.   The tube feet act either independently or in a coordinated manner. They serve to hold the starfish to the substratum, for locomotion, and in the capture and handling of food.

The *digestive system* comprises (1) the *mouth;* (2) the saclike *stomach* which is of two parts, a large lower or cardiac portion with thin folded muscular walls to which five pairs of retractor muscles attach, and a smaller aboral or pyloric portion joined by the ≺-shaped ducts of five pairs of *hepatic caeca* or digestive glands located in the arms; and (3) a short minute *intestine* joined by two rectal caeca and leading to (4) the *anus.*

The hemal or *circulatory system* is reduced and difficult to see; it includes vessels encircling the mouth and five radial vessels, one in each arm beneath the radial canal of the water vascular system.

The *nervous system* includes a circumoral nerve ring with radial nerve cords in the arms. In each arm there is (1) a cord in the epidermis within the ambulacral groove, (2) a pair of deep nerves inside this epidermis, and (3) a cord in the peritoneum on the aboral side. Minute nerves extend to the tube feet, epidermis, and internal structures.

The sexes are separate. A pair of *gonads* lie in the coelom of every arm, and a minute duct from each opens aborally on the central disc.

19-6. Natural history. A starfish spends most of its time quietly attached to some clean solid object. The body seems stiff and rigid and indeed can be broken in parts by rough treatment; yet the animal may voluntarily bend or twist both the disc and arms as when moving about or when its body is fitted into irregular spaces among rocks or other shelter. On a rough or upright surface the animal holds and travels by use of the tube feet, but on sand or a very smooth surface it does so by action of the arms alone. To move, the ray or rays pointing in the given direction are raised slightly, and the tube feet on them are stretched out an inch or so; these grip the new surface and then contract, pulling the body forward. There is no "head," and no one arm that habitually moves forward, although some experiments suggest that the part near the madreporite may often be carried forward. A starfish can be trained experimentally to use a particular arm, and the habit will persist for some time. The animal can progress in any direction over a surface but once started shows coordinated action of the arms and tube feet. If turned upside down, the arms are twisted until some of the tube feet touch and attach to the substratum, and then the entire body slowly folds over so that the oral surface is again downward.

The starfish feeds on mollusks, crustaceans, tube worms, and other invertebrates; deep-water species ingest mud. Small active animals, even fishes on occasion, may be caught by the tube feet, or pedicellariae, and passed to the mouth. With an oyster or a clam, the starfish arches its body over the prey so that the tube feet can grip the opposite valves to pull them apart.   It can exert a continued pull of over 1,300 grams, whereas the adductor muscles of a large bivalve become fatigued by a pull of 900 grams within a half hour, whereupon the shell gapes widely. When this happens, the starfish everts its stomach through the mouth to surround the prey.   The stomach secretes mucus, and the pylorus and caeca give off enzymes to digest the food as it is held; then the stomach and contents are withdrawn into the body.   Any large bits of waste are cast out the mouth since the small intestine serves mainly for excretion.   Starfishes may feed voraciously but also can go for long periods

FIG. 19-7.   Starfish.   An inverted individual turning over (in direction of arrows); *a–e*, same arms in successive positions.   (*After Cole*, 1913.)

without food.   A month-old starfish in an aquarium devoured over 50 young clams in 6 days.   On commercial oyster beds, starfishes may cause serious losses by eating the oysters.   Owners of such beds use a rope drag to capture the starfishes, which are then killed in hot water or carried ashore; or they sprinkle lime on the beds to kill the starfishes.

19-7. Reproduction (Fig. 19-8).   In early summer, eggs and sperm are shed into the sea water, where fertilization occurs.   Cleavage is rapid, total, equal, and indeterminate, yielding on the second day a spherical ciliated *blastula* (0.2 mm. in diameter) that swims.   Invagination produces an elongate *gastrula,* and the blastopore later becomes the anal end as in chordates.   Mesenchyme forms from cells budded off the inner blind end of the archenteron, where also two outpocketings bud off to produce the coelom and its mesodermal lining.   The mouth results from an ectodermal inpocketing, or stomodeum, that connects to the esophagus, stomach, and intestine derived from the archenteron.   Ciliated bands develop on the exterior that serve in locomotion and food capture.   The larva swims anterior end foremost, with a clockwise rotation, and feeds throughout its free existence.   Later, three lobes form on each side of the body to produce the *bipinnaria* larval stage.   Still later, these become modified as elongate and ciliated processes that move and contract, when the larva is termed a *brachiolaria* (2 to 3 mm. long).   After 6 or 7 weeks the larva settles to the bottom, the anterior end becomes a stalk by

which it attaches, and the posterior end enlarges and bends to the left.
Five lobes form on the right side of this posterior part, which becomes the
aboral surface of the future starfish; the left side produces the oral
surface. Skeletal elements appear as the first lobes (arms) become
evident. Two pairs of outgrowths from the coelom (hydrocoele) in each

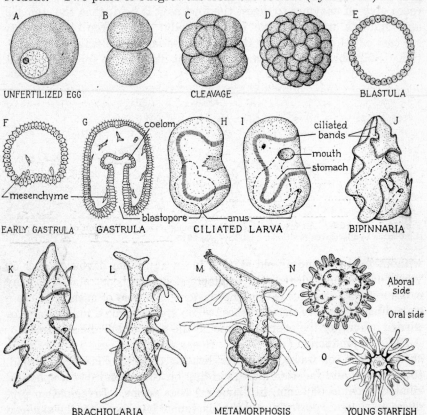

Fig. 19-8. Development of the starfish, *Asterias vulgaris*. The blastula (*E*) and gastrula
(*F, G*) are sectioned; the latter shows migration of mesenchyme cells and budding of coelomic
cavities off the archenteron. The blastopore becomes the anus (*H*), and the stomodeum
invaginates to form the mouth (*I*). The bilaterally symmetrical bipinnaria larva (*J*)
produces three pairs of lateral lobes that lengthen in the brachiolaria larva (*K, L*), as do
others on the ventral surface. The starfish forms on the lower right side of the brachiolaria
(*M*), the upper parts of which are absorbed. (*Adapted from Field; Goto; and Brooks.*)

lobe become the first tube feet and serve for attachment. A complex
internal reorganization occurs during the metamorphosis, but no parts
are cast off. Any bilateral symmetry in the adult is about a different
plane than that in the larva. The female blood starfish (*Henricia*)
produces few large-yolked eggs that are held beneath the disk by arching
the rays; the larval stages are abbreviated, and young emerge as miniature adults.

Starfishes suffer injury in nature and may break off an arm (autotomy) if severely handled.   The arms regenerate readily, and individuals often are seen with one or more of them growing out.   Experimental removal of four or, exceptionally, all arms may be followed by complete regeneration.

Class *OPHIUROIDEA*.   Brittle Stars and Serpent Stars

19-8. Structure.   These animals differ externally from starfishes in having usually a small rounded disc with five distinct arms that are long, slender, jointed, and fragile (Fig. 19-1).   An arm consists of many similar segments, each comprising two central fused ossicles covered by four plates, the laterals with spinelets and the dorsal and ventral spineless. The interior of a segment is almost filled by solid cylindrical ossicles, or "vertebrae," excavated on the proximal face and convex distally so that the adjacent vertebrae articulate with one another by a complex ball-and-socket joint.   Four muscles between each two vertebrae enable the arm to be bent readily.   In the arm is a small tubular coelom, nerve cord, hemal space, and branch of the water vascular system. The small tube feet, or "tentacles," are ventrolateral and without either suckers or ampullae; they are sensory, aid in respiration, and may pass food to the mouth.   All digestive and reproductive organs are in the disc.   The mouth is centered orally and surrounded by five

Fig. 19-9.   Class Ophiuroidea. Basket star, *Gorgonocephalus*.   As illustrated by Rondelet, *De piscibus marinis*, 1551.

groups of movable plates that serve as jaws.   There is a saclike stomach, but no caeca or anus; indigestible wastes are cast out the mouth.   Five pairs of saclike bursae open by narrow slits about the mouth; they function in respiration and receive the gonad ducts.   The madreporite is on the oral surface.   In the basket stars (*Gorgonocephalus*) the arms are repeatedly branched, with tendril-like tips (Fig. 19-9).

19-9. Natural history.   Ophiurans live in shallow to deep water, hiding beneath stones or seaweed or burying themselves in the mud or sand, to become active at night.   They move by rapid snakelike movements, holding to objects by one or more arms and pushing with the others so as to jerk the body along.   They can swim by use of their arms much as a person would do.   Their food is of small crustaceans, mollusks, and other animals and of bottom debris; ophiurans in turn are eaten by fishes.   The arms break or can be cast off easily, and some species can discard the disc except for the mouth framework, such parts being readily regenerated.

The sexes are usually separate and release their sex cells into the sea. The resulting **pluteus** larva has long ciliated arms and after some days undergoes a metamorphosis resembling that of starfishes. Some ophiurans (*Ophioplocus*) rear their young, which have no free-swimming stage, in the bursae.

CLASS *ECHINOIDEA*.   SEA URCHINS, SAND DOLLARS, AND HEART URCHINS

19-10. Structure. The members of this class have rounded bodies lacking free arms or rays and are thickly covered with many *movable spines* (Fig. 19-10). The sea urchins (*Arbacia, Strongylocentrotus*) are

hemispherical in shape, the heart urchins (*Spatangus*) are somewhat ovoid, and the sand dollars, or "sea cakes" (*Echinarachnius, Dendraster*) are disclike. The viscera are enclosed in a test or **shell,** composed of 10 double rows of plates, usually firmly sutured together. Five pairs of these rows, which correspond to the arms of starfishes, are perforated for a double series of long slender **tube feet,** and the other 5 wider rows are interradial areas. On

FIG. 19-10. Class ECHINOIDEA. Sea urchin, *Strongylocentrotus.* The tube feet and spines are in place on the left side of the figure, but removed on the right half.

the plates are series of rounded **tubercles** over which the spines articulate. Each spine has a cup-shaped base fitting over the tubercle and can be moved by muscle fibers around its base. Between the spines are three-jawed **pedicellariae** on long flexible stalks; some echinoids have several kinds. The pedicellariae keep the body clean, capturing small prey, or producing a protective poison. The **anus** is centered on the clear aboral surface and surrounded by enlarged plates containing the five (four or two) **genital openings.** The large **mouth** is on the oral surface, surrounded by five strong sharp **teeth;** these are supported by a complex five-sided framework inside the shell and known as "Aristotle's lantern."

The long **digestive tract** is looped around inside the test (Fig. 19-11). From the mouth a slender esophagus leads to a more expanded stomach that has saclike pouches; the narrow intestine connects by the rectum to the anus. A slender tubelike **siphon,** lined with strong cilia, extends from the esophagus to the beginning of the intestine; presumably, it carries water directly to the latter and may aid in washing out indigestible residues. In sand dollars the mouth is central, but the anus is near the edge of the disc; in heart urchins both the mouth and anus are marginal, at opposite sides of the disc, providing a type of secondary bilateral symmetry.   Ten *gills* protrude from the peristomial membrane about the mouth.   The madreporite is aboral, a ring canal encircles the esophagus, and five radial canals extend meridionally on the interior of the shell, connecting to the tube feet.   A *nerve ring* surrounds the mouth, and the five *radial nerves* accompany the radial canals.   The *gonads* (5, 4, or 2) are attached by strong mesenteries to the inner aboral surface, and from each a fine duct leads to a genital opening.   The larva is termed a *pluteus*. Unlike other echinoderms, the echinoids have only limited ability to regenerate lost parts.

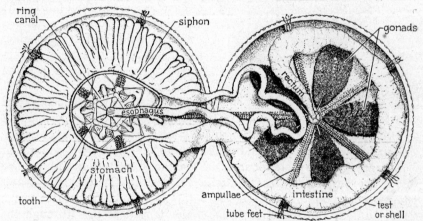

Fig. 19-11.   Sea urchin, *Arbacia*, general structure.   The test has been cut horizontally and the oral half laid to the left; spines omitted.   (*After Coe*, 1912.)

19-11. Natural history.   The urchins live on rocks and mud of the seashore and sea bottom, traveling by the action of their long spines and tube feet.   Some shift to tide pools or hide beneath seaweeds at low tide. Others live in self-excavated depressions in the hard clay or soft rock under shore waters.   The sand dollars live partly buried in sand, pulling themselves over or through it by their short spines and tube feet.   Echinoids keep their bodies clean by movements of their spines and pedicellariae, and wastes from the anus are similarly moved off.   They feed largely on seaweed but may eat any dead animal matter, and they also ingest sand or mud to extract the organic material contained in it.   Fishes, sea stars, and marine carnivores are their chief enemies.

Class *HOLOTHURIOIDEA*. Sea Cucumbers

19-12. Structure.   These are soft-bodied animals covered by leathery skin that contains only microscopic calcareous plates.   *Cucumaria* and *Thyone* are common examples (Figs. 19-12, 19-13).   The body is elongated on the oral-aboral axis.   The anterior mouth is surrounded by 10 to

30 retractile **tentacles,** comparable with the oral tube feet of other echinoderms. The holothurian lies usually with one side (dorsal) uppermost; this in some has two lengthwise zones of tube feet that are tactile and respiratory in function. The ventral side has typically three zones of tube feet, with suckers, that serve in locomotion. The body wall comprises a cuticle over a nonciliated epidermis; beneath is a layer of circular muscles and then five double bands of powerful longitudinal muscles along the radii. The coelom is large, fluid-filled, and undivided. Action of the muscles over the fluid-filled body enables the holothurian to extend or contract its body and to perform wormlike movements.

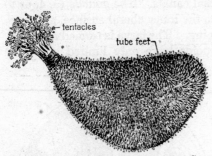

FIG. 19-12.   Class HOLOTHURIOIDEA.   Sea cucumber, *Thyone briareus.*   External features.   (*After Coe,* 1912.)

The digestive tract is slender and S-shaped, within the coelom. A short esophagus leads from the mouth to the oval and muscular stomach; the long intestine is supported by mesenteries and connects to a muscular cloaca ending at the posterior anus. From the cloaca two much-branched tubes, the **respiratory trees,** extend forward in the coelom. Water pumped in and out of these tubes by action of the muscular cloaca serves for respiration and excretion; some water is said to pass through the

FIG. 19-13.   Class HOLOTHURIOIDEA.   Sea cucumber, *Thyone.*   Internal structure; body wall cut lengthwise and laid open.   (*After Coe,* 1912).

walls of the trees to keep the coelom turgid. The water vascular system includes a madreporite within the coelom, a ring canal around the esophagus, and five radial canals that connect to the tube feet along each long muscle band. A nerve ring circles the esophagus, and nerve cords lie along the radii. The sexes are separate (but usually united in *Synapta*). The gonad is brushlike, with fine tubules joining a single duct that opens middorsally behind the tentacles. The free-swimming larva is termed an **auricularia**.

19-13. Natural history. Holothurians lie sluggishly on the sea bottom or burrow in the surface mud or sand with only the ends of the body exposed, but can respond quickly to stimuli if disturbed. Their food is of organic material in the mud or of small organisms taken by the tentacles and pushed into the mouth. They travel by use of the tube feet or by muscular movements of the body. When strongly irritated, *Synapta* will perform violent contractions and fragment the body into two or more pieces; in *Thyone* the body wall is ruptured and various organs are cast out. After such self-mutilation the anterior relic may regenerate lost parts. Some holothurians have a cluster of slender whitish viscous tubes, known as Cuvierian organs, attached to the cloaca; when disturbed, these are thrust out to entangle an enemy. Certain oriental holothurians are collected and dried in the sun, forming the "trepang," or "bêche-de-mer," used for soup.

FIG. 19-14. Class CRI-NOIDEA. Diagram of a simple crinoid. (*From Moore, Historical geology, after Bather.*)

Class *CRINOIDEA*. SEA LILIES AND FEATHER STARS

19-14. Structure and natural history. These flowerlike echinoderms live from below the low tide line to depths of over 12,000 feet. The body disc is a small cup-shaped **calyx** of calcareous plates to which are attached five flexible **arms** that fork to form 10 or more narrow appendages, each bearing many slender lateral **pinnules,** arranged like barbs on a feather. In some species a long jointed **stalk** extends from the lower or aboral surface of the calyx and attaches the crinoid to the sea bottom by rootlike outgrowths (Figs. 19-1, 19-14). Both mouth and anus are on the upper or oral surface of the disc; the anus is often on a raised cone. The oral surface of each arm bears an open ambulacral groove, lined with cilia and containing the tentacle-like tube feet. The food is of microscopic plankton and detritus, caught by the tentacles and conveyed by the cilia to the mouth. There is no madreporite. The aboral nervous system has a central ring, and a cord to each arm. The gonads are usually in the pinnules. Some crinoids shed their eggs directly into the water; with other species they remain attached to the pinnules until hatched. The larva subsists on yolk in the egg, having no mouth. After a few days of free life, it attaches by the anterior end and then the stem, disc, and arms are developed. Crinoids have great powers of regeneration, being able to cast off the arms or even the whole disc and then renew these parts. No animals are known to feed regularly on crinoids. A peculiar small polychaete (*Myzostoma*), is usually found on the arms and disc.

About 2,100 fossil species of crinoids are known. They were especially abundant in Paleozoic time. There are about 800 living species, many of which are attached only during the postlarval stage. Stalked crinoids are gregarious, often forming extensive "gardens" in clear waters, as on coral reefs. Free-living feather stars such as *Antedon* that swim readily by their long arms may also be abundant. Few species of crinoids exceed 8 inches in length, but many are brilliantly colored, yellow, red, white, green, or brown.

CLASSIFICATION

Phylum **ECHINODERMATA**. Echinoderms. Symmetry radial, body usually of 5 radii and 5 interadii, around an oral-aboral axis; no segmentation; body wall with calcareous plates, usually forming a flexible or rigid endoskeleton, with spines and pedicellariae; coelom complex, including a water vascular system with tube feet; digestive tract with or without anus; sexes usually separate but alike; larvae bilaterally symmetrical and free-living before metamorphosis; all marine; about 5,000 species.

Subphylum 1. PELMATOZOA. Body a boxlike calyx of many plates with slender arms bearing food grooves; aboral surface with a hollow jointed stalk for attachment or with footlike cirri.

Class 1. †*CYSTOIDEA*. Calyx of 13 to many plates often irregular and with minute pores; food grooves superficial; Cambrian to Carboniferous. †*Caryocrinus;* †*Edrioaster*, no arms or stalk.

Class 2. †*BLASTOIDEA*. Calyx of 13 plates, regular; no true arms but many fine brachioles; appearance brushlike; food grooves in ambulacra covered; Ordovician to Permian. †*Pentremites.*

Class 3. *CRINOIDEA*. Sea Lilies. Calyx cuplike, symmetrical; arms branched, with open ambulacra; tube feet suckerless; no madreporite, spines, or pedicellariae; Cambrian to Recent. †*Platycrinus;* †*Pentacrinus; Antedon* (*Hathrometra*) *tenella*, Chesapeake Bay to Newfoundland.

Subphylum 2. ELEUTHEROZOA. No stalk or cirri.

Class 1. *ASTEROIDEA*. Starfishes, or Sea Stars. Body star-shaped or pentagonal; arms 5 to 50, more or less flexible, usually not sharply set off from disc; skeleton flexible, usually with short spines and pedicellariae; ambulacral grooves open, with 2 or 4 rows of tube feet; madreporite aboral; stomach large; mostly predaceous; Middle Cambrian to Recent.

Order 1. **Phanerozonia**. Disc and arms margined orally by 2 rows of large plates; papulae all aboral; no crossed pedicellariae; 2 rows of tube feet. *Dermasterias*, skin thick and smooth; *Astropecten; Ceramaster.*

Order 2. **Spinulosa**. Marginal plates inconspicuous; papulae may occur on both surfaces; pedicellariae rare. *Asterina; Patiria; Henricia*, arms slender, cylindrical; *Solaster*, sun star, arms 7 to 14; *Pteraster*, with dorsal brood chamber for young.

Order 3. **Forcipulata**. Marginal plates inconspicuous; pedicellariae with crossed jaws, like scissors. *Asterias, Pisaster*, common starfishes; *Leptasterias; Stephanasterias*, small, rays 5 to 8; *Pycnopodia*, Pacific coast, large, rays 18 to 24, disc soft and flat.

Class 2. *OPHIUROIDEA.* BRITTLE STARS, ETC.   Body of a small rounded and distinct disc with 5 slender, jointed, and flexible arms; tube feet in 2 rows, suckerless, sensory; no pedicellariae; stomach saclike, no caeca or anus; madreporite oral; free-living, active; Mississippian to Recent.

Order 1. **Euryalae.**   Arms often branched, highly flexible, and can turn toward mouth; disc and arms covered by thick soft skin or granules. *Gorgonocephalus,* basket star, arms many-branched.

Order 2. **Ophiurae.**   Arms unbranched, usually cannot turn to mouth; disc and arms usually covered by plates. *Ophiothrix, Ophiopholis, Ophiura,* brittle stars.

Class 3. *ECHINOIDEA.* SEA URCHINS, SAND DOLLARS, ETC.   Body hemispherical, disclike, or egg-shaped; no arms; skeletal plates firmly sutured, forming a test that bears many movable spines and 3-jawed pedicellariae; tube feet with suckers; digestive tract long, slender, and coiled; mouth and anus either central or lateral; Ordovician to Recent.

Order 1. **Cidaroida.**   Anus aboral, central; no peristomial gills. *Eucidaris,* cosmopolitan in tropics.

Order 2. **Centrechinoidea.**   Anus aboral, central; with peristomial gills. *Arbacia, Strongylocentrotus,* sea urchins.

Order 3. **Exocycloida.**   Anus marginal or on oral surface; symmetry secondarily bilateral. *Clypeaster, Echinarachnius, Dendraster,* sand dollars, body depressed; *Spatangus, Lovenia,* heart urchins.

Class 4. *HOLOTHURIOIDEA.* SEA CUCUMBERS.   Body elongated, sausage-or worm-shaped, wall leathery to thin and translucent; no arms, spines, or pedicellariae; skeleton usually of scattered microscopic plates; tube feet usually present; mouth anterior, surrounded by retractile tentacles; digestive tract elongate, S-shaped, anus posterior; cloaca usually with respiratory trees; Cambrian to Recent.

Order 1. **Aspidochirota.**   Tentacles with branches crowded distally on a circular disc. *Holothuria; Stichopus.*

Order 2. **Dendrochirota.**   Tentacles irregularly branched. *Cucumaria, Thyone, Psolus.*

Order 3. **Molpadonia.**   Tentacles small, hand-shaped; no tube feet. *Caudina.*

Order 4. **Apoda** (Synaptida).   No tube feet or respiratory trees. *Leptosynapta, Chiridota.*

References

BATHER, F. A., J. W. GREGORY, and E. S. GOODRICH. 1900. The Echinoderma. *In* E. R. Lankester, Treatise on zoology. London, A. & C. Black, Ltd. Part 3, vi + 344 pp., illus.

COE, W. R. 1912. Echinoderms of Connecticut. *Connecticut State Geological and Natural History Survey, Bulletin* 19, 152 pp. 32 pls., 29 figs.

FISHER, W. K. 1911–1930. Asteroidea of the North Pacific and adjacent waters. *U.S. National Museum Bulletin,* 76 (3 parts), 1,020 pp., 296 pls.

JENNINGS, H. S. 1907. Behavior of the starfish *Asterias forreri* De Loriol. *University of California Publications in Zoology,* vol. 4, pp. 53–185, 19 figs.

MACBRIDE, E. W. 1896. The development of Asterina gibbosa. *Quarterly Journal of Microscopical Science,* n.s., vol. 38, pp. 339–411, pls. 18–29.

————. 1906. Echinodermata. *In* Cambridge natural history. London, Macmillan & Co., Ltd. Vol. 1, pp. 425–623, figs. 185–296.

MEAD, A. D. 1900. Natural history of the starfish. *U.S. Fish Commission Bulletin,* vol. 19, pp. 203–224, pls. 23–26.

MORTENSEN, THEODORE. 1927. Handbook of the echinoderms of the British Isles. Oxford, Oxford University Press. ix + 471 pp., 269 figs.

CHAPTER 20

PHYLUM MOLLUSCA. MOLLUSKS

Members of the Phylum MOLLUSCA (L. *mollis*, soft) have soft unsegmented bodies, consisting typically of an anterior head, a ventral foot, and a dorsal visceral mass. The body is more or less surrounded by a thin fleshy mantle and is commonly sheltered in an external calcareous shell. The phylum comprises five classes of diverse appearance and habits: the chitons (Class AMPHINEURA), tooth shells (SCAPHOPODA), snails and slugs (GASTROPODA), clams, oysters, and other bivalves (PELECYPODA), and the nautili, squids, and octopuses (CEPHALOPODA). Mollusks are of wide distribution in both time and space, having a continuous record since Cambrian time with fully 45,000 living and nearly an equal number of fossil species, many of which are abundant as individuals. They are mostly marine, living along seashores or in shallow waters, but some occur down to great depths and others are pelagic. Various snails and some bivalves inhabit brackish and fresh waters, and other snails and the slugs are terrestrial. Most mollusks are free-living creatures that creep slowly. A few are attached to rocks, shells, or wood, some burrow, others float, and the squids and octopuses can swim freely. Certain mollusks are of major economic importance. Clams, oysters, squids, and others serve as human food, shells of fresh-water clams are cut into buttons, and some bivalves produce pearls. Some snails and slugs feed on cultivated plants, certain fresh-water snails are intermediate hosts for parasitic worms, and the teredos damage wooden ships and wharves.

20-1. Characteristics. 1. <u>Symmetry bilateral</u> (viscera and shell coiled in GASTROPODA and some CEPHALOPODA); <u>3 germ layers</u>; <u>no segmentation</u>; epithelium 1-layered, mostly ciliated and with mucous glands.

2. <u>Body</u> usually <u>short, enclosed in a thin dorsal mantle</u> that <u>secretes a shell</u> of 1, 2, or 8 parts (shell in some, internal, reduced, or none); head region developed (except SCAPHOPODA, PELECYPODA); ventral muscular foot variously modified for crawling, burrowing, or swimming.

3. <u>Digestive tract complete, often U-shaped or coiled</u>; mouth with a radula bearing transverse rows of minute chitinous teeth to rasp food (except PELECYPODA); anus opening in mantle cavity; a large digestive gland ("liver") and often salivary glands.

4. Circulatory system includes a dorsal heart with 1 or 2 auricles and a ventricle, usually in a pericardial cavity, an anterior aorta, and other vessels.

5. <u>Respiration</u> by 1 to many <u>gills</u> (ctenidia) or a <u>"lung"</u> in the mantle cavity, by the mantle, or by the epidermis.

6. <u>Excretion by kidneys</u> (nephridia), either 1 or 2 pairs or 1, connecting to peri-

cardial cavity and veins; coelom reduced to cavities of nephridia, gonads, and pericardium.

7. Nervous system typically of 3 pairs of ganglia (cerebral above mouth, pedal in foot, visceral in body), joined by longitudinal and cross connectives and nerves; many with organs for touch, smell, or taste, eyespots or complex eyes, and statocysts for equilibration.

8. Sexes usually separate (some hermaphroditic, a few protandric); gonads 2 or 1, with ducts; fertilization external or internal; mostly oviparous; egg cleavage determinate, unequal, and total (discoidal in Cephalopoda); a veliger (trochophore) larva, or parasitic stage (Unionidae), or development direct (Pulmonata, Cephalopoda); no asexual reproduction.

20-2. Relationships. Invertebrates with limy shells such as brachiopods, barnacles, snails, clams, and others were confused in classification by early zoologists as they may be by beginning students today. Study of both the shells and soft parts has shown the Mollusca to be a large, well-defined, and homogeneous phylum. The type of cleavage in the egg and the resulting veliger larva in many marine snails, bivalves, and chitons resemble the cleavage and trochophore larva of marine annelids. Adult mollusks differ notably from annelids in the lack of segmentation and reduction of the coelom; the few ganglia in the nervous system and presence of one (or two) pairs of nephridia are possible relics of segmentation in mollusks. The chitons, which are the most primitive of living mollusks, have four lengthwise nerve cords, somewhat as in certain worms. They also have a series of eight dorsal plates that, to some zoologists, are evidence of segmentation. The Annelida and Mollusca were probably differentiated in Pre-Cambrian time, and the classes of Mollusca, including some groups now extinct, were separated soon afterward. Since then the Mollusca have left a long and detailed fossil record by their shells.

20-3. General appearance. The mollusks are of diverse form (Fig. 20-1). Most Amphineura are of elliptical outline, with a large flat foot

Fig. 20-1. Phylum Mollusca. Relations in the five Classes of the shell (heavy lines), foot (stippled), digestive tract (shaded), mouth (*M*), and anus (*A*).

and the body partly covered dorsally by eight overlapping calcareous plates. The Scaphopoda are elongate dorsoventrally and encased in a slender tubular shell open at both ends. Most Gastropoda have a long flat foot and a distinct head with eyes and tentacles, and the viscera are usually housed in a spiral shell, coiled either to the right or to the left. The Pelecypoda are laterally compressed, have a small foot and no head, and the body is within a pair of lateral shells hinged dorsally. In the Cephalopoda the large head bears conspicuous lateral eyes, the mouth is surrounded by 8, 10, or many fleshy arms, and the body is elongate; the shell is usually internal and reduced or lacking.

20-4. Size. Various chitons are $\frac{1}{2}$ to 8 inches long, *Cryptochiton* of the Pacific coast being the largest. The tooth shells are mostly under $2\frac{1}{2}$ inches long, but some grow to 6 inches. The gastropods range from minute snails under 1 mm. in diameter to the Florida conch (*Strombus*) with a shell 10 inches or longer; most species are less than 2 inches in diameter or height. The shells of bivalves are from $\frac{1}{2}$ inch long up to $4\frac{1}{2}$ feet in the "giant clam" (*Tridacna deresa*) of the tropical Pacific, which may grow to weigh 550 pounds. Some squids and octopuses are but 1 inch long, but the giant squid (*Architeuthis*) is recorded with a 20-foot body and 35-foot tentacles, far the largest invertebrate known (Fig. 1-2).

Class *AMPHINEURA*. Chitons, etc.

20-5. Structure. The chiton (Order Polyplacophora, Fig. 20-2) has an elongate elliptical *body* with a convex dorsal surface bearing eight over-

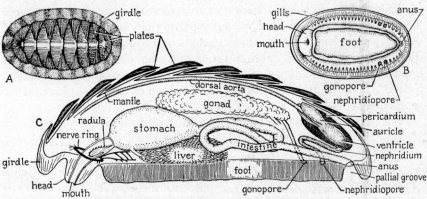

Fig. 20-2. Class Amphineura. The chiton. *A.* Dorsal view. *B.* Ventral view. *C.* Internal structure from the left side, with the shell, mantle, and foot shown in median section.

lapping calcareous valves, or *plates;* these are jointed to one another and covered at the sides (or entirely) by a thick fleshy *girdle* (part of mantle) containing bristles or spines. The *mantle* covers the dorsal and lateral surfaces, and the flat *foot* occupies most of the ventral surface. Between the foot and mantle is a *pallial groove.* Beneath the anterior margin of the girdle is the small *head,* which contains the *mouth* but lacks eyes or tentacles. In the floor of the mouth cavity is a long *radula* with many crossrows of fine **teeth**.   A short **pharynx** leads to the rounded **stomach,** to which the **digestive gland** (liver) connects.   The long and coiled **intestine** ends at the **anus** posteriorly in the pallial groove.   The **heart** lies postero-dorsally in a pericardial cavity; it comprises two auricles and a ventricle connecting to an anterior aorta.   Two slender **excretory organs** drain from the pericardial cavity, one discharging far back in each pallial groove.   In each pallial groove are the **gills,** 6 to 80 in different species. The **nervous system** comprises a ring about the mouth that connects to two pairs of ventral longitudinal nerve cords, the pedal in the foot and pallial in the girdle; the cords have many cross connectives but no ganglia.   Some chitons have eyespots or eyes in the integument over the shells.   The sexes are separate, each having one fused **gonad** from which a duct extends on each side to open posteriorly in the pallial groove.

20-6. Natural history.   Chitons are marine and live on rocks, mostly in shallow waters from the tide lines to moderate depths; some occur down to 13,800 feet.   They cling tightly or creep slowly by use of the foot, but curl up, like a "pill bug," if dislodged.   The dorsal plates protect them against most predaceous enemies.   Their food is of seaweeds and micro-organisms scraped from the rocks by use of the radula.   Some portion of the girdle is raised slightly to admit water about the gills for respiration. Fertilization is external, and the eggs (up to 200,000 in some females) are discharged separately or in long strings.   The larva is usually a trocho-phore.   In the West Indies, chitons are eaten as "sea beef."

The Order Solenogastres comprises small wormlike forms in which the mantle covers the entire body and contains fine limy spicules as the only evidence of a shell.   The foot is a ciliated ridge in a ventral groove or else is lacking.   These animals live on corals or hydroids at considerable depths in the ocean.

Class *SCAPHOPODA*.   Tooth Shells or Tusk Shells

20-7. Structure and natural history.   In the Scaphopoda (Gr. *skaphe,* boat + *podos,* foot) the body is slenderly elongate dorsoventrally, surrounded by the mantle that secretes a tubular shell, open at both ends, and slightly curved and tapered (Fig. 20-3).   Scaphopods are all marine, in shallow waters to depths of 15,000 feet, and live partly buried obliquely in the mud or sand.   The pointed foot protrudes from the larger ventral end of the shell for use in burrowing.   About the mouth are several delicate ciliated and contractile "tentacles" (captacula) with expanded tips; these are sensory and prehensile, serving to capture the microplants and animals used as food.   There is no head; lacking gills, the mantle serves for respiration.   Scaphopods are dioecious; eggs are discharged separately, and after a short larval stage the young animals sink to the bottom.

Scaphopod (Dentalium) shells kept on strings were the money of Indians on the Pacific coast, from California to Alaska; their early trade equivalent was 25 cents for 1⅞-inch shell to $5 for the rare 2½-inch shells.

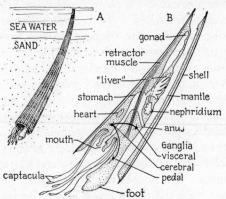

Fig. 20-3. Class Scaphopoda. The tooth shell, *Dentalium*. A. Position in life. B. Internal structure from the left side; diagrammatic.

Class *GASTROPODA*. Snails, Whelks, Conchs, Slugs, etc.

The conspicuous anterior head and long ventral foot of the Gastropoda (Gr. *gaster*, belly + *podos*, foot) are bilaterally symmetrical. The visceral mass is usually contained in a dorsal shell, both being spirally coiled and asymmetrical. The shell is unchambered, of one piece, and called a "univalve." Ancestral gastropods probably had bilateral symmetry throughout; but in living species the digestive tract, anus, heart, gills, kidneys, and some nervous structures have been rotated or coiled, to 180 degrees, and certain parts have disappeared (Fig. 20-5).

20-8. Structure. A common gastropod such as the "garden snail" (*Helix aspersa*, Fig. 20-4), has a fleshy **head** bearing two pairs of retractile **tentacles,** a pair of **eyes** (on tentacles), and a **mouth.** The head joins directly to a muscular **foot,** on top of which is the **shell;** the latter is of calcium carbonate, covered externally by a horny periostracum. A mucous epithelium covers all exposed fleshy parts. On the right side, the **genital pore** opens beside the head, and the small **anus** and larger **respiratory pore** are in the soft mantle margin at the edge of the shell. The **mantle** is a thin membrane that secretes and lines the shell and surrounds the viscera within. All soft parts can be drawn entirely into the shell by the **columella muscle,** which extends internally to the spire at the top of the shell.

The **digestive system** includes (1) the mouth; (2) a muscular pharynx with a dorsal horny "jaw" and ventral radula; (3) a slender esophagus; (4) the large thin-walled crop; (5) a rounded stomach; (6) a long twisted intestine; and (7) the anus. Two flat salivary glands beside the crop

send ducts to the pharynx, and a lobed liver high in the shell connects
to the stomach.   Replacing the gills of other gastropods and mollusks,
the land snail has a *lung* and hence is a "pulmonate."   The lung is
a network of blood vessels in the outer wall of the mantle in the large
mantle cavity within the shell; air enters and leaves by the respiratory
pore.   Blood collected from the body is aerated in the lung and then
pumped by the heart through arteries to the head, foot, and viscera.   The
heart has one auricle and a ventricle.   A single *kidney* drains from the

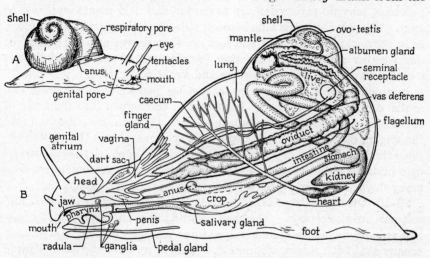

Fig. 20-4.   Class Gastropoda.   Brown garden snail, *Helix aspersa*.   *A*. External features
from the right side.   *B*. Internal structure from the left side.   The lung is indicated by the
branching blood vessels of the mantle cavity that connect to the heart.

pericardial cavity around the heart and discharges into the mantle cavity.
The *nerve ganglia* are condensed, with the cerebral pair dorsal to the
pharynx and the buccal, pedal, and visceral pairs close beneath it; nerves
from the ganglia extend to all organs.   The tip of each posterior tentacle
has an *eye* with cornea, lens, and retina, and also probably an olfactory
organ.   Below the pedal ganglia lie a pair of *statocysts,* the organs of
equilibrium, each containing calcareous bodies, cilia, and sensory cells.
In the epidermis of the head and foot are other sensory structures.

In each individual is a combined male and female *reproductive system.*
High in the shell is the *ovotestis,* which produces both eggs and sperm.
A *hermaphroditic duct* connects to the near-by *albumen gland* of the
female system.   A slender *vas deferens* conducts sperm to the *penis,*
which lies in a sac off the common *genital atrium;* the long *flagellum*
joined to the penis sac presumably forms the spermatophore in which
sperm are transferred at mating.   The *oviduct* (larger than the vas
deferens) leads from the albumen gland to the *vagina,* which in turn

connects to the genital atrium.   To the vagina are connected the slender duct of the **seminal receptacle,** the **"finger" gland,** and the **dart sac.**

20-9. Natural history.   *Helix* is most active at night and in damp weather.   It glides slowly and smoothly by waves of muscular action on the ventral side of the foot, over a "slime track" of mucus that is secreted by the large pedal gland below the mouth.   The food is of green vegetation, moistened by salivary secretions, held by the jaw, and rasped off in small bits by the movements of the radula.   Land snails, when present in numbers, may do severe damage to garden and field plants and even to trees.   By day the snails hide beneath objects on the ground, in crevices, or in burrows; the soft head and foot are then drawn into the shell.   In dry weather a temporary covering (epiphragm) of mucus and lime is secreted to cover the shell aperture and avoid desiccation.

Reproduction is preceded by a mating performance between two snails, during which a "dart" from each is discharged into the body of the other.   Copulation is reciprocal, the penis of each being inserted into the vagina of the other for transfer of a spermatophore; the snails then separate.   Each later deposits one or more batches of gelatinous-covered eggs in damp places or shallow slanting burrows.   Development requires many days and is direct, the young emerging as minute snails.

20-10. Other Gastropoda.   There is infinite variety in the shell and soft parts of gastropods.   The shell may be tall or short, conical, turbanlike, spindle-shaped, or cylindrical, white or variously colored, and plain or ornamented with ridges, spines, etc.   Land slugs have the shell reduced and internal or lacking, and the nudibranchs have only a small coiled shell (protoconch) as larvae and none as adults.   Most gastropods can withdraw completely into their shells, and many of them have a permanent plate (operculum) to cover the aperture.   In most species the shell is right-handed (dextral), being coiled clockwise as seen from the spire, but some are left-handed (sinistral).   In the HETEROPODA the foot is a vertically compressed fin, and the PTEROPODA have a pair of lateral fins near the head; both of these groups swim in the open sea.

The more primitive gastropods (PROSOBRANCHIATA) are chiefly marine and possess two gills; others (OPISTHOBRANCHIATA) have but one gill, nephridium, and auricle, the left of each having disappeared and the true right organ being on the left side.   The gastropods evidently developed in the sea, whence some forms in time migrated to fresh waters; some types invaded the land to become the PULMONATA.   Certain of the later have returned to fresh water where, having a lung instead of gills, they must come to the surface at intervals to respire.   Some gastropods (limpets, nudibranchs) have regained an external bilateral symmetry, but the internal viscera are coiled, implying their derivation from coiled types.

Fig. 20-5. Class Gastropoda. Plan of organization in the 3 Orders, showing rotation of the viscera and crossing of nerve commissures, with loss of the left ventricle, gill, and kidney in Opisthobranchiata, and a lung replacing the gill in Pulmonata. Shell and body outlined, mantle area shaded, nervous system black. *A*, auricle; *V*, ventricle; sex organs omitted. (*Modified from Stempell.*)

The gastropods are very abundant in salt and fresh waters and on land. They occur from the tropics to subpolar regions, to depths of 17,000 feet in the sea and up to 18,000 feet in The Himalayas. Land snails occur from moist tropical regions to arid deserts. A number of them and some slugs have been spread with cultivated plants to places where they were not native, and some marine snails have been trans-

Fig. 20-6. Class Gastropoda. Some marine forms in life and some empty shells. Order Prosobranchiata: *Fissurella*, limpet; *Haliotis*, abalone; *Crepidula*, slipper shell; *Tegula*, turban shell; *Carinaria*, heteropod; *Murex*, rock shell; *Buccinum*, edible whelk. Order Opisthobranchiata: *Tethys*, sea hare; *Clione*, pteropod; *Doris*, nudibranch.

planted with oyster "spat." Most marine gastropods produce large numbers of eggs that develop into a veliger larval stage before metamorphosing to the adult form.

The gastropods are mainly herbivorous, but some (*Buccinum, Urosalpinx*) are predators that bore into and feed on other mollusks. A few are parasites of echinoderms. Many snails are the necessary intermediate hosts for trematode flatworms (Chap. 16). Gastropods are eaten by other invertebrates and by many kinds of vertebrates.   For ancient man and primitive peoples univalves have served as food, and *Helix pomatia* is still eaten commonly in Europe.   Shells of gastropods provided the "money" of various native races, including the wampum of American Indians.

Class *PELECYPODA*.   Bivalves: Clams, Mussels, Oysters, etc.

Members of this class are bilaterally symmetrical and laterally compressed, with the soft body enclosed in a rigid shell of two parts (hence called "bivalves"), and have no head.   The foot usually is wedge-shaped

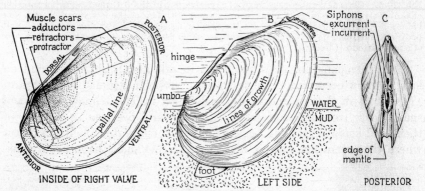

Fig. 20-7.   Class Pelecypoda.   Fresh-water clam, *Anodonta*.   Shell and external features.   Lines radiating from the umbo show the path of the muscle attachments as the shell grows in size.

(Gr. *pelekys*, hatchet + *podos*, foot), and the gills are thin and platelike (whence Lamellibranchiata, an earlier name for the class).   Bivalves inhabit both salt and fresh waters.   Some creep on the bottom, others attach to solid objects, and many of them burrow in sand or mud.   A fresh-water clam or mussel, such as *Anodonta* or *Unio*, will serve to illustrate the anatomy of a bivalve (Fig. 20-7).

20-11. Structure.   The somewhat oval **shell** is a firm exoskeleton that protects the body and provides for muscle attachments.   It is of symmetrical right and left **valves,** the thinner margins of which are ventral and the thicker dorsal.   In the dorsal region are (1) the **hinge teeth** (none in *Anodonta*), which align the valves with each other and serve as a pivot when the shell opens or closes; (2) an elastic **hinge ligament** between the valves that tends to draw them together dorsally and separate their ventral margins; and (3) an anterior swollen **umbo** on each valve, representing its oldest portion.   Around the umbo are many concentric **lines of growth** indicating intervals between successive growth stages, the annual lines being more conspicuous.

The shell (Fig. 20-8) is of three layers: (1) the external **periostracum,** a

thin, colored, horny covering that protects parts beneath from being dissolved by carbonic acid in the water; the umbo on old shells is often
corroded where this layer wears off; (2) a middle *prismatic layer* of
crystalline calcium carbonate; and (3)
the inner *nacre,* or "mother-of-pearl"
lining, formed of many thin layers of
calcium carbonate and having a slight
iridescence. The outer two layers are
produced by the edge of the mantle, and
the nacre by the entire surface of that
membrane. The shell grows in area by
addition around the margin and in thick-
ness by successive deposits of nacre,
being thickest under the umbo.

Fig. 20-8.   Fresh-water clam.   Enlarged cross section of shell and
mantle.

The soft *body* within the shell (Fig.
20-9) consists of (1) a plump median
visceral mass, attached dorsally and
containing various organs; its anteroventral part forms (2) the muscular *foot.*
On each side of these hang (3) a pair of thin *gills,* outside of which is (4) a
mantle lobe. Each mantle lobe is a thin sheet of tissue adhering to the
inner surface of a valve. The free margins of the mantle are muscular
and can be brought together to close the *mantle cavity* within.   Posteriorly

Fig. 20-9.   Fresh-water clam, *Anodonta.*   A. Internal structure as seen with shell,
mantle, and gills of the left side removed.   B. Cross section through the heart region.
Both diagrammatic.   (B, *after Stempell.*)

the mantle margins form two short tubes: a ventral or *incurrent siphon*
and a dorsal or *excurrent siphon*.   Water moves in and out these openings by the action of cilia covering the surfaces within the mantle cavity.

Scars on the inner surface of each valve indicate the attachments of *muscles* (Fig. 20-7*A*). These are the large *anterior* and *posterior* *adductors,* both transverse, which draw the valves together; the *anterior* and *posterior* *retractors,* which draw the foot into the shell, and the *anterior protractor,* which helps to extend the foot.

The *digestive system* includes (1) the small *mouth,* just behind the anterior adductor and between two thin fleshy *labial palps;* (2) a short *esophagus;* (3) a rounded *stomach* dorsally in the visceral mass, and joined by ducts from (4) the paired digestive gland, or *"liver";* (5) the slender *intestine* coiled in the visceral mass above the foot; (6) the dorsal *rectum* surrounded by the heart; and (7) the *anus* opening within the excurrent siphon. A pouch (pyloric caecum) off the stomach usually contains a transparent flexible rod, the *crystalline style,* that provides a starch-reducing enzyme useful in digesting plankton. In the rectum is a longitudinal fold, or *typhlosole,* that increases the surface within that organ (as in earthworms). The mouth has no jaws or radula.

The *circulatory system* comprises a dorsal *heart,* of two auricles joining a muscular ventricle; the latter is around the rectum and within a *pericardial cavity.* The ventricle pumps blood forward in an *anterior aorta* supplying the foot and viscera, except the kidneys and gills, and backward in a *posterior aorta* delivering to the rectum and mantle. Blood oxygenated in the mantle returns directly to the auricles, but that which circulates through other

Fig. 20-10. Fresh-water clam. Diagram of the circulatory system and blood flow.

organs is collected in a *vein* to the kidneys and thence passes to the gills for oxygenation before returning to the heart (Fig. 20-10). Some arterial blood enters vessels lined by epithelium, and some discharges into blood sinuses without cellular lining, as in the foot; some blood also diffuses to intercellular spaces. The blood carries oxygen and dissolved nutriment to all parts of the body; also it disposes of carbon dioxide in the gills and mantle and of organic wastes in the kidneys.

The chief *respiratory organs* (Fig. 20-11) are two pairs of *gills* (ctenidia); a gill is formed of two thin *lamellae* joined around their ventral margins. Each lamella is made of many vertical *gill bars,* strengthened by chitinous rods and connected to one another by horizontal bars, with small *pores* (ostia) between. Cross partitions (interlamellar junctions), between the two lamellae, divide the interior of a gill into many vertical *water tubes.* Dorsally the water tubes of each gill join a common *suprabranchial chamber* that extends posteriorly to the exhalent siphon. There is a slitlike passage from the mantle cavity to the suprabranchial chamber of each inner gill. Blood from veins in the kidneys passes through fine afferent and efferent vessels in the interlamellar junctions for aeration before returning to the heart.

Just below the pericardium are two *kidneys,* which remove organic wastes from the blood and pericardial fluid. Each is a U-shaped tube with a ciliated aperture draining from the pericardial cavity, a glandular region adjacent to the vein, and a bladder discharging through a ciliated opening into the suprabranchial chamber of the inner gill.

Fig. 20-11. Fresh-water clam. Diagrams of gill structure. *A.* Outer left gill partly cut away to show internal structure. ←--, path of water; ←, path of food particles caught in mucus and carried to mouth; ←-, path of rejected particles. *B.* Portion of gill enlarged. ←---, path of blood flow, down in afferent and up in efferent vessels. *C.* Cross section of two gill bars much enlarged to show ciliated surfaces and blood cells.

The *nervous system* includes three pairs of *ganglia,* the cerebral beside the esophagus, the pedal in the foot, and the visceral below the posterior adductor muscle. Each pair of ganglia is joined by a commissure. There are also cerebro-pedal and cerebro-visceral commissures besides nerves to various organs. The *sensory structures* include light-responsive devices in the siphon margins, tactile organs in the mantle edge, a pair of *statocysts* (for equilibration) in the foot, and an *osphradium* in the incurrent siphon over each visceral ganglion. The osphradia are presumably chemoreceptors that test incoming water.

The sexes are separate but alike externally. In each are two much-branched *gonads* about the intestinal coils in the visceral mass, each discharging by a short *duct* near the kidney aperture.

20-12. Natural history. Fresh-water mussels live in ponds, lakes, and streams, some in quiet and others in flowing waters. They may migrate to shallows by night and retire to deeper places by day, and may change their habitats with the seasons. They are usually embedded partly in

428 THE ANIMAL KINGDOM [CHAP. 20

sand or mud or are wedged between rocks, with the valves slightly spread, the mantle margins closed, and the siphons exposed (Fig. 20-7). They can travel slowly by extending the foot between the valves to expand or hook it into bottom materials and then draw the body along by contraction of the foot muscles. This action is aided by the filling and emptying of blood sinuses in the foot. Dragging the shell along leaves parallel furrows in the bottom. The siphons open and close in response to light, touch, and other stimuli. By the action of cilia covering the mantle and gills, water is drawn through the incurrent siphon into the mantle cavity. Organic particles and microorganisms (diatoms, protozoans, etc.), suspended in the water, constitute the food; this is trapped in mucus on the gills or mantle and carried by the beating cilia on these organs to the labial palps and mouth. Food is digested in the stomach, by aid of "liver" secretions, and absorbed in the intestine; any residues pass out the anus. The water provides oxygen for aeration of blood in the gills; it passes through the pores, up the water tubes to the suprabranchial chambers, and out the exhalent siphon, carrying away carbon dioxide and feces, and sex products in season.

20-13. Reproduction. Most mollusks set their eggs and sperm free, but the fresh-water bivalves of the Family UNIONIDAE have a peculiar mode of

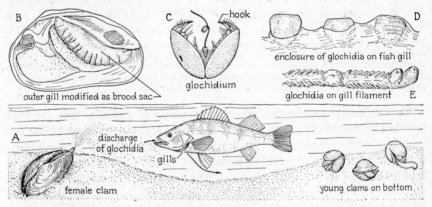

FIG. 20-12. Fresh-water clam. *A.* Diagram of the life cycle. *B.* The female's outer gill modified as a brood sac. *C.* One glochidium. *D.* Enclosure of glochidia by epithelium on gill of a fish. *E.* Glochidia on a gill filament. (*B–D, after Lefevre and Curtis,* 1910.)

reproduction. In a female the ripe eggs pass from the ovaries to the suprabranchial chambers, and there are fertilized by sperm discharged from a male and brought in water entering the female. The eggs become attached by mucus within the water tubes of her gills, which enlarge as *brood chambers* (marsupia). In some species all four gills are used, in others only the outer two or parts of these. Each egg, by total but unequal cleavage, develops into a minute larval **glochidium,** 0.1 to 0.4 mm. wide, with two valves closed by an adductor muscle and a long larval thread; in some (*Anodonta,* etc.) the valves bear hooks ventrally, but others (*Unio, Quadrula, Lampsilis*) lack hooks. The larvae are shed into the water through the female's exhalent siphon, then sink to the bottom or are scattered by water currents. They can open or close their shells but cannot move independently. Hooked glochidia attach to soft exterior parts of fresh-water fishes resting on the bottom; hookless forms clamp to the gill filaments of fishes, being carried in the respiratory water of the latter. In a few hours either type is covered with a capsule formed by migration and mitosis of cells of the host's epithelium. The parasitic larvae feed and grow by absorbing nutrients from the host's body fluids. Later the cyst weakens, the young mollusk opens and closes its valves, extends its foot, and escapes to the bottom to become free-living. In some clams (*Quadrula, Unio*) breeding occurs in summer (May to August), and the glochidial stages last 10 to 70 days depending on the species and water temperature. Others (*Anodonta, Lampsilis*) produce eggs in late summer, and the glochidia are retained in the female until the following spring. Individual fishes in nature may carry up to 20 glochidia, but a fish 3 or 4 inches long may be artificially infected with several hundred that will grow to metamorphosis. The glochidial stage serves to disperse the young over a wide area. At times glochidia in hatcheries cause losses among trout.

20-14. Other Pelecypoda. The bivalves are all aquatic, mostly marine, and chiefly sedentary bottom dwellers. They are commonest from the tide lines into shallow waters, but some occur down to 17,000 feet. Some creep slowly on the bottom, but a large majority of the marine species, including various edible clams, burrow in the sand or mud and extend their siphons up to the water (Fig. 20-13). The sea mussel (*Mytilus*) attaches to solid objects by a "byssus" of threads secreted by glands in the reduced foot. The edible oysters (*Ostrea*) become attached permanently to rocks or shells by a secretion. Some forms (*Pholas*) can burrow in hard clay or soft rocks. The shipworms or teredos (*Teredo, Bankia*) are highly specialized bivalves with very slender bodies and small anterior shells; using the latter they burrow in the wood of ships or wharves immersed in sea water. The scallop (*Pecten*) attaches by a byssus but can free itself and swim by clapping its shells together. Still other bivalves are commensals on echinoderms, some live in the burrows of worms and crustaceans, others are embedded in sponges and the tests of ascidians, and *Entovalva* is parasitic in holothurians.

Some PELECYPODA are enormously abundant. An estimated 4,500,-000,000 clams live on 700 square miles of the Dogger Bank east of England. Shells of the fossil †*Exogyra* of Cretaceous time occur in rocks from New Jersey to Mexico, over 2,500 miles. Oysters, mussels, and others inhabit various coastal waters in large numbers.

In the great majority of PELECYPODA, both ova and sperm are discharged into the water where fertilization occurs, and the zygote develops into a ciliated *veliger larva* somewhat resembling the trochophore of annelids. This in time acquires a shell gland, sinks to the bottom, and becomes a miniature bivalve. Since the hazards in such reproduction are great, these mollusks produce vast numbers of eggs—from 16,000,000 to 60,000,000 may issue from a female oyster in one season.

In the common American oyster (*Ostrea virginica*) of the Atlantic coast the sexes are separate. Eggs and sperm unite in the water, and within

FIG. 20-13. Class PELECYPODA. Positions of some marine forms in life; reduced but not to same scale. Order PRIONODESMACEA: *Nucula; Yoldia; Ostrea*, edible oyster; *Mytilus*, sea mussel with byssus; *Pecten*, scallop. Order TELEODESMACEA; *Mya*, mud clam; *Venus*, quahog; *Tagelus*, jackknife clam; *Ensis*, razor clam; *Pholas*, rock borer; *Teredo*, pileworm or shipworm.

48 hours the larva has a bivalved shell. It swims about for about 2 weeks and grows, then goes to the bottom and moves about by use of the foot, finally settling on the left valve and quickly becoming fixed to some solid object by a secretion from the mantle. The European oyster (*O. edulis*) and the Pacific coast oyster (*O. lurida*) are both protandric, the gonad of an individual first producing sperm and then eggs, in rhythmic alternation. The eggs of *O. lurida* are fertilized and grow to bivalved larvae within the mantle cavity of the parent "female" and then have a brief free existence before attaching. Attached young oysters are called "spat."

20-15. Relations to man. Since man first visited the seashore, he has used bivalves as food. On many coasts are "shell mounds" where ancient peoples for generations ate mollusks and discarded the shells. An Indian shell mound on San Francisco Bay contained over 1,000,000 cubic feet of debris accumulated over an estimated 3,500 years. The United States annually takes more than 130,000,000 pounds of oysters, clams, scallops, and mussels, valued at about $37,000,000. Good natural oyster beds in shallow water are highly valued, some of the starfishes that prey on the oysters are removed, and spat is planted to replace the adult oysters that are harvested by tongs or dredges.   Both the Atlantic oyster and the Japanese oyster (*Ostrea gigas*) have been established on the Pacific coast.   The soft internal parts of oysters are shucked out and consumed fresh, cooked, or canned.   Oyster shell is used on roads and to supply lime for poultry and other needs.   Various kinds of clams are dug by hand, and in many places a limit as to size, number, and season of take has been placed to conserve the stocks.

In the United States, "pearl" buttons for clothing are cut from shells of fresh-water bivalves (Fig. 20-14); no other material withstands repeated laundering so well.   Originally these mollusks were more abundant

FIG. 20-14.   The "pearl" button industry.   Circular blanks cut from shells of fresh-water clams are ground and polished, sometimes dyed, and drilled to receive threads.

in the upper Mississippi drainage than anywhere else in the world, but overfishing has seriously depleted them.   Some species require several years to mature.   The U.S. Bureau of Fisheries has made many experiments seeking to replenish the mollusks and place the industry on a sustained yield basis.   The host fishes can be artificially infected with numbers of glochidia, and the latter have also been reared in an artificial nutrient medium, composed of the chemicals present in the blood serum of fishes.

Pearls are formed about foreign objects between the mantle and shell of bivalves.   A bit of the mantle encloses the object and secretes successive layers of nacre about it, in the manner that the shell lining is produced.   Some pearls form in fresh-water clams and in oysters, but the most valuable kinds come from marine pearl oysters (*Margaritifera*) of eastern Asia.   The Japanese artificially introduce small particles in the mantle and then retain the bivalves (*Meleagrina*) in cages for several years until "culture" pearls are produced.

The burrowing of teredos in wooden marine structures sometimes causes serious damage, since the piles supporting wharves may be weakened and collapse.   An estimated $25,000,000 of such damage occurred in San Francisco Bay in 1917-1921.   Wharves are now constructed of creosoted wood, concrete, or metal to avoid such troubles.

Class *CEPHALOPODA*.   Nautili, Squids, and Octopuses

The Cephalopoda (Gr. *kephale*, head + *podos*, foot) are the most highly developed mollusks.   A common example is the squid of coastal waters, *Loligo pealei* along the Atlantic coast and *L. opalescens* on the Pacific coast.

20-16. Structure and natural history (Fig. 20-15).   The large *head* bears two conspicuous *eyes* and the central *mouth,* which is surrounded by 10 fleshy *arms* bearing cuplike *suckers;* the fourth pair of arms are long retractile *tentacles.*   The slenderly conical *body* has a fleshy triangular *fin* along either side of the tapered end.   The head and body join by a *neck,* around which the free edge of the mantle forms a loose *collar.*   Below the neck is a muscular funnel, or *siphon.*   The skin con-

Fig. 20-15.   Class Cephalopoda.   The squid, *Loligo*.   Internal structure as seen with body wall and arms removed on left side.

tains many *chromatophores,* each with yellow or brown pigment in an elastic capsule surrounded by muscle cells.   These expand and contract rhythmically, causing the animal to be alternately light and dark.   The squid is elongated dorsoventrally, the head is morphologically ventral, and the arms and siphon represent the foot of other mollusks.

In the upper (anterior) wall of the body is a horny "pen," the shell, stiffening the body; a cartilage-like case surrounds the "brain," there is a nuchal cartilage over the neck and similar support for the siphon and fins.   The mantle, fins, siphon, and arms are all muscular.   The *mantle* is a conical envelope surrounding the internal organs.   By its alternate expansion and contraction, water is drawn into and expelled from the mantle cavity.   For respiration alone the water passes into and out of the space between the neck and collar, but for "rocket" locomotion the mantle closes around the base of the siphon and water is forcibly ejected from the latter (Fig. 20-16).   To swim "tail first," the siphon is directed toward the arms; to move head foremost the tip of the siphon is bent around to force the water tailward.   The fins aid in steering and can also be used in swimming.

The digestive system includes (1) the *mouth;* (2) a muscular *pharynx* (buccal mass) with a pair of horny *jaws,* like a parrot beak inverted, and a *radula;* (3) a slender *esophagus;* (4) the saclike muscular *stomach,* joined by (5) a thin-walled *caecum* with a complex valve between; (6) the slender *intestine* and (7) *rectum* extend to (8) the *anus,* which opens into the mantle cavity. Two pairs of *salivary glands* connect to the pharynx, and the long *liver* and a small *"pancreas"* join by ducts to the stomach. The squid eats crustaceans, mollusks, and fishes. It swims forward with the arms together, then darts at the prey by suddenly ejecting water from the siphon; the arms are spread, the prey grasped and drawn to the mouth,

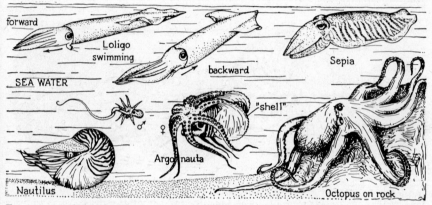

Fig. 20-16. Class Cephalopoda. *Loligo,* squid; *Sepia,* cuttlefish; *Nautilus,* pearly nautilus; *Argonauta,* paper nautilus; *Octopus,* octopus. Variously reduced.

bitten by the jaws, and swallowed. Small bottom animals are quietly covered by the spread arms and then gathered into the mouth.

Above the rectum is the glandular *ink sac,* with a duct opening near the anus; the ink is a dark pigment that can be forced out the siphon to produce an aquatic "smoke screen," under cover of which the squid can escape from an enemy. In each side of the mantle cavity is an elongate *gill.* Blood in veins from body tissues is pumped by a *branchial heart* through capillaries in the gill filaments and then is collected in an auricle on each side; these two join the single ventricle of the *systemic heart,* which sends the blood through arteries to the gut, head, arms, and other organs. A pair of *kidneys* drain from the pericardial cavity around the heart into the mantle cavity. The pairs of *nerve ganglia* are concentrated in the "brain box" around the pharynx. The *eyes* are unique among invertebrates; each has a cornea, lens, anterior and posterior chambers, and retina with rods and can form a real image (Fig. 4-33). They are structurally like those of vertebrates but differently derived. Below the brain are two *statocysts* serving for equilibration.

The sexes are separate, each with one *gonad* near the tip of the mantle cavity and a *duct* opening toward the funnel. At mating, a spermatophore (sperm packet) is transferred by the specialized tip (heterocotylus) of the third right arm on the male to the mantle cavity of the female, where the tip becomes detached and remains. The eggs are large, with much yolk, and are laid in elongate gelatinous capsules. Cleavage is superficial, somewhat as in birds, and there is no larval stage; the young hatch as miniature adults able to swim and feed at once.

20-17. Other Cephalopoda. This class swarmed the seas since Cambrian time and has a fossil record of some 10,000 species (Figs. 9-11 and 9-12). Nautiloids were dominant through Paleozoic times, the ammonites in the Mesozoic, and the dibranchiates (such as *Loligo*) abound

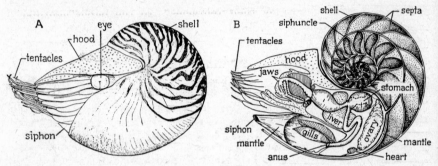

Fig. 20-17. Class Cephalopoda. The pearly nautilus, *Nautilus pompilius*. *A*. External features. *B*. Internal structure; shell and mantle (except at siphon) cut away to midline; jaws, tongue, and radula shown in median section; two left gills removed.

today. Both of the earlier groups had external calcareous shells that varied in size, shape, and ornamentation but were always divided into chambers by transverse septa. The animal probably lived in the outermost compartment, as with the living pearly nautilus. Early forms had slenderly conical shells, an inch to several feet in length. †*Endoceras* of Ordovician time was 15 feet long, the largest shelled invertebrate known; an ammonite, †*Pachydiscus*, of the Cretaceous had a coiled shell 6 feet 8 inches in diameter (Fig. 1-2). The only living relic of this great assemblage is the pearly nautilus (*Nautilus pompilius*) which inhabits the bottom at depths to 1,800 feet in the eastern Pacific and Indian oceans (Fig. 20-17). Its spiral shell is up to 10 inches in diameter, closely coiled in one plane, and divided by septa. The animal lives in the outermost chamber, having previously occupied each of the others in turn as it and the shell grew. The head bears 60 to 90 tentacles without suckers.

The living cephalopods are all predaceous and mostly free-swimming (Fig. 20-16). The squids range from species an inch long to the giant *Architeuthis*, of cold depths off Newfoundland and elsewhere, which is eaten by sperm whales. Small squids like *Loligo* sometimes occur in enormous schools; they are eaten by fishes and marine mammals and also are used as bait by fishermen, especially for cod. Squids are also an article of human food in many countries. The cuttlefish (*Sepia*) of Atlantic waters has a short oval body bordered by fins and possesses long tentacles that are completely retractile. Its internal calcareous shell is the cuttlebone used as a bill sharpener for caged birds, and for centuries its ink has provided the sepia pigment of artists. The devilfishes, or octopuses, vary from 2 inches to 28 feet in spread. They have a flexible bulbous body without a shell and eight long sucker-bearing tentacles. They crawl about rocks and tide pools along the seacoasts but can swim by use of the siphon. Large squid and octopuses are feared more rightly for their dangerously powerful beaks than for their supposed ability to grip a person under water by their tentacles. In the paper nautilus (*Argonauta*) of temperate oceans the female is up to 8 inches long and secretes a shell only as an egg case; the male is only about 1 inch long.

CLASSIFICATION

Phylum **MOLLUSCA.** Mollusks. Symmetry bilateral (viscera and shell coiled in some); no segmentation; body soft, covered by mantle and usually by limy shell of 1, 2, or 8 parts; usually an anterior head and ventral muscular foot; mouth with radula; heart dorsal, with 1 ventricle and 1 or 2 auricles; respiration usually by gills (ctenidia); coelom reduced; nephridia 1, 2, or 4; nervous system with few paired ganglia (cerebral, pedal, visceral), connectives, and nerves; usually dioecious, some monoecious; gonads 1 or 2; usually oviparous; a veliger larva, a glochidial stage, or development direct; mostly in salt or fresh waters, some Gastropoda on land; 45,000 living, 40,000 fossil species.

Class 1. *AMPHINEURA.* Body elongate, shell of 8 plates or none; head reduced; nerve ring around mouth and 2 pairs of ventral nerve cords; no tentacles.

Order 1. **Aplacophora** (Solenogastres). Form wormlike; integument thick, with minute calcareous spicules; foot rudimentary; bottom dwellers at 60 to 6,000 feet, in ooze or on corals and hydroids; about 50 species. *Neomenia*, 20 to 30 mm. long, North Atlantic, hermaphroditic, 2 gonads; *Chaetoderma*, 2 by 25 mm., around North Atlantic to Maine, sexes separate, 1 fused gonad.

Order 2. **Polyplacophora** (Loricata). Chitons. Body elliptical; shell a mid-dorsal row of 8 broad plates, surrounded by fleshy girdle; foot large, flat; gills, 6 to 80 pairs, in groove around foot; sexes separate; 1 gonad; a trochophore larva; on rocks, chiefly in shallow coastal waters; 600 living, 100 fossil species; Ordovician to Recent. *Tonicella, Chaetopleura, Isnochiton, Chiton; Cryptochiton,* with integument over plates.

Class 2. *SCAPHOPODA.* Tooth Shells or Tusk Shells. Shell and mantle slenderly tubular, slightly curved, open at both ends; foot conical; delicate "tentacles" around mouth; no gills; sexes separate; 1 gonad; a veliger larva; marine, in sand or mud, shallow water to 15,000 feet; 200 living, 300 fossil species; Devonian to Recent. *Dentalium, Siphonodentalium.*

Class 3. *GASTROPODA.* Snails, Slugs, Limpets, Whelks, etc. Visceral mass usually asymmetrical in a spirally coiled shell, either right- or left-handed (shell in some conical, reduced, or none); head distinct, with 1 or 2 pairs of tentacles and 1 pair of eyes; foot large, flat; original left auricle, gill, and kidney lacking in some; monoecious or dioecious; 1 gonad, usually with special ducts; mostly oviparous; marine, fresh-water, or terrestrial.

Order 1. **Prosobranchiata.** Shell often large, sometimes thick, rarely absent; usually with calcareous or horny operculum; head often snoutlike with 2 nonretractile tentacles and 2 eyes; foot usually broad; gills anterior to heart; dioecious; eggs usually in capsules, often attached, few ovoviviparous; a veliger larva; mostly marine; 25,000 living, 10,000 fossil species; Cambrian to Recent. *Acmaea, Patella, Fissurella,* limpets, shell flatly conical; *Haliotis,* abalones, shell ear-shaped, aperture large; *Crepidula,* slipper or boat shells; *Littorina,* periwinkles; *Strombus gigas,* giant conch, southern Florida and West Indies, 250 mm. or longer, largest univalve of the United States; *Cypraea,* cowries; *Carinaria* and *Atlanta,* heteropods, pelagic, transparent, foot used for swimming; *Murex,* rock shells; *Buccinum,* edible whelks; *Urosalpinx,* oyster drill; *Bythinia, Viviparus (Paludina),* and *Goniobasis,* all in fresh waters.

Order 2. **Opisthobranchiata.** Shell small or none; body asymmetrical or secondarily symmetrical; 2 pairs of tentacles, eyes at base of posterior pair; with gills (except nudibranchs), posterior to heart; monoecious, gonad single, sex openings separate; all marine; 3,000 living, 300 fossil species; Cambrian to Recent. *Actaeon, Cylichna, Haminea,* with shell; *Tethys,* sea hare, to 30 cm. long, shell vestigial and internal; *Cavolinia, Clione,* pteropods, pelagic, sides of foot expanded as fins; *Polycera, Doris, Aeolis,* nudibranchs or sea slugs, no shell, respire by skin, cerata, or papilla-like gills.

Order 3. **Pulmonata.** Fresh-water and Land Snails, and Slugs. Mostly small; shell a simple spiral (or none); head with 1 or 2 pairs of tentacles, 1 pair of eyes; mantle cavity anterior, its vascular lining an air-breathing lung, opens to a contractile pore on right side; no gills; monoecious; gonad single; mostly oviparous; development direct; chiefly terrestrial; more than 5,000 living, 1,000 fossil species; Devonian to Recent. *Lymnaea, Helisoma (Planorbis), Physa,* all in fresh waters; *Polygyra, Zonites, Helminthoglypta,* all terrestrial, mostly in moist places; *Helix,* European "garden" snails, introduced into the United States; *Testacella haliotidea,* greenhouse slug, with small terminal shell, in greenhouses, preys on earthworms; *Limax, Deroceras (Agriolimax), Ariolimax,* slugs with rudimentary shell in mantle; *Arion,* slugs with no shell.

Class 4. *PELECYPODA* (Lamellibranchiata). Bivalved Mollusks. Shell of 2 lateral valves, usually symmetrical, with dorsal hinge and ligament, and closed by 1 or 2 adductor muscles; mantle of right and left lobes, its margin commonly forming posterior siphons to control flow of water in and out of mantle cavity; no head, jaws, or radula; mouth with labial palps; foot often hatched-shaped, extends between mantle lobes when moving; gills usually platelike; usually dioecious, some protandric; gonad opening into mantle cavity; a veliger larva or glochidial stage; mostly marine, some in fresh water; 11,000 living, 15,000 fossil species.

Order 1. **Prionodesmacea.** Mantle margins usually separate ventrally and behind; siphon imperfect; Ordovician to Recent. *Nucula, Yoldia, Arca; Ostrea,* edible oyster, and *Mytilus,* sea mussel, both attached; *Pecten,* scallop or pecten, swims by clapping shells together; *Anodonta, Unio (Elliptio), Lampsilis, Margaritana,* mussels or clams of fresh water, shells of some used for buttons.

Order 2. **Teleodesmacea.** Margins of mantle more or less connected ventrally and posteriorly; siphons usually well-developed; mostly marine; Devonian to Recent. *Cardium,* cockle; *Mactra,* marine clam, to 15 cm. long; *Venus,* quahog or hard-shell clam; *Macoma; Solen; Ensis,* razor clam; *Mya arenaria,* mud clam, shell delicate; *Pholas,* burrows in clay or rock; *Teredo, Bankia,* shipworms, wormlike, burrow in wood; *Pisidium, Sphaerium,* free-living in fresh water.

Order 3. **Anomalodesmacea.** Mantle margins united ventrally and behind, with 3 or 4 openings for siphons and foot; hinge reduced or none; usually no gills; all marine, usually burrowing; Silurian to Recent. *Thracia, Lyonsia; Cuspidaria,* deep water, Massachusetts and north.

Class 5. *CEPHALOPODA.* Nautili, Squids, and Octopuses. Shell external, internal, or none; head large, eyes conspicuous and complex; mouth with horny jaws and radula and surrounded by 8 or 10 arms, or many tentacles; a siphon; nerve ganglia grouped in head as "brain," in cartilage-like covering; eyes conspicuous; dioecious; development direct; all marine; 400 living, 10,000 fossil species.

Order 1. **Tetrabranchia.** Shell external, coiled in 1 plane, divided by internal septa; 2 pairs of gills and nephridia; siphon 2-lobed; no ink sac; tentacles many, no suckers; eyes without lens.

Suborder 1. †ammonidea. Ammonites. Silurian to Cretaceous. †*Ammonites.*
Suborder 2. nautiloidea. Nautili. Ordovician to Recent. About 2,000 fossil species; 1 living genus of 2 or 4 species: *Nautilus pompilius,* pearly nautilus, eastern Pacific and Indian oceans at depths to 1,800 feet.

Order 2. **Dibranchia.** Shell internal and reduced, or none; body cylindrical or globose, often with fins; arms 8 or 10, with suckers; one pair of gills and nephridia; siphon tubular; an ink sac; eyes with lens.

Suborder 1. decapoda. Ten arms. Triassic to Recent. (Belemnites of Triassic to Cretaceous with internal chambered shell. †*Belemnites.*) Living forms: *Spirula,* shell spiral, internal, deep tropical seas, shells occasional on Atlantic coast; *Sepia,* cuttlefish, Atlantic waters; *Rossia,* body stubby, to 75 mm.; *Loligo,* squid; *Architeuthis,* giant squid.

Suborder 2. octopoda. Eight arms. Cretaceous to Recent. *Argonauta,* paper nautilus; *Octopus,* octopus, or devilfish.

References

Cooke, A. H. 1895. Molluscs. *In* Cambridge natural history. London, Macmillan & Co., Ltd. Vol. 3, x + 459 pp., figs. 1–311.

Haas, F. 1929–1935. Bivalvia [Pelecypoda]. *In* Bronn, Klassen und Ordnungen der Tierreichs. Leipzig, Akademische Verlagsgesellschaft. Vol. 3, Division 3, part 1, xii + 1,337 pp., 563 figs.

Hescheler, K. 1900. Mollusca. *In* Lang, Lehrbuch der vergleichenden Anatomie der wirbellosen Thiere. 2d ed.

Pelseneer, P. 1906. Mollusca. *In* E. R. Lankester, Treatise on zoology. London, A. & C. Black, Ltd. Part 5, 5 + 355 pp., 301 figs.

Pilsbry, H. A. 1939–   . Land Mollusca of North America (north of Mexico). *Philadelphia Academy of Natural Sciences, Monograph* 3, vol. 1, parts 1, 2.

Pratt, H. S. 1935. A manual of the common invertebrate animals. . . . 2 ed. Philadelphia, The Blakiston Co. Mollusca, pp. 556–604, figs. 740–921.

Robson, G. C. 1932. A monograph of the recent Cephalopoda. London, British Museum. 2 vols.

Thiele, G. 1924–1926. Solenogastres, Mollusca. *In* W. Kükenthal, and others, Handbuch der Zoologie. Berlin, Walter de Gruyter & Co. Vol. 5, pp. 1–256, figs. 1–340.

Twenhofel, William H., and Robert R. Shrock. 1935. Invertebrate paleontology. New York, McGraw-Hill Book Co., Inc. Mollusca, pp. 301–405, figs. 110–146.

Ward, H. B., and G. C. Whipple. 1918. Fresh-water biology. New York, John Wiley & Sons, Inc. Mollusca, pp. 957–1,020, figs. 1,403–1,534.

CHAPTER 21

PHYLUM ANNELIDA. SEGMENTED WORMS

In contrast to the various kinds of worms previously discussed, the earthworms, sandworms, and leeches of the Phylum ANNELIDA (L. *annelus*, little ring) have bodies composed of many essentially similar and ringlike segments, or somites. This segmentation usually shows in both external appearance and internal structures including muscles, nerves, and circulatory, excretory, and reproductive organs. Most of the earthworms and their allies (Class OLIGOCHAETA) are inhabitants of damp soil and fresh waters, the marine worms (Class POLYCHAETA) are found chiefly along the seashore, and the leeches (Class HIRUDINEA) are mainly in fresh waters or on moist ground. Members of the small Class ARCHIANELLIDA are all marine. Some species of annelids are free-living, many inhabit burrows or dwell in tubes, some are commensals on other aquatic animals, a few are ecto- or endoparasites, and many of the leeches attach to vertebrates.

21-1. Characteristics. 1. Symmetry bilateral; 3 germ layers; body elongate and usually conspicuously segmented both externally and internally.

2. Appendages are minute rodlike chitinous setae, few to many per somite; POLYCHAETA have fleshy tentacles on the head and the setae borne on lateral fleshy parapodia; most HIRUDINEA lack setae.

3. Body covered by thin moist cuticle over columnar epithelium containing unicellular gland cells and sensory cells.

4. Body wall and digestive tract both with layers of circular and longitudinal muscles; coelom well-developed (except in HIRUDINEA) and divided by septa in OLIGOCHAETA and POLYCHAETA.

5. Digestive tract complete, tubular, extending length of body.

6. A closed circulatory system of longitudinal blood vessels with lateral branches in each somite; blood plasma contains dissolved hemoglobin and free amoebocytes.

7. Respiration by the skin, or by gills in some tube dwellers.

8. Excretory system typically of one pair of nephridia per somite, each removing wastes from the coelom and blood stream directly to the exterior.

9. Nervous system with pair of cerebral ganglia (brain) and connectives to a solid (double) midventral nerve cord extending length of body, with a ganglion and pairs of lateral nerves in each segment; sensory cells and organs for touch, taste, and light perception.

10. Sexes united and development direct (OLIGOCHAETA, HIRUDINEA), or sexes separate and with trochophore larval stage (POLYCHAETA, ARCHIANNELIDA); some OLIGOCHAETA and POLYCHAETA reproduce asexually by budding.

The ANNELIDA resemble the ARTHROPODA in having a segmented body covered by cuticle that is secreted by the epidermis, in the structure of the

438

nervous system, and in forming mesoderm from special embryonic cells. They differ in having a large coelom, only simple unjointed appendages, little or no specialization of somites in different parts of the body, and no succession of larval stages, or molts. The Class ONYCHOPHORA of the Phylum ARTHROPODA shows some annelid features (p. 549). The ANNEL-IDA resemble the MOLLUSCA in embryonic features of cleavage and mesoderm formation; and marine annelids have a trochophore larva (p. 377). The metameric animal may have arisen from an unsegmented stock in forming chains of individuals by asexual fission as occurs in some PLATYHELMINTHES and ANNELIDA, but with the products of fission remaining united and acquiring both structural and physiological unity. Another theory presumes the segmental division of muscles, nerves, coelom, nephridia, etc., within a single individual as seen in the formation of somites by both larvae and adults of some ANNELIDA.

21-2. Size. Some of the smallest OLIGOCHAETA (*Aeolosoma, Chaetogaster*) are under 1 mm. long, but the giant earthworms (*Rhinodrilus fafneri* of Ecuador and *Megascolides australis* of Australia) grow to over 7 feet long and 1 inch in diameter. Most earthworms are only a few inches in length. The smallest POLYCHAETA are minute; *Nereis brandi* of the California coast attains to $5\frac{1}{2}$ feet and *Eunice gigantea* to nearly 10 feet. The leeches range from 10 to 200 mm., most being small.

CLASS *OLIGOCHAETA*. EARTHWORMS, ETC.

This class includes the annelids with few setae per segment (L. *oligos*, few + *chaete*, spine). The large earthworm of Europe and eastern North America, *Lumbricus terrestris*, is a representative oligochaete that may grow to 12 inches long and $\frac{3}{8}$ inch in diameter. It is the basis of the following account.

21-3. External features. The body (Fig. 21-1) is cylindrical and elongate, bluntly tapered at each end, and somewhat depressed posteri-

FIG. 21-1.   Class OLIGOCHAETA. The earthworm, *Lumbricus terrestris*, external features.

orly; the ventral side is flattened and is paler than the dark dorsal surface. There is no distinct head. The body of a mature worm is divided into about 100 to 180 ringlike segments, or **somites,** separated by transverse grooves. The **mouth** is in somite I, overhung by a fleshy lobe, the **prostomium,** and the vertically oval **anus** is in the last somite. The *clitellum* (L., pack saddle) is a conspicuous glandular swelling over somites XXXI–XXXVII; it secretes material forming cocoons to contain eggs. On each somite except the first and last are four pairs of minute bristle-like **setae** that project slightly on the ventral and lateral surfaces. Each seta is a fine chitinous rod, contained in an epidermal seta sac within the body wall, and is secreted by a large cell in the sac. A seta can be moved in any direction and extended or withdrawn by protractor and retractor muscles attached to the sac. The setae serve as holdfast devices when a worm is in its burrow or moving over the ground.

Besides the mouth and anus there are many minute external openings on the body, including (1) a **dorsal pore,** connecting the body cavity and exterior, middorsally in the furrow at the anterior border of each somite from VIII or IX to the anal end; (2) a **nephridiopore,** or excretory opening, lateroventrally on either side of each somite except I–III and the last; (3) the four minute openings of the **seminal receptacles** laterally in the furrows between IX–X and X–XI; (4) the openings of the paired **oviducts** ventrally on XIV; and (5) the openings of the paired **sperm ducts,** with swollen lips, ventrally on XV, from which a pair of glandular ridges extends to the clitellum.

21-4. Body wall. The exterior is covered (Fig. 21-2) by a thin transparent **cuticle,** marked with fine cross striations that produce a slight

FIG. 21-2. Earthworm. Diagram of cuticle and epidermis in perspective. (*Adapted from Hess, 1925; and Langdon, 1895.*)

iridescence. This is secreted by the **epidermis** beneath, a single layer of columnar epithelium that includes many **unicellular glands** producing mucus to pass through pores in the cuticle and keep the latter soft. The cuticle is also perforated by pores over the many **sensory cells** in the epidermis. Both kinds of pores are seen easily in pieces of cuticle stripped off and spread to dry on a glass slide. The epidermis rests on a basement membrane, beneath which is a thin layer of **circular muscles** and a thicker layer of **longitudinal muscles.** The inner surface of the body wall is covered by *peritoneum*. Pigment cells, connective tissue, and blood capillaries occur among the circular muscle fibers. There is no skeleton. The form of the animal is maintained by the elasticity of the body wall over the organs and fluids within. Contraction of the circular muscles elongates the body, contraction of the longitudinal muscles shortens it, and local or differential action of these same muscles produce the bending movements so characteristic of earthworms.

21-5. Internal structure (Fig. 21-3). If the body wall is slit mid-dorsally and spread, the earthworm is seen to consist essentially of two concentric tubes, the outer *body wall* and the straight *digestive tract* within; the space between them is the body cavity, or *coelom*. It is divided into a succession of compartments by the *septa,* which are thin

FIG. 21-3. Earthworm. Internal structure of anterior portion from the left side; body wall and digestive tract cut in median section. Two hearts shown in place; nephridia omitted; reproductive organs of right side included. I, X, XX, somites.

transverse partitions of connective tissue aligned with the grooves on the exterior surface; septa are absent between somites I and II and incomplete between III–IV and XVII–XVIII. The coelom and all organs within it are covered with a thin smooth epithelium, the *peritoneum*. The cavity contains a watery coelomic fluid with free colorless amoebocytes. Small pores in the septa permit this fluid to pass from somite to somite in keeping with movements of the body, and some of it may pass out the dorsal pores to moisten the exterior surface.

21-6. Digestive system. This consists of (1) the *mouth,* followed by a short *buccal cavity* (somites I–III); (2) the *pharynx* (IV–V), with glands to lubricate the food and muscle fibers in its external walls; (3) the slender straight *esophagus* (VI–XIV) joined on either side by three pairs of *calciferous glands* (X–XIV); (4) a thin-walled and enlarged *crop,* or proventriculus (XV–XVI) for storage; (5) the *gizzard* (XVII–XVIII), with thick firm muscular walls and lined internally with cuticle; and (6) the *intestine,* which continues to (7) the *anus.* The intestine is thin-walled and bulges laterally in each somite, and its dorsal wall carries an infolded *typhlosole;* the bulges and typhlosole afford increased surface for digestion and absorption of food. The internal lining is of columnar ciliated epithelium, containing many club-shaped gland cells; next are blood vessels, and then longitudinal and circular muscles; and the exterior of the intestine is covered by rounded yellowish *chloragog cells,* which are modified peritoneum. These cells may aid in fat distribution or elimination of wastes from the blood, and later become free in the coelom.

The food is chiefly of dead leaves, grasses, and other vegetation; it is moistened by saliva-like secretions from the mouth region and then drawn

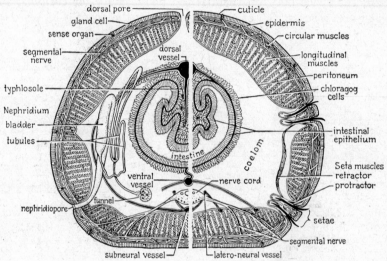

FIG. 21-4. Earthworm. Diagrammatic cross section. Left half shows an entire nephridium and a dorsal pore; but omits setae; right half includes setae but no nephridium.

in by muscular action of the prostomium, "lips," and pharynx. Any organic acids present in the food are neutralized by calcium carbonate secreted by the calciferous glands of the esophagus, so that food undergoing digestion is alkaline in reaction. Food is stored temporarily in the crop and later ground up in the muscular gizzard by aid of sand grains present there. The digestive tract secretes enzymes including pepsin and trypsin acting on proteins, lipase on fats, cellulase on cellulose, and amylase on carbohydrates. Digested material is absorbed in the intestine, and residues are egested through the anus. Small animals on the ground may be eaten, and captive worms will eat bits of fat or meat and dead worms. Earthworms utilize any organic food contained in the earth taken while burrowing.

21-7. Circulatory system. The *blood* consists of a fluid *plasma* that contains free colorless *corpuscles* (amoebocytes). The plasma is colored

red by the **hemoglobin** or respiratory pigment dissolved in it.   The blood circulates to and from all parts of the body in a system of closed **blood vessels** with capillaries.   There are five principal vessels extending lengthwise of the body and five pairs of "hearts" in somites VII–XI. Each somite from XII posteriorly has paired segmental vessels connecting between the longitudinal vessels and various organs; and special vessels serve structures in the anterior somites (Table 21-1; Fig. 21-5).

TABLE 21-1.   BLOOD VESSELS AND PATHS OF CIRCULATION IN THE EARTHWORM

Vessels	Location	Receive blood from	Direction of flow	Deliver blood to
Dorsal (1)	above gut, pharynx to anus	Dorsointestinals Parietals Lateral esophageals	anteriorly	Typhlosole Hearts Pharynx wall
Hearts (5 pairs)	somites VII–XI	Dorsal vessel	ventrally	Subintestinal
Subintestinal or ventral (1)	between gut and nerve cord	The hearts	anteriorly from VII; posteriorly from XI	Nerve cord, I–XX Segmentals (and lateroneurals)
Lateroneural (2)	sides of nerve cord, XX posteriorly	Segmentals	posteriorly	Nerve cord
Subneural (1)	under nerve cord	Nerve cord	posteriorly	Parietals
Segmental	body wall, 1 pair per somite (except first few)	Subintestinal	dorsally	Body wall Nephridia Lateroneurals
Parietal	body wall, 1 pair per somite, XII and posteriorly	Subneural Nephridia Body wall	dorsally	Dorsal vessel
Lateral or esophageal (2)	side of esophagus to X	Anterior end and gut wall	posteriorly	Dorsal vessel in X and XII
Afferent (ventro-intestinal)	gut wall, 2 per somite	Subintestinal	dorsally	Gut wall
Efferent (dorso-intestinal)	gut wall, 2 pairs per somite	Gut wall	dorsally	Dorsal vessel
Typhlosolar	median, 2 per somite	Dorsal vessel	ventrally	Typhlosole Dorsal wall of gut

21-8. Respiration.   There is no organized respiratory system.   Blood circulating in capillaries close to the moist cuticle of the body wall receives oxygen there and gives up carbon dioxide.   The oxygen combines with the hemoglobin in the plasma and is carried to various tissues.   In an emergency an earthworm can survive for several hours without a fresh supply of oxygen.

FIG. 21-5. Earthworm. Circulatory system. *A.* One pair of hearts and other vessels as in somite *X.* *B.* Relations of blood vessels in any somite behind the clitellum. Arrows indicate paths of blood flow. (*Adapted from Johnston and Johnson, 1902; and Bell, 1947.*)

FIG. 21-6. Earthworm. *A.* Ganglia and larger nerves of the anterior end. (*After Hess, 1925.*) *B.* Stereogram of the ventral nerve cord and body wall to show a simple reflex arc. Sensory cells (receptors) in the epidermis connect to sensory fibers that pass in a lateral nerve to the nerve cord; the sensory axone joins through a synapse to a motor nerve that leads to the body muscles (effector). Arrows indicate the direction of nerve impulses.

FIG. 21-7. Earthworm. *A.* An entire nephridium. *B.* Reproductive system in dorsal view, other organs omitted; seminal vesicles cut away on right side.

21-9. Excretory system.   Every somite except the first three and last contains a pair of coiled tubular structures called nephridia that dispose of organic wastes (Fig. 21-7*A*).   Each **nephridium** occupies parts of two successive somites.   A ciliated funnel, or **nephrostome,** lies at the anterior base of a septum beside the nerve cord and connects through the septum by a minute ciliated tubule to the main part of the nephridium in the next somite behind.   The tube there lies in several complex loops of increasing size, with a bladder-like collecting region that connects to the exterior through a **nephridiopore;** the latter opens near the ventral pair of setae. Cilia of the nephrostome and tubule beat so as to draw solid or fluid wastes from the coelom, and organic waste in the blood capillaries may enter the glandular portions of the tube; all such wastes are discharged through the nephridiopore.

21-10. Nervous system.   Above the pharynx (in somite III) is a pair of **suprapharyngeal** (cerebral) **ganglia,** the "brain" (Fig. 21-6*A*).   Two **connectives** extend around the pharynx to the bilobed **subpharyngeal ganglia** (base of somite IV) whence the **ventral nerve cord** extends along the floor of the coelom to the anal somite.   Several nerves connect to the prostomium and mouth region.   The ventral nerve cord in each somite shows an enlarged **ganglion** and gives off three pairs of **lateral nerves** (Fig. 21-6*B*).   The cord and ganglia appear to be single but develop as paired structures.   Each lateral nerve extends around half a somite between the two muscle layers of the body wall and includes both **sensory fibers,** carrying impulses in from the epidermis to the nerve cord, and **motor fibers,** carrying directive impulses outward from the cord to muscles and epidermal cells.   These nerves also include fibers of both types connecting to the nephridia, seta sacs, and other organs.

In the epidermis are many **sense organs,** each of a group of sensory cells surrounded by special supporting cells (Fig. 21-2).   These abound on the anterior end, at the posterior end, on the swollen part of each somite, and in the buccal cavity—the parts of the body most likely to receive stimuli from the environment.   Each sense cell has a hairlike tip projecting through a pore in the cuticle, and a sensory nerve fiber connects to the base of the cell.   Free endings of nerve fibers also occur between cells of the epithelium.   Special **photoreceptor cells** are found in the epidermis and on nerves at both ends of the body.   These cells are most numerous on the prostomium, anterior somites, and anal somite, the parts most sensitive to light; they are lacking on the ventral surface and in the grooves between somites.   Each cell contains a clear transparent organelle ("lens") that focuses light from any direction on a network of neurofibrils ("retina") in the periphery of the cell.   The neurofibrils are probably the actual light receptors, and they connect to sensory nerves.

These photoreceptor cells resemble the visual cells of leeches in structure and function.

21-11. Reproductive system. The earthworm is monoecious, with both male and female sex organs ventrally placed in each individual (Figs. 21-3, 21-7*B*). The *male reproductive system* includes (1) two pairs of minute *testes* (somites X, XI) and back of each (2) a ciliated *sperm funnel* connecting to (3) a short duct, the *vas efferens.* The two ducts on each side connect (in XII) to (4) a *vas deferens* that leads to (5) the *male pore* (XV). The testes and funnels are contained in (6) two pairs of large saclike *seminal vesicles* (in IX to XIII) that extend dorsally around the esophagus. Immature sperm cells separate from the testes to complete their differentiation in the vesicles, and mature sperm are discharged through the funnels and ducts during copulation. The *female reproductive system* includes (1) a pair of *ovaries,* anteriorly in somite XIII, that discharge mature ova into the coelom, whence they are collected by (2) the two *oviducal funnels* (posterior border of XIII) with egg sacs, connecting to (3) the *oviducts* opening on somite XIV. The female system also includes (4) two pairs of *seminal receptacles* (in IX, X) where sperm received in copulation are stored until needed to fertilize eggs in cocoons.

21-12. Natural history. Earthworms live in most lands of the world including oceanic islands and subarctic regions. They are numerous in good soils, with much humus and abundant moisture, but scarce in poor, acid, sandy, or dry situations. They inhabit burrows for protection against enemies and unfavorable climatic conditions. The burrows are nearly vertical at the top, then wind about to various depths, some extending to 6 or 8 feet below the surface. In soft topsoil, a worm makes the burrow by using its slender anterior end as a wedge to enter any crevice and then forces the soil particles outward by swelling its pharynx region. In heavier or deeper soil the worm excavates by actually eating its way. The ingested earth is passed through its digestive tract and deposited on the ground surface as small mounds of feces, or "castings," to be seen commonly wherever worms are plentiful. The upper parts of a regular burrow may be lined with slime, earth from castings, leaves, or fine pebbles, to produce a smooth interior. Earthworms in cold climates retire below the frost line in winter and remain inactive; in arid regions they do likewise in summer to avoid the drought and heat, each rolling up in a close ball.

When the soil is moist and the temperature is moderate, each worm lies by day in the upper part of its burrow, anterior end uppermost. The entrance may be plugged with bits of leafy material. After dark this is pushed aside, and the worm extends its forward end out over the ground surface, to explore, forage, or mate; the posterior end remains in the *dioecious — sexes contained in 2 separate animals*

burrow, holding by the setae, so that if frightened the entire animal can withdraw to safety by a quick contraction of its body. At times a worm will leave its burrow and travel on the surface, and a sudden flooding of the ground, as by a heavy rain, will cause many worms to emerge. This is the basis of an old notion that they "come down in rain"; however, on rare occasions worms have actually been carried by tornadoes!

Experimental study of the reactions of earthworms explains some features of their behavior. They avoid all but the weakest of light, remaining hidden by day, and at night will withdraw quickly if a light is flashed on them; they tolerate a red light but avoid a blue one. They are sensitive to mechanical vibrations such as heavy footfalls on the ground but evidently do not "hear" mere sound vibrations in air. They react favorably to contact, being used to that of the ground surface or the surrounding burrow, and if turned up as in the spading of a garden will seek contact with the earth as well as to avoid daylight. Tactile stimuli are all-important in retaining contact with the ground and burrow. Since respiration depends upon the cuticle being kept moist, they respond positively to a moist environment rather than to dryness. The chemical responses, comparable to taste and smell, are more difficult to study, but it is evident that they serve in the choice of food. Unpleasant or irritating chemical vapors in the air will cause withdrawal into the burrow. Whether different sensory organs respond to tactile and chemical stimuli is unknown.

FIG. 21-8. *A.* Two earthworms in copulation (X = 10th somite). *B.* Secretion of slime tube and cocoon. *C.* Slime tube and cocoon slip forward. *D.* Free tube containing cocoon. *E.* Cocoon. (*A, after Grove,* 1925; *B-D, after Foot and Strobell,* 1902.)

21-13. Reproduction. Earthworms reproduce through much of the year, but most actively in warm moist weather. Mating occurs at night and requires 2 or 3 hours. Two worms stretch out from their burrows and bring their ventral anterior surfaces together, with the anterior ends pointing in opposite directions (Fig. 21-8). The clitellum (XXXI–XXXVII) on each grips somites VII–XII of the other, and a lesser contact of somite XXVI on each is made with XV of the other. Special ventral setae (VI–X, clitellum) of each actually penetrate the body of the other to aid in holding the worms together. Each worm secretes a slime tube about itself, covering somites IX to XXXVI. On each worm a pair of seminal grooves forms (XV to clitellum) along which masses of sperm pass to enter the seminal receptacles of the other (between IX–X and X–XI); after this the worms separate. There is thus reciprocal and cross-fertilization.

Each worm later produces cocoons containing eggs. In *Eisenia foetida*, Foot and Strobell found that captive worms each formed 2 to 10 cocoons at intervals of 3 to 5 days, containing 1 to 28 eggs of which 10 to

FIG. 21-9.   Development of the earthworm; diagrammatic sections (except *E*).   BLASTULA. *A*. Early, with mesoblast cell.   *B*. Growth of mesoblast (mesoderm).   GASTRULA.   *C*. Early longitudinal section.   *D*. Early cross section.   *E*. Later entire gastrula in ventral view.   *F*. Cross section of later gastrula.   *G, H*. EARLY EMBRYO; two layers of mesoderm separate to yield coelom in somites.   *I, J*. LATER EMBRYO; mouth derived from blastopore. (*Adapted from Wilson, 1889; and Sedgwick and Wilson, Introduction to general biology, Henry Holt and Co., Inc.*)

12 develop.   The cocoons of *Lumbricus terrestris* measure about 7 by 5 mm., and each has several eggs of which only 1 develops.   For each cocoon a slime tube is secreted around the clitellum and anterior somites (X–XXXVI), and within this the cocoon forms as a separate secretion over the clitellum; eggs and albumen enter the cocoon while it is still on the clitellum.   The tube and cocoon then slip forward, sperm to fertilize the eggs enter while passing over the seminal receptacles, and as the worm

withdraws from the tube the cocoon closes into a lemon-shaped case that is deposited in damp earth.

Cleavage is holoblastic but unequal, making a hollow blastula of small ectoderm cells above and larger endoderm cells below (Fig. 21-9). Two large mesoblast cells develop on the future posterior surface and later pass inside to lie between the ectoderm and endoderm. The spherical blastula flattens and elongates as an oval plate, the endoderm cells become columnar, and the ectoderm grows down marginally. In gastrulation the ventral surface becomes concave and the edges curl down, meeting first posteriorly. This closure proceeds forward, the endoderm thus invaginating as a tube (future gut) ending with the blastopore (future mouth) at the anterior end. The anus forms much later. Meanwhile two cords of mesoblast cells multiply from behind forward, between ectoderm and gut; they spread as two flat plates giving rise to a series of pockets (the somites) and the body muscles. After gastrulation albuminous material in the cocoon enters the primitive gut (archenteron) to nourish the embryo. Development requires several weeks, since young hatch in 2 to 3 weeks from cocoons kept in a laboratory.

The adult earthworm has some ability to regenerate somites removed at the ends of the body by accident or experiment. At the anterior end no more than 4 will form, and no "head" will form if 15 or more are cut off; regeneration at the anal end often follows loss of somites there. Experiments in grafting have produced worms with two tail ends, short worms from two terminal portions, or extra-long worms by joining parts of three worms.

21-14. Relations to man. Earthworms are of practical use as bait for fishing, and various schemes have been tried to force the worms out of their burrows so that they can be gathered in quantity. These include use of alternating current and pouring irritating chemicals on the ground, but neither is very successful. Large earthworms for bait are sometimes reared in boxes of soil by providing suitable environmental conditions and food. A small white earthworm (*Enchytraeus albidus*) is often grown in soil and used to feed aquarium fishes and small laboratory animals.

The castings of earthworms on lawns are sometimes a nuisance, especially on golf greens, and means have been developed to poison worms where too numerous. In exceptional instances, earthworms burrows may cause loss of water by seepage from ditches in irrigated lands. Some of the small ENCHYTRAEIDAE are thought to damage plants in the ground. Ancient medical writers mention various irrational uses of earthworms in human medicine, and these are still followed in parts of Japan and China.

The long-time effects of earthworms in nature have certain practical aspects. Since earthworms occur by tens of thousands per acre in many soils and burrow actively during much of the year, they exercise a considerable influence on the land, in company with other burrowing animals. The burrows facilitate the entry of air and water, and the castings, in the aggregate, bring quantities of soil to the surface—up to 18 tons per acre in a single year on favorable sites, according to Charles Darwin. The same author noted that layers of gravel or cinders that have been spread over fields are found, after a number of years, to be evenly covered with several inches of topsoil brought up by the worms. In the same way, large stones once on the surface and the floors of ancient stone buildings become gradually embedded in the soil with the passage of centuries. This continued "cultivation" by earthworms is believed gradually to contribute to the depth of arable topsoil over less fertile subsoils. In contrast to this benefit the castings of earthworms on sloping lands tend to be washed away by rain and thus contribute slightly to soil erosion.

Recently there has been a wave of enthusiasm for rearing earthworms to distribute in gardens and orchards in the belief that soil fertility would be quickly improved, but scientific trials show no such benefits.

21-15. Other Oligochaeta. This class includes over 2,400 species, most of which are smaller than *Lumbricus terrestris*. The most common earthworm over North America is the smaller *Allolobophora caliginosa*. The brandling, or "stinking earthworm," *Eisenia foetida*, which is ringed with maroon and yellow, is a favorite fishworm that lives in piles of manure or compost. These two species are commonly used for microscopic study and for experimental work. Earthworms are passive carriers of the gapeworm of fowls (*Syngamus*) and intermediate hosts for a cestode of fowls (*Amoebotaenia sphenoides*) and a lungworm of pigs (*Metastronyglus elongatus*); the latter parasite carries a virus that, in combination with a bacterium, causes swine influenza. Various other oligochaetes inhabit damp banks of lakes and streams and either fresh or foul waters. Some live deep in lakes, some beneath stones or decaying seaweeds of the ocean shore, and a few are marine at shallow depths. Others occur in mountains to 12,500 feet (Kashmir), and some inhabit snow fields from Oregon to Alaska. Most oligochaetes feed on vegetation, but a few are probably carnivorous (*Chaetogaster*). The reddish *Tubifex* lives in tubes on the bottom of polluted waters, feeding on the bottom muck, and probably aids in purifying such places. Some oligochaetes are important in the diet of moles, various birds, amphibians, fishes, and predatory invertebrates.

Worms of the Families AEOLOSOMATIDAE and NAIDIDAE reproduce asexually by transverse fission, with several to many "generations" per year; in some genera no sexual individuals are known. Individuals of *Chaetogaster* and *Aeolosoma* form chains of zooids.

Class POLYCHAETA. Sandworms, Tube Worms, etc.

The Polychaeta (Gr., many bristles) are the segmented worms common along seacoasts. They differ from the Oligochaeta in having (1) a differentiated head with sensory appendages; (2) each body somite with many setae borne on a pair of lateral parapodia; (3) the sexes usually separate and without permanent gonads; and (4) a free-swimming trochophore larval stage.

The clamworm, Neanthes (Nereis) virens (Fig. 21-10), is a representative polychaete that lives near the low-tide line. It hides by day beneath

Fig. 21-10. Class Polychaeta. Clamworm, Neanthes virens. Entire specimen, dorsal view; I–III, somites. (After Newman, and others, Nature of the world and man, University of Chicago Press.)

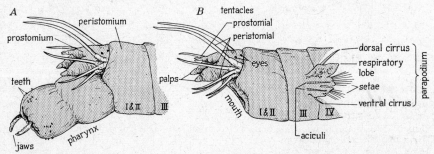

Fig. 21-11. Clamworm. Head region from left side. A. Pharynx extended. B. Pharynx retracted.

stones or in a temporary burrow with only the head protruding; at night it reaches out, crawls over the sand, or swims by lateral wriggling of the body. Large individuals may be 450 mm. long.

21-16. Structure and natural history. The slender elongate *body* is of greenish color, rounded above and flattened ventrally, and is composed of up to 200 or more similar *somites.* A distinct *head* is formed by the prostomium and peristomium (somite I + II). On the prostomium are two short *prostomial tentacles* medially, a pair of stubby conical *palps* laterally, and two pairs of small *eyes* dorsally. The periostomium surrounds the ventrally placed *mouth* and carries four pairs of *peristomial tentacles* dorsally (Fig. 21-11). These specialized sensory organs of touch, smell, and sight are of service in finding food, avoiding enemies, and other activities. On either side of each body somite is a flat *parapodium*

(Gr. *para*, beside + *podos*, foot) formed of two lobes (dorsal notopodium, ventral neuropodium) each bearing a *cirrus* and a bundle of bristle-like *setae*. Within are two needle-like chitinous *aciculi*, which extend into the body and serve to support and move the parapodium (Fig. 21-12). The parapodia serve for locomotion, in both creeping and swimming. The *anus* is in the last somite, on which are two soft sensory *anal cirri*.

The body is covered by *cuticle* over an *epidermis*, and beneath the latter are *muscles*, a thin layer of circular muscles and four large bundles of longitudinal muscles (2 dorsal, 2 ventral). The parapodia are moved

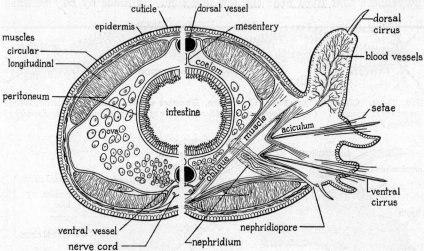

Fig. 21-12. Clamworm. Diagrammatic cross section. Left half with ova free in coelom, right half through parapodium.

by oblique muscles in each somite, and there are special muscles in the head. Within the body wall is the *coelomic cavity*, lined by peritoneum and divided by *septa* between most of the somites as in the earthworm. There are also median dorsal and ventral *mesenteries* between the body wall and gut that divide the coelom of each somite into right and left compartments.

The *digestive tract* is essentially a straight tube and includes (1) the *mouth;* (2) a protrusible *pharynx* with two horny-toothed jaws; (3) a short *esophagus* joined by two large digestive glands; and (4) the *stomach-intestine,* which extends from about somite XII to (5) the *anus*. The food is of small animals, grasped by the jaws.

The *circulatory system* comprises a dorsal vessel and a ventral vessel, both longitudinal, with transverse branches in each somite to the gut, nephridia, body wall, and parapodia. The blood plasma is red, containing dissolved hemoglobin and colorless corpuscles; circulation results from peristaltic contractions of the dorsal vessel. *Respiration* is effected by capillaries in the parapodia and in the body wall.   **Excretion** is performed by paired nephridia that differ from those of the earthworm in being more compact and having much of the ducts ciliated.   The **nervous system** includes a pair of cerebral ganglia in the head with nerves to the tentacles, eyes, etc., and two long connectives joining the midventral nerve cord, which has a pair of ganglia and lateral nerves in each somite.

The sexes are separate.   No permanent reproductive organs are present.   In the breeding season either ova or sperm form from cells of the coelomic peritoneum, and when mature the gametes either pass out through the nephridia or burst through the body wall.   Fertilization occurs by the mixing of ova and sperm in the sea water, and the zygote develops into a ciliated trochophore larva (Fig. 18-1).   This floats about, later to settle and transform into a young worm.

21-17. Other Polychaeta.   Most of the species live from the tide line down to about 20 fathoms, with some in deeper waters, even to 18,000 feet.   Many resemble the clamworm, and others are variously modified in structure and habits; some are brilliantly colored.   The various species crawl on the bottom, hide beneath rocks or plants, dwell in temporary burrows, or live in permanent tubes.   A few swim in the open sea, a few others inhabit fresh water, and the small oval MYZOSTOMARIA are ecto-parasites on echinoderms.   The free-ranging polychaetes are largely carnivorous, some burrowing forms feed on bottom muck, and the tube dwellers subsist mainly on plankton.

The sea mouse, *Aphrodite,* has an oval body with pairs of large plates (elytra) dorsally and is covered by long hairlike setae.   The lugworm, *Arenicola,* is a soft-bodied worm that burrows by ingesting sand or mud and produces castings like an earthworm.   Other species plaster the sandy walls of their burrows with a mucous secretion that binds the sand grains against collapse and produces a smooth lining.   *Terebella* builds a tube of selected sand grains, bits of shell, or other materials, set in mucus. *Pectinaria* cements a tapering tube of fine sand grains, open at both ends, which the worm may carry about.   The minute *Spirorbis* secretes a spiral calcareous tube that is fastened to the surface of rocks or seaweed, and *Hydroides* forms a larger and irregular tube of the same sort.   Some tube dwellers can burrow in rocks or shells.   *Chaetopterus* is a specialized worm living permanently in a parchment-like U-shaped tube, up to ¾ inch in diameter, that is set with both openings just above the mud or sand (Fig. 21-13*A*), at depths to 15 fathoms.   Three pairs of modified parapodia on the middle of its body are modified as fans to draw in water containing oxygen and microscopic organisms.   The mouth is a wide funnel.   Other animals live as commensals in the tube.   *Serpula* and other tube dwellers have a crown of many ciliated tentacles, derived from the prostomial palps, that collect microscopic food; the tentacles contain blood vessels and so serve also as gills for respiration. The tip of one filament is enlarged to form an operculum to close the tube when the worm draws within. Some tube worms, such as *Sabellaria*, often occur in large closely set colonies. Other polychaetes have gills on the parapodia or, exceptionally, at the posterior end.

In some polychaetes the sexes are unlike at maturity, showing secondary sexual characters. The germ cells develop on the peritoneum or blood vessels, usually in the posterior somites, which become different in appearance from the anterior, or nonsexual, part.

A   B

Fig. 21-13.   Order Polychaeta.   *A. Chaetopterus*, a specialized worm dwelling in a secreted tube in the sea bottom. The "fans" are modified parapodia that draw water through the tube. Commensal crabs (*Polyonyx*) also inhabit the tube. (*After Pearse*, 1913.)   *B. Eunice viridis*, the palolo worm. (*From Van Cleave, Invertebrate zoology.*)

In *Syllis* the hinder sexual portion is budded off and develops a head, and the nonsexual part forms a new tail end. In *Autolytus*, regeneration of segments begins before such separation, and the sexual part may divide several times to produce a chain of zooids. In *Syllus racemosa* there is lateral budding that yields branched chains of zooids.

The palolo worm, *Eunice viridis* (Fig. 21-13*B*), of Samoa and Fiji, inhabits burrows in coral reefs at the sea bottom; it produces many posterior segments that become crowded with eggs or sperm. These are cast off as a unit by each worm to rise and swarm at the surface of the sea, when the water becomes milky with the millions of discharged gametes. Swarming occurs regularly on the first day of the last quarter of the

October-November moon, continuing for 2 or 3 days.   Another species (*Leodice fucata*) of the West Indies and Gulf of Mexico swarms in the third quarter of the June–July moon.   Maturation of gametes possibly is stimulated by the light of the full moon and completed 8 or 9 days later when swarming ensues.

CLASS *HIRUDINEA*.   LEECHES

The leeches are aquatic or terrestrial worms, of predatory or parasitic habits, that have enlarged terminal suckers for locomotion and attachment.   Their annelid characteristics include a ventral nerve cord with segmental ganglia and the segmentally arranged nephridia and gonads in the reduced coelom.   They resemble the OLIGOCHAETA in having a clitellum, in being monoecious with formed gonads in a few segments, in producing cocoons, and in lacking tentacles, parapodia, and a larval stage. They differ from other ANNELIDA in the lack of setae (except in *Acanthobdella*) and in the presence of copulatory organs and of genital openings on the midventral line.

21-18. Structure (Fig. 21-14).   The *body* of a leech at rest is elongate or oval in outline and usually flattened dorsoventrally, but is very flexible

FIG. 21-14.   Class HIRUDINEA.   The medicinal leech, *Hirudo medicinalis*.   Internal structure seen in dissection from the ventral side; I-XXV, somites.

and may be greatly stretched, contracted, or dilated.   It consists fundamentally of 34 *somites,* as shown by the nerve ganglia, but the exterior is marked by transverse furrows into many *annuli* (2 to 5 per somite).   At the posterior end is a rounded *sucker,* formed from 7 somites; another sucker (of 2 somites) surrounds the mouth at the anterior end in many species.

The body is covered by *cuticle* secreted by a single-layered *epidermis,* and many unicellular mucous glands open on the surface.   Beneath is a *dermis* with pigment cells and blood capillaries.   The *muscular system* is elaborate and powerful, with circular, longitudinal, oblique, and dorsoventral bands of fibers.   Mesenchyme between the muscles and internal organs reduces the *coelom* to a system of canals and sinuses, from which the nephridia drain and in which the gonads and major blood vessels are located.

The *digestive tract* includes (1) the mouth; (2) a muscular pharynx with unicellular salivary glands and usually either a proboscis or three horny-toothed jaws; (3) a short esophagus; (4) a long crop with up to 20 pairs of lateral pouches or caeca; (5) a slender intestine; (6) a short rectum; and (7) the anus opening before the posterior sucker.   The *circulatory system* is of longitudinal vessels, dorsal, ventral, and lateral, with many cross connections; pulsations in some of these cause the blood to circulate.   *Respiration* is performed by a network of capillaries beneath the epidermis.   *Excretion* is by up to 17 pairs of peculiar nephridia that sometimes are branched and sometimes have closed nephrostomes.   The *nervous system* resembles that of other annelids, with a pair of dorsal ganglia and paired connectives to the ventral nerve cord, which has segmental ganglia.   Four of the anterior ganglia and seven at the posterior end are fused.   Each ganglion gives off several pairs of nerves.   The sensory structures include taste cells in the mouth, tactile organs on the lips and body, one to five pairs of eyes anteriorly, and other eyelike organs (sensillae) on several annuli.

The sexes are united.   The *male reproductive system* includes 4 to 12 pairs of testes lying beneath the crop; those on each side join a vas deferens running anteriorly, and the two ducts enter a median penis to which accessory glands connect.   The penis is within the male genital pore on the midventral surface and toward the anterior end of the body. The *female reproductive system* comprises two ovaries and oviducts joining a single albumen gland and median vagina that opens just behind the male pore.

21-19. Natural history.   Most leeches inhabit fresh waters, a few occur on marine fishes, and some live in moist places on land (Fig. 21-15).   They are largely nocturnal but may be attracted by food during the day.   They travel by looping movements of the body—like a "measuring worm"— and use the suckers for attachment; some also swim by graceful undulations of the body.   Leeches are either scavenging, predatory, or parasitic; some feed on dead animals, and others prey upon small worms, insects, larvae, mollusks, etc.   The group is best known for the bloodsucking habits of some species.   These attach to the exterior or mouth cavity of various vertebrates, from fish to man, some being restricted to one or a few host species.   Such a leech fastens on by its suckers and pierces the skin; then blood is sucked out by action of the muscular pharynx and stored in the distensible crop.   A salivary enzyme (hirudin) prevents coagulation of the blood.   At one feeding a leech may ingest several times its own weight of blood.   Much of the liquid is soon excreted, but the concentrated part of such a "full meal" remains fluid and is digested slowly over a period of several months.

Reproduction takes place in the warmer months.   Copulation and reciprocal fertilization occur in some leeches (HIRUDINIDAE); in others, packets of sperm (spermatophores) are deposited by one leech on the exterior body surface of another, whereupon the sperm penetrate to the ovaries and effect fertilization.   Most leeches produce cocoons containing fertilized eggs, and these are placed either in water or in earth.   In the GLOSSIPHONIIDAE the eggs are attached ventrally to the parent where they develop and where the young remain for a time.

FIG. 21-15.   Order HIRUDINEA.   *Left.*   Leeches in fresh water.   (*After Schmeil.*)   *Right.* Successive stages *A-I*, in locomotion of the medicinal leech.   (*After Uexhull*, 1905.)

Leeches are eaten by various aquatic vertebrates and sometimes are used as fish bait.   In north temperate regions, leeches are a minor nuisance to persons wading or bathing in some waters, but they seldom produce serious effects on mankind or the larger vertebrates.   In some localities they may attach to the buccal cavity of people or mammals when drinking.   The land leeches of southeastern Asia and neighboring islands are extremely abundant and sometimes cause severe injury to human beings.   The most famous member of the CLASS HIRUDINEA is the medicinal leech (*Hirudo medicinalis*) of Europe.   It grows to 4 inches in length, can stretch 8 or 12 inches, and is capable of ingesting a considerable quantity of blood.   Since ancient times, it has been used for "bloodletting" and was in enormous demand during the early nineteenth century when this was a common, though erroneous, method of medical treatment.   It was then collected and even reared in ponds in many parts of Europe.   From 8,000,000 to 57,000,000 were annually imported into France from 1827 to 1854, and considerable numbers were also used in England and in the eastern United States.

CLASS *ARCHIANNELIDA*

21-20. Archiannelids. This is a minor group of small worms that occur along the sea shore. They show some features that resemble larval POLYCHAETA, and they may be either primitive or degenerate. *Polygordius* (Fig. 21-16) becomes 30 to 100 mm. long, having a slender body on which the somites are indistinct externally. The small prostomium bears two sensory tentacles. Most species have no setae or parapodia. The internal organs resemble those of polychaetes but are of simple form.

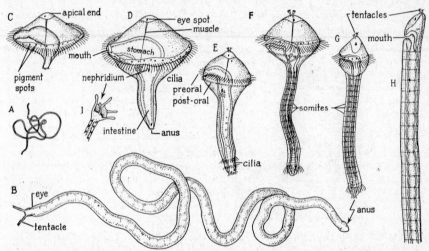

FIG. 21-16. Class ARCHIANNELIDA. *Polygordius.* *A.* Adult, natural size. *B.* Adult, enlarged. *C-H.* Successive stages in growth, beginning with trochophore and showing gradual increase in number of somites. *I.* Nephridium, enlarged. (*After Fraipont*, 1887.)

Each segment of the coelom contains a pair of nephridia. The nervous system lies in the epidermis. The larva is a typical trochophore on which somites are produced posteriorly during metamorphosis. *Dinophilus* is about 2 mm. long, with a relatively broad prostomium bearing two eyes, but no tentacles. There are five or six body segments, each encircled by two bands of cilia that serve for locomotion, and no setae are present.

CLASSIFICATION

Phylum **ANNELIDA.** SEGMENTED WORMS. Body elongate, usually segmented and with paired setae; cuticle thin, nonchitinous; digestive tract complete, usually tubular; coelom usually large; blood system closed; paired nephridia; a pair of dorsal cerebral ganglia connected to solid midventral nerve cord with ganglia and lateral nerves in each somite; world-wide, marine, fresh-water, and on or in soil; more than 6,500 species.

Class 1. *ARCHIANNELIDA.* Size small; segmentation chiefly internal; parapodia and setae usually absent; nervous system in epidermis; usually dioecious; gonads numerous; usually a trochophore larva; marine. *Polygordius; Dinophilus; Chaetogordius.*

Class 2. *POLYCHAETA.* Sandworms, Tube Worms, etc. Body segmented externally and internally, somites numerous, with lateral parapodia that bear many setae; a head region with tentacles; no clitellum; sexes usually separate; no permanent gonads; fertilization commonly external; a trochophore larval stage; asexual budding in some species; predominantly marine; 3,500 species.

Order 1. **Errantia.** Somites alike except in head and anal regions; parapodia alike along entire body; pharynx usually protrusible; free-living or in free or attached tubes; often predatory, some pelagic. *Neanthes (Nereis)*, clamworm, *Aphrodite*, sea mouse; *Syllis*, with asexual budding; *Myzostoma*, ectoparasitic on echinoderms; *Manayunkia speciosa* in Schuylkill River and *Nereis limincola* in Lake Merced, San Francisco, both in fresh water.

Order 2. **Sedentaria.** Body of 2 or more regions with unlike somites and parapodia; prostomium indistinct, head appendages modified or none; pharynx without jaws, usually nonprotrusible; gills anterior or none; in burrows or tubes, feed on detritus or plankton. *Chaetopterus*, no gills; *Cirratulus*, *Amphitrite*, with long gills; *Arenicola*, with branched segmental gills and rudimentary parapodia; *Hydroides*, *Spirorbis*, *Sabellaria*, *Serpula*, in tubes, with anterior gills.

Class 3. *OLIGOCHAETA.* Earthworms, etc. Segmentation conspicuous externally and internally; no head or parapodia; setae usually few per somite; seldom with gills; monoecious, gonads few and anterior; with clitellum secreting cocoon for eggs; no larva, development direct; chiefly in fresh water and moist soil; 2,400 species. *Aeolosoma; Chaetogaster*, commensal on fresh-water sponges, bryozoans, and snails; *Tubifex*, often in delicate tubes in mud; *Enchytraeus*, in soil and on sea beaches; *Pontodrilus*, on seashores; *Bdellodrilus*, *Branchiobdella*, leechlike, commensal on gills of crayfishes; *Eisenia foetida*, the "brandling," in compost or manure piles; *Allolobophora*, *Lumbricus*, in soil.

Class 4. *HIRUDINEA.* Leeches. Body pigmented, usually depressed; a large posterior sucker and often a smaller one at anterior end; no tentacles, parapodia, or setae (one exception); somites 34, subdivided externally into many annuli; a slight clitellum (IX–XI); coelom filled by connective tissue and muscles; monoecious; eggs usually in cocoons; no larva; in fresh or salt water or on land; 290 species.

Order 1. **Acanthobdellida.** No anterior sucker, proboscis, or jaws; 2 pairs of setae each on somites II–IV, coelom segmented. *Acanthobdella*, one species on salmon in Lake Baikal, Siberia.

Order 2. **Rhynchobdellida.** With or without anterior sucker; a protrusible proboscis; no jaws; blood colorless; usually 3 annuli per somite. *Branchellion*, with gills, marine, on rays and skates; *Piscicola*, on bony fishes; *Placobdella*, abundant on turtles and in fresh waters; *Glossiphonia*, in fresh waters.

Order 3. **Gnathobdellida.** An anterior sucker and usually 3 chitinous jaws, but no proboscis; blood red; includes most leeches. *Hirudo medicinalis*, European medicinal leech, introduced in eastern United States; *Haemopis marmoratis*, horseleech, in mud, usually feeds on invertebrates; *Macrobdella decora*, to 300 mm. long, in fresh waters of northern states, attacks man, cattle, frogs, and fish, eats invertebrates; *Herpobdella; Haemadipsa*, tropical land leech, southeastern Asia to Tasmania.

References

Beddard, F. E. 1896. Oligochaeta (Earthworms, etc.) and Hirudinea (Leeches). *In* Cambridge natural history. London, Macmillan & Co., Ltd. Vol. 2, pp. 345–449, figs. 187–225.

Bell, A. W. 1947. The earthworm circulatory system. *Turtox News* (Chicago), vol. 25, no. 5, pp. 89–94, 4 figs.

BENHAM, W. B. 1896. Archiannelida, Polychaeta, and Myzostomaria. *In* Cambridge natural history. London, Macmillan & Co., Ltd. Vol. 2, pp. 239–344, figs. 121–186.

DARWIN, C. 1881. The formation of vegetable mould through the action of worms, with observations on their habits. London, John Murray. vi + 326 pp., 13 figs.

FOOT, K., and E. C. STROBELL. 1902. Further notes on the cocoons of Allobophora foetida. *Biological Bulletin*, vol. 3, pp. 206–213, 3 figs.

GROVE, A. J. 1925. On the reproductive processes of the earthworm, Lumbricus terrestris. *Quarterly Journal of Microscopical Science*, vol. 69, pp. 245–290, pls. 16–17, 3 figs.

HESS, W. N. 1925. Nervous system of the earthworm, Lumbricus terrestris L. *Journal of Morphology and Physiology*, vol. 40, pp. 235–259, 7 figs.

———. 1925. Photoreceptors of Lumbricus terrestris, with special reference to their distribution, structure and function. *Journal of Morphology and Physiology*, vol. 41, pp. 63–93, 18 figs.

KÜKENTHAL, W., and OTHERS. 1928–1934. Handbuch der Zoologie. Berlin, Walter de Gruyter & Co., Vermes Polymera [= Annelida], vol. 2, part 2, xx + 874 pp., 806 figs.

LANGDON, F. E. 1895. The sense-organs of Lumbricus agricola, Hoffm. [= *L. terrestris*]. *Journal of Morphology*, vol. 11, pp. 193–234, pls. 13–14, 2 figs.

MICHAELSEN, W. 1900. Oligochaeta. *In* Das Tierreich. Berlin, Friedlander & Sohn. 10th Lieferung, xxiv + 575 pp., 13 figs.

MOORE, J. P. 1923. The control of blood-sucking leeches, with an account of the leeches of Palisades Interstate Park. *Roosevelt Wild Life Bulletin (Syracuse University)*, vol. 2, no. 1, pp. 9–53, 1 pl., 17 figs.

NACHTRIEB, H. F., E. E. HEMINGWAY, and J. P. MOORE. 1912. The leeches of Minnesota. *Geological and Natural History Survey of Minnesota, Zoological Sciences*, no. 4, 150 pp., 6 pls.

PRATT, H. S. 1935. A manual of the common invertebrate animals. . . . 2d ed. Philadelphia, The Blakiston Co. Annelida, pp. 320–368, figs. 443–502.

STEPHENSON, J. 1930. The Oligochaeta. Oxford, Clarendon Press. xv + 978 pp., 242 figs.

WILSON, E. B. 1889. The embryology of the earthworm. *Journal of Morphology*, vol. 3, pp. 387–462, pls. 16–22.

CHAPTER 22

PHYLUM ARTHROPODA.   JOINT-FOOTED ANIMALS
CLASS CRUSTACEA.   CRUSTACEANS

The Phylum ARTHROPODA (Gr. *arthros*, joint + *podos*, foot) contains most of the known animals, more than 740,000 species, and many of them are enormously abundant as individuals.   It includes the crabs, shrimps, barnacles, and other crustaceans (Class CRUSTACEA), the insects (Class INSECTA), the spiders, scorpions, ticks, and their allies (Class ARACH-NOIDEA), the centipedes (Class CHILOPODA), the millipedes (Class DIPLOPODA), and other less familiar and fossil forms.   The body is seg-mented externally in varying degree and the appendages are jointed, both

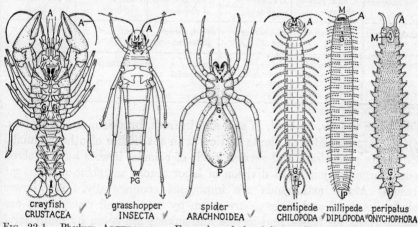

crayfish   grasshopper   spider   centipede millipede peripatus
CRUSTACEA   INSECTA   ARACHNOIDEA   CHILOPODA DIPLOPODA ONYCHOPHORA

FIG. 22-1.   Phylum ARTHROPODA.   Examples of the 6 living Classes in ventral view, showing body divisions, somites, appendages with their divisions, and the body openings. *A*, antennae; *M*, mouth; *P*, anus; *G*, genital opening(s).

being differentiated in form and function to serve special purposes (Fig. 22-1, Table 22-1).   All exterior surfaces are covered by an organic exoskeleton containing chitin.   The nervous system, eyes, and other sense organs are proportionately large and well-developed, making for quick response to stimuli.   This is the only major invertebrate phylum with many members adapted for life on land, apart from moist surround-ings; and the insects are the only invertebrates capable of flight.

Arthropods occur at altitudes of over 20,000 feet on mountains to depths of more than 18,000 feet in the sea.   Different species are adapted

TABLE 22-1. PHYLUM ARTHROPODA. SOME CHARACTERISTICS OF COMMON CLASSES (SEE FIG. 22-1)

CLASSES		*CRUSTACEA* Crustaceans, etc.	*INSECTA* Insects	*ARACH-NOIDEA* Spiders, etc.	*CHILOPODA* Centipedes	*DIPLOPODA* Millipedes
Body divisions		usually cephalo-thorax and abdomen	head, thorax, abdomen	cephalothorax and abdomen	head and long body	head, short thorax, long abdomen
Paired appendages	Antennae	2 pairs	1 pair	none	1 pair	1 pair
	Mouth parts	mandibles 2 pairs maxillae maxillipeds	mandibles 1 pair maxillae labium	chelicerae pedipalpi	mandibles 2 pairs maxillae	mandibles 1 pair maxillae
	Legs	1 pair per somite, or less	3 pairs on thorax (+ wings)	4 pairs on cephalothorax	1 pair per somite	2 (or 1) pairs per somite
Respire by		gills or body surface	tracheae	lung books, or tracheae	tracheae	tracheae
Sex openings		2, hind part of thorax	1, end of abdomen	1, second somite of abdomen	1, end of abdomen	1, third somite near head
Development		usually larval stages	with larvae usually	direct, except mites and ticks	direct	direct
Principal habitat		salt or fresh water, few on land	mainly terrestrial	mainly terrestrial	all terrestrial	all terrestrial

for life in the air, on land, in soil, and in fresh, brackish, or salt waters. Others are parasites of plants and on or in the bodies of other animals. Some are gregarious, and several kinds of colonial insects have evolved social organizations with division of labor among members of different castes. Many arthropods are important economically. The larger crabs, lobsters, and shrimps are eaten by man, small crustaceans are staple foods for fishes, and insects and spiders are eaten by many land vertebrates. The insects are man's chief competitors, eating his crops, stored foods, household goods, or clothing. Some insects and ticks injure or carry diseases to mankind, his domestic animals, and his crops.

22-1. Characteristics. 1. Symmetry bilateral; 3 germ layers; body usually segmented and jointed externally; head, thorax, and abdomen variously distinct or fused (head somites always fused).

2. Appendages one pair per somite or less, each with few to many hinge joints and containing opposed sets of muscles; variously differentiated, sometimes reduced in number or parts, rarely lacking.

3. A hardened exoskeleton containing chitin, secreted by the epidermis, and molted at intervals.

4. Muscles striated, often complex, usually capable of rapid action.

5. Digestive tract complete; mouth parts with lateral jaws adapted for chewing or for sucking; anus terminal.

6. Circulatory system open (lacunar); heart dorsal, distributing blood by arteries to organs and tissues, whence it returns through body spaces (hemocoel) to the heart; coelom reduced.

7. Respiration by gills, trachea (air ducts), lung books, or body surface.

8. Excretion by coxal or green glands or by 2 to many Malpighian tubules joined to gut (segmental nephridia only in *Peripatus*).

9. Nervous system with paired dorsal ganglia over mouth and connectives to a pair of ventral nerve cords, with a ganglion in each somite or ganglia concentrated; sensory organs include antennae and sensory hairs (tactile and chemoreceptor), simple and compound eyes, auditory organs (INSECTA), and statocysts (CRUSTACEA).

10. Sexes usually separate, male and female often unlike; fertilization mostly internal; eggs with much yolk and chitinous shells; either oviparous or ovoviviparous, cleavage superficial; usually with 1 to several larval stages and gradual or abrupt metamorphosis to adult form; parthenogenesis in some crustaceans and insects.

The ARTHROPODA and ANNELIDA are the only invertebrate phyla with conspicuous segmentation. Both show this in the body, muscles, and nervous system. The arthropods differ from the annelids in (1) the absence of cilia; (2) general lack of inter-segmental septa; (3) reduction of the coelom; (4) presence of a lacunar blood system; (5) concentration of excretory organs and gonads; (6) separation of the sexes; (7) presence of an exoskeleton of chitin; (8) jointed appendages; and (9) compound eyes. Some primitive crustaceans (Subclass BRANCHIOPODA) are annelid-like in the structure of the heart and nervous system and grow by adding somites before the terminal part (telson) containing the anus. The peculiar wormlike *Peripatus* (Class ONYCHOPHORA) has segmental nephridia recalling those in annelids, and its anterior end bears some resemblance to a polychaete annelid; but its body lacks internal septa, and its legs are not jointed.

Some zoologists divide the ARTHROPODA into subphyla, including the BRANCHIATA (crustaceans, trilobites), INSECTA or TRACHEATA (insects), CHELICERATA (spiders, etc.), CHILOPODA (centipedes), and PROGONEATA (millipedes, etc.), with several "appendices" for forms of uncertain status. Others recognize five to seven classes, and some join the centipedes and millipedes as the Class MYRIAPODA. Seven classes and several miscellaneous groups are included in this book (see Classification in Chaps. 22 to 24). The sequence of classes is mainly one of convenience, although the trilobites and crustaceans are probably the most ancient. These and some others originated in Pre-Cambrian time. The evidence from fossils and from the morphology of living forms is often conflicting so that it is difficult to construct a genealogical tree for the arthropods.

22-2. Cuticle and chitin. Arthropods are sheathed in an exoskeleton quite unlike either the soft epidermis or the limy shells of other invertebrate phyla. The body covering is a complex noncellular *cuticle* (of two or three layers) containing both fibers and pores and is produced by the single-layered epidermis (hypodermis) immediately beneath. The best known component of the cuticle is **chitin**,[1] a nitrogenous polysaccharide $(C_8H_{13}O_5N)_x$ that is insoluble in water, alcohol, alkalis, dilute acids, or the digestive juices of many animals. Formerly it was thought that the proportion of chitin determined the degree of rigidity in the exoskeleton (hence hard parts were said to be "heavily chitinized"), but later researches show that some soft portions are largely of chitin whereas other firm parts contain little chitin.

The cuticle covers all exterior parts and lines the fore- and hind-gut, respiratory structures, and ducts of surface glands. Its texture varies from smooth to rough, often being sculptured with pits, ridges, or spines and perforated for sensory setae and gland exits (Fig. 23-4). In tracheal tubes and on gills the cuticle is microscopically thin and permeable, and at joints on appendages or between body parts it is soft to facilitate movements. As a general body covering it is commonly flexible and sometimes elastic (nymphs, larvae), but in other cases it is a thick rigid armor, hardened (sclerotized) by chemical substances (*e.g.*, $CaCO_3$ in many crustaceans and millipeds). As a whole. the exoskeleton protects the internal organs, provides attachments for muscles, and forms levers and fulcra between movable parts. On terrestrial arthropods it prevents loss of water and body fluids from the tissues.

Such a jointed but fixed external armor necessarily limits the size of the animal inside. Molt, or ecdysis, is therefore necessary at intervals to permit an increase in size. Most arthropods have four to seven molts. Prior to molt, a new soft exoskeleton grows inside, and the old layer becomes loosened. The latter then opens dorsally, and the animal withdraws slowly, then expands by swallowing air (or water). The new covering soon hardens by chemical change and not solely by exposure to the air or water.

22-3. Size. Because of the limiting weight of the exoskeleton, no arthropod is of great size. Some fossal eurypterids grew to be 9 feet long, and a living Japanese crab (*Macrocheira kämpferi*) spreads to 12 feet with its slender legs. The Atlantic lobster is recorded to 24 inches in length, and a living isopod (*Bathynomus giganteus*) to nearly 14 inches. No living insect exceeds 11 inches in length or spread. The smallest crustaceans, insects, and mites are under 1 mm. long.

Class *CRUSTACEA*. Crustaceans

The Crustacea (L. *crusta*, a hard shell) includes the fairy shrimps, water fleas, barnacles, crayfishes, crabs, and their kin. Most of them are

[1] Chitin also occurs in some sponges, hydroids, bryozoans, brachiopods, mollusks, and annelids, but not in protozoans, echinoderms, or vertebrates.

marine, but many others live in inland waters, and a few, like the sow bugs, are in moist places on land.   Aquatic species inhabit variously the shore, rocks, submerged plants, or open waters; many larvae and some adults burrow, others are pelagic, and a few live deep in the sea.   The great majority are free-living, and some gregarious species occur in vast "schools."   The barnacles are either sessile or parasitic, and certain other crustaceans are commensal or parasitic on various aquatic animals, from hydroids to whales.   Some parasitic species are so greatly modified that their status as crustaceans is shown only in their larval stages.

22-4. Characteristics.   1. Head of 5 fused somites with 2 pairs of antennae, 1 pair of lateral mandibles for chewing, and 2 pairs of maxillae; thorax of 2 to 60 somites, distinct or variously fused; abdominal somites usually distinct, with telson at end; often with a carapace over head and parts of thorax, as a dorsal shield or as 2 lateral valves; appendages variously modified, some usually biramous.

2. Respiration by gills (rarely by body surface).

3. Excretion by 1 or 2 pairs of green glands; no Malpighian tubules.

4. Sexes separate (except in Cirripedia and some parasitic Isopoda); sex openings paired; eggs often carried by female; parthenogenesis in some Branchiopoda and Cladocera.

22-5. The crayfish.   This animal (*Cambarus, Astacus*) serves well for an introduction to both the Arthropoda and the Crustacea (Fig. 22-2).

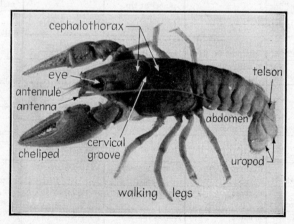

Fig. 22-2.   Class Crustacea.   The crayfish, showing external features.

It is up to 6 inches long and has appendages differentiated to serve special purposes.   The common English names of "crayfish" and "crawfish" (and even the American "crawdad") probably derive from the French name écrevisse (inhabiting a crevice).   Various species of crayfishes inhabit fresh-water streams, ponds, and lakes over much of the world.   *Cambarus affinis* is common in the eastern states, *C. virilis* and others in the Mississippi Valley, and *Astacus nigrescens* occurs from San Francisco

TABLE 22-2. APPENDAGES OF THE CRAYFISH

Somite* and name of appendage	Number and structure of parts			Function
	Protopodite	Endopodite	Exopodite	
I Antennule	3, statocyst in dorsal base	short jointed feeler	short jointed feeler	equilibrium, touch, taste
II Antenna	2, excretory pore in ventral base	long feeler of many joints	thin pointed blade	touch, taste
III Mandible	2, heavy jaw + base of palp	2 distal parts of palp	0	biting food
IV 1st maxilla	2, thin medial plates	1, small, unjointed	0	food handling
V 2d maxilla	2, bilobed plates	1, narrow exopodite and epipodite form scoop (scaphognathite) to draw water over gills		
VI 1st maxilliped	2, broad medial plates + epipodite	2, slender, small	2, slender, minute	touch, taste, food handling
VII 2d maxilliped	2, short, with gill	5, short, stout	2, slender	
VIII 3d maxilliped	2, with gill	5, larger	2, slender	
IX 1st "walking" leg	2, with gill	5, stout; heavy pincer at tip	0	pincer for offense and defense
X 2d "walking" leg	2, with gill	5, slender, small pincer	0	walking, grasping
XI 3d "walking" leg	2, with gill; sex pore in ♀	5, slender, small pincer	0	
XII 4th "walking" leg	2, with gill	5, slender, no pincer	0	walking
XIII 5th "walking" leg	2, no gill; sex pore in ♂	5, slender, no pincer	0	
XIV 1st swimmeret	in ♀, reduced or none			transfer sperm from ♂ to ♀
	in ♂: protopodite + endopodite fused, tubular			
XV 2d swimmeret	in ♂: 2 joints	rolled, conical	filamentous	
	in ♀: same as XVI			
XVI 3d swimmeret	2, short	jointed filament	jointed filament	water circulation in both sexes; carry eggs and young in ♀
XVII 4th swimmeret	2, short	jointed filament	jointed filament	
XVIII 5th swimmeret	2, short	jointed filament	jointed filament	
XIX Uropod	1, short broad	1, flat oval plate	1, flat oval plate, with hinge	swimming, ♂ and ♀; egg protection in ♀

* Some authorities consider that a somite without appendages precedes that bearing the antennule which would make 6 somites in the head and 20 in all.

northward on the Pacific coast.   *C. clarkii* of the Gulf states has become
acclimatized in southern California.   The lobster (*Homarus americanus*)
of salt waters along the Atlantic coast is much larger, but resembles the
crayfish closely in structure.

22-6. External features.   An exoskeleton containing *chitin* covers the
entire body and is hardened except at joints where it is thin and soft to
permit of movements.   The body comprises an anterior rigid *cephalothorax* (head + thorax) and a posterior jointed *abdomen*.   It is composed
of *somites,* or metameres (head 5, thorax 8, abdomen 6), each with a pair
of jointed *appendages* ventrally.   The skeletal elements of a single
somite, as in the abdomen, include a transverse dorsal plate, or *tergum,*
and a ventral crossbar, or *sternum,* joined together at either side by a
lateral *pleuron.*   Somites of the cephalothorax are covered by a continuous *carapace* shielding the dorsal and lateral surfaces.   On this a transverse *cervical groove* marks the division between the head and thorax, and
at the anterior end is a median pointed *rostrum.*

Beneath the rostrum on either side is a *compound eye,* stalked and
movable.   The *mouth* is between the mandibles, and the *anus* opens
ventrally in the broad median *telson* (not a somite) at the end of the
abdomen.   The *gills* are beneath either side of the carapace.   The paired
female sex openings are at the base of the third pair of walking legs on the
thorax, and those of the *male* at the fifth pair.

22-7. Paired appendages (Table 22-2, Figs. 22-2, 22-3).   Unlike the
many simple and solid setae of the earthworm, the crayfish has one pair of

Fig. 22-3.   Crayfish.   Appendages of the right side in ventroposterior view (some omitted),
showing structural differentiation to serve various functions.   *pr,* protopodite; *en,* endopodite; *ex,* exopodite; *ep,* epipodite; *g,* gill.

jointed appendages on each somite; these contain opposed sets of muscles
for their movement.   The joints on the thoracic appendages are not all in
the same plane, so that these members may be moved in various directions.   The appendages on different somites are of parts that differ in

number, structure, and function.   They illustrate, however, the principle
of serial homology in that all are referable to a common form, the two-
branched or *biramous appendage;* this consists of a *protopodite,* typically
of two joints (coxopodite, basipodite), that bears a medial *endopodite* and
lateral *expodite,* each of one to many segments.

The short *antennules* and long *antennae* are mobile sensory structures
that test and receive stimuli from the environment.   The stout *mandibles*
crush the food, which is manipulated by the *maxillae* and *maxillipeds.*
The large *chelae* serve in offense and defense, and the other *walking legs*
(pereiopods) are used for locomotion, handling food, and cleaning the
body.   The abdominal *swimmerets* (pleopods) aid in respiration and
carry the eggs on females, and the wide *uropods,* with the telson, form a
broad terminal paddle for swimming.

22-8. Muscles.   In the crayfish and other arthropods the muscles are
complex and all are contained within the exoskeleton, instead of being a
part of the body wall as in coelenterates and annelids or external to the
skeleton as in vertebrates.   The muscles attaching to many parts are in
opposed pairs, a *flexor* to draw the part toward the body or point of
articulation and an *extensor* to straighten it out.   The largest muscles are
the flexors which bend the abdomen forward under the body when the
crayfish swims backward.

22-9. Digestive system.   This includes (1) the *mouth,* opening above
the mandibles; (2) a short tubular *esophagus;* (3) the large thin-walled
stomach in the thorax that is divided into a swollen anterior *cardiac
chamber* and smaller *pyloric chamber* behind; (4) a short *mid-gut;* (5) the
slender tubular *intestine* extending dorsally in the abdomen to (6) the
anus; and (7) two large *digestive glands* ("liver") beneath the stomach,
each with a duct to the mid-gut (Fig. 22-4).   Food is brought to the
mouth by the chelate second and third pairs of legs, the soft parts being
torn and crushed to small size by the mandibles, then passed through the
esophagus to the cardiac chamber.   Projecting into this are strongly
calcified *teeth,* one median and two lateral, that are moved by muscles
attached outside the stomach and form a *gastric mill* for further grinding
of the food.   The entrance to the pyloric chamber bears many hairlike
setae that permit only fine particles to enter.   Each digestive gland is
three-lobed and composed of many fine tubules that secrete a pancreatic-
like enzyme serving in digestion.   Absorption of digested food occurs in
the mid-gut, possibly also in the "liver."   Hard particles are rejected by
the mouth or cardiac mill, and undigested materials are formed as feces
in the intestine to pass out the anus.   The digestive tract, except for the
mid-gut, is lined by delicate chitin, continuous at the mouth and anus
with the external cuticle; the entire lining is shed at each molt.   At some

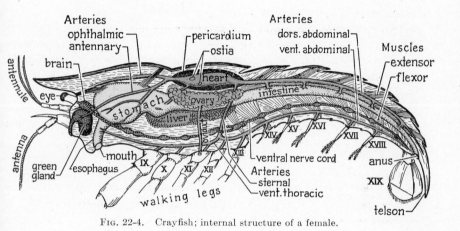

Fig. 22-4.   Crayfish; internal structure of a female.

Fig. 22-5.   Crayfish; Cross section of the body through the heart; arrows indicate the course of blood flow.

seasons the walls of the cardiac chamber have 2 calcareous gastroliths, thought to store lime salts for hardening the exoskeleton after a molt.

TABLE 22-3. PRINCIPAL ARTERIES OF THE CRAYFISH

Artery	Origin	Direction of blood flow	Supplies
Ophthalmic (1) (anterior aorta)	heart	anterior to head	eyes, antennules, brain
Antennary (2)	heart	anteroventral	antennae, green glands, anterior muscles, stomach
Hepatic (2)	heart	ventral	"liver," pyloric stomach, mid-gut
Dorsal abdominal (1) (posterior aorta)	heart	posterior, top of abdomen	intestine, telson, abdominal muscles
Sternal (1)	base of posterior aorta	ventral (passes through nerve cord)	ventral thoracic and abdominal arteries, gonads
Ventral thoracic (1)	sternal artery	anterior, floor of thorax	mouth, esophagus, appendages III–XI*
Ventral abdominal (1)	sternal artery	posterior, floor of abdomen	abdominal muscles, appendages XII–XIX*

* See Table 22-2.

22-10. Circulatory system. The short muscular *heart* is of irregular shape and suspended in a large middorsal *pericardial sinus* of the thorax by 6 ligaments that attach to the sinus walls. Blood in the sinus enters the heart through 3 pairs of *valves* (ostia) and is pumped, by contraction of the heart, into 6 arteries that distribute to all parts of the body (Table 22-3). The arteries contain valves that prevent a return flow. From the finer arteries the blood flows into open spaces, or *sinuses,* between body organs, whence it collects in a large *sternal sinus* in the floor of the thorax and passes in afferent channels leading to the gills. There the CO_2–O_2 exchange of respiration occurs, and the blood returns in efferent channels to the *branchiocardiac sinuses* that lead up the inner sides of the thoracic wall to the pericardial sinus. This *lacunar* or *open system,* distributing between the tissues and without veins, is characteristic of the arthropods and is in striking contrast to the closed circulatory systems of annelids and vertebrates. The nearly colorless *blood plasma* has a dissolved respiratory pigment (hemocyanin) that transports oxygen to the tissues; there are free *amoeboid corpuscles* in the plasma.

22-11. Respiratory system. The *gills* (Figs. 22-5, 22-6) are delicate plumelike projections of the body wall, containing blood channels and located along either side of the thorax in a *gill chamber.* The latter is

covered by a lateral portion (branchiostegite) of the carapace, but open
ventrally and at both ends.   A paddle-like projection (scaphognathite) of

the second maxilla moves back
and forth in a channel under each
side of the carapace to draw water
containing dissolved oxygen over
the gill filaments.   The gills are
arranged in lengthwise rows, the
podobranchiae being attached to
the coxopodites of appendages
VII–XII, and the double row of
arthrobranchiae (anterior ·VII–

Fig. 22-6. Crayfish. The gills (podobranchiae) exposed by removal of the branchiostegite. (*After Huxley.*)

XII, posterior VIII–XII) to the membranes joining these appendages to
the thorax, making 17 on each side.   In the Genus *Astacus* there is one
pleurobranchia on the thorax above appendage XIII.

22-12. Excretory system.   Two large *green glands,* ventral in the head
and anterior to the esophagus, serve to remove organic wastes from the
blood and body fluids.   Each consists of a glandular region, an expanded
"bladder" with thin walls, and a duct opening ventrally on the basal
segment of the antenna.   The cavities in the excretory and genital organs
comprise the only relics of the coelom in arthropods; the spaces within the
body form a *hemocoel,* not comparable with the large coelom of annelids.

22-13. Nervous system.   In the crayfish, this system bears a general
resemblance to that of the earthworm but is proportionately larger (Fig.
22-7).   The *supraesophageal ganglia* ("brain") in the head send nerves

Fig. 22-7. Crayfish. The nervous system in dorsal view.

to the eyes, antennules, and antennae and a pair of *connectives* join the
subesophageal ganglia, behind the mouth, at the anterior end of the
double *ventral nerve cord.*   The fused subesophageal ganglia of the adult
represent six (or five) pairs of ganglia that are separate in the embryo;
nerves from these pass to the mouth appendages, esophagus, green
glands, and anterior muscles.   Along the nerve cord each somite from
VIII to XIX contains a pair of joined ganglia sending nerves to the
appendages, muscles, and other organs.

22-14. Sense organs.   These enable the crayfish to test its environment continually, to find shelter, food, and mates, and to avoid unfavorable surroundings and enemies.   Much of the body is sensitive to *touch,*

especially the chelae, chelipeds, mouth parts, underside of the abdomen, and edge of the telson.   On these regions are many *tactile hairs,* which are delicate plumelike projections of the cuticle, containing fibers connected to sensory nerves.   The *chemical sense* (taste + smell) resides in hairs on the antennules, tips of the antennae, mouth parts, and ends of the chelae.   If meat juice is brought in a fine pipette to any of these, the animal vibrates its mouth parts, becomes excited, and turns toward the stimulus.   Meat placed slightly away from a crayfish is "discovered" when juices diffusing from it through the water reach these sensory organs. The sense of *equilibrium* or orientation to gravity is served by a small chitin-lined sac, the *statocyst,* that opens dorsally under fine hairs on the basal segment of each antennule.   It contains a ridge with many fine upright *sensory hairs* to which sand grains become attached by mucus and serve as *statoliths.*   The action of gravity on the statoliths produces stimuli through the hairs, which are attached to an "auditory" nerve leading to the brain.   Tilting or inverting the body alters the direction of gravitational pull on the statoliths and sets up a changed stimulus to the brain, which leads the animal to right itself.   At a molt, the statolith lining and the sand grains are lost, but new grains are soon acquired from bottom debris.   Proof of their function is had if a freshly molted crayfish is placed in filtered water containing no foreign particles so that no new statoliths can be acquired; its equilibrium will be disturbed.   Should iron filings be placed in such water, some will enter the statocysts; if then a magnet is placed above or at the side of the crayfish, the latter will react by turning its ventral surface toward the magnet.

Each *compound eye* (Fig. 22-8) has an outer rounded surface covered by transparent cuticle, the *cornea,* which is divided into about 2,500 microscopic square *facets.*   The facet is the outer end of a slender tapering visual unit, or *ommatidium.*   Each of these consists of (1) the corneal facet, or *lens;* (2) two *corneagen cells,* which secrete the lens; (3) a *crystalline cone* of four cone cells; (4) *distal pigment cells* about the cone; (5) a long tapering *retinula* of eight cells, which form a central *rhabdome* where they meet; (6) *basal pigment cells* around the retinula; and (7) a *tapetum cell* between the inner bases of the retinular cells.   The inner ends of the retinular cells penetrate the *basement membrane* on which all the ommatidia rest, and each connects through a *nerve fiber* through four *optic ganglia* to the *optic nerve,* which joins the brain.

The eye forms images in two ways (Fig. 22-8*D, E*).   In strong light the pigment is extended to isolate each ommatidium from those adjacent. Light from any small area on an object that passes axially through a lens will reach the light-sensitive retinula and stimulate its nerve fibers, but any rays entering at an angle are refracted into the pigment and absorbed.   Of any object, the eye will form a *mosaic* or *apposition* *image,* the light from different parts registering on separate ommatidia. Any slight shift of the object will stimulate other ommatidia; hence, the compound eye is especially efficient in registering movement. In weak light the pigment recedes toward the distal and basal parts of the ommatidia, the light rays then spread to adjacent ommatidia, and there forms on the retinulae a continuous or *superposition image,* which is probably

FIG. 22-8. Crayfish. The compound eye; diagrammatic. *A.* Entire eye sectioned to show its general structure. *B.* One ommatidium in the light, pigment extended. *C.* Ommatidium in the dark, pigment contracted. *D.* Apposition image formed of separate images on retinulae from points *1, 2, 3* on object. *E.* Superposition image, each retinula receives both oblique and direct rays from more than one point. (*Adapted in part from Imms, Textbook of entomology, E. P. Dutton & Co., Inc.*)

less distinct than the apposition image but provides a proportionately stronger stimulus in relation to the amount of light received.

22-15. Endocrine glands. The *sinus gland* on the eyestalk in various crustaceans produces a hormone that controls the spread of pigment granules in chromatophores of the body epidermis and in the compound eyes, regulates the molt, affects the deposit of lime salts in the exoskeleton, and is also necessary to the continuance of life. The hormone is evidently distributed by the blood stream, as in vertebrates.

22-16. Reproductive system. The sexes are separate in the crayfish, and the female has a proportionately broader abdomen than the male. The first two pairs of appendages on the male's abdomen are tubular, for sperm transfer. The gonads are hollow and three-lobed in both sexes.

In the *male* the two soft white *testes* are fused and lie beneath the pericardial sinus. On each side a slender coiled *vas deferens* extends ventrally to open at the base of the fifth walking leg. In the female the two *ovaries* are of comparable form and location with the testes of the male. Eggs develop in follicles on the inner surface and are discharged through an *oviduct* opening near each third walking leg.

22-17. Natural history. The Genus *Astacus* includes 5 species in western North America and 10 in Europe and western Asia; *Cambarus* comprises about 70 species in North America east of the Rocky Mountains and in Central America. Other genera and species inhabit the Southern Hemisphere. The various species of *Cambarus* are segregated ecologically, some examples being (1) *C. affinis* in ponds, lakes, and slow rivers; (2) *C. acutus* in swifter streams; (3) *C. virilis* in large rivers; (4) *C. bartoni* in upland streams; (5) *C. diogenes* in marshes and meadows where it digs burrows 1 to 3 feet deep, down to the water, and topped by chimneys of mud; and (6) *C. pellucidus*, which is blind and lives in cave waters.

The crayfish is a solitary bottom dweller, hiding by day under stones or in crevices or burrows, where it keeps as much of its body as possible in contact with surrounding objects. The animal faces the entrance of its retreat, with the chelae extended, the antennae waving about, and the "scoops" and swimmerets performing respiratory movements; other appendages are moved at times to receive stimuli or detect food. It grasps any food that passes within reach and will emerge to seize any detected near by and then go back into its retreat. It resists attack by use of the strong chelae and tries to avoid being drawn out of its shelter; if the latter is opened or removed, the animal darts off to a new hiding place. The crayfish can walk forward, sideways, obliquely, or backward with the fourth pair of legs bearing much of the weight. By extending the abdomen, uropods, and telson and then suddenly flexing them under the body, the resistance offered these broad parts by the water enables the animal to "swim" or dart backward, and quick repetition of this action often enables it to escape danger. Crayfishes are most in evidence when feeding actively in spring and early summer; in cold weather they retire to burrows or other safe retreats below the water.

The food includes live insect larvae, worms, crustaceans, small snails, fishes, and tadpoles, besides some dead animal matter. The burrowing species subsist extensively on stems and roots of plants, and other species use some such materials. The enemies of crayfishes, besides mankind, include certain fishes, large salamanders, turtles and water snakes, herons, kingfishers and other birds, and some aquatic mammals.

22-18. Molt. The living crayfish can grow somewhat within its inelastic exoskeleton, but molt (ecdysis) is necessary for an actual increase in body size. The young molt several times per year, and adults less often.

Prior to molt, some inorganic salts are withdrawn from the exoskeleton, a new soft exoskeleton grows beneath and separate from the older, and the muscles and other structures within the appendages soften and are reduced in bulk. The old cuticle then opens dorsally between the carapace and abdomen, and the animal slowly withdraws itself, leaving its former covering complete even to such minor features as the gut lining, eye facets, and setae. Before the new cuticle hardens, an increase in bulk occurs, probably by taking in water. For some days the animal hides away to avoid enemies when in this defenseless condition.

22-19. Regeneration. The crayfish can replace lost parts, chiefly the appendages and eyes, but to a lesser extent than in lower animals such as coelenterates or earthworms. This ability of *regeneration* is greater in the young animals than in older ones. Upon loss or removal of an appendage, the new one is partly formed at the next molt and increases in size with successive molts until it may be fully restored. Removal of the tip of an eye may be followed by normal regeneration, but if the entire structure is cut away, an antenna-like replacement may result. Such regeneration of a part different from that which was removed is called *heteromorphosis*.

22-20. Autotomy. The crayfishes and other crustaceans, particularly crabs, possess the power of self-amputation, or *autotomy,* of the thoracic legs. If a cheliped or walking leg is broken or severely handled, the terminal five segments are cast off—sacrificed to the enemy. The fracture is at a definite breaking plane, marked by a fine encircling line on the basal segment of the endopodite on a cheliped and at the third joint on the others. This procedure is a precaution to avoid undue loss of blood. Across the inside of the appendage, on the proximal side of the breaking plane, there is a diaphragm with a small opening through which the nerves and arteries pass. The joint is fortified by interlocking external spines, and breaking is effected by a special muscle distal to the diaphragm. When the leg is cast off, the aperture is quickly stopped by a blood clot and a small fold or valve, then soon closes by cell growth. A miniature replacement of the limb begins growth, and at subsequent molts this increases toward normal size and complete replacement.

22-21. Reproduction. *Cambarus affinis* of the eastern states mates in March (E. A. Andrews, 1904). The male grasps and inverts a female, stands over her, seizes all her walking legs with his two chelae, and flexes his telson tightly over the end of her abdomen, so that she is held motionless (Fig. 22-9). He uses one of his fifth walking legs to press the tips of the two modified pleopods on his somite XIV against the sperm receptacles (annuli) between somites XII and XIII on her thorax. Sperm then pass in mucus along his pleopods to lodge in her receptacles, after which the animals separate. Some days or weeks later the female cleans her abdomen and pleopods thoroughly, lies upside down with her abdomen sharply flexed, and a slimy secretion issues from glands on the pleopods. Soon the 200 to 400 eggs (2 mm. in diameter) are extruded from the oviducts, fertilized by sperm from the seminal receptacles, and become affixed by the secretion to her pleopods. She later resumes normal position and backs into a shelter, when the eggs hang like berries and are

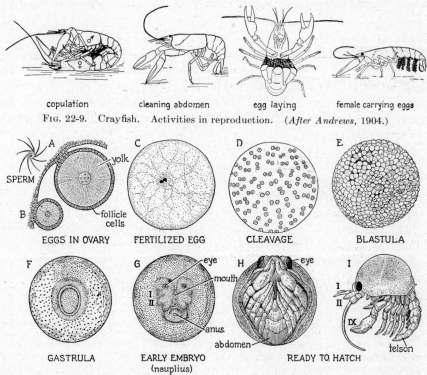

copulation   cleaning abdomen   egg laying   female carrying eggs

Fig. 22-9.   Crayfish.   Activities in reproduction.   (*After Andrews*, 1904.)

SPERM

yolk

follicle cells

EGGS IN OVARY   FERTILIZED EGG   CLEAVAGE   BLASTULA

eye

mouth

anus

abdomen

eye

telson

GASTRULA   EARLY EMBRYO (nauplius)   READY TO HATCH

Fig. 22-10.   Development of the crayfish; figures variously enlarged.   *B*. Eggs in ovary surrounded by follicle cells; when laid they become attached to swimmerets on female (Fig. 22-9).   *D, E*. Cleavage is superficial.   *F*. The shallow gastrula forms beneath the yolk. *F-H*. Ventral views.   *I*. Young removed from egg just before hatching.   (*A, B, from G. B. Howes, Atlas of zootomy, The Macmillan Co.; C-E, after Zehnder*, 1934; *F-I, after Huxley*.)

aerated by movements of the pleopods.   Five or more weeks ensue until hatching.   Each young is a miniature crayfish (Fig. 22-10) about 4 mm. long, transparent, and attached to cuticle molted within the shell before hatching.   Six or more additional molts occur during the first 2 months of life, the young enlarging at each.   They remain attached to the female until the second stage, stay near her a few days more, and then become independent.   By late autumn they are 35 to 50 mm. long and are colored and shaped like the adult.   *Cambarus clarkii* in Louisiana mates in late spring and produces eggs late in summer that hatch in about 15 days. The young grow through the winter, and some are of market size (85 mm.) by February. In the cold waters of Europe, *Astacus fluviatilis* produces eggs in October or November that do not hatch until the following June.

22-22. Other Crustacea. The thousands of species present a wide variety in structure, coloration, habitat, and mode of life, as indicated under Classification and suggested in Figs. 22-11, 22-12. The body is

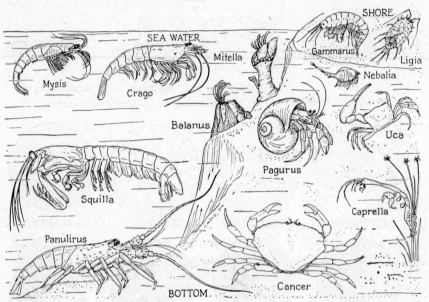

FIG. 22-11. Class CRUSTACEA. Some marine forms in their respective habitats; mostly reduced, but not to same scale. Subclass CIRRIPEDIA, Order THORACICA: *Mitella*, goose barnacle; *Balanus*, acorn barnacle. Subclass MALACOSTRACA, Order NEBALIACEA: *Nebalia*. Order MYSIDACEA: *Mysis*, opossum shrimp. Order ISOPODA: *Ligia*. Order AMPHIPODA: *Gammarus*, sand hopper; *Caprella*, "skeleton shrimp." Order STOMATOPODA: *Squilla*. Order DECAPODA: *Crago*, shrimp; *Panulirus*, spiny rock lobster; *Pagurus*, hermit crab; *Cancer*, edible crab; *Uca*, fiddler crab.

variously elongate or shortened, depressed in crabs, sow bugs, and others, and compressed in shrimps. The appendages of the more primitive BRANCHIOPODA are specialized only on the head region, and those elsewhere serve equally for locomotion, respiration, and egg transport. Strictly pelagic species have many long setae that help to bear them up in the water, and burrowing species have flattened appendages useful for digging. The coloration is varied—red, yellow, green, blue, brown, or black in different species. The pigment is contained in branched chromatophores, and some species change color in response to light intensity and the nature of the background. The nervous system varies from a ladder-like form (BRANCHIOPODA) with paired ganglia in each somite as with annelids, to the crabs which have but a single posterior ganglion, and the parasitic barnacles in which there is but one ganglion serving the whole body.   Some adults and many larvae have a simple median eye in addition to the pair of compound eyes.   The great majority of crustaceans are predaceous, subsisting on other animals of small size; but sow bugs use vegetation mainly, land crabs feed on coconuts, and some bottom dwellers swallow debris from which their food is extracted.   In reproduction the females usually carry the eggs externally, but some have internal brood pouches, and others reproduce parthenogenetically.   Eggs of some fresh-water species are resistant to drought for 2 or more years and may be spread by winds.

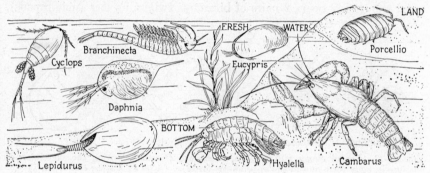

Fig. 22-12. Class Crustacea. Some fresh-water inhabitants in their characteristic habitats. Subclass Branchiopoda, Order Anostraca: *Branchinecta*, fairy shrimp. Order Notostraca: *Lepidurus*. Order Cladocera: *Daphnia*, water flea. Subclass Ostracoda, Order Podocopa: *Eucypris*. Subclass Copepoda, Order Eucopepoda: *Cyclops*. Subclass Malacostraca, Order Isopoda: *Porcellio*, sow bug (on land); Order Amphipoda: *Hyalella*. Order Decapoda: *Cambarus*, crayfish. Some enlarged (*Daphnia, Eucypris, Cyclops*) and others reduced, but not to same scale.

Some of the smaller aquatic crustaceans ("Entomostraca") occur in enormous numbers. In some lakes there are tens of thousands per cubic meter of water and may give distinctive color to the water. Small marine forms often are so abundant, either as larvae or as adults, that whole schools of fishes or whales may subsist chiefly on a single species. In many waters, both fresh and salt, the crustaceans will change through the season, like other members of the plankton, some being most abundant in spring, others in summer, and so on.

22-23. Crustacean larvae. Like some other invertebrates of fresh waters, the young crayfish at hatching resembles the adult except for minor details. Many marine crustaceans, however, have several larval stages, the younger of which are quite unlike the parent animals. These small or minute larvae represent the means of dispersal, especially of sedentary forms. The first three larval stages of the lobster have exopodites on the thoracic legs as in an adult schizopod, so that these are termed "schizopod" or "mysis" larvae.

Shrimps and prawns (*Penaeus*) begin as a minute **nauplius larva** (Fig. 22-13) with an unsegmented body, a simple median eye, and 3 pairs of appendages (the later antennules, antennae, and mandibles). With molt the **metanauplius** and **protozoea** stages appear, the latter with 7 pairs of appendages and beginning somites. Then follows the **zoea,** with distinct cephalothorax and abdomen, 8 pairs of appendages, and 6 more beginning. This molts into the **mysis** (schizopod) larva, having 13 pairs of appendages on the cephalothorax and those of the thorax bearing exopodites that serve in swimming. A further molt yields the adult, with 19 pairs of appendages. In a crab the first or **zoea** larva has a helmetlike carapace with long dorsal and anterior spines, and sessile eyes; the thorax bears 2 pairs of biramous swimming legs (maxillipeds),

Nauplius   Protozoea   Zoea   Mysis   ADULT

FIG. 22-13. Larval stages and adult of a shrimp, *Penaeus*, showing the succession of changes in body form and in the appendages (1–19). (*After F. Müller; and Huxley.*)

and the slender mobile abdomen lacks swimmerets. In the next or **megalops** larva the carapace is broad but lacks spines, the eyes are large and stalked, the thorax has 5 pairs of "walking" legs, and there are functional swimmerets on the abdomen. Both of these minute stages swim in surface waters. Later the megalops sinks to the bottom and molts into typical crab form, with a still broader carapace, the abdomen folded beneath the carapace, and its swimmerets useless for locomotion.

Instances such as these among crustaceans, like comparable cases among the vertebrates, illustrate the **biogenetic law,** or **recapitulation theory,** of Haeckel. This states that "ontogeny recapitulates phylogeny," that the individual in its development passes through stages which represent those in the history of the species or of the group to which it belongs down through time. The progressive acquisition of appendages and their elaboration in successive larvae, the median "cyclops" eye before the paired compound eyes, the increase and segmentation of the thorax, and other features in the sequence of nauplius, zoea, and later larvae are suggestive of a possible course of evolution in the CRUSTACEA. Strict application of the theory is difficult because many ancestral features are abbreviated or omitted, but the concept has stimulated intense interest in embryological studies and has been fruitful in other ways.

22-24. Barnacles.   These are highly modified crustaceans in which the adults are hermaphroditic as to sex, enclosed in a calcareous shell, and of sessile habit.   The common goose barnacles (*Lepas, Mitella*) and rock or ship barnacles (*Balanus*), attach to fixed objects (Figs. 22-11, 22-14);

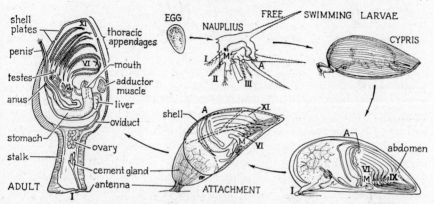

Fig. 22-14. Subclass Cirripedia. Goose barnacle, *Lepas.* Adult with right side of mantle and shell removed. From the egg a free-swimming nauplius larva hatches that feeds and molts to become a cypris larva. The latter attaches by its antennules and cement gland, then transforms to the sessile adult stage. Egg and larvae much enlarged. *M*, mouth; *A*, anus; *I*, antennule; *II*, antenna; *III*, mandible; *VI–XI*, other appendages.

other species fasten only to gorgonians, crabs, sharks, sea turtles, or whales, and still others are parasitic (Fig. 22-16).   The egg develops in the parent's mantle cavity and hatches out a microscopic nauplius larva, which swims, feeds, and molts one to three times in a week or so, with slight changes in form.   Another molt produces the very different *cypris larva,* with a bivalve shell and additional appendages, and containing fat globules for buoyancy.   This stage lasts for 4 days to 10 or 12 weeks in different species; the larva then settles to the bottom and hunts a place of attachment to which it adheres by the antennules, aided by secretion from a cement gland.   In a rather complete metamorphosis the bivalve shell is lost, the body mass alters in form, and the valves of the adult shell appear.   The barnacle thenceforth remains fixed, literally "standing on its head."   When feeding, the long delicate thoracic appendages repeatedly fan out well above the shell opening, then curve and quickly withdraw, to carry food to the mouth.

22-25. Commensal and parasitic crustaceans.   Most species of crustaceans are free-living, but many others are associated with various animals in relations ranging from casual attachment to extreme parasitism. Some crabs dwell in the tubes inhabited by annelid worms (Fig. 21-13*A*), certain copepods, amphipods, and porcelain crabs are regular tenants of the snail shells used by hermit crabs, and other small crabs (*Pinnotheres*) live within the shells of oysters and mussels.   Besides the many

free-living isopods and copepods, others are ectoparasites on various fishes
(Fig. 22-15); their anterior limbs are modified as hooks or suckers, and

Fig. 22-15.　Parasitic Crustacea (Subclass Copepoda) that live on fishes; enlarged.　A.
Caligus, second antennae hooked.　B. Argulus, second maxillae become sucking discs.

some (Aega) have mouth parts specialized to penetrate and suck blood
from their hosts.　Certain forms (such as Cymnothoa) are free-swimming
as larvae but permanently attached as adults, and others are parasitic
also as larvae.　The copepod Lernaea is so far modified as to be of wormlike form.　Isopods of the Suborder Epicarida are all parasitic on prawns
and crabs.　The most extreme of parasitic crustaceans are barnacles of the
Order Rhizocephala, of which Sacculina is a common example (Fig.
22-16).　Its earliest (nauplius) larva resembles that of other crustaceans

Fig. 22-16.　Subclass Cirripedia.　Sacculina, a barnacle parasitic in crabs; I–XI, appendages.　Compare Fig. 22-14.　(After Stempell.)

and barnacles but lacks a digestive tract.　The later (cypris) larva
fastens to a "hair" on a crab, then discards its shell, and burrows into
the host.　It becomes a mere mass of cells that pass in the crab's blood
stream, attach to the intestine, and grow.　When next the crab molts,
part of the parasite protrudes on the crab's abdomen as an ovary, later
to be packed with eggs.　The remaining internal parts become branched
and rootlike, penetrating all parts of the crab's body and absorbing nourishment from its tissues.　The host thenceforth neither grows nor molts,
and its sex organs degenerate so that it cannot breed.

22-26. Relations to man.　Flesh of certain crustaceans is much
esteemed as human food.　In 1946 the commercial fisheries of the United
States took 192,055,000 pounds of shrimp, 147,712,000 pounds of crab,
and 25,747,000 pounds of lobster, valued at a total of $44,021,000.

Some crayfishes are eaten in the Northwest and South.   These and other crustaceans are also eaten in other parts of the world.   Shrimps are captured with seines, but crabs, lobsters, and crayfishes are lured into baited traps (lobster "pots," etc.) of wire, wood, or net.   The leg muscles of crabs and abdominal muscles of the others are either freshly boiled or are canned.   The blue crab (*Callinectes*) of the Atlantic coast is caught and held captive until it molts, then sold in the soft-shelled condition; after removing the viscera the whole animal is cooked and eaten.   The small crustaceans that abound in salt and fresh waters are important links in the food cycle for many fishes and other useful aquatic animals.   Some copepods are the intermediate hosts for worm parasites of man and various vertebrates (Chap. 16).   Crayfishes in the Gulf states often damage fields of cotton and corn by eating the young plants, and occasionally their burrows injure levees.   Sow bugs sometimes eat plants in gardens and greenhouses, and the "gribble," a wood-boring isopod, burrows into and damages wharves in salt water.

CLASS †*TRILOBITA*. TRILOBITES

22-27. Structure.   These primitive marine arthropods, quite abundant during Paleozoic times, had a three-lobed body divided by two lengthwise dorsal furrows.   They were covered by a hard shell that could be rolled up.   On the distinct head was a pair of slender antennae, four pairs of biramous appendages, and often a pair of compound eyes. The thorax was of 2 to 29 short separate somites, and the abdominal somites were fused in a caudal plate.   All somites but the last bore biramous limbs fringed by setae.   The larva began as a pronauplius (protaspis) that gained somites in successive molts.   De-tails of structure and growth have

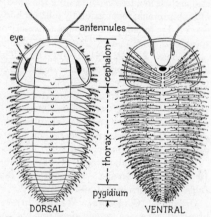

FIG. 22-17.   Class †TRILOBITA.   A trilo-bite, †*Triarthrus becki*, of Ordovician time, ×1½.   (*After Beecher.*)

been learned from many entire and sectioned specimens, especially of †*Triarthrus becki* from the Ordovician shale near Rome, N.Y. (Fig. 22-17).

Trilobites were differentiated in Pre-Cambrian time, were at a peak in the Cambrian and Ordovician, and died out in the Carboniferous save for one Permian genus.   The adults were usually 50 to 75 mm. long, but different species were from 10 to 675 mm. in length.   Many evidently burrowed or pushed through the bottom mud and sand of ancient seas; the larvae and some adults probably swam. Many species were local in occurrence, and others were cosmopolitan.

CLASSIFICATION

Phylum **ARTHROPODA.** JOINT-FOOTED ANIMALS. Body with head, thorax, and abdomen, of like or unlike somites, variously fused, and each typically with a pair of jointed appendages; exoskeleton containing chitin, molted entire at intervals; digestive tract complete, of fore-, mid-, and hind-gut; coelom reduced, body spaces a hemocoel; circulatory system lacunar, heart dorsal; respiration by gills, tracheae, lung books, or body surface; excretion by Malpighian tubules or coxal glands (nephridia rare); brain dorsal, nerve cord ventral, and paired ganglia in each somite or concentrated anteriorly; with simple and compound eyes, antennae, sensory hairs, and statocysts; sexes usually separate, gonads paired, and fertilization internal; cleavage superficial; commonly with larval stages and metamorphosis; some parthenogenesis; terrestrial or aquatic; free-living, sessile, commensal, or parasitic; fully 740,000 species.

(*Note: For classes other than Crustacea and Trilobita, see Chaps. 23 and 24.*)

Class 1. *CRUSTACEA:* CRUSTACEANS. Head (of 5 fused somites) with 2 pairs of antennae, a pair of jaws, and 2 pairs of maxillae; body usually with a dorsal carapace and ending in a telson containing the anus; exoskeleton with lime deposits; appendages often biramous; respiration by gills (or body surface); sex openings paired; eggs usually carried by female; development usually with larval stages; mainly aquatic; 25,000 species.

Subclass 1. BRANCHIOPODA. Thoracic appendages leaflike, margined by gills; end of body forked; parthenogenesis common; mostly in fresh waters; 800 species. Cambrian to Recent.

Order 1. **Anostraca.** Elongate, no carapace; eyes stalked; trunk appendages 11 to 19 pairs. *Artemia salina*, brine shrimp, 10 mm. long, in salty ponds; *Branchinecta; Eubranchipus vernalis*, fairy shrimp, to 23 mm. long.

Order 2. **Notostraca.** Carapace low, oval; somites 40 to 60; eyes sessile. *Lepidurus; Apus*, to 30 mm. long.

Order 3. **Conchostraca.** Carapace bivalved, enclosing compressed body; somites 10 to 27; eyes sessile. Devonian to Recent. *Leptestheria*, Kansas to California; *Lynceus*, eastern states and southward.

Order 4. **Cladocera.** WATER FLEAS. Minute to microscopic; usually with bivalved carapace, which does not enclose head; paired eyes fused, median, and sessile; trunk appendages 4 to 6 pairs; 2d antennae enlarged for swimming jerkily. *Daphnia pulex*, water flea, 2 mm. long; *Alona; Leptodora*, 12–18 mm. long.

Subclass 2. OSTRACODA. Minute; carapace bivalved, compressed, enclosing all the poorly segmented body; only 2 pairs of trunk appendages; fresh or salt waters, mostly on or near bottom; 2,000 species. Ordovician to Recent.

Order 1. **Podocopa.** Carapace unnotched; 2d antenna uniramous. *Eucypris, Darwinula*, both in fresh waters; *Entocythere*, on crayfish gills; *Cythereis*, marine.

Order 2. **Myodocopa.** Carapace notched anteriorly; 2d antenna biramous. *Conchoecia*, northern oceans.

Subclass 3. COPEPODA. Mostly small to microscopic; form various; typically 9 free trunk somites with last 4 lacking appendages, but reduced in parasitic species; 3 ocelli often fused as median eye; eggs on abdomen of female in 1 or 2 egg sacs; fresh and salt waters, free-living, commensal, or parasitic.

Order 1. **Eucopepoda.** No paired compound eyes; genital opening on last thoracic somite. *Calanus finmarchicus,* "brit," 4 mm. long, northern oceans, important food of herring, mackerel, and whales; *Diaptomus, Cyclops,* both in fresh waters; *Asterocheres,* on invertebrates; *Monstrilla,* with intermediate larvae in polychaete worms; *Ascidicola,* male free, female wormlike and commensal in gut of ascidians and echinoderms; *Caligus,* marine, and *Lernaea,* fresh-water, both parasitic on fishes; *Choniostoma,* parasitic on crustaceans; *Salmincola,* dwarf male permanently attached to female that parasitizes gills of trout; *Rhizorhina,* adult female lacks appendages, parasitic on polychaete worms.

Order 2. **Mystacocarida.** Size microscopic; 4 eyespots, no compound eyes; genital opening on 1st thoracic somite. One species, *Derocheilocarus typicus,* damp intertidal sand near Woods Hole, Mass.

Order 3. **Branchiura.** Body flat, carapace disclike, with compound eyes. *Argulus,* parasitic on fishes of fresh and salt waters.

Subclass 4. CIRRIPEDIA. BARNACLES. Adults sessile and attached or parasitic; attach by cement gland on 1st antenna; carapace becomes mantle surrounding body, usually with limy plates; 6 pairs or less of slender and bristly biramous appendages behind mouth used in food gathering; abdomen vestigial; usually hermaphroditic; larvae free-swimming, marine; 800 species. Ordovician to Recent.

Order 1. **Thoracica.** Mantle and 6 pairs of trunk appendages. *Lepas, Mitella,* goose barnacles, body on fleshy stalk; *Balanus,* "acorn shell" or rock barnacle, body in irregular conical shell, no stalk.

Order 2. **Acrothoracica.** Mantle present; fewer appendages. *Alcippe.*

Order 3. **Apoda.** No mantle or trunk appendages. *Proteolepas.*

Order 4. **Rhizocephala.** A mantle but no shell, appendages, or gut; body saclike, with adsorptive "roots" penetrating host. *Sacculina,* parasitic on crabs.

Subclass 5. MALACOSTRACA. LOBSTERS, CRAYFISHES, CRABS, ETC. Body typically of 19 somites (5 head, 8 thorax, 6 abdomen); head fused to one or more thoracic somites; commonly with carapace; abdomen with appendages.

Series 1. LEPTOSTRACA. Order 1. **Nebaliacea.** Carapace bivalved; abdomen of 7 somites; marine. Cambrian to Recent. *Nebalia,* to 12 mm. long.

Series 2. EUMALACOSTRACA. Abdomen of 6 (or less) somites.

Division 1. *SYNCARIDA.* Order 1. **Anaspidacea.** No carapace. *Anaspides,* fresh waters of Australia.

Division 2. *PERACARIDA.* Carapace, when present, leaving 4 or more thoracic somites distinct; females with thoracic brood pouch where young develop.

Order 1. **Mysidacea.** OPOSSUM SHRIMPS. Carapace over much of thorax; uropods forming tail fan; mostly marine; 300 species. Carboniferous to Recent. *Mysis,* Great Lakes and Eurasia.

Order 2. **Cumacea.** Small; carapace with 2 anterior plates often joined over head; abdomen slender, mobile; uropods slender; mostly marine, burrowing in sand or mud. *Diastylis,* 10 mm. long.

Order 3. **Tanaidacea.** Mostly minute; carapace small; 2d thoracic appendage with chela; telson unjointed; marine, to depths of 12,000 feet, in mud or in tubes. *Apseudes, Tanais.*

Order 4. **Isopoda.** PILL BUGS, WOOD LICE, ETC. Body usually depressed dorsoventrally; no carapace; abdomen short, partly or all fused; in salt or fresh waters among plants or under stones, some terrestrial, many parasitic on fish and crustaceans. Devonian to Recent. Marine: *Cirolana; Aega psora,* salve bug of fishermen; *Limnoria lignorum,* gribble, 3 mm. long, burrows in marine timbers, damaging wharves; *Idothea* and *Ligia,* free-living. Fresh-water: *Asellus communis,* to 15 mm. long. Land: *Oniscus asellus* and *Porcellio scaber,* sow bugs; *Armadillium vulgare,* pill bug, rolls up. Parasitic: *Hemioniscus,* on barnacles; *Hemiarthrus,* on decapod crustaceans.

Order 5. **Amphipoda.** SAND HOPPERS, ETC. Body often laterally compressed; no carapace; abdomen flexed ventrally between 3d and 4th somites; telson usually distinct; mostly marine. Tertiary to Recent. *Orchestia*, beach flea, on sand or under seaweed; *Hyalella*, in fresh water; *Gammarus*, in both fresh and salt waters; *Caprella*, body cylindrical, abdomen vestigial, in seaweeds; *Cyamus*, "whale louse," on skin of whales, body narrow, legs with hooked claws, abdomen vestigial.

Division 3. *HOPLOCARIDA.* Order 1. **Stomatopoda.** MANTIS SHRIMPS. Head with 2 movable anterior somites bearing eyes and antennules; marine, on bottom in sand or crevices; 200 species. Carboniferous to Recent. *Squilla; Chloridella empusa*, Florida to Cape Cod, to 250 mm. long, edible.

Division 4. *EUCARIDA.* Carapace large, fused to and covering all of thorax; eyes stalked; gills thoracic.

Order 1. **Euphausiacea.** Thoracic appendages all biramous; marine. *Euphausia*, "krill," to 25 mm. long, often abundant, an important whale food.

Order 2. **Decapoda.** Thoracic appendages mostly uniramous; "walking legs" 10 (5 pairs); mostly marine, some in fresh water, few terrestrial; many edible; 8,000 species. Triassic to Recent. Abdomen elongate: *Crago*, shrimp, and *Penaeus*, *Palaemonetes*, prawns; *Panulirus*, spiny rock lobster; *Homarus*, lobster, on Atlantic shores; *Astacus*, *Cambarus*, crayfishes, in fresh waters. Abdomen short (BRACHYURA, crabs): *Pagurus*, hermit crab, lives in snail shell; *Emerita (Hippa)*, sand crab; *Libinia*, spider crab, legs long; *Cancer*, large edible rock crab; *Callinectes*, edible blue or "soft-shelled" crab of Atlantic coast; *Panopeus*, mud crab; *Uca*, fiddler crab; *Pinnotheres*, oyster or mussel crab, in mantle cavity of oysters and mussels.

Class 2. †*TRILOBITA.* Body 10 to 675 mm. long, divided by 2 lengthwise furrows into 3 lobes; head distinct; abdomen of 2 to 29 somites and a fused caudal plate; all somites except last with biramous appendages fringed by setae; development with larval stages; marine; over 2,000 species. Cambrian to Permian. †*Triarthrus*.

References

BORRADAILE, L. A., and F. A. POTTS. 1932. The invertebrata. New York, The Macmillan Co. ARTHROPODA, pp. 270–469, figs. 199–349.

CALMAN, W. T. 1909. Crustacea. *In* E. R. Lankester, Treatise on zoology. London, A. & C. Black, Ltd. Part 7, fascicle 3, viii + 346 pp., 194 figs.

———. 1911. The life of crustacea. London, Methuen & Co. xvi + 289 pp., 32 pls., 85 figs.

HUXLEY, T. H. 1880. The crayfish, an introduction to the study of zoology. London, Kegan Paul, Trench, Trubner & Co. xiv + 371 pp., 81 figs.

KÜKENTHAL, W., and OTHERS. 1927. Handbuch der Zoologie. Berlin, Walter de Gruyter & Co. Vol. 3, part 1, ARTHROPODA, pp. 211–276, figs. 182–215; CRUSTACEA, pp. 277–1,078, figs. 216–1,171.

PRATT, H. S. 1935. A manual of the common invertebrate animals. . . . 2d ed. Philadelphia, The Blakiston Co. CRUSTACEA, pp. 371–468, figs. 503–638.

SMITH, G., and W. F. R. WELDON. 1909. Crustacea. *In* Cambridge natural history. London, Macmillan & Co., Ltd. Vol. 4, xv + 1–217 pp., figs. 1–135.

SNODGRASS, R. E. 1938. Evolution of the Annelida, Onychophora, and Arthropoda. *Smithsonian Miscellaneous Collections*, vol. 97, no. 6, pp. 1–159, 54 figs.

TWENHOFEL, WILLIAM H., and ROBERT R. SHROCK. 1935. Invertebrate paleontology. New York, McGraw-Hill Book Co., Inc. ARTHROPODA, pp. 406–478, figs. 148–175.

WARD, H. B., and G. C. WHIPPLE. 1918. Fresh-water biology. New York, John Wiley & Sons, Inc. CRUSTACEA, pp. 661–850, figs. 1,011–1,318.

ZEHNDER, H. 1934. Über die Embryonalentwicklung der Flusskrebses. *Acta Zoologica*, vol. 15, pp. 261–408, pls. 1–25, figs. 1–23.

CHAPTER 23

CLASS INSECTA. INSECTS

The grasshoppers, flies, lice, butterflies, beetles, bees, and a host of similar small creatures that comprise the Class INSECTA (L. incised, into distinct parts) number fully 675,000 species. They are the most abundant and widespread of all land animals, being the principal invertebrates that can live in dry environments and the only ones able to fly. These habits are made possible by the chitinous body covering that protects the internal organs against injury and loss of moisture, by the extensions of this covering that form the wings, and by the system of tracheal tubes that enable the insects to breathe air. The ability to fly enables them to find food readily, and under favorable conditions they can multiply rapidly. Insects abound in all habitats except the sea; various kinds are adapted to live in fresh and brackish waters, in soil, on and about plants of all kinds, and on or in other animals. Various species eat all sorts and parts of plants—roots, stems or leaves, sap or blossoms, seeds or fruits; many flower-visiting insects aid in pollination. Others utilize the tissues, fluids, and excretions of animals, and the scavenger insects consume dead animals and plants. Parasitic insects live in the eggs, larvae, or adults of other insects and on many other animals and plants. Some insects transmit diseases—virus, bacterial, protozoan, or others—to plants, animals, and man. Insects in turn are eaten by other insects, spiders, scorpions, and many vertebrates from fishes to mammals. The predaceous and parasitic species serve importantly to regulate the numbers of other insects.

Entomology (Gr. *entomon*, insect + logy) is the science dealing with insects. Many entomologists are engaged in purely scientific studies and others in applied fields. Because of the numbers and many biological relations of insects, they are of great economic significance; some are useful and many are harmful to man's interests.

23-1. Characteristics.[1] 1. Head, thorax, and abdomen distinct; head with one pair of antennae, and mouth parts for chewing, sucking, or lapping; thorax (of 3 somites) with 3 pairs of jointed legs and usually 2 (1 or no) pairs of wings; abdomen of 11 or fewer somites with terminal parts modified as genitalia.

2. Digestive tract of fore-, mid-, and hind-gut; mouth with salivary glands.

3. Heart slender, with an anterior aorta; no capillaries or veins; body spaces a hemocoel (coelom reduced).

[1] Compare Phylum ARTHROPODA, Chap. 22, Table 22-1.

485

4. Respiration by branched cuticle-lined tracheae that carry oxygen from paired spiracles on sides of thorax and abdomen directly to the tissues; some with tracheal or blood gills.

5. Excretion by 2 to many fine Malpighian tubules attached to anterior end of hind-gut.

6. Nervous system of supra- and sub-esophageal ganglia connecting to double ventral nerve cord, with 1 pair or less of ganglia per somite; sense organs include simple and compound eyes, chemoreceptors for smell on the antennae and for taste about the mouth, and various tactile hairs; some with means for sound production and reception; no statocysts.

7. Sexes separate; gonads of multiple tubules with 1 median duct posteriorly; fertilization internal; ova with much yolk and protecting shells; cleavage superficial; development with several molts and direct, or with several nymphal stages and gradual metamorphosis, or with several larval stages and a complete metamorphosis to adult form; parthenogenesis in aphids, thrips, gall wasps, etc.

The earliest known fossil insects were fully winged and give no clue as to their origin. From studies on the comparative morphology of insects, other arthropods, and the annelids, several theories of insect origin have been proposed that would derive them variously from (1) forms resembling the zoea larvae of the higher CRUSTACEA with 3 pairs of appendages on both the head and thorax; (2) other CRUSTACEA that resemble the young of some THYSANURA; (3) the TRILOBITA; (4) the SYMPHYLA, which are like some THYSANURA; or (5) the polychaete worms (ANNELIDA) because of resemblances of the pleura and thoracic appendages of insects to the parapodia of polychaetes. Some authorities believe that winged insects arose from such wingless forms as the THYSANURA, others consider that the winged forms were of separate origin, and some believe the wingless lower orders to be degenerate. The wings may have arisen from thoracic gills or more probably as lateral extensions of the thoracic terga.

23-2. Size. Some insects are smaller than large protozoans and others exceed the smallest of the vertebrates. Some beetles (TRICHOPTERYGIDAE) are but 0.25 mm. long, and some egg parasites (MYMARIDAE) are even smaller. Most insects are 2 to 40 mm. long. The longest include *Pharnacia serratipes* (ORTHOPTERA), 260 mm.; a Venezuelan beetle, *Dynastes hercules*, 155 mm.; and a bug, *Belostoma grande*, 115 mm. long. The wingspread is greatest in some tropical moths, *Erebus agrippina*, 280 mm., and *Attacus atlas*, 240 mm.; some fossil insects (MEGANURA) exceeded 700 mm. in wingspread.

THE GRASSHOPPER, OR LOCUST

To indicate some of the variety in the structure and function of insects, this chapter describes the grasshopper and includes a comparative account of the honeybee. The grasshopper is generalized as to anatomy, has chewing mouth parts, undergoes a gradual or incomplete metamorphosis from the young or nymph stages to the adult, and lives independently for a single season.

Grasshoppers[1] occur over the world, mainly in open grasslands, weed patches, and roadside growths, where they eat grasses and other leafy vegetation.   The following description will serve for any common species

FIG. 23-1. Class INSECTA.   *Left.* Long-winged grasshopper (*Dissosteira longipennis*), $\times 1\frac{1}{8}$.   *Right.* Short-winged or lubber grasshopper (*Brachystola magna*), $\times \frac{3}{4}$.   (*After Walton*, 1916.)

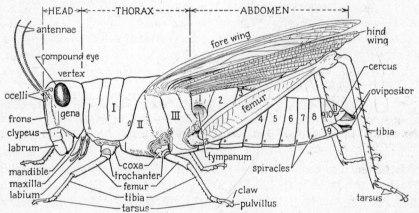

FIG. 23-2.   External features of the grasshopper, a generalized insect.   Female.   *I* to *III*, somites of thorax; *1* to *11*, somites of abdomen.

such as the "Carolina locust" (*Dissosteira carolina*), the "American locust" (*Schistocerca americana*), or the short-winged lubber grasshopper (*Romalea microptera*).

23-3. External features. The body comprises a head of six fused somites, the thorax of three somites with legs and wings, and a long segmented abdomen ending with reproductive organs (Fig. 23-2).   It is covered by an exoskeleton containing chitin, which is secreted by the

---

[1] Order ORTHOPTERA, Family ACRIDIDAE.   A grasshopper is an essentially solitary and resident species, often abundant as to individuals, but which may occasionally migrate.   The term locust applies properly to gregarious and migratory Old World forms (*Locusta*); the North American periodic cicada (*Magicicada*, Order HOMOPTERA), however, is also called "locust."

epidermis beneath and molted periodically in the nymphs to permit of increase in size; adults do not molt.   The exoskeleton is formed into hard plates, or *sclerites,* separated by *sutures* of soft cuticle to permit movement of the body segments and appendages.   Pigment in and under the cuticle provides a variegated and protective coloration by which grasshoppers resemble the environments in which they live.

The *head* (Fig. 23-3) bears one pair of slender, jointed antennae with fine sensory bristles, two lateral *compound eyes* that are unstalked but

FIG. 23-3.   The grasshopper.   *Left.*   Front view of the head.   *Right.*   Mouth parts in anterior view.   Both enlarged.

constructed like those of the crayfish, and three simple eyes, or *ocelli.* Much of the head is enclosed in a fused sclerite or *epicranium,* with a dorsal *vertex,* the lateral cheeks or *genae* and the anterior *frons.*   Below the latter is a broad plate, the *clypeus.*   The mouth parts are of the chewing or mandibulate type, ventral on the head, and include (1) a broad upper lip or *labrum,* hinged to the clypeus; (2) a median tongue-like *hypopharynx* behind the mouth; (3) two heavy blackish lateral jaws or *mandibles,* each with teeth along the inner margin for chewing food; (4) a pair of *maxillae* of several parts and with slender sensory palps at the sides; and (5) a broad median lower lip or *labium,* with two short palps.

The *thorax* consists of the large anterior *prothorax* (with a dorsal saddle-like pronotum), the *mesothorax,* and the posterior *metathorax;* each bears a pair of jointed legs, and the meso- and meta-thorax each a pair of wings.   The sclerites on each somite form a dorsal *tergum* of four fused plates, a *pleuron* of three plates on each side, and a single ventral *sternum.* Each *leg* is a linear series of segments, as follows: (1) the short *coxa,* which articulates to the body; (2) a small *trochanter* fused to (3) the stout *femur;* (4) a slender spiny *tibia;* and (5) the *tarsus* of three parts, the proximal bearing four pairs of ventral *pads* and the distal having a fleshy *pulvillus* beyond two *claws*.   The pulvilli enable the grasshopper to hold onto smooth surfaces, and the claws serve in rough places.   All the legs are used in walking and climbing.   Each metathoracic leg has a large femur containing muscles and a long tibia that serve for leaping.   The narrow *forewings* or *tegmina* are parchment-like.   The *hind wings* are broad and membranous, with many veins, and fold under the forewings

Fig. 23-4.   The wings and body covering of insects; diagrammatic.   *A.* Generalized wing showing the principal veins.   *B.* Cross section of wing and veins.   *C.* Section of body covering at junction of two somites.   *D.* Structure of the body wall.   (*A, B, after Metcalf and Flint; C, D, adapted from Snodgrass.*)

at rest.   Each wing develops as a saclike projection of the body covering, and flattens to a thin double membrane that encloses tubular tracheae surrounded by blood sinuses.   The cuticle thickens around the tracheae to form nervures, or *veins,* that strengthen the wings (Fig. 23-4).   When of full size, the wings become hard and dry but blood flow continues.   The wing veins are of such constant pattern in species and higher groups of insects as to be useful in classification.

The slender cylindrical *abdomen* consists of 11 somites, the terminal ones being modified for copulation or egg laying.   Along the lower sides of the thorax and abdomen are 10 pairs of small openings, the *spiracles* connecting to the respiratory system.

The first abdominal somite is divided about the insertions of the hind legs, with the sternum firmly united to the mesothorax; its tergum contains on either side an oval *tympanic membrane* over an organ of hearing.   On somites 2 to 7 the tergum is ∩-shaped and joins the ⌣-shaped sternum by lateral membranes that permit the abdomen to pulsate in breathing.   In a male, somite 8 resembles those preceding, the terga of 9–10 are fused, and the tergum of 11 forms the suranal plate over the anus; a small spine or *cercus* (relict appendage) projects behind 10, on either side and the long ventral sternum of 9 encloses the male copulatory organ.   In a female, the terga of 8 to 11 and cercus are as in the male, the sternum of 8 is apparently lacking, and that of 9 is elongate; a lateral plate of 10 is present, and the end of the abdomen bears two paired lobes forming the ovipositor (from somites 8–9).

23-4. Muscles. The head contains complex small muscles that move the antennae and mouth parts. In the thorax are large muscles that manipulate the wings and legs. Segmental muscles are most conspicuous in the abdomen but are small as compared with those of the crayfish; some perform the respiratory movements, and others control the reproductive structures.

23-5. Digestive system (Fig. 23-5). The mouth parts surround (1) the *mouth cavity,* from which (2) a slender *esophagus* extends to (3) the large

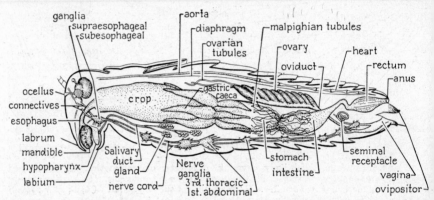

Fig. 23-5. The grasshopper. Internal structure as seen with left side of body wall removed; tracheae omitted. Compare Figs. 22-4, 24-3.

thin-walled *crop.* Below the crop are small branched salivary glands that discharge through ducts opening at the labium. Beyond the crop is (4) a small proventriculus or *gizzard,* lined by plates. The preceding parts comprise the fore-gut. Next is (5) the mid-gut, or *stomach* (ventriculus), joined by (6) a series of six double finger-shaped *gastric caeca.* The hind-gut, or (7) *intestine,* consists of a tapered anterior part, slender middle portion, and enlarged *rectum* that opens at (8) the *anus.* Food is held by the forelegs, labrum, and labium, lubricated by the salivary secretion (which contains some enzymes), and chewed by the mandibles and maxillae; the palps bear organs of taste. Chewed food is stored in the crop, further reduced in the gizzard, and strained into the stomach. There it is digested by various enzymes secreted by the gastric caeca, and absorbed. In the rectum, excess water is withdrawn from the undigested material which is formed into slender fecal pellets and egested through the anus.

23-6. Circulatory system. The slender tubular *heart* lies against the dorsal wall of the abdomen in a shallow *pericardial cavity* formed by a delicate transverse *diaphragm.* Blood enters the heart through pairs of minute lateral openings or _ostia,_ with valves, and is pumped forward by contractions of the heart into a dorsal *aorta* extending to the head.   There it emerges into the body spaces or *hemocoel* (not a true coelom), between the internal organs, and moves slowly backward around these organs, finally to enter the pericardial sinus.   Some blood circulates in the appendages and wing veins.   The system is open, or lacunar, as in other arthropods, there being no capillaries or veins.   The clear blood plasma contains colorless blood cells that act as phagocytes to remove foreign organisms.   The blood serves mainly to transport food and wastes, as there is a separate respiratory system.   The *fat body* is a loose network of tissue in spaces between the organs that stores food reserves, especially in young insects before metamorphosis.

23-7. Respiratory system (Figs. 23-6, 23-7).   The paired *spiracles* connect to a system of elastic ectodermal air tubes, or *tracheae,* that branch

Fig. 23-6.   The grasshopper.   Respiratory system.   Spiracles, tracheal trunks, and air sacs of the left side.   (*Modified from Riley*, 1878.)

Fig. 23-7.   The tracheae of insects.   *A*. Large trunks and branches.   *B*. Cellular wall of a tracheal tube and its internal spiral thread.   *C*. Terminal branches around muscle fibers.   *D*. Fine tracheoles distributed over muscle fibers.   (*After Snodgrass*.)

to all parts of the body.   The finest branches, or *tracheoles,* carry oxygen to and remove carbon dioxide directly from the tissue cells.   The tracheal wall consists of a single layer of thin cells that secretes a lining of cuticle (cast off at molting), and the larger tubes are reinforced by a spiral thread to prevent their collapse.   Longitudinal air trunks connect to the spiracles along either side.   The grasshopper, unlike some insects, has several large thin-walled *air sacs* in the abdomen, where alternate contraction and relaxation of the body wall serve to pump air in and out of the tracheal system.   At inspiration the first 4 pairs of spiracles are open and the posterior 6 are closed and at expiration the arrangement is reversed, so that there is a definite circulation of air in the tracheae. The finest tracheoles contain fluid in which the oxygen dissolves before actually reaching the tissue cells; this oxygen-bearing fluid serves in internal respiration as does the blood of vertebrates. Some harmful insects can be killed by the use of oil films, emulsions, or dusts that cover or clog the spiracles and stop respiration.

23-8. Excretory system. To the anterior end of the hind-gut are joined a number of threadlike *Malpighian tubules;* these lie in the hemocoel and have their free ends closed. The tubule wall is composed of a single layer of large cells that remove urea, urates, and salts from the blood and discharge into the intestine.

23-9. Nervous system (Figs. 23-5, 23-8). The brain, or *supraesophageal ganglia,* in the head comprises 3 pairs of fused ganglia (optic,

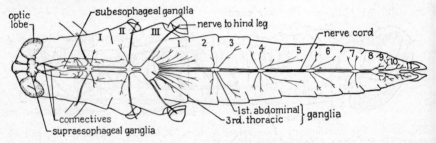

FIG. 23-8. The grasshopper. Nervous system in dorsal view; *I–III,* thoracic somites; *1–11,* abdominal somites. (*After Riley,* 1878.)

antennary, and intercalary) with nerves to the eyes, antennae, and other head organs. It joins by 2 *connectives* around the esophagus to the *subesophageal ganglia,* which are also of 3 pairs (mandibular, maxillary, and labial). From the latter, the ventral *nerve cord* extends posteriorly; it is formed of a series of paired ganglia and longitudinal connectives. Each thoracic somite contains a pair of ganglia with nerves to the legs, wings, and internal organs. There are but 5 pairs of abdominal ganglia as some of those originally separate have become fused. These send nerves to various posterior organs. There is also a visceral or *sympathetic nervous system,* comprised of an esophageal portion with ganglia and nerves connecting to the brain, fore-gut, mid-gut, and heart, and a posterior portion from the last abdominal ganglion to the hind-gut and reproductive system. A fine pattern of peripheral nerves lies beneath the epidermis of the body wall.

23-10. Sense organs. The sensory receptors of the grasshopper differ somewhat from those of the crayfish and are adapted for receiving stimuli from the air and the land environment where this insect lives. They include (1) *tactile hairs* on various body parts, especially the antennae, mouth palps, abdominal cerci, and distal leg segments; (2) *olfactory organs* on the antennae; (3) *organs of taste* on the palps and other mouth parts; (4) the *ocelli,* which are sensitive to light and shade and may form crude images at close range; (5) the *compound eyes,* which function essentially like those of the crayfish; and (6) the *organ of hearing.*   The latter (Fig. 23-15) consists essentially of a stretched tympanic membrane that is set into movement by sound vibrations in the air; this affects a slender point beneath the membrane that is connected to sensory nerve fibers. The grasshopper produces sounds by rubbing the hind tibia, which has a row of minute pegs along the medial surface, against a wing vein to set the latter into vibration.   Each species of grasshopper produces characteristic clacking and trilling notes.

23-11. Reproductive system (Fig. 23-9).   The sexes are separate and show secondary sexual characters in the terminal parts of the abdomen as

Fig. 23-9.   Reproductive systems of insects; diagrammatic.   (*After Snodgrass.*)

described under external features.   In a *male,* each of the two *testes* comprises a series of slender tubules or *follicles,* above the intestine, that are joined to a lengthwise *vas deferens.*   The two vasa unite as a common median *ejaculatory duct,* which is joined by *accessory glands* and opens at the end of the large ventral male *copulatory organ* (edeagus).   In a *female,* each *ovary* is composed of several tapering egg tubes or *ovarioles,* in which the ova are produced, and is joined to an *oviduct.*   The two oviducts unite as a median *vagina* that leads posteriorly and is joined by a small *seminal receptacle* (spermatheca) where sperm received at copulation are stored.   The female tract opens near the ventral *egg guide.*

23-12. Natural history.   In the warm days of early spring the young nymphs hatch from eggs laid the previous autumn.   They resemble the adults but differ in proportions and have no wings or reproductive organs (Fig. 23-11).   They feed on tender vegetation and hide under plants or in crevices to avoid enemies and desiccation.   After a few days the cuticle softens and is molted; the emerging nymph swallows air and increases in volume, and then its fresh cuticle hardens and darkens.   Each individual has five (or six) nymphal stages, and its entire growth period requires 30 to 50 or more days.   The wings first appear as small pads, which become larger at successive molts and unfold to full size after the last molt into the adult stage.

Both nymphs and adults eat many kinds of vegetation, especially succulent types; they often migrate into new feeding grounds and may damage or ruin farm and garden plantings.   Feeding is most active in the midmorning hours of sunny days with little wind.   When food is scarce, these insects will eat cotton or woolen fabrics, wood, and disabled grasshoppers.   The adults of some species, under conditions of crowding, sometimes perform long migrations.   Many were marked with red lacquer in North Dakota one summer and later recaptured 86 to 215 miles away in the direction of prevailing winds.

Grasshoppers have many enemies.   Their eggs are eaten by some beetles, bee flies, moles, skunks, and mice, the nymphs by robber flies and digger wasps, and both nymphs and adults by various large predatory insects and by frogs, reptiles, birds, and mammals of many species.   One-tenth of all insects found in the stomachs of birds examined by the U.S. Biological Survey were grasshoppers and their close allies.   The eggs of grasshoppers are parasitized by certain insects (Fig. 23-39).   Flesh flies (*Sarcophaga*) lay living maggots on adults, and tachinid flies deposit their eggs on grasshoppers in flight; the larvae of both burrow into their hosts and consume the fat tissues.   Parasitized grasshoppers become logy and fail to reproduce, or die.   The parasitic insects thus constitute a factor in grasshopper control.   Both fungus and bacterial diseases also destroy numbers of grasshoppers at times.   Man practices control by spreading poisoned bran baits on which the nymphs and adults feed and also by plowing weed or stubble fields to expose the egg masses.

23-13. Reproduction.   Some days after the adult stage is reached in late summer, the grasshoppers begin to copulate and do so several times.   The male clings to the female's back, inserts his genitalia into her vagina, and transfers spermatozoa.   After a further interval, egg laying (Fig. 23-10) begins and then continues into the autumn. The eggs are 3 to 5 mm. long.   About 20 are laid at a time, and one female may lay up to 10 lots.   The adults die some days after breeding is ended.   In the ovary, each egg is enclosed by a delicate *vitelline membrane* and a brownish flexible shell, or *chorion,* that contains a minute pore, or *micropyle,* through which sperm enter during laying.   The female uses her

Fig. 23-10. A female grasshopper, with greatly extended abdomen, depositing eggs in ground, and, below, a complete "pod," or packet of eggs.   (*After Walton,* 1916.)

ovipositor to form a short tunnel in the ground in which the eggs are placed, surrounded by a sticky secretion that fastens them together as an egg pod.   Development (Fig. 23-11) begins at once and continues for about 3 weeks until the embryo is well formed.   Then a rest, or *diapause,* ensues until spring; growth is resumed, and soon the young hatch and crawl to the ground surface.   The diapause is a means to survive the adverse conditions of cold and lack of food in winter.

FIG. 23-11.   Development of the grasshopper.   *A.* Fertilized egg surrounded by chorion. *B.* Cleavage, nuclei scattered.   *C.* Blastoderm cells surround yolk.   *D.* Germ band formed.   *E.* Early embryo, serosa, and amnion forming.   *F.* Later embryo with somites. *G.* 8-day embryo.   *H.* 15-day embryo.   *I.* 20-day embryo, ready for diapause; *1, 2, 3,* thoracic somites.   *J.* Embryo in diapause.   *K, L.* Blastokinesis, or rotation of the embryo.   *M.* Embryo before hatching.   *N–R.* The 5 nymphal stages with gradual increase in size and development of wing pads.   *S.* Adult with wings.   (*A–F, generalized sagittal sections, after Johannsen and Butt; G, H, ventral views, after Silfer, 1932; K–M, lateral views, after Burkholder, 1934; N–S, modified from Emerton in Riley, 1878.*)

The fertilization nucleus within the egg yolk divides into scattered cleavage nuclei. These migrate to the periphery of the yolk where each is surrounded by cytoplasm and a cell wall, and the cells form an epithelium, or blastoderm, around the yolk. Those of a limited ventral area thicken as a *germ band* that will produce the *embryo,* and the lateral and dorsal cells become the embryonic envelope, or *serosa.* At the ends and sides of the germ band, folds then form; their outer layers, inside the serosa, become the *amnion,* which encloses the embryo in an amniotic cavity. A lengthwise ventral furrow along the germ band folds up to form a layer (mesoderm + ?endoderm) above the germ band. The latter then divides by cross furrows, from before backward, into a linear series of somites that give rise to the head and its appendages, the thorax and its legs, and the segmented abdomen. The future fore-gut, or stomodeum, forms as a pit at the anterior end, and the hind-gut, or proctodeum, similarly at the posterior end. Later the mid-gut forms from endoderm cells, and the gut becomes a continuous tube. The tracheae develop as paired lateral invaginations of ectoderm. The nervous system arises as an infolding of ventral ectoderm into two lengthwise strands of cells that later produce the nerve cords, ganglia, and brain.

The embryo shows six primitive head somites, as follows: (1) preoral, with compound eyes; (2) antennal, and (3) intercalary, respectively homologous with the antennule and antennal somites of the crayfish; (4) mandibular, behind the mouth; (5) maxillary; and (6) labial, with a pair of embryonic appendages that provide the fused labium of the adult. There are six pairs of nerve ganglia in the head, three preoral pairs forming the supraesophageal ganglia and three postoral forming the subesophageal ganglia. Rudiments of abdominal appendages appear on various insects; later these form parts of the external genitalia (ORTHOPTERA, HYMENOPTERA) or produce the larval prolegs (LEPIDOPTERA) or disappear.

THE HONEYBEE

23-14. A social insect. The honeybee, *Apis mellifera* (Order HYMENOPTERA), resembles the grasshopper in general structure but is specialized in many features. It has both sucking and chewing mouth parts, undergoes complete metamorphosis from the wormlike larva through a pupal stage to the flying adult, feeds on nectar and pollen, and lives socially in a permanent colony comprising many individuals of three *castes* (Fig. 23-12). The *queen* lays the eggs; the males, or *drones,* serve only to fertilize new queens; and the thousands of sterile females, or *workers,* build and guard the hive, provide the food for all castes, attend the queen, and rear the young. Wild honeybees live in natural cavities of trees or rocks, but man has partly domesticated this species and houses

it in hives of wood or straw.   Each colony lives amid vertical **combs** of
wax that contain small lateral cells used to store honey or pollen and rear
the young.   Workers collect fluid **nectar** from flowers; this is chemically
altered and stored as the sirupy carbohydrate solution that we call **honey.**
They collect **pollen** ("bee bread") to provide proteins for growth of the

Fig. 23-12.   The honeybee, *Apis mellifera* (Order Hymenoptera); growth stages and 3
adult cases slightly enlarged; portion of comb reduced.   (*After Phillips*, 1911.)

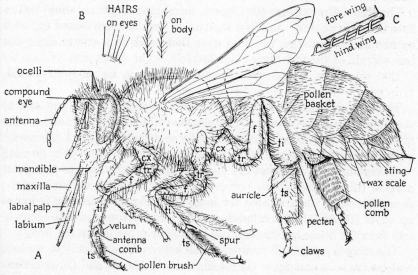

Fig. 23-13.   The honeybee worker.   *A.* Mouth parts, pollen-collecting structures, and
sting. *B.* The hairs.   *C.* The wing-locking mechanism.   Leg segments: *cx*, coxa; *tr*,
trochanter; *f*, femur; *ti*, tibia; *ts*, tarsus.   (*Adapted in part from Casteel*, 1912.)

larvae.   Bees also gather resins from plant buds which, as **propolis,** serve
to cement and varnish crevices in the hive against wind and water.   The
workers have **stings** to protect the colony and its honey against robbery
by other animals, from bees to bears.

23-15. Structure and function.   The body of a bee (Fig. 23-13) is
densely covered by hairs having short lateral barbs where pollen grains
lodge easily.   Unbranched hairs occur on the compound eyes and legs.

On each foreleg, the tibia is margined by an *eye brush* of stiff hairs for cleaning the compound eyes, and its distal end bears a flat movable spine, or *velum*. The latter closes over a bristle-lined notch on the proximal end of the tarsus to form an *antenna comb* through which the antenna is drawn to remove pollen or other foreign material. Long hairs on the large first segment of the tarsus form a cylindrical *pollen brush* to gather pollen from the fore parts of the body. On each middle leg, the flat tarsus has a *pollen brush* to remove pollen from the forelegs and near-by body parts; and the inner distal end of the tibia bears a *spur* used to pick up wax. On the hind leg, the wide tibia is slightly concave externally and margined by incurving hairs to form a *pollen basket* (corbicula). This has a comb of stiff hairs, the *pecten,* at its distal end, and just below is a flat plate, or *auricle,* on the proximal end of the tarsus. The outer surface of the tarsus has a *pollen brush* for cleaning the body posteriorly, and on its inner surface are about 10 rows of stiff downward-pointing spines that form a *pollen comb.*

The thin delicate *wings* (Gr. *hymen,* membrane + *pteron,* wing) lie flat over the back at rest. In flight the two on each side are locked together by fine hooks bordering the hind wing that catch to a groove along the rear margin of the fore wing (Fig. 23-13*C*). The wings may vibrate up to 400 times per second with the tips moving in an ∞-shaped path. Workers are capable of long flights, even to 8 miles.

The smooth *mandibles* of workers serve to gather pollen and also to mold wax in making combs. The maxillae and labial palps form a tube around the slender *tongue,* or labium; by movements of the ligula and a pumping action of the pharynx, fluid nectar is drawn into the large crop, or *honey stomach.* Behind the latter are four triangular lips that form a *valve* (honey stopper) to prevent nectar or honey from entering the stomach except when wanted for food. The slender *intestine* is joined by about 100 *Malpighian tubules,* and the large rectum serves to accumulate feces for discharge through the anus after a bee leaves the hive.

The *sting* is a modified ovipositor and hence is present only in workers and queens. It comprises (1) a hollow dorsal *sheath* and (2) two *darts* grooved along their inner surfaces so they may slide along each other by the action of muscles at their inner bases, (3) at either side a sensory *sting palpus,* and (4) a large median *poison sac* supplied by two acid glands and a slender alkaline gland. The fluid is pumped into the wound made by the darts. A worker dies about 2 days after using its sting, as all the poison apparatus and some adjacent parts pull off in the process. The queen's slender sting serves to combat rival queens and can be used more than once.

Among the numerous adaptive features, each short *antenna* has many olfactory pits that provide a keen sense of smell (1,600 on queen, 2,400 on

worker, 18,900 on drone).   Each *compound eye* has many ommatidia
(4,900 on queen, 6,300 on worker, 13,000 on drone).   The brain is proportionately large.   Bees evidently find their way about and seek food
by both scent and sight.   They can be trained to visit a food supply
having a particular scent or associated with certain colors, except red
which they cannot distinguish from black.   Glands on the abdomen
produce a scent when bees are disturbed and may serve to "mark" new
sources of food afield.   Honeybees have a good sense of orientation, and
each returns to its own hive.   If a hive is moved, the absent workers
return to the old site; but if confined within during the moving, they take
account of the new location upon leaving and will return to it.

23-16. Honey.   A worker bee, upon discovering a food supply in the
field, fills her nectar stomach, returns to the hive, and either deposits the
gathered nectar or feeds young bees.   Then she executes a "dance" that
informs other bees as to the direction and distance of the source.   She
walks a semicircle, returns to the original point, and makes a semicircle
in the opposite direction, a pattern like a compressed ∞ , repeating several
times.   Experiments by von Fritsch show that the location is indicated
in relation to the sun's position.   Clinging to the upright comb, if the
supply is directly toward the sun, the axis is vertically upward; if at an
angle to the sun the axis of the dance is at that angle.   The distance is
indicated by the number of turns in a given interval (*e.g.*, in 15 seconds).
The nature of the food supply is communicated by odor from the plant
source on her body or in the nectar brought.   Other bees keep their
antennae touching the scout during her dance.

When the bee visits a flower, (1) pollen taken by the mandibles is
moistened with honey and (2) mixed with that gathered on the pollen
brushes of the forelegs; (3) it is then taken by the pollen brushes on the
middle legs, which in turn are (4) drawn between the pollen combs of the
hind tarsi; (5) each of the latter is then scraped over the opposite leg to
deposit pollen on the pecten or outer surface of the auricle, and (6) by
flexing the tarsus on the tibia the pollen is pushed upward and packed into
the pollen basket.   The bee thus (Fig. 23-14) accumulates a bulging load
of sticky pollen in both baskets, returns to the hive, and pushes her load
into a cell, to be tamped down by the heads of young workers.   Propolis
is carried similarly but is removed by other workers.

Nectar held in the honey stomach is acted upon by salivary enzymes,
cane sugar being inverted to dextrose and levulose.   Upon returning to
its hive, a worker regurgitates this fluid into a cell of the comb, where the
young "house bees" work it over in their mouths, causing further chemical changes; they evaporate the excess water by fanning with their wings
and then seal the cell with wax.   Honey averages 17 per cent of water
and 77.5 per cent sugars, with small amounts of minerals, enzymes, and

pollen; its color is water-white to dark, and the flavor varies according to the nectar source.

FIG. 23-14. The honeybee. *Pollen gathering* (during flight). *A.* The forelegs remove wet pollen from the head and mouth parts; this is passed to the middle legs which are then drawn between the pollen combs on the hind legs. *B.* Middle legs pat down pollen masses in "baskets" on hind legs. *C.* Pollen from comb on right hind leg is scraped onto the pecten of the left hind leg. *Wax manipulation* (while bee stands on its midlegs) *D, E.* Wax scale is removed from gland pocket by hind leg; and *F, G,* carried forward to the mandibles. (*After Casteel*, 1912.)

23-17. Reproduction. The reproductive system is vestigial in workers but highly developed in queens. About 7 days after emerging a young queen mates with a drone high in the air; his copulatory organs then are torn away to remain in her genital bursa until removed by workers after her return to the hive. The spermatozoa thus received into her spermatheca must serve for all the fertilized eggs she will ever lay. Her ovaries enlarge to fill the long abdomen, and in a day or two she begins to lay. She can control the process of fertilization. Unfertilized eggs produce drones, or males (genetically haploid, 16 chromosomes), and fertilized eggs yield females (diploid, 32 chromosomes). In the season of nectar flow, a queen lays up to 1,000 eggs per day, gluing each to the bottom of a cell. The tiny wormlike *larva* has no legs or eyes. For 2 days all larvae are fed on "royal jelly" produced by pharyngeal glands of young workers. Thereafter, drone and worker larvae receive mainly honey and pollen, but queen larvae continue chiefly on royal jelly, which causes them to develop differently and to become larger. Each larva has several molts and grows; then its cell is capped with wax, and the larva within spins a thin *cocoon.* There, as a *pupa,* it undergoes complete metamorphosis and finally cuts the cell cap with its mandibles to emerge as a young bee. The time of development for each caste is standardized because of the temperature regulation in the hive:

Queen: egg, 3; larva, $5\frac{1}{2}$; pupa, $7\frac{1}{2}$ = 16 days
Worker: egg, 3; larva, 6;   pupa, 12   = 21 days
Drone: egg, 3; larva, $6\frac{1}{2}$; pupa, $14\frac{1}{2}$ = 24 days

To mankind, the honeybee is a symbol of industry and cooperation, gathering food in time of plenty against the needs of winter. When the warmth of spring brings early flowers, the workers gather nectar and pollen, the queen lays rapidly, and new workers soon swell the colony population. Overcrowding leads to *swarming* in which the old queen and several thousand workers emerge as a dense swarm and fly off to a new site previously located by worker scouts. Prior to this, some queen larvae are started in the old colony. One of the queens emerges, usually stings the other queen larvae, is fertilized in a mating flight, and returns to serve the old hive in egg laying. A queen may live for 3 to 5 seasons and lay a million eggs. Drones are produced during active nectar flow; but thereafter, when brood production ceases, they are mostly driven out to starve and die. Many of the workers hatched in autumn survive until spring, but those born earlier in the year use up their energy more rapidly—like a battery—and live only 6 to 8 weeks.

23-18. The hive. Each comb (Fig. 23-12) in a hive is a vertical sheet of wax, fastened to the top (and sides) of a cavity. The *worker cells* where workers are reared and honey or pollen is stored are about 5 mm. across, and the *drone cells,* 6 mm. across, serve to rear drones and for storage. Large vertical peanut-like *queen cells,* open below, are built along the lower comb margins for queen rearing. The wax is secreted as small flakes by glands in pockets under the abdomen on workers. Once formed, the combs are used for years, the cells being cleaned and polished for re-use.

Honeybees are about the only animals that achieve "air conditioning." In summer they fan their wings vigorously to ventilate the hive, to keep the temperature inside at about 33°C. for brood rearing, and to evaporate excess water from honey in open cells. In hot dry weather they carry in water to humidify the colony and to dilute the honey if necessary. During winter, when the stored honey is used as food, they form a compact cluster and produce heat by active body and wing movements. Clusters form at 14°C. (57°F.) or below and can raise the hive temperature to 24 or 30°C., even when the outside air is at or below freezing.

Bee colonies are reduced by dearth of nectar or pollen and by exhaustion of honey stores in winter. Adult bees are eaten by toads, skunks, and bears, the latter having a proverbial liking for honey as well. Two serious "foul brood" diseases cause heavy losses in colonies if unchecked.

OTHER INSECTS

23-19. Form and function. Except for a few degenerate forms, the adults of all insects are alike in having one pair each of antennae and compound eyes, a fused head, a thorax of three somites with six legs (hence called Hexapoda), and a distinct abdomen. Within these limits

members of the various orders, families, and species show great diversity
in details of structure and habits.   Many of their features are adaptive
modifications to particular modes of life as noted here and in the Classification later.

The *coloration* is produced by pigments (chemical), or by surface
structure (physical), or by a combination of these.   Some pigments are
deposited in the exoskeleton and others in the epidermis or deeper.   The
irridescent colors of some beetles, butterflies, and others are produced by
differential interference of light falling upon microscopically fine surface
ridges or parallel plates of chitin.   Many insects are *protectively colored*
so that they resemble their immediate surroundings.   Some that are considered to be bad-tasting are described as *warningly colored,* and some
inoffensive species *mimic* the color or appearance of others that are bad-
tasting or poisonous (Fig. 7-8).

The exterior *cuticle* is often waxy and not easily wetted; this is of
advantage to the insects but causes some difficulty in attempts to control
harmful species by sprays.   The *body* is adaptively streamlined in some
aquatic bugs and beetles, is depressed in cockroaches and others that live
in crevices, and is fusilage-shaped in the fast-flying dragon-flies.   In
many other insects it shows no obvious adaptation to habits.   The hairy
covering on some nocturnal moths may help to insulate them against chilling, and the hairs on many flies and bees serve in the gathering of pollen.

The *antennae* are usually slender and either long or short.   They are
plumed in some gnats and moths and of varied shapes in beetles.   All
insects have *eyes* except some larvae that live concealed from the light,
some adults that inhabit caves or nests of termites or ants, some biting
lice, and the nonsexual castes of some ants and most termites.   The
mouth parts comprise two main types, for either chewing or sucking, as in
the grasshopper and bee, respectively.   Many species with sucking mouth
parts have means for piercing tissues, as in the mosquitoes and fleas
that "bite" other animals and the aphids that puncture plants.

The *legs* are variously modified, for running in tiger beetles, jumping
in fleas, swimming in water bugs and beetles, skating in water striders,
burrowing in mole crickets, and spinning in embiids.   The *wings* are
commonly thin and membranous.   The forewings are hardened as elytra
in beetles; they are leathery in the ORTHOPTERA, and the forward half is
thickened in the HEMIPTERA.   Flies (DIPTERA) and male coccids have
the hind pair represented by minute knobbed halteres (balancing organs),
and the fore pair is reduced on male stylopids.   The primitive insects
(PROTURA to THYSANURA) and lice, fleas, and some other parasitic forms
lack wings; ants and termites are also wingless save for the sexual castes.
The embryo in many insects has abdominal appendages, but there are
rarely any on adults except for the cerci and copulatory organs.   The

muscles are numerous and complex; about 2,000 are present in a caterpillar. Many insects are disproportionately powerful as compared with larger animals; a honeybee, for example, can pull twenty times its own weight and can lift a load equal to four-fifths its weight in flight.

The *digestive system* shows various modifications in relation to food habits. The salivary glands of bloodsucking insects produce anticoagulants that keep the blood fluid during ingestion and digestion. *Respiration* is performed by a tracheal system in most insects, but through the thin body covering in Collembola, some Protura, and some endoparasitic larvae. Adult aquatic insects that dive carry along a film of air on the exterior of their nonwettable bodies or beneath their wings to serve for respiration. Some aquatic larvae, such as those of mosquitoes, must extend their spiracles above the water to breathe, but the larvae of caddis-flies and others have thin *gills*—tracheal, anal, or blood—that take up oxygen dissolved in water. None of these is homologous with the gills of Crustacea. Some larvae that live in bottom muck deficient in oxygen probably satisfy their respiratory needs by oxygen obtained in the metabolism of food.

The *nervous system* is annelid-like in the lowest insects and in many larvae of higher forms, with paired ganglia in each body somite, but in the adults of some flies and others the (posterior) ganglia are concentrated forward in the body. *Sound production* is possible in many Orthoptera (Fig. 23-15), Hemiptera, cicadas, certain moths, some mosquitoes and

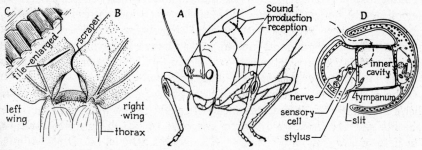

Fig. 23-15. *A.* Fore parts of a katydid showing the location of structures for sound production and reception. *B.* Under surface of the forewings with file and scraper that are rubbed together to produce sounds. *C.* Enlarged detail of the file. *D.* Cross section of foreleg showing the sound receptor or "ear," with paths of sound waves (broken line) and nerve impulses (solid arrow). (*Partly after Dahlgren, 1925.*)

other flies, and some beetles and bees. The mechanism of production varies and in some may be merely incidental to their manner of flight. *Light production* is an ability of glow-worms, fire-flies (Lampyridae) and others, a few of which flash in unison.

23-20. Distribution. Some insects are of exceedingly wide occurrence, over a continent or more, whereas other species are limited to a few acres.

Insects occur from sea level to well above 20,000 feet on the highest mountains. Plant-feeding species are naturally restricted to areas where their food plants grow, but other types are not so closely limited. Surveys by airplanes show that many insects inhabit the air at all times, but especially by day in summer; they are mostly below 1,000 feet, but some have been taken up to 14,000 feet. By such means, species are constantly being carried to new localities. Some beetles and COLLEMBOLA live on seabeaches between the tide lines, and a few water striders (*Halobates*) live on the ocean surface; there are few submerged marine insects.

23-21. Seasonal occurrence. Life on land exposes insects to greater extremes of environmental conditions than are experienced by most inhabitants of the sea and fresh waters. They have especially to withstand seasonal changes in temperature and food supply as between the summer and winter and in the abundance or scarcity of plants. Different species are adapted to these problems in various ways. Many species are abundant in warm seasons and far reduced at other times. Some, such as yellowjackets, overwinter as adults that hide away to hibernate in shelters where their bodily metabolism is far reduced. Others survive as pupae or larvae. In many species all individuals die at the close of the warm season and then are represented only by eggs that will develop and hatch the following spring.

23-22. Sensory perceptions and behavior. Insects respond to many stimuli that provoke sensations in man, including light, chemical stimuli (smell, taste), touch, and sound, but their perceptions differ in both kind and magnitude. They detect chemical stimuli far too delicate for the human nose or tongue, and some react to ultraviolet rays but not to red or infrared. These reactions are of aid in finding food and mates, and shelter for themselves, their eggs, and their young.

The simplest items of response are *reflexes* such as the action of a bee's sting, which will operate reflexly if touched even when severed from the body. The invariable type of response by which an animal orients itself to or away from a stimulus is known as a *taxis*. A *Drosophila* is guided by its olfactory organs to overripe fruit that bears the yeast upon which the fly feeds by a *positive chemotaxis* to certain alcohols and organic acids in the fermenting fruit. Many insects find mates by a similar taxis to the delicate scents emitted by the opposite sex. The moth that flies directly to (and even into) a flame shows *positive phototaxis* and the cockroach that runs for cover when suddenly exposed to a lamp a *negative phototaxis*. Aquatic larvae of caddis-flies often show *positive rheotaxis* by aligning themselves head foremost in a current of water. The term *kinesis* is used to describe undirected locomotor reactions where the speed of movement or frequency of turning depends on the

intensity of stimulation.   The cockroach, besides avoiding light, seeks
shelter in crevices where its body is in contact with the shelter—this is
thigmokinesis.   Taxes and kineses, and some other types of reactions,
enable insects and many other animals to find and inhabit the small
environmental niche or microclimate in which each kind is most successful.

Many other items of behavior in insects are based on ***instincts,*** which
consist of series or chains of coordinated reflexes by the whole organism.
The complex series of events by which a solitary wasp constructs a nest,
deposits an egg, provisions it with paralyzed insects, and skillfully closes
the cell is an example of chain instincts.   Other items of insect behavior
are plastic, or modifiable, and bring to bear some features of experiences
of an individual that are registered as organic memory.   An example here
is the hive bee, which is trained to associate color with a food supply.

23-23. Flight.   Insects, birds, and bats are the only animals capable of
true flight.   The wings of insects (Figs. 23-4, 23-16) are unique structures

Fig. 23-16.   Wing movements in the flight of an insect.   *A. Upstroke:* Contractions of
the tergo-sternal muscles depress the tergum and carry the wing bases downward, each
acting over a wing process as a fulcrum.   Rotation of the wings is produced by still other
muscles.   *C. Downstroke:* Contraction of the longitudinal (and other) muscles causes the
tergum to bulge upward and forces the wing tips downward.   (*After Snodgrass.*)

in being derived as extensions of the body integument quite unlike the
limb-wings of the vertebrates (Fig. 9-1).   The ability to fly enables insects
to escape enemies, to find food and mates more readily, to lay their eggs in
places not easily reached by other animals, to extend their feeding ranges,
and to disperse and occupy new territory.

23-24. Water conservation.   When the ancestors of insects left the
water and moved to the land and air, they experienced changes analogous
to those of amphibians and reptiles as compared with fishes.   The sense
organs became adapted to function in air, the chitinous body covering
served to resist the loss of body fluids by evaporation, and the tracheae
provided a means for breathing air.   All insects save those in humid
environments have a considerable problem in the conservation of body
water that does not beset aquatic animals, since moisture may be lost in
respiration and in evacuating food residues.   The valves in the spiracles
may limit the amount of air (and moisture) exhaled under some conditions, but the more vigorous respiratory movements during flight serve

incidentally to deplete the supply of fluids. Insects in dry situations extract water from food residues in the rectum, and they probably gain some metabolic water as a by-product of the oxidation of food materials within the body.

23-25. Food. Fully half the known species of insects are *phytophagous,* feeding on the tissues or juices of plants. The grasshopper eats a great variety of plants, the potato beetle uses only those of the Family Solanaceae, the larva of the monarch butterfly eats only the milkweeds (Genus *Asclepias*), and that of a common copper butterfly is restricted to a single species of sorrel (*Rumex acetosella*). Most termites and certain beetles subsist on wood, but some of them and certain ants eat fungi exclusively; among such insects are some that produce their own food by planting, fertilizing, and tending "fungus gardens." The *saprophagous* insects include beetles, fly larvae, and others which eat dead animals, and the *carnivorous* species are those which capture and devour insects or other living animals.

23-26. Enemies. Because of their abundance the insects are preyed upon by a great variety of other insects and vertebrates of the land and fresh waters. Insects are subject to many diseases that act to reduce their numbers.

23-27. Reproduction. Fertilization is always internal with insects. Most species are *oviparous* and lay their eggs singly or in clusters, either on or in the ground, on the plants or animals where their larvae feed, or in plant tissues. Those with aquatic larvae oviposit in or near water. The eggs of some hatch in a few hours, but those of some ORTHOPTERA and LEPIDOPTERA require many months before doing so. The aphids and several DIPTERA are *viviparous,* producing living young. The eggs of tachinid flies, which are deposited on other insects, will hatch almost as soon as laid. The living young of tsetse and hippoboscid flies develop within the "uterus" of the female parent where they are nourished by special secretions. *Parthenogenesis,* or reproduction from eggs without fertilization, occurs in aphids, thrips, gall wasps, saw-flies and others (*cf.* drone bee, p. 500). The generations of aphids in spring and summer consist only of females that reproduce by parthenogenesis, but later both sexes are produced in the same manner. These mate, and the fertilized females then lay eggs that remain quiescent over winter to produce females for the next spring. A special type of parthenogenesis known as *paedogenesis* occurs in the fly *Miastor* (CECIDOMYIDAE) and a few other insects. Each larva produces 7 to 30 larvae, and these in turn yield others. Some later larvae pupate to become male and female flies. The chalcid wasps that parasitize eggs of LEPIDOPTERA exhibit *polyembryony;* a chalcid egg begins development, then divides into 100 or more masses each of which grows to be a larva that transforms into a wasp.

23-28. Parasitism and hyperparasitism.   The larvae of tachinid flies (Diptera) and of the ichneumonid, braconid, and chalcid wasps (Hymenoptera) are *parasites* of other insects, and the scelionids (Hymenoptera) are egg parasites.   The parasites weaken or kill their hosts or destroy the eggs and thus serve to control the populations of the latter; but as the supply of host individuals declines, so must that of the parasites, which fluctuate in numbers with their hosts.   This matter is further complicated by *hyperparasitism,* wherein parasites in turn are themselves parasitized by other species.   A tussock moth caterpillar (*Hemerocampa leucostigma*) studied by L. O. Howard was found to have 23 primary parasites (6 Diptera, 17 Hymenoptera), which in turn had 13 secondary parasites, or hyperparasites; the latter were subject to 2 (or 5) tertiary parasites—such are the complexities in the "balance of nature"!

23-29. Gall insects.   The cynipid or gall wasps (Hymenoptera) and the cecidomyids or gall flies (Diptera) are small insects that oviposit in plant tissues.   Some substance then injected or resulting from growth of the larvae causes the plant to produce a characteristic swelling, or *gall.* These are of distinctive form and location (stem or leaf) according to the host plant and the kind of insect involved.   Galls are also produced by some aphids and psyllids (Homoptera) and by certain gall mites (Acarina).

23-30. Number of offspring.   This varies in different insects from the single larva hatched at a time by some viviparous flies to the million eggs, more or less, laid by a queen bee.   The actual number from any one female is less important than the rate of increase; in some species with short life cycles this is very rapid.   The pomace fly (*Drosophila*) lays up to 200 eggs per female, and the entire cycle requires only 10 days at about 80°F.   The house fly may complete its cycle in 8 to 10 days during hot weather.   Parthenogenesis in aphids and others likewise leads to extremely rapid multiplication of the population under optimum conditions of temperature, moisture, and food supply.   The offspring of a single aphid could cover the earth in one season if all survived!

23-31. Growth and metamorphosis.   Since an insect lives in an armorlike exoskeleton, it can change form or increase in size only after a molt, and none molts after attaining the adult stage.   The increase in dimensions at successive molts is a simple mathematical progression (linear increase about $\sqrt[3]{2} = 1.26$).   The primitive Orders Protura to Thysanura attain adult form and size by slightly graded changes and hence are called the Ametabola (Gr. *a,* not + *metabola,* change).   The Hemimetabola (Orthoptera to Thysanoptera) undergo a gradual or incomplete metamorphosis, as with the grasshopper.   The young hatch as small *nymphs,* somewhat resembling the adults, with compound eyes. In the successive stages, or *instars,* the wings appear externally as small wing pads that enlarge at successive molts to become functional in the *adult,* or *imago.* In the Holometabola (Mecoptera to Hymenoptera), the young emerge as small wormlike segmented *larvae* with the head, thorax, and abdomen much alike and with short legs but no wings or compound eyes. The successive larval instars increase in size through several molts. Each then enters a "resting" stage as a *pupa,* within the last larval skin, in a special puparium, or in a cocoon. Many larval organs then break down and are resorbed by phagocytic cells, while new structures for the adult arise concurrently. These profound changes occur before the adult, or *imago,* hatches out. This is complete metamorphosis as seen in the honeybee.

Experimental evidence indicates that both molt and metamorphosis are controlled by *hormones,* which are probably produced by the *corpus allatum.* This gland originates from ectoderm behind the mandibles and comes to lie behind the brain. Its removal at certain critical stages in nymphs of the bug *Rhodnius* will prevent them from molting. Conversely, if removed in early nymphs at certain other times, they will acquire some adult characteristics upon molting. The presence of a hormone is deemed essential for molt, and removal of the gland evidently takes out some substance that inhibits the appearance of adult characteristics. Like vertebrate hormones, this substance is nonspecific and if transplanted will exercise its influence in insects of other genera and orders.

23-32. Social insects. Most insects are *solitary,* each individual living unto itself; the sexes associate only to mate, and the female deserts her eggs or dies after laying. *Gregarious* species assemble in large numbers, as in swarms of locusts and hibernating ladybird beetles. With all such insects the parents usually never see or live coincidently with their offspring. About 6,000 species of insects, however, exhibit social instincts, the female or both parents living cooperatively with their offspring in a common shelter. These conditions begin with *subsocial relations,* as of a female earwig (Order Dermaptera), which guards her eggs and later the young. Cockroaches and crickets, some beetles and bugs, the Embioptera, and the Zoraptera do likewise. A solitary wasp provisions individual egg cells with insects as food for her larvae, which later hatch out and grow independently. True *social life* occurs with all termites, all ants, and certain wasps and bees. The female lives, according to her species, protected within the soil, in cavities in wood, or in a manufactured nest, often in darkness under a lowered temperature and regulated humidity where her muscular movements and catabolism are lessened. She has a lengthened life span, possibly because of these favorable conditions. Queens of some termites and ants may live for several years. With the more primitive, the female merely remains with successive broods or feeds them daily. From this condition there is a graded series to the complex colonial life of termites, ants, and hive bees, which have a division of labor between several castes (pp. 496; 516; 534). The constant association of many individuals in a colony evidently leads to the formation of useful new reflexes and instincts; with different kinds of food and possibly by the action of hormones, these may have led to the origin of castes. The larger populations with social life require an enhanced food supply. The ants show a progression in food habits such as probably occurred in man's history. The lowest kinds hunt insects or flesh. The pastoral ants attend and shelter aphids ("ant cows") from which they obtain honeydew as food, and the harvester ants gather and store seeds in summer to tide them through the winter. Finally, the fungus ants (*Atta*) grow their own pure crops of certain fungi in underground gardens that are fertilized with organic debris; each young queen upon setting out to found a new colony carries a seed stock of fungal hyphae in an infrabuccal pouch.

23-33. Relations to man. Practically every person is affected by some insects, from the apartment dweller who eats honey, wears silk, and swats flies to the poor Indian who is plagued by lice, fleas, and flies and in extremity eats grasshoppers. Economic entomology deals with the several thousand species of insects of importance to agriculture, forestry, and the food industries, and medical entomology with those which affect the health of man and domestic animals.

There are many *beneficial insects.* The bees and other insects that go from flower to flower to gather pollen are essential in cross-fertilizing the blossoms of apples, cherries, blackberries, clover, and other crops, as these will not otherwise set fruit or seed. Hives of bees are placed in orchards or fields to ensure such fertilization. The Smyrna fig, which is grown in California, produces only female flowers; to set good fruit, these need "caprification" (pollination) by a small wasp (*Blastophaga*) that develops only in the small nonedible capri-fig whence it brings pollen. The hive bees of the United States produce about 100,000 tons of honey annually, which serves as human food; they also yield over 1,000 tons of beeswax, which is used in polishes, church candles, and modeling and to wax thread. Raw silk is obtained in the Orient from the silkworm (*Bombyx mori*). The larvae are reared in domestication on a diet of white mulberry leaves, and each spins a cocoon of silk from its salivary secretions. A cocoon yields about 1,000 feet of fiber, and about 25,000 cocoons are unwound to spin 1 pound of silk thread. The shellac of commerce is obtained from waxy secretions of certain lac or scale insects (Coccidae) of India, and the dyes known as "cochineal" and "crimson lake" are derived from the dried bodies of some tropical scale insects of cactus.

Many harmful plant-eating insects are devoured by a host of *pre-*

daceous insects, such as ground beetles, syrphid flies, and wasps. The scale insects that feed on and damage citrus and other trees are eaten by the larvae of ladybird beetles (COCCINELLIDAE), and the latter are a major factor in controlling such pests. Certain species of ladybird beetles have been imported, reared, and liberated in orchards to control scale insects; hibernating masses of these beetles are gathered in the woods and sold for the same use. The parasitic insects that oviposit in the eggs or young of plant-feeding insects and whose larvae destroy the latter are another useful group; some of them are reared artificially and liberated to serve in "biological control" of harmful species. Unfortunately, some such parasites are themselves in turn subject to hyperparasites, which cancels the benefits from the parasitic species.

Other useful insects are the scavenger beetles and flies that clean up the dung and dead bodies of animals. Flesh flies lay quantities of eggs in animal carcasses, which their voracious larvae soon reduce to skin and bone. Ants, termites, and beetles slowly reduce the remains of dead trees and other plants, but termites also do much damage to buildings and other wooden structures. Finally, many insects are indirectly useful as the food for fishes, game birds, fur mammals, and other wild vertebrates and at times for poultry and turkeys.

Many species of *harmful insects* injure farm crops, forests, flower and truck gardens, stored foods, and other property; and others affect the comfort and health of wild and domestic animals and man. The aggregate damage by such insects is estimated at over $1,325,000,000 annually in the United States. Every cultivated plant has more than one insect pest, and each important crop such as corn, cotton, wheat, and tobacco has a hundred or more. These levy a steady toll in damage or loss of crops and in expenditures for control by poison sprays, dusts, and parasites. Some major *native pests* are the potato beetle, chinch bug, and grasshoppers; among the many *introduced pests* are the hessian fly of wheat, European corn borer, cotton boll weevil, and codling moth of apples. Federal and state quarantines are maintained to limit the spread of some of these insects.

Human foods are eaten or ruined by ants, cockroaches, and weevils and are dirtied by house flies; stored cereals are damaged by grain weevils and moths; woolen clothing, carpets, furs, and feathers are riddled by clothes moths and carpet beetles; and books are damaged by silverfish, beetle larvae, and termites. Bedbugs, stable flies, mosquitoes, and the gnats bite man and his animals; attacks of biting lice cause poultry and livestock to become unthrifty; bloodsucking tabanid flies annoy horses, and horn flies do the same to cattle; the larvae of bot flies are a source of irritation in the stomachs of horses; and the larvae of ox warble flies burrow in the backs of cattle, causing them to lose flesh and damaging the hides for leather.

Many insects and some ticks act as intermediate hosts for various diseases of man and the larger animals and plants; a few important examples are given in Table 23-1.

Table 23-1. Examples of Diseases Transmitted by Insects and Ticks

Disease	Causative organism	Carried by	Order
Dutch elm disease.........	*Ceratostomella* (fungus)	Bark beetles (*Scolytus*)	Coleoptera
Cucumber wilt............	*Bacillus tracheiphilus*	Cucumber beetles (*Diabrotica*)	Coleoptera
Curly top of sugar beets....	Virus	Beet leafhopper (*Circulifer*)	Homoptera
Human yellow fever.......	Virus	Mosquito (*Aëdes aegypti*)	Diptera
Bubonic plague of rats and man...................	*Pasteurella pestis*	Fleas (*Xenopsylla* and others)	Siphonaptera
Tularemia...............	*Pasteurella tularensis*	Deer fly (*Chrysops*) and others	Diptera
Human typhus fever.......	*Rickettsia*	Body louse (*Pediculus*)	Anoplura
Human malaria...........	*Plasmodium* (protozoan)	Mosquito (*Anopheles*)	Diptera
Chagas' disease...........	*Trypanosoma cruzi*	Bug (*Triatoma*)	Hemiptera
Filariasis...............	*Wuchereria bancrofti* (nematode)	Mosquitoes (*Culex* and others)	Diptera
Dog tapeworm...........	*Dipylidium caninum*	Louse (*Trichodectes*) and fleas	Mallophaga Siphonaptera
Rocky Mountain spotted fever of man............	*Dermacentroxinus rickettsi*	Tick (*Dermacentor andersoni*)	Acarina
Texas cattle fever.........	*Babesia bigemina*	Tick (*Boophilus annulatus*)	Acarina

Control of injurious insects has become more efficient with recent development of many new organic poisons, of which DDT and benzene hexachloride are conspicuous examples.

23-34. Fossil insects. Despite their fragile nature, remains of insects as fossils have been found in Australia, China, Russia, Europe, and the United States, and over 10,000 species have been described. The oldest are in Upper Carboniferous rocks, about 250,000,000 years old, and include the primitive †Paleodictyoptera, which lasted into Permian time; others (Blattaria) are closely related to living cockroaches. The †Protodonata resembled dragon-flies, and some (†*Meganura*) had a wingspread up to 29 inches! Six existing orders date from the Permian, and others appeared in the Mesozoic. The rising land, colder climates, and appearance of seasonal seed plants of those times evidently stimulated the evolution of pupae to withstand adverse conditions, since the earliest scorpion flies (Mecoptera) are so much like existing species as to suggest

TABLE 23-2.   ORDERS OF THE CLASS INSECTA.

(Characters of adults; exceptions as to wings or other features omitted)

		Orders and common names	Mouth parts		Wings		Distinctive features
			Chewing	Sucking	Fore	Hind	
Subclass APTERYGOTA. AMETABOLA: no metamorphosis		1. Protura	C		none		no antennae
		2. Collembola: springtails	C		none		spring (furcula) on abdomen
		3. Thysanura: bristletails	C		none		body fine-scaled; cerci on abdomen
Subclass PTERYGOTA, typically winged; wings reduced or absent in some. HEMIMETABOLA: young are nymphs with compound eyes, and metamorphosis gradual (incomplete); wings grow externally; metamorphosis gradual		4. Orthoptera: roaches, grasshoppers	C		4 or none leathery	thin	usually with cerci
		5. Dermaptera: earwigs	C		hard, short	thin, fanlike	forceps at end of abdomen
		6. Plecoptera: stone-flies	C		filmy, narrower	pleated, broader	2 long cerci
		7. Isoptera: termites	C		sexual forms with like wings; others wingless		sexual forms pigmented others pale, uncolored
		8. Embioptera: embiids	C		♂ winged; ♀ wingless		tarsi of forelegs enlarged for spinning
		9. Odonata: dragon-flies	C		filmy, not folded nearly alike		large; eyes big; no cerci
		10. Ephemerida: May-flies	C		filmy, not folded larger	smaller	mouth parts vestigial, cerci 2 or 3
		11. Mallophaga: biting lice	C		none		minute, flat
		12. Anoplura: sucking lice		S	none		minute, flat; mouth parts retractile
		13. Corrodentia: book lice	C		4, folded, roofed, or none		a maxillary "pick"
		14. Hemiptera: true bugs		S	half leathery	filmy	a triangular scutellum; base of beak far forward on head
		15. Homoptera: aphids, scale insects		S	texture uniform; 4, 2, or none		base of beak close to thorax
		16. Thysanoptera: thrips		S	fringed with hairs		tarsi bladder-like
HOLOMETABOLA: young are larvae with no compound eyes; wings grow internally; metamorphosis complex (complete)		17. Mecoptera: scorpion flies	C		filmy, roofed nearly alike		head elongate as a beak; cerci short
		18. Neuroptera: ant lions, dobson flies	C		filmy, roofed nearly alike		no cerci
		19. Trichoptera: caddis-flies	C		filmy, roofed		wings hairy-coated
		20. Lepidoptera: moths, butterflies		S	covered by fine overlapped scales		maxillae as coiled proboscis for feeding
		21. Diptera: true flies		S	no hind wings		halteres ("balancers") replace hind wings
		22. Siphonaptera: fleas		S	none		small; body laterally compressed
		23. Coleoptera: beetles, weevils	C		hard, veinless	filmy, folded	prothorax large, mesothorax reduced
		24. Strepsiptera: stylops	C		hind wings only in ♂; none in ♀		♀ maggot-like, having head and thorax fused
		25. Hymenoptera: ants, wasps, and bees	C	S	filmy; 2 pairs or none		base of abdomen usually constricted

♂ = male; ♀ = female; filmy = membranous; roofed = wings at rest over abdomen, thus / \

that complete metamorphosis was an early achievement.   The oldest fossil forms were fully winged and specialized along lines that distinguish the orders to which they belong.   The fossil remains indicate that the orders differed, however, in relative abundance, as the beetles (COLEOP-TERA) comprise only 1 per cent of known Permian insects but nearly 40 per cent of all insect species today.   The flies (DIPTERA) make up 0.3 per cent in the Permian, 5 per cent in Mesozoic, 27 per cent in Tertiary, and 10 per cent of Recent species.

The transparent Baltic amber (fossil resin) of Lower Oligocene, found in the sea off Königsberg, Germany, contains many insects with all external details beautifully preserved and easily seen.   Existing families and genera are common, but extinct species also occur.   Eight kinds of ants are structurally identical with living species, implying survival for 50,000,000 years.   The ants show polymorphism, and some had learned to attend plant lice.   The richest

FIG. 23-17. A fossil fly (†*Megacosmus*) from the Oligocene at Florissant, Colo. (*From Moore, Historical geology.*)

known fossil insect fauna is preserved at Florissant, Colo., near Pikes Peak, in Oligocene lake deposits of volcanic sand and ash that later became shale.   Most of the genera of insects of Tertiary time still survive, others have disappeared (Fig. 23-17), and some (such as the tsetse fly, *Glossina*) are now less widely distributed.

CLASSIFICATION

(Lengths are given for body, not including wings)

Class 3.   *INSECTA* (Hexapoda).   INSECTS.   Head, thorax, and abdomen distinct; 1 pair of antennae; mouth parts for chewing, sucking or lapping; thorax typically with 3 pairs of jointed legs and 2 pairs of wings, variously modified, reduced, or absent; a slender middorsal heart and aorta; respiration by branched tracheal tubes conveying air from spiracles directly to tissues; excretion by Malpighian tubules joined to hind-gut; brain of fused ganglia, double ventral nerve cord with segmental ganglia, often concentrated anteriorly; eyes both simple and compound; sexes separate; sex opening usually single, at end of abdomen; usually oviparous; development after hatching with gradual or abrupt metamorphosis; in all habitats, few in ocean; fully 675,000 species.

Subclass 1.   APTERYGOTA (Ametabola).   Primitively wingless; little or no metamorphosis; abdomen with ventral appendages (styli) besides cerci.

Order 1.   **Protura.**   Minute (0.6 to 1.5 mm.), primitive, mouth parts insect-like; no antennae, true eyes, or wings; 3 pairs of 5-jointed legs; abdomen of 12 somites each of first 3 with pair of minute appendages; first nymphal stage with 9 abdominal somites, 1 added at each molt by division of terminal somite; no metamorphosis; in damp places between decaying leaves, under bark on logs or twigs, or in moss; 60 species.   *Acerentulus* (Fig. 23-18*A*).

Order 2. __Collembola.__ Springtails. Minute to 5 mm.; colored or white; antennae 4-jointed; chewing mouth parts; no wings, compound eyes, or Malpighian tubules, usually no tracheae; abdomen of 6 somites; animal leaps by action of ventral springing organ (furcula) on 4th abdominal somite, when released by hook (hamula) on 3d somite; a ventral tube on 1st somite receives sticky secretion from gland behind labium by which animal adheres to smooth surfaces; no metamorphosis; in damp places under leaves, moss, bark, or stones; food of decaying matter; 1,200 species; Oligocene to Recent. *Papirius fuscus; Sminthurus hortensis,* "garden flea," damages young vegetables; *Achorutes armatum,* in manure, damages mushrooms; *A. nivicola,* "snow flea," sometimes gets into sap at maple-sugar camps.

Fig. 23-18. *A.* Order Protura. *Acerentulus barberi,* 1.0 mm. long. (*After Ewing,* 1940.) *B.* Order Collembola. Springtail (*Entomobrya laguna*), 2 mm. *C.* Order Thysanura. Silverfish (*Lepisma saccharina*), 10 mm.

Order 3. __Thysanura.__ Bristletails. Minute to 50 mm.; antennae long; chewing mouth parts; no wings; body scaly, whitish; abdomen of 11 somites, with 2 or 3 slender jointed cerci at end; run swiftly, avoiding light; no metamorphosis; 1,000 species; Oligocene to Recent. *Lepisma saccharina,* "silverfish" (Fig. 23-18*C*), in buildings, eats starch in books, glazed paper, and clothing, often harmful; *Thermobia domestica,* firebrat, about fire places and bake ovens; *Campodea,* in rotten wood or under leaves and stones; *Japyx,* cerci pincer-like.

Subclass 2. PTERYGOTA. Winged Insects. Wings usually present, sometimes reduced or absent; no abdominal appendages except cerci and genitalia.

Division 1. HEMIMETABOLA (Exopterygota). *Young stages are nymphs with compound eyes; wings develop externally; metamorphosis gradual to adult form.*

Order 4. __Orthoptera.__ Grasshoppers (Locusts), Crickets, etc. Size medium to large; chewing mouth parts; forewings (tegmina) narrow, parchment-like, and veined; hind wings membranous, broad, many-veined, folding fanlike beneath forewings; some wingless; abdomen usually with cerci and ovipositor; metamorphosis gradual; mostly plant feeders; 20,000 species; Carboniferous to Recent (Fig. 23-19).

Blattidae. Cockroaches. Body depressed, head partly under prothorax; antennae long; dark-colored, foul-smelling; hide in crevices, run rapidly in dark; omnivorous, spoil foods, clothing, leather, and books. *Periplaneta americana,* American cockroach; *Blatta orientalis,* oriental cockroach; *Blattella germanica,* croton bug or European cockroach; all in United States.

Mantidae. Praying Mantids. Head free, prothorax long; forelegs enlarged to grasp insects used as food; movements stealthy; mostly tropical. *Stagmomantis carolina,* praying mantis, north to Ohio and New Jersey, 60 mm. long.

Phasmidae. Walkingsticks. Form stick-like, mimicking twigs on which insect rests; wings small or none; meso- and meta-thorax and legs long; slow-moving; feed on foliage; mostly tropical, some to 330 mm. long, some mimic leaves. *Diapheromera femorata,* north to Canada, wingless.

Acrididae (Locustidae). Grasshoppers, Locusts. Body deeper than wide, head and eyes large, antennae short; tarsi 3-jointed; hind legs elongate for jumping; males produce sounds; diurnal; feed on green plants, often damage crops. *Melanoplus femur-rubrum,* red-legged grasshopper; *M. spretus,* Rocky Mountain grasshopper;

Dissosteira carolina, "Carolina locust," and *Schistocerca americana*, "American locust," both of wide distribution; *Romalea microptera*, lubber grasshopper, almost wingless, in southern states; *Locusta migratoria*, winged migratory locust of Old World, cause of biblical locust plagues.

Phasmidae   Mantidae   Blattidae

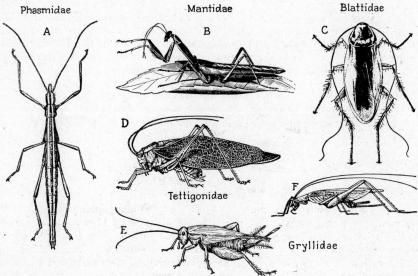

Tettigonidae

Gryllidae

FIG. 23-19.   Order ORTHOPTERA.   *A.* Walkingstick (*Diapheromera*), 75–100 mm. long. *B.* Praying mantis (*Paratenodera*), 70 mm.   *C.* American cockroach (*Periplaneta americana*), 45 mm.   *D.* Katydid (*Microcentrum*), 70 mm.   *E.* Field and house cricket (*Gryllus*), 30 mm.   *F.* Tree cricket (*Oecanthus*), 19 mm.   (*After various authors.*)   See also Fig. 23-1.

TETTIGONIIDAE (Locustidae).   LONG-HORNED GRASSHOPPERS, KATYDIDS, ETC. Form delicate; often green; antennae often longer than body; tarsi 4-jointed; hind legs long for jumping; nocturnal; males produce sounds.   *Microcentrum*, katydid; *Anabrus simplex*, "Mormon cricket," wingless, a crop pest.

GRYLLIDAE.   CRICKETS.   Short, dark-colored; antennae long; tarsi 4-jointed; some wingless; often leap on long hind legs; males produce chirps.   *Gryllus*, field and house crickets; *Gryllotalpa*, mole cricket, burrows in ground; *Oecanthus*, tree crickets, small, greenish white, puncture twigs and berry canes to lay eggs.

Order 5.   **Dermaptera** (Euplexoptera). EARWIGS.   Elongate; chewing mouth parts; forewings short, leathery, no veins; hind wings large, semicircular, membranous, veins radial, fold beneath forewings at rest; some wingless; tarsi 3-jointed; cerci form stout horny forceps at end of abdomen; metamorphosis gradual; feed on green plants and on other insects; hide in crevices, sometimes in buildings; 1,000 species; Jurassic to Recent.   *Labia minor*, 6 mm. long,

FIG. 23-20.   Order DERMAPTERA. European earwig (*Forficula auricularia*), 11–15 mm. long.   (*From W. B. Herms.*)

common; *Forficula auricularia* (Fig. 23-20), European earwig, now a local garden nuisance in eastern states and on Pacific coast; *Anisolabis maritima*, wingless, acclimatized from Europe on beaches of Atlantic coast.

Order 6. **Plecoptera.** STONE-FLIES. Size moderate to large; body soft; mouth parts for chewing, but often absent in adults; antennae long, with setae; wings 4,

membranous, held pleated but flat on back at rest, hind pair larger; tarsi 3-jointed; end of abdomen usually with 2 long many-jointed cerci; nymphs aquatic, often with a tufted tracheal gill behind each leg; live under stones, eat small insects; used as fish bait; adults of weak flight; metamorphosis gradual; 2,000 species; Permian

FIG. 23-21. Order PLECOPTERA. Stone-fly (*Taeniopteryx pacifica*), 13 mm. long. (*After Newcomer*, 1918.)

to Recent. *Pteronarcys; Taeniopteryx pacifica*, "salmon fly," occasionally damages fruit-tree buds in Washington (Fig. 23-21).

Order 7. **Isoptera.** TERMITES. Body soft; thorax joins broadly to abdomen; chewing mouth parts; workers and soldiers wingless, sterile, blind, colorless (hence,

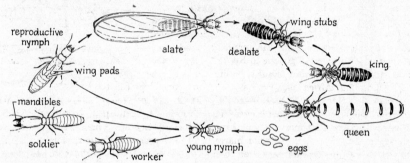

FIG. 23-22. Order ISOPTERA. Castes and life cycle of a termite. (*Modified from Kofoid and others, Termites and termite control, University of California Press.*)

"white ants"); sexual males and females pigmented, with 2 pairs of similar, narrow, membranous wings, carried flat on back at rest and detached after nuptial flight; metamorphosis gradual; 2,000 species, mostly in tropics; Eocene to Recent (Figs. 23-22, 23-23). *Reticulitermes*, subterranean termites, in earth and into dry wood, Mexico to southern Canada; *Kalotermes*, dry-wood termites, in wood, north to Virginia and California; *Zootermopsis*, damp-wood termites, western Canada to Virginia and southward; *Amitermes*, in earth of deserts, Texas to California; *Macrotermes*, in tropics, constructs firm aboveground nests (termitaria) to 30 feet tall, of earth particles cemented by salivary secretions; *Nasutitermes*, in tropics, builds aboveground nests of "carton" (paperlike wood debris); some with "fungus gardens" for food.

FIG. 23-23. Activities of the subterranean termite (*Reticulitermes*). (*Adapted from Light, 1929.*)

Primitive, social, live in closed tunnels within earth, wood, or nests, in colonies of few to thousands of individuals comprising 3 or more castes: (1) **sexuals** (kings and queens), swarm out in flights for dispersal, then settle in pairs, remove wings at preformed breaking joint near base, excavate new nest, mate, and produce colorless, wingless, and sterile young; (2) *soldiers,* heads and mandibles large, used to defend colony (some produce poisonous spray); (3) *workers,* excavate tunnels and build nests, collect food and feed other castes and rear young with aid of older nymphs. *Supplementary reproductives* derived from certain nymphs may become sexually mature and replace king and queen.   Feed on cellulose, which in some termites is digested by symbiotic flagellates (p. 290); termites help to reduce stumps, downed logs, etc., and form humus, but do serious economic damage, especially in tropics, by tunneling in wooden buildings, bridges, posts, and lumber, also in furniture, books, and papers; some attack living trees, and some distribute wood-destroying fungi.

Order 8. **Embioptera** (Embiidina). Embiids. Small; body long, straight-sided, and soft; chewing mouth parts; forelegs with first segment of tarsi inflated, containing spinning organs; cerci 2-jointed; males usually winged, females all wingless; in grass or under objects on ground, construct silk-lined tunnels joined to underground nests; colonial; eat decayed plant matter; tropical and sub-tropical; 140 species; Oligocene to Recent. *Anisembia texana,* Texas; *Gynembia tarsalis,* California (Fig. 23-24); *Oligotoma,* Africa, eastern Asia, etc., introduced in United States.

Fig. 23-24. Order Embioptera. *Embia major,* ×1½.

Order 9. **Odonata.** Dragon-flies, Damsel-flies. Large; body often brightly colored; chewing mouth parts; eyes huge, prominent, with up to 30,000 ommatidia; 2 pairs of transparent membranous wings with complex cross veins, a strong cross vein and notch, or nodus, in anterior margin of each; abdomen slender, elongate; adults strong-flying, predaceous; legs used to capture other insects in flight but not for loco-motion; mate in air; eggs dropped in water or inserted in aquatic plants; nymphs (naiads) aquatic, capture prey with extensible labium having hooklike "jaws" at end; 11 to 15 molts, 3 months to 5 years in water with gradual metamorphosis, climbing out for final molt to winged adult stage; 5,000 species; Permian to Recent (Fig. 23-25).

Suborder 1. anisoptera. Dragon-flies. Hind wings wider at base than forewings; wings held laterally in repose; nymphs with gills in rectum, water for

Fig. 23-25. Order Odonata. Dragon-flies. *Aeschna: A.* Nymph capturing prey, with labium extended. *B.* Nymphal skin. *Libellula: C.* Nymph. *D.* Nymphal skin. *E.* Adult at rest with wings extended. (*After Brehm.*)

aeration drawn in and expelled, aiding also in locomotion. *Gomphus, Anax, Aeschna, Libellula, Sympetrum.*

Suborder 2. ZYGOPTERA. DAMSEL-FLIES. Wings alike, held vertically over back in repose; nymphs with 3 external leaflike caudal gills. *Hetaerina,* ruby spot; *Lestes, Argia.*

Order 10. **Ephemerida.** MAY-FLIES. To 25 mm. long; body soft; mouth parts

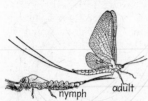

for chewing, but vestigial; antennae short; wings 4, membranous, forewings much larger, all held vertically above body at rest; end of abdomen with 2 or 3 long, many-jointed cerci; nymphs aquatic, with lateral tracheal gills; feed on plant materials; up to 21 molts, few months to 3 years in water; finally float at surface, and flying subimago emerges and soon molts to imago that lives but a few hours or days, reproduces, and dies without feeding; 1,000 species; Permian to Recent. *Ephemera; Leptophlebia; Calliboetis* (Fig. 23-26).

FIG. 23-26. Order EPHEMER-IDA. May-flies. *(From General Biological Supply House.)*

Order 11. **Mallophaga.** BITING LICE. Small, to 6 mm. long; body depressed, flat; wingless; head broad; mouth parts highly modified for chewing (biting); antennae short, 3- to 5-jointed; eyes reduced or none; thorax short, more or less fused; legs short; tarsi 1- or 2-jointed, clawed for clinging to host; no cerci; metamorphosis slight; exclusively ectoparasitic on birds and a few mammals; feed on fragments of feathers, hair, or epidermis; eggs glued to host; 2,100 species, none fossil. *Menopon, Philopterus, Colpocephalum,* various species on different wild birds; *M. gallinae* and *M. stramineum,* common "hen lice" of poultry (Fig. 23-27A, B); *Goniodes, Lipeurus,*

FIG. 23-27. Order MALLOPHAGA. Hen louse (*Menopon stramineum*), 2–2.5 mm. long: *A.* Male. *B* Female. Order ANOPLURA. *C.* Hog louse (*Haematopinus suis*), 5–6 mm. *D.* Human body louse (*Pediculus humanus*), 3 mm. *E.* Crab or pubic louse (*Phthirius pubis*), 2 mm. *(After U.S. Department of Agriculture.)*

on various domestic fowls; *Trichodectes,* various species on wild and domestic mammals; *T. bovis,* on cattle; *T. canis,* on dogs, intermediate host of tapeworm (*Dipylidium caninum*).

Order 12. **Anoplura** (Siphunculata). SUCKING LICE. Small, to 6 mm. long; body depressed, flat; wingless; head narrow; mouth parts modified for puncturing skin and sucking blood, can be withdrawn into head when not in use; eyes reduced or none; antennae short, 5-jointed; thorax fused; tarsi 1-jointed, each with single claw; metamorphosis slight; exclusively ectoparasitic on mammals; feed on blood and transmit various diseases; 300 species, none fossil. (Fig. 23-27C-E). *Pediculus humanus* (or *corporis*), human louse, or "cootie," on head and body, eggs, or nits, on hair or clothing; adults transmit typhus fever, trench fever, European relapsing fever, and other diseases of mankind; related species on apes and monkeys; *Haematopinus suis,* hog louse, on domestic swine; *Polyplax spinulosa,* spiny rat louse; *Echinophthirius horridus,* on harbor seals; others on sea lions, walrus, and fur seals.

Order 13. **Corrodentia** (Psocoptera). Book Lice, etc. Small to minute; antennae slender; chewing mouth parts; prothorax small; wings 4 (or none), veined, membranous, roofed over abdomen at rest; no ovipositor; metamorphosis gradual; 800 species; Permian to Recent.

Suborder 1. zoraptera. Antennae 9-jointed; tarsi 2-jointed; cerci short. *Zorotypus,* 6 species, under 3 mm. long, Texas, Florida, etc., under bark, in humus, near termite nests, etc.

Suborder 2. psocida. Antennae 13- to 50-jointed; a maxillary "pick"; tarsi 2- or 3-jointed; no cerci; feed on starches, cereals, paste, and decaying materials; under bark, in bird's nests, among fungi and carry spores. *Psocus,* bark lice, winged, some under silken tents; *Troctes divinatorius,* book louse, wingless (Fig. 23-28); others winged on trees, etc.

Fig. 23-28. Order Corrodentia. Book louse (*Troctes divinatorius*). 1.0 mm. long. (*After U.S. Dept. Agr., Farmer's Bull.* 1104.)

Order 14. **Hemiptera.** True Bugs. Mostly large; mouth parts piercing-sucking; jointed beak attached far forward on head, composed of labrum with piercing mandibles and maxillae; pronotum large; triangular scutellum between wing bases; wings 4 (or none), forewings thick and horny at bases, membranous behind, crossed at rest; hind wings membranous, fold under forewings; metamorphosis gradual; aquatic or terrestrial; food of plant sap or animal body fluids; many important economically; 40,000 species; Triassic to Recent (Fig. 23-29).

Suborder 1. cryptocerata. Antennae short, under head; no stink glands; aquatic; mostly predaceous.

Fig. 23-29. Order Hemiptera. *A.* Water scorpion (*Ranatra*), 50 mm. long. *B.* Water strider (*Gerris*), 20 mm. *C.* Bedbug (*Cimex*), 5 mm. *D.* Lacebug (*Corythucha*), 3 mm. *E.* Corsair bug (*Rasahus*), 18 mm. *F.* Giant water bug (*Belostoma*), 60 mm. *G.* Squash bug (*Anasa*), 16 mm. *H.* Plant bug (*Lygus*), 6 mm. *I.* Milkweed bug (*Lygaeus*), 12 mm. *J.* Back swimmer (*Notonecta*), 12 mm. (*After various authors.*)

CORIXIDAE. WATER BOATMEN. Swim upright by fringed oarlike hind legs; eat microplants. *Corixa.*

NOTONECTIDAE. BACK SWIMMERS. Swim by long hind legs, with convex dorsal surface downward; bloodsucking; may bite man. *Notonecta.*

NEPIDAE. WATER SCORPIONS. Usually slender, sticklike, 25 to 50 mm. long; long anal breathing tubes; crawl in shallow waters. *Ranatra,* slender; *Nepa,* broad.

BELOSTOMIDAE. GIANT WATER BUGS. To 115 mm. long; beak short but stout, bite severely if handled; often under lights; some females glue eggs to back of male. *Lethocerus (Belostoma),* "electric-light bug," or "toe-biter"; *Abedus, Belostoma.*

Suborder 2. GYMNOCERATA. Antennae movable, as long as head, visible at sides; mostly terrestrial.

GERRIDAE. WATER STRIDERS. Delicate, long-legged, walk on surface film of water; predaceous. *Gerris,* on fresh waters; *Halobates,* on warm oceans even far from land.

REDUVIDAE. ASSASSIN BUGS. Head narrow, beak stout, curved under head into groove of prosternum; predaceous. *Rasahus,* corsair bug, sucks juices of insects, also bites man severely; *Rhodnius* and *Triatoma,* cone noses, suck blood of mammals; *T. protracta,* to 22 mm. long, Texas to California, in nests of wood rats (*Neotoma*) and human dwellings, often infected with *Trypanosoma cruzi,* which causes Chagas' disease in South America (p. 289).

CIMICIDAE. BEDBUGS. Depressed, oval; wing pads only; nocturnal, bad-smelling, bloodsucking. *Cimex lectularius,* common bedbug of man; other species on bats, poultry, and swallows.

PENTATOMIDAE. STINK BUGS. Body oval or shield-shaped; antennae 5-jointed; scutellum over part or all of abdomen; bad-smelling; some predaceous, many plant

egg mass   nymphs (5 instars)   adult

FIG. 23-30. Order HEMIPTERA. Harlequin cabbage bug (*Murgantia histrionica*), adult 10 mm. long. (*After U.S. Dept. Agr., Farmer's Bull.* 1061.)

feeders. *Murgantia histrionica,* harlequin bug (Fig. 23-30), on cruciferous and other plants; *Perillus bioculatus,* eats caterpillars and beetles.

MIRIDAE. PLANT BUGS. To 6 mm. long; no ocelli; forewings with fracture. *Lygus pratensis,* tarnished plant bug, damages many crop plants.

LYGAEIDAE. CHINCH BUGS. With ocelli; antennae below center of eye. *Blissus leucopterus,* seriously harmful to wheat and other cereals.

COREIDAE. SQUASH BUGS. Antennae high on head. *Anasa tristis,* squash bug, harmful to melons, etc.

Order 15. **Homoptera.** CICADAS, APHIDS, SCALE INSECTS, ETC. Mostly small; mouth parts piercing-sucking; base of beak close to thorax; wings 4 (or none), membranous, of like texture throughout, roofed over abdomen at rest; metamorphosis gradual; puncture plants and feed on sap, many destructive, some transmit diseases; 25,000 species; Permian to Recent (Fig. 23-31).

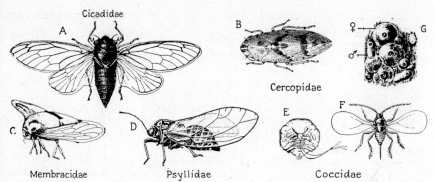

Fig. 23-31.   Order Homoptera.   *A.* Periodic cicada (*Magicicada septendecem*), 25 mm. long. *B.* Spittle bug (*Aphrophora*), 10 mm. *C.* Treehopper (*Platycotis*), 10 mm. *D.* Psyllid (*Paratriozoa*), 1.4 mm. *E–G.* San Jose scale (*Aspidiotus perniciosus*): *E*, female, 1.0 mm.; *F*, male; *G*, scales on tree bark.   (*After various authors.*)

Suborder 1. Auchenorhyncha. Rostrum (free) on head; antennae short, a bristle at end; tarsi 3-jointed; active.

Cicadidae. Cicadas or "Locusts." Usually large; femur of foreleg enlarged; males "sing" loudly, by 2 sets of vibrating plates on fore part of abdomen. *Magicicada septemdecem*, periodical cicada, or "seventeen-year locust," nymph grows 13 or 17 years in ground, sucks sap from tree roots, then emerges as flying adult.

Cercopidae. Spittle Bugs, Froghoppers. To 12 mm. long; ocelli 2 or none; tibiae usually spined; brown; nymphs hide in whipped-up white froth. *Aphrophora.*

Cicadellidae (Jassidae). Leafhoppers. Small; antennae bristle-like, between eyes; can run sidewise. *Circulifer* (*Eutettix*) *tenella*, beet leafhopper, transmits virus causing curly-top disease in sugar beets.

Membracidae. Treehoppers. To 10 mm. long; prothorax variously enlarged and projecting in grotesque shapes. *Ceresa bubalus*, buffalo treehopper, on various trees.

Suborder 2. Sternorhyncha. Small; rostrum apparently arising on thorax; antennae longer, no bristle.

Psyllidae. Jumping Plant Lice. To 3 mm. long; leap by enlarged hind legs. *Psylla pyricola*, on pears; *P. mali*, on apples.

Aphididae. Aphids or Plant Lice. Small to minute, delicate; 2 honeydew tubes (cornicles) dorsal on abdomen; mostly wingless, but males and some females winged; parthenogenesis common (Fig. 23-32); suck sap from plants, much of which is secreted as "honeydew" and often eaten by ants. *Phylloxera*, grape phylloxera, damages roots; *Anuraphis maidi-radicis*, corn root aphid, harmful to roots; *Aphis gossypii*, cotton or melon aphid, on various vegetables.

Aleyrodidae. White-flies. 1 to 3 mm. long, body and wings covered by white powder; nymphs flat, scale-like, sessile; all adults winged. *Trialeurodes vaporariorum*, greenhouse whitefly.

Coccidae. Scale Insects and Mealybugs. Small to minute; males with one pair of wings; females lack eyes, legs, and wings, covered by secreted wax or shell-like scale; many harmful to crop and garden plants. *Saissetia oleae*, black scale, on many host plants, causes great damage; *Aspidiotus perniciosus*, San José scale, quite harmful (Fig. 23-31*E-G*); *Pseudococcus citri*, citrus mealybug, damages various plants; *Tachardia lacca*, lac insect of southeastern Asia, secretion used to make shellac.

Order 16. **Thysanoptera** (Physopoda). Thrips. Mostly minute (0.5 to 8 mm.), slender; mouth parts conical, rasping-sucking; antennae 6- to 9-jointed; wings 4, alike,

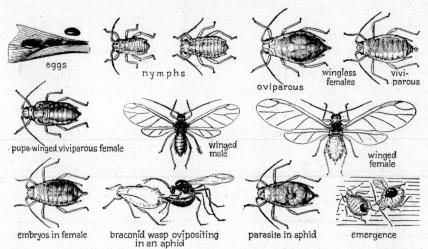

FIG. 23-32. Order HOMOPTERA. Family APHIDIDAE. Spring grain aphid (*Toxoptera graminum*), adult male 1.5 mm. long. Braconid wasp (*Aphidius testaceipes*). (*After U.S. Bur. Entomology Bull.* 110.)

narrow, few veins, fringed by many long hairs, and laid flat on body at rest; some wingless; tarsi 1- or 2-jointed, ending in protrusible "bladder"; no cerci; parthenogenesis common, males unknown in some species; larvae often gregarious; metamorphosis gradual to complete; 1 to 10 generations per year in different species; both larvae and adults scrape epidermis on flowers, leaves, and fruits to suck out juices of plants and leave whitened scars; many species injurious to crops, and some transmit virus diseases of plants; 2,000 species, 125 of these in California; Jurassic to Recent.

FIG. 23-33. Order THYSANOPTERA. Bean thrips (*Hercothrips fasciatus*). (*From Stanley F. Bailey.*)

Suborder 1. TEREBRANTIA. Females with sawlike ovipositor to deposit eggs in epidermis of plants. *Thrips tabaci*, onion thrips, world-wide on hundreds of plant hosts; *Hercothrips fasciatus*, bean thrips (Fig. 23-33), on many cultivated crops; *H. haemorrhoidalis*, greenhouse thrips, on roses, tomatoes; *Scirtothrips citri*, citrus thrips, 0.75 mm. long, damages oranges and lemons.

Suborder 2. TUBULIFERA. Females lack ovipositor, eggs laid on surface of plants; less harmful. *Leptothrips*.

Divison 2. HOLOMETABOLA (Endopterygota). *Young stages are larvae without compound eyes; wings grow internally; metamorphosis complete (complex).*

Order 17. **Mecoptera.** Scorpion Flies. Small to large; antennae and legs long; chewing mouth parts on downward-projecting beak; wings 4, alike, slender, membranous, many-veined, roofed over abdomen at rest; cerci small; some males carry end of abdomen upcurved like scorpion; inhabit dense herbage; larvae and adults carnivorous; larvae caterpillar-like with 3 pairs of thoracic legs and 8 of prolegs on abdomen, live in burrows and feed on ground surface; metamorphosis complete; 300 species; Permian to Recent. *Panorpa*, scorpion fly (Fig. 23-35G); *Bittacus*, resembles crane fly; *Boreus*, on winter snow in northern states.

eggs   larva eating   cocoon   adult
         an insect

Fig. 23-34. Order Neuroptera. Green lacewing-fly (*Chrysopa oculata*), adult 12 mm. long. (*After U.S. Bur. Entomology, Bull.* 110.)

Order 18. **Neuroptera.** Dobson Flies, Ant Lions, etc. Large to small; antennae long; chewing mouth parts; wings 4, alike, large, membranous, many cross veins, roofed over abdomen at rest; tarsi 5-jointed; no cerci; larvae spindle-shaped with grooved suctorial mandibles, carnivorous; metamorphosis complete; 4,000 species; Permian to Recent.

Suborder 1. megaloptera. Veins not forked near wing margins; larvae with chewing mouth parts. *Corydalis cornuta*, dobson fly, male with huge mandibles but harmless, larvae (hellgramites) aquatic for 3 years; *Sialis*, alder fly; *Raphidia*, snake fly, larvae under loose bark.

Suborder 2. planipennia. Veins forked near wing margins; larvae with sucking mouth parts.

Chrysopidae. Lacewings or Goldeneyes. Small; wings delicate, green; eggs on stalks attached to plants; larvae (aphid lions) predaceous, beneficial, feed on aphids. *Chrysopa* (Fig. 23-34).

Myrmeleonidae. Ant Lions. Adults resemble damsel-flies but have knobbed antennae; eggs laid in sand or loose earth; larva, or "doodle bug," makes a conical crater to trap ants, aphids, etc., which fall in and from which it sucks the body fluids. *Myrmeleon, Hesperoleon.*

Fig. 23-35. Order Trichoptera. Caddis-fly: *A.* Larva, 15 mm. long. *B.* Adult (*Phryganea*), 10 mm. *C–F.* Cases of various larvae. *G.* Order Mecoptera. Scorpion fly (*Panorpa*). (*A–F, after Furneaux, Life in ponds and streams, Longmans, Green and Co.; G, Riverside natural history, Houghton Mifflin Co.*)

Order 19. **Trichoptera.** Caddis-flies. Adults 3 to 25 mm. long, soft-bodied; mouth parts rudimentary; antennae and legs long; wings 4, membranous, many longitudinal and few cross veins, roofed over abdomen at rest; body and wings clothed with hairs, scale-like on some; larvae carnivorous, usually aquatic, each species living in distinctive movable case of leaves, plant stems, sand, or gravel, bound by lining of silk secreted by glands opening near mouth; some in rapid water construct nets and funnels to capture prey; often used as fish bait; metamorphosis complete; 3,000 species; Jurassic to Recent. *Limnophilus; Hydropsyche* (Fig. 23-35A-F).

Order 20. **Lepidoptera.** MOTHS AND BUTTERFLIES. Size various, spread 3 to 250 mm.; mouth parts for chewing in larvae, for sucking in adult; usually no mandibles; maxillae joined as coiled tube (proboscis) for sucking fluids; antennae long; eyes large; wings, 4, membranous, usually broad with few cross veins and covered by microscopic overlapping scales; body scaly or hairy; coloration brilliant to obscure; larvae (caterpillar, cutworm, etc.) wormlike with 3 pairs of legs plus prolegs on abdomen; 2 silk glands on labium used to spin cocoon to contain pupa; metamorphosis complete; 140,000 species; Jurassic to Recent (Fig. 23-36).

FIG. 23-36. Order LEPIDOPTERA. Moths. *A.* Fall army worm (*Laphygma frugiperda*), spread 25 to 30 mm. *B.* Tomato-worm moth (*Protoparce sexta*), spread 100 to 125 mm. *C.* Plum-tree borer (*Aegeria*), spread 30 mm. *D.* Gypsy moth (*Porthetria dispar*), spread 50 to 60 mm. *E.* Leopard moth (*Zeuzera pyrina*), spread 60 mm. (*After various authors.*)

Suborder 1. JUGATAE. No coiled proboscis; veins alike on all wings; process of forewing hooked to hind wing in flight.

MICROPTERYGIDAE. Small; mandibles functional. *Micropteryx.*

HEPIALIDAE. Mouth parts vestigial. *Hepialus.*

Suborder 2. FRENATAE. MOTHS AND MILLERS. Mouth with siphoning proboscis; antennae not enlarged at tip; often with ocelli; veins unlike in fore and hind wings; hind wing with one or more strong bristles holding to forewing in flight; mostly nocturnal.

AEGERIIDAE (Sesiidae). CLEAR-WINGED MOTHS. Wings mostly scaleless, transparent; adults resemble wasps but sluggish; larvae bore in wood of trees and shrubs. *Aegeria exitiosa*, peach-tree borer; *Ae. tipuliformis*, currant borer, from Europe.

GELECHIIDAE. Small; larvae burrow in seeds, tubers, twigs, or leaves. *Sitotroga cerealella*, angoumois grain moth, 12 mm. wide, larvae in grains and corn; *Pectinophora gossypiella*, pink bollworm, larvae in cotton bolls, 4 to 6 generations per year.

TINEIDAE. CLOTHES MOTHS. Small, native to Europe, widely naturalized. *Tinea pellionella*, case-making clothes moth, larvae in "silk"-lined case, covered by food debris; destroys woolens, furs, and feathers.

COSSIDAE. CARPENTER OR GOAT MOTHS. Adults large, some spread to 180 mm.; larvae burrow in solid wood of deciduous trees, live 2 or 3 years. *Prinoxystus robiniae.*

TORTRICIDAE. LEAF ROLLERS. Larvae often roll up and feed in leaves. *Carpocapsa pomonella*, codling moth, from southeastern Europe, larvae in fruits of apples and pears, 2 or 3 generations in warm regions, very harmful.

PYRALIDAE. SNOUT MOTHS. Spread to 25 mm.; larvae often concealed, roll in leaves or bore in stems, fruits, or stored materials. *Pyrausta nubilalis*, European corn borer, in eastern states, bores in stems and kills plants; *Plodia interpunctella*, Indian-meal moth, damages dried foods; *Galleria mellonella*, bee moth, larva (wax-worm) eats combs of hive bees.

PSYCHIDAE. BAGWORM MOTHS. Larvae in cases of silk and foliage scraps, females wingless, remain in cases. *Thyridopteryx ephemeraeformis.*

LASIOCAMPIDAE. TENT CATERPILLARS. Adults with proboscis atrophied, cannot feed; larvae spin community web among branches of trees and forage outside. *Malacosoma americana*, tent caterpillar (Fig. 23-37), may defoliate trees.

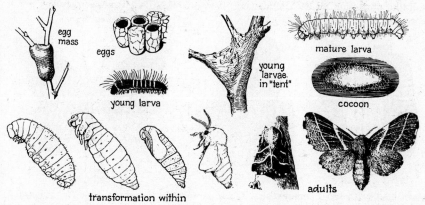

FIG. 23-37. Order LEPIDOPTERA. Life history of the tent caterpillar (*Malacosoma americana*); adult 20 mm. long. Stages in transformation or metamorphosis take place inside the cocoon. Not to scale. (*After Snodgrass, Insects, courtesy of Smithsonian Institution Series, Inc.*)

SPHINGIDAE. HAWK OR HUMMINGBIRD MOTHS. Forewings narrow, flight rapid, hover over flowers at dusk to feed with long proboscis. *Sphinx chersis*, hawk moth; *Protoparce sexta*, tomato worm moth, and *P. quinquemaculata*, tobacco worm moth, both with naked larvae to 100 mm. long, adults spread to 125 mm.

GEOMETRIDAE. MEASURING- AND CANKER-WORM MOTHS. Many resemble butterflies, some females wingless; larvae naked, feed on exposed foliage, and walk by looping body that has legs only near ends, hence called "loopers" or "measuring worms." *Palecrita vernata*, spring cankerworm, on trees.

SATURNIIDAE. GIANT SILKWORM MOTHS. Some yield silk from cocoons. *Samia cecropia*, cecropia moth, North America, wingspread to 165 mm.; *Telea polyphemus*, polyphemus moth, spread to 120 mm.; *Attacus*, in tropics, females spread to 240 mm.

BOMBYCIDAE. *Bombyx mori*, silkworm moth, native to China, entirely domesticated; larvae feed on mulberry leaves and spin dense cocoons that yield the genuine white and yellow silk of commerce—a most valuable insect; larvae subject to pebrine disease (caused by *Nosema bombycis*, a sporozoan) studied by Louis Pasteur.

ARCTIIDAE. TIGER MOTHS. Adults bright-colored; larvae densely hairy, the "wooly bears." *Hyphantia cunea*, fall webworm.

NOCTUIDAE. OWLET MOTHS. Colors somber, some adults spread to 150 mm.; larvae feed variously, some in ground as cutworms. *Heliothis obsoleta*, corn ear worm; *Cirphis unipuncta*, armyworm of North America, larvae sometimes "march" across country in great numbers; *Erebus*, largest moth.

LYMANTRIIDAE. TUSSOCK MOTHS. Larvae thickly covered with hairs. *Porthetria dispar*, gypsy moth, and *Nygmia phaeorrhoea*, brown-tail moth, both of Europe and now in northeastern states, defoliate and kill shade trees.

Suborder 3. RHOPALOCERA. SKIPPERS AND BUTTERFLIES. Mouth with siphoning proboscis; antennae enlarged at tip (hooks only in skippers); no ocelli; veins unlike in fore and hind wings; wings on each side held together by expanded membrane near base of hind wing; wings vertical above body at rest, upper surfaces in contact; diurnal.

HESPERIIDAE. SKIPPERS. Antennae with hooked tips, abdomen heavy; larvae with constriction behind head. *Atalopedes campestris*, field skipper.

PAPILIONIDAE. SWALLOWTAILS. Spread to 125 mm.; bright-colored; usually a tail-like projection on each hind wing; larvae mostly naked; pupae angular, not in cocoons. *Papilio* (Fig. 23-38).

larva   pupa   resting adult   spread adult

FIG. 23-38. Order LEPIDOPTERA. Black swallowtail butterfly (*Papilio polyxenes*); reduced. (*After Webster.*)

PIERIDAE. WHITE AND SULPHUR BUTTERFLIES. Abdomen slender. *Pieris rapae*, cabbage butterfly, wings white, on cabbage, etc. *Eurymus philodice*, wings yellow, on clovers.

NYMPHALIDAE. FOUR-FOOTED BUTTERFLIES. Forelegs reduced, not functional, folded under body; tibiae hairy. *Danaus plexippus*, milkweed or monarch butterfly, tawny and black; *Aglais antiopa*, mourning-cloak butterfly, blackish; *A. californica*, tortoise-shell butterfly, occasionally irrupts and migrates in great numbers; *Vanessa cardui*, painted lady; *Basilarchia archippus*, viceroy, coloration mimics that of monarch (Fig. 7-8).

LYCAENIDAE. BLUES, HAIRSTREAKS, AND GOSSAMERS. Mostly small, delicate, often brown, eyes white-rimmed; front tarsi reduced on males; larvae sluglike. *Lycaena hypophloeas*, the copper; *Feniseca tarquinius*, larvae prey on woolly aphids; *Lycaenophilus*, wings blue, polymorphic; *Strymon melinus*, wings gray.

Order 21. **Diptera.** TRUE FLIES. Forewings transparent, few veins; hind wings represented by short knobbed halteres; some wingless; mouth parts piercing-sucking, or "sponging," often forming a proboscis; body divisions distinct, abdomen of 4 to

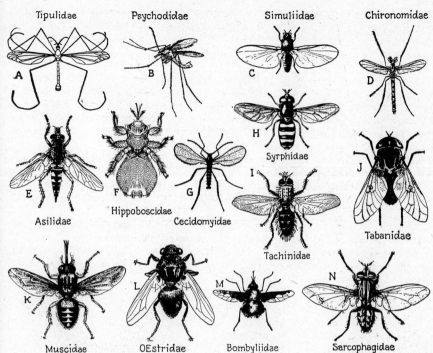

Tipulidae   Psychodidae   Simuliidae   Chironomidae

Asilidae   Hippoboscidae   Cecidomyidae   Syrphidae   Tabanidae

Tachinidae

Muscidae   OEstridae   Bombyliidae   Sarcophagidae

FIG. 23-39. Order DIPTERA. Flies. *A.* Crane fly (*Tipula*), 10 to 25 mm. long. *B.* Sand fly (*Phlebotomus*), 1.5 mm. *C.* Black fly (*Simulium*, 2 mm. *D.* Midge (*Chironomus*), 3 to 10 mm. *E.* Robber fly (*Erax*), 25 mm. *F.* Sheep ked (*Melophagus ovinus*), 6 mm. *G.* Hessian fly (*Phytophaga*), 2.5 mm. *H.* Hover fly (*Syrphus*), 10 mm. *I.* Tachinid fly (*Tachina*), 8 mm. *J.* Horse fly (*Tabanus*), 25 mm. *K.* Tsetse fly (*Glossina*), 13 mm. *L.* Bot fly (*Hypoderma bovis*), 12 mm. *M.* Bee fly (*Bombylius*), 10 mm. *N.* Flesh fly (*Sarcophaga*), 7 mm. (*After various authors.*)

9 visible somites; larvae usually footless; metamorphosis complete; mostly diurnal; 80,000 species; Upper Permian to Recent (Fig. 23-39).

Suborder 1. ORTHORRHAPHA. No frontal lunule (⌒-shaped sclerite) over antennae; larva often with distinct head; pupa naked, emerges from pupa case through T-shaped dorsal opening.

Tribe 1. NEMATOCERA. Antennae long, 6- to 39-jointed.

TIPULIDAE. CRANE FLIES. Slender, like enlarged mosquitoes, legs long and fragile, wings narrow; a V-shaped mark on back; larvae are "leather worms," living about grass roots, or semiaquatic. *Tipula.*

PSYCHODIDAE. MOTH FLIES AND SAND FLIES. To 4 mm. long, woolly, wings velvety; larvae and adults in sewers or damp organic wastes, some larvae in water. *Psychoda; Phlebotomus,* suck blood of vertebrates, carries human "three-day" fever in Mediterranean region and verruga peruana in Peruvian Andes.

CULICIDAE. MOSQUITOES. Slender, delicate; proboscis long and piercing in females; body humped; wings fringed by scales; larvae ("wrigglers") with large head, long abdomen, and breathing siphon, in various waters; adult males suck plant juices; adult females chiefly bloodsuckers, on birds, mammals, and man; abundant, annoying, some transmit serious diseases (Fig. 23-40); 1,500 species. *Culex,* many species;

EGGS

egg raft

LARVAE

surface of water

PUPAE

ADULTS

CULEX   ANOPHELES   AEDES

FIG. 23-40.   Order DIPTERA.   Family CULICIDAE.   Stages in the life cycles of three important types of mosquitoes.   Larvae and pupae in typical postures in the water; adults
posed as when resting or biting.

C. pipiens, common house mosquito, transmits bird malaria; *Anopheles,* some species
transmit *Plasmodium* (SPOROZOA) of human malaria (Fig. 12-20); *Aëdes,* different
species in salt marshes, swamps, tree holes, and snow waters; *Aëdes (Stegomyia)
aegypti,* tropics and subtropics, transmits human dengue and yellow fevers.

CHIRONOMIDAE.   MIDGETS, GNATS, AND PUNKIES.   Mostly minute, delicate,
mosquito-like, mouth parts short, wings scaleless; larvae in water or damp places;
adults often "dance" as swarms in air at end of day; few marine; a few reproduce
parthenogenetically.   *Chironomus,* larvae are "bloodworms," important as fish food;
Ceratopogon and *Leptoconops,* punkies, or "no-see-ums," bite man viciously.

CECIDOMYIDAE.   GALL GNATS.   Minute, mosquito-like, antennae with whorled
hairs; many produce galls on plants, in which larvae are reared; others are predaceous
or parasitic or feed on decaying matter or on plants.   *Phytophaga destructor,* hessian
fly, feeds in stems of wheat, very harmful; *Diarthronomyia hypogaea,* chrysanthemum
gall fly, produces galls; *Miastor,* reproduces by paedogenesis in larvae.

MYCETOPHILIDAE.   FUNGUS GNATS.   Small, delicate, mosquito-like; antennae
and coxae long; in damp woods, basements, etc.; larvae feed on fungus, some gregarious.   *Mycetophila mutica,* in mushrooms and toadstools.

SIMULIIDAE.   BLACK FLIES.   Short, chunky, wings broad; first tarsal joint dilated;
larvae attach by anal end to rocks in running water.   *Simulium,* females suck blood
of domestic birds and mammals and of man; *S. pecuarum,* buffalo gnat.

Tribe 2.   BRACHYCERA.   Antennae short, 3-jointed.

TABANIDAE.   HORSE FLIES.   Stout; eyes large, lateral, often banded; proboscis
projecting; eggs and larvae in water or damp places; male flies suck plant juices and

honeydew, females bloodsucking. *Tabanus*, horse fly, buzzes about and bites horses and cattle; *Chrysops*, deer (and horse) fly; *C. discalis* transmits tularemia from rodents to man.

ASILIDAE. ROBBER FLIES. Large, robust; body bristly; hairy "beard" about mouth; catch insects in air and suck out their juices. *Erax; Asilus.*

BOMBYLIIDAE. BEE FLIES. Densely haired, resembling bees; legs and proboscis long, slender; larvae parasitic or prey on other insects; adults hover and feed in flowers, harmless. *Bombylius.*

Suborder 2. CYCLORRHAPHA. Adults with frontal lunule over antennae; antennae usually 3-jointed with bristle (arista) at end; last larval skin forms hard puparium, enclosing pupa, and opens by circular lid.

Tribe 1. ASCHIZA. No frontal suture around antenna base.

SYRPHIDAE. HOVER FLIES. Bright-colored, no bristles, mimic wasps or bees; larvae prey on aphids or on small insects or (rat-tail maggots) scavenge in filth; adults hover over and feed in flowers. *Syrphus*, hover fly; *Merodon, Eumerus*, bulb flies, larvae damage narcissus, onions, etc.

Tribe 2. SCHIZOPHORA. A seam around antenna base.

TRYPETIDAE. FRUIT FLIES. Tip of abdomen narrow. *Ceratitis capitata*, Mediterranean fruit fly, and *Dacus dorsalis*, Oriental fruit fly, boring larvae of both injure fleshy fruits.

DROSOPHILIDAE. POMACE FLIES. Eyes usually red. *Drosophila melanogaster*, about decaying fruit; much used in genetics (Chap. 6).

ANTHOMYIDAE. ROOT MAGGOT FLIES. Larvae on roots or decaying materials, some carnivorous. *Hylemyia brassicae*, cabbage maggot, and *H. antiqua*, onion maggot, both damage crops.

MUSCIDAE. HOUSE FLIES, ETC. Arista usually plumed to tip; larvae grow in decomposing organic materials; adults about wild and domestic mammals and man, obnoxious and harmful; *Musca domestica*, common house fly (Fig. 23-41), with spong-

larva
eggs   pupa   adult

FIG. 23-41. Order DIPTERA. House fly (*Musca domestica*), 4 to 6 mm. long. (*From W. B. Herms.*)

ing mouth parts, may contaminate food with filth and spread disease; *Calliphora vomitoria*, bluebottle, and *Lucilia caesar*, greenbottle, both "blow" (oviposit on) flesh; *Stomoxys calcitrans*, stable fly, and *Haematobia irritans*, horn fly, both bite domestic mammals; *Cochyliomyia macellaria*, screwworm, maggots in wounds, nose, or navel of domestic mammals, cause injury and death; *Glossina*, tsetse fly, carries trypanosomes of African sleeping sickness (Fig. 12-18*A*).

SARCOPHAGIDAE. FLESH FLIES. Larvae consume dead animals, feces, garbage, etc., or live in insects. *Sarcophaga.*

TACHINIDAE. TACHINID FLIES. Eggs or larvae deposited on insects and destroy the latter; adults feed in flowers. *Gonia*, in cutworms.

OESTRIDAE. BOT FLIES. Adults large, beelike, hairy, about domestic animals. *Gastrophilus intestinalis*, horse bot, eggs, or "nits," laid on hairs, removed by tongue; larvae burrow from mouth to stomach, pupae emerge in feces; *Hypoderma bovis*, larvae live as warbles under skin on back of cattle, hosts become unthrifty, and hides are damaged for leather; *Oestrus ovis*, in sheep, living larvae deposited about nose, live as head maggots in nasal region; *Cuterebra*, under skin of rodents.

Tribe 3. PUPIPARA. Abdomen indistinctly segmented; feet clawed; ovoviviparous, 1 larva at a time.

HIPPOBOSCIDAE. LOUSE FLIES. Body flat, louselike; winged or wingless; abdomen rubbery, expanded; deposit pupae on hosts; ectoparasitic, bloodsucking. *Melophagus ovinus*, "sheep tick," or "ked," 6 mm. long, on domestic sheep, harmful; *Lynchia*, on domestic pigeons; *Ornithoica*, on wild birds.

BRAULIDAE. BEE LOUSE. *Braula coeca*, minute, wingless, on queens and drones of honeybees.

Order 22. **Siphonaptera** (Aphaniptera). FLEAS. Body laterally compressed, tough; no wings; mouth parts piercing-sucking; antennae short, in grooves; eyes simple or none; legs long, adapted for leaping, coxae enlarged, tarsi 5-jointed; eggs laid in habitat of or on host; larvae minute, legless, feed on organic debris; pupae in cocoons; adults periodically ectoparasitic and bloodsucking on birds and mammals, avoid light and seek warmth; metamorphosis complete; 1,000 species; Oligocene to Recent. *Pulex irritans*, human flea, also on rats, etc.; *Ctenocephalides canis*, dog flea, and *C. felis*, cat flea (Fig. 23-42), both on dogs, cats, and man; *Xenopsylla cheopis*,

FIG. 23-42. Order SIPHONAPTERA. Cat flea (*Ctenocephalides felis*), 2.5 mm. long. (*From W. B. Herms.*)

Indian rat flea, transmits *Pasteurella pestis*, that causes bubonic plague; also transmits murine typhus in southern states; *Ceratophyllus*, various species on wild birds and mammals; *Echidnophaga gallinacea*, sticktight flea of poultry, often harmful; *Tunga* (*Dermatophilus*) *penetrans*, chigoe, or jigger, on feet of man and mammals, female burrows in skin, abdomen distends to size of small pea; *Hystricopsylla gigas*, largest flea, 5 mm. long, on some California rodents.

Order 23. **Coleoptera.** BEETLES, WEEVILS. Minute to large, cuticle heavy; chewing mouth parts, some snoutlike; forewings (elytra) thick, leathery, veinless, meet along middorsal line; hind wings membranous, few veins, fold forward under forewings at rest; some wingless; antennae usually 11-jointed; prothorax enlarged, movable; meso- and metathorax united to abdomen; larvae wormlike, usually with 3 pairs of legs; pupae rarely in cocoons; metamorphosis complete; more than 250,000 species; late Permian to Recent (Fig. 23-43).

Suborder 1. ADEPHAGA. Antennae filiform; hind wings with 1 or 2 cross veins.

CICINDELIDAE. TIGER BEETLES. Adults long-legged, bright-colored, run actively in open places, flight fast; larvae in deep burrows, catch insects at surface. *Cicindela*, in sandy places; *Omus*, black, wingless, nocturnal.

CARABIDAE. GROUND BEETLES. Mostly blackish, long-legged, terrestrial, and nocturnal, adults and larvae mainly carnivorous; some burrow, some blind in caves, some emit foul spray if disturbed. *Calosoma*, large, preys on caterpillars and cutworms.

DYTISCIDAE. PREDACEOUS DIVING BEETLES. To 37 mm. long; oval, smooth, shiny; hind legs flat, fringed with hairs, serve as oars in swimming; air stored under elytra when diving; adults and larvae aquatic and predaceous; food of larvae digested externally. *Dytiscus*.

GYRINIDAE. WHIRLING BEETLES. Small, oval, lustrous, eyes divided horizontally; skate rapidly on water surface, gregarious; predaceous. *Gyrinus*.

Suborder 2. POLYPHAGA. Small to minute; antennae various; hind wings lack cross veins.

STAPHYLINIDAE. ROVE BEETLES. Slender; elytra short; scavengers or predators. *Creophilus*, preys on carrion fly maggots; *Myrmedonia*, resembles ants and lives in ant nests; *Termitomimus*, in termite nests, ovoviviparous.

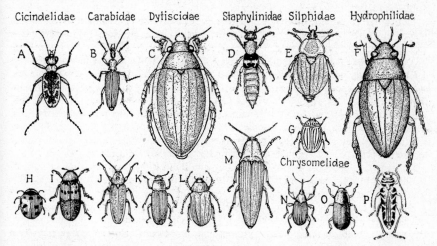

Cicindelidae Carabidae Dytiscidae Staphylinidae Silphidae Hydrophilidae

Chrysomelidae

Coccinell- Dermest- Lampyr- Tenebrion- Scarabae- Elateridae Curculion- Scolyt- Cerambycidae   idae   idae   idae   idae   idae   idae   idae

FIG. 23-43. Order COLEOPTERA. Beetles. Not to scale. (*Mostly from General Biological Supply House.*) *A.* Tiger beetle. *B.* Ground beetle. *C.* Predaceous diving beetle. *D.* Rove beetle. *E.* Carrion beetle. *F.* Water scavenger beetle. *G.* Leaf (potato) beetle. *H.* Ladybird beetle. *I.* Skin beetle. *J.* "Fire-fly." *K.* Darkling beetle. *L.* Lamellicorn beetle. *M.* Click beetle. *N.* Cotton boll weevil. *O.* Bark beetle. *P.* Long-horned beetle.

SILPHIDAE. CARRION BEETLES. Minute to 37 mm. long; many flattened; eat carrion, fungi, or decaying plant material. *Necrophorus*, burying beetle, buries small animals as food for larvae; *Silpha*, some feed on crop plants.

PLATYPSYLLIDAE. One species, *Platypsyllus castoris*, on beaver; flat, blind, and wingless.

HYDROPHILIDAE. WATER SCAVENGERS. Resemble DYTISCIDAE; black, a lengthwise keel under body; eat decaying material in water or damp places. *Hydrous triangularis*, to 27 mm. long.

COCCINELLIDAE. LADYBIRD BEETLES. Many 3 to 6 mm. long, rounded, convex, elytra cover abdomen; bright-colored, spotted; head turned down in notch of prothorax; larvae soft, spiny; both larvae and adults beneficial, preying on aphids and scale insects. *Coccinella* and *Hippodamia*, predaceous; *Epilachna corrupta*, bean ladybird, eats beans and other crops, harmful.

DERMESTIDAE. SKIN BEETLES. Small, dark, hairy; both adults and larvae destructive, eating furs, woolens, meat, and hides. *Anthrenus scrophulariae*, buffalo or carpet beetle, 3 mm. long, very injurious.

LAMPYRIDAE. GLOW-WORMS, FIRE-FLIES. To 12 mm. long, straight-sided; prothorax semicircular over downturned head; nocturnal; with light-producing organs on abdomen. *Lampyris, Photinus.*

ANOBIIDAE. POWDER-POST BEETLES, ETC. Length 3 to 8 mm.; cylindrical or globular, dark. *Sitodrepa panacea,* drugstore beetle, damages stored plant materials and upholstery; *Xestobium rufovillosum,* "deathwatch," larva bores in solid wood, adult taps with head.

BUPRESTIDAE. METALLIC WOOD BORERS. Body iridescent, antennae serrate; larvae with expanded flat prothorax, head minute. *Chrysobothris femorata,* flatheaded apple-tree borer, larva feeds under bark.

ELATERIDAE. CLICK BEETLES. Adults hard, narrow; can snap into air when placed on back, by releasing catch on ventral keel; larvae are tough-skinned "wireworms," some harmful to seeds and roots of crops. *Alaus,* to 45 mm. long; *Melanotus.*

TENEBRIONIDAE. DARKLING BEETLES. Some resemble CARABIDAE, but tarsi 4-jointed; body shape various. *Tenebrio molitor,* "meal worm," larvae damage stored cereals, used to feed caged birds; *Tribolium confusum,* flour beetle, larvae in flour, etc.

MELOIDAE. BLISTER OR OIL BEETLES. Length 7 to 30 mm.; prothorax narrow, necklike; some lack hind wings, some with hypermetamorphosis (extra larval stages and prepupa); adults eat foliage and flowers. *Epicauta,* larvae damage crops; *Lytta,* larvae eat grasshopper eggs; *Meloë, Sitaris,* larvae in nests of solitary bees.

LUCANIDAE. STAG BEETLES. Mandibles enormous in males; front tibiae enlarged for digging in soil; adults feed on honeydew; larvae in roots or wood under ground, some live 4 or more years. *Lucanus.*

SCARABAEIDAE. LAMELLICORN BEETLES. Small to large; body broad, deep, convex; legs spiny; antennae oval, clubbed, of 3 to 7 plates; nocturnal. *Phyllophaga,* larvae, or "white grubs," on grass roots, etc., adults on foliage; *Popillia japonica,* Japanese beetle, destructive, introduced in eastern states; *Macrodactylus,* rose chafer, adults eat leaves of cultivated trees and shrubs; *Scarabaeus sacer,* Egyptian sacred scarab or dung beetle, adults roll up balls of dung for food of larvae.

CHRYSOMELIDAE. LEAF BEETLES. To 12 mm. long; color brilliant, often metallic; adults eat leaves; larvae often in ground, feed on roots; many destructive. *Leptinotarsa decemlineata,* Colorado potato beetle, widespread; *Diabrotica,* cucumber beetles; *Donacia,* larva aquatic, obtains oxygen by piercing plants.

CURCULIONIDAE. WEEVILS OR SNOUT BEETLES. Small to 50 mm.; hard-shelled, often rough-surfaced; snout prolonged; femora often swollen; adults feign death when disturbed; larvae legless, feed within seeds, fruits, stems, or roots; many very destructive to crops. *Anthonomus grandis,* cotton boll weevil; *Conotrachelus nenuphar,* plum curculio; *Sitophilus granarius,* granary weevil; *Phytonomus posticus,* alfalfa weevil (Fig. 23-44).

eggs in stem   larva   pupa   cocoon   adult

FIG. 23-44. Order COLEOPTERA. The alfalfa weevil (*Phytonomus posticus*); adult 3 to 5 mm. long. (*After U.S. Bur. Entomology, Circ.* 137.)

Scolytidae. Bark Beetles. Short, cylindrical; antennae clubbed; adults and larvae feed under bark, "engraving" branched channels. *Scolytus rugulosus*, shothole borer, in various trees; *Dendroctonus*, pine beetle, in various conifers; *Xyleborus*, ambrosia beetle, grows fungus ("ambrosia") for food.

Cerambycidae. Long-horned Beetles. Slender, to 75 mm. long; colors often bright; antennae often exceed body in length; adults eat foliage or soft bark; larvae are roundheaded borers in solid wood. *Saperda candida*, roundheaded apple borer; *Ergates*, "pine sawyer."

Order 24. **Strepsiptera.** Stylops. Minute; metathorax enlarged; mouth parts for chewing, but small (or none); males with fan-shaped hind wings but forewings reduced to clubbed halteres; mobile, live 1 or 2 days; females larva-like, no antennae, eyes, wings, or legs; head and thorax fused; females and larvae permanently parasitic in body spaces of bees, wasps, Homoptera, etc.; absorb nutriment from host and modify structure ("stylopize") of latter; a hypermetamorphosis; 200 species; Oligocene and Recent (Fig. 23-45). *Stylops*, in bee (*Andrena*); *Xenos*, in wasp (*Polistes*).

Fig. 23-45. Order Strepsiptera. *Stylops*, male 2 mm. long. (*After Bohart*, 1941.)

Order 25. **Hymenoptera.** Wasps, Ants, and Bees, etc. Mouth parts chewing or chewing-lapping; wings 4 (or none), small, membranous, few veins, interlocked in

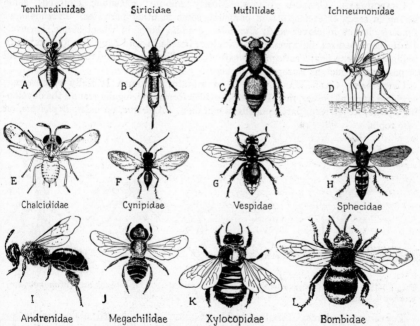

Fig. 23-46. Order Hymenoptera. *A.* Saw-fly or rose slug (*Endelomyia*), 15 mm. long. *B.* Horn-tail (*Sirex*), 30 mm. *C.* "Velvet ant" (*Sphaerophthalma*), 12 mm. *D.* Ichneumon-fly (*Megarhyssa*), to 37 mm. *E.* Chalcid wasp (*Aphytis*), 0.8 mm. *F.* Rose-gall wasp (*Rhodites*), 3 mm. *G.* White-faced hornet (*Vespa maculata*), 12 to 19 mm. *H.* Mud-dauber wasp (*Sphecius*), 12 to 20 mm. *I.* Mining bee (*Andrena*), 6 to 18 mm. *J.* Leaf-cutter bee (*Megachile*), 12 mm. *K.* Carpenter bee (*Xylocopa*), 12 to 20 mm. *L.* Bumble-bee (*Bombus*), 10 to 20 mm. (*After various authors.*)

flight; female with ovipositor for sawing, piercing, or stinging; larvae caterpillar-like or legless; pupae commonly in cocoons; metamorphosis complete; most species solitary, but some social in colonies, others parasitic as larvae; 90,000 species; Jurassic to Recent (Fig. 23-46).

Suborder 1. CHALASTROGASTRA. Abdomen broadly joined to thorax; larvae caterpillar-like, with legs, feed on plants.

SIRICIDAE. HORN-TAILS, WOOD WASPS. Body straight-sided; abdomen with spine at end; female with projecting ovipositor for boring; larvae in wood of trees or shrubs. *Sirex; Tremex*, to 50 mm. long.

TENTHREDINIDAE. SAW-FLIES. Body robust; female with ovipositor concealed and sawlike; parthenogenesis common; larvae eat foliage or bore in stems, etc. *Cimbex americanus*, American saw-fly, wingspread to 50 mm.; *Eriocampoides limacina*, pear or cherry "slug," eats epidermis of tree leaves.

Suborder 2. CLISTOGASTRA. Base of abdomen a narrow "waist" behind thorax; larvae legless.

ICHNEUMONIDAE. ICHNEUMON WASPS or "FLIES." Length 4 to 38 mm.; ovipositor very long (to 150 mm. in *Thalessa*); larvae parasitize caterpillars and other insects, live and pupate in host. *Therion; Ephialtes*.

BRACONIDAE. BRACONID WASPS. Mostly under 3 mm.; like ichneumonids in form and habits, but usually pupate outside of host. *Apanteles congregatus*, on larvae of sphingid moths; *Lysiphlebus testaceipes*, in aphids.

CHALCIDIDAE. CHALCID WASPS. Mostly minute; antennae elbowed; some larvae in seeds or stems, others parasitic, some in other parasites. *Bruchophagus funebris*, larvae in clover seed; *Harmoleta grandis*, larva in wheat stems, harmful; *Blastophaga psenses*, fig wasp, male wingless, breeds in wild capri figs and serves to pollinate Smyrna figs; *Trichogramma minutum*, millions reared and released for control of pest insects such as European corn borer.

CYNIPIDAE. GALL WASPS. Small to minute; abdomen laterally compressed; eggs laid in plant tissues, mainly on oaks, which form swollen galls around the developing larvae; males rare, parthenogenesis common. *Andricus*, on oaks; *Diplolepis*, on rose roots.

adult male   larva   pupa   worker   female

FIG. 23-47. Order HYMENOPTERA. Family FORMICIDAE. The black ant (*Monomorium*); worker 4.5 mm. long. (*From General Biological Supply House.*)

FORMICIDAE. ANTS. Length 2 to 18 mm.; pronotum enlarged; abdominal pedicle narrow; polymorphic, with sexual females (queens), males, and wingless (female) workers; other secondary castes in some species; social, in colonies of few to 100,000; queen removes wings after nuptial flight; she starts colony, later only lays eggs, and is fed liquids from mouths of workers; most species are scavengers and useful in cleaning up dead materials; few predaceous; many eat seeds, often are harmful; some colonize aphids and cause much trouble to agriculture. *Ponera*, primitive, few in colony; *Eciton*, legionary ants of tropics and southern states, no permanent nests, march in large companies, predaceous; *Monomorium*, small black ant (Fig. 23-47), nests in soil or wood; *Solenopsis geminata*, fire ant, stings severely, damages crops; *Pogonomyrmex*, harvester ant, eats seeds and often clears ground about entrance to nest in ground; *Atta*, fungus ant, feeds on fungus cultured on organic debris in underground galleries; *Formica*, builds large "anthills" of debris over nest in ground; *F. sanguinea* rears workers of *F. rufa* to serve as slaves; *Iridomyrmex humilis*, Argentine ant, a great household and agricultural pest, colonizes and attends aphids and scale insects to obtain honeydew as food; *Camponotus*, carpenter ant, large, in dead wood or ground. Many beetles and other insects inhabit ant nests, including (1) scavengers or predators; (2) indifferent guests; (3) true guests, which are fed and even reared by ants; and (4) parasites.

MUTILLIDAE. "VELVET ANTS." Body black, densely covered with colored hair; males winged, females wingless; larvae parasitic in cocoons of solitary wasps and bees. *Mutilla.*

SCOLIIDAE. VESPOID WASPS. Large, black, hairy; larvae parasitic in white grubs or larvae of other scarabaeid beetles. *Tiphia.*

CHRYSIDIDAE. CUCKOO WASPS. Integument hard; colors metallic; adbomen flat beneath, curled under body when attacked; larvae in nest cells of solitary wasps and bees. *Chrysis.*

EUMENIDAE. SOLITARY TRUE WASPS. Make solitary nests, of mud or in plant stems, each with one egg stocked with prey that is stung but not killed to feed larva. *Eumenes.*

VESPIDAE. COLONIAL WASPS. Sting powerful; young females overwinter, and each starts colony that lasts 1 season; nest of paper (chewed wood) with horizontal combs of cells to contain larvae; many small females or workers; males produced in late summer from unfertilized eggs; adults feed on nectar, honeydew, or fruit juices; young carnivorous. *Polistes*, nest flat and open below, 1 female; *Vespa diabolica*, yellow jacket, nest in or above ground, combs enclosed by paper walls; *V. maculata*, white-faced hornet, 12 to 19 mm. long, nests large, enclosed, in trees.

SPHECIDAE. MUD-DAUBER WASPS. Abdomen slender, elongate, enlarged at end; nests in ground or mud cells provisioned with stung prey for food of larvae. *Sphex; Sceliphron.*

BEMBICIDAE. BEELIKE WASPS. Live in separate nests but close together; larvae in unsealed cells, fed daily by adults. *Bembix.*

ANDRENIDAE. MINING BEES. Each female prepares a nest, lays eggs, and feeds nectar and pollen to larvae; nests close together, some with common entrance guarded by a sentinel bee. *Andrena.*

MEGACHILIDAE. LEAF-CUTTING AND MASON BEES. Resemble hive bees, head broad, tongue long, mandibles sharp; nests in plant stems, wood, or earth, and provisioned with nectar and pollen. *Megachile*, leaf-cutter bee, nests lined with discs cut from leaves; *Anthidium*, mason bee, nests of mud, cells lined with plant down, etc.

XYLOCOPIDAE. CARPENTER BEES. Large, black, resemble bumblebees but less hairy; powerful mandibles used to tunnel in solid wood for nest cells. *Xylocopa.*

BOMBIDAE (Bremidae). BUMBLEBEES (HUMBLEBEES). Medium to large, densely haired; tongue long, hence useful in pollinating clover and many other crop plants; overwintering young queens establish new colonies that last 1 season, with queen, many worker females, and drones (males); colonies in mouse nests or rodent burrows surrounded by grass, with wax cells to contain larvae and open cells ("honeypots") for food storage. *Bombus (Bremus).*

APIDAE. HONEYBEES. Eyes hairy; workers with pollen baskets on hind legs; native to Old World, probably Asia. *Apis mellifera*, hive bee (Figs. 23-12 to 23-14).

References

BRUES, C. T.   1946.   Insect dietary.   Cambridge, Mass., Harvard University Press. xxvi + 466 pp., 22 pls.

——— and A. L. MELANDER. 1932. Classification of insects . . . and other terrestrial arthropods [to families]. *Museum of Comparative Zoology, Bulletin*, vol. 73, 672 pp., 1,121 figs.

CARPENTER, G. H. 1921. Insect transformation. London, Methuen & Co., Ltd. x + 282 pp., 124 figs.

DUNCAN, C. D., and GAYLE PICKWELL. 1939. The world of insects. New York, McGraw-Hill Book Co., Inc. ix + 393 pp., 194 figs.

ESSIG, E. O. 1926. Insects of western North America. New York, The Macmillan Co. xi + 1,035 pp., 766 figs.

———. 1931. A history of entomology. New York, The Macmillan Co. vii + 1,029 pp., 263 figs.

FOLSOM, J. W., and R. A. WARDLE. 1934. Entomology with special reference to its ecological aspects. 4th ed. Philadelphia, The Blakiston Co. ix + 605 pp., 5 pls., 308 figs.

HERMS, W. B. 1939. Medical entomology. 3d ed. New York, The Macmillan Co. xix + 582 pp., 196 figs.

HOWARD, L. O. 1930. A history of applied entomology (somewhat anecdotal). *Smithsonian Miscellaneous Collections*, vol. 84, viii + 564 pp., 51 pls.

IMMS, A. D. 1942. Outlines of entomology. New York, E. P. Dutton & Co., Inc. vii + 184 pp., 96 figs.

———. 1949. A general textbook of entomology. 7th ed. New York, E. P. Dutton & Co., Inc. xii + 726 pp., 624 figs.

JOHANNSEN, O. A., and F. H. BUTT. 1941. Embryology of the insects and myriapods. New York, McGraw-Hill Book Co., Inc. 462 pp., illus.

LUTZ, F. E. 1935. Field book of insects. 3d ed. New York, G. P. Putnam's Sons. 510 pp., 100 pls. Popular.

METCALF, C. L., and W. P. FLINT. 1939. Destructive and useful insects. 2d ed. New York, McGraw-Hill Book Co., Inc. xvi + 981 pp., 584 figs.

ROSS, H. H. 1948. A textbook of entomology. New York, John Wiley & Sons, Inc. ix + 532 pp., 434 figs.

SNODGRASS, R. E. 1935. Principles of insect morphology. New York, McGraw-Hill Book Co., Inc. ix + 667 pp., 319 figs.

STEINHAUS, E. A. 1946. Insect microbiology. Ithaca, Comstock Publishing Co. xi + 763 pp., 256 figs. Microbes associated with insects and ticks.

———. 1949. Principles of insect pathology. New York, McGraw-Hill Book Co., Inc. xi + 757 pp., 219 figs. Diseases of insects.

WHEELER, W. M. 1928. The social insects, their origin and evolution. New York, Harcourt, Brace & Co. xviii + 378 pp., 79 figs.

WIGGLESWORTH, V. B. 1939. The principles of insect physiology. London, Methuen & Co., Ltd. vii + 434 pp., 316 figs.

The literature of entomology comprises a great number and variety of books, pamphlets, and periodicals. Besides the many works on general entomology, others are devoted to individual orders, families, or species and to the insect faunas of particular regions, large or small. The *Journal of Economic Entomology* and the *Annals of the Entomological Society of America* are two of the principal periodicals in the United States; others deal with special groups or regions. Many bulletins, circulars, and reports of the Federal government and of the state agricultural experiment stations contain the results of new investigations and provide information for controlling species of economic importance to agriculture, domestic animals, and the public health.

CHAPTER 24

PHYLUM ARTHROPODA. MISCELLANEOUS

This chapter deals with members of the Phylum ARTHROPODA other than the Classes CRUSTACEA, TRILOBITA, and INSECTA; it includes the spiders and their allies (Class ARACHNOIDEA), the centipedes (Class CHILOPODA), the millipedes (Class DIPLOPODA), the peculiar *Peripatus* (Class ONYCHOPHORA), and some forms of uncertain position in classification.

CLASS *ARACHNOIDEA*. SPIDERS AND THEIR ALLIES

The ARACHNOIDEA (Gr. *arachne*, spider + *oid*, like) is a varied assemblage comprising the spiders, mites, ticks, harvestmen, scorpions, whip scorpions, pseudoscorpions, king crabs, and others (Figs. 24-1, 24-2).

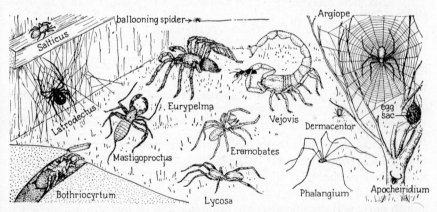

FIG. 24-1.   Class ARACHNOIDEA.   Some common types in their characteristic habitats; not to scale.   Order SCORPIONIDA: *Vejovis*, scorpion.   Order PEDIPALPI: *Mastigoproctus*, whip scorpion.   Order SOLPUGIDA: *Eremobates*, "vinegarone."   Order PSEUDOSCORPIONIDA: *Apocheiridium*, false scorpion.   Order PHALANGIDA: *Phalangium*, "harvestman."   Order ACARINA: *Dermacentor*, tick.   Order ARANEAE: *Bothriocyrtum*, trap-door spider; *Eurypelma*, American "tarantula"; *Lycosa*, wolf spider; *Latrodectus*, black widow spider; *Argiope*, orb-weaving spider with egg case; *Salticus*, jumping spider.

Members of this group differ in body form and the nature of their appendages.   They are mostly free-living terrestrial animals of small size, and the great majority are more numerous in warm dry regions than elsewhere.   Many possess poison glands and poison claws or "fangs" by which they kill insects and other small animals, whose fluids and soft tissues they suck as food.   The spiders and some other arachnoids have

537

also special glands that secrete fine threads of silk.   This material is used
to build nests, shelters, and egg cases and for other purposes.

Some members of this class, because of their peculiar appearance, are
feared by many persons, although the great majority are quite harmless.
Spiders and some others are actually beneficial to man because they feed
upon various kinds of insects.   A few spiders and scorpions, however, do
have bites or stings that may cause man serious illness and even death.
Some mites injure plants, and certain mites and ticks which parasitize man
and animals produce injury, sickness, and death.   Several kinds of ticks
are the intermediate hosts for protozoans and viruses that cause particular
diseases (Chap. 12; Table 23-1).

There is an age-old belief in southern Europe that the bite of a "tarantula" (lycosid spider?) will be followed by melancholy and death unless
cured by dancing, especially to the lively music of a "tarentella," whereby
the poison will be eliminated by perspiration!

24-1. Characteristics.[1]   1. Body usually of distinct cephalothorax and abdomen
(except ACARINA); typically with 6 pairs of jointed[2] appendages: chelicerae, pedipalpi,
and 4 pairs of legs, all on cephalothorax; no antennae or mandibles.

2. Mouth parts and digestive tract mainly suited for sucking; some with poison
glands.

3. Respiration by lung books, tracheae, or gill-books.

4. Excretion by paired Malpighian tubules, or coxal glands, or both.

5. Nervous system with dorsal ganglia (brain) and ventral nerve cord having
paired ganglia, or else concentrated anteriorly; eyes usually simple and in pairs;
tactile hairs or bristles on body.

6. Sexes mostly separate; sex opening single, on second abdominal somite; fertilization usually internal; mainly oviparous; development direct or through a larval stage.

7. Chiefly terrestrial and solitary; either free-living and predaceous, or parasitic.

The ARANCHNOIDEA are of ancient origin, some stocks having been
developed in Cambrian time.   The lack of antennae and lack of mandibles
are distinctive characteristics.   As compared with the INSECTA they have
tracheae and Malpighian tubules but lack wings or a separate head; their
mouth parts and sex openings are different, and all but two orders lack a
larval stage.   The ARACHNOIDEA differ from the CRUSTACEA in the lack of
gills (except MEROSTOMATA) and biramous appendages, and from the CHI-
LOPODA and DIPLOPODA in the body form and in having few appendages.

24-2. Size.   The king crab (*Limulus*) grows to 500 mm. in length.
Most spiders are under 25 mm. long, the extremes being *Microlinypheus*,
which is under 1.0 mm., and *Theraphosa lebondii*, which grows to 90 mm.
long.   The smallest scorpion (*Microbuthus pusillus*) is 13 mm. long and
the largest (*Pandinus dictator*) 160 mm.   The SOLPUGIDA are 8 to 70 mm.

[1] Compare ARTHROPODA, Table 22-1.

[2] For brevity the divisions or segments of appendages are referred to as "joints"—
3-jointed, etc.

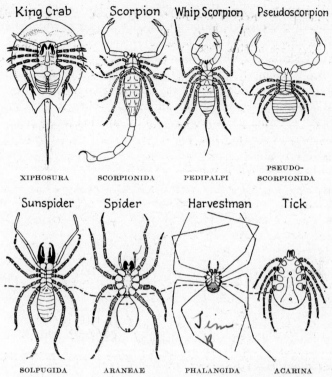

King Crab   Scorpion   Whip Scorpion   Pseudoscorpion

XIPHOSURA   SCORPIONIDA   PEDIPALPI   PSEUDO-SCORPIONIDA

Sunspider   Spider   Harvestman   Tick

SOLPUGIDA   ARANEAE   PHALANGIDA   ACARINA

Fig. 24-2. Class Arachnoidea. Representatives of 8 Orders in ventral view (not to scale), showing general form, division between cephalothorax and abdomen (broken line), chelicerae (black), pedipalpi (outlined), and legs (stippled), with joints in each. (Compare Fig. 22-1.)

long, *Galeodes caspius* being the largest. The smallest mites are under 0.5 mm. long, and the largest tick (*Amblyomma*) is only 30 mm. in length.

24-3. Order Araneae, the spiders. More than 20,000 species of spiders are known. They live in various habitats, from sea level to the highest mountains, from the seashore and fresh-water swamps to the driest of deserts, among rocks, in or on sandy or other soils, in forests, bushes, and grasses, and about buildings. The following general account will apply to most common species.

24-4. External features.[1] The body consists of a distinct *cephalothorax* and an *abdomen,* both rounded and unsegmented and joined by a slender "waist," or *peduncle.* The cephalothorax commonly has eight simple *eyes* anteriorly, and its ventral surface bears six pairs of appendages. Each of the two *chelicerae* has a basal segment and a terminal clawlike fang with a duct near its tip, connecting to a poison gland within

[1] Details of structure may be examined closely on a live spider enclosed in a petri dish under a binocular microscope.

the cephalothorax.   The pair of *pedipalpi* are short, six-jointed, and leg-like, with enlarged bases that form "maxillae" used to squeeze and chew the food; in mature males the tip becomes a specialized container for the transfer of sperm.   There are four pairs of *walking legs,* each of seven joints (coxa, trochanter, femur, patella, tibia, metatarsus, and tarsus) and ending in two or three toothed claws; on some spiders the tip bears a pad of "hairs" (scopula) by which the animal may cling to a wall or similar surface.   All external parts are covered by cuticle bearing many bristles and hairs, some of sensory nature.

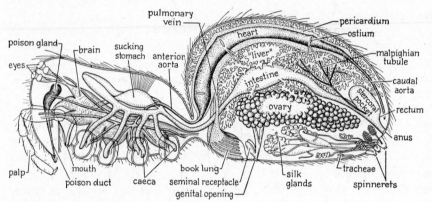

Fig. 24-3.   Class Arachnoidea.   Structure of a spider as seen with left side of body removed.   (*Modified from Leuckart.*)

The external openings are as follows: (1) The minute *mouth,* between the maxillae; all others are ventral on the abdomen and include (2) the *genital aperture* anteriorly in the mid-line and covered by a plate, or epigynum; (3) the slitlike entrances to the two or four *lung books,* or respiratory organs, at each side of the epigynum; (4) a *spiracle* anterior to the anus and connecting to short tracheae; (5) the two or three pairs of bluntly conical *spinnerets,* sometimes jointed, each with many fine tubes through which the "silk" for webs and other purposes is secreted from glands within the abdomen; and (6) the terminal *anus.*

24-5. Internal structure (Fig. 24-3).   The **digestive system** comprises (1) the mouth; (2) a slender esophagus connecting to (3) a sucking stomach operated by muscles extending from its dorsal surface to the cephalothorax; (4) the main stomach in the cephalothorax, with five pairs of caeca, or pouches, one dorsal and one toward each leg; (5) the straight intestine in the abdomen, which is joined by ducts of (6) the much-branched digestive gland ("liver") and extends to (7) the rectum where (8) an enlarged stercoral pocket connects just before (9) the anus.

The *circulatory system* is somewhat like that of insects; the heart is a slender, muscular, and contractile tube dorsally placed in the abdomen, with three pairs of openings, or ostia, and surrounded by a tubular pericardium. From the heart a caudal aorta extends backward, and an anterior aorta sends paired arteries to the stomach, legs, eyes, and poison glands. The colorless blood contains amoeboid corpuscles and dissolved hemocyanin as a respiratory pigment. The heart pumps blood through the aortae and into sinuses among the tissues; thence it passes to the lung books for aeration and returns by "pulmonary veins" to the pericardial cavity to reenter the heart through the ostia.

Respiration is accomplished mainly by the *lung books,* which are peculiar to arachnoids; each is of 15 to 20 leaflike horizontal plates containing fine blood vessels. Air entering the external slit on the abdomen circulates between the plates, where the O_2–CO_2 exchange occurs. The *tracheae,* if present, are like those of insects but restricted to the abdomen. *Excretion* is performed by paired *Malpighian tubules* connected posteriorly to the intestine and by a pair or two of *coxal glands* in the floor of the cephalothorax that empty by ducts between the legs. These glands are considered homologous with the green glands in crustaceans.

The *nervous system* is concentrated, comprising a bilobed ganglion above the esophagus that joins by two thick connectives to a large ventral ganglionic mass, whence nerves radiate to all organs. Paired ganglia occur in the abdomen of young spiders, but not in adults. The *eyes* are simple, with a chitinous lens, epithelial layer, optic rods, and retinal cells; vision is keener in some spiders than in others. The pedipalpi and many of the external hairs are evidently sensitive to touch. The response to sound is uncertain, although some spiders have sound-producing mechanisms. The sense of smell seems well-developed and may reside in minute "lyriform organs" on the body and appendages.

The sexes are separate and often unlike in markings and size, females being larger. The *male* has two testes below the intestine that join by coiled vasa efferentia to a single seminal vesicle leading to the genital opening. In the *female* the two ovaries are large and hollow, each with an oviduct joining the single vagina; two lateral seminal receptacles attach to the vagina.

24-6. Natural history. Spiders are free-living, solitary, and predaceous creatures that feed mainly on insects. Hunting spiders either wait for or wander in search of food, run it down (*Lycosa*), or jump on it (*Salticus*). Other spiders entrap their prey in webs. Small prey is grasped, killed by a quick stroke of the poison-bearing fangs, and "eaten" (sucked out). Larger items of food may first be bound in silk shroud or fastened to the web and then killed. The poison kills invertebrates quickly and that of some large spiders (*Eurypelma*) will overcome small vertebrates. When food is available, spiders feed often, but in captivity some may fast for many weeks. In the majority of species, individuals live only about a year.   The enemies of spiders are mainly birds, lizards, and certain wasps; some ichneumonids (HYMENOPTERA) oviposit in spider cocoons where their larvae hatch quickly and consume many spider eggs.

Spider silk is a proteid secretion of special abdominal glands that passes out the many microscopic tubes in the spinnerets and solidifies into a thread upon contact with the air (Fig. 24-4); it serves many purposes.

FIG. 24-4.   Structural details of spiders.   Ctenid spider: *A*. Front of head.   *B*. Spinnerets on abdomen.   Black widow spider: *C*. Front of head with enlarged pedipalpi of male; *D*. End of leg with claws hooked on web.

Terrestrial hunting spiders pay out a "dragline" as they travel.   Spiderlings are dispersed by climbing to some height and spinning a long thread on which they are carried by the wind; trees sometimes become covered by such gossamer, and numbers of "ballooning" young spiders are occasionally seen by ships at sea.   The most primitive webs are scarcely more than many draglines radiating from a spider's retreat (*Segistra*).   Some (*Amaurobius*) add a sheet of fine silk "carded" by a plate (cribellum) anterior to the spinnerets, and others form a hammock-like sheet over a definite framework (*Tegenaria*).   Some webs are irregular networks of silk (*Latrodectus*).   The orb weavers (*Argiope, Epeira, Miranda*) outline a flat rectangular framework within which radial threads are neatly spaced, and then a spiral of silk bearing sticky droplets is attached for the capture of prey.   The webs are repaired or renewed at frequent intervals.   Snares, shelters, nests for hibernating or mating, and egg cocoons are spun with various kinds of silk by different species.

24-7. Reproduction.   The male, when mature, spins a small web on which a droplet of fluid containing sperm is deposited and then taken into cavities in his pedipalps (Fig. 24-4).   He then seeks a female and may go through a nuptial performance with her before transferring the sperm by inserting his pedipalps in her genital opening.   The female may kill and eat the male after mating, but this is not his invariable end.   Later she spins a padded cocoon in which the eggs are laid.   Females of some species fasten the cocoon to or near the web, and others carry it about; the female *Lycosa* carries the young on her abdomen for some days after they hatch.   The black widow (*Latrodectus mactans*), for example, lays 25 to over 900 eggs in a cocoon and produces one to nine cocoons per season.

Her eggs hatch in 10 to 14 days, and the young remain in the sac for 2 to 6 weeks, leaving after the first molt. Males undergo about five molts before becoming sexually mature, and females seven or eight. At successive molts the spiders increase in size and change in form, proportions, and color pattern.

24-8. Other Arachnoidea (Figs. 24-1, 24-2). The scorpions (SCORPIONIDA) are elongate, with big pincer-ended pedipalpi and a long 12-segmented abdomen bearing a terminal sharp poison claw. They inhabit warm dry regions (to 45°N. in North America), hiding under stones or in shallow burrows by day and running actively at night to catch the insects, spiders, and scorpions used for food. Prey is grasped by the chelicerae and torn slowly apart by the pedipalpi, larger animals first being paralyzed by the sting. The comblike pectines, ventral on the abdomen, are evidently tactile organs. Mating is preceded by a courtship dance, and the female produces living young, which ride for some days on her abdomen.

Whip scorpions (PEDIPALPI) somewhat resemble scorpions but lack poison; their large pedipalpi have pincers, and the first legs are tactile; some have a slender abdominal whip. They live in warm countries, are nocturnal, and prey on insects. The pseudoscorpions (PSEUDOSCORPIONIDA) are like miniature scorpions but lack a sting. Silk from glands near the chelicerae is spun into nests for molt and hibernation. They live under stones, moss, or bark, and some in books or furniture; their food is of minute insects. The vinegarones and sun spiders (SOLPUGIDA) are of spider-like form but lack a "waist"; the pedipalpi are leglike, and the enlarged chelicerae give them an undeserved reputation as dangerous. They lack both poison and silk glands. Their habitat is in warm dry regions. Harvestmen, or daddy longlegs (PHALANGIDA), have compact ovoid bodies and extremely long legs by which they run readily. They lack poison but have "stink" glands for protection. They are common in temperate regions, and their food includes small insects.

The mites and ticks (Order ACARINA) are small to microscopic, with the head, thorax, and abdomen fused closely and unsegmented. The integument is membranous or leathery, sometimes with hard plates or shields. A slender anterior region, often jointed to the body, bears the mouth parts. The eight legs are laterally placed and often bear bristles. The sexes are separate. In most species there hatches from the *egg* a six-legged *larva* that feeds and molts into an eight-legged *nymph* having no genital opening. With further feeding and molt this transforms into the *adult* sexual stage.

Mites (Fig. 24-5) abound as to species and individuals in soil, humus, stored foods, fresh and salt waters, on plants, and as parasites of both plants and animals. Some feed on fresh or decaying plant and animal materials, others suck plant juices, and still others subsist on the skin, blood, or other tissues of land vertebrates.

The ticks (Figs. 24-6, 24-7) feed on the blood of reptiles, birds, and mammals. Upon finding a host the tick's mouth parts pierce the skin, and the sucking pharynx draws in blood, which is kept fluid by a salivary

| Tetrarhynchus red spider | Analges feather mite | Eriophyes gall mite | Sarcoptes mange mite | Demodex follicle mite |

Fig. 24-5.   Order Acarina.   Some representative mites.   All enlarged, not to same scale. (*After Banks*, 1905.)

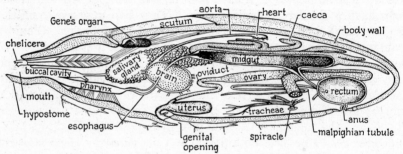

Fig. 24-6.   Order Acarina.   Female Rocky Mountain spotted fever tick (*Dermacentor andersoni*); internal structure, from the left side.   (*After J. R. Douglas*.)

anticoagulant; its stomach expands until "as full as a tick."   In spring the female tick deposits her eggs under shelter on the ground, and hatching occurs a month or so later.   The larvae climb on bushes to wait for appropriate hosts, to which they fasten; then they drop off after feeding and to molt.   In turn, the nymphs and then the adults do likewise. Ticks can survive long periods without feeding, some for a year or more if they fail to find a host animal.   The spotted fever tick normally requires 2 years to complete its life cycle.   Adults of the soft or argasine ticks hide by day and emerge at night to feed briefly, whereas all stages of ixodine ticks remain in place on their hosts for some time.   In the latter the males are smaller, with a scutum covering the whole dorsal surface; the scutum on females is smaller and anterior.

24-9. Relations to man.   The bite of most spiders is harmless to mankind.   Even the large American "tarantulas" (*Eurypelma*) cause no more injury than a wasp.   Females of the Genus *Latrodectus*, however, are distinctly dangerous.   Of four species in various parts of the world, the black widow spider (*L. mactans*) occurs from southern Canada to South America and the West Indies, living in cliffs, piles of rock and lumber, and in outdoor privies and other buildings.   The adult female is shiny black, with an hourglass mark of red beneath the abdomen.   Upward of 400 human cases of poisoning by this spider have been recorded in the United states with about 5 per cent of mortality; most of these are in California, where the black widow causes more poisonings than rattlesnakes.   Severe pain, muscle spasms in the abdomen, and restlessness are common symptoms.   Serum from previous cases and antivenin are used in treatment, with magnesium chloride injections to relieve the muscle spasms.

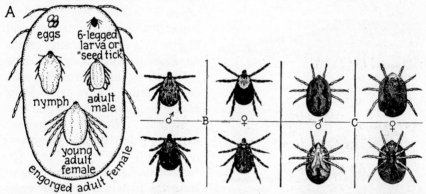

Fig. 24-7.   Order Acarina.   Ticks.   *A*. Texas cattle-fever tick (*Boöphilus annulatus*), ×5.   Smaller stages inside the outline of an engorged female.   (*After U.S. Department of Agriculture.*)   *B*.   Rocky Mountain spotted fever tick (*Dermacentor andersoni*, Family Ixodidae).   *C*.   Relapsing fever tick (*Ornithodorus hermsi*, Family Argasidae).   Upper row, dorsal; lower row, ventral.   (*From W. B. Herms.*)

Some large tropical scorpions have powerful venom.   The state of Durango, Mexico, between 1890 and 1931 reported over 1,700 deaths, chiefly of children, from scorpions.   Treatment by antivenin and bounties for destruction of scorpions decreased the danger in later years. The hairy scorpion (*Hadrurus hirsutus*) of the southwestern United States often stings people, causing severe but transient pain.

Of the mites that suck plant juices, the red spider (*Tetrarhynchus telarius*) causes blisters and injures leaves of orchard trees; the blister mite (*Eriophyes*) injures buds and fruits of pears, apples, grapes, and other crops; and the bulb mite (*Rhizoglyphus hyacinthi*) tunnels in bulbs and roots, whereby fungi and bacteria are able to enter.   The itch mite (*Sarcoptes scabei*) burrows in and irritates human skin; related species cause mange in hogs, dogs, and other mammals; the scab mite (*Psoroptes communis*) produces serious damage to sheep; and the chicken mite (*Dermanyssus gallinae*) causes unthriftiness in fowls.

Ticks, when numerous, may make the host anemic and liable to various diseases or may cause its death. Common species are the fowl tick (*Argas persicus*) on poultry, and the spinose ear tick (*Ornithodorus megnini*) and dog or "wood" ticks (*Dermacentor variabilis* and *D. occidentalis*), which infest both wild and domestic mammals and man. The salivary secretions injected in the biting of some ticks produce severe, slow-healing wounds; certain ticks are intermediate hosts of disease. *D. andersoni* transmits the rickettsia organism causing Rocky Mountain spotted fever, a disease of native rodents and larger mammals in the arid West (Montana to eastern Oregon) that produces serious illness and high

mortality in man. Since 1931 spotted fever has also been recognized in various eastern states from Illinois to New Jersey and North Carolina. Vaccine grown on incubated hen's eggs is now made to protect persons exposed to tick bite. Texas cattle fever of the southern states is due to a sporozoan (*Babesia bigemina*) carried by a cattle tick (*Boophilus annulatus*). In both these diseases the infective agent passes from the female tick to her eggs. Texas cattle fever was the first disease in which an arthropod vector was proved to be the essential agent transmitting the causative organism from infected to healthy hosts.

24-10. King crabs and Eurypterids. The Subclass Merostomata comprises ancient marine arachnoids, with many fossil forms and four living species of king or horseshoe crabs. One of these (*Limulus polyphemus*, Fig. 24-8),

Fig. 24-8. Subclass Merostomata. *A.* Extinct eurypterid (†*Eurypterus*, Order †Eurypterida), in dorsal view. *B, C.* The living king crab (*Limulus polyphemus*, Order Xiphosura). *B*, ventral view; *C*, laterodorsal view; length to 18 inches.

inhabits shallow quiet waters of the Atlantic coast from Maine to Yucatan. Over its body is a shiny dark-brown unsegmented carapace that is arched and of horseshoe shape and joined to a broad hexagonal abdomen with lateral movable spines and a bayonet-like telson. Besides the six pairs of appendages on the cephalothorax, as in other arachnoids, the abdomen bears six pairs of broad thin appendages joined medially.   On the hind surface of the last five pairs are exposed gill-books, each of 150 to 200 leaves containing blood vessels for respiration.   A pair of coxal glands in the cephalothorax serves for excretion.   The nerve ring about the mouth connects to a ventral nerve cord with ganglia.   On the carapace are two lateral compound eyes and two medial simple eyes.

The king crab burrows by shoving its carapace into the sand and pushing with its telson and appendages.   It can walk on the bottom, can swim by flapping the abdominal plates, and may hop by aid of the telson.   It is active by night and feeds on nereid worms and soft mollusks, which are grasped by the chelicerae, aided by the pincers on other appendages, and chewed by the bases of the legs (gnathobases) which serve as jaws.   In early summer the smaller male mounts the female, and groups of small eggs, fertilized externally, are deposited shallowly in sand between the tide lines.   The larva at hatching resembles a trilobite in having a segmented abdomen without appendages or telson, but these features change at the first molt.   The Order Xiphosura dates from the Cambrian and the Genus *Limulus* from Triassic time.

The eurypterids (Order †Eurypterida, Fig. 24-8) were a dominant group in seas of Paleozoic times, before the rise of the cephalopods.   In form they were somewhat scorpion-like, some being up to 9 feet long. They probably swam or crawled on the bottom of salt and brackish waters.

Class *CHILOPODA*.   Centipedes

24-11. Structure and habits.   The centipedes (Fig. 24-9) are of slender, elongate, segmented form and are flattened dorsoventrally.   The head

Fig. 24-9.   Class Chilopoda.   A centipede.   (*After Huxley.*)

bears a pair of long antennae with 12 or more joints, a pair of mandibles, and two pairs of maxillae.   In different species, the body is of 15 to 173 somites.   The first somite bears a pair of four-jointed poison claws, and on each of the other somites except the last two is a pair of small seven-jointed walking legs.   The digestive tract is straight, with two or three pairs of salivary glands at the mouth and two long Malpighian tubules posteriorly for excretion.   The heart extends the length of the body, surrounded by pericardium, with a pair of ostia and of lateral arteries in each somite.   In some somites there are spiracles joining a fused system of tracheal tubes that serve for respiration. The sexes are separate, each having one dorsal gonad and paired accessory glands connected to a ventral genital opening near the posterior end.

Centipedes live mainly in warm countries, hiding by day under stones or logs and running swiftly about at night to prey on earthworms and insects; large species may capture small lizards or mice. Prey is killed quickly by poison from a duct in the poison claw and is chewed by the mandibles. Some centipedes lay eggs, and others are viviparous. The young resemble adults, with the same or a lesser number of somites. Some tropical species are 6 to 8 inches long, and their bites are painful to man. The small agile house centipedes (*Scutigera*) have 15 pairs of extremely long fragile legs. They eat insects and are harmless to man.

CLASS *DIPLOPODA*. MILLIPEDES, OR "THOUSAND-LEGGED WORMS"

24-12. Structure and habits. The millipedes have cylindrical bodies of many somites and the body wall includes deposits of lime salts (Fig. 24-10). Many are brightly colored. On the head are two clumps of

FIG. 24-10.   Class DIPLOPODA.   A millipede (*Spirobolus*).   (*From Haupt.*)

simple eyes and a pair each of short antennae, jaws, and maxillae. The thorax is short, of four single somites, each with one pair of legs. The long abdomen comprises 20 to over 100 double somites, each containing two pairs of spiracles, ostia, and nerve ganglia and bearing two pairs of seven-jointed legs. The digestive and circulatory systems are somewhat as in centipedes. The tracheae are many and separate, each a tufted pouch connected to a spiracle in front of a leg. The gonad is single and ventral, with a duct opening on the third somite. The male has modified appendages (gonopods) on the seventh somite.

Millipedes live in humid dark places under stones or beneath or within rotting logs and shun the light. They travel slowly, with the body extended, and test the route of travel with the antennae. The many legs seemingly move in a series of waves from behind forward. Their food is of dead plant materials, but they also will eat animal matter. Some species roll up in a spiral when disturbed. From some enemies they are protected by a series of "stink" glands that secrete an objectionable fluid. The young at hatching have but six somites and three pairs of legs, others being added in front of the anal somite at the six successive molts during growth.

CLASS *ONYCHOPHORA*

24-13. Onychophora (Gr. *onychus* claw + *phorus*, bearing).   Members of this group are small "walking worms" distributed discontinuously in the Southern Hemisphere, Central America, Mexico, and the West Indies. The 70 species live in dark moist places, in rock crevices, under stones, or beneath bark on rotting logs.

Peripatus capensis, a representative species, is about 50 mm. long, with a cylindrical body but no distinct head (Figs. 24-11, 24-12).   The anterior end bears (1) two short *antennae;* (2) a pair of small *eyes* dorsally; (3) a midventral *mouth* rimmed by a fleshy fold and containing two small horny *jaws* used to tear or grind food; and (4) two blunt *oral papillae,* one at each side of the mouth.   The *skin* is thin and lightly chitinized, with

FIG.   24-11.   Class ONYCHOPHORA.   *Peripatus.* A. Entire animal, natural size.   B, C. Anterior end in lateral and ventral views. (*After Snodgrass, 1938.*)

many transverse rings of fine papillae, each with a spine.   The only features of segmentation are 17 pairs of short stumpy *legs,* each ending

FIG. 24-12.   *Peripatus.*   Internal structure in dorsal view.   (*After Snodgrass, 1938.*)

in two claws; other species have up to 43 pairs of legs.   At the inner base of each leg is a *nephridial opening.*   The *anus* opens at the bluntly conical posterior end, preceded by the single ventral *genital opening.*

The *body wall* includes a thin cuticle, an epidermis, and a thin but complex series of muscle layers, circular, longitudinal, and transverse. Special muscles operate the legs and parts at the anterior end.   Within the body is an undivided cavity, or *hemocoel,* containing the internal organs.   At either side is a large and much-branched *slime gland,* one opening through each oral papilla.   These produce slimy mucus that can be squirted several inches and adheres to any object; it serves for defense and to capture insects and other small animals used as food.   The *digestive system* is a straight tube, from mouth to anus, with a buccal cavity, two large salivary glands, muscular pharynx, short esophagus, long stomach-intestine, and rectum.   The *circulatory system* consists of a single middorsal vessel having muscle fibers in its walls and a pair of openings, or ostia, in each segment.   Many delicate tubular ingrowths of the body wall, termed *tracheae,* presumably serve for respiration.   The *excretory organs* are pairs of nephridia-like structures; each has a sac closed at its inner end, a ciliated funnel and duct, a slightly expanded bladder, and a nephridiopore.   The *nervous system* comprises a pair of oval cerebral ganglia (the brain) above the mouth, several anterior nerves, two circumpharyngeal connectives, and a pair of separate ventral nerve cords without true ganglia that extend the length of the body and have many transverse connections.   The eyes resemble those of annelids.

The sexes are separate, and the reproductive organs are paired, but with a single external opening.   The *male* system includes paired testes, seminal vesicles, vasa deferentia, accessory glands, and an ejaculatory duct.   In the *female* the paired ovaries and oviducts join to a common atrium at the genital opening.   Most species of Onychophora are viviparous, and part of each oviduct is specialized as a uterus where the embryos develop.   In some forms a placenta-like trophoblast develops by which the embryo obtains nourishment from the uterine wall.   A large female may produce 30 to 40 young per year, which at birth resemble adults except in size and color.

The Onychophora resemble annelids in the structure of the eyes, the segmental nephridia, the ciliated reproductive ducts, and the simple gut.   Some of their arthropod characteristics comprise the jaws that are derived from appendages, the body cavity being a hemocoel, the dorsal "heart" with ostia, the coelom reduced to the cavities of the nephridia and reproductive ducts, and the general structure of the reproductive organs; their tracheae somewhat resemble those of insects.   Features peculiar to the Onychophora are the single pair of jaws, scant metamerism, arrangement of the tracheal apertures, nature of the skin, and separate nerve cords with no true ganglia.   *Peripatus* is evidently of an ancient stock, as indicated by its relationship to certain Pre-Cambrian fossils and by its discontinuous distribution at present; it suggests that the Arthropoda may have been derived from an annelid-like ancestor.

N.B

CLASSIFICATION

Class 4. *ARACHNOIDEA.* Body typically of 2 parts (except Acarina); cephalothorax unsegmented (except Solpugida), with 2 chelicerae bearing chelae or claws, 2 pedipalpi variously modified, and 4 pairs of legs; no antennae or true jaws; abdomen either of 6 to 14 somites or undivided and with no locomotor appendages (except Merostomata); respiration by gills, lung books, or tracheae; excretion by Malpighian tubules or coxal glands; sexes usually separate, male often smaller; genital opening anterior on abdomen; mostly oviparous; some with larval stages; mostly predaceous; chiefly terrestrial, some in fresh or salt waters.

Subclass 1. MEROSTOMATA (Gigantostraca). Cephalothorax with compound lateral eyes and broadly joined to abdomen on which are 6 pairs of appendages bearing exposed gills and a terminal bayonet-like telson; aquatic.

Order 1. **Xiphosura.** KING CRABS. Cephalothorax an arched, horseshoe-shaped carapace; abdomen wide, unsegmented; chelicerae 3-jointed, pedipalpi and legs 6-jointed; marine, in shallow waters; Cambrian to Recent. *Limulus polyphemus*, Maine to Yucatan; *Tachypleus*, Japan to Malaysia and India.

Order 2. †**Eurypterida.** EURYPTERIDS. Carapace not expanded; abdomen of 12 somites, narrowed behind; Cambrian to Carboniferous. †*Eurypterus*, †*Pterygotus*.

Subclass 2. ARACHNIDA (Embolobranchiata). Abdomen lacks locomotor appendages; eyes all simple; cuticle often with sensory hairs or scales; pedipalpi usually sensory, modified in male for transfer of sperm to female; no gills; mostly oviparous; no metamorphosis (except ACARINA); chiefly terrestrial.

Order 1. **Scorpionida.** SCORPIONS. Body elongate; cephalothorax (prosoma) compact, broadly joined to abdomen; chelicerae 3-jointed, small; pedipalpi large, 6-jointed, with stout pincers; abdomen long, of 12 ringlike somites, 2d with pair of comblike and tactile pectines; last 6 somites (metasoma) narrow, with a sharp poison claw at end; 4 pairs of lung books; viviparous; nocturnal, in warm regions; 600 species; Silurian to Recent. *Hadrurus hirsutus*, hairy scorpion, and *Vejovis spinigerus*, both to 100 mm. long, Texas to California; *V. boreus*, small, Nebraska to Nevada; *Centrurus*.

Order 2. **Pedipalpi.** WHIP SCORPIONS. Cephalothorax small, narrowly joined to flat abdomen of 11 or 12 somites; 8 eyes; chelicerae small, 2-jointed, chelate; pedipalpi strong, 6-jointed, tarsus of 1st leg an elongate, many-jointed feeler; nocturnal; 150 species; Carboniferous to Recent. *Mastigoproctus giganteus*, to 130 mm. long, with slender terminal whip on abdomen, Florida to Arizona; *Tarantula* (not a tarantula!), 20 mm. long, no whip, Florida, Texas, and California.

Order 3. **Palpigrada.** Size minute; chelicerae stout, 3-jointed, pedipalpi like walking legs; no eyes; abdomen oval, of 11 somites, with slender "tail" of 15 segments; live under stones. *Prokoenenia*, 2.5 mm. long, Texas, California.

Order 4. **Araneae** (Araneida). SPIDERS. Cephalothorax and abdomen both unsegmented, joined by narrow "waist"; chelicerae small, 2-jointed, a poison duct in terminal claw; pedipalpi short, 6-jointed, leglike, the basal joint on each an enlarged "maxilla" for chewing; legs 7-jointed; eyes 8 to none; lung books 2 to 4, some with tracheae; tubercle-like spinnerets on abdomen extrude silk; oviparous, eggs commonly in cocoons; chiefly terrestrial; 20,000 species; Carboniferous to Recent. Some common families and members are (Fig. 24-1):

CTENIZIDAE. TRAP-DOOR SPIDERS. *Pachylomerus* (southeastern United States) and *Bothriocyrtum* (California), nest hole in ground closed by hinged door of earth and silk.

THERAPHOSIDAE. BIRD SPIDERS. *Eurypelma*, American "tarantula," to 48 mm. long, Arkansas and Texas to California; lives on ground or in trees; bite painful but not dangerous to man.

AGELENIDAE. FUNNEL-WEB SPIDERS. *Agelena naevia*, grass spider, web flat with funnel at side, in grass and in houses; *Tegenaria derhami*, house spider, naturalized from Europe, forms webs in corners.

LYCOSIDAE. HUNTING SPIDERS. *Lycosa*, wolf spider, to 25 mm. long; active on ground, hunts prey or builds turrets to watch for prey; female carries egg cocoon and young.

THERIDIIDAE. *Latrodectus mactans*, black widow spider, web irregular, bite dangerous and sometimes fatal to mankind; *Theridion tepidariorum*, house spider, web flat, in corners.

ARGIOPIDAE. ORB WEAVERS. *Miranda aurantia*, orange garden spider, web to 2 feet across, with zigzag band, in grass or bushes; *Epeira marmorea*, with "nest" of leaves at side of web, where spider sits holding a thread to web.

THOMISIDAE. CRAB SPIDERS. Short, wide, with crablike appearance and gait, no web. *Misumena*, bright- or white-colored, live in flowers and mimic color; *Philodromus*, mottled; *Xysticus*, under bark or leaves.

ATTIDAE. JUMPING SPIDERS. Run and jump in all directions, no web. *Salticus scenicus*, on fences and houses; *Phidippus*, on plants, nest baglike, among leaves.

Order 5. **Solpugida** (Solifugae). VINEGARONES. Cephalothorax of 6 somites, 1st to 3d a "head," eyes 4 or 6; chelicerae swollen, 2-jointed, with chelae, and joined to carapace; pedipalpi leglike, 6-jointed; 1st legs tactile, not locomotory; no "waist"; abdomen of 10 somites; no spinning organs; in warm dry regions; 570 species; Carboniferous to Recent. *Eremobates*, vinegarone, southwestern United States; *Ammotreca; Galeodes*, "tarantula" of Egypt.

Order 6. **Pseudoscorpionida** (Chelonethida). FALSE SCORPIONS. Length 1 to 7.5 mm.; unsegmented cephalothorax broadly joined to abdomen of 11 somites; no sting; eyes 2, 4, or none; chelicerae 2-jointed, with comblike serrula handling silk for nests from 2 glands in cephalothorax; pedipalpi large, 6-jointed, chelate; under moss or stones, in trees, or about buildings; 1,000 species; Tertiary to Recent. *Garypus*, California seacoast, to 7.5 mm. long; *Chthonius; Chelifer cancroides*, house or book scorpion, 3.5 mm. long, about buildings.

Order 7. **Podogona** (Ricinulei). Small; movable hood on cephalothorax over small chelicerae; no eyes; abdomen of 6 somites, 1st and 2d forming a "waist"; tropical; Carboniferous to Recent. *Cryptostemma, Cryptocellus*, few specimens known.

Order 8. **Phalangida** (Opiliones). HARVESTMEN, "DADDY LONGLEGS." Body short, ovoid, cephalothorax broadly fused to faintly segmented abdomen; chelicerae 3-jointed, slender; pedipalpi 6-jointed, not chelate; legs 7-jointed, very long and delicate, tarsi many jointed; stink glands on cephalothorax; no lung books or silk glands; sexes much alike; in fields, woods, and buildings; 2,200 species; Carboniferous to Recent. *Phalangium, Liobunum*.

Order 9. **Acarina** (Acari). MITES AND TICKS. Small to microscopic; body compact, ovoid, cephalothorax and abdomen fused; no segmentation; chelicerae and pedipalpi various; legs widely separated, 6- or 7-jointed; respire by trachae or body surface; with larval and nymph stages; free-living or parasitic; world-wide; 6,000 species; Oligocene to Recent (Figs. 24-5 to 24-7).

TETRANYCHIDAE. *Tetranychus*, red spider mites, 0.4 mm., red or yellow, suck leaves of plants making pin-point lesions; female spins silken web.

TROMBIDIIDAE. *Trombicula alfreddugèsi* (*irritans*), larvae are chiggers that puncture and irritate skin of laborers in fields.

HYDRACHNIDAE. WATER MITES. Length 0.5 to 8 mm., colored, in fresh waters or on seaweed. *Hydrachna, Piona*.

HALACARIDAE. Marine, shores and to 3,500 feet deep in ocean. *Halacarus*.

ARGASIDAE. ARGASINE TICKS. No dorsal shield. *Argas persicus*, fowl tick, 8 to 10 mm., on poultry, quail, pigeons; *Ornithodorus megnini*, spinose ear tick, in ears of horses, cattle, sheep, and man; *O. turicata*, 6 to 7 mm., on hogs, cattle, and man; *O. moubata*, carries African tick fever; *O. hermsi*, on wild rodents, transmits *Spirochaeta recurrentis*, cause of relapsing fever in man.

IXODIDAE. IXODINE TICKS. A dorsal shield (Fig. 24-7). *Ixodes ricinus*, castor-bean tick, 3 to 10 mm., on various mammals; *Dermacentor variabilis* and *D. occidentalis*, dog ticks, to 15 mm. long, on domestic mammals and man, common in woods and brush; *D. andersoni*, on domestic and wild mammals and man—this and other species transmit *Dermacentroxenus rickettsi* causing spotted fever in man; *Boöphilus (Margaropus) annulatus*, on cattle, transmits *Babesia bigemina* (SPOROZOA), causing Texas cattle fever (Table 23-1).

PARASITIDAE. Free-living, predaceous, or commensal. *Machrocheles*, in insects.

LAELAPTIDAE. Parasitic or predaceous; to 1 mm. long. *Laelaps*, on wild rodents; *Spinturnix*, on bats; *Halarachne*, in bronchi of seals; *Pneumonyssus* in lungs of Old World monkeys; *Liponyssus bacoti*, tropical rat mite, common on alien rats (*Rattus*); *Dermanyssus gallinae*, chicken mite, attacks poultry and poultrymen; *Allodermanyssus sanguineus*, on house mouse (*Mus*) transmits *Rickettsia akari*, cause of rickettsialpox in man.

GALUMNIDAE (ORIBATIDAE). HORNY OR BEETLE MITES. Cuticle hard. *Galumna* in moss or tree bark, eats decaying matter; *Scutovertex*, on seacoast rocks.

TARSONEMIDAE. Soft-bodied. *Pediculoides ventriculosus*, on insects in stored grain, sometimes troubles workmen.

TYROGLYPHIDAE. Soft-bodied, minute, smooth. *Tyroglyphus siro*, cheese mite; *T. farinae*, in cereals; *Rhizoglyphus hyacinthi*, bulb mite, in bulbs and roots.

ANALGESIDAE. Body elongate, cross-furrowed, 5-jointed legs. *Analgopsis megninia*, feather mite, in bird feathers and quills, not harmful.

SCARCOPTIDAE. ITCH AND MANGE MITES. Body ovoid, legs 8, with suckers, claws, or bristles. *Sarcoptes scabei*, female burrows and oviposits in skin, causing itch in man and mange in domestic animals; *Psoroptes communis*, scab mite of sheep; *Cnemidocoptes laevis*, itch mite of fowls.

ERIOPHYIDAE. GALL MITES. Body elongate, legs 4, anterior; suck juices from plants, stimulating formation of open-ended galls. *Eriophyes*, blister mite, damages buds, leaves, and fruits of trees and shrubs.

DEMODICIDAE. FOLLICLE MITES. Elongate, ringed, 8 legs, 3-jointed. *Demodex folliculorum*, 0.4 mm., in hair follicles and sebaceous glands of man and domestic mammals.

Class 5. *CHILOPODA.* CENTIPEDES. Form elongate, flattened dorsoventrally; head with a pair of jointed antennae, paired jaws, 2 pairs of maxillae, and simple eyes; body of 15 to 173 somites, each with a pair of legs; 1st pair of body appendages 4-jointed, hooklike, with poison duct opening in terminal claws; sex opening midventral on next to last somite; terrestrial; nocturnal; 2,000 species; Tertiary to Recent. *Geophilus*, body thin, 31 to 93 pairs of legs; *Lithobius*, to 30 mm. long, 15 pairs of legs; *Scolopendra*, to 100 mm. long, 21 pairs of legs; *Cermatia (Scutigera) forceps*, house centipede, to 25 mm. long, antennae and 15 pairs of legs all long and slender; eyes compound; in buildings, swift-moving, eats insects.

Class 6. *DIPLOPODA.* MILLIPEDES. Form elongate, usually cylindrical; head with 2 groups of simple eyes and a pair each of short antennae, jaws, and maxillae; thorax of 4 somites, each with 1 pair of legs; abdomen of 20 to over 100 segments (double somites) closely spaced, each with 2 pairs of legs; sex opening midventral on 3d somite; terrestrial in moist places; 7,000 species; Eocene to Recent. *Julus virgatus*, 12 mm. long, 30 to 35 segments; *Spirobolus*, to 100 mm. long, 100 pairs of legs; *Polydesmus*, flattened.

Class 7. *ONYCHOPHORA.* Form elongate, to 200 mm. long; anterior end (no head) with a pair each of eyes, short antennae, and blunt oral papillae; body somewhat cylindrical, unsegmented, with many crossrows of fine papillae and 15 to 43 pairs of stumpy legs; sex opening midventral before anus; terrestrial in moist places; 70 species; Pre-Cambrian and Recent. *Peripatus.*

The following groups of ARTHROPODA *are of uncertain systematic position. The* PYCNOGONIDA, PENTASTOMIDA, *and* TARDIGRADA *are sometimes associated with the*

ARACHONIDEA; *and the* SYMPHYLA *and* PAUROPODA *with the* DIPLOPODA *as a Subphylum* PROGONEATA.

PYCNOGONIDA (Pantopoda). SEA SPIDERS. Mostly small to minute; body short, thin, of 1 cephalic and 3 or 4 trunk somites (or all fused in a disc), abdomen

vestigial; 4 eyes; mouth suctorial, on long proboscis; usually 3 pairs of head appendages, 1 pair being 10-jointed ovigerous (egg-bearing) legs; 4(5 or 6) pairs of long thin walking legs, 8- or 9-jointed; sexes separate, eggs carried by male; development direct, or a 4-legged larva with metamorphosis; marine, on hydroids, anemones, or algae, or under stones, from tide lines down to more than 2,000 fathoms; 500 species; Miocene to Recent. *Pycnogonum; Nymphon; Colossendeis,* spreads to 24 inches; *Achelia.*

PYCNOGONIDA (Nymphon)

PENTASTOMIDA (Porocephalus)

PENTASTOMIDA (Linguatulida). Form worm-like, soft, unsegmented; cephalothorax short, 2 pairs of ventral retractile hooks beside mouth; abdomen elongate, ringed; no circulatory, respiratory, or excretory organs; sexes separate; parasitic. *Linguatula serrata,* larva 5 mm. long, in liver, lung, etc., of rabbit, horse, goat, etc.; adult female to 130 mm. long, male to 20 mm., in nasal cavities of fox, wolf, and dog, occasional in horse and goat, rare in man; *Reighardia,* in gulls and terns; *Sibekia,* in crocodiles; *Kiricephalus,* in water snakes; *Porocephalus crotali,* larva in rodents, adult in rattlesnakes; other species in boas and pythons.

TARDIGRADA

FIG. 24-13. Miscellaneous ARTHROPODA of uncertain position. (*After Banks,* 1915.)

TARDIGRADA. WATER BEARS OR BEAR ANIMALCULES. To 1 mm. long; body cylindrical, rounded at ends, no somites; 4 pairs of stumpy unjointed legs ending in 2 or more claws, last pair at hind end of body; anterior end with retractile snout and teeth; mouth with stylet; no circulatory or respiratory organs; rectal glands for excretion; sexes separate; one gonad; some have larval stages; about 280 species. *Echiniscus,* 0.2 mm. long, in moss on damp roofs, but can resist desiccation; *Macrobiotus,* 0.7 mm., in fresh waters; others marine and terrestrial.

SYMPHYLA. GARDEN CENTIPEDE. To 6 mm. long; white; no eyes; with antennae, jaws, and 2 pairs of maxillae; adult with 12 pairs of legs; sex opening mid-ventral between 4th pair of legs; terrestrial, in damp places with humus. *Scutigerella immaculata,* garden centipede, often injures seeds and young shoots of sugar beets, asparagus, and other crops.

PAUROPODA. Length 0.5–1.8 mm.; antennae 3-branched; no eyes; body cylindrical, of 11(12) somites, with 6 dorsal plates and 9(10) pairs of legs; 4 larval instars; in dark damp places under logs, stones, or leaves, and in soil; 120 species. *Pauropus huxleyi,* eastern states and Europe; others in California.

References

BANKS, N. 1915. The Acarina or mites. *U.S. Department of Agriculture, Office of the Secretary, Report* 108, 153 pp., 294 figs.

COMSTOCK, J. H., and W. J. GERTSCH. 1940. The spider book. 2d ed. New York, Doubleday, Doran & Co., Inc. xi + 729 pp., 766+ figs. Includes other ARACHNOIDEA in brief.

Emerton, J. H.   1902.   The common spiders of the United States.   Boston, Ginn &
     Co.   225 pp., 501 figs.
Fabre, J. H.   1919.   The life of the spider.   New York, Dodd, Mead & Co., Inc.
     404 pp., illus.
Herms, W. B.   1939.   Medical entomology . . . man and animals.   3d ed.   New
     York, The Macmillan Co.   xix + 582 pp., 196 figs.   Arachnoids, pp. 422–541.
Kükenthal, W., and others.   1926–   .   Handbuch der Zoologie.   Berlin,
     Walter de Gruyter & Co.   Vol. 3, part 2, Arachnoidea, Onychophora; vol. 4,
     part 1, Diplopoda, Chilopoda, etc.   About 1,400 pp., 1,800 figs.
Petrunkevitch, A.   1911.   A synonymic index catalogue of spiders of [the]
     America[s].   *American Museum of Natural History, Bulletin*, vol. 29, pp. 1–791.
———.   1933.   . . . The natural classification of spiders based on a study of their
     internal anatomy.   *Connecticut Academy of Sciences, Transactions*, vol. 31, pp.
     299–389.
Pratt, H. S.   1935.   A manual of the common invertebrate animals.   2d ed.   Phila-
     delphia, The Blakiston Co.   Arachnoidea, etc., pp. 468–555, figs. 639–739.
Savory, T. H.   1928.   The biology of spiders.   London, Sidgwick & Jackson, Ltd.
     xx + 376 pp., 16 pls., 121 figs.
———.   1935.   The Arachnida.   London, Edward Arnold & Co., Ltd.   xi + 218
     pp., 8 pls., 99 figs.
Shipley, A. E., C. Warburton, and others.   1909.   Arachnoids, etc.   *In* Cam-
     bridge natural history.   London, Macmillan & Co., Ltd.   Vol. 4, pp. 253–566,
     figs. 152–287.   Good general account.

CHAPTER 25

PHYLUM CHORDATA. LOWER CHORDATES

The Phylum CHORDATA (Gr. *chorda*, string) comprises the lowly tongue worms, tunicates, and lancelets and the "vertebrates"—the lampreys, sharks and rays, bony fishes, amphibians, reptiles, birds, and mammals. The lower chordates are mostly of small size, all are marine, and most tunicates are sessile. All other chordates are free-living and none is strictly parasitic. The vertebrates include practically all living animals of medium to large size, including some huge sharks and whales (Fig. 1-2). Vertebrates occupy all kinds of habitats in salt and

FIG. 25-1. Basic differences between (*A*) a nonchordate (insect) and (*B*) a chordate (salamander) as to location of the nervous system, digestive tract, and heart; diagrammatic.

fresh waters and on land, most of the reptiles, birds, and mammals being strictly terrestrial. Certain fishes, birds, and mammals are gregarious, but most vertebrates are of solitary habit. Some vertebrates are of great importance in human affairs, such as the food and game fishes, the poisonous reptiles, and the many kinds of both useful and harmful birds and mammals. This chapter describes the general features of the Phylum CHORDATA and the structure and natural history of the lower chordates. The major divisions of the phylum are given in Table 25-1.

25-1. Characteristics. The chordates are bilaterally symmetrical, with three germ layers, a segmented body, complete digestive tract, and well-developed coelom. Three outstanding characteristics distinguish them from all other animals—a single dorsal tubular nerve cord, the notochord, and gill slits in the pharynx (Fig. 25-2). These features all form in the early embryo of a chordate, and they persist, are altered, or may disappear in the adult.

The *notochord* is the first supporting structure of the chordate body. In the early embryo it forms above the primitive gut as a slender rod of cells that contain a gelatinous matrix and is sheathed in fibrous connective tissue. In the tongue worms, it is short and anterior. In tunicates, it is present in the tail and only during the larval stages. In the lancelets and higher forms, it extends almost the length of the body. It persists throughout life as the main axial support in lancelets and lampreys, but in the fishes to mammals is later surrounded or replaced by the vertebral column.

TABLE 25-1. MAJOR DIVISIONS OF THE PHYLUM CHORDATA
(For other details, see Classification in Chaps. 11 and 26 to 32.)

	Subphyla		Classes and their principal characteristics	See chap.
ACRANIA. No cranium or brain, etc.	HEMICHORDATA Notochord short, anterior; nerve tissues in epidermis		*ENTEROPNEUSTA.* TONGUE WORMS. Worm-like; gill slits many	25
			PTEROBRANCHIA. Minute; gill slits 2 or none	
	TUNICATA Notochord and nerve cord only in larva; adults contained in secreted tunic		*LARVACEA.* Minute, tadpole-like; tunic temporary; 2 gill slits	
			ASCIDIACEA. ASCIDIANS. Tunic with scattered muscles; many gill slits	
			THALIACEA. CHAIN TUNICATES. Tunic with circular muscle bands	
	CEPHALOCHORDATA Notochord and nerve cord along entire body and persistent, as are the gill slits		*LEPTOCARDII.* LANCELETS. Slender, fishlike, segmented; epidermis 1-layered, no scales; many gill slits	
CRANIATA (vertebrates). With cranium, visceral arches, vertebrae, and brain	AGNATHA No true jaws or paired appendages		†*OSTRACODERMI.* ANCIENT ARMORED FISHES. Scales large, often fused as cephalothoracic shield	26
			CYCLOSTOMATA. CYCLOSTOMES. Skin without scales; mouth suctorial; gills 6 to 14 pairs	
	GNATHOS-TOMATA With jaws and, usually, paired appendages	Superclass *PISCES* Paired fins, gills, and skin with scales	†*PLACODERMI.* ANCIENT FISHES. Jaws primitive; complete gill slit before hyoid	
			CHONDRICHTHYES. SHARKS AND RAYS. Skin with placoid scales; skeleton of cartilage; 5 to 7 pairs of gills in separate clefts	27
			OSTEICHTHYES. BONY FISHES. Skin with cycloid or ctenoid scales; 4 pairs of gills in common cavity under opercula	28
		Superclass *TETRAPODA* Paired limbs, lungs, cornified skin, and bony skeleton	*AMPHIBIA.* AMPHIBIANS. Skin moist, soft, no external scales	29
			REPTILIA. REPTILES. Skin dry, with scales or scutes	30
			AVES. BIRDS. Skin with feathers; fore limbs are wings; warm-blooded	31
			MAMMALIA. MAMMALS. Skin with hair; warm-blooded; suckle young	32

The *nerve cord* forms on the dorsal surface of the early embryo soon after the gastrula stage. Infolding of the ectoderm produces the hollow tubular cord that lies above the notochord. The anterior end becomes enlarged as a simple "cerebral vesicle" in tunicate larvae and in lancelets, but in all vertebrates it thickens and differentiates as the brain, to become progressively more complex in higher forms.   The nerve tissue in tongue worms is diffuse.   In tunicates the cord and vesicle degenerate to a ganglion at metamorphosis.   From the lampreys onward the nerve cord later becomes surrounded by neural arches of the vertebrae that protect it from injury, and the brain is enclosed by a brain box, or cranium.

FIG. 25-2.   Phylum CHORDATA.   Basic features of four subphyla; diagrammatic.

Paired *gill slits* develop on the sides of the embryonic pharynx (digestive tract).   Each is formed by an outpocketing of endoderm in the pharynx and a corresponding inpocketing of ectoderm on the outside of the body; the intervening wall breaks through to form a gill slit.   The characteristic development is seen in a shark or fish in which each slit is margined by many slender filaments containing blood vessels, to form a gill.   Water containing dissolved oxygen passes into the mouth and pharynx and out over the filaments, when blood in the latter gives up its carbon dioxide and acquires oxygen, so that the gill serves the process of external respiration.   All aquatic chordates from tongue worms to amphibians respire by gills.   In amphibians which transform from aquatic larvae to air-breathing adults, the gills are lost at metamorphosis. The reptiles, birds, and mammals all develop several pairs of gill slits during early embryonic life, but they are never functional and soon close; all these animals later acquire lungs for breathing air when they hatch or are born.

25-2. Origin of chordates.   There is no reliable clue as to the origin of the chordates.   No remains of them have been found in Cambrian rocks where animal fossils first are common.   The earliest were probably soft-bodied, without hard skeletal elements likely to be preserved.   The first vertebrates are several groups of fishes in Silurian and Ordovician time. Thenceforth vertebrates are common and often dominant elements in the record of animals of the past and show a progressive series of developments toward the living types of the present day.   The earliest sharks and bony fishes appear in fresh-water deposits, and later both groups invaded the seas.   The amphibians probably derive from crossopterygian fishes.   They appear first in Devonian rocks and were differentiated into three orders by Carboniferous times.   The first salamanders (Cretaceous) and frogs (Jurassic) are distinct, like their modern successors. Reptiles appeared in Permian time and expanded widely into a great variety of dominant types in the Mesozoic era; then most of the orders died out at the end of the Cretaceous. The first bird (†*Archaeopteryx*) appeared in the Upper Jurassic; it was birdlike, with feathers and wings, but had teeth and other reptilian features. The mammals arose from the reptiles, beginning in the Triassic, and differentiated widely in the early Tertiary period. The study of fossils has contributed importantly to the classification of vertebrates and has indicated the probable origins of most of the larger groups.

Resemblances between the lower chordates and some invertebrates have been the basis for several theories of chordate origins, of which the following may be mentioned.

ANNELID THEORY. Annelids and chordates are both bilaterally symmetrical and segmented, with segmental excretory organs, a well-developed coelom, a nerve cord, and longitudinal blood vessels. Inverting an annelid would place its nerve cord dorsal to the digestive tract, and the path of blood flow would resemble that of chordates; however, the mouth would then be dorsal, unlike a chordate, and other dorsoventral relations would be altered. Annelids, moreover, have no structures suggestive of the notochord or gill slits.

NEMERTEAN THEORY. The proboscis sheath and cephalic pits of nemerteans have been compared to the notochord and gill slits, respectively, of chordates. Some paired lateral nerve trunks of the worm are assumed to have migrated dorsally to form a single dorsal cord, while one pair remained lateral, as are lateral branches of the vagus nerve in chordates.

ARACHNID THEORY. Resemblances are seen between Paleozoic eurypterids (arthropods) and early ostracoderms (chordates), both armored with dorsal exoskeletons. Chordates, however, have no arthropod-like appendages, their nerve cord is dorsal and that of arthropods is ventral, and there are other important differences.

ECHINODERM THEORY. The tornaria larva of tongue worms, and the bipinnaria larva of echinoderms are both minute and transparent, with almost identical external ciliated bands and a like number of coelomic cavities, and both have a dorsal pore. Indeed, the first known tongue worm (hemichordate) larva was identified as that of a starfish by a famous zoologist! If chordate ancestry is involved in such small soft larvae, the chance of finding any conclusive fossil record is very remote.

SUBPHYLUM HEMICHORDATA. TONGUE WORMS

The hemichordates are small soft-bodied animals, of sandy or muddy sea bottoms. They possess paired gill slits, a short structure identified as a notochord, and dorsal as well as ventral nervous tissue (Fig. 25-4) and hence are usually considered the lowest members of the Phylum CHOR-DATA, although some zoologists disagree. In the adults, the structure of the gill slits, the chitinous gill bars, and the multiple gonads resemble similar structures in amphioxus.

25-3. Class Enteropneusta. The acorn or tongue worms are slender and 25 to 2,500 mm. long. Most of them live under shallow water; but a few go deeper, and one was dredged at 2,500 fathoms off West Africa. They burrow shallowly by means of a soft proboscis, and a sticky mucus secreted by glands in the skin causes formation of a tubular case of sand and other debris in which each animal lives. About 12 genera and 60 species are known. *Balanoglossus* is world-wide in distribution, and *Saccoglossus* (= *Dolichoglossus*) inhabits both coasts of North America; *S. kowalevskii* occurs from Beaufort, N.C., to Massachusetts Bay and grows to about 175 mm. long. *S. pusillus* of southern California becomes 75 mm. in length and is brilliantly orange; in *S. kowalevskii* the proboscis is yellowish-white, the collar red-orange, and the trunk orange-yellow to green-yellow posteriorly. Some tongue worms have persistent and often unpleasant odors.

The body (Fig. 25-3) comprises a *proboscis*, a *collar*, and an elongated *trunk.* Behind the collar are numerous *gill slits* on either side. Ventral

Fig. 25-3. Subphylum HEMICHORDATA. The tongue worm, *Saccoglossus*, dorsal view. (*After Spengel.*)

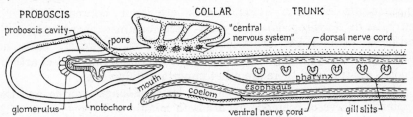

Fig. 25-4. Subphylum HEMICHORDATA. The tongue worm, *Saccoglossus*. Median section of anterior portion; diagrammatic.

to these is a lateral ridge marking the presence of the gonads. Some species have paired transverse ridges, dorsally behind the gills, that indicate the digestive caeca. The *mouth* opens widely at the anterior ventral margin of the collar, behind the proboscis; a dilated *buccal cavity* follows, then the *pharynx,* with U-shaped openings high on either side that connect to the gill pouches. The straight *intestine,* with dorsal *hepatic caeca* ("liver sacs"), leads to the terminal *anus.*

In life the cavities in the proboscis and collar (Fig. 25-4) are believed to fill with water through pores on the dorsal surface; when these parts become turgid, the animal burrows through the sand or mud, aided by muscular movements of the trunk.   The mouth remains open so that a mixture of water and sand containing organic debris if forced into the buccal cavity.   The water passes through the gill slits for respiration, the organic material serves as food, and the sand passes out the anus.

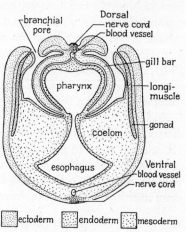

The *circulatory system* includes a middorsal vessel in which colorless blood flows anteriorly (as in annelids) and a midventral vessel.   The two are joined to a "heart," dorsal to the notochord, and there are other branches near the gill slits.   A pulsating vessel has been described in the larva, but its presence in the adult is debatable; contractions of the larger vessels probably cause the blood to circulate.   A small unpaired glomerulus ("proboscis gland") is thought to be the *excretory organ.*

Fig.   25-5.   Subphylum HEMICHORDATA.   Cross section through pharynx region of a hemichordate.   (*Modified from Sedgwick, Textbook of zoology, George Allen & Unwin, Ltd.*)

In the *body wall* (Fig. 25-5), the thick unicellular epidermis contains many mucus-secreting cells; it rests on a basement membrane, beneath which are muscle layers.   The *nervous system* consists of cells and fibers in the base of the epidermis.   Concentrations of these provide a middorsal and a midventral nerve "cord" of small size,

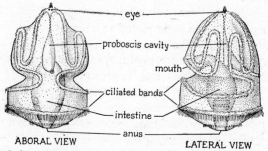

ABORAL VIEW   LATERAL VIEW

FIG.   25-6.   Subphylum HEMICHORDATA.   Tornaria larva of a hemichordate.   (*After Spengel.*)

with a ringlike connective between the two posteriorly in the collar.   A thickened cord, hollow in some species, lies in the collar dorsal to the mouth cavity, and has many nerve fibers in the epidermis of the proboscis.

The *notochord* is a short anterior outpocketing of the digestive tract in the hind part of the proboscis.   There is also a small *proboscis skeleton* of material like chitin or cartilage.   The *coelom* is represented by five cavities, one in the proboscis and a pair each in the collar and the trunk.

The sexes are separate, with multiple *gonads* in two dorsolateral rows from behind the collar to the gastric caeca; each when mature releases its contents immediately to the exterior through a separate pore, and fertilization is external.   In some species the egg produces a small ovoid tornaria larva, quite transparent, and with surface bands of cilia (Fig. 25-6); at metamorphosis the proboscis and collar become evident.   The American species of *Saccoglossus* develop directly without a larval stage. Tongue worms can regenerate the trunk region, proboscis, and collar.

25-4. Class Pterobranchia.   These minute colonial forms (*Cephalodiscus* and *Rhabdopleura*), of both deep and shallow seas, resemble the Enteropneusta in general structure but have only one pair of gill slits or none.   *Cephalodiscus* secretes a "housing" that harbors many individuals, each with a U-shaped digestive tract having the mouth and anus close together.   Pterobranchs reproduce both by budding and sexually.

Subphylum TUNICATA.   Tunicates

Tunicates inhabit the sea, from the polar oceans to the tropics and from shallow beach waters to depths of 3 miles.   Some are free-living, and others become fixed or sessile after a short free larval stage; some are solitary, others are colonial, and some live with the individuals grouped under a common covering.   They vary in size from nearly microscopic forms to others a foot in diameter.   Their methods of reproduction are varied, some sexual, some asexual by budding.   The group name refers to the self-secreted "tunic" or saclike covering over the body.   The best known tunicates are the "sea squirts" or ascidians, which suddenly squirt water from openings in the body covering when touched.

Aristotle (384–322 B.C.) described a simple ascidian as Tethyum, but not until early in the nineteenth century were many species described in detail.   Cuvier then gave the name Tunicata to the group and placed it between the "Radiata" and "Vermes"; later, its members were classified as mollusks.   In 1866 Kowalevsky, by careful study of the developmental stages of a larval ascidian, brilliantly demonstrated the true position of the group to be among the chordates.

The tunicates are best understood by considering first the free-living larva of an ascidian and then the adult.   The larva shows chordate characteristics; but some of these are absent in the adult, and others are obscured by adaptations to the sessile mode of life.

25-5. The larval ascidian.   The small fertilized egg segments to form a blastula and then a gastrula; the embryo elongates and soon hatches as a

free-swimming larva, somewhat resembling a frog tadpole (Fig. 25-7A).
Its tail contains a supporting *notochord* (whence the name Urochordata,
sometimes applied to the tunicates), a dorsal tubular *nerve cord,* and
serial pairs of lateral, segmental muscles.   The other organs are confined
to the anterior and larger head+body region.   The anterior end bears
three mucous or *adhesive glands.*   The *digestive tract* is complete, with

Fig. 25-7. Subphylum Tunicata. Stages in the metamorphosis of a simple ascidian
from the free-swimming larva to the sessile adult.   Arrows indicate entrance and exit
paths of water currents. (*Adapted from Kowalewsky; and Herdman.*)
   A. Larva attaches to a solid object by anterior mucous suckers.
   B. Tail resorbed, notochord and nerve cord reduced.
   C. Notochord disappears, internal organs begin to rotate.
   D. Metamorphosis complete, with rotation (90 to 180 degrees) of internal organs and
external apertures; branchial sac enlarges, tunic (or test) is secreted, and nervous system
reduced to a ganglion.   (See Fig. 25-8.)

mouth, perforate *gill slits,* endostyle, intestine, and anus; there is a *circulatory system* with blood vessels, and a *coelom.*   The *nervous system*
(continuous with the nerve cord in the tail) and sensory structures include
(1) a *cerebral vesicle* and posterior to it (2) a *trunk ganglion,* (3) a
median *optical organ* with retina, lens, pigment, and cornea, and (4) a
pigmented *otolith,* or ear, attached to delicate hair cells (crista acustica).
   25-6. Metamorphosis.   After a few hours or days of free life, the small
larva attaches vertically by its adhesive glands to a rock or wharf pile

(Fig. 25-7). A rapid transformation (retrograde metamorphosis) ensues in which most of the chordate features disappear. The tail is partly absorbed and partly cast off, its notochord, nerve cord, and muscles being withdrawn into the body and absorbed. Of the nervous system only the trunk ganglion persists. The branchial or "gill" sac enlarges, develops many apertures, and is invaded by blood vessels. The stomach and intestine grow. That portion of the body between the point of attachment and the mouth grows rapidly, causing the "body" within to rotate dorsoposteriorly nearly 180 degrees so that the "mouth" is at the upper nonattached end. Finally the gonads and ducts form in mesoderm between the stomach and intestine. The adhesive glands disappear, and the tunic grows upward to enclose the entire animal.

25-7. The adult ascidian. A simple ascidian (*Ciona, Molgula,* etc.) is cylindrical or globose, attached by a *base* or stalk (Fig. 25-8). It is

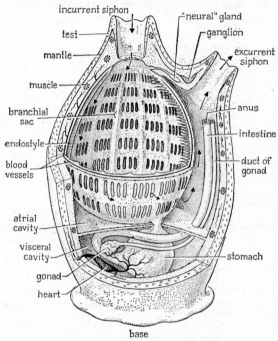

Fig. 25-8. Subphylum Tunicata. Structure of an adult simple ascidian; diagrammatic. Tunic, mantle, and upper half of branchial sac removed on left side. Arrows indicate path of water currents through the animal.

covered with a tough elastic layer, the *test* or *tunic,* of cellulose-like material (which is rare in animals). The test is lined by a membranous *mantle* containing muscle fibers and blood vessels. There are two external openings, the *incurrent siphon* (branchial aperture) at the top and the *excurrent siphon* (atrial aperture) at one side. Water drawn into the incurrent siphon brings minute organisms that serve for food and oxygen for respiration; that passed out the excurrent siphon removes wastes and the sex cells.   Within the test and mantle is the *atrial cavity,* in which is a dilated *branchial sac* having many pores.

The digestive system begins with the *mouth* followed by a circle of hairlike sensory tentacles at the entrance to the branchial sac.   Along the midventral wall of the latter is the *endostyle,* a vertical groove lined with both ciliated and mucous cells where food from the entering water becomes entangled and moved downward.   Feeding only on plankton, the ascidian needs no large appendages to handle food.   From the base of the branchial sac the *esophagus* leads to the dilated *stomach,* which connects to the *intestine;* the latter two organs are outside the branchial sac.   The intestine curves to end at the *anus* below the excurrent siphon.   A *digestive gland* ("liver") connects to the stomach.

The wall of the branchial sac has many pores margined by ciliated cells that beat to move water from within the sac to the atrial cavity, whence it flows to the excurrent siphon.

The circulatory system includes a tubular heart in the *visceral cavity* near the stomach.   To each end is connected a large vessel or *aorta,* one distributing to the stomach, test wall, and one side of the branchial sac, the other to the opposite side of the branchial sac.   In the walls of the latter an intercommunicating series of small vessels surrounds the pores, to constitute the respiratory mechanism.   These "vessels," however, are spaces within the tissues and lack an endothelial lining.   The tunicate is unique in that the path of blood flow reverses at short intervals.

Near the intestine is a structure, without a duct, considered to be excretory in function.   The only relic of the nervous system is a long *trunk ganglion* in the mantle between the two siphons, with nerves to various parts.   Near by is a *neural gland,* possibly of endocrine nature, and somewhat like a pituitary structure.

The ascidians are hermaphroditic, but self-sterile.   The *ovary* is a large hollow gland, on the intestinal loop, with an *oviduct* paralleling the intestine and opening in the atrial cavity near the anus.   The *testes* comprise numerous branched tubules, on the surface of the ovary and intestine, that discharge into a *vas deferens* paralleling the oviduct. Some tunicates also reproduce asexually, by budding.

25-8. Class Larvacea.   These small organisms (to 5 mm. long) live in upper levels of the sea, and swim by contractions of the bent or curved tail.   Some are brilliantly pigmented with orange or violet and when abundant may color the water by their numbers.   Each individual at times secretes a large gelatinous housing or tunic.

25-9. Class Ascidiacea.   In the simple ascidians the individuals are "solitary," that is, each has a distinct and separate test.   Many inhabit shallow waters, but some occur down to 2,900 fathoms.   The compound ascidians (Fig. 25-9) are those in which the "individuals" are buried in a common covering mass or housing, and do not have separate tests. In many of this group, each "individual" possesses a separate incurrent siphon, but several or many (to several hundred) have a common external

aperture ("cloaca") into which their respective excurrent siphons discharge. Compound ascidians reproduce asexually by gemmation and also produce eggs and sperm for sexual reproduction. With most species, development proceeds to the larval stage within the atrium, then the young emerge.

FIG. 25-9.   Subphylum TUNICATA.   A compound tunicate (*Botryllus*) individual with separate incurrent siphons, but common excurrent siphon.   (*After M. Edwards.*)

25-10. Class   Thaliacea. The salpians are highly modified tunicates of peculiar form that live in the open sea and have specialized modes of reproduction.   The body is cask-shaped, surrounded by complete bands of circular muscles, and has the incurrent and excurrent openings at opposite ends.   Some swim by contracting the ringlike muscles so as to force water out the posterior end, and others are wafted about by water currents.   In *Doliolum* (Fig. 25-10) the fertilized egg develops into a free-

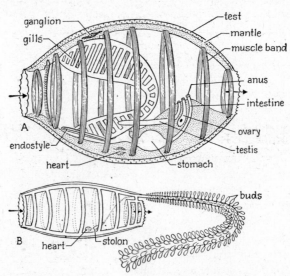

FIG. 25-10.   Subphylum TUNICATA.   A chain tunicate (*Doliolum*).   *A*. Adult of sexual generation.   *B*. Asexual adult ("nurse" stage) with attached chain bearing many buds. Arrows indicate path of water through the animal.   (*Modified from Stempell.*)

swimming tailed larva, somewhat like that of an ascidian. This metamorphoses into a barrel-shaped adult "nurse" stage that by asexual reproduction gives rise to many individuals. Some of the latter eventually produce eggs and sperm. *Salpa* is another type in which, by asexual means, a solitary adult produces long chains of individuals, sometimes several hundred connected to one another. Fragments of such a chain including several animals may break loose from the parent structure. Later these, while still connected or further separated, reproduce sexually. Each gives rise to one or several eggs that remain attached to the parent by a placenta-like structure, analogous to that of higher chordates, where the maternal and embryonic blood circulations are closely related during the course of development. The young that hatch out become the asexual form.

Subphylum CEPHALOCHORDATA. Lancelets

25-11. Amphioxus. This group (Class Leptocardii) comprises about 30 species of fishlike animals (*Branchiostoma*, etc.), commonly called amphioxus, that inhabit tropical and temperate seacoasts. *Branchiostoma virginiae* occurs from Chesapeake Bay to Florida, and *B. californiense* from San Diego Bay southward. The latter grows to 100 mm. long, but most species are smaller. Amphioxus burrows in clean shifting sand of shallow shore waters, leaving only its anterior end protruding. At times it emerges to swim by rapid lateral movements of the body. Amphioxus is of especial zoological interest because it shows the three distinctive characteristics of the Phylum Chordata in simple form and is considered to resemble some ancient ancestor of this phylum.

The **body** is slender, elongate, and laterally compressed, pointed at both ends, and has no distinct head (Fig. 25-11). The low median **dorsal**

Fig. 25-11. Subphylum Cephalochordata. The lancelet or amphioxus (*Branchiostoma*). Adult partly dissected from left side. Natural size about 2 inches long.

fin along most of the body and the **preanal fin** from atriopore to anus are made of fin-ray chambers containing short **fin rays** of connective tissue. The **tail** has a membranous fin. Anterior to the ventral fin, the body is flattened ventrally with a **metapleural fold** along each side. The **mouth** is ventral at the anterior end, the **anus** is on the left side near the base of the tail fin, and the *atriopore* is an additional ventral opening forward of the anus.

The body covering is a single layer of soft *epithelium* in which some cells bear sensory processes; beneath this is a soft connective tissue. The *notochord* is the chief support of the body. It is a slender rod of tall cells containing gelatinous material and is surrounded by a continuous sheath of connective tissue. Other supportive structures include a circular cartilage-like reinforcement in the oral hood, the fin rays, and delicate rods with cross connections in the gill bars. Along each side of the body and tail different species have 50 to 85 <-shaped muscles, or *myotomes,* each of lengthwise muscle fibers and separated from one another by thin septa of connective tissue. Those on the two sides alternate in position— a unique feature. These muscles contract to produce the lateral bending for burrowing and swimming. Transverse muscles in the floor of the atrial cavity, between the metapleural folds, serve to compress the cavity and force water to the exterior.

The straight and simple *digestive tract* begins with the anterior *oral hood,* or vestibule, which is surrounded by about 22 delicate fleshy *buccal cirri;* behind the latter are several ciliated bars. The *mouth* proper is a circular opening in a membrane, or *velum,* posterior in the oral hood. It is guarded by 12 *velar tentacles,* which exclude large particles. Cilia in the hood, during life, producing a rotating effect and are called the "wheel organ." On the cirri and tentacles and within the hood are sensory structures. Behind the mouth is the large compressed *pharynx,* with many diagonal *gill slits* at the sides. There follows the narrow straight *intestine,* which ends at the *anus.* A slender saclike *liver,* thought to secrete digestive fluid, attaches ventrally to the anterior part of the intestine.

The pharynx is suspended dorsally, beneath the notochord, but hangs free in a cavity, the *atrium,* within the muscles of the body wall. The atrium is an external cavity, lined by ectoderm (hence not a coelom), and connects to the atriopore. The pharynx contains a middorsal furrow, the *hyperbrachial groove,* lined with ciliated cells, and midventrally is a corresponding groove, the *endostyle,* having both ciliated and gland cells (Fig. 25-12). Water containing minute organisms is drawn into the mouth by action of the cilia; the food is trapped by mucus in the endostyle and carried posteriorly to the intestine, while the water passes between the gill bars to the atrium and thence to the exterior through the atriopore.

The *circulatory system* is somewhat on the plan of that in higher chordates, but lacks a heart. Besides the definite blood vessels there are open spaces where the colorless blood escapes into the tissues. Blood from the digestive tract flows anteriorly in a *subintestinal vein* to the *hepatic portal vein* entering the liver; thence it collects in a *hepatic vein* and with other blood from the posterior part of the body passes forward in a *ventral aorta* below the endostyle and into branches at each primary gill bar.   Each branch has a small pulsating bulb, and together these function as a heart, forcing blood upward in the gill bars where it is aerated and then collects in the paired *dorsal aortas.*   The latter join behind the pharynx to form a single *dorsal aorta* in which the blood moves posteriorly to supply the body and intestine and finally through capillaries to the venous side.   Some oxygenated blood passes forward in the right dorsal

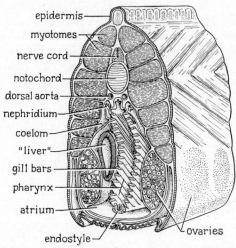

epidermis
myotomes
nerve cord
notochord
dorsal aorta
nephridium
coelom
"liver"
gill bars
pharynx
atrium
endostyle
ovaries

FIG. 25-12.   Subphylum CEPHALOCHORDATA.   Amphioxus.   Enlarged section through pharynx.   (*Adapted from Kükenthal.*)

aorta to the anterior end of the body.   The general course of blood movement in amphioxus is thus like that in higher chordates and opposite to that in invertebrates such as annelids.

   Respiration results from passage of water containing oxygen from the pharynx through 100 or more *gill slits* on each side and past the *gill bars* that contain blood vessels.   This water current is aided by cilia in cells on the gill bars.   The gill system of amphioxus is like that of higher chordates during early larval life, its inner surface being of endoderm and the exterior of ectoderm.   Later the exterior surface of the gill region of amphioxus is enclosed by growth of the covering wall that forms the atrial cavity outside the gills.

   During development the *coelom* is formed of five embryonic pouches as in hemichordates; in the adult amphioxus it becomes reduced and complicated except around the intestine.   The *excretory system* comprises about 100 pairs of small ciliated *nephridia* in dorsal relics of the coelom above the pharynx; they connect the coelom to the atrial cavity, and show some structural resemblance to the nephridia of certain annelid (polychaete) worms. A pair of larger structures, the *"brown bodies,"* dorsal to the intestine may also be excretory in function.

The *nervous system* lies above the notochord; it consists of a single dorsal *nerve cord* with a small central canal. The anterior end is slightly enlarged to form a median *cerebral vesicle,* with a middorsal *olfactory pit,* a small nonsensory *eyespot* of black pigment, and two pairs of "cranial" *nerves.* The cord gives off to each myotome alternately a pair of *nerves,* the dorsal root being both sensory and motor, the ventral only motor in function. In the skin and the mouth region are ciliated cells thought to be sensory in function.

The sexes are separate; about 25 pairs of *gonads* (in 2 rows) bulge into the atrium. Eggs and sperm break into the atrial cavity to pass out through the atriopore, and fertilization is external. The egg is about 0.1 mm. in diameter, with little yolk, and segmentation is holoblastic (Fig. 5-9A). During the breeding season, egg deposition usually occurs about sunset, and by morning a free-swimming ciliated larva is hatched; this feeds and grows for up to 3 months, gradually assuming the adult form and then takes to burrowing in the sand.

Lancelets of the Genus *Asymmetron* have gonads only on the right side.

Amphioxus is usually of purely zoological interest, but in Fukien Province near Amoy, in southern China, a local fishery for these animals has existed for hundreds of years. On a small area of sand where the animals are abundant the catch amounts to over 1 ton per day, and an estimated one billion individuals are taken from August to April each year to be used, either fresh or dried, as human food.

The CRANIATA. Vertebrates

25-12. Characteristics. The Classes Cyclostomata to Mammalia comprise the major part of the Phylum Chordata. They all have an enlarged brain enclosed in a brain case or cranium, and a segmental spinal column of vertebrae that becomes the axial support of the body. Typically the body comprises a head, neck, trunk, and tail. These classes show a progressive series of structural and functional advances in all organ systems besides the features of the notochord, nerve cord, and gill slits mentioned earlier in this chapter under Characteristics (see also Chap. 4).

1. The *integument* becomes a stratified epithelium, of epidermis and dermis, with many mucous glands in aquatic species; most fishes are covered with protective scales; the exterior is cornified on land dwellers, with scales on reptiles, feathers on birds, and hair on mammals; feathers and hair form insulated body coverings.

2. The internal and jointed *skeleton* is of cartilage in lower vertebrates and of bone in higher groups; it supports and protects various organs; the cranium shelters the brain and has paired capsules to contain organs of special sense; a series of visceral

arches supports the gill region, and certain arches become the jaws and other structures of the head region; the vertebral column extends from the base of the cranium to the end of the tail and has neural arches dorsally to house the nerve cord.   Two pairs of appendages, the fins of fishes and limbs of tetrapods, with jointed skeletal supports, are joined to the vertebral column through limb girdles.

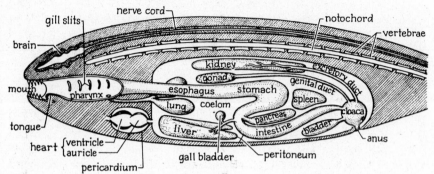

Fig. 25-13.   Diagram of the principal structures in a craniate or vertebrate (both lungs and gills are indicated but rarely occur together).

3. On the skeleton are **muscles** that move its parts and provide for locomotion.

4. The elongate **digestive tract** is ventral to the vertebral column; the mouth contains a tongue and usually teeth; the anus opens at the end of the trunk; the liver and pancreas are 2 large digestive glands that pour their secretions through ducts joined to the intestine.

5. The **circulatory system** includes a well-developed muscular heart of 2, 3, or 4 chambers, located ventral to the digestive tract; its contractions propel the blood through a closed system of arteries, capillaries, and veins, the flow being anteriorly on the ventral side and posteriorly in the dorsal arteries; the blood plasma contains both white and red corpuscles, the latter with hemoglobin as a respiratory pigment; a system of lymph vessels is present; paired aortic arches transport blood from the heart to the gills in lower vertebrates; progressive separation of the respiratory (pulmonary) and systemic blood paths through the heart leads to realization of regulated body temperature in the "warm-blooded" (homoiothermous) birds and mammals.

6. **Respiration** in the lower forms is by paired gills; terrestrial species have lungs developed from outpocketings of the digestive tract.

7. The paired **excretory organs,** or kidneys, discharge through ducts opening near or through the anus; in lower forms they are of segmental nature and drain wastes from both the coelom and the blood; in higher forms they are nonsegmental and drain only from the blood; a bladder for storage of urine occurs in many.

8. The **brain** becomes regionally differentiated as to structure and function; the cerebral hemispheres and cerebellum enlarge, especially in higher forms; there are 10 or 12 pairs of cranial nerves in the head that serve both motor and sensory function, including the paired organs of special sense (smell, sight, and hearing plus equilibration); from the **nerve cord** a pair of spinal nerves serves each primitive body somite; an autonomic nervous system regulates involuntary functions of internal organs.

9. A series of **endocrine glands** (thyroid, pituitary, etc.) provide internal secretions, or hormones, transported by the blood stream, that regulate bodily processes, growth, and reproduction.

10. With rare exceptions the **sexes** are separate, and each has a pair of **gonads** that discharge sex cells through ducts opening into or near the anus.

References on Lower Chordates

Harmer, S. F. 1904. Hemichordata. *In* Cambridge natural history. London. Macmillan & Co., Ltd. Vol. 7, pp. 3–32, illus.

Hatschek, B. 1881. Studien ueber der Entwickelung des Amphioxus. *Arbeiten des zoologische Institute zu Wien*, vol. 4.

Herdman, W. A. 1904. Tunicata and Amphioxus. *In* Cambridge natural history. London, Macmillan & Co., Ltd. Vol. 7, pp. 35–111, 112–138; illus.

Morgan, T. H. 1894. The development of Balanoglossus. *Journal of Morphology*, vol. 9, pp. 1–86, illus.

Ritter, W. E., and B. M. Davis. 1904. Studies on the ecology, morphology, and speciology of the young of some Enteropneusta of western North America. *University of California Publications in Zoology*, vol. 1, pp. 171–210, pls. 17–20.

Spengel, J. W. 1893. Die Enteropneusta. . . . *Fauna und Flora des Golfes von Neapel, Monograph* 18.

Van der Horst, C. J. 1927–1935. Hemichordata. *In* H. G. Bronn, Klassen und Ordnungen der Thierreichs. Leipzig. Vol. 4, part IV, book 2, pp. 1–514, 588 figs.

Willey, A. 1894. Amphioxus and the ancestry of the vertebrates. New York, Columbia University Press. xiv + 316 pp., illus.

References on Vertebrates

(See also Chaps. 26 to 32)

Adams, L. A., and Samuel Eddy. 1949. Comparative anatomy. New York, John Wiley & Sons, Inc. vii + 520 pp., 364 figs.

Bolk, Louis, and others. 1931–1939. Handbuch der vergleichenden Anatomie der Wirbeltiere. Berlin, Urban & Schwartzenberg. 6 vols.

Goodrich, E. S. 1930. Studies on the structure and development of vertebrates. London, Macmillan & Co., Ltd. xxx + 837 pp., 754 figs.

Hyman, L. H. 1942. Comparative vertebrate anatomy. Chicago, University of Chicago Press. xx + 544 pp., 136 figs.

Neal, H. V., and H. W. Rand. 1936. Comparative anatomy [of vertebrates]. Philadelphia, The Blakiston Co. xxi + 739 pp., 540 figs.

Parker, T. J., and W. A. Haswell. 1941. A textbook of zoology. 6th ed. London, Macmillan & Co., Ltd. Vol. 2 on chordates revised by C. Forster-Cooper. xxiii + 758 pp., illus.

Rand, H. W. 1950. The chordates. Philadelphia, The Blakiston Co. xi + 862 pp., 609 figs.

Romer, A. S. 1941. Man and the vertebrates. 3d ed. Chicago, University of Chicago Press. viii + 405 pp., 106 pls., 135 figs.

———. 1949. The vertebrate body. Philadelphia, W. B. Saunders Co. viii + 643 pp., 363 figs.

———. 1945. Vertebrate paleontology. 2d ed. Chicago, University of Chicago Press. viii + 687 pp., 377 figs.

Schimkewitsch, W. 1931. Lehrbuch der vergleichenden Anatomie der Wirbeltiere. Stuttgart, E. Schweitzerbart'sche Verlagsbuchhandlung. ix + 649 pp., 635 figs.

Walter, H. E., and L. P. Sayles. 1949. Biology of the vertebrates. 3d ed. New York, The Macmillan Co. xix + 875 pp., 727 figs.

CHAPTER 26

CLASS CYCLOSTOMATA. CYCLOSTOMES

The Cyclostomata (Gr. *cyklos*, circular + *stoma*, mouth) include the lampreys, hagfishes, and slime eels, all of slender form, which live in salt and fresh waters. These lowest of living vertebrates are jawless, and their nearest allies are the ancient, armored fishlike ostracoderms of Silurian and Devonian times.

A

B

Fig. 26-1. Class Cyclostomata. Representative cyclostomes. *A.* California hagfish (*Polistotrema stouti*), with 12 pairs of gill slits, ×⅓. *B.* Sea lamprey (*Petromyzon marinus*), with buccal funnel, eyes, and 7 pairs of gill slits. (*From Wolcott, Animal biology.*)

26-1. Characteristics. 1. Body long slender and rounded, tail region compressed; median fins supported by cartilaginous fin rays; skin soft and smooth, with many unicellular mucous glands; no scales, jaws, or paired fins.

2. Mouth ventroanterior, suctorial, and margined by fleshy papillae, or tentacles; nasal sac single and median.

3. Skull and visceral arches (branchial basket) cartilaginous; notochord persistent; vertebrae represented by small imperfect neural arches (arcualia) over notochord.

4. Heart 2-chambered, with auricle and ventricle; multiple aortic arches in gill region; blood with leucocytes and nucleated circular erythrocytes.

5. Six to 14 pairs of gills, in lateral saclike pouches off pharynx.

6. Two kidneys with ducts to urogenital papilla.

7. Brain differentiated, with 10 (or 8) pairs of cranial nerves; each auditory organ with 1 or 2 semicircular canals.

8. Body temperature variable (poikilothermous).

9. Gonad single, large, without duct; fertilization external; development direct (hagfishes, and slime eels) or with long larval stage (lampreys).

The vertebrate features of cyclostomes include the differentiated brain and paired cranial nerves, eyes, and internal ears, beginnings of segmental vertebrae, organ systems on the vertebrae pattern, and presence of both red and white blood cells. Cyclostomes differ from other vertebrates in having no differentiated head, jaws, paired appendages, limb girdles, ribs,

573

or reproductive ducts, a single nasal sac and gonad, and but one or two semicircular canals in each "ear."

26-2. Structure of a lamprey (Figs. 26-2, 26-3). The combined head-and-trunk or *body* is cylindrical, and the *tail* is laterally compressed. On the posterior dorsal region and tail are *median fins.* Ventrally on the head is a large cuplike *buccal funnel,* margined by soft papillae and lined within by conical yellow horny *teeth.* The single *nasal aperture* is mid-dorsal on the head, followed by thin skin over the pineal organ. The

Fig. 26-2.   Class CYCLOSTOMATA.   Structure of an adult lamprey (*Entosphenus tridentatus*); left side of body mostly removed.

two large *eyes* are lateral and covered by transparent skin, but lack lids. Behind each are seven rounded *gill apertures.* A row of small lateral *sense pits* extends segmentally along each side of the body and tail. The *anus* opens ventrally at the base of the tail, and close behind is a small *urogenital papilla,* pierced by a duct. The whole animal is covered by smooth epithelium containing many mucous glands but no scales.

26-3. Skeleton. The *notochord* persists throughout life as the axial skeleton; it is a slender gelatinous rod sheathed in tough connective tissue. The other principal *skeletal elements,* all cartilaginous, include (1) the complex skull (cranium and sense capsules); (2) the stout lingual cartilage of the tongue, and a ring of annular cartilage surrounding the buccal funnel; (3) the elaborate paired visceral arches, or "branchial basket," supporting the gill region; and (4) small slender rodlike arcualia dorsal to the notochord, two pairs to most body segments, that represent the neural arches of higher vertebrates.

26-4. Muscular system. The trunk and tail regions are walled by short segmental muscles, in ≥-shaped arrangement, as in other fishes. Radial muscles operate the buccal funnel, and the tongue is moved by stout retractor and smaller protractor muscles.

26-5. Digestive system. The small *mouth* is centered in the buccal funnel and closed or opened by the fore-and-aft piston-like movement of the *tongue.* On the latter are horny teeth like those in the funnel (Fig. 26-4). A short *pharynx* follows, then the tract divides into a dorsal *esophagus* and ventral *respiratory tube;* the entrance to the latter is guarded by a flexible transverse plate, the *velum.* There is no stomach. The posterior end of the esophagus opens, by a valve, into the straight *intestine.* Within the latter is a spiral longitudinal fold (typhlosole), or

Fig. 26-3. Adult lamprey (*Entosphenus tridentatus*); anterior end with left side of body removed to median plane, leaving parts of gill region and muscular body wall.

spiral valve.   The intestine ends at the small **anus.**   The **liver** is usually without a bile duct; it is uncertain whether a "pancreas" is present.

26-6. Circulatory system. The **heart** lies within the cup-shaped posterior end of the branchial basket in a pericardial sac that communi-

cates with the coelom.   It consists of an auricle and a thicker walled ventricle, with a conus arteriosus anteriorly.   Blood from the heart is pumped forward into a **ventral aorta** that distributes in eight pairs of afferent branches to the gill fila- ments, then is collected in a median

FIG. 26-4.   Buccal funnel of lake lam- prey (*Petromyzon*) in ventral view, with many horny teeth; mouth and tip of tongue in center.   (*After S. H. Gage,* 1893.)

dorsal aorta, above the gills, that distributes both anteriorly and pos- teriorly.   The venous system re- turns blood from the head and body and includes a hepatic system through the liver but no renal portal system; lymphatic vessels are also present.

26-7. Respiratory system. There are seven obliquely placed **gill pouches** on either side, between the respiratory tube and the body wall. Each contains many gill filaments with fine capillaries in which the blood is aerated by water in the pouches.   In an adult lamprey the water currents serving for respiration pass both *in* and *out* of the gill openings, a route unlike that in true fishes.   This peculiar method is necessary because the lamprey often attaches by its buccal funnel to food or other objects, when the passage of water through the mouth is impossible; in a larval lamprey the respiratory current passes in through the mouth and out the gill openings as in fishes.

26-8. Excretory system. The two **kidneys** (mesonephroi) are dorsal in the body cavity; a tubular **ureter** extends from each to the **urogenital sinus,** which empties to the exterior through the **urogenital papilla.**

26-9. Nervous system. The forebrain includes large paired **olfactory lobes,** followed by smaller **cerebral hemispheres** attached to the **dien- cephalon;** beneath the latter is a broad **infundibulum** and dorsally a **pineal structure.**   On the midbrain, dorsally, is a pair of large **optic lobes.** In the hindbrain, the **cerebellum** is a small transverse dorsal band, and the ventral **medulla oblongata** is much larger.   Large apertures with choroid plexes containing blood vessels occur between the optic lobes and over the medulla.   Within the brain are four **ventricles,** as in other verte- brates.   There are 10 pairs of **cranial nerves.**   The **nerve cord** is flattened and bandlike.   The dorsal and ventral roots of the paired **spinal nerves** emerge alternately from the cord and are not bound together as in other vertebrates.   There is a poorly defined sympathetic system.

26-10. Sense organs.   The single nasal aperture leads into an *olfactory sac* receiving nerve endings from both olfactory lobes of the brain. Besides the paired *eyes,* an elaborate median *pineal eye* with clear lens and pigmented retina lies behind the nasal aperture.   Each internal ear (organ of equilibrium) has two semicircular canals.   Taste buds occur in the pharynx, and there are *lateral line* sense organs on the sides of the body and the under surface of the head.

26-11. Endocrine glands.   Beneath the infundibulum is a *pituitary body;* a long sac extending posteriorly from the olfactory sac is termed the pituitary pouch.   The endostyle of the larva resembles similar structures in tunicates and amphioxus and is considered to be the forerunner of the thyroid gland of the adult lamprey.

26-12. Reproductive system.   The immature gonad is hermaphroditic but later becomes either male or female in any one individual, so that in adults the sexes are separate (dioecious) as in other vertebrates. At sexual maturity a single large elongate *gonad* fills much of the abdominal cavity.   There is no genital duct; eggs or sperm discharge into the abdominal cavity and pass through paired *genital pores* into the urogenital sinus, thence to the outside.

26-13. Hagfishes and slime eels.   As compared with lampreys, members of the Order Myxinoidia differ in many ways: (1) a soft suctorial mouth with one large dorsal epidermal tooth, but no buccal funnel; (2) four pairs of soft anterior tentacles; (3) nostril terminal and median with canal (and pituitary pouch) under brain to roof of pharynx as channel for water entering to aerate gills; (4) roof and sides of brain case membranous, branchial basket far reduced, arcualia few and posterior; (5) myotomes alternate; (6) gills 6 or 14 pairs, far posterior; (7) segmental pronephros (with nephrostomes) in adult; (8) brain primitive, of 4 lobes, no recognizable cerebrum or cerebellum, dorsal and ventral roots of spinal nerves united; (9) eyes degenerate; (10) each ear with only one semicircular canal; (11) lateral line system far reduced; (12) normally monoecious, eggs large, with shells formed in ovary.

26-14. Natural history.   Lampreys occur in both fresh and salt waters; the hagfishes are marine, some descending to depths of more than 300 fathoms.   Some adult lampreys are nonparasitic.   The parasitic species attach to fishes (Figs. 26-5, 26-6) by suction of the funnel and use of the buccal teeth; a hole is rasped by the lingual teeth and an anticoagulant injected, when the host's blood flows into the mouth of the lamprey. Healthy fishes are attacked and may be killed.   The hagfishes and slime eels burrow into the bodies of fishes and consume the flesh, leaving only a bag of skin and the bones.   Their effects are seen on fishes caught by set nets or lines, but healthy free-swimming fishes also may be attacked.

FIG. 26-5.   Lamprey attaching and feeding; diagrams of the action of the buccal funnel and tongue.   (*After T. E. Reynolds*, 1931.)

A. Buccal funnel is collapsed against an object and its interior volume is decreased by forcing water behind tongue into pharynx.

B. Tongue closes passage between funnel and pharynx; funnel warped out to increase internal volume and degree of suction.

C. Water in hydrosinus is forced behind velum; tongue continues to block oral passage.

D. Velum prevents return of water from gill pouches; tongue is free to move back and forth in rasping flesh.

26-15. Reproduction.

When lampreys, either marine or fresh-water, become sexually mature, in the spring or early summer, the gonads swell and both sexes move into streams, sometimes "riding" on a passing fish or boat.   They seek clear water on riffles in streams, and by use of the buccal funnel move stones on the bottom until a shallow rounded depression, free of silt, is prepared as a nest (Fig. 26-7*A*).   The female then attaches to a stone on the upstream side, and the male fastens to the female, both using their buccal funnels.   Partly entwined, they wriggle back and forth as eggs and sperm are discharged, fertilization being external. The eggs are small (1 mm. in the brook lamprey) and adhesive; they quickly sink and are covered by silt and sand.   A female brook lamprey

FIG. 26-6.   Lamprey attached to a fish. (*After S. H. Gage*, 1929.)

may contain up to 65,000 eggs and that of the large sea lamprey up to 236,000 eggs.   Several pairs usually spawn close together, at times in the same nest.   All adults die after spawning.

FIG. 26-7.   *A*. Lake lampreys and nest; female moored to a large stone and male backing downstream with another stone; eggs shown as white circles in silt of nest bottom.   *B*. Larval lamprey (*Ammocoetes*) in its burrow beneath the water.   (*After S. H. Gage*, 1893.)

The young emerge in a month or so as small larvae and when 12 to 15 mm. long quit the nest to seek quiet water.   There each constructs and inhabits a U-shaped tunnel in the sand and silt but emerges to feed on ooze covering the stream bottom (Fig. 26-7*B*).   Water is drawn into the mouth by ciliary action and passes out through the gill apertures. The food is caught in mucus secreted by the endostyle on the floor of the pharynx, as in amphioxus.

The larvae, known as "ammocoetes," are blind and toothless and have a long life, from at least 3 years (*Entosphenus tridentatus*) to perhaps 7 years (*Ichthyomyzon unicolor*), during which they grow.   When metamorphosis ensues, two courses are pursued by different types of lampreys. In the more primitive group a functional digestive tract is retained, and strong sharp teeth develop; such lampreys feed on fishes, continuing to live and grow in the sea or in large streams or lakes according to the species.   After having existed in this state for a year (perhaps longer in the largest species), they reascend small streams in the spring to spawn and then die.   Members of the second group cease feeding and growth after metamorphosis in August to October; the alimentary tract and teeth partly degenerate, and after 4 to 11 months the animals breed and die. Such degenerate lampreys have developed as offshoots of the normal type at several places, in both eastern and western states and other parts of the world.

In the hagfish the same individual produces sperm and then eggs later, being protandrous.   The eggs are large (10 by 30 mm.) and enclosed in a horny shell that may attach to seaweeds.   Growth to the adult form is direct, without a larval stage.

26-16. Relations to man.   Larval lampreys serve as bait for both commercial and sport fishing, and adult sea lampreys are used to a small extent as food.   Hagfishes often damage fishes caught on lines or in nets.

Lampreys injure or destroy fishes by taking blood and causing secondary infections.

CLASSIFICATION

Class 1. †*OSTRACODERMI*. Ancient Jawless Vertebrates. Small; body usually depressed; covered usually with bony scales and these often fused as a shield covering the head; skull of bone or cartilage; nasal opening 1 (or 2); a pair of eyes and a pineal eye; paired gill slits numerous; median fins on tail and body; some with pectoral lobes behind head.   Ordovician to Devonian; mainly in fresh waters and on the bottom.   †*Cephalaspis;* †*Birkenia;* †*Pteraspis.*

Class 2. *CYCLOSTOMATA* (Marsipobranchii). Body cylindrical, elongate; skin smooth, without scales; mouth suctorial, with horny teeth; nasal aperture single and median; no jaws, paired appendages, or genital ducts; gill compartments 6 to 14 pairs, pouchlike; heart 2-chambered; aquatic.

Order 1. **Petromyzontia.** Lampreys. Mouth surrounded by a large ventral suctorial funnel with many horny teeth; nasal sac dorsal, not connected to mouth; 7 pairs of gill pouches, opening separately; "branchial basket" well developed; eggs small; a long larval stage; nearly world-wide along seacoasts and in streams and lakes. *Petromyzon marinus,* sea lamprey, Atlantic coast from Chesapeake Bay northward and in Europe, grows to 3 feet, spawns in fresh water, landlocked in Finger Lakes, N.Y., Lake Ontario, and spreading westward; *Entosphenus tridentatus,* Pacific lamprey of western shores, routhern California to Alaska, spawns in fresh water; *E. amottenii* and others, brook lampreys, nonparasitic, eastern and middle-western states; *Ichthyomyzon,* brook lamprey, central United States and Canada.

Order 2. **Myxinoidia.** Slime Eels and Hagfishes. Mouth nearly terminal, with 4 pairs of tentacles about margin, no buccal funnel, few teeth; nasal sac near end of head, with a duct to pharynx; eyes beneath skin; gill pores 10 to 14 pairs; "branchial basket" and arcualia poorly developed; eggs large, development direct; marine. *Myxine limosa,* slime eel, Cape Cod northward on the Atlantic coast; *M. glutinosa,* Europe, to 3 feet long; *Bdellostoma,* Chile; *Polistotrema (Eptatretus),* "the borer," Lower California to Alaska.

References

(See also Chap. 28)

Gage, S. H. 1893. The lake and brook lampreys of New York. . . . Ithaca, N.Y., Wilder Quarter-Century Book. Pp. 421–493, 8 pls. Structure, function, and natural history; includes the landlocked form of the sea lamprey.

Hubbs, C. L. 1924. The life-cycle and growth of lampreys. *Michigan Academy of Science, Arts and Letters, Papers,* vol. 4, pp. 587–603, figs. 16–22.

———— and M. B. Trautman. 1937. A revision of the genus *Ichthyomyzon. University of Michigan, Museum of Zoology, Miscellaneous Publications,* No. 35, 109 pp., 2 pls., 5 figs.

Reynolds, T. E. 1931. Hydrostatics of the suctorial mouth of the lamprey. *University of California Publications in Zoology,* vol. 37, pp. 15–34, 3 pls., 2 figs. Anatomy and function of the head region.

Romer, A. S. 1945. Vertebrate paleontology. 2d ed. Chicago, University of Chicago Press. ix + 687 pp., 377 figs.

CHAPTER 27

CLASS CHONDRICHTHYES. CARTILAGINOUS FISHES

The sharks, rays, and chimaeras of the Class CHONDRICHTHYES (Gr. *chondros*, cartilage + *ichthys*, fish) are the lowest living vertebrates with complete and separate vertebrae, movable jaws, and paired appendages.

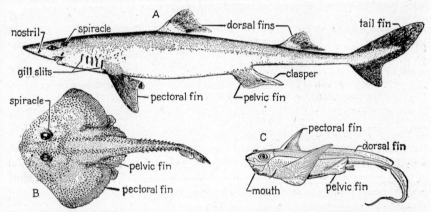

FIG. 27-1. Class CHONDRICHTHYES. *A*. Spiny dogfish or shark (*Squalus acanthias*). *B*. Ray (*Raja*). *C*. Chimaera (*Chimaera colliei*). (*A, after Goode; B, after General Biological Supply House; C, after Dean, Fishes living and fossil, The Macmillan Co.*)

All are predaceous, and practically all are ocean dwellers. The group dates from Silurian time and is represented by many fossil remains, especially teeth, fin spines, and scales. The shark is of especial biological interest, because some of its basic anatomical features appear in early embryos of the higher vertebrates.

27-1. Characteristics. 1. Skin tough, covered with minute placoid scales and having many mucous glands; both median and paired fins present, all supported by fin rays; pelvic fins with "claspers" in males.

2. Mouth ventral, with many enamel-capped teeth; olfactory sacs 2 (or 1), not connected to mouth cavity; both lower and upper jaws present; intestine with spiral valve.

3. Skeleton cartilaginous, no true bone; cranium joined by paired sense capsules; notochord persistent; vertebrae many, complete, and separate.

4. Heart 2-chambered (1 auricle, 1 ventricle), with sinus venosus and conus arteriosus, contains only venous blood; several pairs of aortic arches; red blood cells nucleated and oval.

5. Respiration by 5 to 7 pairs of gills, each in separate cleft (3 pairs in chimaeras).

6. Ten pairs of cranial nerves.

7. Body temperature variable (poikilothermous), dependent upon environment.

8. Sexes separate; gonads typically paired; reproductive ducts discharge into cloaca; fertilization internal; oviparous or ovoviviparous; eggs large, with much yolk, segmentation meroblastic; no embryonic membranes; development direct, no metamorphosis.

The cartilaginous fishes show advances over the cyclostomes in having (1) scales covering the body; (2) two pairs of lateral fins; (3) movable jaws articulated to the cranium; (4) enamel-covered teeth on the jaws; (5) three semicircular canals in each ear; and (6) paired reproductive organs and ducts. They stand below the bony fishes in having (1) the skeleton of cartilage, with no true bone; (2) placoid scales; (3) separate gill clefts; (4) a pair of spiracles connecting to pharynx; and (5) no air bladder.

FIG. 27-2. Possible origin of the fins on fishes from fin folds such as those on amphioxus. Compare Fig. 25-11. (*After Wiedersheim.*)

Several theories have been proposed on the origin of paired fins in fishes. The gill-arch theory of Gegenbaur sought derivation from gill structures—the girdles from gill arches, fin folds from gill flaps, and fin skeletons from gill rays, with backward migration of the pelvic girdle and fins; but there is little to support this theory. That of Balfour and others would derive the paired fins from lengthwise lateroventral fin folds supported by parallel fin rays (Fig. 27-2). As supporting evidence, (1) Amphioxus has such continuous (metapleural) folds joining the ventral caudal fin; (2) a small Devonian fish, †*Climatius*, had five accessory finlets between the pectoral and pelvic fins on each side; (3) †*Cladoselache*, a late Devonian shark, had paired fins with expanded bases supported by many parallel rays; and (4) embryos of some living sharks (*Scyllium*) have lateral skin folds preceding appearance of the paired fins. Other evidence from embryology, anatomy, and paleontology supports the latter theory.

27-2. Size. Dogfishes (*Squalus*) grow to about 3 feet in length and most sharks are under 8 feet long; however, both the great white shark (*Carcharodon carcharias*) and the basking shark (*Cetorhinus maximus*) may exceed 40 feet; and the whale shark (*Rhineodon typus*) reaches 50 feet in length. These are the biggest living vertebrates except whales. Most rays are 1 to 3 feet in length, but the greater devilfish (*Manta birostris*) grows to 17 feet in length and 20 feet across the pectoral fins. The chimaeras are less than 3 feet long.

STRUCTURE OF A DOGFISH, OR DOG SHARK

27-3. External features. The *head* is bluntly pointed, and the *trunk* is spindle-shaped, largest near the pectoral fins, and tapering behind.

There are two separate median *dorsal fins* (each preceded by a spine in the spiny dogfish, *Squalus*), a median *caudal fin,* and two pairs of *lateral fins, pectoral* and *pelvic.* Between the latter on males is a pair of elongated *claspers,* used in mating. The smooth dogfish (*Mustelus*) has also a median *anal fin* ventrally. The *tail* is heterocercal, with the vertebrae extending into the larger dorsal lobe.

Ventrally on the head are two *olfactory sacs* and the wide transverse *mouth;* the *eyes* are lateral and without lids. Five oval *gill slits* open anterior to each pectoral fin and a gill-like cleft, or *spiracle,* behind each eye. The *anus* is between the pelvic fins.

27-4. Integument. The gray-colored *skin* is evenly covered with diagonal rows of minute *placoid scales* (Fig. 27-3), each with a backward

Fig. 27-3. Placoid scales (enlarged). *A.* Skin with scales in surface view. *B.* Median section through a scale. (*After Klaatsch.*)

pointing spine covered by enamel (vitro-dentine) and a basal plate of dentine in the dermis. At the mouth a gradual transition from scales to teeth occurs, indicating the probable origin of vertebrate teeth.

27-5. Skeleton. The entire *skeleton* is of cartilage (gristle) more or less reinforced with limy deposits; the axial parts are the *skull* and the segmented *vertebral column.* Each *vertebra* has a spool-shaped centrum, concave on both ends (amphicoelous), and above this a neural arch to house the nerve cord; in the tail, each also bears ventrally a hemal arch shielding the caudal aorta and vein; the notochord persists in the spaces between vertebrae. The skull is made up of (1) the cranium housing the brain; (2) paired capsules for the olfactory, optic, and auditory organs; and (3) the visceral skeleton, consisting of the jaws, the hyoid arch, and five pairs of branchial arches supporting the gill region. The *appendicular skeleton* includes (1) the U-shaped *pectoral girdle* supporting the pectoral fins; (2) the flatter *pelvic girdle* to which the pelvic fins attach; and (3) the many small jointed cartilages within and supporting each lateral fin. The median fins are supported by dermal *fin rays.*

27-6. Muscular system. The body and tail *muscles* are of segmental character and serve to produce the lateral undulations of the trunk and

tail necessary for swimming.   More specialized muscles serve the paired
fins, gill region, and structures of the head.

27-7. Digestive system.   The broad *mouth* is margined with transverse rows of sharply pointed *teeth;* these are embedded in flesh on the
jaws and frequently replaced by new rows of teeth from behind.   The
teeth serve to grasp prey such as small fishes, which are often swallowed
entire.   A flat *tongue* adheres to the floor of the mouth.   On the sides of
the wide *pharynx* are openings leading to the separate *gill slits* and
spiracles.   The short *esophagus* leads to the J-shaped *stomach,* which
ends at a circular sphincter muscle, the pyloric valve.   The *intestine*
follows and connects directly to the *cloaca*
and *anus.*   In the intestine is a spirally arranged partition, or *spiral valve,* covered
with mucous membrane, that delays the passage of food and offers increased area for absorption (Fig. 27-4).   The large *liver* is of
two long lobes, attached at the anterior end
of the body cavity.   Bile from the liver collects in the greenish *gall bladder* and thence
passes through the *bile duct* to the anterior

Fig. 27-4.   Intestine of dogfish opened to show spiral
valve.   (*After Jammes.*)

part of the intestine.   The *pancreas* lies between the stomach and intestine, its duct joining the latter just below the bile duct.   An elongate
rectal gland, of unknown function, attaches dorsally at the junction of the
intestine and cloaca.

27-8. Coelom.   The stomach, intestine, and other internal organs lie in
the large *body cavity,* or *coelom.*   It is lined with a smooth glistening
membrane, the *peritoneum,* which also covers the organs.   The latter are
supported from the middorsal wall of the coelom by thin *mesenteries,* also
formed of peritoneum.   A transverse *septum* separates the coelom from
the cavity containing the heart.

27-9. Circulatory system.   The *heart* lies beneath the gill region in a
sac, the pericardium; it consists of (1) a thin-walled sinus venosus that
receives blood from various veins, followed by (2) the auricle, (3) the
thick-walled ventricle, and (4) the conus arteriosus.   From the latter,
blood passes anteriorly into the *ventral aorta,* whence five pairs of
afferent branchial arteries distribute to capillaries in the gills for aeration;
four pairs of *efferent branchial arteries* then collect the blood into the
dorsal aorta, which extends along the middorsal wall of the coelom.   The
principal *arteries* are (1) paired external and internal carotids to the head;
(2) paired subclavians to the pectoral fins; (3) coelic to the stomach,
liver, and intestine; (4) anterior mesenteric to the spleen and hind part of
intestine; (5) posterior mesenteric to the rectal gland; (6) several renal and
gonadic (ovarian or spermatic) to the kidneys and reproductive organs;

FIG. 27-5. Spiny dogfish; internal structure.

and (7) paired iliacs to the pelvic fins.   Beyond the latter the caudal
aorta continues in the tail.

In the *venous system,* blood in the caudal vein from the tail passes in
(1) paired renal portal veins to the kidneys.   Other blood from the posterior regions passes forward in (2) the paired postcardinal veins paralleling the kidneys and in (3) paired lateral abdominal veins on either side
of the body cavity.   Paired (4) jugular and (5) anterior cardinal veins
return blood from the head region.   All these veins enter large sinuses
connected to the sinus venosus.   Blood from the digestive tract flows in
(6) the hepatic portal vein to be filtered through capillary-like sinusoids
in the liver, then is collected in (7) the hepatic veins connected to the sinus
venosus.   The blood passes through the heart but once in each circuit
of the body, as in cyclostomes and most fishes, and the heart blood is all
venous (unoxygenated).

27-10. Respiratory system.   By opening and closing the mouth the
shark draws water in and forces it out the gill clefts and spiracles (Fig.
28-6).   The *gills* lining the five pairs of separate clefts (and the spiracles)
are composed of numerous parallel slender filaments that contain capillaries.   The blood from the ventral aorta passes through these capillaries,
discharges carbon dioxide and absorbs oxygen dissolved in the water, and
then continues into the dorsal aorta.

27-11. Excretory system.   The two slender *kidneys* (mesonephroi) lie
immediately above the coelom on either side of the dorsal aorta.   Urine
from each is collected in a series of segmental tubules that join a longitudinal duct, the *ureter,* leading posteriorly, the two emptying through a
single *urogenital papilla* dorsally placed in the cloaca.

27-12. Nervous system.   The shark's *brain* (Fig. 27-6) is of a more
advanced type than that of the lamprey.   From the two olfactory sacs in

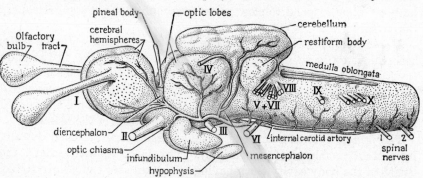

Fig. 27-6.   Brain and nerves of the spiny dogfish from the left side.   I–X, cranial nerves;
1, 2, spinal nerves.

the snout, the large olfactory tracts extend to the *olfactory lobes,* which
attach closely to the paired *cerebral hemispheres* on the *diencephalon.*

Dorsally the latter bears a pineal stalk and *pineal body* and ventrally the *infundibulum* to which is attached the *hypophysis.* All of these structures are part of the forebrain. Two rounded *optic lobes* lie dorsally on the midbrain. The hindbrain comprises the large median dorsal *cerebellum* over the open-topped *medulla oblongata.* Ten pairs of *cranial nerves* serve structures, chiefly of the head, in approximately the same distribution as among other vertebrates (Table 4-7). The spinal *nerve cord* is fully protected by the neural arches of the vertebrae, an advance over the condition in cyclostomes. Paired *spinal nerves* to each body somite emerge between the neural arches of successive vertebrae.

27-13. Sense organs. Sharks depend importantly on olfactory stimuli received from water passing through the two shallow *olfactory sacs* on the snout. The *eyes* are capable of movement by three pairs of muscles attaching the eyeball to the eye socket. The *ears* are entirely within the head and serve the two distinct functions of (1) receiving sound impressions and (2) orientation. There are three semicircular canals at right angles to each other, as in all higher vertebrates. A slender endolymphatic duct extends from each ear to a small opening on the dorsal surface of the head.

The *lateral line* is a slight groove extending along each side of the body and tail. It contains a minute longitudinal canal with numerous transverse openings to the surface. Within the canal are sensory hair cells, segmentally arranged and connected to the lateralis branch of the tenth cranial nerve. On the surface of the head are many *sensory canals* opening in *pores* and containing *pit organs* (neuromasts), with sensory hairs surrounded by groups of supporting cells and connected to sensory nerve fibers. All these structures are derived, embryologically, from the auditory organ and are equivalent to the inner ear of higher vertebrates. They respond to slow pressure stimuli of waves and currents in the water.

27-14. Reproductive system. The sexes are separate. In the *male,* sperm develop in two elongate *testes* placed well anterior in the body cavity; from each testis several *vasa efferentia* lead to a much convoluted *vas deferens* running posteriorly on the ventral surface of the kidney and emptying into the urogenital papilla. At mating, sperm are transferred from the male, by aid of the claspers, into the cloaca of the female.

The *female* system comprises a single large *ovary* attached dorsally by a stout membrane (mesovarium). Two large *oviducts* extend the length of the body cavity, each having at the anterior end a large funnel through which the eggs enter from the body cavity. The anterior portion of each duct is dilated as a *shell gland,* and oviviviparous species like the dogfish have the posterior part enlarged as a *"uterus"* to contain the young during development. The oviducts open separately into the cloaca.

27-15. Other cartilaginous fishes.   Most other sharks resemble the dogfish in general anatomy.   The rays have depressed bodies, flattened dorsoventrally, and the pectoral fins are greatly expanded and broadly joined to the head and trunk so that these fishes are diamond- or disc-shaped in outline from above.   The gill openings are on the flat ventral surface, and the spiracles serve for entry of the respiratory currents of water.   The tail is slender and elongate.   The chimaeras are grotesque appearing fishes.   Their skin is scaleless, the 4 gill slits on either side are covered by a membraneous operculum, and the teeth are fused.

27-16. Natural history.   The cartilaginous fishes inhabit the open sea, shore waters, and bays; a few sharks and rays inhabit rivers above salt water.   Most sharks live in open water and rays on the bottom but the manta and other large rays swim at or near the surface.   Sharks and rays are most numerous in tropical waters, as to both species and individuals, and few penetrate the polar seas.   Small dogfishes and rays are common along all coasts, but the large species may be encountered only rarely.   Some tropical sharks and rays live permanently in fresh waters.

These fishes are all predaceous.   Sharks are active swimmers, seeking prey appropriate to their size, and are usually common about large schools of fishes.   The largest predaceous sharks may capture seals or sea lions, but the big basking and whale sharks feed upon plankton.   The bottom-dwelling rays feed chiefly upon various invertebrates.

27-17. Reproduction.   Fertilization is internal by use of the claspers.   The large eggs undergo meroblastic segmentation and develop slowly (16 to 25 months in the dogfish; 9 to 12 months in chimaera). The primitive heterodont sharks, some dogfishes and rays, and the chimaeras are oviparous, depositing each egg in a brown horny capsule ("mermaid purse") of distinctive shape; some cases have tendrils that affix to seaweeds.   Most of the sharks, dogfishes, and rays, however, are ovoviviparous, retaining the eggs for development internally and giving birth to living young.   The walls of the "uterus" (oviduct) in the female produce numerous loops of blood vessels that lie against the yolk sac of the embryo and provide for the respiration of the latter.   In *Mustelus* a "placenta" forms when the yolk is nearly exhausted, the

SHARK   RAY

A

B

Fig.   27-7.   The   swimming   of cartilaginous fishes.   *A*. Shark (dorsal view) swims by lateral undulations of the trunk and tail.   *B*. Ray (lateral view) swims by flapping movements of the pectoral fins. (*After Marey*.)

embryonic and maternal blood vessels coming close together to transfer nutrients as well. When hatched or born, the young of all sharks and rays resemble their parents, and there is no metamorphosis.

27-18. Relations to man. Sharks are a nuisance to fishermen because they tear nets and steal netted fishes or remove bait or fishes from hooks. Large sharks may capsize or injure fishermen in small boats, and some tropical and subtropical species menace bathers in the sea and large rivers. The great white shark (*Carcharodon carcharias*) has made many attacks on human beings in Australian waters, half of 40 known attacks in New South Wales having been fatal. In north temperate waters, instances of attack by sharks are scarce, but occasional human deaths result from injuries by the spines of sting rays.

Sharks and rays serve mankind as food in the United States and elsewhere. Shark fins are gathered and dried in Ceylon, the Philippines, and California for use in China; they are boiled and yield a gelatinous material favored for soups. Sharkskin tanned with the scales in place (then termed "shagreen") was used in the Old World for casing fine books and jewel boxes, as covering for scabbards and sword handles (affording a firm grip!), and as a sandpaper-like abrasive for polishing wood and ivory. With the scales crushed, the skins make acceptable leather for shoes and bags.

Shark livers yield large quantities of oil, and fisheries for this product have existed for years in Greenland, Iceland, and Norway; a large basking shark yields about 125 gallons of oil. Recently, the oil has been found to contain large amounts of vitamin A, and quantities of sharks have been caught to obtain this material.

27-19. Fossil forms. Earliest of known fossil vertebrates with jaws are the †Placodermi of Silurian to Permian time. The jaws were primitive, and the hyoid unspecialized and followed by a complete gill slit. The latter, in higher Classes, is a spiracle or an ear opening or is closed. Most placoderms had an operculum covering the gills that was developed from the mandibular arch. There were both median and paired fins, but the latter were more variable in number than in later fishes. The first Chondrichthyes appear in mid-Devonian rocks (later than the first bony fishes) but already were well advanced in evolution of the jaws. No true bone is recognized in any shark, fossil or living, and the cartilaginous skeleton seems more likely a degenerate rather than primitive character. Some early types inhabited fresh waters, but the group has been predominantly marine; they were abundant and often well armored in the Paleozoic era but later decreased in numbers and had less armor.

Classification

Class 1. †*PLACODERMI* (Aphetohyoidea). Ancient Fishes. A full-sized functional gill cleft anterior to the unspecialized hyoid arch.

Order 1.   †**Acanthodii.**   A few inches in length; body armored with small diamond-shaped bonelike scales (ganoid-like); each fin except caudal preceded by a spine. Upper Silurian to Permian.   †*Climatius,* †*Acanthodes.*

Order 2.   †**Arthrodira.**   JOINT-NECKED FISHES.   Bony armor of two parts, head and gill region jointed to that of body.   Mainly Devonian.   †*Coccosteus,* †*Dinichthys.*

Order 3.   †**Antiarchii.**   Posterior trunk and tail fishlike, anterior trunk and head each with armor box; fresh water.   Devonian.   †*Pterichthyodes.*

Order 4.   †**Stegoselachii.**   ARMORED SHARKS.   Body covered with bony plates; some of skatelike body form; marine.   Devonian.   †*Gemuendina.*

Class   2.   *CHONDRICHTHYES* (Elasmobranchii).   CARTILAGINOUS FISHES. Living forms with skeleton of cartilage; first gill slit a spiracle; scales minute, placoid; mouth and 2 nasal pits ventral; males with claspers; ova large, much yolk, cleavage meroblastic.

Order 1.   †**Cladoselachii.**   Fins broad at base; no claspers.   Devonian to early Permian.   †*Cladoselache.*

Order 2.   †**Pleuracanthodii.**   Dorsal fin along most of body and tail; fresh water. Late Devonian to Triassic.   †*Pleuracanthus.*

Order 3.   **Selachii.**   SHARKS AND RAYS.   Gills in separate clefts at sides of pharynx; a spiracle opening behind each eye; cloaca present; marine, in open seas, shore waters, and bays.

Suborder 1.   SQUALI (Pleurotremata).   SHARKS.   Body typically spindle-shaped; tail heterocercal; gill slits lateral, 5 to 7 pairs; pectoral fins never greatly enlarged; 1st dorsal fin anterior to pelvics; swim by use of tail.   Carboniferous to Recent. *Chlamydoselachus,* frilled shark, 6 pairs of gill slits; *Heterodontus,* Port Jackson shark, primitive; *Mustelus,* smooth dogfish, to 3 feet long; *Carcharias,* gray shark; *Sphyrna,* hammerhead, to 15 feet long, a large eye-bearing lobe at each side of head; *Rhineodon typus,* whale shark, to 50 feet long, harmless, feeds on plankton sieved from water by gill rakers in pharynx; *Alopias,* thresher shark, large, tail long; *Lamnia nasus,* porbeagle, to 10 feet long, sometimes in groups, eats various fishes; *Cetorhinus maximus,* basking shark, to 40 feet long, feeds like whale shark; *Squalus (Acanthias),* spiny dogfishes, to 3 or 4 feet long, predaceous, common in shore waters; *Squatina,* angel shark, resembles rays but swims with tail, lives on bottom and eats flatfishes, mollusks, and crustaceans; *Pristiophorus* (gill slits, 5 pairs) and *Pliotrema* (6 pairs), saw sharks, resemble *Pristis* but gill slits lateral.

Suborder 2.   BATOIDEA (Raji, Hypotremata).   RAYS.   Body depressed; pectoral fins enlarged and joined to sides of head and body; gill slits ventral, 5 pairs; spiracle highly functional; swim by flapping pectoral fins.   Triassic to Recent; chiefly on bottom in shore waters, some down to 9,000 feet.   *Pristis,* sawfish, to 20 feet long, snout elongate with toothlike scales at sides, used to disable prey; *Rhinobatos,* guitar fish, somewhat sharklike; *Raja,* common rays and skates; *Torpedo,* electric rays, pectoral fins rounded, with many dorsal muscle cells modified as an electric organ producing severe shocks and used to stun prey; *Dasyatis, Urobatis, Aëtobatus,* sting rays, small, tail slender and whiplike, with 1 to 3 saw-edged spines containing poison glands that produce ugly, slow-healing wounds, sometimes complicated by gangrene or tetanus, on bathers and fishermen; *Manta,* manta, or "devilfish," size huge, swims at or near surface.

Order 4.   †**Bradodonti.**   Teeth as crushing plates.   Devonian to Permian.   †*Cochliodus;* †*Psammodus.*

Order 5.   **Holocephali.**   CHIMAERAS.   Gill slits covered by operculum; no cloaca or spiracles; 1st dorsal fin far forward with strong spine; tail slender, whiplike; each jaw with large tooth plate; adults scaleless.   Triassic to Recent.   In cold ocean waters, down to 6,000 feet; 3 genera, 25 species. *Hydrolagus (Chimaera) colliei*, in North Pacific, from California northward, eats fish, invertebrates, and seaweed.

References

(See also Chap. 28)

Bigelow, H. B., and W. C. Schroeder. 1948. Sharks. *In* Fishes of the western North Atlantic. New Haven, Yale University, Sears Foundation for Marine Research, Part 1, pp. 59–576, figs. 6–106.

Daniel, J. F. 1934. The elasmobranch fishes. 3d ed. Berkeley, University of California Press. xii + 332 pp., 270 figs.

Dean, Bashford. 1906. The chimaeroid fishes and their development. *Carnegie Institution of Washington, Publication No.* 32, 194 pp., 11 pls., 144 figs.

Garman, S. 1911. The chismopnea [chimaeroids]. *Museum of Comparative Zoology, Memoirs,* vol. 40, pp. 79–101.

———. 1913. The Plagiostoma [cartilaginous fishes]. *Museum of Comparative Zoology, Memoirs,* vol. 36 (2 parts), xiii + 528 pp., 77 pls. Keys and descriptions; nomenclature somewhat out of date.

Goodrich, E. S. 1909. Chondrichthyes. *In* R. Lankester, Treatise on zoology. London, A. & C. Black, Ltd., part 9, pp. 118–187, figs. 79–155.

Moy-Thomas, J. A. 1939. Palaeozoic fishes. New York, Chemical Publishing Co. ix + 149 pp., illus.

Watson, D. M. S. 1937. The acanthodian fishes. *Royal Society of London, Philosophical Transactions, B,* vol. 228, pp. 49–136, pls. 5–14, figs. 1–25.

CHAPTER 28

CLASS OSTEICHTHYES. BONY FISHES

Many kinds of animals that live in water are called "fishes," from jellyfishes to starfishes, but the word applies properly to the lower aquatic vertebrates. The Greeks knew the fishes as *ichthyes*, and ichthyology is the scientific study of fishes; the common name fish derives from the Latin, *pisces*. The most typical or bony fishes have bony skeletons, are covered by dermal scales, usually have spindle-shaped bodies, swim by fins, and breathe by gills. Various species inhabit all sorts of waters, fresh, brackish, or salt, warm or cold. Fishes have been a staple protein food of mankind since antiquity, and many species provide pleasant recreation for sports fishermen.

28-1. Characteristics. 1. Skin often delicate, with many mucous glands and usually with embedded dermal scales (ganoid, cycloid, or ctenoid); some naked (scaleless), a few with enamel-covered scales; both median and paired fins present (some exceptions), supported by fin rays of cartilage or bone; no limbs.

2. Mouth usually terminal and with teeth; jaws well-developed, articulated to skull; olfactory sacs 2, dorsal, usually not connected to mouth cavity; eyes large, no lids.

3. Skeleton chiefly of bone (cartilage in sturgeons and some others); vertebrae many, distinct; tail usually homocercal; relics of notochord often persist.

4. Heart 2-chambered (1 auricle, 1 ventricle) with sinus venosus and conus arteriosus, contains only venous blood; 4 pairs of aortic arches; red blood cells nucleated and oval.

5. Respiration by pairs of gills on bony gill arches in a common chamber at each side of pharynx, covered by an operculum; usually with an air (swim) bladder, sometimes with duct to the pharynx, and lunglike in DIPNOI and some others.

6. Ten pairs of cranial nerves.

7. Body temperature variable, dependent upon environment (higher in tunas).

8. Gonads typically paired; usually oviparous (some ovoviviparous or viviparous); fertilization external (some exceptions), eggs minute to 12 mm., yolk various in amount; segmentation usually meroblastic; no embryonic membranes; early young sometimes (post larvae) quite unlike adults.

The bony fishes are notable for their bony skeletons, scales, and plates, for the swim bladder, and for advances in the structure of the brain. The tail usually is altered from the heterocercal type of sharks to the homocercal and diphycercal forms (Fig. 28-11). Most modern fishes have less bony armor in the scales than did ancient types, many of which were fully armored (with cosmoid or ganoid scales). The head is encased in a true skull comprised of both cartilage or replacement bones and membrane or

591

dermal bones.   The fins in most bony fishes (Actinopterygii) are supported by numerous parallel dermal rays, but in crossopterygians each paired fin has a single stout central element or lobe (sometimes jointed) that articulates with the limb girdle; this possibly became the limb skeleton in land vertebrates (Fig. 9-3).   The swim bladder is lunglike in some bony fishes, and certain species have perforate nostrils and accessory structures that enable them to breathe air in shallow mucky water.

Fig. 28-1.   Representative bony fishes, of different bodily form.   *A.* Mackerel (*Scomber*), streamlined and fast-swimming.   *B.* Trunkfish (*Ostracion*), body rigid, only fins movable. *C.* Marine sunfish (*Mola*), huge, thin, deep-bodied.   *D.* Globefish (*Chilomycterus*), body spiny, swollen, fins small.   *E.* Sea horse (*Hippocampus*), swims erect by small dorsal fin, tail prehensile.   *F.* Common eel (*Anguilla*), long and highly flexible.   (*After Norman, History of fishes, Ernest Benn, Ltd.*)

28-2. Size.   Some top minnows are under 1 inch in length, and a Philippine goby (*Pandaka*) is only 10 mm. long.   Most fishes are under 3 feet in length.   Some record marine species are the halibut at 9 feet, the tuna at 10 feet, the ocean sunfish (*Mola*) at 11 feet, and the swordfish at 12 feet; the ribbonfish (*Regalecus*) grows to 20 feet long but has a narrow body.   The Columbia River sturgeon grows to $12\frac{1}{2}$ feet and 1,285 pounds, our largest fresh-water fish.

STRUCTURE OF A BONY FISH: THE YELLOW PERCH

28-3. External features (Fig. 28-2).   The body is spindle-shaped, higher than wide, and of oval cross section for easy passage through the water.   The **head** extends from the tip of the snout to the hind edge of the operculum, the **trunk** from this point to the anus, and the remainder is the **tail**.   The large **mouth** is terminal, with distinct jaws that bear fine teeth. Dorsally on the snout are two double **olfactory sacs** ("nostrils"), the **eyes** are lateral without lids, and behind each is a thin bony gill cover or **operculum,** with free edges below and posteriorly.   Under each operculum are four comblike **gills**.   The **anus** and **urogenital aperture** precede the anal fin.   Ichthyologists measure the standard length of a fish from the tip of the snout to the end of the last vertebra, to avoid error from wear of the tail fin; but fishermen include the fin.

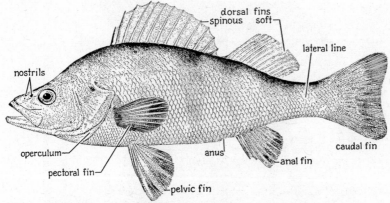

FIG. 28-2.   Yellow perch (*Perca flavescens*); external features.

On the back are two separate **dorsal fins,** on the end of the tail is the **caudal fin,** and ventrally on the tail is the **anal fin;** all these are median. The lateral or paired fins are the **pectoral fins** behind the opercula and the ventral or **pelvic fins** close below.   The fins are membranous extensions of the integument and supported by **fin rays.** All except the first dorsal are flexible, being supported by soft rays which are calcified but with many joints and usually branched.   The first dorsal has 13 to 15 solid calcified **spines,** and there are 1 or 2 similar spines in the anterior edge of the other fins.   The fins aid in maintaining equilibrium, in steering, and in swimming.

28-4. Integument (Fig. 28-4).   The entire body is covered by soft mucus-producing **epidermis** that facilitates easy movement in the water and is a protection against entry of disease organisms.   The trunk and tail bear thin rounded dermal **scales,** in lengthwise and diagonal rows, with their free posterior edges overlapping like shingles on a roof; each lies in a dermal pocket and grows throughout life.   The **lateral line,** along either side of the body, is a row of small pores connected to a lengthwise tubular canal under the scales, in which are sensory organs responsive to slow coarse vibrations in the water.

FIG. 28-3. Yellow perch; general structure. Operculum, pectoral fin, most of the skin and scales, and some trunk and tail muscles have been removed.

28-5. Skeleton.   The scales and fins constitute an exoskeleton.   The endoskeleton consists of the skull, vertebral column, ribs, pectoral girdle, and many small accessory bones (pterygiophores) supporting the fin rays.

The *skull* comprises the *cranium* housing the brain, the *capsules* for the paired organs of special sense (olfactory, optic, auditory), and the *visceral skeleton,* which provides the jaws and the supports for the tongue and gill mechanism.   The skull is so closely affixed to the vertebral column that a fish cannot "turn its head."   *Teeth* are usually present on the premaxillary, dentary, vomer, and palatine bones.

The cranium is composed of cartilage in the embryos and young of bony fishes, as in adult sharks and rays.   Later, this is largely replaced

Fig. 28-4.   Body wall of a bony fish (carp) near the lateral line, showing relations of the epidermis, scales and muscles.   (*Modified from Lankester, Treatise on zoology, A. & C. Black, Ltd.*)

by separate *cartilage bones.*   To these are added many *membrane bones* that result from ossifications in the embryonic connective tissue.   Their origin is explained as follows.   Sharks and rays are closely covered by small placoid scales (dermal denticles) that have bases of bone or dentine; some of these invade the mouth to become teeth, even on the gill bars.   Comparable denticles, as bony plates, cover the head in fossil Ostracodermi.   Bony fishes (and the Tetrapoda) have plates covering the head, originally of the same origin and histologic structure as scales. In more ancient fishes these are complex ("cosmoid" structure); the later fishes presumably lost the outer layers, leaving the bone beneath as membrane bone.

The visceral skeleton comprises seven paired *arches,* first of cartilage and later ossified; these correspond to the arches of sharks and rays, but not to the branchial basket of lampreys.   The upper part (palatoquadrate) of the *mandibular arch* (No. 1) attaches to the cranium, and each half of the upper jaw is formed of two membrane bones (premaxillary and maxillary).   The primitive *lower jaw* (Meckel's cartilage) on each side is supplied with three bones, the dentary, angular, and articular, the latter hinging on the quadrate which attaches to the cranium. The *hyoid arch* (No. 2) is in part a support for the tongue. Four *gill arches* (Nos. 3 to 6) each bear a gill on the outer curvature and a row of small spiny gill rakers on the inner or pharyngeal border; the gill rakers comprise a sieve to prevent escape of food and to protect the gills from injury by large particles. The small last arch (No. 7) has small pharyngeal teeth but no gill.

The adult skull in bony fishes is complex, of about 40 named bones (many paired). Land vertebrates have in the course of time lost various of these and much of the visceral skeleton, with resultant simplification of the skull.

The vertebral column in the perch is composed of many similar and separate *vertebrae;* each consists of (1) a cylindrical *centrum,* concave on both ends (amphicoelous); (2) a small dorsal *neural arch* to contain the spinal cord; above this (3) a slender elongate *neural spine* for muscular attachments; and (4) paired *parapophyses,* laterally on the centrum. Each caudal vertebra (behind the anus) has also (5) a ventral or *hemal arch,* around the caudal artery and vein, and (6) a slender *hemal spine* below (Fig. 4-3). The column ends in an expanded (hypural) bone supporting the tail fin. The vertebrae are bound together by ligaments, and between the centra are relics of the notochord.

Slender paired riblike bones attach to each trunk vertebra and delicate *intramuscular bones* (epipleurals) extend lengthwise between some of the ribs. In the flesh between the spines of the vertebrae are interspinal bones (pterygiophores) that support and articulate the dorsal and anal fin rays.

Each half of the *pectoral girdle* is of several bones (scapular, coracoid, clavicle, etc.), articulated dorsally to the skull and providing attachment for muscles of the pectoral fins. Four short bones with expanded tips (actinosts) and several nodules of cartilage (distal pterygiophores) articulate between the pectoral girdle and rays of each pectoral fin. There is no pelvic girdle; the ventral (pelvic) fins attach to a pubic bone (basipterygium, possibly of fused pterygiophores) having a tendon or ligament to the pectoral girdle but no connection to the vertebral column.

28-6. Muscular system. The substance of the trunk and tail consists chiefly of *segmental muscles* (myotomes), alternating with the vertebrae, that produce the swimming and turning movements. Fish myotomes are broadly $\gtrless$-shaped, in four principal bands, and heaviest along the back. Between successive myotomes are delicate connective tissue septa; when a fish is cooked, these dissolve to leave the myotomes as individual "flakes." The muscles of the fins, gill region, and head are small.

28-7. Digestive system. The large **mouth** has many small conical *teeth* that hold slippery food but are not used for chewing. Mucous glands are numerous, but there are no salivary glands. The small *tongue* is attached to the floor of the mouth cavity and may aid in respiratory movements. The *pharynx* follows, with gills on the sides, and then a short gullet or *esophagus* that leads to the recurved *stomach.* A constriction, the *pyloric valve,* separates the stomach and intestine. Three short tubular *pyloric caeca* attach to the intestine here; their function may be either secretory or absorptive. The *intestine* is the principal area for absorption of digested food; it is short, slightly coiled, and leads to the *anus,* through which undigested food residues pass. The large *liver* lies anteriorly in the body cavity; bile formed within it passes to the *gall bladder* and thence by the bile duct to the intestine. The *pancreas* is usually indistinct. Organs in the body cavity are often surrounded by masses of fat.

28-8. Circulatory system. The two-chambered *heart* lies below the pharynx in the *pericardial cavity,* an anterior portion of the coelom. Venous blood passes into the *sinus venosus,* to the thin-walled *auricle,* thence into the muscular *ventricle,* all separated by valves that prevent reverse flow. Rhythmic contractions of the ventricle force the blood through the *conus arteriosus* and short *ventral aorta* into four pairs of *afferent branchial arteries* distributing to capillaries in the gill filaments. After oxygenation there it collects in correspondingly paired *efferent branchial arteries* leading to the *dorsal aorta,* which distributes branches to all parts of the head and body. The principal *veins* are the paired anterior cardinals and posterior cardinals and the unpaired hepatic portal circulation leading through the liver. The *blood* of fishes is pale and scanty as compared with that of terrestrial vertebrates. The fluid blood plasma contains nucleated oval red cells (erythrocytes) and various types of white cells (leucocytes). The *spleen,* a part of the blood system, is a large red-colored gland near the stomach. A lymphatic system is also present.

28-9. Respiratory system (Figs. 28-5, 28-6). The perch respires by means of *gills,* of which there are four in a common gill chamber on each side of the pharynx, beneath the operculum. A gill consists of a double row of slender *gill filaments;* every filament bears many minute transverse plates covered with thin epithelium and containing capillaries between the afferent and efferent branchial arteries. Each gill is supported on a cartilaginous *gill arch,* and its inner border has expanded *gill rakers,* which protect against hard particles and keep food from passing out the gill slits. In "breathing," the opercula close against the body and the gill arches bulge laterally, whereupon water flows into the opened mouth; then the oral valve closes, the gill arches contract, the opercula lift, and the water is forced out over the filaments. Blood in the filaments gives up its carbon dioxide and absorbs oxygen from the water. The fish needs a constant supply of oxygen-bearing water and soon dies of asphyxiation

Fig. 28-5. Gills of a bony fish (carp). *A.* Gills in the gill chamber with operculum cut away. *B.* Part of a gill showing gill rakers and filaments, with path of blood in the latter; afferent vessels dark, efferent vessels light (in many fishes the gill rakers are slender). *C.* Portion of one filament with thin lamellae containing capillaries where blood is aerated. (*Partly after Goldschmidt, Ascaris, Prentice-Hall, Inc.*)

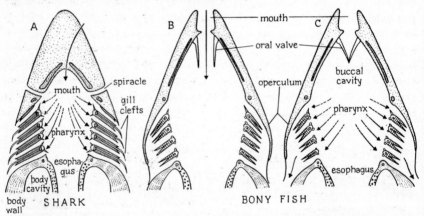

Fig. 28-6. The respiratory mechanism of fishes; diagrammatic frontal sections (lobes of oral valve actually are dorsal and ventral); arrows show paths of water currents. SHARK. *A.* Water enters ventrally placed mouth which then closes and floor of mouth region rises to force water over the gills and out the separate clefts. BONY FISH. *B.* Inhalent, opercula closed, oral valve open, cavity dilated, and water enters. *C.* Exhalent, oral valve closes, buccal cavity contracts, water passes over gills in common cavities at sides of pharynx and out beneath opercula. (*Modified from Boas.*)

if removed from water or if the water is depleted of oxygen. The phrase "to drink like a fish" is a misconception of the respiratory process, since a fish takes little or no fluid into its stomach except with food.

A large thin-walled sac, the **air bladder** or **swim bladder,** occupies the dorsal portion of the body cavity. It is connected to the pharynx by a pneumatic duct in some fishes, but not in the perch. The bladder is filled with gases (O, N, CO_2) and acts as a hydrostatic organ to adjust the specific gravity of the fish to that of the water at different depths. By secretion or absorption of the gases through blood vessels in the wall a fish makes this adjustment slowly as it moves from one depth to another; if a fish is suddenly hauled up from a considerable depth, the greater pressure within the air bladder may, upon reaching the surface, force the stomach out of the mouth.

28-10. Excretory system. The two slender dark *kidneys* lie dorsally between the air bladder and vertebrae. Fluid nitrogenous waste removed from the blood is carried posteriorly from each in a tubular *ureter,* both emptying into a *urinary bladder,* which in turn discharges through the *urogenital sinus* to the exterior.

28-11. Nervous system. The perch *brain* is short, the olfactory lobes, cerebral hemispheres, and diencephalon being smaller and the optic lobes and cerebellum larger than in a shark. There are 10 pairs of *cranial nerves.* The *nerve cord* is covered by the neural arches and gives off a pair of lateral *spinal nerves* to each body segment.

28-12. Organs of special sense. The dorsal *olfactory sacs* on the snout contain cells sensitive to substances dissolved in water. *Taste buds* are present in and around the mouth. The large *eyes* probably focus clearly only on near-by objects but serve to detect moving objects above water, such as a person walking on the bank. The internal *ear* contains three semicircular canals and an *otolith* serving the sense of equilibrium. Opinions differ as to the reactions of fishes to sound; any vibrations that are perceived must be transmitted through the head or body, since fishes have no eardrum or middle ear. The *lateral line system* (Fig. 28-7) has

FIG. 28-7. Body wall of carp in longitudinal section, showing the lateral line sensory system; compare Fig. 28-4. (*Modified from Lankester, Treatise on zoology, A. & C. Black, Ltd.*)

various extensions on the head and evidently detects slight changes in pressure or slow wave or current movements (not over 6 per second) such as might be experienced by a fish swimming close to some solid object from which water movements would be reflected; it is innervated by the lateralis branch of the tenth cranial nerve. This system is considered to survive in land vertebrates as the inner ear.

28-13. Reproductive system. In a *male* the two *testes* enlarge greatly in the breeding season, and at mating the "milt," or sperm, passes in a *vas deferens* from each to emerge from the urogenital aperture. In a *female* the eggs pass from the two united *ovaries* through the *oviducts.*

STRUCTURE OF OTHER BONY FISHES

All bony fishes are enough alike in general form and structure to be recognized as members of the Class OSTEICHTHYES, but they differ among themselves in many details. Many have the general configuration of the perch; the flounders, soles, and some tropical reef fishes are thin-bodied, the eels are slenderly elongate, and the porcupine fishes are globular.

28-14. Scales. Most fishes are covered with *scales* (Fig. 28-8). While usually thin and overlapping, the scales are separate and minute on

FIG. 28-8. Scales of bony fishes, enlarged. *A.* Ctenoid (with fine teeth). *B.* Cycloid. *C, D.* Ganoid (*Lepidosteus*) in surface view and vertical section.

eels, small and tubercle-like on some flounders, and slender spines on porcupine fishes. The overlapping scales of tarpon are up to 2 inches in width, whereas some fishes are scaleless or naked (catfish). The scales are usually bony. On the perch and many others the exposed hind part of each has many tiny spines, making a *ctenoid scale.* Others that lack such spines are termed *cycloid* scales, and still others have *ganoid* scales covered externally by enamel. The heads and bodies of various fishes, living and fossil, are armor-plated with large stout scales, as in the trunkfish; living species so protected are usually small or sluggish.

The scales grow throughout life, increasing in size with the fish. There is no molt of the body covering, although occasional scales may be lost and replaced. On many species growth results in a series of fine concentric ridges that end obliquely on the scale margin. After cessation of growth during winter, the first ridges of the next growth season form

Fig. 28-9.   Scale of 7-pound female rainbow trout, showing concentration of winter growth rings (numbered) which indicate age in years.   (*Enlarged photograph, courtesy of C. McC. Mottley.*)

parallel to the scale margin, making a definite "winter line" (Fig. 28-9). These features make age determination possible in salmon, trout, bass, and others. (Otoliths also yield age data in some fishes.) This provides important data on the rate of growth, age at spawning, and other features for some food and game fishes. The scale pattern is essentially constant in a species; thus, the structure, form, number, and arrangement of scales are of much value in classification.

28-15. Coloration. Bony fishes are variously colored by pigment cells, or **chromatophores,** in the dermis, either outside or beneath the scales. Pigments of black, yellow, orange, and red are present in different species. Combinations of these result in green (black + yellow), brown (red or yellow + black), and other colors. Opaque crystals of **guanine** in other cells (iridocytes) provide the bright silvery or chalky-white appearance on

Fig. 28-10.   Color changes in a flounder (*Rhomboidichthys podas*) some time after being placed on various types of backgrounds. (*After Sumner, from Guyer, Animal biology, Harper & Brothers.*)

various fishes. Interference phenomena, due probably to exceedingly thin layers of material over the pigments, are responsible for the prismatic hues and brilliant iridescence of some species.

Certain fishes change color by concentrating or spreading pigment in the chromatophores; this is slow in some but can be rapid in others. Flounders can simulate closely the sea bottom on which they rest, be it light or dark, uniform or spotty, and of sand, gravel, or other materials (Fig. 28-10). The stimulus to change is received through the eyes, as fish artificially blinded do not respond like normal ones. Some fishes, like brook trout, undergo little or no change in pattern or color but can alter in shade. Fishes living in the perennial darkness of the deep sea are often black.

28-16. Structure. The fins are diverse in form, size, and placement. The pectoral fins are usually near the gill apertures; the pelvics are on the abdomen in trout, near the gill openings on perch, on the throat, or

Fig. 28-11. Types of tails in bony fishes, showing relation of the vertebrae (or notochord) and radials to the caudal fin. *A.* Heterocercal (sturgeon, *Acipenser*). *B.* Abbreviate heterocercal (bowfin, *Amia*). *C.* Diphycercal, equal lobes (lung fish). The homocercal tail, common to many fishes, is shown in Fig. 28-3.

"jugular," in blennies, and lacking in eels. The dorsal fin may be single, multiple, or continuous along the back; salmonids and catfishes have besides the single dorsal, a small fleshy or adipose fin posteriorly. In the top minnow and other viviparous species the anterior part of the anal fin is modified as a copulatory organ (Fig. 28-25).

The skeleton is usually bony but remains partly cartilaginous in certain fishes and completely so in the sturgeon. Accessory skeletal bones are many in the shad and some others. Respiration by gills is the rule, but several species have accessory organs enabling them to breathe air. The air bladder becomes lunglike in the lungfishes (Dipnoi) and a few others. The pyloric caeca are numerous in the mackerels and salmon, few in the perch and others, and absent in the catfish. Salmonoids have no oviducts; the mature eggs discharge through *genital pores* connecting the body cavity to the urogenital sinus and so to the exterior.

NATURAL HISTORY

28-17. Distribution. Fishes occur from the polar seas to the equator, from the surface to depths of more than 12,000 feet and up to 14,000 feet in the Andes. They live variously in open water, on sandy or rocky or muddy bottoms, in the crannies of reefs, in saline bays and estuaries, in fresh or alkaline rivers and lakes, in cave waters, and even in hot springs. Some live only in cold waters of the Arctic, the ocean depths, or deep in lakes; others are restricted to shallow and warm tropical seas; and some minnows live in springs up to 93°F. on the American deserts. Trout thrive in waters at 55 to 70°F. in summer, but some can survive up to 83°F. Most fishes are limited by a temperature range of about 12 to 15°F., but carp and goldfish survive wider extremes. Indeed the carp, mud minnows, and some others will survive temporary freezing; and *Dallia* in Alaska experiences prolonged freezing in winter. Most fishes live either in fresh or in salt water, but sticklebacks and sculpins are at home in either sort, and various species migrate from salt water to fresh for spawning.

Some marine species range widely in the oceans, but most fishes are of restricted distribution, so that along the shores of the continents and in inland waters there are various "fish faunas" as with land animals. Thus of 223 species of bony fishes recorded at Woods Hole, Mass., 26 range predominantly to the north, 169 to the south, and only 28 both north and south of Cape Cod. Individuals may stray or be carried by ocean currents far beyond their normal range, so that stragglers of both arctic and tropical species appear at times on temperate coasts.

28-18. Migration. Many fishes, like birds, perform seasonal migrations. The barracuda and swordfish move north in spring and south in autumn, in a *latitudinal migration.* The salmon, shad, striped bass, and some trout travel from salt water to fresh for spawning and are termed *anadromous;* the fresh-water eel, which reverses this process, is said to be *catadromous.* Cod and herring of the ocean perform an *inshore* migration to spawn on banks or shoals. Some deep-water (bathypelagic) fishes have a daily *vertical* migration.

28-19. Habits. Direct observation of most fishes is seldom possible, so that information as to their habits is obtained chiefly by capturing them with hook and line or nets and sometimes with diving apparatus. Some are active at all hours and many are quiescent at night, but certain species are nocturnal. Tropical wrasses sleep on their sides under a sand blanket. Those of fresh-water streams habitually head against the current to maintain position, facilitate respiration, and catch food, as may be seen in a trout hatchery. Marine species are evidently active at all seasons, but many of those in fresh waters become inactive during the winter, descending to deeper water in lakes and rivers. Some fishes are of solitary habit, whereas others are gregarious and live in schools of various sizes, those of herring numbering a few thousands to many millions of individuals. The schools are often remarkably persistent, each individual retaining its place, save perhaps when feeding.

28-20. Locomotion. The majority of fishes swim by lateral undulations of the tail and tail fin, produced by alternate contractions of the metameric muscles on the two sides. The sidewise sweeps are pronounced in the swimming of an eel (as with a water snake), but of the same general character in most other fishes. The action of the tail and its fin is comparable to that of a man sculling a boat, with one oar at the stern moved from side to side. The other fins serve chiefly to maintain balance and change direction; their lesser role in active movement is indicated by the small size of the fin muscles as compared with the much larger leg muscles of four-footed vertebrates. Some fishes, however, use the other fins for swimming, the dorsal or anal and sometimes the pectorals. Water ejected from the gill chambers in respiration aids in the swimming process.

The relative speed of a fish may be inferred from its shape. The streamlined body of most fishes is efficient for rapid locomotion; the resistance to movement results mainly from inflow of water directly toward the body, behind the region of maximum size. By towing models of various shapes in the water and measuring the power required for each, the "trout" or "mackerel" form proves to offer least resistance. Members of the fast-swimming mackerel tribe have depressions in the surface of the body into which the median fins are depressed when extreme speed is needed. All fishes have numerous epidermal glands that secrete mucus to provide a smooth surface and reduce friction losses in the water. Boats and airplanes built by man imitate the fish form in varying degree; when speed or economy of power is wanted, they are streamlined and provided with an exceedingly smooth exterior surface.

The center of gravity of a fish is usually in the air bladder, and a minimum of movement of the paired fins is necessary to maintain balance or to keep a fixed position in water. Adjustment to depth is facilitated by altering the gases in the air bladder. Fishes deprived of one or two of the paired fins soon learn to compensate for the loss of them.

Trout and salmon and others may jump or leap from the water at times when in pursuit of prey; they swim rapidly up to the surface when momentum alone carries them into the less dense air. Others, like the halfbeaks (HEMIRHAMPIDAE) skitter along the surface, propelled by the tail, which remains submerged. The flying fishes (EXOCOETIDAE) actually leave the water to glide or "volplane." To do this they swim rapidly, then "taxi" with the body above the surface while the submerged tail vibrates laterally (up to 70 times per second), when the pectoral fins may vibrate as a result of bodily movements. They may travel up to 10 m. per second (22 miles per hour). The broad pectoral fins are then instantaneously extended, and the fishes rise and glide for 3 to 8 seconds, traveling 35 to 100 yards. The flights may be repeated at short intervals.

28-21. Food. A few fresh-water fishes and some marine species feed upon aquatic vegetation, and the carp and suckers draw up bottom materials containing algae and minute invertebrates; but most fishes are entirely predaceous. They feed on aquatic invertebrates or other fishes, with occasional captures of birds or mammals by some. Being "cold-blooded," most fishes require no energy to maintain the body temperature; yet their food intake is considerable. A captive trout in winter needs 10 per cent of its body weight in food per week for maintenance, whereas 30 per cent is required for this purpose during the summer. The young of many marine fishes depend importantly on diatoms and small crustaceans; the small fresh-water fishes feed upon small aquatic organisms such as entomostracans and other arthropods, worms, and mollusks; and large fishes everywhere feed predominantly upon other fishes Tunas and other large active fishes have greater food needs as their body temperature is several degrees above that of the sea.

28-22. Enemies. Fishes serve as staple food for other fishes, for water snakes, some turtles and alligators, many kinds of sea birds, herons and kingfishers, and mammals such as seals, mink, otter, and bears. The eggs and young of fishes are devoured by a host of aquatic animals. Man is an important enemy of fishes.

28-23. Reproduction. Some tropical species may reproduce at almost any season, but in temperate latitudes most fishes breed in the spring or early summer. Many trout, however, spawn in autumn or winter, the brook trout from October to December. Most fishes have but one annual laying, but captive top minnows can produce up to six broods in one season.

The majority of fishes are oviparous, although many individual species and all members of some groups are viviparous. The top minnows and the viviparous perches (EMBIOTOCIDAE) bear but few young at a time, whereas most oviparous fishes produce many eggs. Brook trout lay 80 to more than 5,600 according to size, Atlantic salmon up to 17,000, the cod to over 6,000,000, and the ocean sunfish to 300,000,000. The bodies of females are often swollen with the maturing eggs just before laying, and changes in coloration or other features, such as the hooked jaws of salmon, may occur in males for the mating season. Courting performances precede actual spawning among various kinds of fishes. Many fishes change their habitat to spawn, some marine forms resorting to shallow waters and trout and salmon often ascending small tributary streams. In some species a definite pairing occurs before the eggs and milt (spermatozoa) are put forth. The eggs, when extruded, may remain separate (cod, trout) or adhere in large clumps (herring). Eggs of some marine fishes float near the surface, others remain suspended at a depth, and some sink to the bottom.   Some fresh-water fishes attach their egg masses to aquatic vegetation, and others provide "nests"; nests or "redds" of trout and salmon are shallow depressions on the bottom, cleared of fine debris by active movement of the parents, and gravel or sand is swept over the eggs, after deposition, to protect them from predators.   The male stickleback (*Gasterosteus*) constructs a globular nest of fine vegetable fibers bound together with a sticky secretion from the kidneys, and he later guards the eggs and small young.   The eggs of viviparous perch

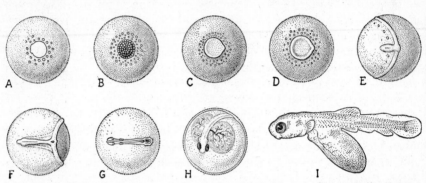

Fig. 28-12.   Early development of the trout, a bony fish.   *A*. Germinal disc (white) concentrates after fertilization.   *B*. Meroblastic segmentation.   *C, D*. Gastrula forming, blastodisc elongates in axis of future embryo.   *E*. Primitive streak begins, blastodisc spreads.   *F*. Neural tube forms, blastoderm surrounds yolk.   *G*. Embryo with eye and ear vesicles and 18+ somites.   *H*. "Eyed egg"—embryo with large eyes; blood vessels spread over yolk.   *I*. "Yolk sac" stage of hatched embryo.   (*A–G, after Henneguy,* 1888.)

and of top minnows are retained for development within the ovaries of the female, whereas in the sea horse (*Hippocampus*) the eggs are transferred to a brood pouch on the male.   Males of some marine catfishes and of African fresh-water cichlids carry the eggs in the mouth during development.

The eggs of bony fishes usually are small.   The time required for development varies with the species and also with the water temperature. Eggs of some marine fishes hatch as small transparent larvae within a few hours, and those of most tropical fresh-water species hatch in 20 to 48 hours.   By contrast, the eggs of brook trout need about 44 days at 50 to 52°F., about 33 days at 57°F., and 90 days or more at below 40°F.

The young of some viviparous fishes resemble their parents when hatched; other young are quite larval upon emergence and gradually assume the form of the adult.   Flounders and soles (Heterosomata) when hatched are bilaterally symmetrical with an eye on each side, but at an early age one eye begins to "migrate" to the opposite side, which thenceforth is the upper surface as the fish lies on the bottom.   The lower nasal pit shifts about 30 degrees, but there is little asymmetry of the brain.

The period of growth until sexual maturity varies with the species and also with the local water temperature. Young of the top minnow (*Gambusia*) may mature and breed before four months of age, in the same summer that they are hatched; yet they stop breeding and growing before they die. The king salmon of the Yukon River, by contrast, requires 5 or 6 years before spawning. Most fishes live to breed in several successive seasons, but individuals of the Pacific salmon (*Oncorhynchus*) grow to sexual maturity, breed once, and then die.

28-24. Relations to man. Fishes have been important as human food from the time of Paleolithic man, who left fishbones in his "kitchen middens," to the present day. The world fisheries take 35 billion pounds worth over $800,000,000 annually and employ thousands of persons. Many species are edible and a variety is used by different nations, but a few are of major importance in any one region.

Fishes are captured by spears, baited hooks, nets, and traps. The spear or harpoon is of undated origin, and the hook, net, and net sinker were used by Neolithic man in Europe. The baited hook began as an angular piece of bone, shell, or wood on a line of plant fiber or animal sinew, and as such was used by American Indians, Eskimos, and others; today it is essentially the same, a J-shaped wire with a recurved barb at the tip. Cod and halibut today are caught commercially on a long line with several hundred short laterals, each bearing a baited hook. Angling (Aryan *ank*, to bend) is of ancient origin; use of the pole and line was illustrated as early as 1400 B.C. The fly was known to Martial (A.D. 43–102), and Aelian (A.D. 170–230) described an artificial fly of wool and feathers, much as used by modern sport anglers.

The fish trap is a wicker basket with a funnel entrance and bait inside; it is still employed, as is the weir, or rack, a temporary dam with a funnel entrance, placed across salmon streams by Indians of the Pacific Northwest.

Nets originally were made of plant fibers. In the commercial fisheries of today they are of twine and are chiefly of four types. (1) The *trawl* is a flattened conical bag, to 100 feet long, with an open mouth tapering to a slender "purse" guarded by flaplike valves; it is drawn slowly along the sea bottom by two lines ("warps") attached to the sides of the mouth and pulled by a vessel. (2) The *seine* is a long net, used either from the shore or a vessel, having floats along the upper edge and (lead) weights on the lower. It is let out around a school of fishes gradually to encircle them; in a "purse" seine the bottom is drawn together by a running line. (3) The *gill net* stands vertically in the water, with floats above and weights below, and the ends attached to a buoy or ship; free-swimming fishes push into the diamond-shaped meshes and, if of appropriate size, the mesh catches them behind their gills (opercula). (4) The *trap net* (fyke or pound) has a funnel-shaped opening through which fish enter a closed bag.

The flesh of most fishes is white (or reddish) and flaky in texture. It contains 13 to 20 per cent of protein and has a food value of 300 to 1,600 calories per pound, depending on the oil content (to 17 per cent in salmon). Fishes deteriorate rapidly after being caught and must either be consumed soon or preserved. Packing in ice has long been employed. With modern artificial refrigeration, including quick freezing, vessels can work far from home ports and return their catch in good condition; frozen fish can be transported far inland or stored.

Fishes used as human food are prepared in many ways. Fresh fishes are usually cooked, although some are eaten raw in the Orient. The oldest means of preservation was to split, gut, and dry them in the air. Along northern seacoasts the cod, haddock, and others are split, cleaned, and packed in layers of salt, then spread and dried on racks in the sun, to become the salt fish of commerce. Herring are often pickled in strong brine. Fishes to be smoked are cleaned and briefly salted, then hung in dense wood smoke for several hours or days. Red herring, bloaters, and kippers are herring that have been subjected to different types of smoking; haddock, smoked originally at Findon in Scotland and now similarly prepared in both Europe and America, are known as "finnan haddies." Some mackerel, eels, and salmon are also smoked. Canning is the most modern method of preservation and is used commonly for Pacific salmon, California pilchards or "sardines," tuna, herring, anchovies, and others; the small canned "sardines" of Europe are young pilchard. The fishes are cleaned, rinsed, cut to size, and packed by hand in cans, with the addition of oil (fish, olive, cottonseed) and salt; spices, pickles, or sauce are often added for flavoring; the cans are then sealed and cooked (sterilized) in large steam retorts.

Crude fish oils are used in paints and insecticidal sprays, and refined oils from livers of cod and other species comprise a concentrated source of vitamin D. The scraps from canneries as well as entire fishes of some species are ground and dried into meal, used for feeding poultry and for fertilizer. Liquid glues are rendered from heads and trimmings of fishes, and the linings of swim bladders provide isinglass, used for clarification of wines and jellies.

Sport fishing, an important recreation, is an outdoor interest for thousands of persons and a source of food. Millions of dollars are spent each year by anglers in pursuit of trout, salmon, perch, bass, and other game fishes. In the United States the Federal and state governments rear millions of trout and some other fishes in hatcheries and plant them in streams and lakes to replace some of those taken by fishermen.

Captive fishes of many kinds in ponds and aquaria are kept and bred by fish fanciers and other persons, and many public institutions maintain large glass-fronted aquaria where both native and foreign fishes are displayed. The keeping of fishes in artificial ponds is an ancient practice of the Orient, the Romans, and the Aztecs of Middle America. Artificial rearing was on record in Europe in the fourteenth century and is now a widespread practice. Intensive pond culture of fishes, especially carp in Central Europe and the Orient, supplies considerable protein to human populations in those regions. Recent experiments in the United States and elsewhere have shown that addition of natural or chemical fertilizers to fish ponds will increase the diatom–algae–invertebrate food chain upon which fishes depend, and up to 250 pounds of fish may be produced in an acre of water.

The top minnow (*Gambusia affinis*) has been propagated and distributed widely in many waters where it was not native, to aid on control of mosquitoes and malaria, by devouring mosquito larvae.

Fishes have been influenced adversely by many activities of mankind. Overfishing has depleted stocks of some desirable species. Many streams and lakes are contaminated by sewage and chemical wastes and rendered less suitable for fishes. Dams for flood control, hydro-electric power, and irrigation make barriers that interfere with the migrations, spawning, and other activities of various fishes. On many salmon and trout streams, fish ladders have been constructed that consist of a series of small pools at successively higher levels and connected by miniature waterfalls up which the migrating adults may pass.

28-25. Fossil fishes. Bony fishes probably arose from primitive fishes in Silurian time. The Subclasses PALAEOPTERYGII (ancient fins) and CHOANICHTHYES (lobe fins) were numerous and widespread before the modern NEOPTERYGII (new fins) appeared. The PALAEOPTERYGII, of predaceous habit, were dominant in Paleozoic time and continued through the Mesozoic but are now represented only by the African bichir (*Polypterus*), and spoonbill (*Polyodon*) of the Mississippi Valley, and the sturgeons (ACIPENSERIDAE) of the Northern Hemisphere.

Of the crossopterygians, the Order †RHIPIDISTIA of the Devonian and Carboniferous, with rounded lobelike fins, simple teeth, and bodies covered by ganoid scales, are probable ancestors of the amphibians. The Order COELACANTHINI exhibits what is perhaps the most remarkable range of all known extinct fishes, occurring almost unchanged from Lower Carboniferous to Cretaceous (A.S. Woodward). Even more remarkable is the capture of a 5-foot living coelacanthid (*Latimeria chalumnae*) in a fish trawl at about 40 fathoms, off East London, South Africa, on Dec. 22, 1938. It has a cartilaginous skeleton, tubular vertebrae, small spiracles, and an obscure lateral line. The Superorder DIPNOI (lungfishes) flourished during the Paleozoic and dwindled in the Triassic; but, in the latter period, species resembling the living *Neoceratodus* of Australia were of almost world-wide occurrence. The five living species of lungfishes in Australia, Africa, and South America were formerly considered primitive and possible ancestors of the amphibians but are now looked upon as somewhat degenerate forms, with some specializations, including (1) reduction in the dermal bones, (2) elongation of the body and median fins, (3) change of the tail from heterocercal to symmetrical form, and (4) replacement of ganoid plates by thin cycloid scales.

Fig. 28-13.   Fossil fish (†*Priscacara*, Family Cichlidae) from Eocene Green River Shale, Kemmer, Wyoming.   (*Photograph by T. I. Storer.*)

The earliest recognized modern fishes (Neopterygii) are the †Semionotidae of the Triassic and Jurassic.   Unlike the older Palaeopterygii, these were slow-swimming bottom dwellers having small mouths with specialized teeth for feeding upon shellfishes; yet they retained ganoid scales.   The family gave rise to various offshoots, most of which in turn became extinct during Cretaceous time, save for the bowfin (*Amia*) and gar pike (*Lepidosteus*) still living in North America.   A variety of other fishes appeared through Tertiary times, of which many became extinct and others led on to the Recent fishes of the present day.   Most of the modern families and a few existing genera probably date from the Eocene.

Fossil remains of fishes are abundant, and some are so well-preserved that details of the soft parts can be determined in addition to the form of the body, fins, scales, and skeleton (Fig. 28-13).   Numerous individuals of a species are sometimes discovered in a single slab of stone, suggesting that schools of fishes were killed suddenly by some catastrophe and then entombed by sediments that later became converted into stone.

CLASSIFICATION

Class *OSTEICHTHYES* (Pisces of many authors).   Bony Fishes.   Skeleton more or less bony; skin usually with embedded dermal (bony) scales of cycloid or ctenoid form, some with ganoid scales; both paired lateral and median fins usually present, and supported by fin rays; no pelvic girdle; mouth usually terminal; gills present throughout life, not in separate clefts; air bladder usually present; heart 2-chambered; no cloaca; ova small, segmentation meroblastic; Devonian to Recent, in salt, brackish, and fresh waters; about 25,000 species.

Subclass 1. PALAEOPTERYGII. ANCIENT FISHES. Dermal fin rays of dorsal and anal fins usually more numerous than their internal skeletal supports; clavicles present (except in BELONORHYCHII); nostrils not connected to mouth cavity.

Order 1. †**Archistia.** Body usually covered with ganoid scales; tail heterocercal; head covered with bones; snout short; teeth conical; vertebrae without centra; Lower Devonian to Jurassic. †*Cheirolepis*, †*Platysomus*.

Order 2. **Cladistia.** Body slender, elongate, covered with thick rhomboid enameled scales; base of pectoral fins narrow and scale-covered; dorsal fin of 8 or more finlets each with a spine anteriorly; tail seemingly diphycercal; vertebrae amphicoelous, with bony centra; air bladder lunglike, possibly an accessory respiratory organ; larvae with slender external gills; Paleozoic and Recent (none known between). Africa. *Polypterus* (Fig. 28-14), tropical Africa; *Calamoichthys*, eel-like, Nigeria and Congo.

FIG. 28-14. Bichir (*Polypterus bichir*, Order   FIG. 28-15. Sturgeon (*Acipenser sturio*.
CLADISTIA). Length to 36 inches.   Order CHONDROSTEI). Length to 10 feet.
(After Norman, Guide to fish gallery, British Museum.)

Order 3. **Chondrostei.** STURGEONS, SPOONBILL. Body naked (scaleless) or with longitudinal rows of bony (ganoid) scutes; snout prominent; tail heterocercal; no teeth; skeleton largely cartilaginous; notochord persistent and unsegmented; vertebrae acentrous; Lower Jurassic to Recent.

POLYODONTIDAE. Two living species: *Polyodon spathula*, spoonbill or paddlefish, Mississippi drainage and south in streams, to 6 feet long, with paddle-shaped snout, practically scaleless; food of small invertebrates strained by gill rakers from bottom mud; *Psephurus*, Yangtze River.

ACIPENSERIDAE. STURGEONS. About 24 species; sharklike, mouth ventral and with barbels, 5 rows of enlarged bony scutes along body; food of worms, mollusks, small fishes, and aquatic plants; flesh palatable, eggs preserved as caviar, lining of swim bladder made into isinglass for clarifying jellies. *Acipenser sturio*, common sturgeon (Fig. 28-15), on both sides of Atlantic Ocean, and *A. transmontanus*, great white sturgeon, along Pacific coast, both ascend large rivers to spawn; *A. fulvescens*, rock sturgeon, and *Scaphirhynchus platorhynchus*, shovel-nosed sturgeon, both in Mississippi drainage, restricted to fresh water.

Order 4. †**Belonorhynchii.** Body with 4 series of bony scutes; caudal fin symmetrical; snout and lower jaw very long; vertebrae acentrous; Lower Jurassic and Triassic. †*Belonorhynchus*.

Subclass 2. NEOPTERYGII (Ganoids + Teleostei). MODERN FISHES. Vertebra with centra and usually amphicoelous; dermal rays of dorsal and anal fins equal in number to internal radial skeletal supports; no clavicles; caudal fin homocercal (rarely, abbreviate heterocercal); scales cycloid or ctenoid (ganoid in some fossils); nostrils not connected to mouth cavity; Upper Permian to Recent.

Order 1. **Protospondyli.** Tail abbreviate heterocercal; the living species with thin overlapping cycloid scales; Upper Jurassic and Lower Tertiary; one Recent species. *Amia calva*, bowfin (Fig. 28-16), Great Lakes to Texas and Florida; air bladder large, cellular, aids in respiration; feeds on fishes and invertebrates; eggs deposited in a crude nest and guarded by male.

Order 2. **Ginglymodi.** GAR PIKES AND ALLIGATOR GARS. Vertebrae solid, opisthocoelous; scales ganoid, in oblique rows; snout and lower jaw long; teeth stout, conical; Eocene to Recent. *Lepidosteus osseus*, long-nosed gar (Fig. 28-17), Great Lakes and Mississippi Valley to coastal streams of Florida, snout and body slender, grows to 5 feet; *L. spatula*, alligator gar, lower Mississippi Valley, grows to over 9 feet; all voracious, preying on smaller fishes.

FIG. 28-16. Bowfin and nest (*Amia calva*, Order PROTOSPONDYLI). Length to 24 inches. (*After Norman, Guide to fish gallery, British Museum.*)

(*Note: The remaining* NEOPTERYGII, *comprising the "Telostei" or bony fishes proper, now in 29 orders, include all but a few of the living fishes; Orders 4 to 8 and 10 to 13 have only soft rays in the fins, but many of the others have some or all fins with one or more hard calcified spiny rays.*)

Order 3. †**Halecostomi.** Vertebral centra annular or amphicoelous. Mesozoic. †*Pholidophorus.*

Order 4. **Isospondyli.** HERRING, SALMON, TROUT, ETC. Tail homocercal; fins without spiny rays; pelvic fins abdominal; air bladder with open duct to pharynx (no auditory ossicles); pyloric caeca usually numerous; Jurassic to Recent.

FIG. 28-17. Long-nosed gar (*Lepidosteus osseus*, Order GINGLYMODI). Length to 5 feet. (*After Norman, Guide to fish gallery, British Museum.*)

FIG. 28-18. Shad (*Alosa sapidissima*, Order ISOSPONDYLI). Length to 30 inches. (*After Goode, 1884.*)

ELOPIDAE. TARPONS. Medium to large, in salt water, prized for sport. *Tarpon atlanticus*, common off Florida.

CLUPEIDAE. HERRINGS. Small, chiefly in salt water, often in schools numbering millions along both sides of North America, coming shoreward to spawn. *Clupea harengus*, common herring, over 50,000,000 pounds netted annually in New England waters and up to 3,000,000,000 pounds per year in Europe; marketed fresh, salt, smoked, or pickled, also used for bait; young canned as "sardines" in Norway; *Sardinops caerulea*, pilchard or California sardine, large tonnages formerly taken annually along Pacific coast for canning and for reduction to fish oil and meal; *Sardinia*, sardine of Spain and Italy; *Alosa sapidissima*, shad (Fig. 28-18), native to Atlantic coast and introduced on Pacific coast, enters rivers to spawn, much esteemed for eating.

SALMONIDAE. SALMONS, TROUTS, ETC. A small adipose fin on back. In cool waters of Northern Hemisphere, much prized for game and food. *Oncorhynchus*, Pacific salmon (Fig. 28-19), 5 species central California to Alaska, others in Asia; millions of pounds taken in nets, used fresh or canned; spawn in fresh water, young migrate to sea and mature in 2 to 8 years, return to fresh water, spawn once, and die; *O. tschawytscha*, Chinook or tyee salmon, averages 30 pounds, some over 100 pounds; other species smaller. *Salmo salar*, Atlantic salmon, eastern North America and Europe, spawns more than once as do trouts; *S. gairdnerii*, rainbow trout, resident in fresh waters of Pacific coast, California to Alaska, has a sea-run race the "steelhead trout"; *S. clarkii*, cutthroat trout, Colorado and central California northward; *S. trutta*, brown or Loch Leven trout of Europe, widely introduced in United States; *Salvelinus fontinalis*, eastern brook or speckled trout (Fig. 28-20), Iowa and Allegheny Mountains to Saskatchewan and Labrador; *Coregonus*, whitefish, and *Thymallus*, grayling, northern states to Canada and Alaska. Various trout and salmon have been transplanted to many new localities. Many millions of trout and salmon are reared artificially and planted annually by Federal and state game departments.

Fig. 28-19. Chinook or king salmon and young (*Oncorhynchus tschawytscha*, Family Salmonidae). Length 2 to 5 feet. (*U.S. Bureau of Fisheries.*)

Fig. 28-20. Eastern brook trout (*Salvelinus fontinalis*, Family Salmonidae). Length to 18 inches. (*After Norman, Guide to fish gallery, British Museum.*)

Order 5. **Haplomi.** Pikes and Mud Minnows. Fins with soft rays only; pelvic fins abdominal; air bladder with duct to pharynx; no pyloric caeca; Miocene to Recent.

Esocidae. Pikes. Slender-bodied with large mouths and conspicuous teeth, feed on other fishes. *Esox lucius*, common pike or pickerel, Arkansas and Minnesota eastward, other species there and in Eurasia; *E. masquinongy*, muskellunge, upper Mississippi basin, Great Lakes and northward, grows to 8 feet and over 100 pounds, a choice game fish.

Order 6. **Iniomi.** Lantern Fishes, etc. Air bladder usually absent; deep-sea forms with phosphorescent spots on sides; Cretaceous to Recent; shore waters and deep sea to 2,500 fathoms. *Myctophum*, lantern fishes, deep seas; *Synodus*, lizard fishes, tropical seas.

Order 7. **Giganturoidea.** Lower lobe of caudal fin elongate; pectoral fins long with many rays, placed high above the small gill openings; pelvic fins absent; fin rays soft; no air bladder; Atlantic and Indian oceans. *Gigantura*, several species.

Order 8. **Lyomeri.** Gulpers. Body eel-shaped, naked; mouth very large; fin rays soft; tail long and slender, without caudal fin; ribs and pelvic fins absent; oceanic, at considerable depths. *Saccopharynx*, several species.

Order 9. **Ostariophysi.** Characins, Electric Eels, Suckers, Minnows, and Catfishes. Anterior vertebrae fused, and lateral elements of 4 vertebrae detached to form small auditory ossicles (Weberian organ) between air bladder and ear; air bladder of 2 or 3 parts, usually with duct to pharynx; Eocene to Recent; fully 5,000 species, all in fresh waters except some catfishes.

Suborder 1. cyprinoidea. Normally scaled. Characins, mostly small with silvery sides, many in Central and South America, some in Africa. Gymnotids, slender, long tapering tail and anal fin, no dorsal or pelvic fin, South and Central America;

Electrophorus electricus, electric eel, Orinoco and Amazon drainages in South America, grows to 8 feet, with modified muscular tissue along lower surface capable of producing powerful electric shocks.

CYPRINIFORM OR CARPLIKE FISHES. No adipose fin; mouth toothless and protractile.

CATOSTOMIDAE. SUCKERS. *Catostomus, Carpiodes*, and others, more than 60 species in North America and 2 in eastern Asia, with fleshy lips to suck up bottom mud containing small animals and plants used as food.

CYPRINIDAE. CARPS, CHUBS, ROACHES, MINNOWS, ETC. Teeth in pharynx used to grind food; about 1,500 species. *Cyprinus carpio*, common carp, native to fresh waters in eastern Asia, where reared for food and ornament for centuries; introduced into Europe in thirteenth century and brought from Germany (hence "German" carp) to United States in 1872 where now widespread and abundant, with domestic races such as mirror carp (large scales) and leather carp (scaleless); *Carassius auratus*, goldfish (Fig. 28-21), also native to Asia and long under domestication, with many artificial breeds or races of peculiar form; daces and minnows, many native to North America, of small size, often erroneously thought to be young fishes; *Notropis*, minnows, eastern North America; *Ptychocheilus lucius*, "white salmon" of Colorado River basin, grows to 5 feet and 80 pounds, the largest North American cyprinid.

FIG. 28-21. Goldfish (*Carassius auratus*, Order OSTARIOPHYSI). Length to 12 inches. (*After Goode*, 1884.)

FIG. 28-22. Catfish or bullhead (*Ameiurus melas*, Suborder SILUROIDEA). Length 6 to 10 inches. (*After Goode*, 1884.)

Suborder 2. SILUROIDEA. CATFISHES. Mouth with teeth, nonprotractile, and usually with sensory barbels; body either naked (scaleless) or with bony plates; over 30 species in fresh waters of United States, others in salt water and southward, American species naked and with adipose fin (Fig. 28-22). *Ameiurus nebulosus*, bullhead or horned pout, native to most quiet waters east of Rocky Mountains and introduced in the West; *Ictalurus lacustris* (*punctatus*), channel or spotted catfish, in clear flowing waters from Great Lakes region to Gulf states; *Galeichthys, Arius*, shallow coastal seas.

Order 10. **Apodes.** EELS. Body elongate and slender; dorsal, caudal, and anal fins continuous, caudal sometimes lacking; pelvic fins usually absent; gill openings small; scales minute or absent; air bladder with duct; no oviducts; mostly marine; Cretaceous to Recent. *Anguilla*, fresh-water eels (Fig. 28-23), grow to maturity in fresh-water streams, adults migrate to sea in autumn, spawn in deep water, and die, the delicate transparent larvae (leptocephali) swim near the surface of the sea, feeding and growing, to enter the rivers perhaps a year later; *A. bostonensis* American eel, of Atlantic coast, spawns near Bermuda islands; *Muraena*, morays, marine, highly predaceous, many of striking coloration, abound in crevices of coral reefs.

Order 11. **Heteromi.** Body slender; tail long, with elongate anal fin below tapering to a point, but no caudal fin; pelvic fins abdominal; no oviducts; oceanic at considerable depths. *Notacanthus*.

Order 12. **Synentognathi.** Garfishes, Halfbeaks, Flying Fishes. Dorsal fin above anal; pectorals high on body; lower pharyngeals united as 1 bone; marine. *Strongylura, Belone,* garfishes; *Scomberesox,* skipper; *Hemirhamphus,* halfbeak; *Exocoetus, Cypselurus,* flying fishes, chiefly in warm seas, emerge to glide in air over the water (Fig. 28-24).

Fig. 28-23. Fresh-water eel (*Anguilla bostonensis,* Order Apodes). Length to 4 feet. (*After Goode,* 1884.)

Fig. 28-24. Flying fish (*Cypselurus,* Order Synentognathi.) Length to 15 inches. (*After Norman, Guide to fish gallery, British Museum.*)

Order 13. **Cyprinodontes** (Microcyprini). Top Minnows and Cave Fishes. Size small; mouth protractile; lateral line weak; pelvic fins abdominal or absent; many viviparous; chiefly in North America, either fresh or salt waters; feed chiefly near the surface, on small animals or plants; some with conspicuous courtship performances. *Typhlichthys,* eyeless cave fish, in streams of limestone caves, Indiana to Alabama; *Cyprinodon macularius* and others, desert minnows, in scat-

male

female

Fig. 28-25. Top minnow or "mosquito fish" (*Gambusia affinis,* Order Microcyprini). Natural size. (*After Garman,* 1895.)

Fig. 28-26. Sea horse (*Hippocampus,* Order Solenichthyes). Length to 6 inches. (*After Norman, Guide to fish gallery, British Museum.*)

tered springs, streams, and artesian waters, southern Nevada and southeastern California to Sonora; *Fundulus heteroclitus,* common killifish, in brackish coastal waters, Canada to Florida; *Gambusia affinis,* top minnow (Fig. 28-25), in fresh waters, reared and planted widely to control mosquito larvae; *Anableps,* "four-eyed" fish, pupil of eye divided with upper half for vision in air and lower for seeing in water.

Order 14. **Salmopercae.** Trout-perches. Dorsal and anal fins preceded by 1 or 4 spines; North America (only 3 species). *Percopsis; Columbia.*

Order 15. **Solenichthyes.** PIPEFISHES, SEA HORSES, ETC. Body either elongate and slender or else head at right angles to body; mouth suctorial, at end of tubular snout; male usually with a brood pouch under the tail to shelter the eggs until hatching; marine. *Syngnathus*, pipefishes, slender, covered with ringlike exoskeleton of enlarged plates, fins minute; *Hippocampus*, sea horse (Fig. 28-26), head enlarged and at right angles with body, swims in vertical position by undulations of dorsal fin.

Order 16. **Anacanthini.** CODS, POLLACKS, HAKES, BURBOTS, ETC. Fins soft-rayed; pelvics often many-rayed, and thoracic or jugular in position; caudal fin, when present, formed mainly of dorsal and anal rays, without expanded hypural; air bladder without duct; Northern Hemisphere, mosty marine bottom dwellers; of great commercial importance. *Gadus morhua*, codfish (Fig. 28-27), both sides of North Atlantic,

FIG. 28-27. Common cod (*Gadus morhua*, Order ANACANTHINI). Length to 4 feet. (*After Goode*, 1884.)

FIG. 28-28. Mackerel (*Scomber scombrus*, Order PERCOMORPHI). Length to 18 inches. (*After Goode*, 1884.)

fished from ancient times, over 100,000,000 pounds taken annually in American fisheries, and twice this amount of haddock (*Melanogrammus aeglefinus*) being sold fresh or salted; *Merluccius*, hake; *Lota*, burbot (in fresh water).

Order 17. **Allotriognathi.** Eyes large; teeth feeble or none; occasional spiny fin rays; marine, mostly oceanic. *Lampris regius* (*luna*), opah; *Trachypterus*, ribbonfish; *Regalecus*, oarfish, slender, to 20 feet long.

Order 18. **Berycomorphi.** Pelvic fins usually with more than 5 soft rays; caudal fin generally with 19 principal rays (17-branched); some spiny rays; Cretaceous to Recent; marine, mostly in deep water. *Holocentrus*, squirrelfish.

Order 19. **Zeomorphi.** Anal fin preceded by 1 to 4 spines forming separate fins; marine. *Zeus faber*, "John Dory."

Order 20. **Percomorphi.** PERCHES, ETC. Dorsal and anal fins with both spiny and soft fin rays; pectoral arch attached to skull by forked post-temporal; Upper Cretaceous to Recent; world-wide, in both fresh and salt waters; about 80 families, diverse in form and habits.

CENTRARCHIDAE. FRESH-WATER BASSES AND SUNFISHES. Many species in eastern states, prized for sport fishing. *Huro salmoides*, large-mouthed black bass; *Micropterus dolomieu*, small-mouthed black bass; *Lepomis gibbosus*, sunfish; *Pomoxis annularis*, crappie.

PERCIDAE. FRESH-WATER PERCHES. *Perca flavescens*, yellow perch; *Etheostoma*, *Hadropterus*, etc., darters, eastern United States.

CICHLIDAE. CICHLIDS. Nearly 600 species in tropical America and Africa.

EMBIOTOCIDAE. SURF FISHES OR VIVIPAROUS PERCHES. California to Japan.

SCOMBRIDAE. MACKERELS, ETC. More than 100,000,000 pounds of mackerel (*Scomber scombrus*, Fig. 28-28) taken annually by fishermen of United States.

THUNNIDAE. TUNAS, ETC. Includes tunas, yellowfin, bluefin or horse mackerel, skipjack, bonito, and others, some of large size. More than 200,000,000 pounds obtained commercially in United States fisheries each year.

Other important families are the SERRANIDAE (sea basses), SCIAENIDAE (drums), MULLIDAE (red mullets), LABRIDAE (wrasses), GOBIIDAE (gobies), LUTIANIDAE (snappers), Blennidae (blennies), Sphyraenidae (barracudas), Mugilidae (gray mullets), and Atherinidae (silversides).

Order 21. **Scleroparei.** Mail-cheeked Fishes. A bony stay (second suborbital) across cheek, from below eye toward operculum; many with extra spines on head or body; chiefly marine, some in fresh water, many bottom dwellers in shallow or deep waters. *Sebastes*, rose fish or ocean perch; *Scorpaena*, scorpion fish; *Cottus*, sculpin; *Gasterosteus*, stickleback (Fig. 28-29), male builds nest of sticks and a secretion, then guards eggs.

Fig. 28-29. Stickleback (*Gasterosteus aculeatus*, Order Scleroparei). Length to 4 inches. (*After Norman, Guide to fish gallery, British Museum.*)

Fig. 28-30. The sand dab, a "flat fish" (*Hippoglossoides platessoides*, Order Heterosomata*). Length to 24 inches. (*After Goode, 1884.*)

Order 22. **Hypostomides.** Dragonfishes. Size very small; body enclosed in a broad bony box, tail in bony rings; tropical seas of Old World. *Pegasus.*

Order 23. **Heterosomata.** Flatfishes. Asymmetrical, with both eyes on one side of head and movable; body strongly compressed; dorsal and anal fins greatly elongate, fringing the body (Fig. 28-30); bottom dwellers, lying on side, under surface usually unpigmented; Upper Eocene to Recent; usually marine, on bottom in coastal waters; important food fishes, sought commercially; early young bilaterally symmetrical, but fish soon lies on one side and "lower" eye migrates around so that both eyes are on upper surface. *Hippoglossus*, halibut; *Paralichthys*, flounder; *Symphurus*, sole; *Achirus*, round sole.

Order 24. **Discocephali.** Remoras. Upper surface of head with flat oval adhesive disc (modified spinous dorsal fin), transversely furrowed, by which the fish attaches itself to a shark or other object in the water; other fins normal and used for ordinary swimming; warm seas. *Echeneis, Remora,* remoras, or "suckfishes" (Fig. 28-31).

Order 25. **Plectognathi.** Trigger-fishes, Trunkfishes, Puffers, Head Fishes, etc. Body form various, some rounded or globose, some inflate by swallowing water; jaws short, powerful, teeth usually strong incisors or forming a sharp-edged beak; scales generally spiny or bony; gill openings small; warm seas; form and habits diverse. *Balistes*, triggerfish; *Diodon*, porcupine fish; *Mola mola*, ocean sunfish, body short, high, compressed (Fig. 28-1), anal and dorsal

Fig. 28-31. Remora or "suckfish" (*Remora*, Order Discocephali). Length to 21 inches. Dorsal fin converted to muscular sucker on head for attaching to other marine animals. (*After Norman, Guide to fish gallery, British Museum.*)

fins enlarged, literally no tail, skin leathery, specimens of 250 to 400 pounds occasional off New York, the largest nearly 11 feet long and 1 ton in weight off California.

Order 26. **Malacichthyes.** No spinous rays; skeleton weakly ossified, body limp; median fins long with many rays; Pacific Ocean. *Icosteus.*

Order 27. **Xenopterygii.** CLING-FISHES. Naked; large subcircular adhesive disc on abdomen, by which the fish attaches to stones or shells; shore waters, tropic and temperate. *Gobiesox,* clingfish.

Order 28. **Haplodoci.** TOADFISHES. Head depressed, mouth wide; a spinous dorsal fin and long soft-rayed dorsal and anal fins; bottom of tropical and subtropical seas. *Opsanus,* toadfish; *Porichthys,* singing fish or "midshipman."

Order 29. **Pediculati.** ANGLER FISHES, DEEP-SEA FISHES. "Spinous" dorsal fin of a few flexible rays, the first located on head and with dilated bulb at tip; some luminescent organs; shore waters or ocean depths. *Lophius piscatorius,* angler fish (Fig. 28-32), broad, soft-bodied, with huge mouth, and to 4 feet in length, on both sides of North Atlantic down to 60 fathoms, captures fish,

FIG. 28-32. Angler fish (*Lophius piscatorius,* Order PEDICULATI). Length to 4 feet. (*After Norman, Guide to fish gallery, British Museum.*)

marine invertebrates and birds; *Ceratias, Melanocetus,* etc., deep-sea anglers, at 1,500 to 6,000 feet, mostly small, of blackish color, with a luminescent "bulb"; male minute and early attaches permanently to female, their bodies and blood streams growing together, such "parasitism" probably an adaptation to ensure mating in the dark depths of the sea.

Order 30. **Opisthomi.** Body eel-shaped; dorsal fin preceded by separate small spines; anterior nostril tubular on fleshy tentacle at end of snout; fresh waters of Africa and southeastern Asia. *Mastacembelus.*

Order 31. **Symbranchii.** SYMBRANCHOID EELS. Shaped like eels; dorsal and anal fins without fin rays and continuous with caudal; no pectoral fins; gill openings fused as transverse ventral slit; Africa, India and tropical America in fresh-water streams. *Synbranchus.*

Subclass 3. **CHOANICHTHYES.** Nostrils connecting to mouth cavity; each paired fin with large median lobe (sometimes cross jointed), and dermal fin rays along sides.

Superorder 1. **CROSSOPTERYGII.** LOBE-FINNED FISHES. Premaxilla and maxilla present.

Order 1. †**Rhipidistia.** Head normal, skull ossified; teeth on both premaxilla and maxilla; a "pineal" eye; tail heterocercal. Devonian to Carboniferous. †*Osteolepis.*

Order 2. **Coelacanthini** (Actinistia). Head short, deep; skull with much cartilage; teeth only at tip of premaxilla and dentary; no pineal eye; tail 3-pronged. Devonian to Cretaceous. †*Eusthenopteron,* †*Macropoma.* Also Recent: *Latimeria chalumnae,* one off South Africa.

Superorder 2. **DIPNOI** (Dipneusti). LUNG FISHES. Body long, slender; no premaxilla or maxilla; teeth forming pair of plates on palate and one on inner edge of each lower jaw; air bladder lunglike;

FIG. 28-33. Lungfishes (Superorder DIPNOI). *A.* African (*Protopterus*), length to 32 inches. *B.* South American (*Lepidosiren*), length to 32 inches. *C.* Australian (*Neoceratodus*), length to 40 inches or more. (*After Norman, Guide to fish gallery, British Museum.*)

paired fins narrow; Devonian to Recent (many fossil forms; food of invertebrates and plants (Fig. 28-33).

CERATODONITIDAE.   †*Ceratodus*, Triassic to Cretaceous, almost world wide; *Neoceratodus forsteri*, only living species; scales large, cycloid, overlapping; fins leaf-like; in Burnett and Mary rivers, Queensland, Australia; inhabits quiet pools that become stagnant during dry season when the fish rises to surface and takes air into lung.

LEPIDOSIRENIDAE.   Body eel-like, scales small, fins filamentous; inhabit swamps and in dry season retire to vertical burrows ("nests") in mud, lined with mucus. *Lepidosiren*, South America, makes burrow at bottom of water and deposits eggs in tunnel, guarded by male; *Protopterus annectens* and 2 other species of central Africa retire to burrows in mud where mucus dries to form a "cocoon" with lid and tubular aperture leading to mouth of fish for respiration; spawns after return of water.

References

(References for Chap. 27 are included)

BERG, L. S.   1940.   Classification of fishes, both recent and fossil.   *Travaux de l'institut zoologique de l'académie des science de l'URSS*, vol. 5, part 2, pp. 87–517, 190 figs; also available in facsimile lithoprint edition.   1947.   Ann Arbor, Mich., J. W. Edwards.   Best recent summary; text in both Russian and English.

BRIDGE, T. W., and G. A. BOULENGER.   1904.   Fishes.   *In* Cambridge natural history.   London, Macmillan & Co., Ltd.   Vol. 7, pp. 139–760, figs. 90–440.   General account and systematic review.

CURTIS, B.   1949.   The life story of a fish, his morals and manners.   New York, D. Appleton-Century Co., Inc.   xii + 284 pp., illus.

DEAN, B.   1895.   Fishes, living and fossil.   New York, The Macmillan Co.   xiv + 300 pp., 344 figs.

—— and OTHERS.   1916–1923.   A bibliography of fishes.   New York, American Museum of Natural History.   3 vols., 2,124 pp.

GOODRICH, E. S.   1909.   Cyclostomes and fishes.   *In* E. R. Lankester, Treatise on zoology.   London, A. & C. Black, Ltd.   Part IX: 1, pp. 58–578, figs. 39–515.

JORDAN, D. S.   1905.   A guide to the study of fishes.   New York, Henry Holt & Co., Inc.   2 vols., 1,271 pp., 506 figs.

—— and B. W. EVERMANN.   1896–1900.   The fishes of North and Middle America . . . *U.S. National Museum, Bulletin* 47 (4 volumes), ci + 3,313 pp., pls. I–CCCXCII.   Keys and technical descriptions; comprehensive.

—— and ——.   1902.   American food and game fishes.   New York, Doubleday, Doran & Co., Inc.   xlix + 573 pp., illus.   Popular.

——, ——, and H. W. CLARK.   1930.   Checklist of the fishes . . . of North and Middle America. . . . *U.S. Commissioner of Fisheries, Report for* 1928, part 2, 760 pp.   Scientific and common names and distribution of 4,137 species and subspecies; many errors.

NEEDHAM, P. R.   1938.   Trout streams.   Ithaca, N.Y., Comstock Publishing Co., Inc.   x + 233 pp., 74 figs.   Trout biology and management in North America.

NORMAN, J. R.   1931.   A history of fishes.   London, Ernest Benn, Ltd.   xv + 463 pp., 8 pls., 147 figs.   Modern general account of fishes.

—— and F. C. FRASER.   1938.   Giant fishes whales and dolphins.   New York, W. W. Norton & Co., Inc.   xxvii + 361 pp., illus.

RADCLIFFE, W.   1936.   Fishing from the earliest times.   2d ed.   London, John Murray.   xxi + 494 pp., illus.   Historical to A.D. 500; many ancient quotations.

TRESSLER, D. K.   1923.   Marine products of commerce.   New York, Chemical Catalog Co., Inc.   762 pp., 257 figs.   Gathering, processing, and preserving fishes and other sea products.

WALTON, ISAAK. 1653. The Compleat Angler. 5th ed. (1676) and later editions with Charles Cotton. The classical discussion of the delights of fishing.

Many reports, bulletins, and other publications of the U.S. Bureau of Fisheries (now part of the Fish and Wildlife Service, U.S. Department of the Interior) deal with the fishes and fisheries of the United States and dependencies. Various state game and conservation departments issue publications on the fishes of their states. The *Transactions* of the American Fisheries Society, *Annual Reports* of the North American Wild Life Conference, the quarterly periodical *Copeia*, other journals, and many books contain materials on fishes and the fisheries.

CHAPTER 29

CLASS AMPHIBIA. AMPHIBIANS

The AMPHIBIA include the living salamanders (Subclass CAUDATA), the toads and frogs (Subclass SALIENTIA), the limbless tropical caecilians (Order GYMNOPHIONA), and various fossil forms of Carboniferous and Permian times. The Class name (Gr. *amphi*, dual + *bios*, life) appropriately indicates that most of the species live partly in fresh water and partly on land. In both structure and function the amphibians stand between the fishes and reptiles, but with greater resemblance to the latter, being the first group among the chordates to live out of water. Several "new" features adapt them for terrestrial life, such as legs, lungs, nostrils connecting to the mouth cavity, and sense organs that can function in both water and air. Amphibians occupy a minor role in nature, although some species are abundant as individuals. They serve as food for various vertebrates, a few species are used for biological teaching and research, and frog legs are a table delicacy.

29-1. Characteristics. 1. Skin moist and glandular; no external scales.

2. Two pairs of limbs for walking or swimming (no paired fins); toes 4–5, or fewer, hind toes webbed (no limbs on caecilians, no hind limbs on SIRENIDAE); any median fins lack fin rays.

3. Nostrils 2, connected to mouth cavity and with valves to exclude water; eyes often with movable lids; eardrums external on toads and frogs; mouth usually with fine teeth; tongue often protrusible.

4. Skeleton largely bony; skull with 2 occipital condyles; ribs, if present, not attached to sternum.

5. Heart 3-chambered, 2 auricles and a ventricle; 1 (or 3) pair of aortic arches; red blood cells nucleated and oval.

6. Respiration by gills, lungs, skin, or the mouth lining, separately or in combination; gills present at some stage in life history; vocal cords in toads and frogs.

7. Brain with 10 pairs of cranial nerves.

8. Body temperature variable (poikilothermous), dependent upon environment.

9. Fertilization external or internal; mostly oviparous; eggs with some yolk and enclosed in gelatinous coverings; cleavage holoblastic but unequal; no embryonic membranes; usually an aquatic larval stage with metamorphosis to adult form.

The AMPHIBIA are the lowest and earliest TETRAPODA (Gr. *tetra*, four + *podos*, foot), or land vertebrates. They undoubtedly were derived from some fishlike ancestor, possibly in Devonian times. The transition from water to land involved (1) modification of the body for travel on land while retaining the ability to swim, (2) development of limbs in place of paired fins, (3) change of the skin to permit exposure to the air, (4) replacement of gills by lungs, (5) changes in the circulatory system to provide for respiration by the lungs and skin, and (6)

FIG. 29-1. Tiger salamander (*Ambystoma tigrinum*, Subclass CAUDATA, Order MUTABILIA) Length to 11 inches.

acquisition of sense organs that function in both air and water. In the early larvae of all amphibians and in such salamanders as retain the gills throughout life, there are multiple aortic arches as in fishes. After metamorphosis, the other salamanders and the toads and frogs have but one pair of arches, as in reptiles. The amphibian skull is simpler, with fewer bones than in fishes, but the limb muscles are more complex than those of the lateral fins in fishes. The caecilians are probably specialized relics of an ancient stock to which many fossil species of Paleozoic time belong. The salamanders and the frogs and toads

FIG. 29-2. A caecilian or limbless amphibian of the tropics (*Ichthyophis glutinosus*, Subclass STEGOCEPHALIA, Order GYMNOPHIONA). (*After Sarasin.*)

represent two lines of descent distinct since before the Cretaceous. Some primitive fossil labyrinthodonts probably were ancestral to the oldest reptiles and so to all higher land vertebrates.

29-2. Size. Most salamanders are 3 to 8 inches long. The giant salamander (*Megalobatrachus japonicus*) grows to 69 inches, whereas a Mexican salamander is only 1½ inches in length. The giant frog (*Rana goliath*) of the African Cameroons grows to 12 inches in head-and-body length, the American bullfrog (*R. catesbeiana*) to 8 inches, and a toad (*Bufo marinus*) of Mexico to South America to 8½ inches long and 2½ pounds in weight; the smallest salientian is a Cuban tree toad (*Phyllobates*) only ⅜ inch when grown. Most toads and frogs are 2 to 5 inches long. The largest caecilian (*Typhlonectes compressicauda*) grows to a meter or more. Various fossil amphibians were from a few inches to as much as 15 feet in length.

29-3. General appearance. Salamanders have the head and neck distinct, the trunk elongated and cylindrical or depressed dorsoventrally and a long tail, rounded to oval in land dwellers, but finlike in aquatic species. The limbs are of about equal size save in a few eel-like species. Toads and frogs have the head and trunk joined in a broad depressed body, no neck or tail, small fore limbs, and long hind limbs with webs between the toes; usually the mouth is broad, the eyes are large, and the eardrums exposed. Caecilians are limbless and wormlike, with annulate bodies, and their skin contains small internal scales.

STRUCTURE OF AMPHIBIANS

29-4. External features. The detailed description of the frog in Chap. 2 will serve as an account of the general structure and physiology of an amphibian. The present chapter discusses features of other amphibians. The skin on salamanders and caecilians adheres closely to the muscles of the body. On most amphibians the external surface is smooth and glistening; it is rough on terrestrial newts (*Triturus*, etc.) and on toads bears many groups of *poison glands* in small or large rounded warts, over the back, sides, and legs. (Handling toads does not produce warts on human skin.) The coloration of many salamanders and toads is bright and contrasted, of green, yellow, red, brown, or black. The pattern is fixed on most species, and changes are slight; tree toads, however, undergo great changes in coloration with different conditions of background, illumination, light, temperature, and humidity (Fig. 29-3).

| bright green | dark green | gray green | citron yellow | gray, black-flecked |

Fig. 29-3. Changes of pigment distribution in the dermis of the European tree toad (*Hyla arborea*) as they affect color. Melanophores, darkly stippled; lipophores, lightly stippled; guanophores, with short lines; epidermis omitted. (*After W. J. Schmidt*, 1920.)

The palms and soles of the *feet* bear small cornified tubercles; on the hind foot in the spadefoots (*Scaphiopus*) and some other toads the innermost tubercle becomes a horny cutting spade that these animals use to dig backward into the ground when seeking shelter. The tree toads (Hylidae), some frogs (Phyllobatidae), and some *Rana* in Asia have expanded discs on all toes by which they can adhere to and climb on vertical surfaces; some members of these families are exclusively arboreal. The webbing of the hind toes is least in strictly terrestrial toads and widely developed in the more aquatic amphibians, being notably large in the Pipidae.

29-5. Skeleton and muscles.   The *skeleton* in salamanders resembles that of other elongate vertebrates in having many vertebrae (up to 100 in *Amphiuma*); some caecilians have over 200.   Ribs are present in salamanders, caecilians, and some toads.   The pelvic girdle of salamanders is short, and caecilians lack both limbs and girdles.   The whole skeleton in both these groups is more fully ossified than in a frog.   Most amphibians have fine teeth on the upper jaw and roof of the mouth (vomers, palatine, or sphenoid); some salamanders have teeth on both jaws, but toads are toothless.   The teeth are somewhat conical, fastened to the surfaces of the bones, and replaced by growth of a new tooth beside the old one.

Segmental *muscles* are conspicuous on the trunk and tail of all salamanders and caecilians, and many show external skin furrows between adjacent muscles.   Gill-bearing species have special muscles to move the gills and to open or close the gill slits.   The upper segment of each limb stands out laterally from the body, with a conspicuous angle at each elbow or knee, thus ⌐°⌐, as in four-legged reptiles.

29-6. Respiration.   The *heart* in larvae is fishlike, with one auricle and a ventricle, and all the heart blood is venous (unoxygenated).   Adults have two auricles and a double circulation of the blood through the heart. The pulmocutaneous arteries distribute blood to both lungs and skin in all adult amphibians without gills.

Amphibians have more diverse means for *respiration* than any other group in the animal kingdom, a condition that reflects their transitional place between aquatic and land habitats.   In different species the gills, lungs, skin, and buccopharynx serve separately or in combination.

Three pairs of external *gills* occur in the embryos and larvae (Fig. 29-4) of all amphibians and persist in the adults of some strictly aquatic

Fig. 29-4.   Gills of amphibian larvae; enlarged insets show finer structure of gill filaments.

salamanders (*Necturus*, *Amphiuma*, and *Siren*, but not *Cryptobranchus*). By pumping action of the mouth cavity, water is drawn in through the nostrils and forced out the gill slits, to pass the filaments where the respiratory exchange occurs. *Necturus* waves its bushy gills in the water and does not use the mouth in respiration.

Save for the dipnoan fishes, amphibians are the lowest vertebrates with **lungs.** These are usually simple sacs with a few shallow internal partitions that contain blood vessels (Fig. 2-16). The mechanism of lung respiration in all amphibians is as described in Chap. 2. In aquatic species the lungs serve also as hydrostatic organs, being inflated to assist the animals when floating. Reduction of lungs has occurred in some salamanders that inhabit swift mountain streams (*Rhyacotriton*), and lungs are absent in the American land salamanders (PLETHODONTIDAE).

The skin of all amphibians contains many blood vessels served by the cutaneous arteries, whereby the skin functions like a lung. This enables many aquatic species to remain submerged for long periods and to hibernate in ponds during the winter.

In many amphibians respiration is buccopharyngeal; pulsations by the floor of the mouth cavity move air in and out of the nostrils and aeration of the blood occurs in vessels under the mucous membrane lining the mouth cavity.

The larynx in toads and frogs contains elastic muscular **vocal cords** that can be set into vibration by air forced from the lungs to produce the familiar croaking notes; the pitch of the notes is varied by changing the tension of the cords. Many species also have thin vocal pouches on the chin, median in toads but lateral and paired in some frogs. Vibrating air passes into and distends the pouches, which act as resonators to amplify the sound. Each species has characteristic notes and calls, readily identifiable by students of natural history. The bullfrog utters deep notes, and many small tree toads have shrill and far-carrying calls. Salamanders lack vocal cords, yet some occasionally utter faint squeaks.

NATURAL HISTORY

29-7. Distribution. Amphibians are most abundant in moist temperate regions and live in fresh water or in damp places; none inhabits salt water. They are scarcer in high altitudes and latitudes although a tree toad and a frog occur to over 12,000 feet in the Sierra Nevada of California, a toad reaches 15,400 feet in The Himalayas, and a frog ranges within the Arctic Circle. Some toads and tree toads inhabit the arid southwestern states and desert regions elsewhere; the spotted toad (*Bufo punctatus*) occurs from Texas to eastern California, including Death Valley. In these dry places the animals remain in underground burrows by day and become active only at night.

The mud puppy (*Necturus*), hellbender (*Cryptobranchus*), congo eel (*Amphiuma*), mud eel (*Siren*), and the tongueless toads (*Pipa, Xenopus*) are strictly aquatic. The bullfrog and green frog live in or close to permanent water, the leopard frog in grasslands, and the wood frog on the damp floor of forests. Many salamanders hide beneath logs, stones, or moss or in burrows of other animals. Some tree toads and frogs are partly arboreal, and others in the tropics are completely so. Toads are terrestrial, and each individual usually has a regular retreat to which it returns after a night of foraging. The tropical caecilians burrow in moist earth.

29-8. Seasonal activity. All amphibians must avoid temperature extremes and drought because they have no regulation of body temperature and can lose water easily from the soft skin. In regions with severe winters, the frogs and aquatic salamanders hibernate during the cold season by going deep into lakes or streams that do not freeze. Toads and terrestrial salamanders then burrow or otherwise go into the ground below the frost line. During hibernation all bodily processes are lessened, the heartbeat is very slow, and the animal subsists on materials stored within its body, including glycogen in the liver. The mild climate of some southern states permits many amphibians there to be above ground at all seasons. In the lowlands of California many are active during the mild winter rainy season, but in the hot dry summer some aestivate in below-ground retreats. The spring emergence with species that hibernate is conditioned by temperature, to which each responds differently; some approximate times of emergence for species at Ithaca, N.Y., are as follows: late March, *Ambystoma punctatum* and *Rana sylvatica;* April 1,

Hyla crucifer and *R. pipiens;* early April, *Bufo americanus* and *R. palustris;* late May, *R. clamitans;* mid-June, *R. catesbeiana.*

29-9. Food. Adult amphibians and the larvae of salamanders eat only live moving animals such as insects, crustaceans, worms, and small mollusks. Large aquatic species also take small fishes, the bullfrog sometimes catches small fishes, birds, or mammals, and big amphibians will devour small individuals of their own or other species. Toads in gardens are beneficial to man because of their destruction of insects.

Fig. 29-5. Tongues of a plethodont salamander and a frog as extended to capture prey.

The aquatic larvae of toads and frogs feed mainly on algae and on bits of dead animals in the water, as their peculiar mouth parts do not permit swallowing large items (Figs. 2-20, 29-4).

29-10. Enemies. Frogs and tree toads are staple foods of turtles, snakes, herons, certain hawks, raccoons, and large fishes. The acrid secretions of the warts on toads protect these animals from many predators, although they are eaten by hog-nosed snakes and garter snakes. Raccoons and skunks are reported to roll toads underfoot to get rid of these secretions before eating them. Puppies soon learn by bitter experience to leave toads alone, and adult dogs rarely attack them. For the same reason, newts are seldom eaten by other animals. Amphibian larvae are preyed upon by large water bugs and beetles and by dragon-fly nymphs as well as by the various enemies of adult amphibians.

   29-11. Reproduction. Most amphibians mate in water, where their eggs are deposited and hatched and where the resulting larvae live and

FIG. 29-6.   Some amphibian eggs and their gelatinous coverings; diagrammatic.

grow until they metamorphose into the adult stages.   Each species has a characteristic breeding place where several to many adults may congregate, such as a large quiet lake or pond, a stream, or a transient pool. Some species breed on land, and some have peculiar modes of reproduction, mentioned below.   With toads and frogs, the males, upon entering the water, begin croaking to attract females.   As each "ripe" female enters, she is clasped by a male, who clings on her back.   When ready, she extrudes her eggs, and the clasping male discharges sperm, or "milt," over them to effect fertilization (Fig. 2-20).   The pair then separates, and the female soon quits the water.   With both aquatic and terrestrial salamanders there is a courting performance in which the male noses about or may mount the female, but he eventually deposits one or more gelatinous spermatophores (sperm packets) on the bottom or ground.

These are taken up into the cloaca of the female and serve to fertilize her eggs internally before they are laid .

Eggs of amphibians are covered with one or more gelatinous coatings. The coats on eggs of aquatic species swell after laying until an egg mass may exceed in bulk the female that laid it.   The coverings protect the eggs against shock and drying and also make attacks by enemies more difficult.   The form of egg mass and jelly coats are distinctive for each species (Fig. 29-6). Toad eggs are in long strings, those of frogs in tapioca-like masses, and those of some aquatic salamanders in small clumps; a few species deposit the eggs individually.   Eggs of land salamanders (Plethodontidae) are often attached by a stalk to some object. A small frog (*Sminthillus*) of Cuba lays but one egg, some land salamanders deposit about 30, small frogs and tree toads produce up to 1,000, the bullfrog up to 25,000, and one large toad (*Bufo marinus*) may lay up to 32,000 eggs at one time.

The time and rate of development vary widely among species and with differences in water temperature.   Eggs of the spadefoot (*Scaphiopus*) may yield young toads in a month, whereas larvae of the bullfrog commonly require 2 years before they metamorphose into frogs. The larval stages of many frogs and toads last for several months.

Salamander larvae (Fig. 29-7) resemble their parents in general form, having limbs and feet early in life and a mouth that enables them to be predaceous feeders.   Their larval characteristics of gills, gill slits, a dorsal fin on the tail and back, and peculiarities in the hyoid apparatus are usually lost at metamorphosis.

Toads and frogs produce larvae known as "tadpoles" or "polliwogs"; the head and body form a single ovoid mass, and the long tail has median fins above and below.   Their external gills are replaced by internal gills covered by a delicate membrane (operculum).   The limbs develop late in larval life, and the fore limbs are hidden within the operculum until metamorphosis.   True jaws are lacking; on the face are two horny plates that serve to scrape algae and other minute food from objects in the water. The intestine is long, slender, and spirally coiled.   The metamorphosis is a conspicuous change that involves (1) growth of a wide mouth and loss of the horny jaws; (2) loss of the gills, closure of the gill slits, and development of lungs; (3) emergence of the forelegs; (4) reduction in length of the intestine from the long (herbivorous) type to the short (carnivorous) form of the frog; and (5) resorption of the tail and median fins.   While these changes are occurring, the young inhabit shallow water where both gill and lung respiration are possible and where insect food may be captured. They may emerge before the tail stub is resorbed and then inhabit damp ground, often hiding in crevices to avoid desiccation.   Thousands may appear suddenly during a shower, thus accounting for the age-old belief of an occasional "rain of toads."

1⅓ days   6⅔ days   10⅓ days

14⅙ days   15⅔ days   18⅔ days

22⅔ days   26 days

36⅔ days

Fig. 29-7.   Mud puppy (*Necturus maculosus*, Order PROTEIDA).   Development and adult.
(*From Noble, Biology of the amphibia.*)

In the hellbender (*Cryptobranchus*) and the HYNOBIIDAE fertilization is
external, the male discharging sperm over eggs laid in a nest in the water.
Fertilization is internal in the American bell toad (*Ascaphus*).   Eggs of
some land salamanders (PLETHODONTIDAE) are deposited in damp cavities and often guarded by the female; some hatch as larvae that have an
aquatic stage, but others complete development within the egg to emerge
as miniature adults.   Certain frogs also complete their development

while in the egg membranes. In both cases the embryos have broad thin gills that serve for air breathing in a manner analogous to the allantoic respiration in embryos of reptiles and birds. The male obstetrical toad (*Alytes*) of Europe entwines the egg strings about his hind legs until the larvae are ready for release into water. The female tongueless toad (*Pipa*) carries her eggs in separate dermal pockets on her back until they metamorphose, and the marsupial frog (*Gastrotheca*, Fig. 29-8),

Gastrotheca pygmaea   Gastrotheca marsupiata   Cryptobatrachus evansi

Fig. 29-8. Brood pouches of some tropical tree toads (Hylidae), opened to show eggs within. (*After Noble, Biology of the amphibia.*)

carries her egg mass sheltered dorsally under a flap of skin. Certain tropical frogs prepare a nest of gelatinous froth for the eggs; in some species the larvae drop into water, and others complete their development in the nest. The European salamander (*Salamandra salamandra*) is ovoviviparous, the female retaining her few embryos internally for 10 to 12 months, when they are released into water. The European alpine salamander (*S. atra*) retains one or two embryos that develop completely before birth.

Some ambystomid salamanders produce perennial larvae that reach adult size and even breed while retaining the gills and other larval features. This condition, known as **neoteny,** occurs in the tiger salamander (*Ambystoma tigrinum*) in Colorado, near Mexico City, and elsewhere, and also in *Dicamptodon ensatus* of the Pacific coast.

Several salamanders that have gills as adults also retain larval features in the head bones and the structure of the skin (*Necturus, Proteus, Amphiuma, Siren,* and *Pseudobranchus*); these have been termed "permanent larvae"; they differ in the degree of approach to adult structure.

Small amphibians may breed at two years of age, but larger forms mature more slowly. The length of life is known only for specimens in zoological gardens, a few records being: giant salamander, 55 years; European toad, 36 years; tiger salamander, 25 years as a larva and 11 years as an adult.

Live toads or frogs are occasionally reported as being found in cavities of rocks or trees where, inferentially, they had been imprisoned for years;

it seems likely that such animals had some means of exit and had not been long "imprisoned," because captive amphibians even in favorable surroundings but without food will gradually waste away.

William Buckland, Dean of Westminster and lecturer in geology at Oxford University, England, once experimented on this oft-debated subject. Twelve circular cells (12 inches deep by 5 inches in diameter) were made in porous limestone, and 12 smaller ones (6 by 5 inches) in compact siliceous sandstone. On Nov. 26, 1825, a toad was placed in each cell (sealed with a glass plate and a sheet of slate, both set in clay) and buried in earth at a depth of 3 feet. On Dec. 10, 1826, all the toads in the sandstone were dead and much decayed; most of those in the limestone were alive, and two had gained weight (possibly from small invertebrates that entered the cells, one of which had a cracked glass), but the last died before the end of the second year. Other toads, put into closely stoppered holes in apple trees, died within a year.

29-12. Relations to man. Amphibians furnish art motifs (Fig. 29-9) and play a role in the religions of primitive peoples. A toad-shaped amulet from near the river Nile is dated at 3400 B.C., and a Chinese

Fig. 29-9. Amphibian motifs in the art of American Indians. *A.* Frog pursued by snake (on basket of Guiana Indians, *from Roth*). *B.* Tadpole design (Hopi pottery, *from Fewkes*). (*After Frost*, 1932.)

sacrificial vessel in the form of a toad belongs to an ancient dynasty (2205 to 1122 B.C.). Aesop (560 B.C.) included frogs among his fables, and Aristophanes (448–380 B.C.) dramatized their croaking choruses. The dances and myths of some American Indians used frogs, sometimes personified, and Indian sorcerers employed the bodies or parts of frogs and toads in their magic. Roasted frogs, seasoned with soy, have been employed to treat consumption and other diseases in Japan. Toads, long used in Chinese medicine, may have some therapeutic value because of the digitalis-like secretions in the skin.

Erroneous beliefs about amphibians are common, such as that a croaking frog predicts rain, that the toad bears a jewel in its head, and that salamanders can endure fire (burning a log in the woods may force an individual sheltered within to emerge).

Mark Twain's humorous story "The Celebrated Jumping Frog of

Calaveras County" is now the basis for an annual "jumping-frog contest" at Angels Camp, Calif., with pet bullfrogs from all over the United States.

Frogs are used for elementary courses in biology, for research in physiology and pharmacology, for fish bait, and for human food. The gathering and sale of frogs to supply these needs is a minor part of the fisheries industry. Many thousands are caught annually in various states, and in some localities the supply has been depleted. In Louisiana, during 1938, a total of 715,540 pounds of frogs was taken, valued at $107,331. Frogs are taken by hand, with nets, with spears, or by shooting. Live frogs may be stored for some weeks or months at low temperatures until needed. Others are killed at once, cleaned, and refrigerated or quick-frozen; some frog flesh has even been canned. With species such as the leopard frog only the hind legs are used, but the bullfrog has enough flesh to warrant eating the entire animal. Frog meat is of delicate flavor, somewhat like veal or chicken. The axolotls of lakes near Mexico City are also used as food.

"Frog farming" has long been a topic of discussion and experiment, but no successful long-continued frog farm is known. So-called "farms" are merely favorable marshes where natural reproduction is high. Artificial rearing is impracticable because (1) no satisfactory supply of living moving food for frogs has been developed; (2) losses from disease and predators such as snakes, herons, and raccoons may be large where frogs are concentrated; (3) frogs of different sizes must be separated lest the big individuals eat the smaller ones; and (4) the low average price per adult does not provide an adequate return for the two or more years required to rear a frog from the egg to market size. Despite these limitations, there have been many efforts to rear frogs in artificial ponds. Many persons have purchased "breeding stock" and "lessons in frog culture" from unscrupulous promoters and have built ponds, only to have their efforts end in failure.

29-13. Fossil amphibians. The earliest recognized amphibians (†*Ichthyostega*) occur in Devonian rocks of Greenland. They had narrow skulls 6 to 8 inches long and were of some size. They possibly were derived from crossopterygian fishes that inhabited shallow fresh-water pools and streams, had both aquatic and aerial respiration, and possessed fins with skeletal supports from which the tetrapod limb could be derived. The Devonian was evidently a time of season droughts, when the chances of survival were greater for an animal that could leave a drying pool to travel over land and seek water elsewhere. Only the development of limbs made this possible. By Carboniferous time, with its coal swamps, there were three distinct orders of ancient amphibians. The skull became flattened and roofed with bone, and many had external armor of bony plates, possibly as protection against large eurypterids (arthropods) then in fresh waters.   Those amphibians had elongate bodies from a few inches to perhaps 15 feet in length.   Some were aquatic and some terrestrial.   Early forms had one occipital condyle and five toes on the hand, unlike modern amphibians.   Two orders died out in the Permian and the third in the Triassic.   Some of the last types were permanently aquatic, and several had degenerated to become limbless, like eels or snakes.   The connection between these early orders and modern amphibians is not bridged by intermediate fossils.   Salamanders appeared in the Cretaceous and were distinct from the earliest frogs, which appeared in the Jurassic; the latter may have been derived from fossil branchiosaurs. Both these modern types show degenerative trends in the skull by loss of bones.   There is no fossil record of the caecilians.

CLASSIFICATION

Class *AMPHIBIA* (Batrachia).   AMPHIBIANS.   Living forms with moist glandular skin and no external scales; typically with 2 pairs of limbs (no paired fins); 2 nostrils connecting to mouth cavity; skull with 2 occipital condyles; heart 3-chambered; respiration by gills, lungs, or skin; eggs with gelatinous coverings, usually laid in water; larvae usually aquatic; adults aquatic or in moist places on land; Devonian to Recent; more than 2,500 living species.

Subclass 1.   STEGOCEPHALIA.   Cranium and cheeks completely roofed with bony plates; fossil species often with armor of small overlapping scales ventrally, some also with dorsal scales.

Order 1.   †Leptospondyli.   Small, like salamanders or eels; each vertebra usually with centrum and neural arch of one piece; ribs articulated between adjacent vertebrae.   Carboniferous and Permian.   †*Lysorophus;* †*Diplocaulus.*

Order 2.   †Phyllospondylii.   BRANCHIOSAURS.   Small, like salamanders or snakes; vertebrae tubular, with nerve cord and notochord in common cavity; 3 pairs of gills on broad arches during long larval life, but none in adult.   Devonian to Permian. †*Ichthyostega,* †*Branchiosaurus.*

Order 3.   †Labyrinthodonti.   Small to large, of salamander or crocodile form; both jaws with large teeth having greatly folded dentine; body usually armored with dermal plates.   Lower Carboniferous to Upper Triassic.   †*Eogyrinus,* to 15 feet long; †*Eryops* (Fig. 29-10), crocodile-like, to 9 feet long; †*Capitosaurus.*

Fig. 29-10.   A fossil amphibian (†*Eryops,* Order LABYRINTHODONTI).   Length to 9 feet (*After Noble, Biology of the amphibia.*)

Order 4.   Gymnophiona (Apoda).   CAECILIANS.   Body slender, wormlike, no limbs or limb girdles; skull compact, roofed with bone; vertebrae many; ribs long; skin smooth, with transverse furrows, and both slime glands and "squirt glands" (discharging an irritating fluid); some with mesodermal scales embedded in skin; a small protrusible tentacle between eye and nostril; eyes lidless, often beneath skin or maxillary bones; tail short, anus near end of body; male with protrusible copulatory organ. No known fossils; about 55 Recent species.

Caeciliidae. In tropics: India to Philippines, Borneo, Java, and Seychelles; east and west Africa; Mexico to Argentina. *Ichthyophis* (Fig. 29-2); *Gymnopis*. Live, crawl, and burrow in moist ground; feed on invertebrates; eggs usually 24 to 30 per female, to 6 mm. in diameter, each in gelatinous covering, deposited in moist ground near water; some complete larval development in egg, others with aquatic larvae. *Typhlonectes*, northern South America, aquatic throughout life and viviparous, producing about 6 embryos that grow to 150 mm. long before birth.

Subclass 2. CAUDATA (Urodela). Salamanders, Newts, etc. Body elongate, with distinct head, trunk, and tail; limbs of about equal size; larvae, if aquatic, resemble adults in form and have teeth in both jaws; about 150 species.

Order 1. **Proteida.** Body depressed, tail with fin; gills permanent, bushy; no eyelids; lungs present; permanently aquatic.

Proteidae. *Necturus maculosus*, mud puppy or water dog (Fig. 29-7), Arkansas River to the Carolinas and Hudson River, in clean or polluted waters, moving or quiet; to 12 (or 17) inches long, rusty-brown, with blackish spots; eats small fishes, mollusks, crustaceans, aquatic insects, and worms; often taken on baited fishhooks; mates in autumn when females take up spermatophores deposited by males; eggs laid in May or June, 18 to 180 in "nests," attached individually by jelly stalks to undersides of stones and guarded by female; hatch out in 38 to 63 days, larvae 22 mm. long; growth slow, about 6 years to full size; *N. punctatus*, the Carolinas; *Proteus anguineus*, "olm" of southeastern Europe, in waters of deep caves, unpigmented, eyes under skin.

Order 2. **Mutabilia.** True Salamanders. Adults without gills (except *Amphiuma*); lungs present (except Plethodontidae); skull with paired vomers.

Crytobranchidae. Body depressed, skin soft, flabby, with fleshy folds at sides; no eyelids; vomerine teeth in arc parallel to jaw; permanently aquatic; Oligocene to Recent. *Cryptobranchus alleganiensis*, hellbender (Fig. 29-11), Louisiana to Ohio and

Fig. 29-11.   The hellbender (*Cryptobranchus alleganiensis*, Order Mutabilia).   Length to 24 inches.   (*After Noble, Biology of the amphibia*.)

New York, in running water with rock slabs; to 24 inches long; food as with *Necturus;* fertilization external; in late summer, mates and lays over 300 eggs in rosary-like strings; larvae hatch in November, require several years to mature. *Megalobatrachus japonicus*, giant salamander, eastern China and Japan in cold brooks, to 69 inches long. †*Andrias scheuchzeri*, Miocene in Europe, first referred to several centuries ago as "*Homo diluvii testis*" (human victim of the deluge).

Hynobiidae. Asiatic Land Salamanders. Small; with eyelids; vomerine teeth in V behind nares; fertilization external; metamorphosis complete. Northern Asia, Chungking to Ural Mountains. *Hynobius* (Fig. 29-12); *Ranodon*, lives in brooks.

(*In other salamanders the male has cloacal papillae, the female a seminal receptacle, and fertilization is internal.*)

FIG. 29-12.   Asiatic land salamander (*Hynobius*, Family HYNOBIIDAE).   Length to 6 inches.   (*After Noble, Biology of the amphibia.*)

AMBYSTOMIDAE.   Teeth in transverse row across posterior margins of vomers, none on palatine bones; with eyelids; vertebrae amphicoelous; adults usually terrestrial; limited to North America.   *Ambystoma*, 13 species; *A. tigrinum*, tiger salamander (Fig. 29-1), whole United States and to central Mexico, adults about 8 inches long, larva often perennial as "axolotl"; *A. opacum*, marbled salamander, eastern states, eggs laid in moist places; *Dicamptodon ensatus*, Pacific coast, to 10½ inches long, larvae often perennial; *Rhyacotriton olympicus*, Oregon and Washington, in mountain streams, lungs only ¼ inch long.

SALAMANDRIDAE.   Teeth in roof of mouth behind nares and diverging posteriorly; with lungs but no gills; eyelids present; vertebrae opisthocoelous.   Europe, eastern Asia, and North America.   *Triturus viridescens*, American newt or eft (Fig. 29-13), Atlantic coast to Hudson Bay and Texas, with reddish spots along sides, to 4 inches long, eggs single, in water; *T. torosus* and others, Pacific coast newt, or "water dog," California to southern Alaska, brown above and orange beneath, to 9 inches long, eggs in small masses in

FIG. 29-13.   American newt or eft (*Triturus viridescens*, Family SALAMANDRIDAE), in courtship performance; male above. Length to about 4 inches.   (*After Noble, Biology of the amphibia.*)

water; *T. cristatus*, European crested newt, male brilliant with dorsal crest in breeding season; *Salamandra salamandra*, European "fire" salamander, black with yellow spots, to 6 inches long, adults terrestrial, eggs retained and develop for 10 months in female, then released in water to complete larval growth; *S. atra*, European Alpine salamander, young 1 or 2, complete development in female, no aquatic stage.

AMPHIUMIDAE.   Body cylindrical, elongate; no eyelids; adults with lungs, gills, and gill clefts; limbs small, toes 2 or 3.   *Amphiuma means*, "congo eel" (Fig. 29-14),

FIG. 29-14.   "Congo eel" (*Amphiuma means*, Family AMPHIUMIDAE).   Length to 36 inches.   (*After Noble, Biology of the amphibia.*)

Louisiana to Missouri and Virginia, in swamps and rice fields, grows to 36 inches long, feeds on mollusks, crayfishes, and small fishes.

PLETHODONTIDAE.   LUNGLESS SALAMANDERS.   Mostly under 6 inches long; a minute nasolabial groove from each nostril to upper lip; teeth on vomers and also behind on parasphenoids; eyelids present; no lungs or gills; skin delicate; about 80 species in the Americas (eastern Canada to Bolivia and Lower California to Alaska, none in Great Basin or Rocky Mountains); 1 in southern South America, 2 in southern Europe; most adults terrestrial in moist places where eggs are deposited, guarded by female, and young emerge with no larval stage; few in cold brooks with aquatic larvae. *Gyrinophilus porphyriticus*, purple salamander; *Pseudotriton ruber*, red salamander; *Desmognathus fuscus*, dusky salamander (Fig. 29-15); *Plethodon glutinosus*, slimy

Fig. 29-15. Lungless salamanders (Family PLETHODONTIDAE). *Above.* Arboreal salamander (*Aneides lugubris*). Length to 6½ inches. *Below.* Dusky salamander (*Desmognathus fuscus*), female with eggs. Length to 4¼ inches. (*After Noble, Biology of the amphibia.*)

salamander; *Batrachoseps attenatus*, slender salamander of Pacific coast, with small legs; *Aneides lugubris*, arboreal salamander of California (Fig. 29-15*A*), sometimes oviposits in holes in trees; *Eurycea bislineata*, two-lined salamander; *Typhlomolge rathbuni*, blind, nearly colorless, permanently aquatic and neotenic, in underground waters at San Marcos, Texas.

Order 3. **Meantes.** Body slender, elongate; no hind limbs or eyelids; gills persistent; jaws with horny covering; fertilization probably external; strictly aquatic.

SIRENIDAE. *Siren lacertina*, "mud eel," Virginia and Indiana to Florida and Texas, in muddy ditches and ponds, grows to 30 inches, 3 pairs of gills; *Pseudobranchus striatus*, South Carolina to Florida, to 7 inches long, 1 pair of gill slits, burrows.

Subclass 3. SALIENTIA (Anura). TOADS AND FROGS. Head and trunk fused, no neck or tail; mouth usually wide; forelegs short, hind legs enlarged for leaping and with webs between toes; vertebrae 10, the last a slender urostyle; ribs reduced or none; skin mostly free from muscles beneath; egg deposition and fertilization usually external, by "clasped" pair of adults; larva (tadpole) with fused ovoid head-and-body and long tail with median fins, usually aquatic; metamorphosis conspicuous; over 1,700 species.

Order 1. **Amphicoela.** Vertebrae amphicoelous; 2 relict "tail" muscles.

ASCAPHIDAE (Liopelmidae). "BELL TOADS." Only 2 genera; *Liopelma*, 2 species, the only amphibians native to New Zealand; *Ascaphus truei* (Fig. 29-16), northwestern California to Washington and Montana, in or near cool mountain streams; in mating, male grasps female around pelvis, and fertilization is internal (unique in SALIENTIA)

FIG. 29-16.   Male American "bell" toad (*Ascaphus truei*, Family ASCAPHIDAE) of north-western United States.   Head-and-body length to 2 inches.   Enlarged inset shows cloacal appendage in ventral view.   (*After Noble, Biology of the amphibia.*)

by use of external tail-like copulatory organ on male; larva with ventral sucking disc for adhering to stones in swift stream waters.

Order 2. **Opisthocoela.**   Vertebrae opisthocoelous; free ribs in either larva or adult.

DISCOGLOSSIDAE.   Tongue and eyelids present; adults with ribs.   †*Latonia*, Upper Miocene; *Discoglossus; Bombina*, fire-bellied toad of Old World, with black and bright red or yellow on undersurface; *Alytes obstetricans*, European midwife toad, strings of eggs laid by female are gathered around hind legs of male and carried until hatching, when larvae are released in water.

XENOPIDAE.   CLAWED TOADS.   No tongue; feet fully webbed; three inner hind toes with black horny claws; strictly aquatic.   Africa.   *Xenopus*, used in human pregnancy tests.

PIPIDAE.   No tongue or eyelids; feet fully webbed; slender front toes end in cluster of short dermal papillae; strictly aquatic; eggs carried in separate pockets on back of female, young fully metamorphosed when hatched. Northern South America.   *Pipa*, Surinam toad.

Order 3. **Anomocoela.**   Sacral vertebrae procoelous; no free ribs.

PELOBATIDAE.   SPADEFOOT TOADS.   Hind foot with horny cutting spade on inner margin; pupil of eye elliptical; Northern Hemisphere to Philippine Islands.   *Pelobates*, in Old World; *Scaphiopus holbrookii*, Texas and Florida to Massachusetts; *S. couchii*, Oklahoma to Arizona; *S. hammondii* (Fig. 29-17),

FIG. 29-17.   A spadefoot toad (*Scaphiopus hammondii*, Family PELOBATIDAE). Head-and-body length to 2½ inches. (*From Storer, 1925.*)

Montana to Texas and westward; strictly nocturnal, hiding by day in burrows, seldom seen except when spawning; eggs laid in temporary pools after rains in spring or summer; development through metamorphosis requires about 1 month.

Order 4. **Procoela.** Vertebrae procoelous; urostyle with double condyle.

†Palaeobatrachidae. *†Palaeobatrachus*, Jurassic to Miocene, Europe.

Bufonidae. True Toads. No maxillary teeth; a large parotoid gland behind each eye; ventral parts of pectoral girdle overlap (arciferous); practically world-wide. *Eleutherodactylus; Leptodactylus; Bufo*, common toads, skin rough, many warts; terrestrial and nocturnal, hiding under logs, stones, etc., or in burrows by day; enter water briefly to spawn; eggs in gelatinous strings; over 100 species, 16 in United States. *B. americanus*, American toad, Hudson Bay southward and eastward; *B. fowleri*, Fowler's toad, Texas to Michigan and eastward; *B. cognatus*, Great Plains toad, Kansas to Wyoming and Arizona; *B. boreas* (Fig. 29-18), Pacific states to Alaska; other species more local.

Fig. 29-18. The California toad (*Bufo boreas halophilus*, Family Bufonidae). Head-and-body length to 4⅓ inches. (*From Storer*, 1925.)

Fig. 29-19. A tree toad (*Hyla arenicolor*, Family Hylidae) of the American Southwest. Head-and-body length to 1⅝ inches. (*From Storer*, 1925.)

Brachycephalidae. Halves of pectoral girdle more or less fused ventrally. New World tropics. *Brachycephalus; Dendrobates.*

Hylidae. Tree Toads. Mostly under 2 inches; teeth in upper or both jaws; terminal bone of each digit claw-shaped; all toes with expanded "adhesive" discs, used to climb trees, rocks, etc. (Fig. 29-19); voice often loud; eggs usually in water; commonest in American tropics. *Hyla versicolor*, tree toad, Minnesota to Texas and eastward; *H. regilla*, Lower California to British Columbia; *H. crucifer*, spring peeper, Manitoba, Kansas, and eastward; *Acris gryllus*, cricket frog, central Canada and Texas eastward; *Gastrotheca*, "marsupial frog" (Fig. 29-8), South America, egg mass carried on back, exposed or in skin sac, whence young frogs hatch.

Order 5. **Diplasiocoela.** Pectoral girdle fused to sternum (firmisternal).

Ranidae. True Frogs. Teeth in upper jaw; tongue usually forked posteriorly; eggs usually in tapiocalike masses; Jurassic to Recent; world-wide except South America and Antipodes; only *Rana* with 22 species and subspecies in United States, the commonest being:

R. *catesbeiana*, bullfrog, Texas to southern Canada and eastward; introduced in western states; inhabits permanent ponds; length 6 to 8 inches; eardrum large, equals (♀) or exceeds (♂) eye; back and sides green with diffuse brown spots (Fig. 2-1).

R. *clamitans*, green frog or spring frog, Arkansas to southern Canada and eastward; lives in or near water; length 3 to 5 inches; head thick; eardrum equals (♀) or exceeds (♂) the eye; slight dorsolateral folds; color various, bright green to brownish above; sides with dark blotches; back granular.

R. *palustris*, pickerel frog, Arkansas to Hudson Bay and eastward; inhabits brooks, ponds, and wet meadows; length 3 to 2½ inches; skin smooth; dorsolateral folds broad; brownish above, with 4 rows of squarish dark-brown patches; legs with dark crossbands.

R. *pipiens*, leopard frog or grass frog, North America east of the Sierra-Cascade mountains and into

Mexico, in damp grass, meadows, etc.; length 3 to 5 inches; skin very smooth; dorsolateral folds narrow; upper surface brassy to brownish green with 2 (1 to 3) rows of brownish spots, each narrowly margined with white; other spots along sides; dark crossbands on legs (Fig. 2-1).

R. sylvatica, wood frog, Ohio and South Carolina to Nova Scotia; on ground in damp woods; length 2 to 3 inches; dorsolateral folds present; ear region dark; back pale to dark brown, sometimes irregularly spotted.

R. aurora, red-legged frog, Lower California to Vancouver Island; in ponds; length 3 to 5 inches; slight dorsolateral folds; yellowish to dark brown or gray above, with diffuse spots; undersurface reddish posteriorly.

POLYPEDATIDAE. OLD WORLD "TREE FROGS."   An intercalary cartilage in digits. Africa, eastern and southeastern Asia; mostly arboreal. *Polypedates (Rhacophorus),* eggs usually laid in gelatinous foam over water, whence tadpoles drop into water.

MICROHYLIDAE. "NARROW-MOUTH TOADS."   Head small, narrow. Cosmopolitan; arboreal to burrowing. *Microhyla carolinensis,* narrow-mouth toad (Fig. 29-20) Virginia and Indiana to Texas; nocturnal, hides in ground by day; larva aquatic

FIG. 29-20. Narrow-mouth toad (*Microhyla carolinensis,* Family MICROHYLIDAE). Length to 1½ inches. (*After Noble, Biology of the amphibia.*)

with median spiracle, toothless expansible mouth, and no nares until metamorphosis; in some species the "larva" completes metamorphosis within the egg capsule.

References

(See also Chap. 2)

BARBOUR, T.   1934.   Reptiles and amphibians, their habits and adaptations.   2d ed. Boston, Houghton Mifflin Co.   xxii + 129 pp., illus.

BISHOP, S. C.   1943.   Handbook of salamanders . . . of the United States, of Canada, and of Lower California.   Ithaca, N.Y., Comstock Publishing Co. xiv + 555 pp., 144 figs.

COPE, E. D.   1889.   The Batrachia of North America.   *U.S. National Museum, Bulletin* 34, 525 pp., 86 pls., 119 figs.   Comprehensive but out of date.

DICKERSON, M. E.   1906.   The frog book.   New York, Doubleday, Doran & Co., Inc.   xvi + 253 pp., 16 + 95 pls., 35 figs.   Popular; SALIENTIA of the United States.

DUNN, E. R.   1926.   The salamanders of the Family Plethodontidae.   Northampton, Mass., Smith College.   viii + 441 pp., 3 pls., 86 figs.

———.   1942.   The American caecilians.   *Museum of Comparative Zoology, Bulletin* 91, pp. 439–540.

GADOW, H.   1901.   Amphibia and Reptilia.   *In* Cambridge natural history.   London, Macmillan & Co., Ltd.   Vol. 8, xiii + 668 pp., 181 figs.

Livezey, R. L., and A. H. Wright.   1947.   A synoptic key to the salientian eggs of the United States.   *American Midland Naturalist*, vol. 37, pp. 179–222, 82 figs.

Noble, G. Kingsley.   1931.   Biology of the Amphibia.   New York, McGraw-Hill Book Co., Inc.   xiii + 577 pp., 174 figs.   Modern, technical; structure, function, life histories, and classification.

Rosel von Rosenhof.   1758.   Historia naturalis ranarum nostrativum.   Nuremberg, J. J. Fleishmann.   6 + 115 pp., 24 col. pls.   Earliest comprehensive account of the toads and frogs of Germany; text in parallel columns of Latin and German.

Stejneger, L., and T. Barbour.   1943.   A checklist of North American amphibians and reptiles.   5th ed.   *Museum of Comparative Zoology, Bulletin* 93, xix + 260 pp.   Scientific names and distribution.

Wright, A. A., and A. H. Wright.   1949.   Handbook of frogs and toads . . . of the United States and Canada.   3d ed.   Ithaca, N.Y., Comstock Publishing Co., Inc.   xi + 652 pp., 163 figs.   Keys and descriptions.

Articles on amphibians appear in many periodicals, especially in the quarterly *Copeia* published by the American Society of Ichthyologists and Herpetologists. For many states and Canadian provinces there are state or local lists giving the distribution and natural history of amphibians occurring in those areas.

CHAPTER 30

CLASS REPTILIA. REPTILES

The Class REPTILIA includes the lizards and snakes (Order SQUA-MATA), the turtles and tortoises (Order CHELONIA), the crocodiles and alligators (Order LORICATA), and the New Zealand tuatara (*Sphenodon punctatum*, Order RHYNCHOCEPHALIA). These represent only 4 of the 14 known orders that flourished during Mesozoic time, the Age of Reptiles,

FIG. 30-1. Class REPTILIA. American alligator. A representative reptile. Length to 10 feet or more. (*From E. L. Palmer.*)

when they were the dominant animals. Reptiles are the first group among vertebrates adapted for life in dry places on land. The dry cornified skin and scales resist loss of moisture from the body and facilitate living on rough surfaces. The class name refers to the mode of travel (L. *rept*, creeping), and the study of reptiles is called "herpetology" (Gr. *ereptos*, reptile).

30-1. Characteristics. 1. Body covered with dry cornified skin (not slimy), usually with scales or scutes; few surface glands.

2. Two pairs of limbs, each typically with 5 toes ending in horny claws and suited to running, crawling, or climbing; limbs paddle-like in marine turtles, reduced in some lizards, and absent in a few other lizards and in all snakes (vestiges in boas).

3. Skeleton completely ossified; skull with one occipital condyle.

4. Heart imperfectly 4-chambered, 2 auricles and a partly divided ventricle (ventricles separate in crocodilians); one pair of aortic arches; red blood corpuscles nucleated, biconvex, and oval.

5. Respiration always by lungs; cloacal respiration in aquatic turtles.

6. Twelve pairs of cranial nerves.

7. Body temperature variable (poikilothermous), according to environment.

8. Fertilization internal, usually by copulatory organs; eggs large with much yolk, in leathery or limy shells; usually laid, but retained in female for development by some lizards and snakes.

9. Embryonic membranes (amnion, chorion, yolk sac, and allantois) present during development; young when hatched (or born) resemble adults; no metamorphosis.

641

The reptiles show advance over the amphibians in having (1) a dry scaly integument suited to life in dry environments, (2) limbs suited for rapid locomotion, (3) further separation of the oxygenated and unoxygenated blood in the heart, (4) complete ossification of the skeleton, and (5) eggs suited for development on land with membranes and shells to protect the embryo. Reptiles lack the insulated body covering, regulated body temperature, and some other features of birds and mammals.

30-2. General appearance. The crocodiles and alligators and most lizards have elongate bodies with distinct head, neck, trunk, tail, and four limbs. Turtles are sheltered in a two-part shell from which the limbs, head, and tail protrude. Snakes have narrow cylindrical bodies and lack limbs, and some slender lizards are limbless. The fossil reptiles were of diverse form, some resembled mammals, others birds, and many were unlike any creature now living, some having armor, spines, or horns.

30-3. Size. The fossil reptiles were small to large, a few being the largest terrestrial animals ever known. Of living reptiles, the South American anaconda grows to 33 feet long, the Komodo lizard (*Varanus komodoensis*) to 9½ feet, and the marine leatherback turtle may exceed 7 feet. Some land tortoises of the Galápagos Islands exceed 4 feet in length, but none weighs over 250 pounds. A crocodile killed about 1825 in Luzon, Philippine Islands, was about 21 feet long. A snake (*Leptotyphlops*) of Syria is the size of a steel knitting needle, and a lizard (*Lepidoblepharis*) of Panama is about 2 inches long.

In the United States, the Florida diamondback rattlesnake becomes 8 feet long, the Gila monster about 19 inches, and the alligator snapping turtle exceeds 2 feet. A record American alligator measured 19 feet, but few now exceed 10 feet. Most North American snakes are 10 to 60 inches long, and the lizards usually under 12 inches.

FIG. 30-2. Head and mouth of the alligator.

STRUCTURE OF A REPTILE: THE ALLIGATOR

30-4. External features. The elongate *body* comprises a distinct head, neck, trunk, and tail; each of the short *limbs* bears toes tipped with horny claws and with webs between. The long *mouth* is margined with conical teeth, set in sockets. Near the tip of the snout are two small *external nares*. The *eyes* are large and lateral, with upper and lower eyelids, and a transparent *nictitating membrane* moves backward beneath the lids.

The small *ear* opening is behind the eye and under a flap of skin. The *anus* is a longitudinal slit, behind the bases of the hind limbs.

30-5. Integument. The tough leathery *skin* is sculptured into rectangular *horny scales* over most of the trunk and tail. The scales are generally in transverse and lengthwise rows, with furrows of softer skin between. The cornified exterior is not molted, and surface wear is replaced by additional cornified layers from the epidermis beneath. Adults have an exoskeleton of separate bony *dermal plates* under the dorsal scales from neck to tail; these are rectangular or oval, often pitted, and some have a median keel. Three pairs of epidermal *musk glands* occur on the lower side of the head, inside the mouth, and just within the cloaca.

30-6. Skeleton (Fig. 30-3). The massive *skull* includes an elongate snout, and bones of the skull are usually pitted in old adults. The long

FIG. 30-3.   Skeleton of the crocodile.   (*Adapted from Claus.*)

lower jaw articulates at each side of the posterior margin of the skull on a fixed quadrate bone. Ventrally on the cranium is the long *hard palate* above which are passages from the external to the internal nares.

The *vertebral column* comprises five types of vertebrae: 9 cervical, 10 thoracic, 5 lumbar, 2 sacral, and about 39 caudal. On the cervical vertebrae are short free *cervical ribs;* the thoracic vertebrae and sternum are connected by *thoracic ribs,* with cartilaginous ventral extensions, and between the sternum and pubic bones there are 7 pairs of V-shaped *abdominal ribs* held in a longitudial series by ligaments.

The *pectoral girdle* on each side comprises a dorsal scapula and ventral coracoid, both flattened; their junction provides an articulation for the *fore limb.* The latter includes the humerus, radius and ulna, two rows (3+3) of carpals, and the metacarpals and phalanges of the five toes. The *pelvic girdle* on each side include an ileum, ischium, and pubis, with the acetabulum at their junction as a socket for articulation of the femur. The bones of the *hind limb* are the femur, tibia and fibula, the tarsals, and the metatarsals and phalanges of the toes.

30-7. Muscular system. As compared with a frog, the alligator has more diversity in its muscles, in keeping with the greater variety of its movements both on land and in water. The muscles of the head, neck, and limbs are well-differentiated, though less in bulk than in a mammal. The segmental muscles of the vertebral column and ribs are conspicuous.

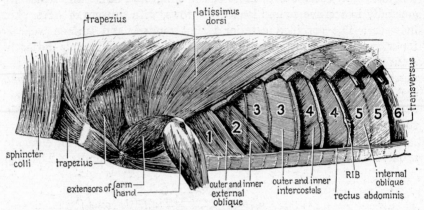

Fig. 30-4. Muscles of a lizard (*Lacerta*). Behind the "arm" successive muscle layers are removed to reveal those beneath: 1, outermost layer; 6, innermost layer. (*After Nierstrasz & Hirsch.*)

30-8. Digestive system. The large *mouth* (Fig. 30-2) can open widely and has stout *teeth* used for offense and defense and also to grasp and twist large items of prey. A flat *tongue* lies in the floor of the mouth cavity but cannot be protruded. On the hind margin of the tongue there is a transverse fold opposite a similar one (velum palatinum) on the palate; when pressed together these shut off the mouth cavity from the pharynx, so an alligator in water may open its mouth without having water enter its lungs. Beyond the short *pharynx* is the *esophagus,* a slender tube leading to the *stomach.* The latter comprises a large spherical or fundus region and a smaller pyloric portion on the right side. This connects to the coiled *small intestine,* which joins the larger *rectum* leading to the *cloaca* and *anus.* The *liver,* of two lobes, lies anterior to the stomach, and the *pancreas* is in the first or duodenal loop of the intestine; the ducts of both enter the fore part of the intestine. The cloaca is a common end for the digestive, excretory, and reproductive systems.

30-9. Circulatory system. The *heart* lies in the anteroventral part of the thorax; it comprises a small *sinus venosus,* two *auricles,* and two *ventricles.* The ventricles are completely separated in crocodilians but imperfectly so in other reptiles. Blood from the veins passes in turn through the (1) sinus venosus, (2) right auricle, (3) right ventricle, (4) pulmonary artery to each lung, (5) pulmonary veins from lungs, to the (6) left auricle, and (7) left ventricle. It emerges in a pair of *aortic* *arches* that pass dorsally around the esophagus; from the base of the right arch two *carotid arteries* lead to the neck and head, and a *subclavian artery* to each fore limb.   The two aortic arches join dorsally as a *dorsal aorta* and distribute to organs in the body cavity and to the hind limbs and tail. Venous blood is collected (1) by an *anterior vena cava* on each side from the head, neck, and fore limb; (2) by a single middorsal *posterior vena cava* from the reproductive organs and kidneys; (3) by a *hepatic portal vein* from the digestive tract that breaks to capillaries in the liver and collects as a short *hepatic vein;* and (4) by an *epigastric vein* on each side of the abdominal cavity from the posterior limbs, tail, and body. All these veins empty into the sinus venosus.

30-10. Respiratory system. Air enters the *external nares* and passes above the hard palate to the *internal nares* behind the velum and thence through the *glottis* in the pharynx, just behind the base of the tongue.   The glottis is composed of three cartilages and contains the paired *vocal cords;* it connects to the tubular *trachea,* which is reinforced with rings of cartilage.   The trachea extends to the fore part of the thorax to divide into two short *bronchi,* one to each lung.   The *lungs* are divided by higher interior partitions than in the frog and contain the pulmonary capillaries.

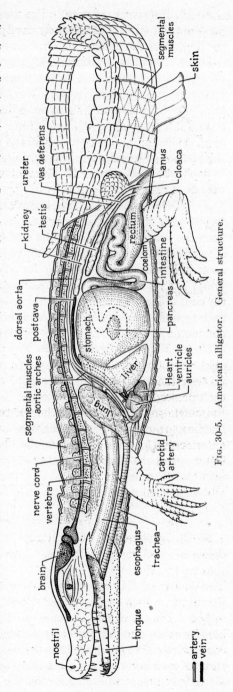

Fig. 30-5. American alligator. General structure.

30-11. Excretory system. The two flat lobular *kidneys* lie in the posterior dorsal part of the body cavity; a *ureter* from each extends back to the side of the cloaca.

30-12. Nervous system. Dorsally the *brain* shows two slender olfactory lobes connected to the large cerebral hemispheres; behind the latter are two oval optic lobes. Next is the median pear-shaped cerebellum, which is larger than in amphibians. The medulla oblongata is spread laterally below the cerebellum, then narrows to the spinal *nerve cord*. Ventrally, between the bases of the cerebral hemispheres, are the optic tracts and optic nerves, followed by the infundibulum and the hypophysis. There are 12 pairs of *cranial nerves* and paired *spinal nerves* to each body somite.

30-13. Sense organs. There are *taste buds* on the tongue and *olfactory organs* in each nasal cavity. The eyes have *lachrymal glands* to keep the cornea or surface of the eyeball moist when out of water. The ears are of the type characteristic of land vertebrates. Each ear has a short *external auditory canal* under a flap of skin, with a *tympanic membrane* at the inner end, a tympanic cavity or middle ear, and an inner ear containing three semicircular canals and the organ of hearing. From each tympanic cavity a *Eustachian tube* leads medially, the two having a common opening on the roof of the pharynx behind the internal nares.

30-14. Reproductive system. The paired gonads and ducts are much alike in young of the two sexes. In mature males two roundish *testes* lie near the ventromedial borders of the kidneys; a *vas deferens* from each passes back to enter the cloaca just anterior to the ureter and joins the single median *penis* on the ventral floor of the cloaca. In adult females two *ovaries* are similarly attached near the kidneys. Near the anterior end of each kidney is the open funnel of an *oviduct,* and the latter runs backward to the cloaca. Eggs form in the ovaries and pass into the funnels; in the oviducts, each is fertilized and covered with albumen, shell membranes, and shell before being laid.

STRUCTURE OF OTHER REPTILES

30-15. Integument. On all reptiles the skin comprises a stratified epidermis and complex dermis. The epidermis produces layers of cells that pass to the surface, become cornified, and provide the body covering. The epidermal cells are bound to one another by many fine intercellular "bridges," which resist mechanical displacement.

The dermis is chiefly of connective tissue and contains pigment cells, blood vessels, and nerves; in some species it includes dermal bones. The connective tissue fibers are in definite layers nearly parallel to the surface; those of each layer are approximately at right angles to fibers immediately above and below, and all are "on the bias" at about 45 degrees to the body axis. Small fibers extend up through the dermis and into the epidermis, binding the whole skin together. This structural arrangement provides mechanical strength, as in a woven fabric, yet is elastic so that the skin can stretch, as when a snake is swallowing large food or a lizard puffs up in its courting performance. The pattern of dermal scales is essentially constant on each species, and the form and arrangement of the scales are useful in the classification of reptiles.

The outer cornified epidermis is molted at intervals by lizards and snakes, from two to six times a year by the latter. Prior to a molt the epidermal cells produce a new cuticle beneath the older one. The latter then loosens by cell dissolution at its base, with some production of moisture between new and old layers. In snakes, this secretion clouds the cuticle over the eye, which is lost at the molt, and probably impairs the animal's vision, whence the common belief that "snakes go blind in August" when many of them molt. The "slough" of snakes and of small-limbed or limbless lizards comes off in one piece, first becoming free about the mouth when it is caught on some rough object and the animal wriggles out. The old covering of a snake becomes turned inside out, but some lizards literally crawl out of the old skin, and others molt the cuticle in pieces. The horny scutes of turtles are lost individually, at irregular intervals. The rattle of a rattlesnake results from retention of the heavier cornified covering at the end of the tail in successive molts (Fig. 30-11).

The pigment cells, or *chromatophores,* include both melanophores (black or brown) and lipophores (yellow, orange, or red); there are also *guanophores* in which color results, not from pigment, but from light diffraction by minute particles within the cells. Some lizards and many snakes have color patterns of brillance and beauty, comprising stripes or bands of alternating colors, spots small or large, and diamond or rectangular markings. Chameleons change color conspicuously, and some other reptiles undergo slight change, but many are fixed as to both pattern and intensity. Abnormalities in coloration include partial or complete "albinos" lacking some or all pigment and black individuals in which melanin is more abundant than usual; examples of both occur among rattlesnakes and other serpents. Control of pigment change in reptiles is ascribed to the adrenal glands.

30-16. Turtles. The body is incased in a more or less oval shell, consisting of a layer of platelike bones in definite pattern and closely sutured to one another, over which there is a covering of cornified scutes, also of regular arrangement (Fig. 30-6). The dorsal convex portion is the *carapace,* and the flatter ventral part the *plastron.* The thoracic vertebrae and ribs are usually consolidated with the bony carapace. Soft-shelled turtles have leathery integument, not divided into scutes, and the shell is poorly ossified. The head, tail, and limbs of turtles protrude between the two parts of the shell and in most species can be drawn completely within the margins for safety. Their jaws lack teeth but bear stout cornified sheaths serving to crush their food. The toes end in horny claws that are useful in crawling, climbing, or digging. On terrestrial tortoises the feet are stumpy, and on marine turtles the limbs are flipperlike, for swimming. The excretory system includes a bladder, and the urine is fluid. The male has an erectile penis on the ventral wall of the cloaca. In the cloaca of aquatic turtles are thin-walled vascular sacs that serve as "cloacal gills" when the animals are submerged.

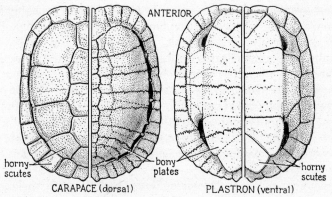

ANTERIOR

horny scutes   bony plates   horny scutes

CARAPACE (dorsal)   PLASTRON (ventral)

Fig. 30-6. The shell of a turtle (*Chrysemys*) showing the arrangement of external horny scutes over the bony plates beneath.

30-17. Sphenodon. The tuatara, only living member of the Order Rhynchocephalia, is restricted to New Zealand. It is lizard-like in superficial appearance but has various primitive characters including (1) three temporal bridges in the skull, (2) a widely roofed mouth, (3) firm adfixture of the quadrate, (4) a well-developed median pineal eye, (5) persistent abdominal ribs, and (6) absence of a copulatory organ.

30-18. Lizards. The general body configuration is varied, many species being slender, some compressed laterally, and some flattened dorsoventrally as with the horned toads. The limbs may be long or short, stout or delicate; they are reduced on some, and entirely lacking in a number of limbless lizards ("glass snake," Anniellidae, etc). Practically all the limbless forms live in the soil, through which they progress by wriggling in the manner of a worm. In some rapidly running lizards the long slender tail serves as a counterbalance, but in sluggish forms it is short and stumpy. The tail vertebrae in many species are incompletely ossified at their centers; if such a lizard is grasped by the tail, the latter separates at one or another of these "breaking points" and the animal scuttles off to freedom; in time it regenerates the tail.

The skin is usually flexible, is loosely attached to the body, and contains many scales arranged in rows, longitudinal, transverse, or diagonal. On most lizards the scales of the back and sides overlap behind, like shingles on a roof. Individual scales are variously smooth, pitted, or have a longitudinal keel. The ventral surface commonly bears small scales. An external eardrum is usually evident on each side of the head.

The tongue may be only slightly mobile or freely extensible; in chameleons it can be "shot" several inches beyond the snout to capture insects on the mucus-coated tip. The jaws are variously provided with teeth, usually short and alike, but differentiated as to form in the Old World AGAMIDAE. A bladder is present in lizards, but the excretory wastes are semisolid as in birds and most reptiles, being passed from the cloaca as whitish material (urates) with the feces. The male has two hemipenes in the sides of the cloaca; at copulation these are everted to enter the cloaca of the female.

30-19. Snakes. Loss of appendages and elongation of the body are an "experiment of nature" in several groups of vertebrates, including the eels and morays among fishes, the caecilians among amphibians, and the worm lizards (AMPHISBAENIDAE), silvery lizards (ANNIELLIDAE), "glass snake" and "slowworm" (ANGUIDAE), and other lizards, besides all the snakes. Vestiges of the pelvic girdle and hind limbs persist in the boas, pythons, etc. The snakes also lack limb girdles, a sternum, eyelids, external ear openings, and a bladder, and they show numerous specializations in form and function of other parts in the body.

Snakes vary considerably as to the size of the head and the length and diameter of the body. Most of the vipers have a broad, somewhat triangular head, but in other poisonous species and many harmless snakes it is narrow. The big tropical boas and some vipers and rattlesnakes are heavy-bodied, but racers, tree snakes, and others are quite slender. The tail may be long and tapered or short and blunt, and in the rattlesnakes it bears the cornified rattle.

As in lizards, the skin of snakes bears rows of scales, either smooth as on king snakes, or keeled as on rattlesnakes, garter snakes, and others (Fig. 30-7). The ventral surface on all except worm snakes has one row of large transverse scales (ventrals or gastrosteges) from chin to anus, and either one or two rows (caudals or urosteges) on the tail.

The eyes are covered with transparent cuticle; on worm snakes the vestigial eyes are beneath opaque scales. There is no external ear membrane or opening in snakes. The skull is delicate, and several of the bones can move upon one another. Teeth, having a backward slant, are present on the jaws and on bones in the roof of the mouth; they serve

Fig. 30-7. The scales of snakes. *A.* Head of ring-necked snake. *B.* Snake body with smooth scales. *C.* Snake body with keeled scales. *D.* Lower surface of a snake in the anal region showing the enlarged ventral scales on body and tail. (*Adapted from Blanchard,* 1924.)

to hold food while being swallowed. Poisonous snakes have a pair of specialized teeth, or "fangs," on the two maxillary bones of the upper jaw that conduct the venom used to kill prey; these are fixed in the cobra and its allies but folded back when not in use in rattlesnakes and other vipers. The serpent tongue is narrow, flexible, and ribbonlike, with a forked tip, and can protrude through a notch in the lower jaw when the mouth is closed; it aids in the sense of smell, bringing chemical stimuli to the Jacobson's organs in the nasal cavity. The digestive tract is essentially a straight tube, from mouth to anus, practically all the other internal organs are elongated, and the right lung is reduced or absent. Hemipenes are present in the male, as in lizards.

In long snakes the vertebrae number 200 to 400 (Fig. 30-8). The segmental body muscles of a snake are very slender and exceedingly

Fig. 30-8. Skeleton of a snake showing the loss of limbs, limb girdles, and sternum, and the greatly increased number of vertebrae and ribs all practically alike in structure.

numerous, connecting vertebrae to vertebrae, vertebrae to ribs, ribs to ribs, ribs to skin, and skin to skin. Many of them extend from one body segment to the next, but others connect, by tendons, between segments far removed from one another. This arrangement makes possible the graceful sinuous movements of a snake.

Locomotion in snakes is usually due to the backward pressure of lateral loops of the body against irregularities on the surface of the ground, as can be seen by examining a snake track on soft soil. Forward movement is accomplished at times by "hitching," part by part, the skin and body alternately, dragging the ventral scales on the ground, and producing a straight smooth track.   The sidewinder, or "horned rattlesnake" (*Crotalus cerastes*) progresses by a curious looping of the body at a sharp angle with its path of travel.

Snakes neither chew nor tear their food but swallow it entire.   They can utilize prey greater in diameter than their own bodies by reason of a series of adaptive modifications, which include: (1) junction of the two mandibles anteriorly by an elastic ligament; (2) loose attachment of the quadrate bone on either side to both the skull and mandible; (3) and movement of bones of the palate.   In consequence of these three features the mouth can be widely distended to engulf a large food item. Other modifications are (4) the slender backward-pointing teeth on the jaws and palate, which prevent the food from slipping forward, once swallowing has begun; (5) absence of a sternum (breastbone) and ribs

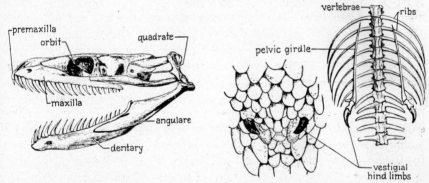

Fig. 30-9.   Skeletal features of a python.   *Left.* Skull with quadrate articulation of lower jaw that permits distension of the mouth when swallowing.   *Center.* External appearance of pelvic region with black horny caps on vestigial hind limbs.   *Right.* Vestigial pelvic girdle and limb bones.   (*From Guide to reptile gallery, British Museum.*)

free of any bony articulation ventrally, so that the thorax may be dilated; (6) presence of soft, elastic skin between scales on the back and sides of body, permitting wide distension; (7) thin and easily stretched walls of esophagus and stomach; and (8) placement of the glottis far forward, between the jaws and just behind the sheath for the slender tongue, which permits of respiration during the swallowing of food.

NATURAL HISTORY

30-20. Distribution.   Most reptiles, both species and individuals, are in tropical and subtropical regions; their numbers decline rapidly toward the poles and in high altitudes.   Thus, Louisiana has 22 kinds of turtles, 9 lizards, 40 snakes, and the alligator, but northern Alberta has only 1, a garter snake.   North America, north of Mexico, has about 347 kinds of reptiles—65 turtles, 175 lizards, 205 snakes, the crocodile, and the alligator.   Turtles and snakes are more numerous in humid regions such as the southeastern states, and lizards in arid territory like that of the American Southwest.

Reptiles occupy a wide variety of habitats, including sandy and rocky deserts, soil both dry and wet, brushy areas, tropical and temperate forests, fresh-water and salt-water marshes, open streams and lakes, brackish or saline lagoons, and the open ocean.   Large pythons and boas dwell in the tropics, the crocodilians in swamps or rivers or along seacoasts, the biggest turtles in the ocean, the giant land tortoises on arid oceanic islands, and some of the larger lizards (VARANIDAE) in dryish places.   Most lizards and snakes are terrestrial, but some climb rocks and trees.   The black snake and striped racers ascend bushes and trees in search of food, and some tropical serpents are predominantly arboreal. Small geckos and other lizards seek shelter in crevices of rocks, trees, or buildings, snakes often use rodent burrows, and some lizards and snakes burrow into sand by aid of an upturned (rostral) plate on the snout. Most turtles live in and about water, but box turtles inhabit the open floor of forests, and the land tortoises inhabit dry ground exclusively.

30-21. Activity.   Being "cold-blooded" or poikilothermous, reptiles are influenced markedly by the environmental temperature.   In the tropics they are active throughout the year but elsewhere experience a period of dormancy dependent upon the length and severity of the cold season.   In the southern states this is brief, but to the north and in mountainous regions there is a long hibernation, when the bodily activities drop to a low level.   Lizards and snakes enter crevices in the ground to hibernate, rattlesnakes and some other snakes den up in numbers in caves or large burrows, and fresh-water turtles go to the bottoms of ponds.

In temperate regions, reptiles are active during the daylight hours of the warmer months.   In desert and semidesert regions they behave similarly during the moderate weather of spring and autumn but in midsummer are most active in the early morning and late afternoon, remaining quiet or sequestered during the hottest midday hours.   Some desert snakes are always nocturnal, and others, including rattlesnakes in the southwestern states, become night prowlers during the hotter months.

Contrary to common belief, reptiles cannot withstand unlimited quantities of heat, although some seek and are most active in temperatures but a few degrees below that which is fatal to them.   Rattlesnakes, sand lizards (*Uma*), and desert iguanas (*Dipsosaurus*) native to deserts of the American Southwest are most active at temperatures of 35 to 40°C. (95 to 104°F.), but a rise in body temperature to over 45°C. (113°F.) is quickly fatal.   Lacking a mechanism for heat dissipation, they are soon killed by overheating.

30-22. Food. Most reptiles feed chiefly on animals; the land tortoises, large and small, some turtles, and a few lizards such as the American chuckwalla (*Sauromalus*) and desert iguana subsist upon vegetation. The large crested Galápagos iguana (*Amblyrhynchus cristatus*) is unique in that it dives into the sea to obtain seaweeds (marine algae), which constitute its sole food.

Lizards and small snakes feed upon insects and other small invertebrates, small turtles capture aquatic invertebrates, and large lizards, turtles, snakes and crocodilians capture various vertebrates from fishes to mammals. Many snakes can take prey considerably large in diameter than their own mouths and bodies, because of specializations already discussed (Fig. 30-10). The total intake of food by reptiles is small

Fig. 30-10. A gopher or bull snake that has just swallowed a house mouse. Extreme distension of the body skin causes the rows of scales to be widely separated during swallowing and early stages of digestion. The glottis opening just inside the lower jaw permits respiration to continue. (*Photograph by T. I. Storer.*)

in amount as compared with that necessary for birds and mammals. Lizards and turtles forage daily during warm weather, but many snakes seek food only at intervals.

Lithe and agile snakes such as racers and some speedy desert lizards capture their prey "on the run," other reptiles stalk theirs, and heavy-bodied snakes and crocodilians often lie in wait for animals to stray near by. Small prey is grasped at once and swallowed, as a garter snake does with a small fish or frog. Turtles and crocodilians tear up large items of food. Nonvenomous snakes that feed upon land vertebrates commonly encircle the prey quickly with one or more coils of the body, then tighten down and "constrict" the victim until death results from asphyxiation; this is the practice of boas, king snakes, and others. The

poisonous snakes strike with their fangs and inject venom, whereupon
the victim quickly dies.

30-23. Enemies. Bullfrogs occasionally capture small snakes and
newly hatched turtles and alligators. Snapping turtles eat snakes,
several kinds of snakes eat turtle eggs, and some lizards prey upon other
lizards. Racers, king snakes, coral snakes, moccasins, copperheads, and
even the little ring-necked snakes feed in varying degree upon other
serpents, king snakes reputedly being immune to the venom of poisonous
snakes. The great king cobra of southeastern Asia is reported to subsist
exclusively on serpents. Crows, hawks, and owls are the most important
bird predators upon reptiles, followed by herons, jays, shrikes, the road
runner, and others. The secretary bird of Africa (*Gypogeranus serpen-
tarius*), a long-legged relative of the hawks, preys commonly on snakes.
Of mammals the skunks, raccoons, badgers, foxes, and coyotes feed upon
reptiles, and some ground squirrels occasionally eat lizards.

Man kills many snakes, and his destruction of harmful rodents may
reduce the food for large snakes. Many snakes and turtles are killed
by automobiles on highways, whence they are retrieved by hawks and
crows. Some reptiles die from freezing during hibernation. Reptiles
are subject to the attacks of various parasites, ticks being common on
the necks of lizards and snakes, and worms in the intestine and elsewhere;
blood parasites are numerous.

30-24. Life span. In captivity, several tortoises have survived beyond
100 years, various turtles for 20 to 90 years, occasional crocodiles and
large snakes for 25 to 40 years, and smaller species for a few years to 20
or more.

30-25. Reproduction. In their manner of reproduction, the reptiles are
intermediate between the fishes and amphibians and the mammals.
Fertilization is always internal among reptiles, yet most species deposit
their eggs for development outside the body. Internal development
may have begun as a regular phenomenon among reptiles, since some
strictly oviparous turtles and snakes retain their eggs temporarily when
conditions for deposition are unfavorable. When this happens in the
European ring snake (*Tropidonotus*) the embryos develop, so that after
laying only 3 weeks (instead of the usual 7 or 8) ensue until hatching.
Internal development is the rule for vipers, rattlesnakes, water and
garter snakes, and the sea snakes. In certain genera of lizards, some of
the species lay eggs and others produce living young. Thus, the American horned toads (*Phrynosoma*) are all ovoviviparous except *P. cornutum*,
but the reverse is true with the fence lizards (*Sceloporus*), only one species
being ovoviviparous.

In adaptation to life on land, reptile eggs resemble somewhat those of
birds, being covered by a tough flexible shell with a shell membrane

inside, both produced in the oviduct.   The shells are hardened by deposition of limy salts in crocodilians and some turtles.   The shape is usually elongately oval but spherical in the eggs of land tortoises and sea turtles. An abundance of yolk is provided to nourish the embryo, so that the size of the egg is often large in proportion to that of the female.   Segmentation is of the meroblastic type, as with birds.   During development the embryo is surrounded by embryonic membranes, the **amnion** and **chorin** and the **allantois;** these constitute a "new" feature of vertebrates, first occurring in reptiles, and are an adaptation to protect the delicate embryo against desiccation and physical shock during development.   Prior to hatching a calcareous **egg tooth** develops on the tip of the upper mandibles, as in birds; it serves to cut the egg membrane and shell at hatching, then drops off.

The number of eggs produced annually by a female varies from nearly 400 in a sea turtle (*Caretta*) to a single egg in the house gecko (*Sphaerodactylus*).   Small pond turtles lay 5 to 11 eggs, the smaller snakes and lizards about 10 to 20, and the American alligator 30 to 60; and garter snakes have produced over 70 living young in a single brood.   The eggs are deposited in natural cavities below or within rocks or logs, beneath vegetable debris, or in earth or sand.   Some tropical lizards lay in the nests of ants or termites.   Female turtles leave the water and seek sandbanks or hill slopes where they excavate cavities by digging with the hind feet; after laying the eggs the site is covered, sometimes so skillfully that the nest cannot be found.   Crocodilians make nests of vegetable debris in which the eggs are incubated at temperatures slightly above the environment by decomposition of the nest material.   Most reptiles desert their eggs after laying, but the female alligator defends her nest and keeps it moist, and in some snakes such as the large tropical pythons she encircles the eggs during development.   During this "incubation" a rise of 2 to 4°C. occurs in body temperature above that of the environment.   The duration of development in different reptiles is from a few weeks to several months; the New Zealand tuatara is unique in requiring about 13 months.

In ovoviviparous reptiles that retain eggs in the oviduct of the female for development, the "shell" is but a thin membrane.   Blood vessels of the embryo soon grow out on either the yolk sac or the chorion and lie close to maternal vessels on the inner surface of the oviduct ("uterus"), providing respiration for the embryo in an arrangement functionally equivalent to the placenta in mammals.   When development is completed, such eggs are "laid" and the young "hatch" at once.

Young reptiles, at hatching, usually resemble their parents in form and coloration.   An exception is the black snake or racer (*Coluber constrictor*) in which the young are marked with dark blotches and the adults are uniformly colored. The young of most reptiles are independent from the time of hatching; those of some snakes may remain with the mother for a brief period, and those of the American alligator continue with the female through the first winter.

It has long been alleged that parent snakes sometimes swallow their young for protection, but no bona fide confirmatory evidence has ever been obtained. The digestive juices of snakes are so powerful that should this happen the young could scarcely emerge unharmed.

30-26. Relations to man. Many kinds of snakes and lizards benefit man by feeding upon harmful rodents and insects. Some snakes constitute one factor in the regulation of the rodent population, but these or other species also prey upon the eggs of game and song birds in season.

Skins of crocodiles and alligators have long been used for fancy leather, and in recent years those of large snakes and lizards have been made into shoes, purses, and similar articles. An estimated 2,500,000 skins were taken for such purposes in India alone during 1932, with others from Malaysia, the Philippines, Africa, and South America. Reptile leathers are durable, afford variety in pattern, color, and surface, and can be dyed with various colors, but the wild populations cannot long withstand exploitation at a high rate.

Turtles have been useful chiefly for food. Flesh of the green turtle, both fresh and dried, has been in such demand that the fisheries for it on tropical islands have been far depleted. The Galápagos giant land tortoises, once enormously abundant, were levied upon by Pacific Ocean mariners for three centuries as a source of fresh meat; during the whaling period from 50 to 300 were removed by each ship, and an estimated 100,000 were taken during the nineteenth century. Some species were exterminated and the reduced populations of others are now protected. The smaller turtles of fresh and brackish waters in the United States also serve as food, especially the snapper, diamondback terrapin, and soft-shelled turtles. Other small turtles find some use in biological laboratories. The real tortoise shell for combs and other fancy articles is obtained from the marine hawksbill turtle.

Snakes have long been objects of fear and superstition to mankind. They are often objects of veneration and worship in the folklore of many primitive peoples. The Hopi Indians on the mesas of northern Arizona have an annual ceremonial lasting for 9 days, part of which is a snake dance. For this, live snakes, including rattlesnakes, are gathered, washed, and then carried in the mouths of certain priests of the tribe in a ceremonial dance, after which the snakes are returned alive to the desert. Many old and erroneous beliefs about snakes still persist among people in civilized countries, despite the amount now known about the structure and biology of snakes and their place in nature as one group of predaceous animals.

30-27. Poisonous reptiles.   The two species of *Heloderma,* one of which is the Gila monster of the American Southwest, are the only poisonous reptiles other than snakes.   The venom of these lizards is as poisonous as that of rattlesnakes, but the mechanism for venom transfer is poorly developed, and only rarely are human beings injured or killed by it, usually in handling the animals.

Venomous snakes occur on all the continents and on many large islands, except Madagascar and New Zealand, but are fewer in temperate North America and Europe than in the tropics.   Venom serves for the capture of their small prey but is used defensively against large animals and man; their presence is a hazard of varying degree for mankind. Among the crowded populations of India, snake poisoning causes several thousand human deaths annually.   In Brazil some 5,000 deaths per year were earlier ascribed to snakes.   For the United States no accurate figures are available, but several hundred persons are bitten annually, and it has been estimated that 150 deaths result chiefly from rattlesnakes in the South and Southwest.   The differences noted are due to the differing densities of human and snake populations, to the habit of certain peoples of going barefooted, and in India in part to religious beliefs that keep the people from killing snakes.

In North America, north of Mexico, the snakes poisonous to man include 2 coral snakes, the moccasin, the copperhead, and 20 kinds of rattlesnakes.   The coral snake has a small head and eye, an elliptical pupil, and the body marked with transverse rings of red, black, and yellow, each black ring being bordered by yellow.   All other dangerous snakes in this region are "pit vipers," with wide heads, vertically ellip-

Fig. 30-11.   Rattlesnake.   *A.* Mechanism of the head in striking.   The spheno-pterygoid muscle (1) contracts to rock the fang forward at right angles to the head; upon entering the victim's flesh the external pterygoid (2) and spheno-palatine (3) contract to draw the fang more deeply; then the anterior temporal muscle (4) draws up the lower jaw and compresses the poison gland to force venom through the duct and fang into the wound.   All head and neck muscles relax for withdrawal.   The whole process requires but an instant. *B, C.* The dry cornified rattle in external view and frontal section to show how the segments are held loosely together.   (*After Grinnell and Storer, Animal life in the Yosemite, University of California Press.*)

tical pupils, and a pit between the nostril and eye on each side of the head. The tail on the moccasin and copperhead is slender-tipped; on all rattlesnakes it is blunt and ends with the characteristic rattle. The coral snake occurs from states of the Mexican border and Gulf north to Indiana and North Carolina; the copperhead from Massachusetts to Illinois and southward; and the moccasin from Virginia and Illinois southward. Rattlesnakes occur from southern Canada southward, being more numerous as to species and individuals in the arid Southwest.

The *venom* is secreted in a pair of glands, one on either side of the upper jaw, each connected by a duct to a fang. Reserve fangs develop behind the functional pair to replace the latter when lost (as with teeth in all snakes). Venom is a complex of organic materials having various physiological effects, and each kind of venom has distinctive characteristics and different toxicity. Some of the many components are (1) proteolysins, causing local pain, swelling, and necrosis, especially in vipers and rattlesnakes; (2) cardiotoxin, producing low blood pressure and heart failure, in the cobra, coral snake, and some viperids; (3) hemorrhagin, destroying endothelium of capillaries with bleeding in tissues and organs, in viperids; (4) neurocytolysins, affecting various nervous tissues especially centers for respiration, in cobras; and (5) antibactericidin, which inhibits ordinary bactericidal action of blood corpuscles. Venom of the cobra and related snakes (Elapidae) affects particularly the respiratory centers and death results from asphyxiation; that of rattlesnakes and vipers (Viperidae) affects the heart and nervous system more severely.

Rattlesnakes and other pit vipers strike from an S-shaped posture of the body; the fangs are buried in the victim, the snake's lower jaw clamps upward, muscles over each poison gland force the venom through the hollow fangs into the flesh, and then the head is withdrawn—all with amazing rapidity (Fig. 30-11). The venom of vipers and rattlesnakes usually travels slowly in the lymphatic circulation so that the approved *treatment for rattlesnake bite* is now to (1) apply a tourniquet encircling the bitten part, toward the heart from the bite; (2) disinfect and make X-shaped cuts about 1/4 inch deep near the bite; (3) apply suction by a rubber bulb, or other device, and continue this for 12 to 15 hours; and (4) administer antivenin, if available. Potassium permanganate, coal oil and whisky, cautery with hot irons, and other procedures long advocated are without particular value and are often harmful to victims of snake bite.

Efforts to treat victims of snake bite date from antiquity, and many irrational means, chemical and others, have been tried. In 1887 Sewell discovered that the repeated injection of minute sublethal doses of rattlesnake venom into pigeons caused development of a substance in the latter, an **antibody,** which made the birds immune to subsequent larger doses.   Such antibodies (antisera) are now produced for use against various diseases such as diphtheria and tetanus as well as snake bite. For the latter, horses are gradually immunized to snake venom, then the blood serum is withdrawn to serve as **antivenin,** which is injected into a victim of snake bite.   Since each kind of venom has distinctive qualities, no single antivenin will serve against all snakes.   Antivenin useful for cases of rattlesnake bite is now available in the Americas, and other types are produced for the snakes of other lands.

Some primitive peoples use snake venom to prepare poisoned arrows for killing game and for warfare, as did a few tribes of American Indians. Snake venom has also been tried by modern physicians for treatment of various diseases, but such use is largely irrational because of the complexity of venom.   Furthermore, some venoms contain spores of the dangerous gas gangrene bacillus (*Bacillus welchii*).   However, an extract of water moccasin venom now serves to check persistent bleeding in some diseases, and cobra venom has been employed to relieve the severe pain in human cases of inoperable cancer.

30-28. Fossil reptiles.   The living reptiles, although numerous, are mostly small and occupy a minor role among existing animals.   During the Mesozoic era, or Age of Reptiles (Triassic to Upper Cretaceous), they were the dominant vertebrates and occupied most of the animal habitats then available, from semideserts and dry uplands through marshes and swamps to the open ocean.   They varied in size from small to large, some far exceeding elephants in length and weight, and were greatly diversified as to structure and habits.   Many were of peculiar form as compared with modern vertebrates, whereas others were evidently of attractive appearance and graceful in their movements.

The most primitive reptiles resembled early amphibians so closely that it is difficult to separate the two groups, but this is good evidence as to the origin of reptiles.   A few remains that are certainly reptiles have been found in deposits of Pennsylvanian time; during the Permian reptiles became numerous and began to radiate in both structure and manner of life.   By the end of that period they had largely replaced the amphibians, by the end of Triassic time practically all the major groups of reptiles had appeared, and during the Jurassic and Cretaceous these attained a climax as to numbers of species and individuals and also in diversity of form and manner of life.   Then, with the end of the Cretaceous, most reptilian stocks disappeared.   Only four have survived to the present.   The later reptiles gave origin to the mammals.

The most important evolutionary achievement of the reptiles was to become adapted for terrestrial life apart from water.   The acquisition of a dry cornified integument to prevent loss of moisture from the body and the production of eggs capable of development on land were significant in this adaptation.

The small primitive reptiles had slender bodies and tails, and four short five-toed limbs. From this generalized form some of the lines of radiation or specialization were (1) increase in size, as to the huge proportions of the brontosaurs; (2) acquisition of defensive armor, including plates in the skin and horns or spines on the head, as by some dinosaurs; (3) lightened build, for rapid running on four legs or two, as with other dinosaurs; (4) adaptation to flight, by increased length of fore limb and tail and development of flight membranes of skin by the pterodactyls; and (5) adaptation to strictly aquatic life, with paddle-like limbs and a fusiform body in the case of ichthyosaurs and others.

†Brontosaurus (Fig. 1-2) and †Brachiosaurus attained to lengths of 75 and 80 feet, respectively, and †Diplodocus to 87½ feet, the largest terrestrial animals ever known. They may have weighed 25 to 35 tons and used more than ¼ ton of food per day. †Stegosaurus (Fig. 30-12) had a series of enormous bony plates in a dorsal crest extending from the neck to the end of the tail. †Triceratops bore a skull scarcely equaled as to size and weight by any other animal save the modern whales, with a sharp cutting beak on the upper jaw, a short stout horn on the nose, and a pair of long forward-pointing horns on the top of the head. Many of these reptiles went about on "all fours," but others could stand, kangaroo-like, on their hind feet, with the tail for a brace. Armor and defensive horns or spines are believed to have been characters of the herbivorous forms only. The brains of these huge dinosaurs were proportionately small; that of the 10-ton †Triceratops may have weighed only 2 pounds, and that of the 18-foot †Stegosaurus had an estimated weight of only 2.5 ounces.

The flying reptiles, or pterodactyls (Figs. 30-12, 9-1), were of lighter build. The head was long; the fifth "finger" was greatly elongated and with the hind limbs and base of the tail supported the flight membrane, in a manner somewhat similar to that seen in modern bats. One form (Pteranodon) had a wingspread of 25 feet. The marine ichthyosaurs were whale-like in appearance but had four (instead of two) paddle-like limbs used for steering and a large tail fin. The Mesozoic reptiles included both herbivorous and carnivorous species. Nests of dinosaur eggs discovered in Mongolia prove that certain of these ancient reptiles were oviparous like their successors.

Remains of fossil reptiles have been found on all continents (except Antarctica) and are abundant in some rocks of the western states, especially in Wyoming, Utah, and Colorado. Many species are well known from numerous complete skeletons that have been excavated, studied, and mounted in museums.   The Dinosaur National Monument near Jensen, Utah, has a display of partly exposed skeletons and of restorations that show how some of these animals appeared in life.   Footprints of Mesozoic reptiles, made on the shores of ancient waters, occur in sandstones of the Connecticut Valley and elsewhere in the United States.

Fig. 30-12.   Restored skeletons of fossil reptiles; all much reduced but not to same scale. DINOSAURS: *Stegosaurus*, length to 18 feet, with huge dorsal armor; *Ceratosaurus*, of bipedal form and large size; *Brontosaurus*, length to 75 feet.   ICHTHYOSAUR: marine and fishlike, limb girdles reduced and limbs paddle-like for swimming.   PLESIOSAUR: length to 50 feet, marine, with long neck and stout paddle-like limbs.   PTERODACTYL: *Rhamphorhynchus*, fifth finger elongated to support flight membrane (compare Fig. 9-1).   (*After Marsh and others.*)

There has been much speculation as to why the ancient reptiles disappeared so suddenly, geologically speaking.   One theory suggests that the earliest mammals preyed upon the eggs of the huge reptiles; another and more plausible explanation is that change in climate, as by reduction in temperature or altered moisture relations, affected either the reptiles themselves or their habitats, or both, adversely.   Disappearance of the late Mesozoic reptiles evidently gave opportunity for the mammals, which then were very small in size, to begin the spectacular development that was their history in the Tertiary era.

The following outline indicates the diversity of reptiles in past geologic time.[1] Groups with living representatives are indicated by boldface type; all others are extinct.

Subclass I. ANAPSIDA.
    Order 1. Cotylosauria. Stem Reptiles. Permian, *Seymouria.*
    Order 2. **Chelonia.** Turtles. Permian, *Eunotosaurus;* Cretaceous, *Archelon;* Recent, *Chrysemys.*
Subclass II. ICHTHYOPTERYGIA.
    Order 3. Ichthyosauria. Ichthyosaurs. Marine. Triassic, *Merriamia;* Jurassic, *Ichthyosaurus;* Cretaceous, *Ophthalmosaurus.*
Subclass III. SYNAPTOSAURIA.
    Order 4. Sauropterygia. Plesiosaurs, etc. Marine. Jurassic, *Plesiosaurus;* Cretaceous, *Elasmosaurus.*
Subclass IV. LEPIDOSAURIA.
    Order 5. Eosuchia. Ancient Two-arched Reptiles. Upper Permian to Jurassic. *Proterosuchus.*
    Order 6. **Rhynchocephalia.** Triassic to Recent. *Sphenodon,* 1 living species.
    Order 7. **Squamata.**
        A. **Lacertilia.** Mosasaurs. Cretaceous, *Tylosaurus.* Lizards. Jurassic to Recent. *Scelporus, Eumeces,* etc.
        B. **Ophidia.** Snakes. Cretaceous to Recent. *Pituophis, Crotalus.*
Subclass V. ARCHOSAURIA. Ruling Reptiles.
    Order 8. Theodontia. Phytosaurs, etc. Triassic, *Ornithosuchus, Mystriosuchus.*
    Order 9. **Loricata.** Alligators, etc. Jurassic, *Stenosaurus;* Recent, *Alligator.*
    Order 10. Pterosauria. Flying Reptiles. Jurassic, *Rhamphorhynchus;* Cretaceous, *Pteranodon.*
    Order 11. Saurischia. "Reptile-like" Dinosaurs.
        A. Theropoda (bipeds). Jurassic, *Compsognathus;* Cretaceous, *Tyrranosaurus.*
        B. Sauropoda (quadrupeds). Jurassic, *Brontosaurus, Diplodocus, Brachiosaurus.*
    Order 12. Ornithischia. "Bird-like" Dinosaurs.
        A. Ornithopoda (bipeds). "Duckbills," etc. Jurassic, *Camptosaurus;* Cretaceous, *Trachodon, Corythosaurus.*
        B. Stegosauria. Jurassic, *Stegosaurus.*
        C. Ankylosauria. Armored Dinosaurs. Cretaceous, *Ankylosaurus.*
        D. Ceratopsia. Horned Dinosaurs. Cretaceous, *Triceratops.*
Subclass VI. SYNAPSIDA (forms leading toward mammals).
    Order 13. Pelycosauria. Permian and Carboniferous, *Dimetrodon, Edaphosaurus.*
    Order 14. Therapsida. Mammal-like Reptiles. Permian and Triassic, *Cynognathus.*

CLASSIFICATION

Class *REPTILIA.* Reptiles. (Characteristics of living forms.) Skin dry, cornified, usually with scales or scutes; limbs typically 4, each with 5 clawed toes, but reduced or absent in some; skeleton bony, 1 occipital condyle; Permian to Recent; terrestrial, fresh-water, or marine, in tropics and warm temperate regions; over 4,000 species.

Order 1. **Chelonia** (Testudiniata). Turtles, Tortoises, and Terrapins. Body broad, incased in a rigid "shell" of rounded dorsal carapace and flat ventral plastron, joined at sides, and covered by polygonal scutes or leathery skin; no teeth, jaws with horny sheaths; quadrate immovable; thoracic vertebrae and ribs usually fused to shell; anus an elongate slit; one copulatory organ; oviparous, eggs laid in holes, or "nests,"

Fig. 30-13. Young leathery turtle (*Dermochelys coriacea*). Inhabits tropical oceans, adults to 7¼ feet long. (*After Guide to reptile gallery, British Museum.*)

[1] Condensed from A. S. Romer, 1937. Man and the vertebrates, University of Chicago Press.

dug and covered by females; Triassic to Recent; world-wide except New Zealand and western South America; in fresh or salt waters or on land; more than 225 species.

Suborder 1. ATHECA. Large; ribs and vertebrae separate from shell; skin thick, smooth, and leathery with polygonal plates; limbs paddle-like; fore limbs slender, nearly as long as body.

DERMOCHELIDAE. *Dermochelys coriacea*, leathery turtle, in tropical oceans, occasional on American coasts (Fig. 30-13).

Suborder 2. THECOPHORA. Thoracic vertebrae and ribs fused to carapace.

Superfamily A. CRYPTODIRA. Carapace covered with horny shields; neck bends in vertical S-curve if retractile; pelvis not fused to carapace or plastron.

CHELYDRIDAE. SNAPPING TURTLES. Plastron small, cross-shaped; head, neck, and limbs large, cannot be withdrawn into shell; tip of upper jaw hooked; North and Central Americas. *Chelydra serpentina*, common "snapper," Gulf coast to southern Canada (Fig. 30-14); *Macrochelys temminckii*, alligator snapper, Missouri, Georgia, and southward, length to 24 inches, vicious, powerful, food chiefly vertebrates.

FIG. 30-14. Snapping turtle (*Chelydra serpentina*). Length to 14 inches. (*From E. L. Palmer.*)

DERMATEMYIDAE. Tail short; Mexico and Central America. *Dermatemys.*

KINOSTERNIDAE. MUSK and "MUD" TURTLES. Both ends of plastron hinged; odor musky in life; North and Central Americas. *Sternotherus*, musk turtles, Missouri and southern Canada eastward and southward, head large, plastron reduced; *Kinosternon*, mud turtles, eastern states, Colorado River and southward, in muddy streams.

PLATYSTERNIDAE. Head large; temporal region completely roofed; mandible hooked; tail long; southern Asia. *Platysternum megalocephalum.*

TESTUDINIDAE. COMMON TURTLES, TERRAPINS, AND LAND TORTOISES. Pubic and ischiadic symphyses firmly joined; Eocene to Recent; world-wide, except Australian region; includes most chelonians. *Chrysemys*, painted turtle, Atlantic coast to eastern Washington, in clear waters (Fig. 30-15); *Malacoclemmys*, diamondback

FIG. 30-15. Painted turtle (*Chrysemys picta*). Length to 6 inches. Common in fresh waters. (*From E. L. Palmer.*)

terrapins, Massachusetts to Texas, in salt and brackish waters, esteemed for eating; *Emys, Clemmys*, semi-box and mud turtles; *Terrapene*, box turtles, plastron with transverse hinge, Arizona to Atlantic coast; *Testudo*, giant land tortoises of Galápagos

Islands and islands of Indian Ocean, some over 4 feet long; *Gopherus*, smaller land tortoises, Florida to southeastern California (Fig. 30-16); both of latter groups strictly terrestrial and vegetarian.

CHELONIDAE. SEA TURTLES. Large; limbs flipper-like; shell covered with smooth horny shields; Upper Cretaceous to Recent; tropical and subtropical seas, occasional on coasts of United States; come ashore only to lay eggs. *Caretta*, loggerhead, Atlantic coast, big-headed, 2 nails on each front flipper, to 4 feet long and 500 pounds; *Eretmochelys*, hawksbill turtle, to 24 inches long, upper jaw hooked, overlapping dorsal scutes provide true "tortoise shell" of commerce (Fig. 30-17); *Chelonia*, green turtle, much prized for food, occasional adults to 3½ feet and 400 pounds.

FIG. 30-16. Desert tortoise (*Gopherus*). Length to 11½ inches. On land in arid southern states. (*From E. L. Palmer.*)

FIG. 30-17. Young hawksbill turtle (*Eretmochelys*). In warm seas; length to 24 inches. (*After Guide to reptile gallery, British Museum.*)

Superfamily B. PLEURODIRA. Neck folds sideways under front of carapace; pelvis fused to carapace and plastron.

PELOMEDUSIDAE. Neck completely retractile; South America, Africa, and Madagascar. *Podocnemis,* "tartaruga."

CHELYIDAE. SNAKE-NECKED TURTLES. Head and neck long, not completely retractile beneath shell; South America, Australia, and New Zealand. *Chelys*, matamata; *Chelodina.*

CARETTOCHELYIDAE. Limbs flat, paddleshaped; shell soft; New Guinea; 1 species. *Carettochelys insculpta*, highly aquatic.

Superfamily C. TRIONYCHOIDEA. Body flat, oval; skin smooth, leathery; scant bony shell; head long, snout tubular; feet broadly webbed; only 3 inner digits with claws; Cretaceous to Recent.

TRIONYCHIDAE. SOFT-SHELLED TURTLES. North America, Africa, Asia, and Malay Archipelago. *Trionyx*, Gulf states to St. Lawrence River; *T. spinifera*, most common; *T. ferox*, to 18 inches long (Fig. 30-18).

FIG. 30-18. Young soft-shelled turtles (*Trionyx ferox*). In fresh waters of eastern United States. (*After Guide to reptile gallery, British Museum.*)

Order 2. **Rhynchocephalia.** Living representative lizard-like; scales granular; a middorsal row of low spines; quadrate immovable; mandibles joined by ligament; vertebrae amphicentrous; abdominal ribs present; anal opening transverse; no copulatory organ in male; Permian to Eocene, and Recent; New Zealand. One living species, *Spenodon punctatum,* "tuatara" (Fig. 30-19), length to 30 inches; lives on land and in water and burrows; eats fishes, insects, and worms; eggs about 10, with hard white shells, laid in holes in ground and requiring about 13 months to hatch.

Order 3. **Squamata.** LIZARDS AND SNAKES. Skin with horny epidermal scales or shields; quadrate bone movable; vertebrae usually procoelous; copulatory organ (hemipenes) double and eversible; anal opening transverse.

Suborder 1. SAURIA (Lacertilia). LIZARDS. Body usually slender; limbs typically 4, sometimes reduced or absent; mandibles fused anteriorly; pterygoid in contact with quadrate; eyelids usually movable; pectoral girdle well-developed (or vestigial); tongue usually entire; bladder ordinarily present; length usually under 12 inches (a few over 6 feet); mostly oviparous, some ovoviviparous; food chiefly insects and small invertebrates, some herbivorous; tropics and temperate regions, on continents and islands; 2,500 species.

(*Note: Of the 26 families, 6 entirely fossil, some are omitted here.*)

FIG. 30-19. Tuatara (*Sphenodon punctatum*). Length to 30 inches. The only reptile native to New Zealand and only living member of the Order RHYNCHOCEPHALIA.

FIG. 30-20. Common gecko (*Tarentola mauritanica*) of the Mediterranean region. Length to about 6 inches. (*After Guide to reptile gallery, British Museum.*)

Division A. *ASCALABOTA.* Usually more than 4 rows of scales per body segment; scales, when overlapping (imbricate), with wide free margin posteriorly.

GEKKONIDAE. GECKOS. Small; toes often with rounded adhesive plates or pads for climbing; eyes usually lack movable lids; vertebrae amphicoelous; tongue protrusible; many can produce sounds; egg shells calcified; world-wide, in warm regions; some climb rocks, trees, and buildings, other slender forms live on sandy deserts; 300 species. *Phyllodactylus* and *Coleonyx,* native to southwestern United States and Mexico; *Hemidactylus* and *Sphaerodactylus,* probably introduced at Key West, Fla. (Fig. 30-20).

IGUANIDAE. NEW WORLD LIZARDS. Limbs normal; teeth usually alike (homodont) and fixed to sides of jaws (pleurodont); tongue fleshy, not protractile; eyelids complete; chiefly in the Americas; includes most North American lizards, a majority of them west of the Mississippi River. *Anolis carolinensis,* American "chameleon," North Carolina to Texas, skin color changes readily, green on leaves, etc.; *Scleoporus* (Fig. 30-21), "swifts," on rocks, trees, or ground, *S. undulatus* in eastern states; *Phrynosoma,* horned toads (Fig. 30-22), body broad, flat, and spiny, enlarged "horns" (scales) on head, eastern Washington and Kansas to California and Mexico, live on dry ground and sand; *Uta,* utas; *Crotaphytus,* collared lizards (Fig. 30-23); *Sauromalus,* chuckwalla; *Callisaurus,* gridiron tail; *Iguana, Cyclura,* etc., iguanas, Mexico and southward, some to 6 feet long, body compressed, tail long, a middorsal crest of lancelike spines; active in running and climbing; feed on leaves, fruits, some insects, and small vertebrates; used for human food in tropics.

AGAMIDAE. OLD WORLD LIZARDS. Limbs normal; teeth usually differentiated (heterodont) and attached to edges of jaws (acrodont); tongue short, thick; some with

FIG. 30-21. Fence lizard (*Sceloporus biseriatus*). Length to 7 inches; lives on ground, rocks, and fences in western states. (*From Van Denburgh.*)

FIG. 30-22. The horned toad (*Phrynosoma*), a common lizard on dry ground and sand in the arid western states; length to 5½ inches. (*From Van Denburgh.*)

FIG. 30-23. Collared lizards (*Crotaphytus collaris*). Length to 13 inches. The sexes differ in coloration. Lives on rocks and open ground in western states. (*From Van Denburgh.*)

throat sacs or dorsal spines; southern Europe, Africa, Asia, and Australia; over 200 species. *Agama; Draco,* "flying dragon," long ribs covered by membrane and used to volplane from a height; *Moloch,* Australia, somewhat like a horned toad.

CHAMAELEONTIDAE. CHAMELEONS. Head angular; body high and narrow; tail prehensile; toes opposed (2 vs. 3) for grasping; tip of tongue expanded and mucus-coated, can be "shot" several inches beyond head; eyes large, move independently; eyelids fused over eyeball, with small central circular aperture; teeth acrodont; lungs

with air sacs; Africa, Madagascar, and India.
changes color readily (Fig. 30-24).

Division B. *AUTARCHOGLOSSA.*
Less than 4 transverse rows of ventral
scales to each body segment; scales
when imbricate with narrow free margin
posteriorly.

XANTUSIIDAE. NIGHT LIZARDS.
Small; dorsal scales granular, ventral
scales squarish and nonimbricate; fem-
oral pores present; southwestern United
States to Central America, and Cuba.
Xantusia.

SCINCIDAE. SKINKS. Limbs or toes
often reduced, sometimes absent; scales
commonly smooth and round-margined
(cycloid), with dermal ossifications beneath; tongue with scale-like papillae,
tip feebly indented; viviparous; Old

Chamaeleo (Chamaeleon), chameleon,

FIG. 30-24. A chameleon (*Chamaeleo chamaeleon*). Length to 6 inches. Native to
warm regions of the Old World. Specialized
with compressed body, prehensile tail, grasping toes, and protrusible tongue. (*After
Guide to reptile gallery, British Museum.*)

World tropics, Australia, and Pacific islands; few in the Americas. *Eumeces fasciatus*,
and *E. skiltonianus*, blue-tailed skinks, in United States (Fig. 30-25).

FIG. 30-25. Blue-tailed skink (*Eumeces skiltonianus*). Length to 7½ inches. Terrestrial,
often under rocks or logs. (*From Van Denburgh.*)

LACERTIDAE. OLD WORLD LIZARDS. Limbs normal; posttemporal fossa roofed;
intermaxillary unpaired. Europe, Asia, and Africa. *Lacerta.*

TEIIDAE. NEW WORLD LIZARDS. Slender; limbs reduced in some; temporal
fossa not roofed; ventral scales usually squarish and nonimbricate; tongue long and
bifid, with scale-like papillae; the Americas and West Indies. *Cnemidophorus*, whip-
tailed lizard; *Ameiva; Tupinambis.*

AMPHISBAENIDAE. "WORM" LIZARDS. Body elongate, wormlike; limbs and
girdles rudimentary or absent; tail short, blunt; skin soft, folded into numerous rings;
eyes and ear openings concealed; subterranean; tropical America, the West Indies,
and Africa. *Bipes biporus*, southern Lower California, fore limbs present, each with
5 toes; *Rhineura floridiana*, in Florida, no limbs.

VARANIDAE. MONITORS. Large, trunk and limbs stout, neck and tail long;
scales small, smooth; teeth large, pointed, and pleurodont; tongue long, smooth,
deeply bifid, and protrusible; Africa, southern Asia, and islands southeast to Australia.
Varanus; V. salvator, Ceylon and Malay, to 8 feet; *V. komodoensis*, to 9½ feet.

PYGOPODIDAE. SNAKELIKE LIZARDS. Body snakelike; no fore limbs; hind limbs
small, under flat flaps of skin; scales rounded; tail long and fragile; no eyelids; Australia, Tasmania. *Pygopus.*

HELODERMATIDAE. BEADED (POISONOUS) LIZARDS. Trunk and tail stout, rounded,
limbs short; dorsal scales beadlike, over bony tubercles (osteoderms); ventral scales
flat; tongue fleshy, protrusible; teeth bluntly fanglike, grooved, with poison glands

opening on outer "gum" of lower jaw; venom potent, bite fatal to small animals, rarely to man; 3 species, 2 are the only poisonous lizards. *Heloderma suspectum*, Gila monster, Arizona and Mexico to southern Utah and Nevada, pink and black, to 19 inches (Fig. 30-26); *H. horridum*, beaded lizard, Mexico and Central America, yellow and much black; *Lanthanotus*, Borneo, nonpoisonous.

Fig. 30-26.   The Gila monster (*Heloderma suspectum*) of the American Southwest.   Length to 19 inches.   This and a related species are the only poisonous lizards.   (*From Van Denburgh.*)

ANGUIDAE.   ALLIGATOR LIZARDS, ETC.   Body slender, a deep fold in skin along each side; limbs small or none; tail long, fragile, regenerates readily; tongue delicate, retracts into thick base; scales usually rectangular over thin bony plates; southwestern United States to northern South America, Europe, and India.   *Gerrhonotus*, in United States and Mexico, limbs small; *Ophisaurus ventralis*, glass snake, New Mexico, Wisconsin, and Indiana southward and eastward, limbless, the very fragile tail about ⅔ of total length; *O. apus*, Europe; *Anguis fragilis*, slowworm or blindworm, Europe, western Asia, and northern Africa.

ANNIELLIDAE.   SILVERY FOOTLESS LIZARDS.   Slender, limbless; eyes and ear openings concealed; scales smooth, soft; subterranean; California.   *Anniella* (2 species).

ZONURIDAE.   WHORLED LIZARDS.   Limbs present or absent; scales often strongly keeled and in conspicuous transverse rows; South Africa, Madagascar.   *Zonurus*.

Suborder 2.   SERPENTES (Ophidia).   SNAKES.   No limbs, feet, ear openings, sternum, or urinary bladder; mandibles joined anteriorly by ligament; eyes immobile and covered by transparent scales, no lids; tongue slender, bifid, and protrusible; left lung reduced; teeth slender and conical, usually on jaws and on roof of mouth (palatine and pterygoid bones); about 1,700 species.

TYPHLOPIDAE.   WORM SNAKES.   Eyes vestigial, under opaque scales; teeth only on transversely placed maxillary bones, none on lower jaw; scales thin, overlapping, cycloid, in multiple rows over whole body; tropics and subtropics of both hemispheres, subterranean.   *Typhlops*.

LEPTOTYPHLOPIDAE.   WORM SNAKES.   Like TYPHLOPIDAE, but teeth only on lower jaw; vestiges of femur and all pelvic bones present; southwestern United States to Brazil, the West Indies, Africa, and southeastern Asia; subterranean. *Leptotyphlops*.

(*Note: The following families of snakes all have the eyes exposed and functional and only one row of large transverse scales along the belly.*)

BOIDAE.   PYTHONS, BOAS, ETC.   Vestiges of pelvic girdle and hind limbs persist, latter usually as spines at each side of anus (Fig. 30-9); world-wide, except New Zealand; variously on ground, or in trees of tropical jungles, or in dry, rocky, or sandy places; includes largest living serpents, also smaller species.   *Python reticulatus*, regal python of Malay region, to 29 feet long; *P. molurus*, Indian python, to 25 feet; *Eunectes murinus*, anaconda of South America, to 33 feet; *Charina bottae*, rubber snake, Montana to California, to 20 inches long (Fig. 30-27).

FIG. 30-27.   The rubber snake (*Charina bottae*), a small boa of the western United States. Length to 20 inches.   (*Photograph by T. I. Storer.*)

ANILIDAE (Ilysiidae).   Vestiges of pelvic girdle and hind limbs present, latter appearing as spines at side of vent; head small; tail very short and blunt; supratemporal and quadrate bones very short; scales small, smooth, and iridescent; southern Asia; South America.   *Anilius* (*Ilysia*).

UROPELTIDAE.   BURROWING OR "EARTH" SNAKES.   Head small and pointed; eyes small; tail short, ending in peculiar large shield; scales smooth and shining; supratemporal bone absent; no vestiges of hind limbs or pelvic gridle; ovoviviparous; southern India and Ceylon.   *Uropeltis.*

FIG. 30-28.   A garter snake (*Thamnophis o. atratus*).   Length to 28 inches.   (*From Van Denburgh.*)

FIG. 30-29.   A racer (*Masticophis semilineatum*) and its eggs.   Native to the American Southwest.   Length to 50 inches.   (*From Van Denburgh.*)

XENOPELTIDAE.   Dentary bone loosely attached to articular; scales smooth, iridescent; southeastern Asia.   One species, *Xenopeltis unicolor.*

COLUBRIDAE.   COMMON SNAKES.   Facial bones movable; squamosals loosely attached to skull; maxillaries horizontal, forming most of upper jaw; both jaws with teeth.

Series A.   AGLYPHA.   HARMLESS SNAKES.   All teeth solid, none grooved; mostly oviparous; nearly world-wide; includes majority of harmless snakes, mostly terrestrial

(Figs. 30-28 to 30-31). *Natrix*, water snakes, and *Thamnophis*, garter snakes, aquatic in varying degree, feed on frogs and fishes; *Coluber* and *Masticophis*, racers, speediest of snakes in United States; *C. constrictor*, black snake, climbs readily, preys on small vertebrates including birds; *Pituophis*, bull snakes and gopher snakes, terrestrial; *Lampropeltis*, milk and king snakes, feed in part on reptiles, including rattlesnakes.

Series B. OPISTHOGLYPHA. One or more pairs of grooved teeth (fangs) on posterior parts of maxillary bones of upper jaw; usually with venom, but most species not very poisonous to man; world-wide, except New Zealand. *Boiga* (*Dipsadomorphus*), tree snakes; *Oxyrhopus; Tantilla*, of American Southwest, small and not particularly harmful to man.

FIG. 30-30. The gopher or bull snake (*Pituophis catenifer*). Length to 52 inches. (*From Van Denburgh.*)

FIG. 30-31. A king snake (*Lampropeltis zonata*), marked with red, black, and white cross bands. Length to 33 inches. (*From Van Denburgh.*)

Group a. PROTEROGLYPHA. POISONOUS SNAKES. A pair (or more) of short, rigid, erect, venom-conducting teeth (fangs), grooved or perforated, on maxilla in anterior part of upper jaw; all dangerously poisonous.

HYDROPHIIDAE. SEA SNAKES. Tail compressed, used for swimming; venomous and dangerous to man; viviparous; in tropical seas. *Hydrophis; Hydrus platyurus*, along Pacific coast from southern Mexico to northern South America, feeds on small fishes.

ELAPIDAE. TERRESTRIAL POISONOUS SNAKES. Tail round, tapered, not compressed; venom powerful, dangerous to man; world-wide, except northern North America and northern Eurasia. *Naja*, cobra; *Bungarus*, krait; *Denisonia; Micrurus* (*Elaps*), coral snake, colored with bands of black, red, and yellow, slow to bite and considered harmless, but strong venom causes occasional human deaths; *M. fulvius*, Ohio and North Carolina to Gulf States; *M. euryxanthus*, southern Arizona and New Mexico southward.

Group b. SOLENOGLYPHA. Paired erectile fangs in front of upper jaw, one on each maxillary bone and folded backward when not in use; maxillary short, thick, and movable in vertical plane; facial bones movable; poisonous; usually viviparous.

VIPERIDAE. OLD WORLD VIPERS. No pit between nostril and eye. Eurasia, Africa, and southern India. *Vipera*, viper; *Cerastes*, horned viper; *Bitis*, puff adder.

CROTALIDAE. PIT VIPERS, RATTLE-SNAKES. A pitlike depression on each side of upper jaw between nostril and eye; some with horny rattle at end of tail; the Americas (*Agkistrodon* also in Asia, west to Caspian Sea).

Tail without rattle: *A. piscivorus*, water moccasin, Virginia and Illinois southward, in swampy places; *A. mokasen*, copperhead, Massachusetts and Illinois to Gulf coast; on drier land; *Bothrops*, f e r-d e-l a n c e, tropical Americas and West Indies; *Lachesis*, bushmaster, Panama to Peru and Brazil.

Tail with rattle of cornified epidermis: *Sistrurus*, pigmy rattlesnakes, and *Crotalus*, rattlesnakes; about 40 species and varieties in Western Hemisphere, 20 in United States; *C. horridus*, timber

FIG. 30-32.   The Indian cobra (*Naja tripudians*), with the "hood" expanded and in the striking position; length to 6½ feet; native to the Old World and highly poisonous. (*After Guide to reptile gallery, British Museum.*)

or banded rattlesnake, Maine to Florida and west to Iowa and Texas; *C. viridis* (*confluentus*), prairie rattlesnake, Great Plains to Pacific coast; *C. atrox*, western diamond back rattlesnake, Texas to eastern California; *C. adamanteus*, eastern diamond back rattlesnake, North Carolina and Louisiana to Florida, to 8 feet in length; *C. cerastes*, sidewinder or "horned rattlesnake," southwestern deserts, travels by angular loops of body.

FIG. 30-33.   A Pacific rattlesnake (*Crotalus viridis*), in the striking position and with the rattle elevated.   Dangerously poisonous.   (*Photograph by T. I. Storer.*)

Order 4. **Loricata** (Crocodilia). ALLIGATORS, CAIMANS, GAVIALS, AND CROCODILES. Body long; head large and long, jaws powerful, rimmed with numerous bluntly conical teeth; 4 short limbs ending in clawed toes with webs between; tail long, heavy, and compressed; skin thick and leathery, with horny scutes, those on back and belly rectangular and reinforced beneath by dermal bones; ear opening small, protected by small flap of skin; tongue not protrusible; heart 4-chambered, with separate ventricles; no bladder; oviparous; eggs deposited in "nests" of decaying vegetation; Triassic to Recent; tropics of New and Old Worlds and Australia, and Gulf states; about 23 species.

CROCODYLIDAE. *Crocodylus americanus,* American crocodile, southern Florida and Greater Antilles to Ecuador and Colombia, snout narrow; *C. niloticus,* Africa and river Nile, dangerous to man, many deaths; *Alligator mississippiensis,* American alligator, southern North Carolina to Florida and Rio Grande in Texas; in water and swamps and on land; constructs burrows; hibernates October to April; old males with loud voices; food of animals—insects to dogs and hogs—but rarely attacks man; female constructs conical nest of decaying vegetation, deposits 30 to 60 eggs incubated by decay in nest for about 60 days; young $8\frac{1}{2}$ to $9\frac{1}{2}$ inches at hatching, grow 12 inches or so per year; at 10 years, males 110 inches long, weighing 250 pounds, females 87 inches and 113 pounds (Fig. 30-1).

References

(See also works by Barbour, Gadow, and Stejneger and Barbour in Chap. 29)

COPE, E. D. 1900. Crocodilians, lizards and snakes of North America. *U.S. National Museum Report for* 1898, pp. 153–1,270, 36 pls., 347 figs. Technical; somewhat out of date.

DITMARS, RAYMOND L. 1926. Reptiles of the world. New York, The Macmillan Co. 23 + 373 pp., 89 pls. Popular.

———. 1936. The reptiles of North America. New York, Doubleday, Doran & Co., Inc. xvi + 476 pp., 135 pls. Popular.

McILHENNY, E. A. 1935. The alligator's life history. Boston, The Christopher Publishing House. 117 pp., 18 illus.

POPE, CLIFFORD, H. 1937. Snakes alive and how they live. New York, The Viking Press. xii + 238 pp., illus.

———. 1939. Turtles of the United States and Canada. New York, Alfred A. Knopf. xviii + 343 pp., 99 illus.

SCHMIDT, K. P., and D. D. DAVIS. 1941. Field book of snakes of the United States and Canada. New York, G. P. Putnam's Sons. xiii + 365 pp., 34 pls., 103 figs.

SMITH, H. M. 1946. Handbook of lizards [of the United States and Canada]. Ithaca, N.Y., Comstock Publishing Co. xxi + 557 pp., 135 pls., 136 figs., 41 maps.

VAN DENBURGH, J. 1922. The reptiles of western North America. *California Academy of Sciences, Occasional Papers, No.* 10, 2 vols., 1,028 pp., 128 pls. British Columbia to Lower California and Utah.

Papers on reptiles will be found in the quarterly journal *Copeia,* in various scientific and popular journals, and in many books of travel dealing with tropical and other regions. Descriptive accounts of the native reptiles, their distribution and natural history, are available for many states and local areas in *Copeia,* museum publications, and other documents.

CHAPTER 31

CLASS AVES. BIRDS

Birds are the best known and most easily recognized of all animals, because they are common, active by day, and easily seen. All birds have feathers that clothe and insulate their bodies to make a regulated body temperature possible, and those of the wings and tail provide for flight (Fig. 31-1); no other animals possess feathers. The ability to fly

FIG. 31-1.   Class Aves.   The American robin (*Turdus migratorius*), a representative bird. The contour feathers insulate the body against loss of heat and form a smooth streamlined exterior surface; the large feathers of the wings and tail provide extended surfaces for flight. The beak or bill is of bone, with a smooth cornified covering, and serves as both mouth and hands.   The slender lower legs or shanks and the feet also have a cornified covering. (*After U.S. Biological Survey.*)

enables birds to occupy some habitats denied to other animals and to move about actively. The habits of birds are known in great detail through studies by many professional and amateur students. The distinctive coloration and voices of birds appeal to human eyes and ears, and many birds species are of economic importance because of their food habits. Certain kinds are hunted as game, and the few domesticated species contribute to man's food supply. The ancient classical names for birds (Gr. *ornis*, L. *aves*) are perpetuated in the name of the class and the term "ornithology," the study of birds.

31-1. Characteristics.   1. Body covered with feathers.
2. Two pairs of limbs; anterior pair modified as wings for flight; posterior pair adapted for perching, walking, or swimming (with webs); each foot usually with 4 toes; shanks and toes sheathed with cornified skin.
3. Skeleton delicate, strong, fully ossified; mouth a projecting beak or bill, with horny sheath; no teeth in living birds; skull with one occipital condyle; neck very

flexible, often long; pelvis fused to numerous vertebrae but open ventrally; sternum enlarged, usually with median keel; tail vertebrae few, compressed.

4. Heart 4-chambered (2 auricles, 2 separate ventricles); only the right aortic (systemic) arch persists; red blood corpuscles nucleated, oval, and biconvex.

5. Respiration by compact lungs attached to ribs and connected to thin-walled air sacs extending between internal organs; voice box (syrinx) at base of trachea.

6. No bladder, excretions semisolid; females usually with only left ovary and oviduct.

7. Twelve pairs of cranial nerves.

8. Body temperature regulated (homoiothermous).

9. Fertilization internal; eggs with large yolk, covered with hard limy shell, and deposited externally for incubation; segmentation meroblastic; embryonic membranes (amnion, chorion, yolk sac, and allantois) present during development within the egg; young at hatching either fully formed, feathered, and able to run about (precocial), or helpless, naked, and requiring further growth in a nest (altricial), but always fed and cared for by parents.

Birds represent a significant advance over all lower animals in having (1) an insulated body covering; (2) complete separation of venous and arterial circulation in the heart, with (3) regulated body temperature and (4) high rate of metabolism; (5) the ability to fly; (6) highly developed voice, hearing, and sight; and (7) specialized care for the young. In all these features they stand above the reptiles and are comparable only with the mammals, from which they differ notably in the type of body covering, in the ability to fly, and in the manner of reproduction.

31-2. Size. The largest living birds include the ostrich of Africa, which stands fully 7 feet tall and weighs 300 pounds or more, and the great condors of the Americas with a wingspread up to 10 feet; the smallest is Helena's hummingbird of Cuba, $2\frac{1}{4}$ inches long and weighing about $\frac{1}{10}$ ounce; no bird, living or fossil, approaches the largest fishes or mammals in size.

STRUCTURE OF A BIRD: THE DOMESTIC FOWL

31-3. External features. The chicken or fowl has a distinct *head,* a long flexible *neck,* and a stout spindle-shaped *body* or trunk. The two fore limbs, or *wings,* are attached high on the back and have elongate flight feathers (remiges); the wings are deftly folded in Z-shape at rest and extended in flight. On each *hind limb* the two upper segments are muscular, whereas the slender lower leg or *shank* contains tendons but no muscle and is sheathed with cornified scales, as are the four *toes* which end in horny *claws.* The short *tail* bears a fanlike group of elongated tail feathers (rectrices).

The mouth is extended as a pointed bill or *beak,* covered with cornified epidermis, with two slitlike *nostrils* on the upper mandible. The *eyes* are large and lateral, each with an upper and lower *eyelid;* beneath these is the membranous *nictitating membrane,* which can be drawn independently across the eyeball from the outer corner. Below and behind each eye is an ear opening, or *auditory aperture,* hidden under special feathers. The fleshy median *comb* and lateral *wattles* on the head and the cornified spurs on the legs are peculiar to the chicken, pheasant, and a few other birds. Below the base of the tail is the vent or *anus.*

FIG. 31-2. Development of a contour feather. *A, B.* Early stages, as seen in section. *C.* Stereogram of later stage.

31-4. Integument. The skin is soft, flexible, and loosely attached to the muscles within. It lacks glands save for the *oil gland* above the base of the tail, which secretes an oily substance ordinarily thought to serve for "dressing" the feathers but which probably is used to keep the bill from becoming brittle.

31-5. Feathers. These distinctive epidermal structures provide a light-weight, flexible, but resistant body covering, with innumerable dead air spaces useful as insulation; they protect the skin from wear, and the thin, flat, and overlapping wing and tail feathers form surfaces to support the bird in flight.

Growth of a feather begins, like the scale of a reptile, as a local *dermal papilla* thrusting up the overlying epidermis (Fig. 31-2). The base of this *feather bud* sinks into a circular depression, the future *follicle* which will hold the feather in the skin. The outermost epidermal cells on the bud become a smooth cornified sheath (periderm) within which other epidermal layers are arranged in parallel ribs, a larger median one forming the future shaft and the others producing the barbs. The central soft dermal pulp (original dermal papilla) contains blood vessels and is wholly nutritive, drying upon completion of growth so that the feather is purely an epidermal structure. Pigment for coloration is deposited in the epidermal cells during growth in the follicle, but not thereafter. When growth is completed, the sheath bursts and is removed by preening, when the feather spreads to its completed shape.

1. CONTOUR FEATHERS. These provide the external covering and establish the contour of the bird's body, including the enlarged flight feathers of the wings and tail; several thousand are present on a chicken.

Each consists of a flattish *vane,* supported by the central *shaft,* which is an extension of the hollow *quill* attaching to the follicle. Each half of the vane is of many narrow, parallel, and closely spaced *barbs* joining the sides of the shaft. On the proximal and distal side of each barb are numerous smaller parallel *barbules,* and these are provided with

minute *barbicels* or *hooklets,* serving to hold opposing rows of barbules loosely together (Fig. 31-3).

The shaft is nearly straight in long flight feathers of the wing and of the tail, but curved in many body feathers so that their tips lie nearly parallel to the body and overlap one another to produce a smooth exterior surface. Many of the body feathers have a secondary shaft or after-shaft and vane, attached to the junction of the principal shaft and quill. Smooth muscles and elastic fibers in the skin enable a bird to ruffle or raise its feathers away from the body, to facilitate their rearrangement when bathing and preening and to increase the insulation value of the feather covering during cold weather.

2. DOWN FEATHERS. Young chicks and many other birds at hatching are covered with soft downy plumage, providing excellent insulation. A down feather has a short quill, a reduced shaft, and long flexible barbs with short

Fig. 31-3. *Above.* Types of feathers. *Below.* Stereogram of the parts in a contour feather; *, two proximal barbules cut to show curved edge along which the hooklets slide to make the feather flexible.

barbules. Down is also present beneath the contour feathers on ducks and various other water birds.

3. FILOPLUMES. Minute hairlike feathers, of unknown function, are sparsely distributed over the body, as seen on a plucked fowl. These grow in clusters near the follicles of some contour feathers; each has a long threadlike shaft, with a few weak barbs and barbules at the tip.

4. BRISTLES. Some birds have hairlike growths that are modified feathers, each with a short quill and slender shaft, with a few vestigial

barbs at the base.   These are seen about the mouths of flycatchers and whippoorwills, but there are none on the chicken.

The varied coloration of feathers results chiefly from pigments deposited during growth; these include acid-soluble melanins of black, brown, or dull yellow and ether-soluble lipochromes, either red or yellow. Blue, green, and iridescent markings, as on neck feathers of some poultry and on hummingbirds, are due to microscopically thin plates (lamellae) in the surface structure of these feathers, with dark pigment beneath. A feather once grown changes color only by wear, fading, or other discoloration.   Normal abrasion of the light-colored tips of some feathers reveals darker colors in more proximal parts, causing a change in pattern. Absence of pigment locally or generally causes partial or complete albinos.

Feathers grow only on certain areas or feather tracts (pterylae) of the skin, between which are bare spaces (apteria), as can be seen upon parting the feathers of a bird in hand (Fig. 31-4).   The assemblage of

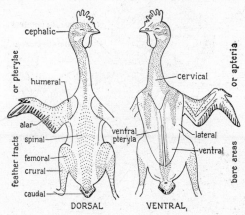

FIG. 31-4.   Feather tracts of the domestic fowl.   (*After Nietsch.*)

feathers on a bird at any one time is called a *plumage,* and the process of feather replacement is known as *molt.*   The molt is an orderly and gradual process so that portions of the body are not left bare; the large feathers on the wings and tail are molted in symmetrical pairs so that flight is not impaired.   The molt may be partial, involving only certain feather tracts, or complete as is usual in the late summer or autumn, and requires several weeks.   Molt involves the loss of an old feather and growth of a new one in each follicle.   The feather tracts, plumages, and molts of various species and higher groups of birds are distinctive and differ in varying degree.

31-6. Skeleton.   The bird skeleton (Fig. 31-5) is delicate as compared with that of most reptiles or mammals, and many of the bones contain air

cavities.   It is modified in relation to flight, bipedal locomotion, and the
laying of large eggs with hard shells.   The bones of the cranium are
separate in young birds but fused, with obliteration of most sutures, in
adults.   The **brain case** is rounded, the *orbits* sheltering the eyes are
large, and the *jaws* (premaxillae + maxillae, and mandibles) project
forward as the bony *beak*.   The lower jaws are fused to one another
anteriorly and articulate posteriorly on either side with the movable
quadrate connecting to the squamosal on the cranium.   The skull
meets the vertebral column nearly at a right angle and articulates on
a single *occipital condyle* with the first neck vertebra.

The long and flexible neck contains about 16 elongate ***cervical verte-***
brae, each with saddle-shaped (heterocoelous) articular surfaces on the

Fig. 31-5.   Skeleton of the domestic fowl.   (*Adapted from Ellenberger und Baum.*)

centra that permit free movements of the head in feeding, preening, and
other activities.   The *trunk vertebrae* are closely fitted together and
nearly rigid; those of the thorax have rib articulations laterally, and the
remainder are fused to form the solid *synsacrum* to which the pelvis
attaches.   No lumbar region is evident.   The four free ***caudal vertebrae***
and the compressed terminal *pygostyle* (= 5 or 6 fused vertebrae) are

freely movable on one another to allow for action of the tail feathers (rectrices) attached over the pygostyle.

The *bony thorax* protects the internal organs and provides a rigid support for the flight mechanism yet is capable of slight expansion and contraction for respiration. It consists of (1) the *vertebrae* dorsally, (2) the flat *ribs* laterally, and (3) the breastbone or *sternum* ventrally, with a median keel (carina) below to which the pectoral flight muscles attach. Each thoracic rib has a distinct vertebral and a sternal part, the two joining nearly at a right angle; the second cervical and first four thoracic ribs each bear posteriorly an *uncinate process* overlapping the rib next behind and strengthening the thorax.

The *pectoral girdle* on each side consists of (1) the long swordlike *scapula* (shoulder blade) lying parallel to the vertebrae and over the ribs, (2) the *coracoid* as a stout stay between the scapula and sternum, and (3) the *clavicle* hanging vertically from the scapula; the two clavicles are fused at their ventral ends to form the V-shaped *furcula* or "wishbone." The three bones meet dorsally on either side to form a circular canal as a pulley for the pectoralis minor muscle that lifts the wing.

Each fore limb attaches high on the dorsal surface, the *humerus* articulating in the glenoid fossa on the coracoid. The "forearm" contains the *radius* and *ulna* as in other land vertebrates. The remainder of the wing bones are greatly modified to provide stabilized supports for the flight feathers (remiges). Only two *carpals* (radiale and ulnare) and but three *digits* (II, III, IV) are evident, the other carpal bones being fused to the three metacarpals and forming the *carpometacarpus* of two elongate bones. In the "hand" the anterior or second digit bears the bastard wing (alula), the next or third is longest and of two segments, and the innermost or fourth has one. The outermost and principal flight feathers or *primaries* are supported on digits III and IV, the *secondaries* on the radius and ulna, the *tertiaries* on the humerus. Two membranous extensions of skin on the fore and hind borders of the limb (anterior and posterior patagium) hold the quills of the flight feathers against twisting during flight.

The *pelvic girdle* is a broad thin saddle firmly united to the synsacrum, but widely open ventrally, permitting easy passage of large eggs in the female. Each half consists of the large *ilium* anteriorly, the *ischium* posteriorly, and the slender *pubis* ventrally; where the three meet a socket, the *acetabulum,* receives the head of the thighbone.

Each leg consists of (1) the rounded *femur,* or thighbone; (2) the long and triangular headed *tibiotarsus,* which is paralleled by the slender and often incomplete *fibula;* (3) the fused *tarsometatarsus,* or shank; (4) a knee bone or *patella,* held in ligaments before the femur-tibiotarsal joint; and (5) the four *toes,* three in front and one behind, each of several bones. Of the tarsals, or ankle bones, seen in other vertebrates, the proximal row in birds is fused to the tibia and the distal row to the metatarsus; the latter consists of three fused metatarsals, distinguishable only at the ends of the bone.

31-7. Muscular system. In the bodies of most lower vertebrates, segmental muscles predominate over nonsegmental ones, but the reverse is true among birds and mammals, where the limb muscles are enlarged for rapid activity. In birds these muscles show specializations related

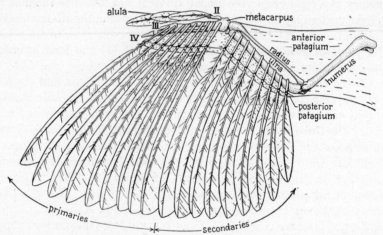

Fig. 31-6. Spread left wing of a white-crowned sparrow from the dorsal side, dissected to show how the flight feathers are supported, primaries on the "hand" and secondaries on the "forearm," by the bones and also the membranous patagium. II–IV, digits.

to flight and bipedal locomotion. Movement of the wings in flight is due chiefly to the large pectoral muscles of the breast, the "white meat" of chickens and turkeys, which form a major fraction of the entire musculature on a bird (Fig. 31-7*B*). On either side the **pectoralis major** originates on the outer part of the sternal keel and inserts on the ventro-lateral surface of the head of the humerus; its contraction moves the wing downward and lifts the bird's body in flight. In other land vertebrates the fore limb is raised by muscles on the dorsal surface of the body, but in birds such movement is also due to a ventral muscle, the **pectoralis minor**. This originates on the keel (inside or medial to p. major) and tapers dorsally to a strong tendon passing through the ringlike junction of the clavicle, coracoid, and scapula to insert on the dorsoposterior surface of the humerus. Since both these muscles are symmetrically paired and the members of each pair in turn exert an equal and opposite pull, the thin keel of the sternum affords an adequate place for their attachment. Other smaller muscles about the head of the humerus provide for minor changes in the movements of the wings. The tail feathers are moved vertically or horizontally and spread or brought together by muscles about the follicles of those feathers.

The shanks and feet contain no muscle, probably as an adaptation to prevent loss of heat from these unfeathered parts.   Movements of the toes are due to tendons connected to muscles in the upper segments of the legs.   The tendons move through spaces lubricated by fluid, and their action on the toes is directed through loops of tendon ("pulleys").   The slender *ambiens* muscle, which originates on the pelvis, has a long tendon crossing the knee to insert on the toes.   When a bird squats on its perch, the tension on this muscle and tendon causes the toes to flex and grasp the support, and thus the bird, in resting or sleeping, is automatically clamped to its perch (Fig. 31-7*A*).

Fig. 31-7. *A*. Perching mechanism of a bird. From muscles on the thigh and lower leg tendons pass behind the "heel" (tarsal joint) and shank, then through an annular ligament beneath the foot to insert separately on the toes. When a bird squats down for resting or sleeping, this arrangement flexes the toes and holds the bird firmly to its perch. (*Adapted from Wolcott.*) *B*. Diagram of the pectoral muscles (major and minor) that move the bird's wings in flight.

31-8. Digestive system. The *tongue* is small and pointed, with a horny covering.   The *mouth cavity* is roofed with elongate *palatal folds,* a short *pharynx* follows, then the long tubular and muscular *esophagus* extends to the base of the neck where it dilates into a large soft-walled *crop,* in which food is stored and moistened.   The stomach comprises a soft anterior *proventriculus* with thick walls secreting the gastric juices, and the disc-shaped *ventriculus,* or *gizzard,* with walls of thick dense musculature, lined internally by heavily cornified epithelium.   Here the food is ground up by action of the muscular walls, aided by bits of gravel or other hard particles swallowed for the purpose—these are, functionally, the "hen's teeth." The *intestine* is slender, with numerous coils, and leads to the larger *rectum;* at the junction are two elongate *caeca* or blind pouches, which increase the digestive surface of the gut. Beyond is the dilated *cloaca,* the common exit for undigested food wastes and materials from the excretory and reproductive organs, ending with

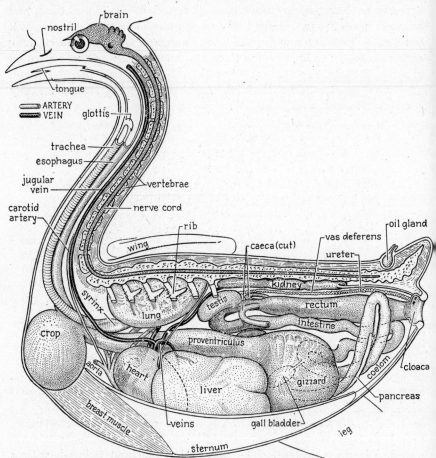

FIG. 31-8.   The domestic fowl; internal structure.   The two caeca are cut off.

the external aperture, the *vent* or *anus.*   Dorsally the cloacal wall bears a small outgrowth, the bursa of Fabricius, of unknown function.   The large reddish *liver* is bilobed, with a gall bladder and two bile ducts.   The *pancreas* usually has three ducts; all the ducts discharge into the anterior loop of the intestine.

     31-9. Circulatory system.   The bird *heart* has two thin-walled auricles and two distinct thick-walled ventricles, separating completely the venous and arterial blood streams.   This is undoubtedly a factor in the develop-

ment of a regulated body temperature.   The sinus venosus is incorporated
in the right auricle.   Blood from the two precaval and one postcaval vein
enters the right auricle, passes to the right ventricle and thence by the
pulmonary artery to capillaries in the lungs for oxygenation.   It all
returns in the pulmonary vein to the left auricle, then the left ventricle, ·
and into the single *right aortic arch.*   The latter gives off two innominate
arteries, each with three large branches, the carotid to the head and neck,
brachial to the wing, and pectoral to the breast muscles of flight.   The
arch continues dorsally and posteriorly as the *dorsal aorta* serving the

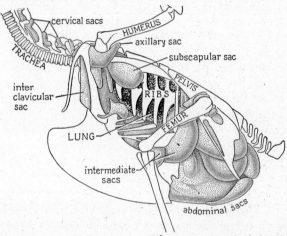

FIG. 31-9.   Respiratory system of a pigeon.   The air sacs are stippled and bones are outlined; attachments of the lungs to the ribs are indicated.   (*After Muller*, 1910.)

internal organs and remainder of the body.   The venous system retains
some reptilian features.   Two precavals collect anteriorly and the single
postcaval vein is short, formed of two large iliac veins draining from the
hind limbs and body.   A *hepatic portal system* is present as in other
vertebrates, but the renal portal system in the kidneys is reduced.   A
special adaptation is the cross connection in the jugular veins below the
head that prevents stoppage of circulation if one vein is compressed by
movements of the head or neck.   The small rounded *spleen* lies near the
stomach.

Behind the pericardial sac containing the heart, a delicate *oblique
septum* separates the heart and lungs from the other viscera.

31-10. Respiratory system (Fig. 31-9).   The *external nares* on the beak
connect to *internal nares* above the mouth cavity.   In the pharynx
and just behind the tongue is the slitlike *glottis* of the *larynx.*   To the
latter is joined the flexible windpipe or *trachea,* which is reinforced by
hooplike cartilages, partly calcified.   The trachea continues down the
neck to the voice box or *syrinx,* within which are the vocal muscles.

From the syrinx a short *bronchus* leads to each *lung.* The latter are small, inelastic, and closely attached by connective tissue to the ribs and vertebrae in the dorsal part of the thorax. The lungs are penetrated by many interconnected air passages, the *bronchioles,* and by branches of pulmonary blood vessels. To the bronchioles are attached numerous thin-walled *air sacs* that extend out between organs in the body cavity, to spaces around neck vertebrae, and to cavities in the larger bones. The lungs are attached to the ribs and dilated by slight movements of intercostal muscles between the ribs, the sternum moving downward and the ribs bowing laterally, whereupon air is drawn into the lung cavities; slight contraction of the thorax reverses the flow. Such movements are possible despite the rigid nature of the thorax necessary for flight. At inspiration, air rushes through the bronchioles and on into the air sacs, then passes in reverse direction at expiration. This rapid flow of air *through* the lung and past the pulmonary capillaries explains why birds can be served by small and dense lungs, although they have the highest respiratory needs of all animals because of their high body temperature and active life. The air sacs are the principal means of dissipating the heat resulting from muscular contraction and other metabolic activities. Experiments have shown that if the air sacs are opened the bird continues to respire and live although the body temperature rises; if the attachments of both lungs to the ribs are severed, it dies quickly of asphyxiation. The air sacs do not "decrease the bird's specific gravity," as commonly stated. The songs and calls of birds are produced by air forced across muscles in the syrinx, which vibrate like reeds and can be varied in tension to give notes of different pitch.

31-11. Excretory system. The paired *kidneys* are dark-brown three-lobed structures attached dorsally beneath the pelvis. From each a slender duct, the *ureter,* extends posteriorly to the dorsal wall of the cloaca; there is no bladder. Semisolid nitrogenous waste (with a high concentration of urates) passes slowly down the ureters and out the cloaca with the feces, as whitish material on the latter.

31-12. Nervous system. The bird *brain* is proportionately larger than that of a reptile and is short and broad. The olfactory lobes are small (poor sense of smell), the cerebral hemispheres are large and smooth, and the optic lobes on the midbrain are conspicuously developed (keen sight). The cerebellum has increased surface with many superficial folds (many activities of coordination). The *nerve cord* and paired *spinal nerves* are essentially as in other vertebrates. The thoracic or brachial plexus, serving the great muscles of flight, is especially large.

31-13. Sense organs. The sense of *smell* is poorly developed; choice and rejection of food materials probably depend on the *taste* buds in the roof of the mouth and at the sides of the tongue, aided by pressure receptors on the bill and tongue.   The eye is proportionately larger than in other vertebrates, and the sense of *sight* phenomenally keen.   The exposed surface of the eye, beneath the eyelids, is covered by the *cornea,* a transparent layer that is kept moist by secretions of the tear glands.   A protective ring of 12 to 20 bony *sclerotic plates* is embedded in the outer tissues of the eyeball; the *lens* is biconvex, with different curvatures on the outer and inner surfaces, and is surrounded externally by the pig-mented *iris diaphragm,* which gives color to the eye and regulates the amount of entering light.   The anterior chamber, before the lens, contains watery *aqueous humor,* and the posterior chamber behind is filled with gelatinous *vitreous humor.*   In the latter is a peculiar comblike *pecten,* of unknown function but thought possibly to aid in nutrition or accommodation or screening the retina.   The light-sensitive *retina* contains a multitude of minute rods and cones, their small size being considered a basis for the keen vision of birds.   Color vision is acute, and accommodation, or adjustment of focus to objects at different distances, is very rapid, as necessary in the quick changes from near to distant vision during flight and in other activities.

The sense of *hearing* is highly developed.   A short *external auditory canal* at the posterior-lateral angle of the head leads to the *tympanic membrane* or eardrum.   From the latter a bone, the *columella auris,* transmits sound waves across the middle-ear cavity to the "oval window" of the inner ear as with reptiles and amphibians.   From the *middle ear* on each side a *Eustachian tube* leads to the pharynx, the two having a common opening at the back of the palate.   The "cochlea" of the inner ear is a short, blind-ended tube, larger than in reptiles but less developed than in mammals.

31-14. Endocrine glands.   The *pituitary* (hypophysis) is below the base of the brain.   The *thyroid,* of two lateral lobes, lies beneath the jugular vein near where the subclavian and carotid arteries originate.   The *pancreas* contains the islets of Langerhans.   The paired *adrenals* are on the ventral surface of the kidneys, each being 8 to 10 mm. long.   The endocrine secretions of the *gonads* regulate the secondary sexual char-acters, especially those of plumage.   In many species of birds the males and females differ in feather characteristics, and in chickens and turkeys the wattles and comb are unlike in the two sexes.

Complete removal of the left ovary and rudiment of the right in a brown Leghorn hen is followed by permanent assumption of typical male plumage.   If only the left ovary is removed in a young hen, the male plumage is acquired; but later, with growth of the right ovary, there is often a return toward female plumage.   If the left ovary is removed after a hen has acquired her typical plumage, she assumes that of the male.   Secretions of the female gonad therefore suppress the male plumage, but if eliminated the latter type develops. Similar results have been obtained in the Rouen duck, pheasant, ostrich, European bullfinch, and chaffinch. Complete removal of the testes in a male chicken results in a *capon,* with feathering much like that of a male. Castration of a male duck eliminates the brown eclipse plumage·that normally replaces the green of the head and neck during the molt of the flight and body feathers. Implanting an ovary in a chicken capon usually is followed by assumption of female plumage, but implantation of a testis into a normal or castrated hen (*poulard*) has no effect on its plumage. In the turkey, guinea fowl, or pigeon, removal of the testis is not followed by plumage changes.

The Sebright bantam is a domestic race of chickens selected to have essentially the same plumage in both sexes; castration of either sex results in a more distinctive type of male feathering; the gonads·in this race are assumed to be hermaphroditic, containing both male and female components.

A feather during its growth in the follicle is sensitive to changes in concentration of the gonad hormone circulating in the blood stream. If several of the normal black feathers are plucked from the breast of a male brown Leghorn, new ones of the same kind soon begin to grow. If, however, female gonad hormone is injected in small amounts, after about 2 weeks a salmon-colored crossbar will appear across each feather at the part in active stage of growth when the hormone was injected. The salmon color is characteristic of breast feathers on a normal female.

31-15. Reproductive system (Fig. 31-10). In the *male* the two oval and whitish *testes* are attached near the anterior ends of the kidneys.

Fig. 31-10. Urogenital systems of the domestic fowl, in ventral view. Cloaca opened to show exits of the ducts.

From each testis a much convoluted **vas deferens** extends posteriorly parallel to the ureter; in many birds it is dilated as a **seminal vesicle** just before entering the cloaca on a papilla close to the urinary opening. In the cloaca of ducks and ostriches there is a median copulatory organ or **penis,** as in the alligator; this is present only as a vestige in the chick for a few days after hatching, when it provides a means of determining the sex of downy young. The testes become enormously enlarged in the breeding season. Sperm developed in the testes are accumulated in the seminal vesicles, to be transferred from the cloaca of the male to that of the female while in contact during the act of mating.

The **female** system usually develops only on the left side. The **ovary** is near the left kidney, and close by is the open expanded funnel or **infundibulum** of the **oviduct;** the duct extends posteriorly and enters the cloaca. In nonlaying birds the ovary is small, containing minute eggs, and the duct is also small, but in the season of egg laying both are much enlarged. The ova then become numerous, and each receives its full quota of yolk before being released individually. A mature ovum escapes from its ovarian follicle into the abdominal cavity, is grasped by active gaping movements of the funnel, to enter the oviduct; there it moves slowly down by the action of muscles in the walls and bands of cilia on the inner surface of the duct. Fertilization probably occurs in the upper oviduct; albumen (egg white) is added by glands in the middle portion; and the shell membranes and shell are secreted by glands in the posterior part or "uterus," after which the egg is ready to lay. An egg completed early in the day is soon deposited but if formed later is usually retained overnight. A rudimentary right ovary is commonly present and may enlarge to function if the left one is removed.

STRUCTURE OF OTHER BIRDS

31-16. Adaptive features. As a group the birds are more like one another than are members of other classes of vertebrates. Differences among various birds are often adaptive, enabling each kind to perform its necessary activities more efficiently. The external form is usually fusiform or spindle-shaped, like two cones with their bases together; this shape offers minimum resistance to the air during flight or to water in diving, facilitates passage through vegetation, and sheds water easily.

The **coloration** is varied and striking. A few birds are all of a color, as black crows and some blackbirds and the white egrets, but the feathers of most species are marked with spots, stripes, or bars. The pattern often resembles somewhat that of the environment, and such **protective coloration** renders the bird less visible; this is aided by **countershading,** the upper parts which receive stronger lighting being darker than the undersurface. Birds of arid regions tend to be pale-colored, and those of humid places are darker.   Males are often more brilliant than and marked differently from females.   In some species both sexes acquire a *nuptial plumage* by a spring or prenuptial molt and return to duller colors for the winter by a postnuptial molt in late summer.

The *bill* is at once a mouth and hands, serving to obtain and "handle" food, to preen the feathers, to gather and arrange nest materials, and for other purposes, including defense (Fig. 31-11).   The cornified covering

Fig. 31-11.   Some types of beaks and bills in birds.

grows continually to replace that lost by wear.   The form of bill usually indicates the food habits of a bird, being slender in species that probe into crevices or capture insects, stouter but still elongate in woodpeckers which dig in wood, wide but delicate in swallows and flycatchers which capture living insects in flight, stout and conical in seed-eating finches and sparrows, sharp-edged in flesh-eating hawks, owls, shrikes, and parrots, and with serrated margins in ducks that sieve small materials from water.   The *tongue* in most birds cannot be extended; but in woodpeckers it can be protruded beyond the bill for capturing insects in wood, and in hummingbirds it is an extensible siphon for obtaining nectar from flowers.

The *wings* (Fig. 31-6) are the means of active flight.   Their vigorous downward strokes serve to raise the bird's body in the air, and various tilting and banking movements aid in altering the manner of flight. Short rounded wings are characteristics of species that fly in and about vegetation such as quail and many sparrows and warblers; long slender wings are possessed by birds that fly actively in the open like the swallows, falcons, and terns; broad wings of large area are found in eagles, hawks, and others that habitually soar and circle.   The penguins, auks, and some other waterfowl use their wings to "fly" under water.   The ostrich, kiwi, and a few other birds have degenerate wings and cannot fly.

The bird's *tail* is a group of large feathers attached fanlike over the pygostyle.   It serves as a rudder in flight, as a counterbalance in perching, and for display in courting by the males of many species.   The tail may be spread or folded and elevated, depressed, or tilted to direct the course of flight.   Long slender tails are common in birds of trees and thickets such as jays and towhees, broad tails are seen in pigeons which check their flight suddenly, and the tail is small in species that live on open water like ducks and seafowl, or in the air as do swallows and swifts.   Creepers, woodpeckers, and some others that forage on vertical surfaces have tail feathers with stiffened shafts that help to support the body when these birds are at work.

The *feet* of birds serve variously for running or climbing, for support of the body at rest, for arranging nest materials, and in some species for handling food and for offense (Fig. 31-12).   The most usual arrangement

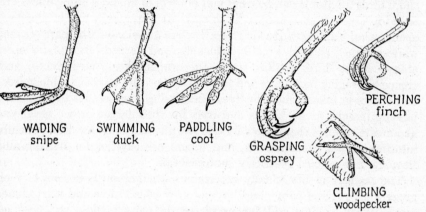

WADING   SWIMMING   PADDLING   GRASPING   PERCHING
snipe   duck   coot   osprey   finch

CLIMBING
woodpecker

FIG. 31-12.   Some types of feet in birds.

of three toes in front and one behind enables a bird living about vegetation to perch easily on twigs and branches.   Stout feet for scratching are common to quail and other ground dwellers, slender toes and sharp claws are possessed by those that inhabit the stems and foliage of plants, webs between the toes occur in most birds that swim on or in the water, and hawks and owls have sharp curved claws for clutching the animals that are their prey.   The legs are long in waders such as herons and also in some that inhabit open lands, like the ostrich.

The *skeleton* varies in the length and proportion of parts and in other features.   The neck is short in many foliage-inhabiting birds but is greatly elongated and has many vertebrae in herons, swans, cranes, and others.   The *crop* is used by some birds to carry food for the young, which are fed either by regurgitation or by putting their heads down the parent gullet.   In adult pigeons, while rearing young, the epithelial lining sloughs off as "pigeon milk" used to nourish squabs in the nest.   In some flesh-eating birds such as the kingfisher there is no distinct crop, and the stomach is a thin-walled distensible sac.   The intestine tends to be shorter in birds which subsist upon animal food than in those which eat plant materials.   Both left and right ovaries are developed in some hawks.

NATURAL HISTORY

31-17. Distribution. Birds occupy all continents, the seas, and most islands, penetrating the Arctic to 80°N. and the Antarctic, and occur from sea level to above timber line on mountains, even to above 20,000 feet on Mount Everest. Despite the ability to fly they conform to the "laws" of animal distribution, each species occupying a definite geographic range and particular kind of habitat. Albatrosses and petrels live on the open ocean except when nesting, gulls, auks, and murres occur along seacoasts, shore birds inhabit ocean beaches and borders of inland waters, ducks are found in marshes and on open fresh and salt water, rails live in marshes, meadow larks and savanna sparrows dwell in grasslands, fox sparrows and white-crowned sparrows inhabit thickets, and horned larks prefer open areas. Many birds utilize trees—the woodpeckers, nuthatches, and creepers foraging on trunks and large branches, the warblers, chickadees, and others in foliage, and the flycatchers using tree perches to watch for passing insects, as do hawks and owls for their larger prey. Swallows and swifts capture their insect food in the air, and some hawks soar when hunting. Owls, woodpeckers, and others use cavities for nesting and sleeping, but no bird is strictly subterranean.

The manner of life usually determines whether birds are solitary or gregarious. Insect eaters and birds of prey usually live and hunt alone; quail, ducks, robins, and juncos scatter in pairs to nest but flock at other seasons; and some seafowl, pigeons, and blackbirds are always in companies.

In polar regions the species are few but numerous as to individuals. In temperate lands, 150 to 200 kinds of birds may occur in a locality at various seasons. Tropical regions tend to have many species. Birds sometimes occur in enormous aggregations, such as "rafts" of 100,000 ducks and "clouds" of blackbirds in rice fields; the now extinct passenger pigeon once "darkened the sky" with its numbers in eastern states. There is an average of two birds per acre over the United States at the opening of the nesting season.

31-18. Activity. Birds are active at all seasons, by reason of being "warm-blooded" (only the poorwill is known to hibernate). Diurnal species are busy from dawn to dusk, and owls and whippoorwills feed at night. All spend some time preening their feathers, and many bathe to aid this process. Diurnal land birds sleep at night, with the head turned back on or beneath a wing. Water birds may sleep by day, floating and dragging a foot to keep from drifting.

The body temperature is regulated and usually above that of the environment. The daytime temperature of adults is about 105 to 108°F., varying with the species. Poultry and passerine birds have a daily

rhythm of 107 to 108° by day and down to 104°F. at night. Activity
and the amount of food in the stomach vary the temperature. Young
of house wrens and others are "reptilian" at birth when they assume the
temperature of the environment, but their heat regulation develops within
a few days.

The ability to fly gives greater opportunity to seek food and escape
enemies and makes long migrations possible. Quail have a short direct
flight, others can remain awing for longer periods, and the swallows,
swifts, terns, and some hawks are in the air much of the time. The speed
of flight varies from 20 to 50 or more miles per hour.

31-19. Voice. Most birds can utter calls and songs. Cormorants and
pelicans are voiceless, some species have only a fixed call, and most "songbirds" (Order PASSERIFORMES, Suborder OSCINES) have definite songs.
Crows and jays use various notes to convey different "ideas" to others
of their species, and the parrots, mynas, magpies, and mockingbirds have
the power of mimicry.   The average pitch in songs of 59 passerine species
studied by Brand is 4,280 cycles per second, or above the highest note
(C_7) on the piano. Bird notes serve (1) to assemble gregarious species;
(2) to advertise nesting territory and attract mates; (3) for directional
calls between parents and young; and (4) to warn in the event of danger.
Some notes are used at all times of year, some songs and calls only during
the nesting season, and a few only during migration. The calls and songs
serve for identification of bird species by man, once he has learned them,
as the voice of each is usually distinctive.

31-20. Migration. Some birds such as the bobwhite are strictly
resident, but many species *migrate,* or shift regularly from one region
to another with the change of seasons. Most migration is north and
south, or *latitudinal;* birds move into the wide land masses of the north
temperate and subarctic regions, where there are facilities for feeding and
nesting during the warmer months, and then retire south for the winter.
A lesser and opposite movement occurs in the Southern Hemisphere,
where the seasons are reversed. Some birds perform *altitudinal migrations* into mountainous regions for the summer and return to the lowlands to winter; this occurs in the Rocky Mountains and the Cascade-
Sierra Nevada systems of western North America.

Most species use established routes for migration and travel more or
less on schedule, arriving and disappearing regularly, "according to the
calendar" (Fig. 31-13).   Ducks and other waterfowl are influenced more
by storms in autumn and the presence of open water in spring. Small
warblers, thrushes, and sparrows migrate at night and stop to rest and
feed by day; crows, blackbirds, hawks, and geese travel by day but stop
to forage in suitable places; swallows and swifts migrate by day, capturing
their insect food en route.   Ducks, shore birds, gulls, and others migrate

either at night or by day. Some birds migrate close to the earth, and others up to 3,000 or 5,000 feet but rarely higher. Although individuals may fly at 30 to 50 miles per hour, they stop to feed, are passed by others, then go on; hence the "migration front" progresses rather slowly, averaging about 25 miles per day for many species. Some birds migrate only short distances, but small insect eaters such as flycatchers, warblers, and vireos that nest in the United States and Canada spend the winter in Mexico, Central America, or northern South America. Many migrants

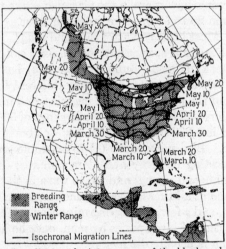

Fig. 31-13. Summer (breeding) and winter ranges of the black-and-white warbler (*Mniotilta varia*), a migratory species. The advance during the spring migration is shown by isochronal lines that connect points of arrival on certain dates. (*From U.S. Fish and Wildlife Service.*)

"follow the sun"—like human tourists—and never experience the rigors of winter, whereas some Arctic species move to temperate regions for winter and retire to cooler latitudes in summer. Results from marking individual birds with numbered leg bands show that many return to places previously occupied. Both the summer and winter ranges of species are well-defined.

Some migrants follow obvious landmarks such as rivers, mountain ranges, or coast lines; but others pass over the sea or lands without directional features, and young may precede their parents on the first migration. Birds evidently are guided by instinct impressed on the nervous system in some way through countless generations. The urge to migrate is related in part to the endocrines of the gonads, since experimental induction of gonad development in winter may cause individuals to migrate before their usual season, and individuals of migratory species that remain during the summer in their winter habitats usually prove to have defective gonads.

In addition to regular migrations there are vagrant movements of young out from their nesting ranges in later summer and of roving flocks searching for food in winter. Some species occasionally "irrupt" or leave their normal habitat when food shortage occurs, and move in numbers to areas they do not ordinarily occupy. Snowy owls of the Arctic move south every few winters when their food supply of rodents becomes scarce in the north, and large numbers then appear in the northern United States.

31-21. Food. The high and regulated body temperature of birds, their great activity, and their light weight place on them a large requirement for food of high energy value, well above that for most other animals. They cannot long survive without food and many must literally "eat to live." Quail and other gallinaceous birds eat much leafy vegetation, but most others use concentrated materials such as seeds or fruits of plants and various animals including worms, arthropods, mollusks, and vertebrates. Some seed eaters turn to insects for food during the nesting season. Many small flycatchers, warblers, and vireos are almost exclusively insectivorous; fish are the staple diet of loons, cormorants, pelicans, terns, herons, and kingfishers; frogs are eaten by herons; both snakes and lizards are captured by some hawks; the "bird hawks" (sharp-shinned, Cooper's, goshawk, duck hawk) feed chiefly on birds; and rodents and rabbits bulk large in the diet of many hawks and owls. Vultures feed only on carrion—dead animals— but ravens and some hawks also use such food. Crows and jays can subsist on a variety of materials, both plant and animal, but some birds are narrowly restricted; hummingbirds live on nectar of flowers and small insects, and sapsuckers eat the cambium and sap of trees, with some insects. The robin uses insects and other animal food in summer but forages largely on berries in winter.

Nestlings may eat more than their own weight in a day, and adults of many small species eat one-quarter to one-half their weight daily. The crop and stomach may be filled twice a day or more often, and digestion is rapid for animal materials. Several hundred seeds may be present in the crop and stomach of a finch at one time, and carnivorous birds often gorge themselves when meals are infrequent.

31-22. Enemies. These are mostly among the higher vertebrates although some fish and bullfrogs occasionally capture birds. Racers, bull snakes, and others eat eggs and young in the nesting season, and one African snake feeds extensively on eggs, having ventral processes on the vertebrae that serve to puncture the shells. The bird hawks, some other hawks, and a few owls take birds for food. Weasels, wildcats, house cats, and foxes are common bird predators, and other carnivores take birds as opportunity affords. Man "preys" on game birds, often kills useful hawks and owls and other species, and at times has to destroy birds that damage crops.   Migrant birds and young in the nest are sometimes killed by stormy weather.

Birds have various worm parasites, protozoans, bacteria, and viruses. The western duck sickness, due to *Bacillus botulinus,* type *C,* occurs at times in shallow warm waters of western North America that contain decaying vegetation, and has killed thousands of ducks.   Freshening the water and other artificial means serve to reduce these losses.

31-23. Reproduction.   Fertilization is always internal, and all birds lay eggs with large yolks and hard calcareous shells, which must be warmed or *incubated* for growth of the embryos.   In all birds except the "brush turkeys" (Megapodes) of Australia, either one or both parents sit upon the eggs to supply the necessary heat.   The young of chickens, quail, ducks, shore birds, and others are *precocial,* being well formed, fully covered with down, and able to run about at once when hatched, whereas those of songbirds, woodpeckers, pigeons, and others are blind, naked, and helpless when hatched and must be fed and cared for in the nest; these are termed *altricial.*

Each species has a characteristic season of reproduction, usually a few weeks in spring or summer—horned owls in February or March, goldfinches in July, and so on.   Breeding activities follow increase in the size and functioning of the gonads and are controlled by endocrines.   The latter are, in turn, evidently affected indirectly by light, since experimental exposure of birds in winter to an increased "length of day," even with a 40-watt electric light, will cause enlargement of the gonads, song, mating behavior, and even egg production long before the normal season of reproduction.

The breeding season for many species begins with the males uttering their characteristic songs at frequent intervals, and many go through *courting performances* in the presence of females.   Each male takes up and defends a *territory* suitable to the needs of a pair for the period necessary to rear a brood.   The territorial requirements of each species are different in features such as location, size, cover, food plants, etc.   Other males of the same species and predaceous enemies are not tolerated. When a female joins him, the pair proceeds with nest construction, mating, egg laying, incubation, and care of the young.   In some species both sexes participate fully, whereas in others one sex performs most of the duties.   Colonial waterfowl such as murres, cormorants, or gulls on rocky sea cliffs usually do not organize territories, since suitable nesting places are scarce although large common feeding areas are readily available.   Brood production usually leaves the parents with worn plumage, which is renewed at the postnuptial molt.

Some waterfowl and a few land birds lay on bare rocks or ground, but most species construct a *nest* to hold the eggs during incubation, and,

with altricial birds, to shelter the young (Fig. 31-14).   It may be a mere
depression in soil or gravel (killdeer), a few bits of vegetation (gulls), a
loose framework of twigs (doves), or a cuplike structure woven of grasses
or other plant materials (many songbirds).   The kingfisher and some
swallows dig a nest tunnel in a stream bank, the woodpecker excavates a
gourd-shaped nest cavity in a tree, and some swallows build nests of mud.
Owls, bluebirds, titmice, and others use natural or artificial cavities,
including man-made nest boxes.

Fig. 31-14.   Some types of bird nests.   *Left.* Killdeer, eggs laid on ground.   *Center.*
Valley quail, eggs in a lined depression.   *Right.* Cliff swallow, nests formed of mud pellets
and closely placed in a dense colony on a rock.   (*Photographs by T. I. Storer.*)

The average number of *eggs* laid by a female in one clutch is smallest
among species nesting in safe locations and largest among ground nesters
exposed to great hazards.   The murre and the band-tailed pigeon lay but
1, the mourning dove 2, large hawks 2 or 3, most small land birds 3 to 5,
and the bobwhite and California quail average 14 to a set.   The *shells*
are white with owls and woodpeckers, plain blue with the robin, and of a
common ground color overlaid with darker spots, streaks, or blotches in
many species.   Shore birds and some others nesting on bare places have
eggs that are *protectively colored,* closely resembling their average surroundings.   The usual ovoid or "egg" shape permits the eggs being
closely placed and covered by the parent during incubation.   The size
of the egg and duration of incubation are in general related to the size of
the parent, although precocial species have larger eggs and longer incubation than altricial birds of the same bulk.   *Incubation* with many small
land birds requires about 14 days, the domestic fowl 21 days, pheasants
21 to 26 days, many ducks and the larger hawks 28 days, and the ostrich
42 to 60 days.   Young of small altricial species require about a week after
hatching before they leave the nest.

All young birds require *care after hatching.*   This includes feeding,
guarding, and brooding (for protection against chilling or wetting) or

shielding against undue heat of the sun (Fig. 31-15).   The young of precocial species are led away from the nest almost at once by the parents.

FIG. 31-15.   *Left.* Precocial young killdeer hatched with a full covering of down, eyes open, and able to get about at once.   *Right.* Helpless (altricial) young of the wood pewee still in the nest some days after hatching; the down has grown out, the contour feathers are just appearing, the eyes are still closed, and the young must be fed by the parents. (*Photographs by T. I. Storer.*)

With altricial species the parents are busy from dawn to dusk, seeking food and carrying it to the nest, removing excrement, and brooding; growth is rapid, and the young leave as soon as their flight feathers are fairly grown (Fig. 31-16).   The young are attended and defended by the adults for some time.   Family groups form the nuclei for winter flocks with gregarious birds such as blackbirds or quail; among solitary forms such as hawks and insect eaters the young scatter or are driven away by the parents, and all take up independent life. Adults and young of both sexes then become essentially alike in behavior until the next breeding season.

FIG. 31-16.   Young goldfinch after leaving the nest but barely able to fly; some down still on the head, lax contour feathers of the juvenal plumage on the body, and wing and tail feathers not fully grown. (*Photograph by T. I. Storer.*)

31-24. Relations to man.   Primitive people use wild birds for food and garments.   Means for capturing birds are figured on many decorations in ancient Egypt and adjacent regions. Ducks, quail, herons, and other birds down to small finches have been sought as game in Europe for centuries, and today small songbirds are regularly marketed in some Mediterranean countries.   Early settlers in North America used game birds for food, and later enormous numbers of wild ducks, geese, prairie chickens, pigeons, and shore birds were sold in city markets, but wild populations cannot withstand such continued slaughter. The great auk and passenger pigeon became extinct, and many others were far reduced. Ducks, geese, quail, and other game birds are now sought by several million hunters every year in the United States, under legal restrictions as to season, bag limit, and manner of capture. Means are now being developed to increase the supply by "game management."

Bird feathers of distinctive color or shape serve native peoples and modern women for ornamentation. Indians of the Middle West used wing and tail feathers of golden eagles for ceremonial headdresses, and feathers of flickers and valley quail served Pacific coast tribes for decora-

TABLE 31-1. THE PRINCIPAL DOMESTICATED BIRDS, THEIR CLASSIFICATION AND PLACES ON ORIGIN

Order and family	Domesticated stocks	Wild stock whence derived	Place of origin
Struthioniformes STRUTHIONIDAE	Ostrich	*Struthio camelus*, ostrich	Africa
Anseriformes ANATIDAE	Ducks, most breeds	*Anas platyrhynchos*, mallard	Europe
	Muscovy duck	*Cairina moschata*	Central America or northern South America
	Geese, most breeds	*Anser albifrons*, gray lag goose	Europe
	Mute swan	*Cygnus olor*	Europe
Galliformes PHASIANIDAE	Fowls, all breeds	*Gallus bankiva*, jungle fowl	India
	Pheasants	*Phasianus colchicus* and other wild pheasants	Caucasus; northern Asia
	Peacock, or peafowl	*Pavo cristatus*	India
MELEAGRIDAE	Turkey	*Meleagris gallopavo*	Mexico
NUMIDIDAE	Guinea fowl	*Numida meleagris*	Africa
Columbiformes COLUMBIDAE	Pigeons, all breeds	*Columba livia*, rock pigeon	Western Asia or Egypt
Psittaciformes PSITTACIDAE	Shell parakeet, or budgerigar	*Melopsittacus undulatus*	Australia
Passeriformes FRINGILLIDAE	Canaries, all breeds	*Serinus canarius*	Western Europe

tion. Late in the nineteenth century feathers of wild birds were used extensively to decorate women's hats, but this trade threatened the stocks of many birds in various countries; decorative feathers now come from domesticated poultry and ostriches.

Fig. 31-17. Fossil birds. *Left.* Restoration of the Jurassic "lizard-bird" (†*Archaeopteryx*). *Right.* Skeletons of cretaceous toothed birds (†*Ichthyornis*, †*Hesperornis*). (*After Marsh.*)

Many small birds consume harmful insects and weed seeds, but they are only one agency in reducing such pests and their economic importance to agriculture has been overrated.   Most hawks and owls feed upon rodents that are injurious to crops and so are beneficial, although a few of them destroy poultry, game birds, and songbirds.   Certain birds sometimes damage crops by eating newly planted seeds or young plants, or the mature seeds, fruits, and berries, and control then is necessary.

Bird study with field glasses or camera is a healthful outdoor recreation for many people, and there are numerous organizations devoted to this subject, the American Ornithologists' Union and the National Audubon Society being the largest in North America.

For centuries man has kept wild birds as pets in cages and aviaries. Until recently this traffic depended upon capture of adults or young birds in the wild, but aviculturists now breed many species in captivity, and the drain on wild stocks has lessened.

31-25. Domestic birds.   The greatest economic contribution of birds to man's welfare is from the species he has domesticated, the "barnyard" fowls or poultry—chickens, turkeys, ducks, and geese—that serve for food, supply eggs, and provide feathers for pillows and beds.   Several others have been domesticated for aesthetic reasons (Table 31-1).

31-26. Fossil birds. Fossil remains of birds are scarcer than those of some other land vertebrates because their delicate skeletons are less likely to be preserved. Birds are probably derived from reptiles, possibly the birdlike dinosaurs, as the two groups have many similar features.

The oldest bird relics are in two slabs of limestone from the Upper Jurassic near Solnhofen in southern Germany, that contain impressions of the birdlike †*Archaeopteryx* (Fig. 31-17). This was the size of a large pigeon, with elongate jaws having bony teeth, but no horny sheaths. The wing had four (not three) digits, each with a claw, and bore long flight feathers. The long tail had more than 13 separate vertebrae, and the long tail feathers as a lateral fringe, a pair to each segment. The head, neck, and part of the body were bare. Toothed birds lived during Cretaceous time, 14 kinds having been found in Kansas and Montana; of these, †*Hesperornis* was a highly aquatic and flightless form about 6 feet long, and †*Ichthyornis* was a smaller flying type somewhat resembling modern birds.

From the Tertiary (Eocene) onward the birds lack teeth and become progressively more modern in structure and appearance. The terrestrial †*Diatryma* of the Eocene in Wyoming was about 7 feet tall with a huge bill but abortive wings. The oldest known passerine bird is †*Paleospiza belli*, about the size of a bluebird, from the Miocene of Colorado. Few birds are known from Oligocene or Pliocene, but remains are common in the Pleistocene of California, Florida, and elsewhere, and it is possible to visualize the avifauna of that time for several places. The asphalt pits of Rancho La Brea in Los Angeles, Calif., have yielded about 60 species, including †*Teratornis merriami*, a giant condor larger than any now existing; 36 of the species are still living. About 350 kinds of fossil birds have been recorded in North America, and 165 of them continue in the present-day avifauna.

CLASSIFICATION

Class *AVES*. Birds. Body covered with feathers; fore limbs modified as wings, usually adapted for flight, hind limbs for walking, perching, or swimming, usually 4 toes, never more; mouth extended as a beak, no teeth (in living birds); skull with one occipital condyle; pelvis fused to numerous vertebrae, forming a synsacrum, open ventrally; heart 4-chambered; lungs compact, with air sacs; voice box at base of trachea; no bladder; body temperature regulated; oviparous; Upper Jurassic to Recent; 8,600 species.

Subclass 1. ARCHAEORNITHES. "Lizard Birds." Three fingers and metacarpals separate, each with a claw; tail elongate, with more than 13 vertebrae, each with a pair of rectrices; no pygostyle; both jaws with teeth in sockets (alveoli); Upper Jurassic, in Germany. †*Archaeopteryx*, 2 known specimens (Fig. 31-17).

Subclass 2. NEORNITHES. Metacarpals fused, 2d finger longest; caudal vertebrae 13 or fewer, and compressed; sternum either keeled or flat; Cretaceous to Recent.

Superorder A. †ODONTOGNATHAE. New World Toothed Birds. Teeth present, in furrows on jaws; Cretaceous (Kansas and Montana); 14 species. †*Hesperornis*, †*Ichthyornis* (Fig. 31-17).

Superorder B. PALAEOGNATHAE. Walking Birds. Teeth absent; wings reduced, usually flightless; tail vertebrae free; coracoid and scapula small.

Order 1. **Struthioniformes.** Ostriches. Flightless; terrestrial; sternum without keel; pubic symphysis present (unique in birds!); pygostyle absent; only 2 toes (3d and 4th) on each foot; head, neck, and legs very sparsely feathered; feathers without aftershaft; Miocene to Recent; Africa and Arabia. *Struthio camelus*, ostrich (Fig. 31-18), largest living bird, to over 7 feet tall and weight of 300 pounds or more; inhabits arid lands in flocks of 3 to 20; omnivorous; at nesting a male defends 4 or 5 females that lay up to 30 eggs in one nest, male usually incubates; feathers of adults used by women as decorative plumes, plucked from living birds on ostrich farms in Africa and United States.

Fig. 31-18. The ostrich (*Struthio camelus*, Order Struthioniformes) of Africa and Arabia; to over 7 feet tall; each foot with two toes; body and wing feathers lax, cannot fly. (*Photograph by National Zoological Park.*)

Order 2. **Rheiformes.** Rheas. Flightless; terrestrial; sternum unkeeled; 3 front toes on each foot; head and neck partly feathered; feathers without aftershafts; Miocene to Recent; South America. *Rhea*, to 4 feet tall, on open lands.

Order 3. **Casuariiformes.** Cassowaries and Emus. Flightless; terrestrial; sternum unkeeled; 3 front toes on each foot; wings small; neck and body densely feathered; feathers with aftershaft nearly equal to shaft; Pliocene to Recent. Australia: *Dromaeus*, emu, to 5 feet tall, in sparsely wooded regions. New Guinea and near-by islands: *Casuarius*, cassowary, to over 5 feet tall, bare skin on head and neck, helmetlike casque on head, in forest, nocturnal.

Order 4. **Dinornithiformes.** Moas. Flightless; terrestrial; sternum reduced and unkeeled; coracoid, scapula, and wing bones reduced or absent; hind limbs massive, 3 or 4 toes; feathers with large aftershaft; Recent, but extinct for several centuries; New Zealand. *Dinornis*, several species, one 8 feet tall; eggs to 5½ by 7¾ inches.

Order 5. **Aepyornithiformes.** Elephant Birds. Flightless; terrestrial; sternum short, broad, and unkeeled; wings vestigial; 4 toes; Recent, but extinct for several centuries; Madagascar. *Aepyornis*, about 10 feet tall; eggs to 9½ by 13 inches, largest known animal eggs.

Order 6. **Apterygiformes.** Kiwis. Flightless; terrestrial; bill long and slender with nostrils at end; plumage hairlike; wing degenerate (humerus vestigial, only one digit, no flight feathers); sternum unkeeled; 4 toes, body plumage fluffy, hairlike, without aftershafts; New Zealand. *Apteryx*, kiwi (Fig. 31-19), several species, mostly under 24 inches long; nocturnal; omnivorous; nest in burrows, eggs 1 or 2, about 3 by 5 inches.

Order 7. **Tinamiformes.** Tinamous. Wings developed for flying; sternum keeled; pygostyle absent; egg shells with high gloss; southern Mexico to southern

Fig. 31-19.   Kiwi (*Apteryx*, Order Apterygiformes), wings vestigial, plumage hair-like; native to New Zealand.

South America.   *Tinamus, Rhynchotus,* tinamous, size medium, flight direct, but usually run; used as game birds.

Superorder C. NEOGNATHAE.   Modern Birds.   Teeth absent; sternum keeled, wings well-developed; tail vertebrae 5 or 6; pygostyle present; fore limb with metacarpals joined and fingers included in wing; Eocene to Recent.

(*Note: All birds of the following orders possess the ability to fly except the penguins and an occasional species in other orders.*)

Order 8.   **Sphenisciformes.**   Penguins. Flightless; fore limbs ("wings") paddle-like, adapted for swimming, the bones much compressed; metatarsus incompletely fused; 4 toes, all directed forward, feet completely webbed; feathers small, scale-like, covering entire body (no apteria); thick layer of fat beneath skin; stand erect on metatarsi; dive readily and swim by alternate strokes of fore limbs; nest in colonies on rocky islands or ice; southern oceans north to Galápagos Islands; about 20 kinds (Fig. 31-20). *Aptenodytes forsteri,* emperor penguin, shores of Antarctica, to 48 inches tall; other species smaller.

Fig. 31-20.   Penguins (Order Spheni-sciformes).   The paddle-like wings serve for swimming but not for flight; native to the Southern Hemisphere. (*Photograph by National Zoological Park.*)

Order 9.   **Gaviiformes.**   Loons.   Legs short, at end of body; toes fully webbed; patella lacking, replaced functionally by enlarged rotular process of tibia; tail of 18 to 20 short stiff feathers; flight swift, direct, adept at diving; feed on fish; northern part of Northern Hemisphere; 4 species. *Gavia immer,* common loon (Fig. 31-21).

Order 10.   **Colymbiformes.**   Grebes.   Tail a rudimentary tuft of downy feathers; legs far back on body; patella very large; tarsus compressed; feet lobed; on quiet fresh water, some on bays or ocean margins; adept at diving, "at flash of a gun"; food of small aquatic animals, some plant materials. *Colymbus auritus,* eared grebe; *Podilymbus podiceps,* pied-billed grebe or "dabchick."

FIG. 31-21. Loon (*Gavia immer*, Order GAVIIFORMES). Length 28 to 36 inches; strictly aquatic; native to Northern Hemisphere. (*After Hoffmann, Birds of the Pacific states, Houghton Mifflin Co.*)

Order 11. **Procellariiformes.** ALBATROSSES, FULMARS, AND PETRELS. Nostrils tubular; horny sheath of bill compounded of several plates; skull with large nasal glands; hind toe rudimentary or absent (diving petrels); plumage compact, "oily" in texture; wings long, narrow; young downy when hatched; strictly oceanic, nest usually on islands.

DIOMEDEIDAE. Albatrosses. Mostly large and on southern oceans, often follow ships at sea. *Diomedea exulans*, wandering albatross, wingspread over 10 feet.

PROCELLARIDAE. *Puffinus*, shearwaters; *Oceanodroma*, petrels or "Mother Carey's chickens," small, nest in crevices or burrows.

Order 12. **Pelecaniformes.** PELICANS, CORMORANTS, BOOBIES, GANNETS, ETC. All 4 toes included in foot web; nostrils vestigial or absent; a gular pouch on throat (except in tropic birds); aquatic; young naked at hatching.

PELECANIDAE. PELICANS. Body heavy, bill to 18 inches long, pouch used to scoop fish from water. *Pelecanus erythrorhynchos*, white pelican, on inland fresh waters of the West; *P. occidentalis*, brown pelican, coastwise in Gulf states and California.

PHALACROCORACIDAE. CORMORANTS. *Phalacrocorax*, many species, practically world-wide, on both coasts of North America, nests on sea cliffs, islands, and some inland waters; slender-bodied with small pouch, fish by diving; captives (with ring on neck) used by Orientals to catch fish.

SULIDAE. *Sula*, booby, tropic birds; *Moris bassana*, gannet.

Order 13. **Ciconiiformes.** HERONS, STORKS, IBISES, AND FLAMINGOS. Long-necked and long-legged wading birds, with either decorative plumes (herons), bare areas on head (storks), or bill abruptly decurved at middle (flamingos); little or no web between toes (except flamingos); young naked; chiefly tropical and subtropical, usually about water; food chiefly of fish and other aquatic animals; many nest in colonies in trees.

ARDEIDAE. HERONS AND BITTERNS. *Ardea herodias*, great blue heron (Fig. 31-22); *Butorides virescens*, green heron; *Nycticorax*, night heron; *Casmerodius albus*, American egret, and *Egretta thula*, snowy egret, both with pure white plumage and nuptial plumes (aigrettes) on back in nesting season.

PHOENICOPTERIDAE. *Phoenicopterus ruber*, flamingo, Brazil to Florida Keys, mandibles bent, forming box with ser-

FIG. 31-22. Great blue heron (*Ardea herodias*, Order CICONIIFORMES), length 42 to 50 inches; a long-legged water bird that eats fishes, frogs, and small mammals. (*After Hoffmann, Birds of the Pacific states, Houghton Mifflin Co.*)

rated margins, bird feeds with head inverted sieving small animals from water; nest in dense colonies, eggs on cylindrical mounds of mud.

Order 14. **Anseriformes.** Ducks, Geese, and Swans. Bill broadened, covered with soft cornified epidermis containing numerous sense pits, with harder "nail," or cap, at tip; margins of bill with many transverse horny ridges (lamellae); tongue fleshy; legs short; feet webbed; tail usually short, of many feathers; nests lined with down; eggs plain, without spots; young downy when hatched; world-wide; over 200 species; the "waterfowl" of hunters, prized for sport and eating; many kept as captives (Fig. 31-23).

Fig. 31-23.   Order Anseriformes.   Whistling swan (*Olor columbianus*), pin-tail duck (*Dafila acuta*), lesser snow goose (*Chen hyperboreus*), Canada goose (*Branta canadensis*). (*Photograph by T. I. Storer.*)

Anatidae. Surface ducks (tip up, do not dive in feeding): *Anas platyrhynchos*, mallard, or "greenhead"; *Dafila acuta*, pintail or "sprig"; shoveller, teal, wood duck, etc. Diving ducks (more often on salt waters): *Nyroca valisineria*, canvasback; *N. americana*, redhead; scaups, goldeneyes, eiders, scoters, etc. Geese (neck longer): *Branta canadensis*, Canada goose, several subspecies; *Chen*, snow goose; *Anser*, white-fronted goose. Swans (neck very long): *Cygnus columbianus*, whistling swan, winters in United States.

Palamedidae. Screamers. In South America, bill slender, feet not webbed. *Palamedea.*

Order 15. **Falconiformes.** Vultures, Kites, Hawks, Falcons, and Eagles. Bill stout, hooked at tip, with soft naked skin (cere) at base; mandibles sharp-edged; feet usually adapted for grasping, with sharp curved claws; predaceous, active by day; flight strong, rapid in some; food variously of vertebrates and smaller animals. Carrion feeders: *Cathartes aura*, turkey vulture or "buzzard," with red head; *Coragyps atratus*, black vulture, chiefly in southeastern states, head black; *Gymnogyps californianus*, California condor, head yellow, wingspread to 9 feet, local in southern California. Bird hunters: *Accipiter cooperi*, Cooper's hawk, *Astur atricapillus*, goshawk. Broad-winged soaring types, feed largely on rodents: *Buteo borealis*, red-tailed hawk; *Aquila chrysaëtos*, golden eagle. Fish-eating: *Haliaeetus leucocephalus*, bald eagle, the United States emblem. Narrow-winged speedy hunters:

Falco peregrinus, duck hawk, used in falconry; *F. sparverius*, American sparrow hawk (Fig. 31-24) feeds largely on insects.

FIG. 31-24. Sparrow hawk (*Falco sparverius*, Order FALCONIFORMES), length 10 inches; feeds on insects and small mammals. (*After Hoffmann, Birds of the Pacific states, Houghton Mifflin Co.*)

Order 16. **Galliformes.** GROUSE, QUAIL, PHEASANTS, TURKEYS, ETC. Bill short; feathers with aftershaft; feet usually adapted for scratching and running; young downy at hatching and precocial; the "upland game" of hunters, several species domesticated, many gregarious ground dwellers where all of them nest; food chiefly of plant materials (Fig. 31-25).

FIG. 31-25. Order GALLIFORMES. Two important upland game birds of North America. Bobwhite quail (*Colinus virginianus*), length 10 inches. Ruffed grouse (*Bonasa umbellus*), length 16 to 19 inches. (*From Pennsylvania Game News.*)

TETRAONIDAE. GROUSE. *Bonasa umbellus*, ruffed grouse, in broad-leaved woods; *Dendragapus*, blue grouse, in conifers; *Lagopus*, ptarmigan, north to Arctic, turns white in winter; *Tympanuchus*, prairie chicken; *Centrocercus urophasianus*, sage hen, in sagebrush of West.

PERDICIDAE. PARTRIDGES AND QUAILS. *Perdix perdix*, European or Hungarian partridge, introduced successfully in northwestern prairie regions of United States and Canada; *Colinus virginianus*, bobwhite or eastern quail; *Lophortyx californica*, valley quail of Pacific coast.

PHASIANIDAE. PHEASANTS. Native to Asia, widely introduced; *Phasianus colchicus torquatus*, ring-necked pheasant, in many states; *Pavo cristatus*, peacock or pea fowl; *Gallus*, jungle fowl and domestic chickens.

MELEAGRIDAE. *Meleagris gallopavo*, wild turkey, eastern North America to Mexican plateau, also domesticated.

OPISTHOCOMIDAE. *Opisthocomus hoazin*, hoatzin, a peculiar species in South America, inhabits trees and feeds on leaves; young with claws on first 2 digits of wing, used for climbing until wing feathers are grown.

Order 17. **Gruiformes.** CRANES, RAILS, COOTS, ETC. Feathers with after-shaft; either of large size and strong flight, inhabiting open marshes or prairies (cranes) or of medium to small size, of weak flight (occasionally flightless), and shy inhabitants of marshes (rails); young downy when hatched.

GRUIDAE. CRANES. Some bare skin about head; Northern Hemisphere and Africa. *Grus mexicana*, sand hill crane, tall, gray-colored, nests in temperate North America, often flocks on marshes in winter.

RALLIDAE. RAILS, COOTS, ETC. Size of chickens or smaller, neck and legs not elongate. *Rallus*, rails, body compressed, live in marshes, slip readily through vegetation; *Fulica americana*, coot or "mud hen," with lobate toes, common on ponds, diving or swimming, over much of North America; *Gallinula*, gallinule, toes elongate, used to walk on lily pads in ponds.

Order 18. †**Diatrymiformes.** Large, flightless, wing atrophied; bill huge; 4 toes on each foot. Eocene of western United States. †*Diatryma*.

Order 19. **Charadriiformes.** SHORE BIRDS OR "WADERS," GULLS, AUKS, ETC. Toes usually webbed at least at base; plumage dense and firm; more or less long-legged (shore birds), strong-winged (gulls), or with only 3 toes and legs far back on body (auks); eggs heavily spotted; young downy when hatched.

SHORE BIRDS. On seabeaches or inland watery flats—"the strand"—probing for food in sand, mud, or shallow water; many nest in Arctic regions and migrate far south for winter; formerly hunted for market. *Oxyechus vociferus*, killdeer (Fig. 31-26), often inland; *Philohela minor*, American woodcock, in

FIG. 31-26. Killdeer (*Oxyechus vociferus*, Order CHARADRIIFORMES), length 11 inches. A common "shore bird," often along inland waters. (*After Hoffmann Birds of the Pacific states, Houghton Mifflin Co.*)

woods of eastern states; *Capella*, snipe, in marshy places; *Pisobia*, sandpiper.

LARIDAE. GULLS AND TERNS. On seashores and inland waters; long-winged and commonly gray-backed, white beneath. *Sterna*, terns, fish activity over water, plunging to capture prey; *Larus*, gulls, feed on aquatic animals in surface waters or on shore and on garbage about harbors.

ALCIDAE. AUKS, MURRES, PUFFINS, ETC. Flight in air swift, direct; swim and dive readily, "fly" under water; nest in dense colonies on sea cliffs or in burrows, each pair with one egg; on seacoasts of Northern Hemisphere. *Plautus impennis*, great auk, or garefowl, 24 inches tall, North Atlantic coasts, south to Massachusetts, extinct since 1844; *Uria aalge*, murre, eggs earlier collected for market; *Fratercula*, puffin.

Order 20. **Columbiformes.** PIGEONS AND DOVES. Bill usually short and slender, with thick soft skin (cere) at base; tarsus usually shorter than toes; crop large, producing "pigeon milk" to feed small young; eggs unmarked, usually white; young naked; world-wide.

COLUMBIDAE. *Columba fasciata*, band-tailed pigeon (Fig. 31-27), forested portions of Pacific coast; *Ectopistes migratorius*, passenger pigeon, formerly in forested regions of eastern North America, killed extensively for market, extinct since about 1900; *Zenaidura macroura*, mourning dove, over whole of United States.

FIG. 31-27. Band-tailed pigeon (*Columba fasciata*, Order COLUMBIFORMES), length 15 inches; native to woods of Pacific Coast states; sometimes in large flocks. (*After Hoffmann, Birds of the Pacific states, Houghton Mifflin Co.*)

Order 21. **Cuculiformes.** CUCKOOS, ROAD-RUNNER, AND ANIS. Toes 2 in front and 2 behind, outer hind toe reversible; feet not adapted for grasping; tail long; bill moderate; many Old World cuckoos "parasitic," the female laying egg in nest of other small birds, for incubation and rearing; young cuckoo usually "elbows out" rightful owners; the two North American cuckoos, *Coccyzygus*, not parasitic; *Geococcyx californianus*, road-runner, Kansas to Texas and California, terrestrial, legs and tail long.

Order 22. **Psittaciformes.** PARROTS. Beak stout, narrow, sharp-edged and hooked at tip; upper mandible movable on frontal bone of skull; bill with soft cere, often feathered; tongue fleshy; toes 2 in front and 2 behind, outer hind toe not reversible; feet adapted for grasping; plumage brilliant, green, blue, yellow, or red; in forests of tropics and subtropics, many gregarious and with loud voices; food chiefly of fruits. *Rhynchopsitta pachyrhyncha*, thick-billed parrot, Mexico north to southern Arizona; *Conuropsis carolinensis*, Carolina paroquet, small, formerly to Wisconsin and Colorado, now only local in Florida.

Order 23. **Strigiformes.** OWLS. Head large and rounded; eyes large and directed forward, each in a disc of radial feathers; ear opening large, often with flaplike cover, sometimes asymmetrical; beak short; feet adapted for grasping; claws sharp; plumage soft-textured and lax; eggs white; young downy at hatching; active chiefly by night; hide in retreats by day; nest in natural cavities; food of land vertebrates especially mammals, some birds, and arthropods. *Tyto alba*, barn owl (Fig. 31-28); *Bubo virginianus*, horned owl; *Otus asio*, screech owl; *Nyctea nyctea*, snowy owl, in Arctic, sometimes invades northern states in winter; *Speotyto cunicularia*, "burrowing owl," inhabits burrows in ground dug by squirrels, etc.

Order 24. **Caprimulgiformes.** NIGHTHAWKS, WHIPPOORWILLS, ETC. Bill small and delicate, but mouth wide and margined with long bristle-like feathers (none in

Fig. 31-28.   Order Strigiformes.   Great horned owl (*Bubo virginianus*), length 18 to 23 inches.   Barn owl (*Tyto alba*), length 15 to 21 inches.   (*After Grinnell and Storer, Animal life in the Yosemite, University of California Press.*)

nighthawks); legs and feet small and weak, not adapted for grasping; plumage soft and lax; active mostly at dusk and by night, food of night-flying insects captured in air; do not build nests. *Antrostomus vociferus*, whippoorwill, woods of eastern states, named for its call; *Phalaenoptilus nuttalli*, poorwill, brushy areas of western states, 2-syllabled call; both forage near ground; *Chordeiles minor*, nighthawk, usually forages high in air.

Order 25. **Micropodiformes** (Apodiformes). Swifts and Hummingbirds. Size usually small; legs very short and feet very small; wings pointed; bill small and weak (swifts), or slender with long tubular tongue (hummingbirds); eggs white; active by day, food captured on the wing; most species migrate south to winter.

Micropodidae (Apodidae). Swifts. Nests in rock cavities or trees and fastened with salivary secretion; latter used in Orient for "bird's-nest soup"; over 400 species, 4 in United States. *Chaetura pelagica*, chimney swift, eastern North America.

Trochilidae. Hummingbirds. Only in Western Hemisphere, over 500 species, mostly in tropics, 9 in United States; length 2¼ to 8½ inches; plumage brilliant, iridescent especially on head and neck of males; food of nectar, small insects, and spiders taken from blossoms by the tubular protrusible tongue and needle-like bill; nests small, exquisitely felted of mosses, plant down, and spider web; eggs 2, young naked, fed by regurgitation. *Archilochus colubris*, ruby-throated hummingbird (Fig. 31-29), Alberta to central Texas and eastward; others chiefly in California and far western states; *Selasphorus rufus*, rufous hummingbird, to 61°N. in Alaska for nesting.

Fig. 31-29.   Ruby-throated hummingbird (*Archilochus colubris*, Order Micropodiformes), length 3 inches. Male above, female on nest. (*After U.S. Biological Survey.*)

Order 26. **Coliiformes.** COLIES OR MOUSE BIRDS. Small, passerine-like; 1st and 4th toes reversible; tail very long; Africa. *Colius.*

Order 27. **Trogoniformes.** TROGONS. Bill short and stout, with bristles at base; feet small and weak; plumage brilliant, often green, but soft and lax. *Trogon ambiguus,* coppery-tailed trogon, Mexico and southern Arizona; *Pharomacrus moccino,* quetzal, Central America, one of the most beautiful of birds.

Order 28. **Coraciiformes.** KINGFISHERS, ETC. Third and 4th toes fused at base; bill strong; includes also motmots, bee eaters, rollers, hoopoes, and hornbills, mostly in tropics. *Megaceryle alcyon,* belted kingfisher (Fig. 31-30), on fresh waters

FIG. 31-30. Belted kingfisher (*Megaceryle alcyon,* Order CORACIIFORMES), length 11 to 14 inches; lives about water. (*After Hoffmann, Birds of the Pacific states, Houghton Mifflin Co.*)

FIG. 31-31. The flicker (*Colaptes,* Order PICIFORMES), length 13 inches, a woodpecker that forages both in trees and on the ground. (*After U.S. Biological Survey.*)

over much of North America, captures small fishes and frogs by diving from a perch; excavates horizontal tunnel in stream bank for nest.

Order 29. **Piciformes.** WOODPECKERS, JACAMARS, PUFFBIRDS, BARBETS, HONEY GUIDES, AND TOUCANS.

PICIDAE. WOODPECKERS. Tail feathers stiff with pointed tips; bill stout, awl-like; tongue roughened or with barbs near tip, and protrusible; toes 2 in front and 2 (or 1) behind, not reversible; mostly in forests, cling to tree trunks, dig insects and larvae out of wood, and excavate nest cavities in trees; some on cactus in southwestern deserts. *Dryobates (Dendrocopus) villosus,* hairy woodpecker; *D. pubescens,* downy woodpecker; *Sphyrapicus*, sapsuckers, eat cambium of trees; *Colaptes*, flickers (Fig. 31-31), forage also on ground; *Balanosphyra formicivora bairdi*, California woodpecker, stores many acorns individually in holes drilled in trees.

Fig. 31-32.   Chipping sparrow (*Spizella passerina*, Order Passeriformes), length 5½ inches; common in much of North America.   (*After U.S. Biological Survey.*)

Order 30. **Passeriformes.** Perching Birds. Toes 3 in front and 1 behind, adapted for perching and neither reversible nor united; includes great majority of all known birds, 4 suborders, 69 families. Suborder Oscines, "Songbirds" (52 families), so named because of structure of vocal cords; many produce beautiful songs, others are poor songsters, practically all have call notes. Size from that of raven and crow to small chickadee; in all types of habitats, some strictly terrestrial, a majority in trees and shrubs; the ouzels or dippers (*Cinclus*) swim and dive in cold fresh-water streams, and flycatchers and swallows capture insects in flight. Usually build nests, some elaborate, eggs 3 to 8, variously colored, young naked and blind at hatching, require feeding and care by parents before becoming independent. Food varied, chiefly of small size, many strictly insectivorous, some exclusively seed eaters, others have mixed diet. Common examples: *Corvus*, crow, raven; *Melospiza*, song sparrow; *Dendroica*, wood warblers; *Turdus*, American robin (Fig. 31-1).

ORDER PASSERIFORMES. FAMILIES IN NORTH AMERICA, NORTH OF MEXICO

Suborder TYRANNI
  Cotingidae
    Cotingas
  Tyrannidae
    New World Flycatchers
Suborder OSCINES
  Alaudidae
    Horned Larks
  Hirundinidae
    Swallows
  Corvidae
    Crows, Magpies, Jays
  Paridae
    Chickadees, Titmice
  Sittidae
    Nuthatches
  Certhiidae
    Creepers

Chamaeidae
  Wren Tits
Cinclidae
  Dippers, or Water Ouzels
Troglodytidae
  Wrens
Mimidae
  Thrashers, Mockingbirds,
    Catbirds
Turdidae
  Thrushes, Robins, Bluebirds
Regulidae
  Kinglets
Motacillidae
  Pipits, Wagtails
Bombycillidae
  Waxwings
Ptilogonatidae
  Phainopeplas

Laniidae
  Shrikes ("butcherbirds")
Sturnidae
  European Starling
    (introduced)
Vireonidae
  Vireos
Mniotiltidae
  Wood Warblers
Icteridae
  Blackbirds, Orioles,
    Meadow Larks
Thraupidae
  Tanagers
Fringillidae
  Grosbeaks, Finches,
    Sparrows, Towhees,
    Buntings

References

Allen, G. M. 1925. Birds and their attributes. Boston, Marshall Jones Co. xiii + 338 pp., illus. Structure and habits.

American Ornithologists' Union. 1931. Checklist of North American birds. 4th ed. Lancaster, Pa., American Ornithologists' Union. xix + 526 pp. Scien-

710 *THE ANIMAL KINGDOM* [Chap. 31

tific and common name and geographic range for each living species and subspecies north of Mexico; also a list of fossil species. Supplements to check list
appear at intervals in *The Auk*.

AUDUBON, JOHN JAMES. 1937. The birds of America. New York, The Macmillan
Co. 500 colored plates (9 by 12½ inches) with footnotes and index. A popular
reproduction of the famous elephant folio of the same title with plates about
28 by 38 inches, published 1827–1838 by this renowned naturalist-artist, in which
all birds of North America then known were shown in color. In 1831–1839 he
issued 5 text volumes, "Ornithological Biography," on the anatomy and habits
of birds, and in 1840–1844 the two works were combined and reissued as 7 octavo
volumes. The indefatigible Audubon collected the specimens and notes, painted
the pictures, wrote the text, obtained subscriptions, and directed the printing;
the most stupendous work on natural history ever produced in North America.

BENT, A. C. 1919– . Life histories of North American birds. *U.S. National
Museum, Bulletins* 107 . . . 197 . . . (18 published, others planned). Detailed
account of habits, migration, and nesting for each species; many illustrations.

EVANS, A. H. 1900. Birds. *In* Cambridge natural history. London, Macmillan
& Co., Ltd. Vol. 9, xvi + 635 pp., illus. Systematic account of structure, classification, and habits.

GROEBBELS, F. 1932, 1937. Der Vogel. Berlin, Verlagsbuchhandlung Gebrüder
Borntraeger. Vol. 1, xii + 918 pp., 234 figs; vol. 2, xvi + 547 pp., 141 figs.
A detailed technical compilation; vol. 1, digestive system, food and nutrition,
respiratory and circulatory systems; vol. 2, reproduction; several thousan i
references.

HELLMAYR, C. E., C. B. CORY, and B. CONOVER. 1918–1949. Catalogue of birds
of the Americas and the adjacent islands. *Field Museum of Natural History,
Zoological Series*, vol. 13, 15 parts.

KNOWLTON, F. H. 1909. Birds of the world. New York, Henry Holt & Co., Inc.
ix + 873 pp., illus. Structure, distribution, and habits of the orders and families,
with mention of many species.

PETERS, J. L. 1931– . Checklist of birds of the world. Cambridge, Mass.,
Harvard University Press. 7 vols. to 1951.

PYCRAFT, W. P. 1910. A history of birds. London, Methuen & Co., Ltd. xxxi
+ 458 pp., illus. Classification, structure, habits, and evolution.

RIDGWAY, R. 1900– . Birds of North and Middle America. *U.S. National
Museum, Bulletin* 50, parts (vols.) I–IX (unfinished). Technical keys, descriptions of plumages, measurements, and geographic distribution.

STRONG, R. M. 1939. A bibliography of birds. *Field Museum of Natural History,
Zoological Series*, vol. 25, 937 pp.

Many special periodicals deal solely with birds, the more important for North
America being as follows: *The Auk* (published by the American Ornithologists'
Union), chiefly on North American birds; *The Condor* (Cooper Ornithological Club),
especially for western North America; *The Wilson Bulletin* (Wilson Ornithological
Club), especially for the Middle West; and *Bird Banding* (Northeastern Bird Banding
Association), particularly for studies on banded birds; *Audubon Magazine*, formerly
Bird-Lore (National Audubon Society), popular. Many separate books, museum
publications, and articles in scientific journals contain extensive accounts of the birds
in various regions, states, provinces, and smaller geographic areas.

CHAPTER 32

CLASS MAMMALIA. MAMMALS

The mammals are the "highest" group in the animal kingdom. They include the moles, bats, rodents, cats, monkeys, whales, horses, deer, man, and other living forms besides a host of extinct species and orders. All are more or less covered with hair or fur, and are warm-blooded. Laymen often apply names such as "quadruped," "four-footed beast," "beast," or simply "animal" to members of this class, but the term

Fig. 32-1.   Class Mammalia.   The Norway or house rat (*Rattus norvegicus*), a representative mammal; body covered with hair, nose bearing sensory vibrissae, lips soft and movable, external ears thin, feet with fleshy sole pads, toes with claws, and slender tail serving mainly for balancing.

"mammal" is distinctive and preferable.   The class name refers to the mammary glands on females that supply milk for suckling the young. Parental care of the offspring is most highly developed among mammals and reaches its climax in the human species (Chap. 33).   Various mammals live in all sorts of habitats from polar regions to the tropics and from the sea to the densest forests and driest deserts.   Many are of retiring habits or nocturnal so that they are seldom seen.   They are a dominant group and play a leading role in the present-day world.   Mammals generally are of great aesthetic interest; some wild species are hunted as game and others for their fur.   Some rodents and flesh eaters damage man's crops and livestock, and certain species are reservoirs of disease.   The domestic mammals provide man with food, clothing, and transportation.

32-1. Characteristics.   1. Body usually covered with hair (scant on some), which is molted periodically; skin with many glands (sebaceous, sweat, scent, and mammary).

711

2. Skull with 2 occipital condyles; neck vertebrae usually 7; tail usually elongate and mobile.

3. Nasal region usually elongate; mouth with teeth (rarely absent) in sockets or alveoli, on both jaws and differentiated in relation to food habits; tongue usually mobile; eyes with movable lids; ears with external fleshy pinnae.

4. Four limbs; each foot with 5 (or fewer) toes and variously adapted for walking, running, climbing, burrowing, swimming, or flying; toes with horny claws, nails, or hoofs and often fleshy pads (no hind limbs in cetaceans or sirenians).

5. Heart completely 4-chambered (2 auricles, 2 distinct ventricles); only the left aortic arch persists; red blood cells nonnucleated, usually circular.

6. Respiration only by lungs; larynx with vocal cords; a complete muscular diaphragm separating lungs and heart from abdominal cavity.

7. A urinary bladder; excretions (urine) fluid.

8. Twelve pairs of cranial nerves; brain highly developed, both cerebrum and cerebellum large.

9. Body temperature regulated (homoiothermous).

10. Male with copulatory organ (penis); testes commonly in a scrotum external to abdomen; fertilization internal; eggs usually minute, without shells, and retained in uterus (modified oviduct) of female for development; embryonic membranes (amnion, chorion, and allantois) present; usually with a placenta affixing embryo to uterus for nutrition and respiration; young nourished after birth by milk secreted from mammary glands of female.

The insulated body covering (hair and subcutaneous fat) and the complete separation of venous and arterial blood in the heart make the regulated body temperature possible. With this go a high rate of metabolism and a consequent large requirement for food. The teeth are usually conspicuous and differentiated. The senses of sight, hearing, and smell are highly developed. Mammals are consequently keen and active. The large cerebellum and cerebrum provide for a high degree of coordination in all activities and for learning and a retentive memory.

32-2. Size. The smallest mammals are some shrews and mice less than 2 inches in head-and-body length and weighing only a fraction of an ounce. Others range variously in size up to the elephants; some are over 11 feet tall and weigh up to 14,500 pounds. The large whales are the biggest mammals; the blue whale (*Balaenoptera musculus*) which grows to 105 feet long and 119 tons in weight is the largest known animal.

STRUCTURE OF A MAMMAL: THE DOMESTIC CAT

The cat is a member of the Order CARNIVORA (L. *caro*, flesh + *voro*, devour) that feeds typically on small mammals and birds. Its forward-directed eyes, keen senses, and silent tread on padded feet make it an effective hunter. The lithe body and sharp claws enable it to pounce upon and grasp prey easily, and the sharp shearing teeth facilitate the cutting of flesh.

32-3. External features. The entire body is densely covered with *hair* or fur, and consists of a rounded *head,* short *neck,* narrow *trunk,* and long

flexible *tail.*   Each of the slender *fore limbs* has five *toes* provided with
fleshy *pads* and curved retractile *claws.*   The *hind limbs* are stouter,
providing the principal power in locomotion; each has four toes and
claws.   A cat walks on its toes and hence is digitigrade (L. *digitus,*
finger + *gradior,* to step), whereas man is plantigrade in that he walks
on the whole foot and a horse is unguligrade, walking on the enlarged
nails, or hoofs (Fig. 32-6).

On the head are two narrow *nostrils* below the movable tip of the nose,
and the *mouth* is bordered by thin fleshy *lips.*   Each large eye has two
fleshy *eyelids,* margined with fine hairs or *eyelashes;* and beneath the
lids is a transparent *nictitating membrane* that moves across the eyeball
from the outer angle.   About the eyes and nose are long sensory hairs,
the *vibrissae* or "cat whiskers."   Behind the eyes are two thin fleshy
external ears (pinnae), each with an external auditory canal leading
into the head.   The trunk comprises a narrow chest or *thorax,* sheltered
by the ribs, and the broader *abdomen* posteriorly; along the ventral
surface on the female are four or five pairs of small elevated *teats* or
mammae, through which the milk or mammary glands open.   The *anus*
is anterior to the base of the tail, and close below is the *urogenital opening.*
In males the *scrotum,* containing the testes, hangs beneath the anus.

32-4. Integument.   The *skin* is soft and thin except for the thickened
cornified pads of the feet.   It consists of a stratified epidermis and dermis
beneath, which is attached loosely to the body musculature.   The skin is
covered densely with closely spaced *hairs.*   All the hairs collectively are
termed the coat or *pelage.*

Each hair (Fig. 4-2) grows from a *hair papilla* at the base of a deep
tubular pit or *hair follicle,* that is embedded in the skin and lined by
epidermis.   Each follicle is joined to a small *sebaceous gland* that provides an oily secretion (sebum) to lubricate the hair.   The follicles lie
slantingly in the skin, and to each is attached an *erector muscle* by which
the hair may be made to "stand on end" when the cat is either cold or
angry.   The hair, when grown, is a nonliving epidermal product subject
to wear and fading and therefore is periodically renewed by molt, usually
in autumn.   The hairs drop out individually, and new ones grow from
the same follicles.   An individual hair (Fig. 32-9) is covered by *cuticular
scales* over a tubular *cortex* that surrounds an inner *medulla.*   The
coloration of hair and hence of the pelage is dependent upon the kind of
pigment granules present in the cortex.   These may be black, brown,
red, or yellow.   The blue color of some cats is due to the combined effect
of pigment and of light-interference phenomena in the cortex and cuticle.
White cats lack pigment.

32-5. Skeleton.   The skeleton is largely of bone, with cartilage over
joint surfaces, on parts of the ribs, and in a few other places (Fig. 32-2).

The movable bones are joined by ligaments and moved by muscles. Besides the cartilage and membrane bones (Chap. 3), certain tendons contain ossifications known as *sesamoid bones;* the most conspicuous of these is the kneecap, or *patella,* but others occur on the feet.   As in the skeletons of other land vertebrates, the skull, vertebrae, ribs, and sternum comprise the axial portion and the limbs and limb girdles the appendicular part.

The rounded *skull* is a hard case with all the bones closely united by irregular *sutures* that may be obliterated in later life.   The anterior or facial region contains, dorsally the *external nares* and the large *orbits* that shelter the eyes, and ventrally there is a flat *palate* margined by the teeth of the upper jaw.   Outside of each orbit is a conspicuous horizontal bar, the *zygomatic arch.*   The larger cranial region of the skull encloses the brain.   Exits or foramina for the cranial nerves are seen in various bones.   Below each posteroventral corner of the skull is a small petromastoid bone that contains the inner ear with its three ossicles. On the posterior surface is a large *foramen magnum* through which the nerve cord connects to the brain, and at either side of this is a rounded *occipital condyle* by which the skull articulates to the first vertebra or axis.   The *lower jaw,* which also bears teeth, consists of a single bone on each side that articulates to the squamosal bone of the cranium.

The *vertebral* or *spinal column* forms a flexible support for the body and shelters the nerve cord.   The centra of adjacent vertebrae are separated by *intervertebral discs* of dense fibrocartilage.   The column comprises five regions: (1) the short neck of 7 *cervical vertebrae;* (2) the

Fig. 32-2.   Skeleton of the domestic cat.

13 *thoracic vertebrae* on which the movable ribs articulate; (3) the 7 *lumbar vertebrae* of the lower back; (4) the 3 *sacral vertebrae* which are fused for attachment of the pelvic girdle; and (5) the 16 to 20 slender *caudal vertebrae* in the tapered tail.   The 13 pairs of *ribs* and the slender midventral *sternum* (of six sternebrae) form a flexible "thoracic basket" that protects vital organs within and also performs respiratory movements.   The cat has nine pairs of true ribs (joined individually to the sternum), three pairs of false ribs (with their cartilage ends combined), and one pair of floating ribs (with no cartilage).

The *pectoral girdle* attaches by muscles to the thorax and supports the fore limbs.   On each side it comprises a flat triangular shoulder blade or *scapula* which receives the head of the humerus, and a delicate collarbone or *clavicle* in near-by muscles.   The *fore limb* comprises a humerus; distinct radius and ulna; seven carpal bones; five metacarpals (innermost short); and the phalanges of the toes.   The *pelvic girdle* attaches rigidly to the sacrum; each half (the innominate bone, or hip-bone) consists of an anterior dorsal *ilium,* a posterior *ischium* with a tuberosity on which the cat sits, and the ventral *pubis.*   At the junction of the three bones is a cuplike socket or *acetabulum,* in which the head of the femur articulates.   The two pubes and ischia join in symphyses ventrally below the vertebrae.   The bones of each *hind limb* are the femur; separate tibia and fibula; seven tarsals of the ankle; four long metatarsals (and a vestige of the innermost, or first), and the phalanges.

32-6. Muscular system (Fig. 32-3).   As compared with most other vertebrates, the mammals have a lesser bulk of segmental muscles on the

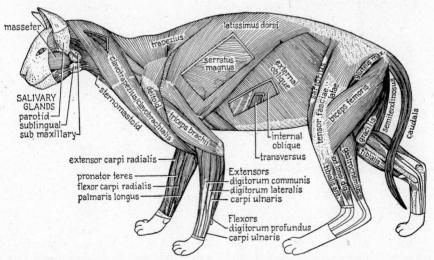

Fig. 32-3. Superficial muscles and salivary glands of the domestic cat; some of the muscles are cut to show others beneath.

vertebrae and ribs and more elaborately developed muscles on the head, neck, and limbs.   The cat has facial muscles that permit some degree of "expression" in relation to emotional states.   The limbs have been rotated so that the elbow is posterior and the knee is anterior and both limbs project ventrally; this is quite unlike the laterally projecting limbs of amphibians and reptiles.   The forearms and thighs are incorporated under the skin of the trunk; yet the limbs are capable of considerable rotation.   The cat's ability to "land on all fours" when dropped results from the freedom in its skeletal articulations and the diversity of muscular movements that it can make.   A distinctive mammalian characteristic is the dome-shaped transverse muscular partition or *diaphragm,* covered by peritoneum, that separates the coelom into an anterior *thoracic cavity* containing the heart and lungs and the *abdominal cavity* behind with the other viscera.

32-7. Teeth.   In the mammalian mouth the teeth grow like those of other vertebrates, but they are fixed in sockets and of a definite number. In various mammals the teeth are specialized in form and function according to the kind of food used, those of the cat being adapted for cutting and tearing flesh.   On each tooth (Fig. 32-13) the exposed part or *crown* is covered by hard white *enamel* over a bonelike *dentine* that contains a pulp cavity.   The base or *root* of the tooth, below the gums, is fixed by bony *cement* in a socket or *alveolus* in the jaw.   Like most mammals the cat has four kinds of teeth: short *incisors* at the ends of the jaws, to cut or scrape off food; slender stabbing *canines* used to seize or kill prey and in fighting; and angular *premolars* and *molars* for shearing and crushing the food (Fig. 32-12).   Incisors, canines, and premolars comprise the "milk teeth" of a kitten; these later are all replaced, and there are added the molars having no milk predecessors. The teeth are alike on the two sides but differ in the upper and lower jaws.   All the teeth collectively form the *dentition,* and their number is expressed as a dental formula that indicates those of the upper and lower jaws on one side.   The dental formula is:

for a kitten $\qquad i\frac{3}{3},\ c\frac{1}{1},\ p\frac{3}{2} \times 2 \qquad = 26,$

and for a cat $\qquad I\frac{3}{3},\ C\frac{1}{1},\ P\frac{3}{2},\ M\frac{1}{1} \times 2 = 30.$

32-8. Digestive system (Fig. 32-4).   The mouth cavity is margined by the thin soft *lips,* within which are fleshy *gums* around the bases of the *teeth.*   The lips and cavity are lined with soft mucous membrane.   The *tongue* is a flexible muscular organ, attached ventrally and supported by the hyoid bones; its rough and cornified upper surface contains four kinds of *papillae* and microscopic *taste buds.*   The mouth cavity is roofed by the

cerebrum

cerebellum

medulla

spines of vertebrae

respiratory cavity

palate

mouth cavity

larynx

carotid artery

trachea

esophagus

pre cava

pulmonary arteries and veins

heart

hepatic vein

thoracic cavity

lung

nerve cord

coeliac artery

sternum

diaphragm

gall bladder

liver

stomach

spleen

kidney

adrenal gland

dorsal aorta

post cava

pancreas

small intestine

large intestine

coelom

hepatic portal vein

ureter

bladder

iliac a. & v.

caudal aorta and vein

rectum

anus

penis

testis

vas deferens

Cowper's gland

prostate gland

artery

vein

* * part of small intestine omitted

Fig. 32-4.   The cat; internal structure.

palate, its anterior part or *hard palate* being formed of bone and crossed by fleshy ridges that help in holding food; behind is the short fleshy *soft palate,* which closes the respiratory passage above during swallowing. At either side of the soft palate is a soft reddish *tonsil,* of lymphoid tissue and of unknown function. Four pairs of *salivary glands* pour watery and mucous secretions through ducts into the mouth to moisten the food; these are (1) the *parotids,* below the ears; (2) the *submaxillaries,* behind the lower jaws; (3) the *sublinguals* near the preceding; and (4) the *infraorbitals* below the eyes.

The *pharynx* is the cavity behind the mouth where respiratory and food paths cross. Into its dorsal surface there open the *internal nares* from the nasal cavity above the palate, and behind these are two slitlike openings of the *Eustachian tubes.* Behind the tongue and ventral in the pharynx is the respiratory opening, or *glottis;* when food is passing this is covered by an anterior flap, the *epiglottis.* The *esophagus* is a narrow muscular tube through the thorax to the enlarged *stomach* behind the diaphragm. The stomach connects, through a *pyloric valve,* to the slender and coiled *small intestine.* To the anterior portion of the latter are joined ducts of the digestive glands, the large brownish *liver* of several lobes, and the small whitish *pancreas.* At the junction of the small and large intestine there is a short blind sac or *caecum* (but no appendix). The *large intestine* extends up the left side and across the abdomen, then descends on the right to a short muscular *rectum* opening at the *anus.* Unlike other vertebrates, most of the mammals have no cloaca; the digestive, excretory, and reproductive systems have separate external openings.

32-9. Circulatory system. The red blood corpuscles of mammals are unlike those of all lower vertebrates in being round, biconcave, and nonnucleated. The *heart* lies in the thoracic cavity, enclosed in a delicate sac of pericardium. It is completely four-chambered, as in birds, with two auricles and two thick muscular ventricles. The course of blood through the heart and lungs is the same in the cat and the bird, but in the mammal it leaves the left ventricle of the heart through a *left aortic arch.* Shortly the arch gives off an *innominate artery* (relict of the right arch), whence the two *common carotid arteries* arise, and the innominate continues as the *subclavian* artery to the right fore limb. The arch gives off a left subclavian and then turns as the *dorsal aorta,* which extends posteriorly. The latter gives branches to the internal organs, body wall, and posterior limbs, then continues as the *caudal artery* of the tail.

The *venous system* includes paired *jugular veins* from the head and neck and *subclavian veins* from the fore limbs; these all join as a *precaval vein,* which enters the right auricle. The *postcaval vein* returns blood from the tail, hind limbs, kidneys, gonads, and dorsal muscles. From the digestive organs a *hepatic portal system* carries blood to the liver, whence *hepatic veins* join the postcava as the latter enters the right auricle.   There is no renal portal system.   The *spleen* is a slender dark mass behind the stomach.

32-10. Respiratory system.   Air enters the *nostrils* to pass above the palate through a maze of coiled turbinate bones covered by mucous epithelium, where it is cleaned and warmed.   Behind the soft palate it crosses the pharynx to enter the *glottis.*   This is the opening in the voice box or *larynx* (Adam's apple in man), a framework of several cartilages that contains the *vocal cords* by which the cat's calls and squalls are produced.   From the larynx the air passes down the flexible wind pipe or *trachea,* which is reinforced against collapse by C-shaped cartilages.   The trachea continues into the thorax to divide into two *bronchi.*   These distribute air through subdividing branches that terminate in the microscopic *alveoli* of the lungs.   The alveoli are surrounded by pulmonary capillaries in which the O_2-CO_2 exchange of external respiration occurs.   The lungs are spongy elastic structures, each of three lobes. The exterior of the lungs and interior of the thorax (pleural cavity) are lined by smooth peritoneum, the *pleura.*   The mechanics of breathing in mammals differs from that in other land vertebrates.   By muscular action the ribs are drawn forward and the diaphragm is flattened posteriorly; this enlarges the pleural cavity and creates a slight negative pressure around the lungs; the latter thereupon expand and draw in air (inspiration).   When the diaphragm and rib muscles relax, the thorax is slightly compressed and air in the lungs is forced out (expiration).

32-11. Excretory system.   The two **kidneys** lie in the lumbar region above the peritoneum.   They remove organic wastes, excess water, and salts from the blood stream.   The liquid urine passes from each kidney down a duct, the *ureter,* to be stored in the distensible *bladder* that lies midventrally below the rectum.   At intervals the muscular walls of the bladder are voluntarily contracted to force the urine out through the single *urethra.*   In a female this empties at the urogenital aperture, but in a male the urethra traverses the penis.

32-12. Nervous system.   The general pattern of the mammalian nervous system is like that of other land vertebrates, but the *brain* is proportionately larger.   The sizable *olfactory lobes* and brain stem are covered by the greatly enlarged *cerebral hemispheres.*   The exterior of these is convoluted with elevations (gyri) separated by furrows (sulci); this increase of cerebral tissue is in keeping with the greater degree of intelligence displayed by the cat.   The two hemispheres are joined internally by a transverse band of fibers, the *corpus callosum,* peculiar to mammals. The *cerebellum* likewise is large and conspicuously folded, being formed of a median and two lateral lobes (Figs. 4-23, 4-27).   Its greater development is related to the fine coordination in the cat's activities.   There are 12 pairs of **cranial nerves** and from the **nerve cord** a pair of **spinal nerves** passes to each body somite, as in other vertebrates. The trunks of the **sympathetic system** lie close below the vertebrae.

32-13. Sense organs. The organs of taste, smell, sight, and hearing in the cat are essentially like those of man as to location and function (see Chap. 4). Sound waves collected by the movable external pinna of the ear pass into the external auditory canal that leads to the eardrum, or tympanic membrane. The middle ear of a mammal has three auditory ossicles (malleus, incus, stapes) that transfer vibrations to the inner ear. This is unlike the ears of birds, reptiles, and amphibians, which have only a single bone (columella). A further difference occurs in the cochlea of mammals, which is spirally coiled.

32-14. Endocrine glands. In the cat these comprise the pituitary, thyroid, parathyroids, adrenals, islets of Langerhans, and gonads. Their functions are much as in other mammals (see Chap. 4).

32-15. Reproductive system (Figs. 32-5, 5-4). In a male the two **testes** lie within the **scrotum,** a skin-covered double extension of the

FIG. 32-5.   The cat.   Urogenital organs in ventral view; bladder turned aside.   Compare Fig. 5-15.

abdominal cavity suspended below the anus. From each testis the spermatozoa are gathered in a network of minute tubules, the **epididymus,** to enter the sperm duct, or **vas deferens.** This, together with blood vessels and nerves, comprises a **spermatic cord** that enters the abdomen through a small **inguinal canal.** The two vasa deferentia enter the base of the urethra, which is a common urinogenital canal through the male copulatory organ, or **penis.** The latter lies in a short canal below the anus and projects posteriorly. During copulation the penis serves to transfer sperm into the vagina of a female. Two small accessory glands, the **prostate gland** around the base of the urethra and the Cowper or **bulbourethral glands** posteriorly, provide secretions that aid in the transfer of sperm.

The female has, behind the kidneys, two small *ovaries.* These show minute surface vesicles or *Graafian follicles,* each containing an ovum. Lateral to each ovary is the funnel or *ostium,* joining a slender coiled *oviduct.* The latter is continued backward as a thick-walled *horn of the uterus.* Posteriorly the two horns unite medially as the *body of the uterus* from which the *vagina* extends between the bladder and rectum to the *urogenital opening.* Ventral in the latter is a minute rod, the *clitoris,* corresponding to the penis of the male.

In reproduction, ova are discharged by the Graafian follicles and enter the ostia. In the oviducts they are fertilized by sperm that migrate up from the vagina after copulation. The fertilized ova settle separately against the inner wall of the uterine horns and become implanted. The foetal membranes of the developing embryo form a *placenta* (Fig. 5-15) through which the embryo receives nourishment and oxygen and disposes of wastes by way of the maternal blood circulation. The *period of gestation,* from fertilization until birth, is 60 days.

STRUCTURE OF OTHER MAMMALS

32-16. External features. The many kinds of mammals differ in size, form, proportions, nature of the pelage, and coloration. Swift-running species have narrow bodies and long limbs, large sedentary species are heavy in all respects, and the whales, seals, and others that swim have spindle-shaped bodies as with fishes and birds. The mammalian *head* is generally large because of the greater size of the brain and usually has an elongate snout. The *eyes* of rodents, hoofed animals, and other plant feeders are laterally placed (to watch on both sides for enemies); those of primates, bats, and carnivores are directed forward to provide binocular vision. The *external ears* are large and mobile in the deer, horses, and hares, which graze, reduced in the ground squirrels and pocket gophers, which burrow, and small or absent in seals and other swimming mammals. The *neck* is long in grazing mammals such as deer and horses and of extreme development in the tree-browsing giraffe; it is short in burrowing types and not evident in whales. The *trunk* is cylindrical in the agile weasels, casklike in the ponderous elephants, boat-shaped in whales, compressed in deer and other speedy runners, and depressed in the burrowing gophers and moles. Mammalian *tails* are of diverse form and serve variously—being brushlike "fly swatters" in hoofed mammals, stout for support and balance in kangaroos, flat as rudders in whales, beavers, and muskrats, prehensile for grasping in opossums and some monkeys, and variously shaped as stabilizers in running and jumping rodents, especially tree squirrels.

The *limbs* are slender and tapered in the agile deer and antelopes, huge and stumplike in the elephants and hippopotamuses which are of great weight, much shortened and with broad palms in the burrowing moles, and paddle-like in the seals and whales.   Kangaroos, jerboas, and kangaroo rats have elongate hind legs, feet, and tail that serve for their jumping or bounding gait.   The bats have long delicate fore limbs and fingers to support their thin flight membranes, or wings.   Other so-called "flying" mammals, squirrels, lemurs, and marsupials, however, have normal limbs with lateral extensions of skin along the body, and these animals merely volplane down from a height.

The mammalian *foot* (Fig. 32-6) ends typically in five toes; hence, man and other primates are generalized in this respect.   Narrowing

Fig. 32-6.   Mammalian feet (left hind limb).   *A*. Human, generalized with 5 toes and walks on entire foot.   *B*. Dog, with 4 toes, "heel" raised, and walks on fleshy pads under toes.   *C*. Horse with only one toe (3d), "heel" raised, and walks on cornified hoof over tip of toe.

of the foot and reduction in the number of toes occur particularly in running mammals.   The horse has evolved from a five- or four-toed ancestor through a three-toed stage to the modern type with but one toe on each foot.   The cattle, sheep, and deer are "cloven-hoofed," with the third and fourth toes persisting and the second and fifth showing as small relict dewclaws.

32-17. Body covering.   The *integument* produces hair and various horny or cornified structures, and it contains many glands.   Where well-protected by hair, the epidermis is delicate; where subjected to heavy wear, it forms a dense cornified coating such as the calluses on the human palms or soles and the foot pads of bears, mice, etc.   The claws, nails, and hoofs of various mammals and the horns of cattle, sheep, and Old World antelope (but not the antlers of deer) are also cornified structures, composed of keratin and resistant both to wear and to chemical disintegration.   Growth in all of them is continuous from the base (nail,

hoof, or horn bed) to compensate for external wear.   Horns are supported
by a bony core.   Antlers of deer, etc., are annual growths of dense connective tissue that later become calcified (Figs. 32-7, 32-8).

FIG. 32-7.   Structure and growth stages of horns and antlers; diagrammatic sections.   *A.*
Prong-horned antelope.   *B–D.* Horns of cow or sheep.   *E–I.* Antlers of a deer or elk.
Compare Fig. 32-8.

A. Mountain Sheep   B. Prong-horned Antelope   C. White-tailed Deer

FIG. 32-8.   Horns and antlers.   *A.* The mountain sheep has thick permanent hollow horns
(of keratin), each over a bony core.   *B.* The prong-horned antelope has thin hollow horns
over bony cores and the horns are molted annually.   *C.* The white-tailed deer has solid calcified antlers that are shed and grow anew each year.

The *pelage* or covering of hair varies in length, density, texture, and
color in different species.   It is heaviest on Arctic mammals, ample on
those in temperate lands, and thin and short on tropical species.   The
elephant, rhinoceros, hippopotamus, and manatee are, like man, sparsely
haired.   Whales are naked save for a few bristles about the lips.   The
coat on many mammals is differentiated into a dense fine *underfur*
for body insulation, and a lesser number of heavier long *guard hairs*
that protect against wear.   About the nose and eyes of carnivores and
rodents are long sensory *vibrissae,* with the base of each hair surrounded
by sensory nerve fibers.   As the animal moves about, these receive
touch stimuli.   A rat deprived of its vibrissae does not run freely and

behaves abnormally.   Spiny anteaters, hedgehogs, and porcupines are covered by sharp pointed quills (modified hairs) that protect against enemies.   Scales, with hairs between, occur on the tails of beavers, muskrats, and many rats and mice; the pangolins (*Manis*) are entirely covered by scales.   The armadillo has a jointed armor of epidermal scutes over bony plates (as in turtles) and a few hairs project from beneath the scutes.

The pelage is molted periodically, usually in autumn so that a new coat is provided for winter.   The *molt* is gradual so that the body is always covered.   Deer and others have also a spring molt that yields a

FIG. 32-9.   Structure of mammalian hairs.   (*After Hausman.*)

shorter sparser pelage for the summer.   In northern regions the weasels and hares have a brown summer coat that is replaced by one of white for the season of snow; the animals are thus less conspicuous in both seasons. Each hair usually grows to a definite length and stops, but on the scalp of mankind and the manes and tails of horses the growth is continuous.

The various *color patterns* of mammals result from differences in pigmentation of the hair.   Some, like black or white foxes, are practically solid color, but stripes, spots, bars, or other markings are common. Most species show differences in color on parts of individual hairs.

Whales and seals have a thick layer of subcutaneous fat (blubber) that insulates the body against loss of heat in water; blubber is the source of oil in the whaling industry.

32-18. Glands.   The superficial *glands* include (1) sebaceous glands, as described for the cat; (2) scent glands of various types; (3) mammary glands that produce milk; (4) sweat glands on the horse and man; and (5) lachrymal (tear) glands that moisten and cleanse the surface of the eye.   Examples of *scent glands* are the suborbital and metatarsal (leg) glands of deer, the middorsal glands of peccaries and some squirrels, those between the toes and on the tail in the dog family, those between the toes of sheep and other ruminants, and those about the anal region in rabbits, muskrats, beavers, skunks, weasels, etc.   The secretions may be abundant and odoriferous (skunks) or scant and delicate (squirrels).   The

secretions serve variously (1) to convey information by an odor or scent track for animals of the same or other species; (2) to bring the sexes together for mating; and (3) as a means of defense.   Such extensive use of scent is related to the keen sense of smell in mammals as compared with other vertebrates. *Mammary glands* (Fig. 32-10) usually occur only on females but are present on males in primates and some other mammals.   They become activated late in pregnancy by action of a hormone (prolactin from the anterior pituitary), to provide milk during early growth of the young, and then recede.   In bats and primates the mammae are on the thorax (breast), but on the abdomen in other species.   The nipples are usually more numerous than the average number of young in a litter—2 in the human fe-

FIG. 32-10. Human mammary gland in saggital section; nonlactating. (*After Testut.*)

male, mare, and ewe, 4 in cattle and some rodents, and 10 to 12 in swine. *Sweat glands* produce a watery secretion that by evaporation from the surface of the skin serves to cool the body.

32-19. Dentition.   The *teeth* are differentiated (heterodont) and usually not alike (homodont) as in most lower vertebrates.   In each mammalian order or species they are specialized for the kind of food used; an isolated tooth will usually reveal the identity and food habits of the species to which it belongs.   The teeth are narrowly conical in moles and bats which feed on insects, sharp for shearing and piercing in flesh eaters such as the cat, flattened and with low cusps for crushing various foods in squirrels, pigs, and human beings, and of rasplike structure with many enamel ridges for grinding green vegetation in hoofed animals and many rodents.   The incisors of rodents have enamel only on the anterior surface, and the softer dentine behind wears away more rapidly so that these teeth are always of chisel-like form for gnawing stems, seeds, or other foods.   Teeth may be short-crowned as in cats or long-crowned as in the cheek teeth of horses; they may have distinct roots in which growth soon ceases, or may be rootless and grow from a persistent pulp as with the incisors of rodents.   Among higher mammals a full dentition never exceeds 44 teeth, and many species have fewer; the dental formula in the mole and pig is $I\,\dfrac{3}{3},\ C\,\dfrac{1}{1},\ P\,\dfrac{4}{4},\ M\,\dfrac{3}{3} \times 2 = 44$, and in

the beaver and house rat is $I\,\dfrac{1}{1},\ C\,\dfrac{0}{0},\ P\,\dfrac{0}{0},\ M\,\dfrac{3}{3} \times 2 = 16.$

The tusks of pigs are enlarged canines, and those of elephants are upper incisors.   Adult monotremes, some edentates, and whalebone whales lack teeth entirely.

FIG. 32-11.   Some types of mammalian skulls and teeth; not to same scale. *Mole* (Order INSECTIVORA): teeth fine and conical for grasping insects and worms. *Mule deer* (Order ARTIODACTYLA): lower incisor teeth close against fleshy pad on the upper jaw to nip off vegetation which is ground between the enamel-ridged cheek teeth (premolars and molars); no canines. *Beaver* (Order RODENTIA): two pairs of chisel-like incisors used for gnawing; no canines; premolars and molars cross-ridged with enamel to grind food. *Dog* (Order CARNIVORA): incisors small, canines large for stabbing, and cheek teeth differentiated for shearing and crushing.

32-20. Digestive tract.   The intestine is short in species that consume such concentrated foods as insects or flesh, and long in rodents and hoofed mammals which eat grass or leafy vegetation.   All the latter have a large *caecum* that provides additional space for such bulky food while undergoing slow digestion.   In the cattle, deer, antelope, camels, etc., or ruminants, which "chew the cud," the stomach is of four compartments (rumen, reticulum, omasum, abomasum; Fig. 32-14).   The food of these large and defenseless mammals is gathered rapidly, mixed with saliva, chewed but slightly, and passed into the rumen. After feeding the animal seeks a safe quiet place to ruminate. In small masses or cuds, the

Fig. 32-12. The two dentions of the dog. *Above.* The temporary or "milk" teeth of a puppy, all of which are later replaced. *Below.* The adult or permanent teeth.

Fig. 32-13. Structure of mammalian teeth in diagrammatic sections; on the molar teeth the arrows indicate the plane of section for the figure above or below.

food is regurgitated, thoroughly chewed, and then reswallowed. It then passes in turn through the other compartments, the first three of which are specialized parts of the esophagus and have cornified linings with ridges or folds that subject it to further abrasion.

In healthy mammals the *body temperature* is closely regulated; the means and extremes for a few domestic animals are: horse 100°F. (99.1–100.8); sheep 102.3 (100.9–103.8); dog and cat 101.5 (100.5–102.5); rabbit 103.1 (101.5–104.2).

Fig. 32-14. The 4-compartment stomach of the cow, a ruminant animal. Grasses and similar roughage pass down (*A*) the esophagus to the rumen, return (*B*) to the mouth for rechewing or rumination, and then pass (*C*) into the reticulum. Grain and other concentrates go at once into the reticulum. The food while being digested is moved successively (*D*) to the omasum, (*E*) abomasum, and (*F*) small intestine.

NATURAL HISTORY

32-21. Distribution. Mammals utilize practically all parts of the earth—land, water, and air. The walrus and some seals live in the Arctic seas and ice, other seals and sea lions along temperate ocean shores, the whales and porpoises in the open sea, and manatees and certain seals are restricted to tropical waters.   The beaver, muskrat, mink, and otter inhabit fresh waters.   Grasslands, brushlands, and forests are the homes of many rodents, carnivores, and hoofed animals.   Still other mammals live in dense tropical jungles, on the treeless Arctic tundras, and in many desert regions.   Tree squirrels, lemurs, many monkeys, and some small carnivores live chiefly in trees, moles and pocket gophers are strict inhabitants of the soil, and the insect-eating bats find their forage at night in the air.   Different mammals range in altitude from sea level to high mountains where some mountain sheep and conies live above timber line.   Each kind of mammal has a definite geographic range. The habitat limitations may be narrow as with a beaver which requires soft-barked trees as food and quiet fresh water for shelter, or wider as with house rats which accommodate themselves to various environments. Many rodents, carnivores, and bats are active only at night, but chipmunks and squirrels (except flying squirrels) are diurnal.   Hoofed mammals forage either by day or by night, but in hot climates many of them rest during midday hours.

32-22. Populations. Many mammals are nocturnal or secretive and escape notice by man; their presence is revealed by tracks, droppings, or other "signs," but trapping or hunting is necessary to determine their numbers or to obtain other information.   The mountain lion, mink, and many rodents live solitarily.   Wolves and hyenas may hunt in packs, the prairie dog (*Cynomys*) and other western ground squirrels inhabit colonial burrows, and buffaloes, antelopes, fur seals, and sea lions often live in herds.   Social groups occur among some primates.

The population density varies with available cover and food.   In favorable places, small shrews and mice may number 50 to 100 per acre and large ground squirrels from 2 to 10 per acre; American deer average 25 to 40 acres per animal, and the black bear up to a township (36 square miles) for each individual.   Marine species, having large areas of the sea for foraging, often assemble in herds on the shore.   The number of species is least in polar regions and greatest in the tropics.

In many species the general population is rather constant unless modified by drought, flood, food shortage, human interference, or similar factors.   It reaches an annual peak when the young appear and then declines until completion of the next breeding season.   Cyclical fluctuations in population occur with meadow mice or voles (*Microtus*), lemmings (*Synaptomys*), with snowshoe hares, arctic foxes, and other species in northern states, Canada, Alaska, and northern Europe, and with cottontails and kangaroo rats of temperate lands.   The cycle is about 4 years in meadow mice and about 10 or 11 years in arctic foxes and hares. Meadow mice and house mice (*Mus musculus*) occasionally "irrupt" with great local increase of numbers for a short time. The causes of all these fluctuations are being studied but are not yet understood.

32-23. Nests and shelters. Many mammals provide shelters where they rest, sleep, avoid inclement weather, and rear their young. Natural crevices amid rocks serve wood rats, conies, and some carnivores. Holes in trees are used by mice, chipmunks, raccoons, opossums, and black bears. Bats resort to caves, trees, or buildings. Tree squirrels, some wood rats, and certain mice build nests amid the foliage of trees. Rabbits, ground squirrels, badgers, coyotes, and skunks dig burrows in the ground. Moles and pocket gophers spend their lives in elaborate systems of tunnels beneath the ground surface. Beavers construct dams to form ponds where they can float logs and build moundlike houses of sticks and mud for shelter. Deer and moose in regions of heavy snow trample out winter yards where they can move about and forage. Many of the small rodents shred plant fibers lengthwise to form a fine "excelsior" that is felted into a warm soft nest.

32-24. Voice. A few mammals are practically voiceless and some are heard rarely, but many use their voices often and for various purposes, including the expression of "emotions" and transfer of "ideas" between individuals. The calls and notes serve to (1) warn of danger, (2) intimidate enemies, (3) assemble gregarious species, (4) bring the sexes together for mating, and (5) locate parents or young. The "language" is usually of stereotyped calls but is more varied among the primates, leading toward the articulate speech of mankind. The voice is powerful in the African lion, elk, and moose and also in the howler monkeys of tropical America and some fruit bats. Small bats emit short bursts of ultrasonic notes that echoing from nearby objects serve to guide them in flight and may aid in capturing prey (10 to 60 bursts per second, each of 0.005 second duration, frequency 50,000 cycles per second).

32-25. Food. The hoofed mammals and most rodents (along with insects) are primary converters of vegetation, since they subsist on plant materials, and they in turn serve as food for flesh-eating animals. The *herbivorous* mammals include horses, cattle, bison, and others which *graze* on grasses and herbs, and the deer, goats, elephants, and giraffes which *browse* on leaves and twigs of shrubs and trees. Rabbits eat grasses, herbs, and bark; ground squirrels and chipmunks consume many seeds (hence are spermophiles); tree squirrels eat nuts of hardwoods and conifers; beavers feed exclusively on the inner bark or cambium of willow and aspen, and porcupines take that of coniferous trees. *Omnivorous* mammals are those which take both plant and animal materials; examples are the house rats, raccoon (Fig. 32-15), bears, pigs, and man. The *carnivorous* mammals or flesh eaters include the cats, weasels, mink, seals, whales, and others. The small bats are exclusively *insectivorous,*

and moles, shrews, skunks, and others subsist largely on insects.   Some
ground squirrels eat insects, and the western grasshopper mouse (*Ony-
chomys*) is mainly insectivorous.   Small mammals have disproportionately large food requirements; some mice eat nearly their own weight of
food daily, and a shrew has been known to consume its own weight in
insects during 24 hours.   If plant-eating mammals become too abundant,
they may denude areas of vegetation so that many of their kind will

Fig. 32-15.   Proportions of different foods taken by an omnivorous mammal, the raccoon
(*Procyon*), in fall and winter.   (*From Hamilton, American mammals.*)

eventually starve.   This occurs in mouse irruptions and has happened
with deer in Pennsylvania and on the Kaibab Plateau in Arizona.
Rodents and deer may forage on farm crops, coyotes and wildcats often
kill sheep or turkeys, and foxes prey on poultry.

Mammals overcome a seasonal scarcity of food in several ways.   The
buffalos of the Great Plains performed a regular *migration* to northern
grasslands for the summer and retired to others farther south for the
winter.   Some mule deer in the western states migrate up on the Sierra-
Cascade and Rocky Mountains to summer in high altitudes and retreat
to winter in the foothills when deep snow blankets the higher ranges.
Herds of antelope and zebras in Africa shift about in keeping with supplies
of forage grasses.   Some bats, like insectivorous birds, leave their
northern summer habitats when insects become scarce and migrate
southward to winter.   Sporadic migrations, probably due to food shortage, occur with tree squirrels in the eastern states and with lemmings in
Norway and Sweden.

Squirrels, chipmunks, and kangaroo rats gather seeds in their cheek
pouches and *store* them by burying in the ground.   Pocket gophers do
likewise with roots.   The cony (*Ochotona*) cuts and cures various plants

as "hay" during the summer; this material is stored in dry, well-aired spaces ("barns") among the rocks of its high mountain habitat, to be eaten when the region is blanketed with winter snow.   Moles are reported to store earthworms below ground on occasion.

Winter sleep or *hibernation* is practiced by ground squirrels, chipmunks, bats, and bears to tide over the winter scarcity of food.   During hibernation all bodily metabolism drops to a low level; the respiration and heartbeat are slowed, and the body temperature is far reduced. Excess fat is accumulated prior to hibernation and serves as fuel to maintain life through the dormant period when no food is eaten.   Squirrels usually hibernate in underground nests, bears in hollow logs or caves, and bats hang up in caves or buildings.   Some northern ground squirrels hibernate for about two-thirds of the year; with bears the duration varies with latitude, and bats may fly out during a warm spell in winter.

32-26. Enemies.   Herbivorous mammals fall prey to various flesh-eating animals according to size.   Cattle are eaten by tigers, antelopes and zebras by African lions, American deer by mountain lions, wolves and coyotes, and so on, down to small mice, which are eaten by weasels. Hawks and owls prey on mice, rats, and rabbits, and some large snakes take many rodents.   Man is a major enemy of many mammals.   He hunts game species, traps fur bearers, and kills in various ways the predators that levy on domestic livestock and rodents that forage on crops.   Mammals are hosts to various parasites and diseases that may reduce their vitality or cause death, and some of these are probably important in the regulation of mammalian populations.   Ticks, lice, fleas, roundworms, and flatworms are among the common parasites (Chaps. 16, 17, 23, 24).   Many protozoan, bacterial, and virus diseases are peculiar to mammals (Table 23-1).

32-27. Reproduction.   Fertilization is always internal with mammals, and the young are nourished by milk after birth.   The lowest mammals are the duck-billed platypus and spiny anteater (MONOTREMATA); they lay reptile-like eggs of some size which are probably incubated.   The opossums, kangaroos, and other MARSUPIALIA have minute eggs that develop for some days in the uterus.   Then the immature "larvae" crawl out to the ventral pouch or marsupium on the abdomen of the female, where they attach firmly to the mammary nipples for nutrition and remain until their development is completed.   In all the other higher mammals the minute eggs are retained for a longer period of development in the uterus, which becomes modified for their reception and nourishment.   The circulatory system of the embryo quickly comes into close relation, but not direct connection, with maternal blood vessels in the uterus by development of the placenta, which provides a mecha-

nism for diffusion of food and oxygen to the embryo and for removal of
waste products (Chap. 5).

Fig. 32-16.   Types of uteri.   *A.* Duck-billed platypus (Monotremata); separate oviducts (uteri) enter a urogenital sinus joined to the cloaca.   *B.* Rabbit (Lagomorpha); uterus
duplex, of separate "horns" joined to a common vagina.   *C.* Cow (Artiodactyla); uterus
bicornate, "horns" partly fused.   *D.* Human (Primates); uterus simplex, with a common
central chamber, and no "horns."

Most mammals have rather definite mating seasons, often in winter or
spring.   Many produce but one brood a year, some have more than one,
and the alien house mouse and rats may breed at any season.   The
reproductive seasons of domestic animals have been modified by artificial
selection.   Males of some mammals produce viable sperm throughout the
year even though the females have a restricted season of reproduction.
In rodents, the testes enlarge and descend into the scrotum to become
functional during the mating season, then decrease in size and return into
the abdomen.   Male elk "bugle" and become more pugnacious during
the mating period, and other mammals have special mating calls between
the sexes, as with domestic cats and cattle.

Female mammals experience a recurrent *estrus cycle,* or "heat"
period.   This is marked by a series of cellular changes in the uterus and
vagina and by differences in behavior of the female.   The successive
stages are termed anestrum (quiescent period), proestrum (preparation
for mating), estrum (acceptance of male), and metestrum (regressive
changes).   Discharge of ova from the ovary occurs usually late in estrus
or soon thereafter.   The female rat is in heat for a few hours about every
4 days, the cow has recurrent periods lasting about 24 hours every 18 to
21 days, and the female dog is in estrus for 6 to 12 days about every
6 months.   Female rabbits and ferrets will usually breed at any time.
Estrus, pregnancy, and lactation are regulated by hormones of the
pituitary gland and ovaries; environmental factors such as the length of
day and temperature effect pituitary activity in these respects.

The relations between the sexes during the reproductive season are
various.   In some carnivores the male remains with the female and
helps to gather food until the young are weaned.   Many other mammals

are promiscuous in mating, one or more males simply attending a female for a day or so until she is served.   Polygamy, the mating of one male with several or many females, is the habit of sea lions, fur seals, cattle, wild horses, and elk.   A sexually active male gathers a group of females, defends them against the other males with whom he may fight, and copulates with each female as she comes into heat.

The period of gestation, or pregnancy, usually varies with size.   The time in days for some common mammals is as follows: house mouse, 21; Norway rat, 21.5 to 22; domestic rabbit, 30 to 32; ferret, 40; black fox, 51; house cat and domestic dog, 60; guinea pig, 68; swine, 114; sheep and goats, 149; mule-tailed deer, 203 to 208; marten 259 to 275; cow, 280; horse, 336; elephant, about 20 months.

FIG.   32-17.   Young   mammals.   *Above.* Rats, born naked, blind, and helpless; require nursing and care in a nest before becoming independent.   *Below.*   Jack rabbit, fully haired and with eyes open at birth, able to move about at once.   (*Photographs by T. I. Storer.*)

The number of young produced at one time is usually inversely proportional to size; elephant and horse, 1; sheep and deer, 1 or 2; carnivores, 3 to 5; rodents, 2 or 3 to 8 or 9.   The black rat averages 6 and the Norway rat about 8, but females of the latter may have up to 15 embryos at one pregnancy.   Experimental injection of gonadotropic hormone into 28-day old rats, followed by breeding, has yielded up to 33 embryos and 23 live young from one female!   Large mammals usually produce but one young per year, but smaller species with short gestation time and multiple broods are more prolific.   A pair of captive meadow mice has produced 13 to 17 litters totaling 78 to 83 young in 1 year, and a pair of white (Norway) rats over 1,500.

The *precocial* young of hares and jack rabbits (*Lepus*), deer, and domestic livestock are fully haired at birth, have their eyes open, and are able to move about at once (Fig. 32-17).   In contrast, the *altricial* young of true rabbits (*Oryctolagus*), most rodents, and carnivores are naked, blind, and helpless when born and require further development in a nest before being able to get about.   The young of all mammals are given more or less parental care and guarding before they scatter to become independent.

Some small mice may breed a few weeks after birth, whereas the larger land mammals require several years before sexual maturity; large whales, however, breed in the second or third year of life.

The average span of life is scarcely a year in some small rodents and shrews and is generally proportional to size in the larger species; yet no mammals, even among captives, attain the average life span of mankind.

32-28. Relations to man. From the earliest times to the present day, mammals have served or harmed man in various ways. He has depended on some of them for food, clothing, and other necessities, but others have been a physical menace or a source of disease, and some are injurious to his possessions. The early cave paintings of primitive man in Europe depict the chase and the defense against large predators; the great interest in hunting by all peoples demonstrates this continuing relation between man and mammals.

Eskimos in the Arctic use whale and seal blubber as fuel oil, caribou skins for clothing, seal hides for footwear, and skins or intestines of other species for boats. The Plains Indians were supported largely by the buffalo, using its flesh for food, its hides for teepees (tents), and its sinews for sewing. Tanned deerskins served many Indian tribes as clothing. Civilized races in northern countries have used animal pelts as clothing for many centuries, and much of the early exploration of North America was done by trappers in search of new sources of furs. Today, the demand for fur garments supports an industry employing thousands of trappers, tanners, and dyers, garment manufacturers, and retailers. Dense natural furs of soft texture and pleasing colors bring the highest prices. Beavers and martens have been exterminated by trapping in many places, and other species are now far reduced. Millions of muskrats, skunks, and opossums are still taken in the United States, and lesser numbers of other fur bearers. The rearing of valuable species such as black fox and mink on fur farms has become successful and already contributes an appreciable number of furs annually. Pelts of rabbits, house cats, muskrats, and others are dyed, clipped, or otherwise altered to resemble the more expensive furs.

Civilized man hunts now for pleasure and recreation. The moose, elk, deer, mountain sheep, and bears are "big game," sought for their heads, hides, and meat; lesser forms such as the raccoons, opossums, rabbits, and tree squirrels are pursued by thousands of hunters. Excessive hunting has exterminated the bison, elk, mountain lion, and wolf in many places.

Live mammals, especially the larger or rarer kinds, are of interest to most persons; hence, they are exhibited in many zoological gardens, and in the national parks they are protected so that many visitors may see them at close range.   To many persons the sport of hunting mammals with a camera surpasses that with a gun.

The harmful mammals include those which damage crops or domestic animals, those which harbor disease, and the large mammals which are dangerous to man himself.   Rabbits, woodchucks, and some mice will forage in truck patches, gardens, and fields of alfalfa or clover and may gnaw the bark of trees.   In the western states, ground squirrels damage grainfields and other crops, and pocket gophers eat roots of plants in gardens and fields.   The burrows of these and other rodents often cause loss of water in irrigated areas.   The alien house rats and house mice are a widespread scourge.   From their homes in Europe and Asia they have been spread by shipping and commerce to many lands.   They gnaw into or invade all sorts of buildings, consume all kinds of foodstuffs, and destroy much property.   The carnivores, or "predatory mammals," in nature feed on other animals appropriate to their size, from rodents to deer.   Wolves, coyotes, wildcats, and bears also prey at times on domestic cattle, sheep, hogs, and poultry.   Since the beginning of agriculture, mankind has endeavored to control the damage by rodents to his crops and property and by predators to his livestock.   Active campaigns, under the auspices of governmental agencies, are conducted in many parts of the United States against harmful mammals.

Some important diseases in mammals that may be transmitted to man are plague, typhus, and ratbite fever in house rats; plague, relapsing fever, spotted fever, and tularemia in various wild rodents; and trichina in rats, pigs, and cats.

32-29. Domesticated mammals.   Several mammals have been domesticated to serve man's needs (Table 32-1).   The horse and ox serve for transport and draft, the cattle, sheep, and goats provide meat and milk, the pig affords meat, and all yield hides to tan into leather.   The wool and hair of sheep and goats is spun into yarn or thread and woven into fabrics.   The dog is a guardian and friend, is used in hunting, sometimes is a beast of burden, is eaten by some primitive races, and was bred for "wool" by Indians of the North Pacific coast.   Domestication probably began in Asia many centuries ago (Chap. 33), and the wild ancestors of several domestic stocks are native to that continent.   The first domestic animal remains in Europe are with the Swiss lake dwellings (New Stone Age) and being unlike local wild mammals were probably brought "out of the east" whence various human migrations came.

For successful domestication a mammal must have a moderate degree of intelligence and be of gregarious habit.   The cat "that walks alone" is almost too intelligent and readily reverts to the wild or feral state. Of all mammals now domesticated, only the rabbit cannot be reared in groups; this is because of a disease, coccidiosis (Chap. 12), that decimates rabbits when kept together.

Many special types of horses, cattle, sheep, pigs, and dogs have been developed to suit particular needs, by artificial selection in breeding. Some of these differ greatly from their wild ancestors in size, conforma-

Table 32-1.   The Domesticated Mammals, Their Classification and Places of Origin

Order and family	Domesticated stocks	Wild stock whence derived	Place of origin
Rodentia			
Leporidae	Domestic Rabbits, all breeds	*Oryctolagus cuniculus,* European gray rabbit	Europe
Muridae	Golden Hamster	*Mesocricetus auratus*	Syria
	White-footed Mice	*Peromyscus leucopus* and *P. maniculatus*	United States
	Cotton Rat	*Sigmodon hispidus*	Southeastern United States
	White and Colored Mice	*Mus musculus,* house mouse	Asia or Europe
	White Rat	*Rattus norvegicus,* Norway rat	Western Asia
Caviidae	Guinea Pig	*Cavia porcellus*	South America
Carnivora	Domestic Dogs, *Canis familiaris*	*Canis lupus,* wolf	Europe and Asia
Canidae	Black and Silver Foxes	*Vulpes fulva,* American red fox	Northeastern Canada and United States
Felidae	Domestic Cats, *Felis catus*	*Felis silvestris,* European wildcat	Europe
Mustelidae	Mink	*Mustela vison*	United States
	Ferret, *Mustela furo*	*Mustela eversmanni,* polecat	Asia
Perissodactyla	Domestic Horses:		
Equidae	western draft types	*Equus caballus fossilis*	Europe
	oriental speed types	*Equus przewalski*	Western Asia
	Gray Asses	*Equus onager*	Western Asia
	White Asses	*Equus asinus*	Northern Africa
Artiodactyla	Pigs or Swine, European	*Sus scrofa,* European wild boar	Europe
Suidae	Asia and Southeastern Europe	*Sus vittatus*	Southeastern Asia
Camelidae	Arabian Camel, or Dromedary	*Camelus dromedarius*	Mongolia
	Bactrian Camel (2-humped)	*Camelus bactrianus*	Mongolia
	Llama	*Auchenia glama*	South America
	Alpaca	*Auchenia peruana*	South America
Cervidae	Reindeer	*Rangifer tarandus*	Northern Euorpe
Bovidae	European Cattle, *Bos taurus*	*Bos primigenius,* aurochs, or ur, and ? *B. brachyceros*	Europe
	Asiatic Cattle, *Bos indicus*	? *Bos sondaicus,* banteng	Southern Asia
	Water Buffalo	*Bufellus bubalis*	Southern Asia
	Yak	*Poephagus grunniens*	Tibet
	Sheep, ordinary breeds	*Ovis musimon,* mouflon	Southern Europe
	Merino, Fat-tailed	*Ovis argal*	Western Asia
	Goats, ordinary breeds	*Capra aegagrus*	Western Asia
	Kashmir and Angora	*Capra falconeri*	Western Asia

tion, color, reproductive ability, and other features, although no new animals have been created. Examples of such breeds among cattle are the Hereford (beef), Holstein-Friesian (heavy milk producers), Jersey (high butterfat content of milk), and Brown Swiss of triple purpose (meat, milk, and draft).   Recently domesticated animals such as the mink and black fox have been changed but slightly.

Domestic mammals and birds provide most of the protein for human food, aside from fish, and also many other necessities of modern life. The livestock industry, which breeds and rears domesticated mammals and birds, is consequently a valuable part of modern agriculture.   The packing industry slaughters these animals, distributes meat products, and recovers by-products and hence is also important in all civilized countries.

32-30. Fossil mammals.   The mammals probably arose from the cynodont reptiles of Triassic time, which had differentiated teeth.   The earliest forms were small, but later stocks increased in size and became varied in structure.   Marsupials and insectivores appeared in the Cretaceous, and from the latter group the higher placental mammals are considered to have arisen.   With the close of the Cretaceous most of the reptiles disappeared and the mammals "blossomed forth."   First came a series of archaic stocks, mostly of ungainly form (Orders †Taeniodonta, †Creodonta, †Condylarthra, †Amblypoda), and then shortly the modern types appeared.   The Cenozoic era (Paleocene to Pleistocene) is called the Age of Mammals because members of this class were dominant throughout.   About half the known orders of mammals consist entirely of extinct forms, and all the others contain, besides the living representatives, some or many that have died out.

Some important structural features of mammals, as compared with reptiles, are (1) two occipital condyles instead of one; (2) each ramus of the lower jaw of one bone, not several; (3) articulation of the jaw directly on the skull, not through the quadrate; (4) teeth differentiated and of only two sets (milk, permanent), instead of alike with many replacements; and (5) centra of vertebrae and long bones ossifying from three centers instead of one.

The factors that led to development of the mammals have been inferred to be the increasing aridity from Permian time onward which placed a premium on speed of locomotion, and the colder glacial climates in which animals with regulated body temperature that progressed with their bodies off the ground would be more likely to survive.

Some early mammals were exceedingly abundant, to judge from the quantities of their teeth and skeletons that have been found.   Fossil relics of carnivores, whales, proboscidians, horses, camels, and others are sufficiently numerous to enable paleontologists to trace their probable evolution in some detail.   The phylogeny of some groups can be traced through several geological periods in one continent.   In other cases a stock suddenly appears in the rocks and provides little or no clue to its immediate ancestry or probable path of migration.

For example, the elephants and mastodons (Chap. 9) began in the Eocene as small creatures with no evidence of a proboscis and only slightly enlarged incisors (tusks). They developed into a variety of forms, with either two or four tusks, and with cheek teeth of increasing size and complexity. The largest was †*Elephas imperator*, 13½ feet in height. They spread to several continents and were common over North America during the Pleistocene but then largely died out. Living forms are restricted to Africa and India.

The horses began with †*Eohippus*, which averaged 11 inches high at the shoulder and had four front and three hind toes. They increased in height, the lateral toes were shortened and gradually lost, and the cheek teeth became long-crowned with more complex enamel folds. Their direct phylogeny can be traced from Eocene to Pleistocene in North America. The modern genus (*Equus*) appeared in upper Pliocene, spread to South America and Eurasia and later to Africa, and then became extinct in the Americas at the end of the Pleistocene. All Recent "wild" horses in North America are descended from domestic horses brought by explorers and settlers since the fifteenth century.

CLASSIFICATION

Class *MAMMALIA*. Mammals. Body usually covered with hair; skin with various glands; skull with 2 occipital condyles; jaws usually with differentiated teeth, in sockets; limbs adapted for walking, climbing, burrowing, swimming, or flying; toes with claws, nails, or hoofs; heart 4-chambered, with left aortic arch only; lungs large and elastic; a diaphragm between thoracic and abdominal cavities; male with a penis; fertilization internal; eggs small or minute, usually retained in uterus of female for development; females with mammary glands that secrete milk to nourish the young; body temperature regulated (homoiothermous); Triassic to Recent; 4,400 living species (many subspecies) and numerous fossil forms.

Fig. 32-18. An egg-laying mammal, the duck-billed platypus (*Ornithorhynchus anatinus*, Order Monotremata) of Australia. (*After Vogt and Specht, The natural history of animals, Blackie & Son, Ltd.*)

Subclass A. PROTOTHERIA.

Order 1. **Monotremata** (Ornithodelphia). Monotremes or Egg-laying Mammals. Coracoid and precoracoid present; no external pinna on ear; teeth only in young, adults with horny beak; cloaca present; ureters open in dorsal wall of urogenital passage; testes abdominal; penis conducts only sperm; oviducts distinct, entering cloaca separately; no uterus or vagina; mammary glands without nipples; females oviparous; Australian region. *Ornithorhynchus anatinus*, duck-billed platypus (Fig. 32-18), eastern Australia and Tasmania, 18 to 20 inches long; ducklike bill, internal cheek pouches, feet broadly webbed, tail flat and beaver-like, male with rooster-like spur on heel, connected to poison gland; aquatic, constructs burrows; food of freshwater invertebrates, carried in cheek pouches; during spring (August to December) female constructs nest in burrow and lays 1 to 3 eggs, each about ½ by ¾ inch, with strong flexible white shell; probably incubated; young about 1 inch long when hatched, "nurse" by lapping up milk secreted by scattered "mammary" glands on abdomen of female. *Tachyglossus*, spiny anteater, several species, Australia, Tasmania, New Guinea, and Papua. *T. aculeatus*, of Australia, 17 inches long, beak elongate cylindrical, tongue extensile, body covered with coarse hairs and spines, limbs short, toes 3 to 5 with claws; nocturnal, feeds upon ants found under stones; female lays 1 egg, probably carried in pouch (marsupium) on abdomen.

Subclass B.   †ALLOTHERIA.   Order 1.   †**Multituberculata.**   Jurassic to Eocene.

Subclass C.   THERIA.   Marsupials and Placental Mammals.   Ear usually with external pinna; teeth usually present in both young and adults and differentiated as to form and function; cloaca usually absent; ureters open into base of bladder; testes of males usually in a scrotal sac, vasa deferentia and bladder opening through a common urethra in penis; females with each oviduct differentiated into upper

Fig. 32-19.   American or Virginia opossum (*Didelphis virginianus*, Order Marsupialia); Head-and-body to 20 inches long, tail 13 inches.   (*Photograph by D. R. Dickey.*)

Fallopian and lower uterine portions, both opening into a distinct and elongate vagina; mammary glands with nipples; females produce living young (viviparous).

Infraclass 1.   †PANTOTHERIA.   Order 1.   †**Pantotheria.**   Jurassic.   Order 2. †**Symmetrodonta.**   Jurassic.

Infraclass 2.   METATHERIA.

Order 1.   **Marsupialia.**   Marsupials or Pouched Mammals.   Epipubic bones usually present; coracoid an apophysis on scapula; incisor teeth not equal in the 2 jaws; female usually with marsupium (ventral pouch) or marsupial folds surrounding nipples on abdomen; uterus and vagina double; usually no placenta; eggs fertilized internally and begin development in uterus, but after a few days the premature "larvae" leave and crawl to marsupium where each attaches closely by its mouth to a mammary nipple and remains (as a "mammary foetus") until fully formed; thereafter small young retreat to marsupium for shelter; Cretaceous to Recent.

Didelphidae.   Opossums.   In the Americas.   *Didelphis virginianus,* Virginia opossum (Fig. 32-19), southern New England and Wisconsin to Gulf states and Texas, introduced into California; tail scaly and prehensile; hides by day in hollow tree near water; omnivorous.   Up to 22 embryos, mammae only 13; "larvae" when 12¾ days old (11 mm. long) crawl to marsupium and remain attached to nipples for 50 to 60 days, then become free but return to pouch during following month.

Adults feign death, or "play 'possum," when disturbed; favored for hunting and eating in southern states.

CAENOLESTIDAE.   *Caenolestes,* two species in Andes of South America.

(*Note: All other living marsupials are restricted to Australia, where they are the dominant mammals; many have the fore and hind limbs about equal, but others have long hind legs as in kangaroos; they range in size from small mice to large man-sized kangaroos.*)

DASYURIDAE.   Limbs alike: carnivorous or insectivorous. *Thylacinus,* marsupial wolf, size of large dog; *Sarcophilus,* Tasmanian devil; *Dasyurus,* tiger cat; *Phascogale,* size of a rat; *Sminthopsis,* pouched mouse, 3 to 5 inches long.

NOTORYCTIDAE.   Foreclaws enlarged; subterranean, insectivorous. *Notoryctes,* marsupial mole, 6½ to 8 inches long.

PERAMELIDAE.   Terrestrial and burrowing, largely insectivorous. *Perameles,* bandicoot.

PHALANGERIDAE.   Claws sharp, hallux opposed; arboreal, herbivorous. *Phalanger,* cuscus; *Petaurus,* flying phalanger (like flying squirrel); *Phascolarctus,* koala or "teddy bear."

PHASCOLOMYIDAE.   Terrestrial and burrowing, herbivorous. *Phascolomys,* wombat.

MACROPODIDAE.   Hind legs, feet, and tail elongated; habitat various, herbivorous. *Macropus,* kangaroo, open forest or plains (Fig. 32-20); *Petrogale,* rock wallaby, about rocks; *Lagorchestes,* hare wallaby, like hare or jack rabbit; *Dendrolagus,* tree kangaroo, arboreal.

FIG. 32-20.   A marsupial mammal (Order MARSUPIALIA) of Australia; female kangaroo with young in the pouch; long tail of female not shown. (*Photograph by San Diego Zoological Society.*)

Infraclass 3.   EUTHERIA.   PLACENTAL MAMMALS.   No marsupial bones or pouch; coracoid only a process on scapula; vagina single; foetus developed entirely within body of female, attached by a placenta to wall of uterus, and with growth of chorion.

Order 1.   **Insectivora.**   MOLES, SHREWS, ETC.   Size small; snout usually long and tapered; feet usually 5-toed, with claws, inner toes not opposable; teeth rooted, tuberculate; Cretaceous to Recent; Northern Hemisphere, West Indies, and Africa.

TALPIDAE.   MOLES.   *Scalopus, Scapanus* (Fig. 32-21), etc.   Eyes covered, palms enlarged, foreclaws large; pelage short, velvety; most species strictly subterranean, in "mole runs" at ground surface and in deeper tunnels from which earth is pushed out on surface

FIG.   32-21.   Mole (*Scapanus latimanus,* Order INSECTIVORA), length 6½ inches. Lives in ground, using large claws and palms for burrowing.

as "mole hills"; food chiefly insects and worms, some sprouted seeds.

SORICIDAE.   SHREWS.   *Sorex,* etc.   "Mouselike," eyes not covered, feet and tail normal; pelage soft, short; forage on surface of ground and in animal burrows, feeding voraciously on insects, small invertebrates, and some rodents; *Echinosorex albus,* Borneo, largest, to 653 mm. long.

ERINACEIDAE. HEDGEHOGS. *Erinaceus*, in Old World, pelage with spines on back.

Order 2. **Dermoptera.** "FLYING LEMURS." Resemble flying squirrel in appearance; the four limbs equal and included with tail in a wide, thin, fur-covered "parachute" (patagium); incisor teeth 2/3. Southeastern Asia and adjacent islands. One living genus, *Galeopithecus*, 2 species, nocturnal, in trees, glide on extended membranes; feed on leaves and fruits.

Order 3. **Chiroptera.** BATS. Flying mammals; size small; fore limbs and 2d to 5th digits greatly elongated, supporting a thin integumental flight membrane, or wing, that includes hind limbs (and tail in some); only 1st digit (2d also in fruit bats) of fore limb with claw; hind feet small, with sharp curved claws; teeth sharp; mostly nocturnal, capable of true flight; Paleocene to Recent; world-wide.

Suborder 1. MEGACHIROPTERA. FRUIT BATS OR "FLYING FOXES. Africa and s. Asia to Australia; often in great flocks; sleep by day on tree branches, hanging head downward with wings folded cloaklike around body; feed on fruits, sometimes damaging orchards. *Pteropus edulis*, of Java, largest species, head and body about 12 inches, wingspread to 5 feet.

FIG. 32-22. Mexican free-tailed bat (*Tadarida mexicana*, Order CHIROPTERA), length 4 inches, wing spread about 12 inches. Hangs upside down by day in caves or buildings on sharp hind claws; climbs with aid of foreclaws, and flies at night to capture insects for food. (*Photograph by T. I. Storer.*)

Suborder 2. MICROCHIROPTERA. INSECTIVOROUS BATS OR "FLITTERMICE." Hang by hind claws head downward during day, in crevices of rocks or trees or in caves or buildings; some gregarious, others solitary; forage independently at night, in open air or beneath trees; feed on flying insects. *Myotis*, *Eptesicus*, brown bats; *Tadarida mexicana*, free-tailed bat (Fig. 32-22), roosts in companies of a dozen to millions, as in Carlsbad Caverns, N.M., the accumulated droppings (guano) under roosts in dry caves gathered for fertilizer; *Desmodus*, vampire bat, in American tropics, with enlarged canine teeth punctures large blood vessels on horses, cattle, and occasionally man and laps up the streaming blood as food; transmits a form of rabies and a disease of horses (trypanosomiasis).

Order 4. **Primates.** LEMURS, MONKEYS, APES, AND MAN. Limbs elongate, "hands" and "feet" enlarged, each of 5 digits with flattened or cupped nails; innermost (great) toe and thumb or both, usually opposable, for climbing; orbit usually directed forward and surrounded by bony ring; molars tuberculate; usually but one young at a birth; Paleocene to Recent; chiefly tropical and subtropical, most species arboreal; structure more generalized than in many other mammals, but with highest functional development of nervous system and intelligence; food chiefly fruits and seeds, some eat animal materials.

Suborder 1. LEMUROIDEA. LEMURS. Second toe with claw, others with nails; tail long, never prehensile, rarely absent; coloration often conspicuous; hair thick; Madagascar, Africa, southeastern Asia to Philippines and Celebes; solitary, tree-dwelling, many crepuscular or nocturnal; food of plant materials and small animals. *Lemur.*

Suborder 2. TARSIOIDEA. TARSIERS. Eyes protruding; ears large, thin; tarsal region of foot long, 2d and 3d toes with claws, tips of all digits with rounded pads; tail long ratlike, not prehensile; Philippines and Indo-Australian islands. *Tarsius* (1 or more species), size of red squirrel, solitary, tree-inhabiting, nocturnal, agile, jumps like a frog; food chiefly insects and lizards.

Suborder 3. ANTHROPOIDEA. MONKEYS, APES, MAN. Digits with flattened or cupped nails; tree-inhabiting or terrestrial, diurnal.

Superfamily 1. CEBOIDEA (Platyrhinii). NEW WORLD MONKEYS. Central and South America, wide flat interval between nostrils, no cheek pouches.

FIG. 32-23.—Mountain gorilla (*Gorilla gorilla*, Order PRIMATES). (*Photograph by San Diego Zoological Society.*)

HAPALIDAE. MARMOSETS. Size of squirrels; head often with lateral tufts; tail not prehensile. *Hapale.*

CEBIDAE. Form and color varied; tail prehhensile in some. *Ateles,* spider monkey, very slender; *Alouatta* howlers, voice loud; *Cebus,* capuchins, mostly small.

Superfamily 2. CERCOPITHECOIDEA (Catarrhini). OLD WORLD MONKEYS. Nostrils directed downward, a narrow space between; often with internal cheek pouches; tail never prehensile, ischial tuberosities on buttocks with calloused, exposed skin. *Nasalis,* proboscis monkey, in Borneo; *Semnopithecus,* langur, in India, includes sacred hanuman of the Hindus; *Colobus,* in Africa, hair long, black-and-white; *Cynocephalus,* baboons, mandrill, etc., head stout, doglike, tail short, disposition savage; *Macacus,* macaques or rhesus monkeys, Asia (one species at Gibraltar), used as pets and in biological research.

Superfamily 3. HOMINOIDEA. ANTHROPOID APES AND MAN. No tail or cheek pouches.

PONGIDAE. ANTHROPOID APES. *Hylobates,* gibbon, and *Siamanga,* siamang, southeastern Asia and Malay Archipelago, body slender, limbs long, height to 3 feet; chiefly arboreal, travel easily through trees, but walk slowly on ground, using only the feet; voice powerful, often used; diet omnivorous. *Pongo (Simia) satyrus*, orang-utan, Sumatra and Borneo, in swampy forests; skull high-topped, face flattish, brain man-like; to 54 inches tall; hair long, lax, and reddish, old males often with beard; lives in trees and constructs crude nests; diet of plant materials. *Gorilla gorilla* (Fig. 32-23), gorilla, West and east Central Africa, in forests; body and limbs heavy, males to 65 inches high and over 500 pounds in weight; hair and skin black; walks on soles of feet aided by knuckles of hands, with body inclined; lives chiefly on ground and in family groups; food of plant materials. *Pan (Anthropopithecus) troglodytes*, chimpanzee (Fig. 32-24), West Africa, in forests, to 54 inches tall, weight to 150 pounds;

FIG. 32-24. Chimpanzee (*Pan troglodytes*, Order PRIMATES). (*Photograph by San Diego Zoological Society.*)

head rounded, ears large, forearms short, feeds on plant materials; resembles human beings more than other anthropoids.

HOMINIDAE. *Homo sapiens*, mankind (Chap. 33).

Order 5.   †Tillodontia. Paleocene-Eocene.

Order 6.   †Taeniodonta. Eocene.

Order 7.   **Edentata** (Xenarthra). SLOTHS ETC. Teeth reduced to molars in anterior part of jaws and without enamel; Eocene to Recent.

MYRMECOPHAGIDAE. ANTEATERS. *Myrmecophagus*, in tropical America; head and snout elongate; tongue slender, protrusible, and sticky; no teeth; forefeet with stout curved claws used to open ant and termite nests; hair long.

BRADYPODIDAE. ARBOREAL SLOTHS. *Bradypus*, in tropical America, molar teeth present, all feet with long curved claws by which sloth hangs upside down on tree branches; hair long, slopes dorsally; food of leaves, fruits, and birds.

DASYPODIDAE. ARMADILLOS. *Dasypus (Tatu)* (Fig. 32-25). Texas to South America, with dorsal horny protective shell over bony plates in the skin and commonly divided by transverse furrows of softer skin so that animal can curl up when disturbed. *D. novemcincta*, nine-banded armadillo, southern Texas.

Order 8.   **Pholidota.**   Body covered by large overlapping horny plates with sparse hair between; no teeth, tongue slender and used to capture insects.   *Manis*, pangolin or scaly anteater, Africa and southeastern Asia.

Order 9.   **Lagomorpha.**   PIKAS, HARES, AND RABBITS.   Size moderate to small; toes with claws; tail stubby; incisors chisel-like grow continually, 2/1 × 2 (2d upper incisor small, behind 1st); no canines; premolars 3/2; molars unrooted; total cheek teeth to 6/5, those of upper jaw wider; palate broad; jaw motion only lateral; elbow joint nonrotating; Eocene to Recent; more than 300 species and subspecies; food of leaves, stems, and bark.

FIG. 32-25.   Armadillo (*Dasypus novemcinctus*, Order EDENTATA), length to 32 inches. (*After Wolcott, Animal biology.*)

OCHOTONIDAE.   PIKAS OR CONIES·(not HYRACOIDEA).   *Ochotona*, California and Colorado to Alaska and Asia, at high altitudes; about 6 inches long, ears rounded, legs equal, tail vestigial; live about rock piles and gather plants for "winter hay."

LEPORIDAE.   HARES AND RABBITS (Fig. 32-26).   Ears long, hind legs elongate for jumping, feed on leaves and stems of plants.   *Lepus americanus*, snowshoe hare (rabbit), turns white in winter; *L. campestris*, etc., "jack rabbit," arid western states; both surface dwellers, young fully haired when born; *Sylvilagus*, American cottontail, lives about thickets, digs burrows, young born naked and blind; *Oryctolagus cuniculus*, European gray rabbit, source of all domestic breeds, introduced and widespread in Australia and New Zealand.

Order 10.   **Rodentia** (Glires).   RODENTS OR GNAWING MAMMALS.   Usually small; limbs usually with 5 toes and claws; incisors 1/1 × 2, exposed, chisel-like, and rootless, growing continually; no canines; a wide gap (diastemma) between incisors and canines; premolars 2/1 or fewer; molars 3/3 (rarely 2/2); upper and lower cheek teeth about equal sized; palate narrow; jaw motion both fore-and-aft and lateral; elbow joint rotates; Eocene to Recent; world-wide, on all continents and many islands, from sea level to above 19,000 feet in Himalayas, from dry deserts to rain forests, some in swamps and fresh waters, none marine; includes majority of living mammals, more than 6,400 species and subspecies (1,500 of the 2,500 mammals in North America, from Panama northward); size varies from mice only 2 inches long to capybara (*Hydrochoerus* of South America) 48 inches long, but few exceed 12 inches; food chiefly of leaves, stems, seeds, or roots, some partly or largely insectivorous; smaller species often abundant, and with high reproductive potential; serve as staple food for many carnivorous mammals, birds, and reptiles.

SCIURIDAE.   SQUIRRELS.   Mostly diurnal, feed chiefly on seeds and nuts.   *Sciurus*, tree squirrels (red, gray, fox, etc.) in forested regions, often sought by hunters; *Citellus*, ground squirrels, on open lands of western states, make burrows in ground, feed on seeds and grasses, some damage crops, and a few carry diseases transmissible

FIG. 32-26. Order LAGOMORPHA. *Above.* Jack rabbit (*Lepus californicus*, a hare), living in open areas. *Below.* Cottontail (*Sylvilagus*), living about thickets. *Right.* Brush rabbit (*Sylvilagus*), native to the Pacific coast, inhabits dense brushy chaparral. (*From Storer*, 1949.)

to man; *Tamias, Eutamias,* chipmunks, about logs, brush, and rocks; *Marmota,* woodchuck, ground hog, or marmot, in meadowlands, feeds on grasses; *Glaucomys,* flying squirrel, with broad membranes along sides of body, in forests, nocturnal.

GEOMYIDAE. POCKET GOPHERS. With external fur-lined cheek pouches to carry food; strictly subterranean in self-constructed burrows; vegetarian; southern and

western North America. *Geomys, Thomomys.*

HETEROMYIDAE. POUCHED MICE. With fur-lined cheek pouches; forage on surface of ground at night, chiefly on seeds; in arid southwestern North America. *Dipodomys,* kangaroo rat; *Perognathus,* pocket mouse.

MURIDAE. RATS AND MICE. *Microtus,* meadow mice or voles, in grasslands; *Peromyscus,* white-footed or deer mice, widespread over North America; *Sigmodon,* cotton rats; *Neotoma,* wood rats or pack rats; *Ondatra zibethica,*

FIG. 32-27. The muskrat (*Ondatra zibethica,* Order RODENTIA), length to 22 inches. Specialized for life in marshes; a muskrat house at right (see Fig. 8-2).

muskrat (Fig. 32-27), in marshes, pelt valuable for fur. Also, the Old World rats and house mouse, spread by commerce and shipping to all civilized countries, common in much of North America, damage property and food supplies and carry various diseases, including plague, typhus, and ratbite fever.   *Rattus norvegicus*, Norway rat (Fig. 32-1); *R. rattus*, black and roof rats; *Mus musculus*, house mouse.

ERETHIZONTIDAE.   PORCUPINES.   *Erethizon*, protectively covered with slender, pointed quills (modified hairs); feeds on cambium of coniferous trees.

CASTORIDAE.   BEAVERS.   *Castor*, North America and Europe, formerly common; head and body to 30 inches long; tail flat, oval, scaly; body pelage soft, a desirable fur; builds dams and ponds, to float logs cut for food and to contain houses for shelter; feeds on cambium of aspen, willow, etc.

Order 11.   **Cetacea.**   WHALES, DOLPHINS, AND PORPOISES.   Size medium to very large; body usually spindle-shaped; head elongate, often pointed, joined directly to body (no neck region); some with a fleshy dorsal "fin"; fore limbs (flippers) broad and paddle-like, digits embedded, no claws; no hind limbs; tail long, ending in two broad transverse fleshy flukes, and notched in mid-line; teeth when present alike, lacking enamel; nostrils 1 or 2 on top of head; ear openings minute; body surface smooth, no hairs save for few on muzzle; no skin glands except mammary and conjunctival glands; a thick layer of fat (blubber) under skin, affording insulation; stomach complex; Eocene to Recent; oceanic, over the world, always in water, die from crushing of internal organs if stranded on shore; whales may dive to 3,600 feet when wounded and can remain submerged many minutes without breathing; upon reaching surface, warm moist air is blown from lungs, forming a "spout" as condensed by cooler air over ocean; mate and bear young in the sea, sometimes in shallow water, young large at birth and suckled like those of other mammals.

Suborder 1.   †ARCHAEOCETI.   ZEUGLODONTS.   Eocene to Oligocene.

Suborder 2.   ODONTOCETI.   TOOTHED WHALES.   Teeth 2 to 40 in various species. *Physeter catodon*, sperm whale or cachalot, to 60 feet long, head squarish, about one-third total length; food of large squids and some fishes; a large "reservoir" in head

FIG. 32-28.   Humpback whale (*Megaptera novaeangliae*, Order CETACEA), length to 50 feet; female suckling young.   (*After Scammon, Marine mammals*, 1874).

yields sperm oil, a fine lubricant; ambergris, formed in the stomach, is used in perfume. *Delphinus delphis*, common dolphin, to 7 feet long, and *Phocaena phocaena*, harbor porpoise, both feed on fishes; 4 species of dolphins native to rivers in China, India, and

South America; *Orcinus*, killer whale, most aggressive cetacean, attacks large fishes, seals, porpoises, and even big whales; *Monodon monoceros*, narwhal, of Arctic, with but 2 teeth, of which one in male is a slender twisted tusk 8 to 9 feet long—the "unicorn" of European fables.

Suborder 3. MYSTICETI. No teeth; mouth with numerous parallel horny plates of "whalebone" on sides of upper jaw, used to strain small animals from water; food chiefly of krill (*Euphasia*, a schizopod crustacean about 2 inches long, often enormously abundant). *Balaena*, "right" whale, no dorsal fin; *Balaenoptera* (*Sibbaldia*) *musculus*, blue whale, with fin on back and lengthwise grooves on throat; the largest living animal, to about 105 feet long, young 23 feet long at birth, 52 feet at weaning, and 74 to 77 feet long when sexually mature in 2d winter of life; *Rhachianectes glaucus*, California gray whale, of Pacific coast, now scarce.

Order 12. **Carnivora.** CARNIVORES. Small to large; toes usually 5 (at least 4), all with claws; limbs mobile, radius and ulna, tibia and fibula, complete and separate; incisors small, usually 3/3; canines 1/1, as slender "fangs"; uterus bihorned; placenta zonary.

Suborder 1. †CREODONTA. Eocene to Miocene.

Suborder 2. FISSIPEDIA. DOGS, CATS, BEARS, ETC. Toes separate; Eocene to Recent; native to all continents except Australia and New Zealand, where some now introduced; the flesh eaters or predatory animals, but some eat plant materials; pelts of many are valuable furs, hence the principal fur bearers.

CANIDAE. *Canis nubilis*, wolf, once common in Europe and America, now far reduced; *C. latrans*, coyote or "prairie wolf," usually under 30 pounds in weight; open regions of arid West, but has spread to Alaska; eats rodents, deer, antelope, domestic sheep, and some plant material; *Canis*, domestic dogs, derived in Old World (Table 32-1); *Urocyon*, gray fox, in brushlands; *Vulpes*, red fox, chiefly in woodlands, domesticated "black" and "silver" phases now reared commonly on fox farms yielding more than 200,000 pelts annually.

PROCYONIDAE. *Procyon lotor*, raccoon (Fig. 32-15), over most of United States, especially near streams, tail black-and-white banded, food of frogs, fishes, crayfishes, fruits, a favorite for night hunting, pelts used for coats; *Ailurus*, panda, in Himalayas; *Ailuropoda*, giant panda, mountains of western China, feeds on bamboo.

URSIDAE. BEARS. *Thalarctos maritimus*, polar bear, Arctic regions to southern limit of pack ice, pelage white and dense, feet fully furred, teeth pointed, food of fishes and seals; *Euarctos americanus*, "black" bear (also with cinnamon or "brown" phase) in forests of North America from subarctic regions to Mexico, climbs readily, adults occasionally to 600 pounds, hibernates in midwinter, when young (8 to 9 inches long) are born, omnivorous; *Ursus horribilis*, etc., grizzly bears, size large, strictly terrestrial, originally in open and brushy areas, Mexico to Arctic and Great Plains to California, mostly exterminated; *U. gyas*, etc., brown bears of Alaska, strictly terrestrial, size huge, some possibly to 1,500 pounds, omnivorous.

FIG. 32-29. Striped skunk (*Mephitis*, Order CARNIVORA), length to 18 inches. (*After Pennsylvania Game News.*)

MUSTELIDAE. FUR BEARERS. Many strictly predatory, eat birds, mammals, or fishes. *Martes*, marten, fisher, in woods; *Gulo*, wolverine; *Mustela*, weasels, stoats, and ferrets, live in burrows; *Taxidea*, badger, on open lands; *Mephitis*, striped skunk

(Fig. 32-29), and *Spilogale*, spotted skunk, both with nauseating secretion (containing mercaptans), eat small vertebrates, insects, and fruits; *Mustela vison*, mink, and *Lutra*, river otter, both aquatic; *Enhydra lutris*, sea otter, California to Alaska, lives in ocean surf, feeds on marine invertebrates.

FELIDAE. CATS. *Felis leo*, lion, of Africa, and *F. tigris*, tiger, eastern Asia and India, both large and dangerous to man; *F. catus*, house cat, widely feral in United States; *F. cougar*, etc., mountain lion (also cougar, puma, or panther), the Americas, but exterminated in many eastern states; to about 7 feet and 160 pounds, food of deer, sometimes colts and livestock, practically never attacks man; *Lynx canadensis*, Canada lynx, and *L. rufus*, wildcat, both with short tails.

VIVERRIDAE. Mostly small, bodies slender. Africa and southern Asia. *Herpestes mungo*, common mongoose, of India, introduced into Jamaica and Hawaii; *Viverra*, civet, scent glands used to make perfume.

HYAENIDAE. HYENAS. *Hyaena*, Africa and southern Asia, doglike in size and form, gray or brown with spots or stripes, jaws powerful, teeth large.

Suborder 3. PINNIPEDIA. SEALS AND SEA LIONS. Size medium to large, males usually much larger than females; body spindle-shaped, limbs formed as flippers or paddles for swimming with toes included in webs; tail very short; Miocene to Recent; oceans and seacoasts, gregarious; food chiefly of fishes.

OTARIIDAE. EARED SEALS. *Eumetopias stelleri*, Steller sea lion, California to Alaska; *Zalophus californianus*, California sea lion, smaller, central California southward; *Callorhinus alascanus*, northern fur seal, adults haul out on rocky shores of Pribilof Islands in Bering Sea through summer, in assemblages (rookeries) numbering thousands. An adult male (bull) controls a group (harem) of about 60 females (cows); each female usually produces 1 young (pup), nurses it on land, later breeds; at end of summer entire population (herd) puts to sea for ensuing 9 months; summer population about 3,600,000, under supervision of United States government; more than 60,000 three-year males (bachelors) taken annually to provide sealskins of commerce.

ODOBAENIDAE. WALRUSES. S k i n thick, sparsely haired; 2 upper canine teeth form tusks up to 3 feet long, used to dig mollusks and crustaceans on sea bottom, and used by man as ivory. *Odobaenus*, in Arctic, to 10 feet long.

PHOCIDAE. E A R L E S S O R H A I R SEALS. Hind feet cannot be turned forward, hence less agile on land. *Phoca vitulina*, harbor seal (Fig. 32-30),

FIG. 32-30. Harbor seal (*Phoca vitulina*, Order CARNIVORA, Suborder PINNIPEDIA), length 5 feet; a marine, fish-eating "carnivore" of seacoasts. (*After Goode*, 1884.)

common on coasts and bays of North America and elsewhere; *Mirounga*, sea elephant, to 18 feet long, occasional off southern California.

Order 13.   †**Condylarthra.**   Paleocene to Eocene.

Order 14.   †**Litopterna.**   Paleocene to Pleistocene.

Order 15.   †**Notungulata.**   Paleocene to Pleistocene.

Order 16.   †**Astrapotheria.**   Paleocene to Miocene.

Order 17.   **Tubulidentata.**   AARD VARKS. Body stout, somewhat piglike, sparsely haired; ears and snout long; mouth tubular, with slender protrusible tongue; milk teeth numerous, permanent teeth fewer (no incisors or canines), unrooted, no enamel;

toes 4, 5, with heavy claws; Pliocene to Recent. Africa. One genus *Orycteropus* (2 or 4 species), nocturnal, claws open nests of ants and termites and captures the insects with its sticky tongue.

Order 18.   †**Pantodonta** (Amblypoda).   Paleocene to Eocene.

Order 19.   †**Dinocerata**.   Paleocene to Eocene.

Order 20.   †**Pyrotheria**.   Paleocene to Oligocene.

Order 21.   **Proboscidea**.   Elephants.   Massive; head large, ears broad and flat, neck short, body huge, legs pillar-like, skin thick (pachyderm), loose, and sparsely haired; nose and upper lip a long flexible muscular proboscis, containing nasal passages, with nostrils at tip; 2 upper incisors elongated as tusks; each molar tooth with many transverse rows of enamel on exposed grinding surface, only 1 tooth (or 2) functional

Fig. 32-31.   Indian elephant (*Elephas maximus*, Order Proboscidea).   (*Photograph by National Zoological Park.*)

at a time in each side of jaw; feet clublike, toes 5, 3 (or 4) each with small nail-like hoof, weight borne on elastic pad behind toes.   Eocene to Recent.   Africa and southeastern Asia; inhabit forests and tall grass; gregarious, in herds of 10 to 100; feed upon trees, grasses, and bamboos, adults eating 600 to 700 pounds daily; gestation period about 20 months, young about 3 feet tall, weighing 200 pounds at birth; maximum recorded age about 50 years.

Elephantidae.   *Elephas maximus* (*indica*), Indian elephant (Fig. 32-31), India to Ceylon and Borneo, tusks to 9 feet long; used for transport and in circuses; *Loxodonta africana*, African elephant, to over 10 feet in height, ears huge; tamed for transport in war and pageants by Carthaginians and Romans but not often since; *E. cyclotis*, pigmy elephant, West Africa, under 7 feet tall, ears small.

Order 22.   †**Embrithopoda**.   Oligocene.

Order 23.   **Hyracoidea**.   Coneys.   Small; 4 toes on fore limb, 3 on hind; ears and tail short; incisors 1/2; no canines; Oligocene to Recent; Africa and Syria.   One genus, *Procavia* (*Hyrax*), about 14 species; superficially like guinea pigs, but related to hoofed animals; inhabit rocky areas or trees.

Order 24.   **Sirenia**.   Manatees or "Sea Cows."   Size large, body spindle-shaped; fore limbs paddle-like, no hind limbs, tail with lateral flukes, not notched; muzzle blunt, mouth small, lips fleshy; no external ears; teeth with enamel; hairs few, scattered; stomach complex; Paleocene to Recent; tropical and subtropical seas and rivers; herbivorous.

Three families, each of one genus: *Trichechus*, manatees, in warm rivers of Florida, West Indies, Brazil, and West Africa; *T. latirostris*, Florida manatee (Fig. 32-32), to 12 feet long; *Halicore dugong*, dugong, Red Sea and coasts of India, New Guinea, and Australia; *Hydrodamalis (Rhytina) stelleri*, Steller sea cow, large, formerly on island shores in North Pacific Ocean, exterminated by hunters in 1854.

Order 25. **Perissodactyla.** Odd-toed Hoofed Mammals. Size large; legs elongate; foot with odd number of toes, each sheathed in cornified hoof, and functional axis of leg passing through middle (3d) toe; stomach simple; Eocene to Recent; Eurasia, Africa, and tropical America.

Equidae. Horses, Asses, and Zebras. One functional digit and hoof on each leg (in Recent forms); inhabit open plains or deserts, diet of grass. *Equus caballus*, horse, man's principal means of transport and work for centuries, with 50 or 60 domestic races, from Shetland pony 42 inches high at shoulder and weighing scarcely 300 pounds to Shire and Percheron stallions 6 feet high, weighing to

Fig. 32-32. Manatee (*Trichechus*, Order Sirenia), length to 12 feet. (*After Goode*, 1884.)

2,600 pounds and over; *E. asinus*, ass, adapted to desert life, domesticated as donkey, or burro, for riding and transport; the mule is an F_1 hybrid of male ass ("jack") and female horse ("mare"), with stamina of ass and size of horse; *E. zebra*, zebra (Fig. 32-33), native to open lands of Africa, seldom domesticated.

Tapiridae. Tapirs. Toes 4 on front feet, 3 on hind feet; in tropical forests. *Tapirella*, 2 species, Central America and northern South America; *Tapirus*, Malay Peninsula, Borneo, and Sumatra.

Fig. 32-33.   Zebra (*Equus zebra*, Order Perissodactyla), about 48 inches high at shoulder; native to Africa. (*Photograph by National Zoological Park*.)

Rhinocerotidae. Rhinoceroses. *Rhinoceros*, in woody or grassy areas in Africa south of Sahara Desert and in southeastern Asia; large and heavy-bodied, hide thick and armor-like; 1 or 2 median "horns" on snout; toes 3.

Order 26. **Artiodactyla.** Even-toed Hoofed Mammals. Size various; legs usually long; 2 (rarely 4) functional toes on each foot, each usually sheathed in a cornified hoof; axis of leg between toes; many with antlers or horns on head; all but pigs with reduced dentition, a 4-compartment stomach, and ruminate, or "chew the cud"; Eocene to Recent; all continents except Australia. Size from antelope (dik-diks) no bigger than a hare to heavy buffalo and hippopotamus; some domesticated (Table 32-1), others important as big game; 4 suborders and 22 families, 13 families extinct and others all with fossil species.

Fig. 32-34.   Hippopotamus (*Hippopotamus amphibius*, Order Artiodactyla), length to 12 feet.   (*Photograph by National Zoological Park.*)

Suborder 1. Bunodontia. Pigs and Allies.   No horns or antlers, teeth 38 to 44, canines enlarged as curved tusks.

Tagassuidae.   Peccaries or New World Pigs.   Patagonia to southern United States; *Pecari angulatus*, southern Texas and Arizona.

Suidae.   Old World Pigs.   Many in southern Asia; *Sus scrofa*, European wild boar, source of most domestic pigs; *Phacochoerus*, wart hog, in Africa.

Hippopotamidae.   Hippopotamuses ("horse of the river").   Body and legs very stout, skin heavy but scantily haired, adept at swimming, feeds on aquatic plants.   *Hippopotamus amphibius*, Nile River and south in Africa (Fig. 32-34), to 12 feet long; *Choeropsis liberiensis*, pigmy hippopotamus, in West Africa, smaller.

Fig. 32-35.   Bactrian or two-humped camel (*Camelus bactrianus*, Order Artiodactyla), of Asia.   (*Photograph by National Zoological Park.*)

Suborder 2.   Pecora.   Ruminants.   Teeth 32, canines small or none; stomach of 4 parts (Fig. 32-14).

Camelidae.   Feet soft and broad (no hoofs), 1 pair of upper incisors.   *Camelus*, camel and dromedary (Fig. 32-35), in Africa and Asia, used for riding and transport; *Auchenia*, llama and alpaca, in western South America, provide transport, flesh, hides, and wool.

Tragulidae.   Chevrotains or "Mouse Deer."   Intermediate between pigs, camels, and deer; some no bigger than large rodents.   *Tragulus*, southeastern Asia.

(*Note: Next 4 families have 4 pairs of incisor-like teeth at front of lower jaw, none in upper.*)

CERVIDAE. DEER, ETC. Head of male with pair of solid calcareous antlers, shed and grown anew each year; in Northern Hemisphere. *Rangifer*, reindeer and caribou, in northern regions, antlers in both sexes; *Alces americanus*, moose, in Canada, Maine, North Dakota, and Yellowstone Park, adult male (bull) to 6 feet at shoulder and 900 to 1,400 pounds in weight, enters water, feeds on aquatic plants; *Cervus canadensis*, American elk (wapiti), formerly over much of United States except deserts, now restricted, males to 5 feet high and 500 pounds; *C. elaphus*, European red deer; *Odocoileus*, American deer, males of larger races to 42 inches high and 300 pounds in weight: *O. virginianus*, white-tailed deer, Atlantic coast to eastern Oregon (Fig. 32-8); *O. hemionus*, black- and mule-tailed deer, western North America.

GIRAFFIDAE. GIRAFFES, ETC. Africa. Neck and legs very long. *Giraffa camelopardalis*, giraffe, 18 to 20 feet tall, head with 3 to 5 skin-covered "horns"; browses on foliage of mimosa and other trees; *Ocapia*, okapi, smaller, neck shorter.

ANTILOCAPRIDAE. One species, *Antilocapra americana*, prong-horned antelope (Fig. 32-8), on treeless plains and deserts from Great Plains to California, now reduced and mostly on reservations; adults 36 inches high, weight to 125 pounds; both sexes with pair of permanent bony horn cores on head, on which compressed black horns with lateral prongs grow and are shed annually.

BOVIDAE. HOLLOW-HORNED RUMINANTS. Horns hollow, paired, unbranched, composed of keratin, growing slowly and continuously from base, over bony cores on frontal bones, usually in both sexes, larger in males; over 35 genera in Northern Hemisphere, southeastern Asia and Africa. *Ovis canadensis* (and others), mountain sheep, or bighorn (Fig. 32-8), Mexico, Rocky Mountains, and California to Alaska, on rugged mountains; males (rams) to 40 inches high and 300 pounds, with horns to 40 inches long; *Oreamos montanus*, mountain goat, Idaho and Washington to Alaska, coat long, shaggy, and white, horns short, black; *Bison bison* (Fig. 32-36),

FIG. 32-36.   American bison (*Bison bison*, Order ARTIODACTYLA).   (*Photograph by National Zoological Park.*)

American buffalo or bison, formerly Texas and Great Plains to southern Canada, with hump over shoulder and long crinkly hair on fore parts; adult bulls to 70 inches high and 1,800 pounds but cows smaller; millions formerly on flat lands but slaughtered for meat and hides, now few on reservations and in parks; *Bison bonasus*,

European wisent, nearly extinct; *Bos taurus, Bos indicus,* domestic cattle (Table 32-1); *Bibos (Bos) gaurus,* gaur, India and Burma; *Bibos sondiacus,* banteng, southeastern Asia, Borneo, and Java; *Ovibos moschatus,* musk ox, on treeless Arctic lands from Hudson Bay to 83°N., to 52 inches high and over 500 pounds; African antelopes, many species of various sizes.

References

Anthony, H. E.   1928.   Field book of North American mammals.   New York, G. P. Putnam's Sons.   xxv + 625 pp., 32 col. pls., 175 figs.   Characteristics, measurements, distribution, and habits in brief for all mammals north of Mexico.

Audubon, John James, and J. Bachman.   1851–1854.   The quadrupeds of North America.   3 vols.   New York, V. G. Audubon.   155 pls. and text.   First issued (1845–1848) as "The Viviparous Quadrupeds of North America" in 3 folio vols. containing 150 plates and a separate text (1846–1853) of 3 quarto vols.; combined as "The Quadrupeds . . . " of 3 royal octavo vols.   The first elaborate work on mammals of North America.

Beddard, F. E.   1902.   Mammalia.   *In* Cambridge natural history.   London, Macmillan & Co., Ltd.   Vol. 10, xii + 605 pp., 285 figs.   Structure, classification, and habits.

Cahalane, V. H.   1947.   Mammals of North America.   New York, The Macmillan Co.   x + 682 pp., illus.

Flower, W. H., and R. Lydekker.   1891.   An introduction to the study of mammals living and extinct.   London, A. & C. Black, Ltd.   xvi + 763 pp., 357 figs.

Hamilton, W. J., Jr.   1939.   American mammals: their lives, habits, and economic relations.   New York, McGraw-Hill Book Co., Inc.   xii + 434 pp., 92 illus.

———.   1943.   The mammals of eastern United States.   Ithaca, N.Y., Comstock Publishing Co.   432 pp. 183 figs.

Henderson, J., and E. L. Craig.   1932.   Economic mammalogy.   Springfield, Ill., Charles C. Thomas.   x + 397 pp.   Much detailed information and many references.

Miller, G. S., Jr.   1924.   List of North American recent mammals.   *U.S. National Museum, Bulletin* 128, xvi + 673 pp.   Scientific name and geographic range for each species and subspecies.

Seton, E. T.   1925–1928.   Lives of game animals.   New York.   Doubleday, Doran & Co., Inc.   4 vols., illus.   Extensive account of hoofed mammals, carnivores, and some rodents.

Simpson, G. G.   1945.   The principles of classification and a classification of mammals.   *American Museum of Natural History, Bulletin* 85, xvi + 350 pp.   Technical; both fossil and Recent groups down to genera.

Weber, Max.   1927.   Die Saügetiere.   Einführung in die Anatomie und Systematik der recenten und fossilen Mammalia.   2d ed.   Jena, Gustav Fischer.   xxxix + 1,342 pp., 886 figs.   Detailed, modern; vol. 1, anatomy; vol. 2, systematic review of genera, mentioning many species.

The *Journal of Mammalogy* (quarterly, since 1919, published by the American Society of Mammalogists) is the principal periodical.   Museums, universities, etc., publish state lists or books on mammals.   The U.S. Departments of Agriculture and the Interior have many circulars and bulletins on the economic and other relations of mammals.   The *North American Fauna* (60 numbers, issued by the U.S. Biological Survey; now U.S. Fish and Wildlife Service) includes accounts of mammals of various states and regions.   Information on game and fur bearers may be found in books on hunting, shooting, and trapping.

CHAPTER 33

MANKIND

33-1. Man's place in nature. The place of man, *Homo sapiens*, in the realm of living things has long been a topic of great interest to himself. Primitive races have various myths that imply human origin from animals, inanimate materials, or other sources. To many other peoples, man is the creation of a supernatural power. Biologists view the origin and position of man objectively, using knowledge of the structure and physiology of the human body, its embryonic development, and the historic, prehistoric, and fossil records of mankind on earth. On this basis, the human species belongs in turn to the following groups:

1. Animal Kingdom, in requiring complex organic food, etc.
2. Phylum CHORDATA in having a notochord and gill arches and pouches during embryonic development and a dorsal brain and nerve cord throughout life.
3. Group CRANIATA (vertebrates) in having a cranium and segmented spinal column.
4. Class MAMMALIA in having hair and mammary glands.
5. Order PRIMATES in having 4 generalized limbs each with 5 digits bearing nails.
6. Superfamily HOMINOIDEA in lacking cheek pouches and a tail.
7. Family HOMINIDAE (as distinguished from the Family PONGIDAE, or anthropoid apes) in the possession of many features, including
   a. Brain with far greater functional ability and of larger size (minimum human, 1,000 cc.; maximum gorilla, 650 cc.); brain case larger than face.
   b. Face flatter and more vertical, brow ridges reduced, lower jaw less protruding, teeth more evenly sized.
   c. Hair long and of continuous growth on head, but sparse and short on body,
   d. Hands more generalized, thumbs better developed; leg 30 per cent longer than arm, and straight; big toe not opposable to other toes.
   e. Skeleton and soft parts of different configuration and proportions.

The human species habitually walks erect on two feet, is terrestrial in habits, highly gregarious, and omnivorous in diet, and commonly uses cooked food. By contrast the anthropoid apes (gorilla, chimpanzee, orang-utan, gibbon) are semierect in posture, literally "four-handed," chiefly tree dwellers, slightly gregarious, and fruit eaters.

The human race is notable for its extreme variability in many small structural features as compared with most animal species.

Mankind surpasses all other living organisms in many functional abilities such as (1) the construction and use of tools, (2) modification of the environment to his own advantage, (3) possession of articulate speech and language, (4) formation of a complex social life, and (5) formation of mental and abstract concepts. These are possible by reason of having generalized hands, but more importantly by the superior development of the human brain as to size, structure, and functional capacity. By use of articulate speech, language, writing, and records, mankind is able to assemble and transmit accumulated knowledge to succeeding generations by teaching and otherwise. Material, social, cultural, and ethical advances have thus resulted. With all other animals, transmission of abilities between generations is limited to such instincts and reflexes as are fixed by heredity.

33-2. Size. Normal human adults are 56 to 78 inches tall, although occasional midgets are only 18 to 36 inches high and exceptional giants (due to excessive pituitary function) grow to 9 feet. Native races vary in average height from 51 inches (African pygmies) to 72 inches (Patagonian and Australian natives). Peoples lacking suitable food or living in extreme climates tend to be small, but active races in temperate lands and with better food are taller. In the United States a definite increase in average height is noted with recent generations, due to improved nutrition and more healthful living. Daughters of college alumnae at Vassar College, Stanford University, and elsewhere average 1.1 to 1.5 inches taller than their mothers; and native-born children of immigrants average taller than their parents. In most races the males are taller than the females, American men averaging 68 inches and the women 64 inches.

The weight varies with race, sex, height, and age, that of white males averaging about 150 pounds and of females 130 pounds. Exceptional fat (obese) persons have weighed 400 to 700 pounds, and occasional individuals of average height weigh scarcely 50 pounds. Increase in weight after maturity is usually due to accumulation of fat.

33-3. Structure and function. Some distinctive features of mankind are dealt with in this chapter, and certain other details of human morphology and physiology are described in Chap. 4. Man's many mammalian characteristics will be evident upon comparing these two accounts with that on mammals in Chap. 32.

33-4. Integument. Human skin is thin and delicate, except for calluses (functional adaptations) on the palms of "horny-handed sons of toil" and on the soles of the feet, especially among barefoot natives. The skin coloration results from the presence of blood capillaries containing red cells (with hemoglobin) in the dermis and also of pigment, including melanin (black) and carotene (yellow). The white, yellow, brown, and black races differ as to the amounts of melanin pigment occurring as microscopic granules in outer layers of the skin. Blonds of the white race have less melanin than brunets and women usually less than men. The yellow tinge of the palms, soles, and eyelids is ascribed to carotene. Pigmentation is commonly more pronounced in races exposed to severe sunlight. The tanning or darkening of the skin in white persons is a defensive mechanism of the body against exposure to undue amounts of ultraviolet radiation.

The human skin differs from that of most mammals in containing sweat (sudoriferous) glands. These produce a watery perspiration, containing some salts and excretory products. When the perspiration appears as moisture on the surface (sensible perspiration), its evaporation aids in cooling and regulating the body temperature.

33-5. Hair. Human hair is mammalian as to structure and manner of growth but differs (1) in being long or dense chiefly on the head; (2) in amount, distribution, and form at various ages of an individual; (3) between the sexes as to amount and length; and (4) in amount and structure between races of men.

Long hair of continuous growth on the scalp is a distinctive human characteristic not shared by any other mammal. The eyebrows and eyelids (lashes), external ear canals, and nostrils all bear specialized hairs. The body elsewhere has a scant covering, and the lips, soles, palms, outer (extensor) surface on the terminal segment of each finger, and parts of the genitalia are hairless.

The human foetus at about the twentieth week is covered with fine soft hair (lanugo); this is lost at or before birth. Scalp hair at birth may be dark or pale and dense or scant. With growth the color may change. Body hair is scant during childhood but begins to grow at puberty (14 ± years) especially in the armpits (axillae) and in the pubic region. As boys become men, the beard and chest hairs grow out. Dense facial hair is characteristic of males after puberty; women have varying small amounts, and there are occasional "bearded ladies."

Further changes occur later in life, when the hair gradually becomes gray and then white through failure of the hair papillae to produce pigment—but no one's hair ever "turns white overnight," despite popular belief to the contrary. The head hair usually becomes sparse with advancing years, and definite patterns then develop, leading to graying of the scalp and beard and, on men, to baldness, or loss of hair. These are probably hereditary changes, although pathological ones also occur; baldness is probably transmitted by females, but not evidenced by them. Certain men become gray or bald much earlier than others, and some never become bald. Some of the patterns are gray hair on the temples, a dark patch on top of the scalp, a bald spot on the crown or above each eye, a completely bald crown, a dark beard with white patch on each cheek, or a gray beard with black moustache. Curiously enough, for each type of human hair pattern, one or another occurs in some species of lower primate!

Racial differences in human hair are exemplified by the straight black hair of Orientals and American Indians, the kinky hair of Negroes, and the yellowish hair of Scandinavians. In cross section the hair varies from nearly round in Mongolians to elliptical in kinky-haired Hottentots.

All human hairs are replaced at intervals, those of the eyebrows and eyelashes every few months and scalp hairs at from a few months to 4 or 5 years. There is evidence of slight "spring" and "autumn" molts in human beings. The scalp includes about 100,000 hairs.

33-6. Skeleton. The human cranium is a rounded bony box, lacking the sagittal crest of many other mammals. The occipital condyles are ventral or caudal rather than posterior, in keeping with the upright posture, the brain case is larger, the nasal region is short, and the lower jaw is U-shaped rather than V-shaped. The skull increases in size until about seven years and again at puberty, and final closure of the sutures may be delayed until old age.

Fig. 33-1   Change in outline and relative shape of the human mandible with age.   (*Altered from Heitzmann.*)

The human teeth are less conspicuously differentiated than in other mammals, and of nearly equal height. The first or deciduous (milk) teeth number 20, and the permanent or adult dentition includes 28 to 32, depending on how many of the third molars (wisdom teeth) appear, these being irregular as to time and manner of eruption.

Other notable features of the human skeleton are the absence of caudal (tail) vertebrae and the complete and generalized skeleton of the limbs, hands, and feet.

33-7. Muscular system. The 500 or more muscles of the human body are much like those of other mammals. The names for muscles that were first applied by early anatomists to the human subject serve in the main for mammals as well, with minor differences as to origin, insertion, and size. Most of the peculiarities of human muscles relate to the upright

TABLE 33-1. APPROXIMATE AGE FOR ERUPTION AND LOSS OF TEETH IN HUMAN BEINGS

	Incisors		Ca-nines	Premolars		Molars		
	Cen-tral	Lat-eral		1st	2d	1st	2d	3d
Deciduous teeth								
Erupted (months).....	6–8	7–9	17–18	14–15	18–24	None present		
Shed (years).........	7	8	10	10	11–12			
Permanent teeth								
Erupted (years):								
Upper..............	7–8	7–8	12–13	8–11	11–12	6–7	12–14	17–20
Lower..............	7–8	8–9	12–13	10–11	11–12	6–7	14–16	16–20

posture, the support of the body and walking on the "hind" limbs, and to the greater flexibility of the arms, hands, and fingers. Of especial interest are the facial muscles (Fig. 33-2), just beneath the skin, that make possible the expression of pleasure, anger, and other emotional states. The greatest refinement of these occurs in the white race, particularly in the center of the face; in Mongolians, Negroes, and others, they are more extended, especially (m. orbicularis orbis) around the eye. Man and the primates have the greatest development of facial muscles; a few carnivores such as the cat may indicate pleasure and anger, but in all vertebrates below the mammals the face is a rigid mask. The facial muscles have had a long and interesting evolution traceable back through the verte-brates to the sharks!

FIG. 33-2. The facial mus-cles of man. (*After Huber*, 1930.)

33-8. Internal organs. The human viscera do not differ conspicuously from those of various mammals. The organs within the abdominal cavity are supported by mesenteries attached to the posterior wall, and a large sheet called the greater omentum hangs apron-like between the intestines and the inner front wall of the abdomen. It is composed of four layers of peritoneum and contains deposits of fat, serving to cushion the internal organs and protect them against loss of heat.

33-9. Nervous system. The human brain (Fig. 4-27) is notable for proportionately large size and the great development of the cerebral hemispheres (gray matter). These have a much convoluted surface and are spread so as to cover completely the other parts of the brain.

The average human brain weighs about 1,250 (women) to 1,350 grams (men), and the volume is around 1,500 cc. Brain size and mental ability are not closely correlated, although the brains of people of distinction tend to be somewhat larger; two extremes were Baron Georges Cuvier (1,830 grams) and Anatole France (1,190 grams). The human brain far surpasses that of other animals in proportionate size as well as functional development. Thus a dog, gorilla, and man of about equal weights have brains of 135, 430, and 1,350 grams, respectively.

NATURAL HISTORY

33-10. Distribution. Man inhabits a wider geographic range than any other animal, from the Arctic ice to islands beyond the southern continents, from sea level to over 20,000 feet in some mountain regions, on islands and continents, and from moist tropical jungles to the driest of deserts. The local races in these various habitats differ as to stature, configuration, and coloration, in mode of life, foods and shelters utilized, and in social organization and customs. The white race thrives best in north temperate regions and does not persist in many tropic localities without renewed immigration.

33-11. Numbers. The total human population of the earth is unknown. Pearl and Gould give the following estimates, in millions of persons:

A.D. 1650	1700	1760	1820	1840	1860	1880	1900	1920	1935
453	471	550	814	969	1,150	1,341	1,520	1,641	2,057 or 2,073

The 1935 estimate is based on careful study of all recent data. The present trend suggests approximate stabilization around A.D. 2100, with 2,645,000,000 people. The fivefold increase in the past three centuries is probably due in part to improved agricultural practices and latterly to public health measures.

Human beings now average about 40 per square mile on the world land area of 51,700,000 square miles, but they are unequally distributed because of concentration in cities and on more fertile lands. About 52 per cent live on 5 per cent of the land (394 per square mile), 25 per cent on 14 per cent (96 per square mile), and the other 23 per cent on 81 per cent of the land (9 per square mile).

The ultimate human population of any region depends upon the fertility of the soil and also, in arid regions, upon the availability of water for irrigation. Human populations in Asia Minor, North Africa, and parts of the United States have decreased because of depletion of soil fertility, loss of top soil by erosion, and increasing aridity.

33-12. Factors regulating human populations. Man surpasses animals in being able to control his environment in some degree, as by (1) *food production* (agriculture) and *food storage* (warehouses, canning, refrigeration) against seasonal shortage and deterioration; (2) improved *shelter* for adults and offspring against unfavorable weather and against enemies (housing, flood protection, police protection, national defense); (3) *destruction of animal enemies* (wolves, rats and mice, household insects); (4) *reducing competition* from other animals (fencing crops and livestock; shooting, trapping, or poisoning species that attack his food, crops, and domesticated livestock); and (5) *control of diseases* that attack human beings (sanitation, immunization). By such artificial means, modern man in civilized countries has increased in numbers over the population possible for primitive natives.

Human beings are reduced in numbers by several agencies, some being comparable to those affecting wild animals; these include the following: (1) *food shortage* or famine due to crop failure, as from unfavorable weather, especially in densely populated lands such as China and India where food reserves are scant or unequally distributed; malnutrition (improper diet) may lead to physical impairment with greater susceptibility to disease and death; (2) *inadequate shelter,* especially during the cold of winter outside the tropics; (3) *calamities in nature,* including floods, hurricanes, volcanic eruptions, etc.; (4) *enemies,* such as large predatory mammals (lion, tiger) and poisonous snakes, which cause many deaths in less civilized regions; (5) *warfare,* a form of competition between races or nations for land, natural resources, trade routes, or other desired features of human environment; war and slavery have long been major factors in depopulation; and (6) *disease,* uncontrolled as among primitive peoples, the result of neglect as is common among "civilized" peoples, or uncontrollable as with epidemic influenza; probably the largest single factor in reducing populations.

Where many diseases are under control by public-health measures in civilized countries, fewer individuals die in childhood or early life from disease. Proportionately more die from diseases of later life or from old age (senility). Explosions, fire, earthquake, shipwreck, and transportation accidents cause many deaths in modern civilizations.

33-13. Reproduction. During the childhood of human beings the features relating to sex are usually undeveloped. When an individual reaches about 14 (10 to 17) years of age, conspicuous changes take place that lead toward sexual maturity and the ability to reproduce. This time is known as *puberty.* There then appear gradually the characteristics that differentiate the sexes. With males the beard and body hair begin growth, the shoulders broaden, the voice becomes deeper pitched, and·more attention is paid to the opposite sex.   In females the mammary glands and hips enlarge, subcutaneous fat is deposited, the reproductive

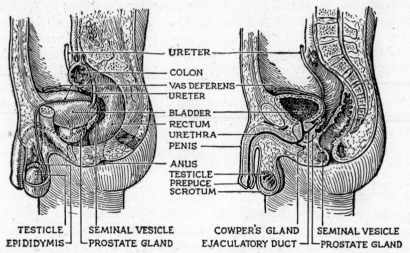

URETER
COLON
VAS DEFERENS
URETER
BLADDER
RECTUM
URETHRA
PENIS
ANUS
TESTICLE
PREPUCE
SCROTUM

TESTICLE   SEMINAL VESICLE   COWPER'S GLAND   SEMINAL VESICLE
EPIDIDYMIS PROSTATE GLAND   EJACULATORY DUCT PROSTATE GLAND

FIG. 33-3. The male urogenital system of mankind. *Left.* In perspective. *Right.* Median section. (*From Baitsell, Human biology.*)

tract begins a series of cyclic changes, and the attentions of young men become of interest.

Healthy females from puberty onward experience a recurrent discharge of blood, mucus, and epithelial cells from the lining of the uterus, termed **menstruation** (L. *menses*, months); on the average, this occurs every 28 days (1 lunar month) and lasts 4 or 5 days.   Menstruation is regulated by endocrine secretions (especially from the corpus luteum of the ovary) and prepares the uterus for implantation of an ovum.   It usually ceases during pregnancy and lactation and stops if the ovaries are removed.   Menstruation gradually stops at about age forty-five to fifty, and its cessation (the menopause) marks the end of reproductive ability.   This "change of life" is a time of physiological and emotional distress for many women.   There is no comparable cycle in the male.

Each ovary in a female child contains perhaps 50,000 immature ova, all of which disappear before puberty.   New ova are then developed from the germinal epithelium covering the ovary, and one (occasionally more) is released to pass down the oviduct some days after each menstruation, possibly 400 ova in all during the life of an average woman.

Exceptional human females only eight or nine years old have borne children, but there is usually a time after menstruation begins (the menarche), termed "adolescent sterility," before pregnancy occurs in any considerable percentage of young women.   In the white race of north

OVIDUCT
(FALLOPIAN TUBE)
OVARY
ROUND LIGAMENT
UTERUS
URETER
BLADDER
RECTUM
CLITORIS
LABIUM MINUS
ANUS
LABIUM MAJUS

URETHRA   VAGINA   URETHRA VAGINA

Fig. 33-4. The female urogenital system. *Left.* In perspective. *Right.* Median section. (*From Baitsell, Human biology.*)

temperate latitudes, first children are common only at about age twenty. The time at which a young male becomes capable of procreation varies with individuals, and the same is true as to cessation of potency, as some men of advanced age have become fathers.

If, as a result of sexual union, an ovum in a female is fertilized, it becomes implanted in the mucosa of the uterus, begins embryonic devel-

placenta   wall of
                                                  uterus

foetal
arteries
and veins
in the
umbilical
cord

maternal
arteries
and veins
of the
uterus

Fig. 33-5. Section of the human uterus with a foetus connected by the umbilical cord to the placenta; maternal blood circulation indicated by broken arrows, embryonic circulation by solid arrows. (*Adapted from Ahlfeld and Spanner.*)

opment, and is surrounded by embryonic membranes. Shortly a placenta develops whereby the maternal and embryonic circulations are brought close together for transfer of nutrients, removal of wastes, and respiration (Fig. 33-5). The human embryo normally requires about 280 (243 to 298) days from conception to birth. In the vast majority of cases a single infant is produced. Twins occur about once in 88 births, triplets once in 7,600, and quadruplets once in 670,000; some families produce a greater percentage of twins. About 50 instances of quintuplets are known, but only exceptionally, as with the Dionne quintuplets, do all survive. The average infant weighs about 7 pounds (3,250 grams) at birth but may be from less than 5 to 13 pounds or more.

33-14. Sex ratio. The sexes are not produced in equal numbers. The ratio at birth is about 105 to 106 males per 100 females, and even more disproportionate before birth. A higher mortality rate occurs in males, before birth and during the early years of life, so that from about age forty to eighty the females decidedly outnumber the males.

33-15. Growth. The human individual has the longest period of development after birth of any living creature, and its growth curve (age to weight) differs both quantitatively and qualitatively from that of other animals, except the chimpanzee (Fig. 33-6). Five stages may be recog-

FIG. 33-6. Comparison of growth curve for weight in mankind and mammals (guinea pig and cow). (*After Brody*, 1927.)

nized in mankind, as follows: (1) *prenatal,* 9 months; (2) *infantile,* birth to 10 months; (3) *early childhood,* 10 months to 4 or 5 years; (4) *juvenile,* 4 or 5 to about 14 years, the time of puberty; and (5) *adolescent* plus postadolescent, 14 to 20 or 22 years. Accelerated growth occurs in the prenatal and puberty periods, with retardation in the juvenile and postadolescent stages. Little or no living tissue is added after the latter, any subsequent increase in weight being due chiefly to the addition of fat, dehydration of tissues, and further mineralization of bone. The extreme length of the juvenile period, about 10 years, is a most distinctive human characteristic as compared with other animals.

33-16. Length of life. The extreme limit of life is the *life span,* which is about 100 years for mankind, the longest lived animal. Accounts of persons living 900 years are purely legendary, and reports of those living well over a century must be carefully authenticated. Christen J. Drakenburg of Denmark (1626–1772) of nearly 146 years and Henry Jenkins of Yorkshire, England (1501–1670) of 169 years are exceptional instances of longevity. Reports of extreme age among Indians and Negroes are often unsupported by documentary records. The human

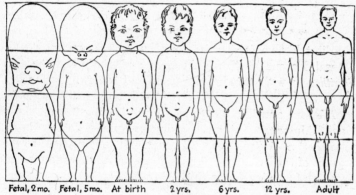

Fetal, 2 mo.   Fetal, 5 mo.   At birth   2 yrs.   6 yrs.   12 yrs.   Adult

FIG. 33-7.   Changes in proportions of the human body with age.   (*From Baitsell after Stratz.*)

life span has not changed materially within historic times, since the agerage age at death of 52 eminent Greeks and Romans of antiquity was 67 years, a figure close to that of similar persons today. The Biblical "threescore years and ten" is still a fair approximation.

The *mean length of life* is the average number of years lived by all persons born at a given period. This is least among primitive and tropical native populations. With white populations of the North Temperate region, it has increased during the twentieth century, with improved sanitation, control of communicable diseases, corrective surgery, and bettered nutrition. For white persons in the United States the average in 1901 was 49.24 years; in 1910, 51.49 years; and in 1936, 60.18 for males and 64.36 for females.

In ancient Egypt and Rome the *average expectation of life* during the first 5 years was never over 30 years, whereas in the United States in 1944 for age 20 it was 51.3 for girls and 46.4 for boys. This results from great reductions in infant mortality and the other factors just mentioned.

HISTORY OF MANKIND

33-17. The fossil record. An understanding of the gradual evolution of mankind from prehuman ancestry has been obtained in the last century since the significance of fossils has been recognized. The available evidence points to derivation of existing races from stocks dating back to early Pleistocene time and those in turn from earlier primates. The story is a continuous one, but for convenience it may be divided into (1) the fossil record, from bones, especially skulls and teeth, always rare and usually fragmentary; (2) the prehistoric record (Recent, to about 5000 b.c. but before the invention of writing) based on tools, weapons, and other evidence from places of habitation; and (3) the historic record (about 5000 b.c. in Egypt and later elsewhere), from the earliest accounts usually carved upon stone (Fig. 8-9).

The earliest known fossil primates (*Notharctus*) are small and found in the basal Eocene of North America and Europe. The first apes (*Propliopithecus*) with a reduced muzzle and somewhat enlarged brain case are in the Oligocene. Anthropoid stocks branched widely during the long Miocene and Pliocene epochs, some leading toward the modern gorilla and chimpanzee, others showing prehuman features in the jaws and molar teeth. *Dryopithecus* of Europe and India is close to the point of divergence of the two lines. The subsequent record of human ancestry rests upon the following forms (Fig. 33-8).

Java Ape Man, *Pithecanthropus erectus*. Old Pleistocene from near Trinil, Java. Skullcap, portion of mandible, femur, and 3 teeth, 1891; 4 more femurs, 1931; cranium and mandible with 4 teeth, 1937; 4 skulls in all up to 1945. Skull low-vaulted with heavy brow ridges, estimated cranial capacity (brain volume) about 750 to 900 cc.; imprint of brain on interior of skullcap suggests extremely primitive human status, possibly with power of speech; femur somewhat curved, suggesting only semierect posture. No associated stone implements.

Peking Man, *Sinanthropus pekinensis*. Pleistocene near Peking (Peiping), China. One tooth, 1903; many others, broken mandibles, and 15 skulls or fragments up to 1943. Crania small, low-vaulted, brow ridges well-developed, capacity 915 to 1,220 cc.; imprint of brain suggests better development for motor control of speech, but "thinking area" deficient. With numerous crude stone implements, seemingly, some of deer antler and bone, and definite evidence of use of fire.

Piltdown Man, *Eoanthropus dawsoni*. Possibly early Pleistocene; Sussex, England. Fragments of cranium, part of mandible, and few teeth, 1908 and later. Forehead upright, brow ridges slight, cranium well-rounded, capacity estimated at 1,200 to 1,400 cc. Combines advanced human characteristics with others far retarded. Associated mandible apelike, may not pertain to skull. With some crudely chipped flint implements and one 16-inch tool of bone from an extinct elephant.

Heidelberg Man, *Homo heidelbergensis*. Second (or first) warm interglacial period of mid-Pleistocene. Mauer (near Heidelberg), Germany. One complete mandible with teeth, 1907. Stronger and more massive than that of any living people. Teeth robust, jaw muscles evidently powerful, chin not prominent; form intermediate between simian and human, possibly ancestral to Neanderthal man.   No associated implements.

NEANDERTHAL MAN, *Homo neanderthalensis.*   Pleistocene, 3d and 4th warm interglacial periods.   Crimea to Germany, France, and Spain; also central Asia (southeast of Aral Sea).   First found ?1700; again at Gibralter, 1848; described from Neanderthal Valley near Düsseldorf, Germany, 1861; others subsequently totaling nearly 100 individuals, in caves and rock shelters.   Cranium flattened and elongate, also widened laterally and bulging at back; forehead sloping, brow ridges heavy but arched, cranial capacity 1,300 to 1,600 cc.   Impressions of brain convolutions on

FIG. 33-8.   Skulls of prehistoric species and races of mankind; all but the Cro-Magnon are restored in varying amount.   (*After various authors.*)

interior simpler than in modern man.   Face large and prominent, jaws protruding (prognathous); lower molars large and deep-bodied.   Posture slightly stooping, head and neck inclined forward, as suggested by slight curvature of femur and vertebral column, attachments for heavy neck muscles, and more posterior position of foramen magnum in skull; males 63 to 65 inches high.   Remains found in debris and in definite burials in floors of caves and rock shelters, often associated with chipped stone tools and weapons (Mousterian culture) and evidence of fire.   Estimated age 100,000 years.

RHODESIAN MAN, *Homo rhodesiensis.*   Probably Pleistocene.   In cave at Broken Hill, Rhodesia, South Africa.   One skull, 1921.   Cranium compressed, orbits huge, with most massive brow ridges, capacity about 1,280 cc.   Upper jaw and palate "gigantic," but teeth distinctly of human character.   Nondescript stone implements and quantities of broken animal bones (?food relics) in the debris-filled cave with the skull, may relate either to this or another race.

CRO-MAGNON MAN, *Homo sapiens fossilis.*   Close of Glacial period onward.   Many specimens since 1864; caves of northwest Italy and France to Czechoslovakia and Poland.   Related races in Africa.   Cranium high, face broad and upright, carnial capacity 1,590 cc.; males to 70 inches high, robust.   Remains often in caves, with stone implements, sculpture, and paintings.   Estimated age 40,000 B.C. and later.

Miscellaneous Remains.   (1) Java, 1938, skull fragments of *Pithecanthropus robustus*, heavier than *P. erectus*.   (2) Java, 1941, part of a giant jaw (*Meganthropus paleojavanicus*) heavier than any known hominid relic.   (3) From chemist shops in Hongkong, 1935–1939, possibly originally from caves in South China, three huge molars (*Gigantopithecus blacki*) of human type, each 5 or 6 times the bulk of those in modern man.   (4) Java, 1933, eleven crania of *H. soloensis*, Ngandong man, in ancient lime-cemented gravels of the Solo River, near Ngandong, resemble but differ from *H. neanderthalensis*.   Associated animal fossils indicate late Pleistocene, probably the 3d interglacial period.   Rude bone implements and many split bones with the remains. (5) In caves of Palestine, near Mount Carmel (1925–1932), 13 individuals, including several complete skeletons.   Characteristics of both Neanderthal and Cro-Magnon, but showing greater variability than in most modern communities; associated with Mousterian-like stone implements.

33-18. Modern man   (*Homo sapiens*).   After the Old Stone Age of the Neanderthal and Cro-Magnon, there were several transitional stocks in Europe (Mesolithic; Tardenoisian culture, with very small flints). New broad-headed people appeared, and narrow-headed races came from the south.   Cro-Magnon art was replaced by conventional silhouettes of men and animals, tools were improved, some being fitted to the side of a shaft. Remains of huts and of flint implements include axes and adzes for felling trees and building boats.   There are also millstones, implying agriculture with cereal production, and crude pottery.

The New Stone Age came with waning of the glacial cold.   The people polished their chipped stone implements, made pottery, wove textiles, and were food producers rather than food gatherers.   In Europe, they included narrow-headed light-statured Mediterraneans in the south, broad-headed stocky swarthy Alpines in the center and east, and narrow-headed tall blond Nordics to the north.   These by complex mixing and with some additional invasions from the east, have formed the present racial stocks of Europe.   The New Stone Age was followed by the Ages of Copper, Bronze, and Iron; these lead to the early civilizations recorded in history of the eastern Mediterranean and thence onward to the modern Age of Steel and steel alloys and plastics.

The "cradle of the human race" was presumably in Central Asia, whence stocks radiated in various directions, especially westward; such migrations also occurred in the historical period, which, geologically speaking, began but yesterday (Fig. 8-9).

33-19. Man in the Western Hemisphere.   The time and route of man's arrival in the Americas is a controversial topic.   The native races of the Western Hemisphere differ less among themselves in physical features and language than do races in the Old World.   American Indians are much like some stocks of eastern Asia.   The route of entry was probably near Bering Strait between Asia and Alaska, where but 30 miles of shallow water separate the two continents and solid ice sometimes connects the two shores in winter.   In New Mexico, at Folsom and near Clovis, finely worked flint tools are associated with remains of extinct native species of elephant, bison, and horse, tentatively estimated to be about 10,000 years old.   Claims for man earlier in the Americas have not been substantiated as yet, although more evidence on early man in North America is being found.

Prior to the discovery of America by Columbus in 1492, two great human cultures had developed, one by the Incas in the Andes of South America, from Colombia to Chile, at elevations up to 13,000 feet, and another by the Mayas and Aztecs of Central America.   The Maya chronology points to a beginning date in 3400 (or 3140) B.C.   The Inca civilization dates from about A.D. 1000 but rests on other earlier cultures extending backward to before the Christian era.   Of the old empire of the Mayas, chiefly in Guatemala and Honduras, the earliest dated relic is a stone from near Tres Zapotes, Veracruz, dated Nov. 4, 291 (or 31) B.C.   That empire ended about A.D. 600, and a new one culminated in the tenth to twelfth centuries but declined before the Spanish explorers arrived.   Those civilizations had none of the Old World domestic animals except the dog; their agricultural plants were exclusively of the New World and included maize or corn, beans, squashes, manioc or cassava, sweet potatoes, cotton, tobacco, peppers, tomatoes, and peanuts.   Some tribes of North American Indians practiced agriculture but were far less advanced culturally than either the Incas or Mayas.

33-20. Shelter.   The anthropoid apes live in tropical forests and have little need of shelter; at most, they construct crude nests of leaves and branches in trees.   Man, long a dweller on the earth both in and beyond the tropics, requires protection against weather and enemies.   During the Glacial period, early man in Europe lived in natural caves.   The hunting Plains Indians of North America, who followed buffalo and other game, made conical shelters (teepees) of animal skins supported on poles; nomad tribesmen with herds of sheep and goats in Central Asia today use crude tents of skins or woven fabrics of animal fibers.   The oldest fixed human shelters in Egypt were of wattle (woven sticks); sun-dried (adobe) bricks later served as building material in the eastern Mediter- ranean countries.   Rough (unhewn) stones were first employed to form burial tombs in the Mediterranean region, in England (at Stonehenge), and in Scandinavia.   Dressed stone for building was possible only after the discovery of copper and development of copper tools for shaping the stone.   Structures wholly of wood were built in forested regions as by the "Danube people," who moved up the river of that name about 2600 B.C.; such structures are made by Indians of the Pacific Northwest today.   Man has continued to use all these materials, improving his work with wood and stone by invention and development of iron and steel tools. To these have been added, in the past century, concrete (with reinforcement) and iron or steel for construction.

33-21. Food. Mankind was first a *food gatherer,* either hunting wild animals for their flesh and marrow (using the hides for clothing), or gathering wild roots, seeds, and fruits, as did many tribes of American Indians in recent centuries. Later he became a *food producer,* when flesh-producing animals were domesticated and reared in captivity and seeds were planted and tended to produce more abundant harvests. In Arizona these two stages existed side by side up to the last century with the hunting Apaches and the agricultural Papagos. Conscious food production is solely an attribute of the later human races. Man and the cultivated cereals now exist symbiotically as neither can survive without the other. The only instinctive food producers among animals are a few specialized fungus-growing ants and termites and some ants that colonize aphids ("ant cows") on plants to afford honeydew for the ants.

Domestication of animals (Tables 31-1, 32-1) to furnish meat for food, hides for clothing, and fibers for weaving and for use in draft and transport began in the distant past. The Stone Age people who invaded Europe after the Glacial period may have had the first domestic dogs. Horses for transport and cattle for milk production are on record in Asia Minor about 3000 B.C. but probably were used earlier in western Asia. Sheep and asses were under domestication in early Egypt. The gathering and planting of seeds of native wheat and barley began long ago, as did the use of scythes of wood with blades of flint. Storage of harvested grain in pits lined with mud and straw began in Egypt between 5000 and 4000 B.C. The plants of native human races in the New World, before the time of Columbus, have already been mentioned. Of all living creatures only mankind uses cooked food.

33-22. Implements. Use of fire is associated with Peking man of the early Pleistocene; later its use spread to all peoples. The spear is known from Mesolithic time. A progressive series in the development of tools (artefacts) can be traced from association with the older human relics down to the present day (Fig. 33-9). Presumptive evidence suggests that at first stones of convenient size and shape (eoliths) were selected as tools. Then crude implements of flint were formed through flaking off chips by striking with another stone (percussion method of Paleolithic time, the Early Stone Age). The wedge-shaped fist ax was one of the earliest tools thus produced. Next the flints were shaped more accurately through flaking off bits by pressure with a piece of deer antler (pressure method of the later Paleolithic). Still later, such implements were smoothed by grinding on some abrasive stone (polished implements of the Neolithic or New Stone Age). Meanwhile some races had made awls, needles, and fishhooks of bone, antler, or mollusk shell. These all belong

to the prehistoric period.　Finally, copper was discovered and smelted
into metallic form by the use of fire (about 3000 B.C. in eastern Europe
and 2000 B.C. in the west).　By heating and hammering, it became possible to fashion tools suited to special tasks.　Small amounts of tin (from
Bohemia, before 2000 B.C.) added to the copper produced bronze, an
alloy of lower melting point yet of superior hardness and better suited to
making edge tools (about 1800 B.C. in Europe).　In turn, there followed
the recovery of iron by smelting (Roman times), and much later the

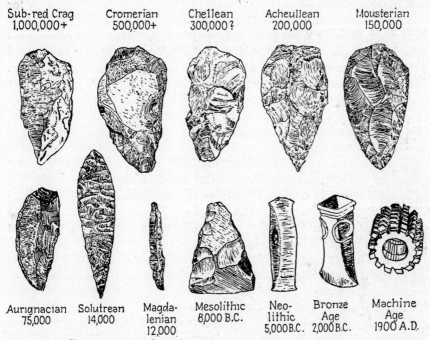

FIG. 33-9.　Evolution of cutting tools used by mankind.　Names are of the successive
human "cultures" recognized by anthropologists, and figures are estimated age in years,
B.C.　(*After Fairchild and Hart, 1929.*)

production of steel by adding a trace of carbon to the iron.　The special
alloys of steel and other metals in the twentieth century are but a further
development of this ancient practice.

　　Other early inventions of fundamental significance in the social development of mankind were (1) drawing as first practiced on cave walls by
Paleolithic man in France and Spain; (2) pictorial records (hieroglyphics)
leading to phonetic signs and writing (Egypt, about 3500 B.C.); (3) baking
of clay to make pottery; and (4) clay tablets and then papyrus sheets on
which written records were preserved.　In the realm of mechanics, the
wheel for carts and much later for machines and the arch in stone construction were great advances, as were the boat and sail for water trans-

port.   Development of counting and computation systems led to means for calculating the movements of heavenly bodies, determination of the length of the year, the size of the earth, etc., and slowly paved the way for the scientific research and technical knowledge of the present day.

33-23. Energy supplies.   During the past 500,000,000 years a fraction of the organisms living on the earth have been entombed in sediments under conditions that preserved some of their energy content derived from solar radiation.   Coal, oil shale, petroleum, and natural gas are rich in such "fossil energy."

Through his long early history man existed almost entirely on energy from food, perhaps 2,000 gram-calories per day, with a little added heat later from wood fires.   In the ecologic complex of nature he was merely one animal species competing for the immediate products of solar energy.   Civilization is essentially a means for using more energy, both current and fossil supplies.   It has upset the ecologic balance to favor increase in numbers of the human species at the expense of the environment, and this process goes on at an ever accelerated rate.   Wind and water power are derived from replaceable resources, and wood for fuel may be strictly replaceable for a small human population.   Beasts of burden are sustained by the recurrent supplies of solar energy in their plant foods, but with some eventual decline in fertility of crop lands.   Modern civilization, however, with its enlarged human populations and complex activities depends largely on "mining" the fossil energy from past geological periods, a nonrenewable resource.

33-24. The future of civilized man.   Against man's ingenuity in devising machines to multiply the results of his labor must be set the effects of increasing the human population and of the consequent greater struggle for lands (territory) and the natural resources required in modern life. He has already modified his environment profoundly by agriculture, drainage, irrigation, deforestation, planting, and the construction of huge cities with manifold biological requirements.   Unwise use of land has destroyed the productive capacity of many areas by loss of topsoil through erosion by water and wind.   Commerce and agriculture have spread pests, parasites, and diseases to countries and continents where these were not native and where they levy on the human population, its domestic animals, and its agriculture.   Efforts to alleviate sickness and suffering by applying the discoveries of modern medicine have offset some of the effects of natural selection that formerly eliminated less fit individuals from the population.   Such individuals now produce offspring that may in the end be less suited to natural survival.   Modern knowledge of the mechanism of heredity and its application in the field of eugenics has as yet made only small beginnings to offset some of these adverse features.   There have been great losses of good human germ plasm from the human race through wars, immigration, and other later developments of human "society." Man's future, as a species, will depend upon his ability to recognize and take account of these many changes when planning the manner of life for later generations.

CLASSIFICATION

All living human beings belong to the one highly variable species, *Homo sapiens*. They are divided into numerous races, all able to produce fertile offspring when intercrossed. A *race* is a stock of common ancestry and physical characteristics, whereas a *people* is the assemblage of individuals occupying a given area; the two terms are not synonymous. The culture and languages of a people are of sociological interest but do not necessarily indicate its origin, as some habits and inventions are borrowed from other peoples and some develop independently. The races have been blended by intermarriage following migrations, war, conquest, and slavery so that few are sharply distinct. Their number is uncertain, classification is difficult, and anthropologists disagree as to how they should be divided. Many races of Africa, Europe, and Asia are variously mixed, and no true races have yet resulted from settlement of the Americas by Europeans.

The characters most useful for classification are (1) hair form—straight, smooth, wavy, or curly, and its color and amount; (2) skin color—white, yellow, brown, red, or black; (3) form of head—the length to breadth ratio, long, medium, or short, and other measurements; (4) facial features—general shape, form of forehead, shape and proportions of nose, lips, and jaw, and color and form of eyes; and (5) stature or average height of mature adults—pigmy up to 58 inches; short to 62 inches; medium to 66 inches; tall to 68 inches; very tall, over 68 inches.

Group I. NEGROIDS. Hair woolly.

1. **Negrillo.** Congo Pigmy. Skin yellow; hair very short, dark rusty-brown; stature 53½ to 56 inches. Equatorial Africa, in forests.

2. **Bushman.** Skin yellow, hair short, often knotted; buttocks enlarged (steatopygia) in females; stature to 60 inches. Africa, Kalahari Desert. Hottentot of southwest Africa is Bushman × Bantu.

3. **Negro.** Skin dark brown to black; head long; forehead often bulging; legs short; stature tall, to 68 inches. Guinea coast, formerly also tropical Africa.

4. **Nigritian.** Nile Negro. Skin very dark; head long; forehead retreating; legs long; stature to 70 inches or more. Upper Nile Valley and eastern Sudan.

5. **Bantu.** Skin black, chocolate, or yellow; head various; stature 66 to 68 inches. Central and South Africa.

6. **Negrito.** Skin dark to medium; head medium; hair short; stature short, 57 to 60 inches. Philippines, Malay Peninsula, Andaman Islands, Dutch New Guinea.

7. **Melanesian** (and **Papuan**). Skin chocolate; head long, high; face squarish or ovoid; stature to 63 inches. New Guinea to Fiji and Marshall Islands.

Group II. MONGOLOIDS. Hair usually straight, stiff, and black, sparse on face.

1. **Eskimo.** Skin yellow-brown; head long, face round and flat; stature to 66 inches. Arctic coasts of Greenland, North America, and northeastern Asia.

2. **Northwestern Amerind.** North Coast Indian. Skin and hair lighter than Northern Amerind. Washington to southeastern Alaska.

3. **Northern Amerind.** Red Indian. Skin red to yellow; head long to short; face large, oval; nose straight or convex; tall, 66 to 69 inches. Plains and eastern woodlands of North America.

4. **Neoamerind.** Skin reddish to warm yellow; nose straight to concave; head short. Western North America, Central and South America.

5. **Patagonian** (Tehuelche). Skin deep brown; head short; face square; very tall, 68 to 72 inches. Southern South America.

6. **Ugrian** (Lapp, Tungus, Chukchi). Skin yellow-white to brown; hair black to reddish; head flat; cheekbones prominent. Arctic Eurasia, Scandinavia to Siberia.

7. **Northern Mongol.** Skin pale yellow to brown; face oval to round; stature medium to tall. Northcentral Asia.

8 **Southern Mongol.** Skin pale yellow; face squarish; cheekbones prominent; stature medium. China and Indo-China.

9. **Indonesian** (Malaysian). Skin yellow to light brown; hair black; head long; face elliptic; cheekbones prominent; nose flat or concave; stature short. South China to East Indies.

10. **Polynesian.** Skin yellow to light brown; hair straight or wavy; head various; face elliptic, nose prominent; stature tall. Hawaii to New Zealand, and Samoa to Easter Island.

11. **Turko-Tatar.** Skin yellowish-white; head short, high; face long, oval; nose straight; lips thick. European Turkey across central Asia.

Group III. CAUCASOIDS. Hair smooth to wavy.

1. **Australian.** Skin dark brown; hair straight to wavy; head long, forehead retreating, jaw prominent; nose flat; stature medium. Australia.

2. **Ainu.** Skin light brown; hair black; face and body very hairy; head long; nose broad, concave; stature short. Islands of northeastern Asia.

3. **Dravidian.** Skin brownish-black; hair brownish-black, curly, abundant; head long; stature short. Southern India.

4. **Indo-Afghan.** Skin light brown; hair black, wavy; head and face long; eyes dark; stature tall. Northwestern India.

5. **Ethiopian** (Hamite). Skin reddish-brown to brown-black; hair brown to black; head long; face oval; stature medium. Northeastern Africa.

6. **Berber.** Skin usually pinkish-white; hair black to brown, curly; head long; face various; eyes brown; stature medium. Northwestern Africa.

7. **Armenoid** (Assyroid). Skin swarthy; hair abundant, dark brown, wavy; head short; nose narrow, hooked; eyes brown; stature medium. Northeast of Mediterranean Sea.

8. **Arab** (Semite). Skin tawny-white; hair black; face elliptical; nose convex; stature medium. Arabia.

9. **Ibero-insular** (Pyrenean). Skin tawny-white; hair black to dark brown; head long; nose straight; stature short. Northern Spain and Western Isles.

10. **Littoral** (Atlanto-) **Mediterranean.** Skin tawny-white; hair black; head medium; face long, oval; nose straight; stature medium. Western Ireland to Spain, the Mediterranean, and eastward.

11. **Alpine.** Skin pale-tawny; hair light brown to black; head short; stature medium to tall. Central France to Russia, Persia, and eastward.

12. **Nordic.** Skin reddish-white; hair yellow, reddish, or pale brown; head and face long; eyes blue or gray; nose and chin prominent; stature tall. Northern Europe.

References

BAITSELL, G. A. 1950. Human biology. 2d ed. New York, McGraw-Hill Book Co., Inc. xvii + 730 pp., 361 figs.

BOAS, F., and OTHERS. 1938. General anthropology. Boston, D. C. Heath & Co. xi + 718 pp., illus.

Boule, M. 1923. Fossil men. Translated by Ritchie. Rev. ed. Edinburgh, Oliver and Boyd. viii + 532 pp., illus.

Breasted, J. H. 1935. Ancient times. 2d ed. Boston, Ginn & Co. xiii + 823 pp., illus. From prehistoric man through the Roman Empire.

Burkitt, M. C. 1933. Old Stone age. New York, The Macmillan Co. xiv + 254 pp.

Childe, V. G. 1934. New light on the most ancient East. New York, D. Appleton-Century Co., Inc. xviii + 327 pp., illus.

Haddon, A. C. 1925. The races of man and their distribution. New York, The Macmillan Co. vii + 201 pp., 10 pls.

Hooton, E. A. 1947. Up from the ape. Rev. ed. New York, The Macmillan Co. xxii + 788 pp., 41 pls., 68 figs.

Kroeber, A. L. 1948. Anthropology. New York, Harcourt, Brace & Co. xii + 856 + xxxix pp., 42 figs.

MacCurdy, G. G. 1932. The coming of man. New York, The University Society. vi + 157 pp., 58 figs. Simple account of pre-man and prehistoric man.

Osborn, H. F. 1923. Men of the old stone age. 3d ed. New York, Charles Scribner's Sons. xxviii + 559 pp., illus.

Sollas, W. J. 1924. Ancient hunters. 3d ed. New York, The Macmillan Co. xxxv + 589 pp., illus.

GLOSSARY

L. = Latin; Gr. = Greek.

Definitions of many other terms not included in the glossary can be found by referring to the index for the pages on which they occur in the text.

Pronunciation is indicated by the division of words into syllables (by hyphens) and by accent marks; on long words with two accented syllables both the primary ('') and the secondary (') accents are shown.

Ab-do'men. The major body division posterior to the thorax; behind the diaphragm in mammals. (L.)

Ab-duc'tor. A muscle that draws a part away from the axis of the body or a limb, or separates two parts. (L.*ab*, away +*duco*,lead)

Ab-o'ral. Opposite the mouth. (L.*ab*, from +*os*,mouth)

Ab-sorp'tion. The selective taking up of fluids or substances in solution by cells or absorbent vessels. (L.*ab*, from +*sorbeo*,suck in)

Ac-cli'ma-tize. To become habituated to an environment where not native. (L.*ad*,to +*clima*,climate)

Ac'i-nus. A small terminal sac in a lung or multicellular gland. (L.,grape)

Acquired character. One that originates during the life of an individual owing to the environment or a functional cause.

Ad'ap-ta''tion. The fitness of a structure, function, or entire organism for a particular environment; the process of becoming so fitted. (L.*ad*,to +*apto*, fit)

Ad-duc'tor. A muscle that draws a part toward the median axis or that draws parts together. (L.*ad*,to +*duco*, lead)

Ad'i-pose. Pertaining to fat. (L.*adeps*, fat)

Ad-sorp'tion. Adhesion of an extremely thin layer of gas molecules, dissolved substance, or liquid to a solid surface. Compare Absorption. (L.*ad*,to +*sorbeo*,suck in)

A-e'ri-al. Living or occurring in air. (Gr.*aer*,air)

Aes'ti-vate. Passing the summer in a quiet, torpid condition. (L.*aestas*, summer)

Af'fer-ent. A vessel or structure leading to or toward a given position. (L.*ad*, to +*fero*,bear)

Al'bin-ism. Lack of pigment when normally present. (L.*albus*,white)

Al'i-men''ta-ry. Pertaining to food, digestion, or the digestive tract. (L. *alimentum*,food)

Al-lan'to-is. An embryonic membrane out-pocketed from the hind-gut and serving for respiration and excretion in embryos of reptiles and birds; becomes part of umbilical cord and unites with the chorion to form the placenta in mammals. (Gr.*allas*,stem +*eidos*,form)

Al-le'le. The alternative forms of a gene, having the same locus in homologous chromosomes; also, the alternative forms of a Mendelian character. (Gr.*allelon*,of one another)

Al-le'lo-morph. See Allele.

Alternation of generations. Metagenesis.

Al-ve'o-lus. A small cavity or pit; a tooth socket; a minute terminal air sac in a lung; a terminal unit in an alveolar gland; one droplet in an emulsion. (L.,a small cavity)

Am'i-no acid. Any organic acid containing an amino radical (NH_2); amino acids are the "building stones" of proteins.

Am'ni-on. The innermost thin double membrane, filled with watery amniotic fluid, that encloses the developing embryo of a reptile, bird, or mammal. A similar single membrane around the insect embryo. (Gr.,foetal membrane)

A-moe'boid. Putting forth pseudopodia like an amoeba or a white blood cell. (Gr.*amoibe*,change)

Am-phib'i-ous. Capable of living either on land or in water, as a frog. (Gr. *amphi*, on both sides +*bios*,life)

Am'phi-coe''lous. Concave at both ends, as the centrum of some vertebrae. (Gr.*amphi*,on both sides +*koilos*,hollow)

Am'phi-mix''is. Union of egg and sperm nuclei to form a zygote; mingling of the germ plasm of 2 individuals. (Gr.*amphi*,on both sides +*mix*)

Am-pul'la. A small bladderlike enlargement. (L.,flask)

A-nab'o-lism. Constructive stages in metabolism, including digestion to assimilation. (Gr.*ana*,up +*ballo*, throw)

A-nal'o-gy. Similarity of external features or function, but not of structural plan or origin. (Gr.*analogia*,ratio)

An-am'nia. Vertebrates in which the embryo is not enclosed by an aminon during development—the cyclostomes, fishes, and amphibians. (Gr.*an*,without +*amnion*)

A-nas'to-mo''sis. A union or joining as of 2 or more arteries, veins, or other vessels. (Gr.*ana*,again +*stoma*, mouth)

An-ten'na. A sensory appendage, especially on arthropods, not concerned with light perception or sight. (Gr. *ana*,up +*teino*,stretch)

An-ter'i-or. The forward-moving or head end of an animal, or toward that end. Opposite of posterior. (L.*ante*, before)

An'ti-mere. One of the several similar or equivalent parts into which a radially symmetrical animal may be divided. (Gr.*anti*,against +*meros*, part)

A'nus. The posterior opening of the digestive tract. (L.)

A-or'ta. A large artery, especially one connected to the heart. (Gr.*aorte*, artery)

A-or'tic arch. A large artery arising from the heart in vertebrates; one of paired arteries connecting the ventral aorta and dorsal aorta in the region of the pharynx or gills.

Ap'i-cal. At the apex or top, as of a conical structure. (L.)

Ap-pend'age. A movable projecting part on a metazoan body having an active function. (L.*ad*,to +*pendeo*, hang)

A-quat'ic. Pertaining to or living in water. (L.*aqua*,water)

Ar-bor'e-al. Pertaining to or living in trees, as tree-inhabiting animals. (L. *arbor*, tree)

Ar-chen'ter-on. The primitive, digestive cavity of a metazoan embryo, formed by gastrulation. (Gr.*archo*, rule +*enteron*,intestine)

Ar'ter-y. A tubular vessel conveying blood away from the heart. (Gr. *arteria*,artery)

A-sex'u-al. Not related to sex; not involving gametes or fusion of their nuclei.

As-sim'i-la''tion. Incorporation of digested nutriment, after absorption, into living protoplasm. (L.*ad*,to +*similis*,like)

A'sym-met''ri-cal. Without symmetry.

A'tri-um. An outer cavity or chamber, as an auricle of the heart. (L., court)

Au''di-to'ry. Pertaining to the organ or sense of hearing. (L.*audio*,hear)

Au'ri-cle. The receiving chamber (atrium) of the heart; also, the external pinna of the ear in mammals. (L.)

Au'to-some. Any ordinary chromosome as contrasted with a sex chromosome. (Gr.*autos*,self +*soma*,body)

Au-tot'o-my. The automatic "voluntary" breaking off of a part by an animal. (Gr.*autos*,self +*temno*,to cut)

Au''to-tro''phic nu-tri'tion. That process by which an organism manufactures its own food from inorganic compounds, as in a plant. (Gr.*autos*,self + *trepho*,to feed)

Ax′i-al skel′e-ton. That part of the vertebrate skeleton in the axis of the body—skull, vertebrae, ribs, and sternum.

Ax′is. A line of reference or one about which parts are arranged symmetrically. (L.)

Ax′on. Ax′one. The process of a nerve cell that conducts impulses away from the cell body of which it is a part. (Gr.,*axon*,axle)

Bi-lat′er-al sym′me-try. Symmetry of a kind so that a body or part can be divided by one median plane into equivalent right and left halves, each a mirror image of the other.

Bi-ra′mous. Consisting of or possessing 2 branches, as a crustacean appendage. (L.*bis*,twice +*ramus*,branch)

Blad′der. A thin-walled sac, or bag, that contains fluid or gas.

Blas′to-disc. The germinal area on a large yolked egg that gives rise to the embryo. (Gr.*blastos*,germ +*diskos*, platter)

Blas′to-mere. One of the early cells formed by the division of an ovum. (Gr.*blastos*,germ +*meros*,part)

Blas′to-pore. The mouthlike opening of a gastrula. (Gr.*blastos*,germ +*poros*, passage)

Blas′tu-la. Early stage of an embryo, usually a hollow sphere of cells. (Gr.dim.of*blastos*,germ)

Blood. The fluid that circulates in the vascular system of many animals.

Bod′y cav′i-ty. The cavity between the body wall and internal organs of an animal. See Coelom.

Bra′chi-al. Referring to the fore limb or pectoral appendage. (L.*brachium*, forearm)

Bran′chi-al. Referring to gills. (Gr. *branchia*,gills)

Bron′chus. One of the larger divisions of the trachea conveying air into the lungs. (Gr.*bronchos*,windpipe.)

Buc′cal. Pertaining to the mouth or cheek. (L.*bucca*,cheek)

Bud. Part of an animal that grows out to produce a new individual.

Bur′sa. A pouch, or sac, as the bursa of a joint. (Gr.hide or skin)

Cae′cum; pl. cae′ca. A pouch or saclike extension on the digestive tract, closed at the outer end. (L.*caecus*, blind)

Cal-car′e-ous. Composed of or containing calcium carbonate ($CaCO_3$). [L. *calx* (*calc*),lime]

Cap′il-la-ry. A minute tubular vessel with walls composed of a single layer of thin cells, through which diffusion may occur; commonly in a connecting network between arteries and veins. (L.*capillus*,hair)

Car′di-ac. Pertaining to or near the heart. (Gr.*kardia*,heart)

Car-niv′o-rous. Eating or living on flesh or other animals. (L.*caro*,flesh +*voro*, eat)

Cas-tra′tion. Removal of the gonads, or sex glands, especially of the male. (L.*castro*,to castrate)

Ca-tab′o-lism. Destructive metabolism; the breaking down of more complex substances in protoplasm. (Gr.*kata*, down +*ballo*,throw)

Cau′dal. Pertaining to the tail, or posterior part of the body. (L.*cauda*,tail)

Cell. A small mass of living matter usually containing a nucleus or nuclear material; the fundamental unit of structure and function in plants and animals. (L.*cella*,small room)

Cel′lu-lar. Pertaining to or consisting of cells. (L.dim.of*cella*,small room)

Cel′lu-lose. The carbohydrate forming the wall of plant cells; also in the mantle of tunicates.

Cen′trum. The spool-like body of a vertebra, which bears various processes. (L.,center)

Ce-phal′ic. Pertaining to or toward the head. (Gr.*kephale*,head)

Ceph′a-lo-tho″rax. A body division with the head and thorax combined. (Gr.*kephale*,head +*thorax*,chest)

Cer'e-bel''lum. The anterior development from the hindbrain. (L.dim.of *cerebrum*,brain)

Cer'e-bral. Of or pertaining to the brain as a whole or the anterior dorsal (cerebral) hemispheres; also to the anterior brainlike nerve ganglia of various invertebrates. (L.*cerebrum*, brain)

Cer'e-brum. The dorsal anterior part of the vertebrate forebrain, consisting of 2 "hemispherical" masses. (L.,brain)

Cer'vi-cal. Pertaining to a neck. (L. *cervix*,neck)

Chae'ta. See Seta.

Char'ac-ter, Characteristic. A distinguishing feature, trait, or property of an organism. (Gr.)

Che-lic'-e-ra. One of the most anterior pair of appendages on arachnoids such as spiders, scorpions, and the king crab. (Gr.*chele*,claw +*keras*,horn)

Che'li-ped. The first thoracic appendage (pincer) of a crayfish and related crustaceans. (Gr.*chele*,claw +L.*pes* foot)

Chi'tin. The nonprotein secreted in the exoskeleton on arthropods and some other animals. (Gr.*chiton*,tunic)

Chlo'ro-phyll. The green pigment of plants and certain animals, involved in photosynthesis. (Gr.*chloros*,green +*phyllon*,leaf)

Cho'a-na. A funnel, especially the opening between the nasal passages and pharynx (or mouth). (Gr.)

Chon'dro-cra''ni-um. The cartilaginous skull of cyclostomes and elasmobranchs; also that part of the embryonic skull in higher vertebrates first formed as cartilage. (Gr. *chondros*, cartilage +*kranion*,skull)

Chor-da'ta. The phylum of animals with a notochord, persistent or transient; includes the vertebrates, amphioxus, tunicates, and tongue worm; the chordates. (L.*chorda*,cord or string)

Cho'ri-on. The outer double membrane surrounding the embryo of a reptile, bird, or mammal; in mammals it unites with the allantois to form the placenta; the outer membrane of an insect egg. (Gr.,membrane)

Chro'ma-tin. The easily and deeply staining substance in a cell nucleus, conspicuous in the nuclear network and in the chromosomes at mitosis. (Gr. *chroma*,color)

Chro''ma-to-phore'. A pigment cell containing granules or coloring material and responsible for color markings on many animals. (Gr.*chroma*,color +*phero*,bear)

Chro'mo-mere. An individual chromatin granule in a chromosome. (Gr. *chroma*,color +*meros*,part)

Chro'mo-somes. Characteristic deeply staining bodies, formed of chromatin in the nucleus of a cell during mitosis, that bear the genes or determiners of heredity. (Gr.*chroma*,color +*soma*, body)

Cil'i-um; pl. cil'i-a. A microscopic hairlike process attached to a free cell surface; usually numerous, often arranged in rows, and capable of vibration. (L., eyelid)

Cir'rus; pl. cir'ri. A small, slender, and usually flexible structure or appendage. (L.,tuft of hair)

Cleav'age. The early stages in the division of an egg cell into many cells.

Clo-a'ca. The terminal portion of the digestive tract in many insects; the common passage from the digestive, excretory, and reproductive organs in various vertebrates. (L.,sewer)

Co-coon'. A protective case or covering about a mass of eggs, a larva or pupa, or even an adult animal.

Coe'lom. The body cavity or space between the body wall and internal organs in many metazoan animals, lined with peritoneum (mesoderm). (Gr.*koilos*,hollow)

Col'o-ny. A group of organisms of the same species living together; colonial. Opposite of solitary. (L. *colonus*,farmer)

Com-men'sal-ism. The association of 2 or more individuals of different species in which one kind or more is benefited and the others are not harmed. (L. *cum*,together+*mensa*,table)

Com-mu-ni-ty. A group of organisms of one or more species living together and related by environmental requirements. (L.*communis*,common)

Com-pressed'. Reduced in breadth; flattened laterally. (L.*com*,together+ *premo*,press)

Con-ver'gent. Approaching each other or tending toward a common point. (L.*con*,together+*vergo*,incline)

Cop'u-la''tion. Sexual union. (L.*copulo*,join together)

Co'ri-um. The dermal portion of the skin beneath the epidermis. The dermis. (L.,skin,hide)

Cor'ne-a. The outer transparent coat of an eye. (L.*corneus*,horny)

Cor'pus-cle. A small or minute structure or a cell free or attached, as a blood corpuscle or bone corpuscle. (L.dim.of *corpus*,body)

Cor'tex. The outer or covering layer of a structure. (L.,rind,bark)

Cra'ni-al. Of or pertaining to the skull or brain, as a cranial nerve. (Gr. *kranion*,skull)

Cra'ni-um. The skull, specifically the brain case. (Gr.*kranion*,skull)

Crop. A thin-walled and expanded portion of the digestive tract, primarily for food storage.

Cross fer'til-i-za''tion. Union of an egg cell from one individual with a sperm cell from another. Opposite of self-fertilization.

Cu-ta'ne-ous. Pertaining to the skin. (L.*cutis*,skin)

Cu'ti-cle. A thin noncellular external covering on an organism. (L.dim.of *cutis*,skin)

Cyst. A resistant protective covering formed about a protozoan or other small organism during unfavorable conditions or reproduction; a small sac or capsule. (Gr.*kystis*,bladder)

Cy'to-plasm. That part of a cell outside the nucleus and within the cell

membrane. (Gr.*kytos*,hollow +*plasma*,form)

Cy'to-some. See Cytoplasm.

Def'e-cate. To discharge food residues (feces) through the anus. (L.*de*,from +*faex*,lees)

Den'drite. The process on a nerve cell that conducts impulses to the cell body; often branched. (Gr.*dendron*, tree)

De-pressed'. Flattened vertically, from above. (L.*de*,down+*preno*,press)

Der'mal. Pertaining to the skin, especially the inner connective-tissue layers of vertebrate skin. (Gr.*derma*,skin)

Der'mis. The deeper or "true" portion of the skin beneath the epidermis in a vertebrate, derived from mesoderm. (Gr.*derma*,skin)

Deu'ter-o-plasm. Substance other than the nucleus and cytoplasm in a cell, especially yolk in an egg cell. (Gr. *deuteros*,second+*plasma*,form)

Di'a-phragm. A dividing membrane, as the diaphragm of the ear; the muscular partition between the thoracic and abdominal cavities in mammals. (Gr. *dia*,through+*phragma*,fence)

Di-ges'tion. The process of preparing food for absorption and assimilation. (L.)

Dig'it. A finger or toe; one of the terminal divisions of a limb in tetrapods. (L.*digitus*,finger)

Dig'i-ti-grade. Walking on the toes. (L.*digitus*,finger+*gradior*,to step)

Di-mor'phism. Existing under 2 distinct forms. (Gr.*di*,two+*morphe*,form)

Di-oe'cious. With the male and female organs in separate individuals. (Gr. *di*,two+*oikos*,house)

Dip'lo-blas''tic. Derived from 2 embryonic germ layers, ectoderm and endoderm. (Gr.*diplous*,double+*blastos*,germ)

Dip'loid. The dual or somatic number of chromosomes (2*n*), the normal number in all but the matured germ cells of any particular organism. (Gr.*diplous*,double+*eidos*,form)

Dis-sim′i-la″tion. The chemical disintegration of protoplasm, usually by oxidation, with release of energy; catabolism. (L.*dissimilis*,different)

Dis′tal. Away from the point of attachment or place of reference. (L. *disto*,stand apart)

Di-ver′gent. Going farther apart; separating from a common source. (L.*di*, doubly +*vergo*,incline)

Di-ur′nal. Pertaining to the daytime. (L.*dies*,day)

Dom′i-nant char′ac-ter. A character from one parent that manifests itself in offspring to the exclusion of a contrasted (recessive) character from the other parent. (L.*dominor*,rule)

Dor′sal. Toward or pertaining to the back, or upper surface. (L.*dorsum*, back)

Duct. A tube by which a liquid or other product of metabolism is conveyed, as of a secretion from a gland; usually opening on a surface or in a larger compartment. (L.*duco*,lead)

Duct′less gland. A gland that elaborates and secretes a hormone, or "internal secretion," directly into the blood stream; an endocrine gland.

E-col′o-gy. The relations of an organism to its environment. (Gr.*oikos*, home +*logy*)

Ec′to-derm. The outer germ layer or cell layer of an early embryo. (Gr. *ektos*,outside +*derma*,skin)

Ec′to-par″a-site. One that lives on the exterior of its host. (Gr.*ektos*,outside +parasite)

Ef-fec′tor. A structure that transforms motor impulses into motor action. (L.*efficio*,effect, bring to pass)

Ef′fer-ent. A structure leading away from a given point of reference, as an efferent artery. (L.*ex*,out +*fero*,carry)

E-gest′. To discharge unabsorbed food or residues from the digestive tract. (L.*e*,out +*gero*,bear)

Egg. A germ cell produced by a functionally female organism; an ovum.

Em′bry-o. A newly forming young animal in the stages of development before hatching or birth. (Gr.)

Em′bry-og″e-ny. The process of development of the embryo. (Gr.*embryon* +*genesis*,generation)

Em′bry-on″ic mem′branes. Cellular membranes formed as part of an embryo during its development and necessary for its metabolism; the amnion, chorion, and allantois of reptiles, birds, and mammals, and of insects.

En-am′el. The dense whitish covering on teeth of vertebrates, the hardest substance produced by animal bodies.

En′do-crine. A ductless gland; also, its internal secretion or hormone, which is diffused into and carried by the blood stream. (Gr.*endon*,within +*krino*,separate)

En′do-derm. The layer or group of cells lining the primitive gut, or archenteron, in an early embryo, beginning in the gastrula stage. (Gr. *endon*,within +*derma*,skin)

En′do-par″a-site. One that lives within its host. (Gr.*endon*,within +parasite)

En′do-skel″e-ton. An internal supporting framework or structure. (Gr. *endon*,within +skeleton)

En′do-style. The ventral ciliated groove in the pharynx of tunicates, amphioxus, and larval lampreys, used in food getting; homologous with the thyroid gland of vertebrates. (Gr. *endon*,within +*stylos*,column)

En′do-the″li-um. Layer of simple squamous cells lining the inner surface of circulatory organs and other closed cavities. (Gr.*endos*,within + *thele*,nipple)

En′ter-on. The digestive cavity, especially that part lined by endoderm. (Gr.,intestine)

En-vir′on-ment. The total of conditions surrounding an entire organism.

En′zyme. A substance produced by living cells that in minute amount causes specific chemical transformation such as hydrolysis, oxidation, or reduction but that is not used up in the process; a ferment or catalyst. (Gr.*en*,in +*zyme*,leaven)

Ep′i-der″mis. A layer of cells (sometimes stratified) covering an external surface; the ectodermal portion of the skin of most animals; secretes cuticle on some animals. (Gr.*epi*,upon + *derma*, skin)

Ep′i-did″y-mis. The efferent tubules of the testes. (Gr.*epi*,upon +*didymos*, testicle)

E-piph′y-sis. The end or other external part of a bone that ossifies separately; also, the pineal body, a dorsal outgrowth on the diencephalon of the vertebrate brain. (Gr.*epi*,upon + *phyto*,to grow)

Ep′i-the″li-um. A layer (or layers) of cells covering a surface or lining a cavity. (Gr.*epi*,upon +*thele*,nipple)

E-ryth′ro-cyte. A red blood cell or corpuscle; characteristic of vertebrates. (Gr.*erythros*,red +*kytos*,hollow vessel)

E-soph′a-gus. That part of the digestive tract between the pharynx and stomach. (Gr.)

Eu-sta′chi-an tube. The passage between the pharynx and middle ear in land vertebrates. (Eustachio, an Italian anatomist)

E-vag′i-na″tion. An outpocketing from a hollow structure. (L.*e*,out from + *vagina*,a sheath)

E′vo-lu″tion. The process by which living organisms have come to be what they are, structurally and functionally, complex forms being derived from simpler forms; hence, descent with modification. (L.*evolvo*,unroll,unfold)

Ex-cre′tion. Waste material resulting from metabolism and discharged from the body as useless; also the process of its elimination. Compare Secretion, and Feces. (L.*excerno*,separate, secrete)

Ex′o-skel″e-ton. An external supporting structure or covering. (Gr.*exo*, outside, +skeleton)

F₁, F₂, etc. Abbreviations for 1st filial, 2d filial, etc., indicating the successive generations following crossbreeding.

Fac′tor. An agent or cause; in genetics, a specific germinal cause of a hereditary character; same as gene.

Fas′ci-a. A sheet of connective tissue covering an organ or attaching a muscle. (L.,a band)

Fau′na. All the animal life in a given region or period of time.

Fe′ces. Excrement; unabsorbed or indigestible food residues discharged from the digestive tract as waste. (L., dregs)

Fer′til-i-za″tion. Union of two gametes (egg and sperm) to form a zygote and initiate the development of an embryo. (L.*fertil*,fruitful from *fero*,to bear)

Fi′ber. A delicate threadlike part in a tissue. (L.)

Fi′bril. A small fiber. (L.)

Fin. An extension of the body on an aquatic animal used in locomotion or steering.

Fis′sion. Asexual reproduction by division into 2 or more parts, usually equivalent. (L.*findo*,split)

Fla-gel′lum. A long lash or threadlike extension capable of vibration; on flagellate protozoans and on collar cells of sponges. (L.,little whip)

Flame cell. A type of hollow terminal excretory cell in certain invertebrates that contains a beating (flamelike) group of cilia.

Foe′tus. The later stages of an embryo while within the egg or uterus. (L., offspring)

Fol′li-cle. A minute cellular sac or covering. (L.dim.of *follis*,bag)

Food vac′u-ole. An intracellular digestive organelle.

Fo-ra′men. An opening or perforation through a bone, membrane, or partition. (L.*foro*,bore)

Fos′sil. Any relic of an organism buried in the earth or rocks by natural causes in past geologic time. (L.*fodio*,dig)

Free-liv'ing. Not attached or parasitic; capable of independent movement and existence. Compare Sessile.

Fron'tal. Of or pertaining to the front, or forehead; also, a plane or section parallel to the main body axis and at right angles to the sagittal plane. (L. *frons*,the brow)

Func'tion. The activity or action of any part of an organism. (L.*functio*,to perform)

Gam'ete. A mature reproductive or germ cell, either male (sperm) or female (ovum). (Gr.*gamos*,marriage)

Gam'e-to-gen''e-sis. The process of formation of mature germ cells, or gametes; maturation.

Gan'gli-on; pl. gan'gli-a. A group or concentration of nerve cell bodies, set apart, and acting as a center of nervous influence.

Gas'tro-der''mis. Lining of the digestive cavity in coelenterates. (Gr.*gaster*, stomach +*derma*,skin)

Gas'tro-vas''cu-lar. Serving for both digestion and circulation.

Gas'tru-la. Early stage in embryonic development; an invaginated blastula. (Gr.*gaster*,belly)

Genes. The units of inheritance, which are transmitted from one generation to another in the gametes and control the development of characters in the new individual; the factors, or hereditary determiners.

Gen'i-tal. Referring to reproductive organs or the process of generation. (L.*gigno*,beget)

Gen'o-type. The internal genetic or hereditary constitution of an organism without regard to its external appearance. Compare Phenotype. (Gr.*genos*,race +*typos*,impression,form)

Germ cell. A reproductive cell in a multicellular organism.

Germ lay'er. One of the (2 or 3) fundamental cell layers (ecto-, endo-, mesoderm) in an early embryo of a multicellular animal from which tissues and organs of the adult are formed.

Germ plasm. The material basis of inheritance; the gametes and the cells and tissues from which they form, considered as a unit.

Ger'min-al va'ri-a''tions. Those due to some modification in the germ cells.

Gill. An organ for aquatic respiration.

Giz'zard. A heavily muscled portion of the digestive tract.

Gland. An organ of secretion or excretion. (L.*glans*,acorn)

Glo-mer'u-lus. A small rounded clump of vessels; the knot of capillaries in a renal corpuscle. (L.dim.of *glomus*, ball)

Glot'tis. The opening from the pharynx into the trachea. (Gr.*glotta*,tongue)

Gly'co-gen. A carbohydrate (polysaccharid) stored in the muscles and liver; "animal starch." (Gr.*glykys*, sweet +*gen*,come into being)

Gon'ad. A reproductive organ (ovary, testis, or hermaphrodite) in which gametes (ova or sperm) are produced. (Gr.*gonos*,generation,seed)

Gre-ga'ri-ous. Habitually living in groups, flocks, etc., of numerous individuals. (L.*grex*,herd)

Gy-nan'dro-morph. An individual in a dioecious species having one part of the body female and another part male in constitution. (Gr.*gyne*, woman +*aner*,man)

Hab'i-tat. The natural or usual dwelling place of an individual or group of organisms. (L.*habitus*,condition)

Hair. A slender filamentous growth on the skin of mammals and on the exposed surfaces of some anthropods.

Hap'loid. The single or halved number of chromosomes (*n*) as found in matured germ cells. (Gr.*haplous*,single +*eidos*,form)

Hem'al. Pertaining to the blood or the blood-vascular system. (Gr.*aima*, blood)

Hem'o-coel. Portion of a body cavity reduced in size and functioning as part of a blood-vascular system. (Gr. *aima*,blood +*koilos*,cavity)

Hem'o-glo"bin. The coloring matter of red corpuscles in vertebrate blood and of blood plasma in some invertebrates; a protein containing iron that combines with and transports oxygen to the tissues. (Gr.*aima*,blood + globe)

He-pat'ic. Pertaining to the liver. (Gr.*hepar*,liver)

He-pat'ic por'tal sys'tem. A system of veins leading from the digestive tract to capillaries (sinusoids) in the liver of a vertebrate.

Her-biv'o-rous. Feeding only or chiefly on herbs, grasses, or other vegetable matter. (L.*herba*,grass+*voro*,devour)

He-red"i-tar'y. Passing by inheritance from one generation to another.

He-red'i-ty. The transmission of characters, physical and others, from parent to offspring; the tendency of offspring to resemble their parents. (L.*heres*,heir)

Her-maph'ro-dite. An animal with both male and female reproductive organs. (Gr.*Hermes*+*Aphrodite*)

Het'er-o-zy"gote. An individual produced by union of 2 germ cells that contain unlike genes for a given character, either both genes of an allelomorphic pair or 2 different genes of an allelomorphic series. Compare Homozygote. (Gr.*heteros*,another+*zygon*, yoke)

Hi'ber-nate. Passing the winter in an inactive or torpid condition. (L. *hiberno*,pass the winter)

Hol'o-blas"tic. Cleavage in which an entire egg cell divides. (Gr.*holos*, whole+*blastos*,germ)

Hol'o-phyt"ic nu-tri'tion. Nutrition involving photosynthesis of simple inorganic chemical substances, as in green plants and some flagellate protozoans. (Gr.*holos*,whole+*phyton*,plant)

Hol'o-zo"ic nu-tri'tion. Nutrition requiring complex organic foodstuffs, and characteristic of most animals. (Gr. *holos*,whole +*zoön*,animal)

Ho-mol'o-gous. Of like source in structure and embryonic development from primitive origin. (Gr.*homos*,same+ *lego*,speak)

Ho-mol'o-gous chro'mo-somes. A pair of chromosomes having relatively similar structure and value, one from each parent. (Gr.*homologos*,agreeing)

Ho-mol'o-gy. Fundamental similarity; structural likeness of an organ or part in one kind of animal with the comparable unit in another resulting from descent from a common ancestry. Compare Analogy. (Gr.)

Ho'mo-zy"gote. An individual produced by union of 2 germ cells that contain like genes for a given character. Compare Heterozygote. (Gr.*homos*, like+*zygon*,yoke)

Hor'mone. A chemical regulator or coordinator secreted by cells or ductless glands and carried in the blood stream. See Endocrine. (Gr.*hormao*, urge on,spur)

Host. An organism that harbors another as a parasite. (L.*hospes*,entertainer)

Hy'a-line. Glassy or semitransparent. (Gr.*hyalos*,glass)

Hy'brid. The offspring of 2 parents that differ in 1 or more heritable characters; a heterozygote. (L.*hybrida*,mongrel)

Hy-per'tro-phy. Abnormal increase or overgrowth in the size of a part or organ. (Gr.*hyper*,over+*trepho*, nourish)

In-breed'. To mate related animals or plants.

In-gest'. To take food into a place of digestion. (L.*in*+*gero*,bear)

In-her'i-tance. The sum of all characters that are transmitted by the germ cells from generation to generation. (L.*in*,in +*heres*,heir)

In'stinct. An inherited type of action, invoked by a certain stimulus and often of complex nature, combining associated reflex acts and leading to a particular end.

In-teg'u-ment. An outer covering, especially the skin of a vertebrate and its derivatives. (L.*intego*,to cover)

In'ter-cel"lu-lar. Between or among cells.

In-tes′tine. That part of the digestive or alimentary canal between the stomach and anus (or cloaca). (L. *intus*,inside)

In′tra-cel″lu-lar. Within a cell or cells.

In-vag′i-na″tion. An inpocketing or folding in, as of the vegetal pole of a blastula to form the gastrula. (L. *in+vagina*,a sheath)

In-ver′te-brate. Any animal without a dorsal column of vertebrae; protozoans to amphioxus, inclusive.

Ir′ri-ta-bil″i-ty. The capacity of responding to stimuli. (L.*irrito*,excite)

Joint. A place of union between two separate bones or other hardened structures. (L.*junctus*,from *jungo*,to join)

La′bi-al. Pertaining to the lips.

La-mel′la. A thin sheetlike layer. (L. *lamina*,plate)

Lar′va. The early and usually active feeding stage of an animal, after the embryo, and unlike the adult. (L., mask)

Leu′co-cyte. A white blood cell or corpuscle. (Gr.*leukos*,white+*kytos*, hollow vessel)

Lim′y. Calcareous; containing calcium salts, especially $CaCO_3$.

Lin′gual. Pertaining to the tongue. (L.,tongue)

Link′age. Inheritance of characters in groups, probably because their genes lie in the same chromosome.

Lip′oid. Of fatty nature. (Gr.*lipos*,fat)

Lo′pho-phore. A ridge about the mouth region bearing tentacles in some invertebrates. (Gr.*lophos*,crest+*phero*,bear)

Lu′men. The cavity in a gland, duct, vessel, or organ.

Lu′mi-nes″cence. Emission of light as result of chemical reactions within cells. (L.*lumen*,light)

Lung. An organ for aerial respiration.

Lymph. Colorless blood fluid (without red blood cells) found among tissues and in lymph capillaries or vessels. (L.*lympha*,water)

Lym-phat′ic sys′tem. A system of delicate vessels in vertebrates that lead from spaces between tissues to large veins entering the heart; part of the circulatory system.

Lymph′o-cyte. A white blood cell with one large undivided and nongranular nucleus; present in blood and lymph vessels. (L.*lympha*,water+Gr.*kytos*, hollow vessel)

Man′di-ble. The lower jaw of a vertebrate; either jaw of an arthropod. (L.*mandibula*,jaw)

Ma-rine′. Pertaining to or inhabiting the sea, ocean, or other salt waters. (L.*mare*,sea)

Mat′u-ra″tion. Final stages in preparation of sex cells for mating, with segregation of homologous chromosomes so that each cell or gamete contains half the usual (diploid) number.

Mei-o′sis. See Maturation.

Mem′brane. A thin soft sheet of cells or of material secreted by cells.

Mer′o-blas″tic. Cleavage of an egg in which only part of the protoplasm divides, leaving the yolk undivided; characteristic of eggs with much yolk. (Gr.*meros*,part+*blastos*,germ)

Mes′en-chyme. Part of the mesoderm in a vertebrate embryo that produces connective and circulatory tissues. (Gr.*mesos*,middle+*chyma*,fluid)

Mes′en-ter-y. The sheet of tissue that suspends organs in the body cavity and is continuous with the peritoneum lining that cavity. (Gr.*mesos*,middle +*enteron*,intestine)

Mes′o-derm. The embryonic cells or cell layers between ectoderm and endoderm. (Gr.*mesos*,middle+*derma*, skin)

Mes′o-gle″a. The gelatinous filling between the outer and inner cell layers of a two-layered animal such as a jellyfish. (Gr.*mesos*,middle+*gloios*, glutinous)

Me-tab′o-lism. The sum of the constructive and destructive processes (anabolism and catabolism), mainly chemical, that occur in living organisms. (Gr.*metabolos*,changeable)

Met'a-gen''e-sis. Alternation of sexual and asexual reproduction in the life cycle of certain animals; alternation of generations. (Gr.*meta*,after +*genesis*, origin)

Met'a-mere. Any one of a series of homologous parts in the body, as with annelids, arthropods, or chordates; a somite. (Gr.*meta*,after + *meros*,part)

Me-tam'er-ism. Segmental repetition of homologous parts (metameres).

Met'a-mor''ph-osis. Marked change in form from one stage of development to another, as of a larva to an adult. (Gr.)

Met'a-ne-phrid''i-um. A tubular excretory organ, the open inner end draining from the coelom and the outer discharging to the exterior, as in the earthworm. (Gr.*meta*,after +*nephros*, kidney)

Met'a-zo''a. Multicellular animals with cells usually arranged into tissues; includes all animals above the sponges. (Gr.*meta*,after +*zoön*,animal)

Mi'cron; pl. micra. The unit of microscopic measurement, 1/1,000 of a millimeter; represented by μ (Greek letter mu). (Gr.*mikros*,small)

Mi-to'sis. Indirect cell division, characterized by the appearance of a fibrous spindle and a definite number of chromosomes, which split longitudinally to form 2 equal sets of daughter chromosomes; the latter diverge to opposite poles of the spindle to become parts of the 2 new nuclei. (Gr.*mitos*, thread)

Mo'lar. The posterior permanent teeth of a mammal. (L.*molo*,grind)

Molt. To cast off an outer covering such as cuticle, scales, feathers, or hair.

Mo-noe'cious. Having both male and female gonads in the same individual; hermaphroditic. (Gr.*monos*,single + *oikos*,house)

Mon'o-hy''brid. The offspring of parents differing in 1 character. (Gr. *monos*,single +L.*hybrida*,mongrel)

Mon'-o-phy-let''ic. From a single known evolutionary derivation. (Gr. *monos*,single +*phyle*,tribe)

Mu'cous. Secreting mucus or similar sticky slimy substance, as by a mucous cell, gland, or membrane. (L.)

Mu-ta'tion. Abrupt and heritable modification of a character; also, the change in a gene responsible for it. (L. *mutatus*,changed)

Mu'tu-al-ism. Jointly beneficial and obligatory association between individuals of 2 different species. (L. *mutuus*, exchanged)

My'o-tome. A muscle segment or somite. (Gr.*mys*,muscle +*temno*,cut)

Na'ris; pl. na'res. The opening of the air passages, both internal and external, in the head of a vertebrate. (L., nostril)

Na'sal. Pertaining to the nose.

Nat'u-ral se-lec'tion. The elimination of less fit individuals in the struggle to live.

Ne-phrid'i-um. A tubular excretory organ found in mollusks, annelids, arthropods, and other invertebrates. (Gr.*nephros*,kidney)

Neph'ro-stome. The ciliated entrance from the coelomic cavity into a nephridium, or kidney tubule. (Gr. *nephros*,kidney +*stoma*,mouth)

Nerve. A bundle of nerve fibers lying outside the central nervous system.

Nerve cord. A compact cord, composed of neurons and usually with ganglia, forming part of a central nervous system.

Neu'ral. Pertaining to the nervous system. (Gr.*neuron*,nerve)

Neu'ron. A nerve cell with cytoplasmic extensions (dendrites, axon) over which nervous impulses pass.

Noc-tur'nal. Active at night. (L.*nocturnus*,nightly)

No'to-chord. The elastic cellular axial support formed ventral to the nerve cord in the early embryo of all chordates; later surrounded or supplanted by the vertebrae in most vertebrates. (Gr.*notos*,the back +*chorde*,string)

Nu-cle′o-lus. An oval mass within the nucleus of most cells; of uncertain function but disappears during mitosis. (L.dim.of *nucleus*)

Nu′cle-us. A differentiated structure of specialized protoplasm within a cell, refractile and with deeply staining chromatin, that controls metabolic activities; in cells of all organisms except bacteria. (L.dim.of *nux*,nut)

O-cel′lus. A small simple eye as on many invertebrates. (L.dim.of *oculus*, eye)

Oc′u-lar. Pertaining to the eye.

Ol-fac′to-ry. Pertaining to the sense of smell. (L.*olfacto*,smell)

Om-niv′o-rous. Eating all kinds of food; feeding upon both plants and animals. (L.*omnis*,all+*voro*,eat)

On-tog′e-ny. Development of the individual. (Gr.*on*,being+*gen*,become)

O′ö-sperm. A fertilized egg, a zygote. (Gr.*oön*,egg+*sperma*,seed)

O-per′cu-lum′. The plate covering the gills of a bony fish; also, the plate serving to cover the opening of some snail shells. (L.)

Oph-thal′mic. Pertaining to the eye (Gr.*ophthalmos*,eye)

O-pis′tho-coe″lous. Concave behind, as the centrum of some vertebrae. (Gr.*opisthen*,behind+*koilos*,hollow)

Op′tic. Pertaining to the eye or sense of sight. (Gr.*optos*,seen)

O′ral. Pertaining to or near the mouth. (L.*os*,mouth)

Or′bit. The eye socket. (L.*orbis*,circle)

Or′gan. Any part of an animal performing some definite function; a group of cells or tissues acting as a unit for some special purpose. (Gr.*organon*,instrument)

Or-gan-elle′. A specialized part in a protozoan that performs some special function (like an organ in a metazoan). (Gr.dim.of *organon*,instrument)

Or′gan-ism. A single plant or animal; one that functions as a unit.

Os-mo′sis. Diffusion through a semipermeable membrane. (Gr.*osmos*, pushing)

Os′ti-um; pl. os′ti-a. An opening to a passage, usually guarded by a valve or circular muscle. (L.*os*,mouth)

O′tic. Pertaining to the ear. (Gr.*otikos*, pertaining to the ear)

O′to-lith. A concretion of calcium salts in the inner ear of vertebrates or in the auditory organ of some invertebrates. (Gr.*otikos*,pertaining to the ear+*lithos*,stone)

O′va-ry. The organ in which the egg cells multiply and are nourished. (L.*ovum*,egg)

O′vi-duct. The tube by which eggs are conveyed from the ovary to the uterus or to the exterior. (L.*ovum*,egg+*duco*,lead)

O-vip′a-rous. Egg-laying; producing eggs that hatch outside the mother's body. (L.*ovum*,egg+*pario*,produce)

O′vo-vi-vip″a-rous. Producing eggs that are incubated and hatched within the parent's body, as with some fishes, reptiles, and invertebrates. (L.*ovum*, egg+*vivus*,alive+*pario*,produce)

O′vum. An egg, the sex cell of a female. (L.)

P. The first parental generation—parents of a given individual of the F_1 generation.

Palp. A projecting part or appendage, often sensory, on the head or near the mouth in some invertebrates. (L. *palpo*,stroke)

Pa-pil′la. Any nipple-like structure, large or small. (L.,nipple)

Par′a-site. An organism that lives on or in another more or less at the expense of the latter (the host). (Gr. *para*,beside+*sitos*,food)

Pa-ren′chy-ma. Soft cellular substance filling space between organs. (Gr. *para*,beside+*en*,in+*chyma*,fluid)

Par′the-no-gen″e-sis. Development of a new individual from an unfertilized egg, as in rotifers, plant lice, etc. (Gr.*parthenos*,virgin+*genesis*,origin)

Path′o-gen″ic. Causing or productive of disease. (Gr.*pathos*,suffering+*genesis*,origin)

Pec'to-ral. Pertaining to the upper thoracic region, or breast. (L.*pectoralis,* pertaining to the breast)

Pe-lag'ic. Pertaining to the open sea, away from the shore. (Gr.*pelagos,* open sea)

Pel'vic. Pertaining to the posterior girdle and paired appendages of vertebrates; the posterior abdominal region of a mammal. (L.,a basin)

Pe'nis. The copulatory organ of a male for conveying sperm to the genital tract of a female. (L.)

Pen'ta-dac''tyl. Having 5 fingers, toes, or digits. (Gr.*pente,*five +*daktylos,* finger)

Per'i-car''di-um. The cavity enclosing the heart; also, the membranes lining the cavity and covering the heart. (Gr.*peri,*around +*kardia,*heart)

Pe-riph'er-al. To or toward the surface, away from the center. (Gr.*peri,* around +*phero,*to bear)

Per'i-stal''sis. Rhythmic involuntary muscular contractions passing along a hollow organ, especially of the digestive tract. (Gr.*peri,*around +*stalsis,* constriction)

Per'i-to-ne''um. The thin serous membrane (mesodermal) that lines the body cavity and covers the organs therein in many animals. (Gr.*peri,*around + *teino,*stretch)

Phag'o-cyte. A white blood cell that engulfs and digests bacteria and other foreign materials. (Gr.*phagein,*to eat +*kytos,*hollow vessel)

Phar'ynx. The region of the digestive tract between the mouth cavity and the esophagus; often muscular and sometimes with teeth in invertebrates; the gill region of many aquatic vertebrates. (Gr.,throat)

Phe'no-type. The external appearance of an individual without regard to its genetic or hereditary constitution. Compare Genotype. (Gr.*phaino,*show +*typos,*impression,type)

Pho'to-syn''the-sis. The formation of carbohydrates from carbon dioxide and water by the chlorophyll ın green plants or flagellate protozoans in the presence of light. (Gr.*phos,*light +*synthesis,*place together)

Phy-log'e-ny. The history (evolution) of a species or higher group. (Gr. *phylon,*race +*gen,*become)

Pig'ment. Coloring matter.

Pin'na. A wing or fin; also, the projecting part of the external ear in mammals. (L.,feather)

Pla-cen'ta. The organ by which the foetus (embryo) of higher mammals is attached in the uterus of the mother and through which diffusible substances pass for the metabolism of the foetus. See Chorion. (L.,flat cake)

Plan'ti-grade. Walking on the whole sole of the foot, as a man or bear. (L.*planta,*sole +*gradior,*walk)

Plas'ma. The fluid portion of blood or lymph. (Gr.,a thing molded)

Pleu'ra. The membrane covering the lung and lining the inner wall of the thorax. (Gr.,rib,side)

Plex'us. A network of interlaced nerves or blood vessels. (L.,a plaiting)

Pol'y-mor''phism. Existence of individuals of more than one form in a species. (Gr.*polys,*many +*morphe,*form)

Pol'y-phy-let''ic. From more than one known evolutionary derivation. (Gr. *poly,*many +*phyle,*tribe)

Por'tal vein. One that divides into capillaries before reaching the heart. (L.*porta,*gate)

Pos-te'ri-or. The hinder part or toward the hinder (tail) end, away from the head. Opposite of anterior. (L., following)

Pred'a-tor. An animal that captures or preys upon other animals for its food. (L.*praeda,*booty)

Pre-hen'sile. Adapted for grasping or holding. (L.*prehendo,*seize)

Prim'i-tive. Not specialized; the early or beginning type or stage. (L.*primus,* first)

Pro-coe'lous. Concave in front, as the centrum in some vertebrae. (Gr.*pro,* before +*koilos,*hollow)

Proc′to-de″um. The ectoderm-lined terminal part of the digestive tract near the anus. (Gr.*proktos*,anus + *hodos*,a way)

Pro-tan′dry. Production of sperm and later of eggs by the same gonad. (Gr.*protos*,first + *aner*,man)

Pro′to-ne-phrid″i-um. An invertebrate excretory organ (of 1 or more cells), the inner end closed and either branched or with one terminal cell (solenocyte). (Gr.*protos*,first + *nephros*, kidney)

Pro′to-plasm. Living substance; the complex colloidal physicochemical system that constitutes living matter and is the viscid, semifluid material of animal and plant cells. (Gr.*protos*, first + *plasma*,form)

Prox′i-mal. Toward or nearer the place of attachment or reference of the center of the body. Opposite of distal. (L.*proximus*,nearest)

Pseu′do-po″di-um. A flowing extension of protoplasm used in locomotion or feeding by a cell or protozoan. (Gr. *pesudes*,false + *podion*,foot)

Pul′mo-na-ry. Pertaining to the lungs. (L.*pulmo*,lungs)

Ra′dial sym′me-try. Having similar parts arranged around a common central axis, as in a starfish.

Ra′mus. A branch or outgrowth of a structure. (L.,branch)

Re′cent. The present or Holocene epoch in geology. Compare Fossil. (L.*recens*,fresh)

Re-cep′tor. A free nerve ending or sense organ capable of receiving and transforming certain environmental stimuli into sensory nerve impulses. (L.,receiver)

Re-ces′sive char′ac-ter. A character from one parent that remains undeveloped in offspring when associated with the corresponding dominant character from the other parent. (L.*recessus*, a going back)

Rec′tum. The terminal enlarged portion of the digestive tract. (L.*rectus*, straight)

Re-duc′tion di-vi′sion. That division of the maturing germ cells by which the somatic or diploid number of chromosomes is reduced to the haploid number.

Re′flex ac′tion. Action resulting from an afferent sensory impulse on a nerve center and its reflection as an efferent motor impulse independent of higher nerve centers or the brain. An automatic response to a stimulus. (L.*re*, back + *flecto*,bend)

Re-gen′er-a″tion. Replacement of parts lost through mutilation or otherwise.

Re′nal. Pertaining to a kidney. (L. *renes*,kidneys)

Re′pro-duc″tion. The maintenance of a species from generation to generation.

Res′pi-ra″tion. Obtaining oxygen from the surrounding medium and giving off carbon dioxide. (L.*re*,back + *spiro*, breathe)

Ret′i-na. The cell layer of an eye containing the receptors of light impulses. (L.*rete*,net)

Re-ver′sion. The reappearance of ancestral traits that have been in abeyance for one or more generations. (L.*re*,back + *verto*,turn)

Ros′trum. A projecting snout or similar process on the head. (L.,beak)

Ru′di-men″ta-ry. Incompletely developed or having no function. Compare Vestigial. (L.*rudis*,unwrought)

Ru′mi-nant. A herbivorous land mammal that chews a cud, as a cow or deer. (L.*rumen*,throat)

Sa′crum. The posterior part of the vertebral column that is attached to the pelvic girdle. (L.from *sacer*, sacred,offered in sacrifice)

Sag′it-tal. Of or pertaining to the median anteroposterior plane in a bilaterally symmetrical animal, or a section parallel to that plane. (L. *sagitta*,arrow)

Sal′i-va-ry. Pertaining to the glands of the mouth that secrete saliva. (L. *saliva*,spittle)

Sap'ro-phyte. An organism that lives upon dead organic matter. (Gr.*sapros*,rotten +*phyton*,plant)

Scan-so'ri-al. Pertaining to or adapted for climbing. (L.*scando*,climb)

Sec'on-da-ry sex'u-al char'ac-ters. Those characters which distinguish one sex from the other, not functioning directly in reproduction.

Se-cre'tion. A useful substance produced in the body by a cell or multicellular gland; also, the process of its production and passage. Compare Excretion. (L.*secretus*,separated)

Sed'en-ta-ry. Remaining in one place. (L.*sedeo*,sit)

Sed'i-men''ta-ry. In geology, rocks formed of calcium carbonates, clay, mud, sand, or gravel, deposited in water or depressions on land and cemented or pressed into solid form. Fossils occur in such rocks. (L.*sedimentum*,settling)

Seg'ment. A part that is marked off or separate from others; any of the several serial divisions of a body or an appendage. Compare Somite.

Sem'i-nal. Pertaining to structures or fluid containing spermatozoa (semen). (L.*semen*,seed)

Sense or'gan. An organ containing a part sensitive to a particular kind of stimulus.

Sep'tum. A dividing wall or partition between two cavities or structures. (L.*sepes*,fence)

Se'rous. Secreting watery colorless serum, as by a gland or serous membrane. (L.)

Se'rum. The plasma of blood that separates from a clot and contains no cells or fibrin. (L.)

Ses'sile. Permanently fixed, sedentary, not free-moving. (L.*sedeo*,sit)

Se'ta (chaeta). A bristle or slender, stiff bristle-like structure. (L.,bristle)

Sex chro'mo-somes. Special chromosomes different in males and females and concerned in the determination of sex; the X and Y chromosomes.

Sex-lim'i-ted char'ac-ter. A character belonging to one sex only; commonly a secondary sexual character.

Sex-linked char'ac-ter. A character the gene of which is located in the sex chromosome.

Sex'u-al u'nion. Temporary connection of a male and female for transfer of sperm into the female's reproductive tract.

Si-li'ceous. Containing silica or silicon dioxide (SiO_2). (L.*silex*,flint)

Si'nus. A cavity in a bone or an enlargement in a blood vessel. (L.,fold, hollow)

Skel'e-ton. The hardened framework of an animal body serving for support and to protect the soft parts; it may be external or internal and either solid or jointed. (Gr.)

Sol'i-ta-ry. Living alone; not in colonies or groups. (L.*solus*,alone)

Sol'ute. A substance that will dissolve or go into solution, as salt in water. (L.*se*,apart +*lus*,set free)

Sol'vent. A fluid capable of dissolving substances.

So'ma, So-mat'ic. Pertaining to the body or body cells, as contrasted with germ cells. (Gr.*soma*,body)

So'mite. A serial segment or homologous part of the body; a metamere. (Gr.*soma*,body)

Spe'cial-ized. Not primitive; adapted by structure or function for a particular purpose or mode of life.

Spe'cies. (pl. also **species**). The unit in classification of animals or plants. (See Chap. 11)

Sperm. See Spermatozoa.

Sper'ma-to-zo''a. The matured and functional male sex cells or male gametes. (Gr.*sperma*,seed +*zoön*,animal)

Spir'a-cle. In insects, an external opening to the tracheal or respiratory system; in cartilaginous fishes, the modified first gill slit. (L.*spiraculum*,air hole)

Spore. A cell in a resistant covering, capable of developing independently into a new individual. (Gr.*spora*, seed)

Stat′o-cyst. An organ of equilibrium in some invertebrates. (Gr.*statos*, standing + *kystis*,bladder)

Stat′o-lith. A calcareous granule in a statocyst.

Stim′u-lus. A change in the external or internal environment capable of influencing some activity in an organism or its parts.

Sto′mo-de″um. The ectoderm-lined portion of the mouth cavity. (Gr. *stoma*,mouth + *hodos*,a way)

Strat′i-fied. A series of layers, one above another. (L.)

Stra′tum. A layer or sheet of tissue (anatomy); a layer or sheet of sedimentary rock (geology). (L., covering)

Su′ture. Line of junction between 2 bones or between 2 parts of an exoskeleton. (L.*suo*,sew)

Sym′bi-o″sis. Interrelation between 2 organisms of different species; see mutualism, parasitism. (Gr.*syn*,together + *bios*,life)

Sym′phy-sis. A union between 2 parts. (Gr.*syn*,together + *phyein*,grow)

Syn-apse′. The contact of one nerve cell with another, across which impulses are transmitted. (Gr.*syn*,together + *hapto*,unite)

Syn-ap′sis. Temporary union of the chromosomes in pairs preliminary to the first maturation division. (Gr. *syn*,together + *hapto*,unite)

Syn-cyt′i-um. A mass or layer of protoplasm containing several or many nuclei not separated by cell membranes. (Gr.*syn*,together + *kytos*, cell)

Sys-tem′ic. Portion of the circulatory system not directly involved in respiration.

Tac′tile. Pertaining to the organs or the sense of touch. (L.*tactus*,touch)

Tec′tin. The organic material in skeletons of some protozoans; pseudochitin.

Ten′don. A connective tissue band attaching a muscle. (L.*tendo*,to stretch)

Ten′ta-cle. An elongate flexible append-

age usually near the mouth. (L. *tento* from *teneo*,hold)

Ter-res′tri-al. Belonging to or living on the ground or earth. (L.*terra*,earth)

Tes′tis; pl. tes′tes. The male germ gland or gonad, in which spermatozoa are formed. (L.)

Tet′ra-pod. A vertebrate typically with 4 limbs—the amphibians, reptiles, birds, and mammals. (Gr.*tetra*,four + *pous*,foot)

Tho′rax. The major division of an animal next behind the head; in land vertebrates, the part enclosed by the ribs. (Gr.)

Tis′sue. A layer or group of cells in an organ or body part having essentially the same structure and function. (L.*texo*,weave)

Tra′che-a. An air tube; the windpipe of land vertebrates from the glottis to the lungs; part of the respiratory system in insects and other arthropods. (Gr.*trachys*,rough)

Trip′lo-blas″tic. Derived from 3 embryonic germ layers—ectoderm, endoderm, and mesoderm. (Gr.*triplous*, threefold + *blastos*,germ)

Tro′cho-phore. An invertebrate larva, commonly pear-shaped and with an equatorial band of cilia. (Gr.*trochos*, wheel + *phoros*,bearing)

Tym′pa-num. A vibrating membrane involved in hearing; the eardrum, or tympanic membrane. (Gr.*tympanon*, drum)

Um-bil′i-cal cord. The cord containing blood vessels supported by connective tissue that unites the embryo or foetus of a mammal with the mother during development in the uterus. (L.*umbilicus*,navel)

Un-guic′u-late. Having claws, as a cat. (L.*unguis*,claw)

Un′gu-late. Having hoofs, as a deer or horse. (L.*ungula*,hoof)

Un″gu-li-grade′. Walking or adapted for walking on hoofs. (L.*ungula*,hoof + *gradior*,to step)

Unit character. A trait that behaves more or less as a unit in heredity, and may be inherited independently of other traits.

U-re'ter. The duct carrying urine from the kidney to the urinary bladder or to the cloaca. (Gr.from *ouron*,urine)

U-re'thra. The duct by which urine is discharged from the bladder to the outside in mammals; joined by the vasa deferentia in the male. (Gr. from *ouron*,urine)

U'ri-no-gen''i-tal. See Urogenital.

U'ro-gen''i-tal. Pertaining to the excretory and reproductive organs and functions. (L.*urina*,urine +*genitalis*, genital)

U'ter-us. The enlarged posterior portion of an oviduct in which eggs may be retained for development. (L.,womb)

Vac'u-ole. A minute cavity within a cell, usually filled with some liquid product of protoplasmic activity. (L. dim.of *vacuus*,empty)

Va-gi'na. The terminal portion of the female reproductive tract, which receives the copulatory organ of a male in mating. (L.,sheath)

Valve. In animals, any structure that limits or closes an opening; the thin folds in veins, lymph vessels, or hearts or the circular muscles about a tubular exit; also, either external shell of a bivalve mollusk, brachiopod, or some crustaceans.

Vas; pl. va'sa. A small tubular vessel, or duct, especially one leading from the testis. (L.,vessel)

Vas'cu-lar. Pertaining to vessels or ducts for conveying or circulating blood or lymph. (L.dim.of *vas*,little vessel)

Vein. A vessel carrying blood from capillaries toward the heart. (L.*vena*, vein)

Ven'tral. Toward the lower side or belly; away from the back. Opposite to dorsal. (L.*venter*,belly)

Ven'tri-cle. The muscular chamber in a heart; also, a cavity in the brain of a vertebrate. (L.dim.of *venter*,belly)

Ver'te-bra. One of the segmental structural units of the axial skeleton or spinal column in a vertebrate. (L., joint)

Ver'te-brate. An animal having a segmental "backbone" or vertebral column; the cyclostomes to mammals. (L.*vertebratus*,jointed)

Ves'sel. A tubular structure that conveys fluid, especially blood or lymph. (L.*vascellum*,dim.of *vas*,vase)

Ves-tig'i-al. Small or degenerate but representing a structure that formerly was more fully developed or functional. Compare Rudimentary. (L.*vestigium*, footstep,a trace)

Vil'lus; pl. vil'li. A minute fingerlike projection; especially those numerous on the intestinal lining of vertebrates. (L.*villus*,shaggy hair)

Vis'cer-a. The organs within the cranium, thorax, and abdomen, especially the latter. (L.,internal organs)

Vis'cer-al skel'e-ton. The supporting framework of the jaws and gill arches and their derivatives, in vertebrates.

Vis'u-al. Pertaining to sight.

Vi'ta-min. An organic substance that is an essential food factor needed in minute amounts for normal growth and function. (L.*vita*,life +*amin*,a chemical radical)

Vi-vip'a-rous. Producing living young that develop from eggs retained within the mother's body and nourished by her blood stream, as with most mammals. (L.*vivo*,live +*pario*,to bear)

X,Y chromosomes. Chromosomes associated with sex in many animals.

Yolk. Fat or oil droplets stored within or with an egg for nourishment of the future embryo.

Zy'gote. A fertilized egg resulting from the union of 2 gametes of opposite kind, ovum and sperm. (Gr.*zygon*, yoke)

INDEX

All numbers refer to pages. Numbers in boldface refer to pages on which illustrations occur. Scientific names of genera and species are in italics and those of higher groups in small capitals. Names of fossil species or groups are preceded by a dagger (†). The index omits incidental references to common structures such as stomach, heart, etc., but contains entries for pages where these are described in detail. Such items may be sought under entries to Digestive system, Circulatory system, etc., or to an animal type such as Cat, Crayfish, etc.

A

Aard vark, 747–748
Abalone, 268, **423,** 436
Abdomen, **18**
    arthropod, **461,** 462, **465–467, 487, 489–490, 539**
    cat, **716**
    man, **76**
Abductor muscle, 26
Abedus, 520
Abomasum, **726**
Aboral end, 259, 403, **404**
Absorption of food, 27, 78–80
Abyssal, **199,** 200
Acanthias, 589
Acanthobdella, 455, 459
ACANTHOBDELLIDA, 459
ACANTHOCEPHALA, 186, **267,** 376, 387–389
†*Acanthodes,* 589
†ACANTHODII, 589
Acanthometron, 309
ACARI, 552–553
ACARINA, **537, 539,** 543–546, 552–553
Accessory sex organs, 119
Accipiter, 703
Acerentulus, 513, **514**
Acetabulum, **23,** 24
Acetylcholine, 101
Achatinella, 238
Achelia, 554
Achirus, 617
Achorutes, 514
Aciculum, **452**
Acid, amino, 45
    ascorbic, 83
    fatty, 45
    hydrochloric, 78
Acipenser, 272, 602, **611**
ACIPENSERIDAE, 609, **611**
Acmaea, 268, 436
ACOELA, 346, 351, 361
ACOELOMATA, 257, 265
Acontium, **335**
Acquired characteristics, 170, 230

ACRANIA, 270, 557
ACRIDIDAE, 487, 514–**515**
Acris, 638
Acromegaly, 118
Acropora, **337,** 341
ACROTHORACICA, 483
Actaeon, 436
Actinia, 340
ACTINARIA, **321,** 340
ACTINISTIA, 618
ACTINOMYXIDIA, 309
Actinophrys, 264, 308
ACTINOPTERYGII, 592
Actinosphaerium, **283**
Actinotrocha larva, 395
ACTINOZOA, 265
Activator, 47
Acuaria, 369
Adamsia, 340
Adaptations, 190–193, **214, 215,** 236–237, 649–651
Adaptive convergence, **191**
Adaptive mutations, 236
Adaptive radiation, 191
Adder, puff, 671
Addison's disease, 118
Adductor muscle, 26, **424, 425**
ADELOCHORDA, 270
ADEPHAGA, 530
Adipose tissue, 55
Adjustor neuron, 101, **107**
Adolescent, 762
Adrenal gland, **18,** 21, 34, 38, **116**–118
Adrenalin, 38, 117
Adrenotropic hormone, 118
Aëdes, 511, **528**
Aega, 480, 483
Aegeria, **524**
AEGERIIDAE, **524**
AELOSOMATIDAE, 450
Aeolis, 436
Aeolosoma, 439, 450, 459
Aepyornis, 700
AEPYORNITHIFORMES, 700
Aeshna, **517,** 518
Aëtobatis, 589
Afferent neuron, 101, **107**

Agama, 666
AGAMIDAE, 666
Agassiz, Louis, **251,** 254
Age, of animals, 206–208, 659–662, 736–737
    of earth, 212
Agelena, 551
AGELENIDAE, 551
Agglutinins, 87
Agglutinogens, 87
Agkistrodon, 671
Aglais, 526
Aglantha, 339
AGLYPHA, **669**–670
AGNATHA, **271,** 557
Agriolimax, 436
Ailuropoda, 746
Ailurus, 746
Ainu race, 772
Air bladder, **594,** 598–599
Air sacs, bird, 93, **683,** 684
    grasshopper, **491**
ALAUDIDAE, 709
Alaus, 532
Albatross, 702
Alberta, 384
Albertus Magnus, 245
Albumen of egg, **97, 130,** 687
Alces, 751
ALCIDAE, 705
Alcippe, 483
ALCYONACEA, 340
ALCYONARIA, 340
Alcyonidium, 392
Alcyonium, 340
ALEYRODIDAE, 521
Algae, 187
Alien animals, 204–205
Allantois, **142,** 655
Allantosoma, 307
Allele, 151, 160
Allelomorph, 151
Alligator, 272, **641, 642**–646, 662, 672
    brain, **103**
Alligator gar, 612
Allodermanyssus, 553
Allogromia, 308

793

Cat, organ systems, sensory, 719
   skeletal, 713–715
   parasites of, 359, 530
   teeth of, 716
   tiger, 739
   wild, 735, 747
Catabolism, 46
Catadromous, 603
CATARRHINI, 741
Caterpillar, **192, 525, 526**
Catfish, **614**
Cathartes, 703
CATOSTOMIDAE, 614
Catostomus, 614
Cattle, 80, 169, **731,** 735, 752,
   762, 768
   heredity in, 150, 169
   horns, **722**
Cattle fever, 295, 511
Caucasoid race, 772
CAUDATA, **634–636**
Caudina, 415
Cavia, 735
CAVIIDAE, 735
Cavolinia, 436
CEBIDAE, 741
CEBOIDEA, 741
Cebus, 741
CECIDOMYIDAE, **527,** 528
Cell division, **51–53**
Cell inclusions, **49,** 277, **278**
Cell membrane, **49**
Cell mouth, **74, 285,** 286, **296**
Cell theory, 48–49, 253
Cells, 17, 48–51, 253, 263
   formative, 347, **348**
Cellulose digestion, 80, 290, 517
Celsus, 243
Cement of tooth, 716, **726**
Cement gland, **382, 388, 479**
Cenozoic period, **206**–208
Centaur, **242**
Centipede, **2, 9, 270, 461,** 462,
   547–548, 553
   garden, 270, 554
   house, 548, 553
CENTRARCHIDAE, 616
CENTRECHINOIDEA, 415
Centriole, **49, 51**
Centrocercus, 704
Centromere, **51**
Centrosome, **49**
Centrum, 23, 66, **67, 105**
Centrurus, 551
Cepedea, 309
Cephalanthus, 395
†*Cephalaspis*, 271, 580
CEPHALOCHORDATA, **271,** 557,
   558, 567–570
Cephalodiscus, 271, 562
CEPHALOPODA, **206,** 223–**224,**
   268, 417, 418, **432**–435, 437

Cephalothorax, 462, **465,** 467,
   539
Ceramaster, 414
CERAMBYCIDAE, **531,** 533
Cerastes, 671
Ceratitis, 529
Ceratium, 287, 308
Ceratius, 618
CERATODONTIDAE, **618,** 619
†*Ceratodus*, 619
Ceratophyllus, 530
Ceratopogon, 528
†*Ceratosaurus*, **661**
Cercaria, **354**
Cercomonas, **289**
CERCOPIDAE, **521**
CERCOPITHECOIDEA, 741
Cercus, **487,** 489, 512, **514, 515,**
   517
Cerebellum, **35,** 60, **76,** 102, 103,
   109, 585
Cerebral cortex, **103, 109**
Cerebral ganglia, planaria, **347,**
   348
Cerebral hemispheres, 34, **35,**
   102, 103, 109, 585
Cerebratulus, 266, 380
Cerebrospinal fluid, 35
Cerebrum, **35, 76, 103, 109**
Ceresa, 521
Cereus, 337
CERIANTHARIA, **321,** 341
Cerianthus, **321,** 337, 341
Cermatia, 553
CERTHIIDAE, 709
CERVIDAE, 735, 751
Cervus, 751
CESTIDA, 344
CESTODA, **357–360,** 361
CESTODARIA, 356–357, 361
CESTOIDEA, **266,** 345, **356–360,**
   361
Cestum, 265, **342,** 344
CETACEA, **745**–746
Cetorhinus, 582, 589
Chaetae (*see* Setae)
Chaetoderma, 435
Chaetogaster, 439, 450, 459
CHAETOGNATHA, **2,** 263, 268, 376,
   396–397
Chaetogordius, 458
Chaetonotus, 266, **385**
Chaetopleura, 435
Chaetopterus, 269, 453, 454, 459
Chaetura, 707
Chagas' disease, 289, 511, 520
Chain reflex, 108
CHALASTROGASTRA, **533,** 534
CHALCIDIDAE, **533,** 534
CHAMAEIDAE, 709
CHAMAELEONTIDAE, 666–**667**
Chamaleo, **667**
Chameleon, 665–**667**

Chamois, **241**
Characin, 613
Characters, 256
CHARADRIIFORMES, **705**
Charina, **669**
Cheilosis, 82
Cheilospiura, 369
CHEILOSTOMATA, 392
†*Cheirolepis*, 611
Chela, crayfish, **465, 467,** 468
Chelicera, 462, **539,** 543, **544**
CHELICERATA, 463
Chelifer, 552
Cheliped, **465**
Chelodina, 664
CHELONETHIDA, 552
Chelonia, 664
CHELONIA, 641, **662–664**
CHELONIDAE, **664**
Chelydra, **663**
CHELYDRIDAE, **663**
CHELYIDAE, 664
Chelys, 664
Chemical cycles in nature, 177–
   179
Chemotaxis, 504
Chen, 703
Chevrotain, 750
Chicken, 674–687, 705
   brain, **103**
   egg, 130
   embryo, **136,** 140, **141, 142**
   heredity in, **153**–154, 157–**158**
   parasites of, **369,** 450, **518,** 530,
     544, 545, 552, 553
   (*See also* Fowl)
Chigger, 552
Chigoe, 530
Childhood, 762
Chilomastix, 308
Chilomonas, 307
Chilomycterus, **592**
CHILOPODA, **270, 461,** 462, 463,
   547–548, 553
Chimaera, mythical, **242**
Chimaera, 272, **581,** 589–590
Chimpanzee, **742**
Chinch bug, 520
Chipmunk, 744
Chiridota, 415
CHIRONOMIDAE, **527,** 528
Chironomus, **527,** 528
CHIROPTERA, **740**
Chitin, 65, 463–464
Chiton, **2, 9,** 268, **418**–419, 435
Chiton, **268, 417,** 435
Chlamydomonas, 307
Chlamydoselachus, 589
Chloragog cells, **442**
Chloridella, 484
Chlorohydra, 187, 323, 339
CHLOROMONADINA, 307
Chloroplast, **285,** 286